SMITHSONIAN INSTITUTION

UNITED STATES NATIONAL MUSEUM

Bulletin 178

CATALOG OF THE TYPE SPECIMENS OF MAMMALS IN THE UNITED STATES NATIONAL MUSEUM, INCLUDING THE BIOLOGICAL SURVEYS COLLECTION

By

ARTHUR J. POOLE and VIOLA S. SCHANTZ

UNITED STATES

GOVERNMENT PRINTING OFFICE

WASHINGTON : 1942

For sale by the Superintendent of Documents, Washington, D. C. - - - - - - - Price $1.25 (paper cover)

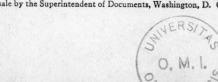

ADVERTISEMENT

The scientific publications of the National Museum include two series, known, respectively, as *Proceedings* and *Bulletin*.

The *Proceedings* series, begun in 1878, is intended primarily as a medium for the publication of original papers, based on the collections of the National Museum, that set forth newly acquired facts in biology, anthropology, and geology, with descriptions of new forms and revisions of limited groups. Copies of each paper, in pamphlet form, are distributed as published to libraries and scientific organizations and to specialists and others interested in the different subjects. The dates at which these separate papers are published are recorded in the table of contents of each of the volumes.

The series of *Bulletins*, the first of which was issued in 1875, contains separate publications comprising monographs of large zoological groups and other general systematic treatises (occasionally in several volumes), faunal works, reports of expeditions, catalogs of type specimens, special collections, and other material of similar nature. The majority of the volumes are octavo in size, but a quarto size has been adopted in a few instances in which large plates were regarded as indispensable. In the *Bulletin* series appear volumes under the heading *Contributions from the United States National Herbarium*, in octavo form, published by the National Museum since 1902, which contain papers relating to the botanical collections of the Museum.

The present work forms No. 178 of the *Bulletin* series.

ALEXANDER WETMORE,
Assistant Secretary, Smithsonian Institution.

WASHINGTON, D. C., *March 6, 1942.*

CONTENTS

	Page
Introduction	1
Outstanding authors and collectors of type specimens	2
Arrangement	2
Summary of the list of types	4
Explanation of symbols	4
Order ARTIODACTYLA: Even-toed ruminants	6
Family Antilocapridae: Pronghorns	6
Genus *Antilocapra* Ord	6
Family Bovidae: Cattle, antelope, sheep, goats	6
Genus *Adenota* Gray	6
Genus *Alcelaphus* Blainville	7
Genus *Bison* Hamilton Smith	8
Genus *Cephalophus* Hamilton Smith	8
Genus *Connochaetes* Lichtenstein	8
Genus *Egocerus* Desmarest	8
Genus *Gazella* Blainville	9
Genus *Kobus* A. Smith	9
Genus *Nesotragus* von Düben	10
Genus *Oreotragus* A. Smith	10
Genus *Oryx* Blainville	10
Genus *Ourebia* Laurillard	10
Genus *Ovis* Linnaeus	11
Genus *Prodorcas* Pocock	13
Genus *Pseudois* Hodgson	13
Genus *Redunca* Hamilton Smith	13
Genus *Rhynchotragus* Neumann	14
Genus *Rupicapra* Blainville	14
Genus *Strepsiceros* Frisch	15
Genus *Sylvicapra* Ogilby	15
Genus *Tragelaphus* Blainville	16
Family Cervidae: Deer	16
Genus *Alces* Gray	16
Genus *Capreolus* Gray	16
Genus *Cervus* Linnaeus	17
Genus *Mazama* Rafinesque	18
Genus *Muntiacus* Rafinesque	18
Genus *Odocoileus* Rafinesque	19
Genus *Rangifer* Hamilton Smith	24
Genus *Rusa* Hamilton Smith	25
Family Hippopotamidae: Hippopotamuses	25
Genus *Hippopotamus* Linnaeus	25
Family Moschidae: Musk-deer	25
Genus *Moschus* Linnaeus	25

Order ARTIODACTYLA: Even-toed ruminants—Continued.   Page

Family Suidae: Pigs_____ 26
    Genus *Phacochoerus* F. Cuvier_____ 26
    Genus *Sus* Linnaeus_____ 26
Family Tayassuidae: Peccaries_____ 28
    Genus *Pecari* Reichenbach_____ 28
    Genus *Tayassu* Fischer_____ 30
Family Tragulidae: Chevrotains, or mouse deer_____ 30
    Genus *Tragulus* Brisson_____ 30
Order CARNIVORA: Flesh-eaters_____ 38
Family Bassariscidae: Cacomistles_____ 38
    Genus *Bassariscus* Coues_____ 38
    Genus *Jentinkia* Trouessart_____ 40
Family Canidae: Dogs_____ 40
    Genus *Alopex* Kaup_____ 40
    Genus *Canis* Linnaeus_____ 41
    Genus *Icticyon* Lund_____ 46
    Genus *Lupulella* Hilzheimer_____ 46
    Genus *Otocyon* Müller_____ 46
    Genus *Schaeffia* Hilzheimer_____ 46
    Genus *Urocyon* Baird_____ 47
    Genus *Vulpes* Oken_____ 49
Family Felidae: Cats_____ 52
    Genus *Acinonyx* Brookes_____ 52
    Genus *Felis* Linnaeus_____ 53
    Genus *Lynx* Kerr_____ 60
Family Hyaenidae: Hyaenas_____ 61
    Genus *Crocuta* Kaup_____ 61
Family Mustelidae: Weasels, minks, martens, skunks, otters, badgers_ 61
    Genus *Aonyx* Lesson_____ 61
    Genus *Conepatus* Gray_____ 61
    Genus *Enhydra* Fleming_____ 63
    Genus *Grison* Oken_____ 63
    Genus *Gulo* Pallas_____ 64
    Genus *Ictonyx* Kaup_____ 64
    Genus *Lutra* Brisson_____ 64
    Genus *Martes* Pinel_____ 66
    Genus *Mellivora* Storr_____ 67
    Genus *Mephitis* Geoffroy and Cuvier_____ 68
    Genus *Mustela* Linnaeus_____ 69
    Genus *Spilogale* Gray_____ 75
    Genus *Taxidea* Waterhouse_____ 78
    Genus *Vormela* Blasius_____ 79
Family Procyonidae: Raccoons, coatis, kinkajous_____ 79
    Genus *Bassaricyon* J. A. Allen_____ 79
    Genus *Nasua* Storr_____ 80
    Genus *Potos* Geoffroy and Cuvier_____ 80
    Genus *Procyon* Storr_____ 81
Family Protelidae: Aard wolves_____ 85
    Genus *Proteles* Geoffroy_____ 85
Family Ursidae: Bears_____ 85
    Genus *Euarctos* Gray_____ 85
    Genus *Selenarctos* Heude_____ 86
    Genus *Ursus* Linnaeus_____ 86

Order CARNIVORA: Flesh-eaters—Continued.   Page
  Family Viverridae: Civets_____ 100
    Genus *Arctictis* Temminck_____ 100
    Genus *Arctogalidia* Merriam_____ 101
    Genus *Atilax* Geoffroy and Cuvier_____ 102
    Genus *Bdeogale* Peters_____ 103
    Genus *Genetta* Oken_____ 103
    Genus *Hemigalus* Jourdan_____ 103
    Genus *Ichneumia* Geoffroy_____ 104
    Genus *Mungos* Geoffroy and Cuvier_____ 104
    Genus *Myonax* Thomas_____ 104
    Genus *Nandinia* Gray_____ 105
    Genus *Paguma* Gray_____ 105
    Genus *Paradoxurus* Geoffroy_____ 105
    Genus *Viverricula* Hodgson_____ 108
Order CETACEA: Whales, porpoises_____ 108
  Family Balaenopteridae: Finbacks_____ 108
    Genus *Balaenoptera* Lacépède_____ 108
  Family Delphinidae: Porpoises_____ 108
    Genus *Delphinus* Linnaeus_____ 108
    Genus *Globicephala* Lesson_____ 109
    Genus *Grampidelphis* Iredale and Troughton_____ 109
    Genus *Lagenorhynchus* Gray_____ 109
    Genus *Lissodelphis* Gloger_____ 110
    Genus *Phocaena* Desmarest_____ 110
    Genus *Phocoenoides* Andrews_____ 112
    Genus *Pseudorca* Reinhardt_____ 112
    Genus *Sagmatias* Cope_____ 112
    Genus *Stenella* Gray_____ 113
    Genus *Tursiops* Gervais_____ 113
  Family Iniidae: River dolphins_____ 113
    Genus *Lipotes* Miller_____ 113
  Family Kogiidae: Pigmy sperm whales_____ 114
    Genus *Kogia* Gray_____ 114
  Family Ziphiidae: Beaked whales_____ 114
    Genus *Berardius* Duvernoy_____ 114
    Genus *Mesoplodon* Gervais_____ 115
    Genus *Ziphius* G. Cuvier_____ 115
Order CHIROPTERA: Bats_____ 115
  Family Emballonuridae: Sheath-tailed bats_____ 115
    Genus *Emballonura* Temminck_____ 115
    Genus *Taphonycteris* Dobson_____ 116
    Genus *Taphozous* Geoffroy_____ 117
  Family Hipposideridae: Horseshoe bats_____ 117
    Genus *Coelops* Blyth_____ 117
    Genus *Hipposideros* Gray_____ 117
  Family Megadermidae: False vampires_____ 118
    Genus *Lavia* Gray_____ 118
    Genus *Megaderma* Geoffroy_____ 119
  Family Molossidae: Free-tailed bats_____ 119
    Genus *Chaerephon* Dobson_____ 119
    Genus *Cheiromeles* Horsfield_____ 120
    Genus *Eumops* Miller_____ 120

Order CHIROPTERA: Bats—Continued.
 Family Molossidae: Free-tailed Bats—Continued.   **Page**
  Genus *Molossus* Geoffroy _____ 121
  Genus *Promops* Gervais _____ 122
  Genus *Tadarida* Rafinesque _____ 122
 Family Natalidae: Long-legged bats _____ 124
  Genus *Chilonatalus* Miller _____ 124
  Genus *Natalus* Gray _____ 125
  Genus *Phodotes* Miller _____ 126
 Family Noctilionidae: Hare-lipped bats _____ 126
  Genus *Noctilio* Linnaeus _____ 126
 Family Phyllostomidae: Leaf-nosed bats _____ 126
  Genus *Ardops* Miller _____ 126
  Genus *Artibeus* Leach _____ 126
  Genus *Brachyphylla* Gray _____ 127
  Genus *Carollia* Gray _____ 128
  Genus *Centurio* Gray _____ 128
  Genus *Chilonycteris* Gray _____ 129
  Genus *Chiroderma* Peters _____ 129
  Genus *Ectophylla* H. Allen _____ 129
  Genus *Erophylla* Miller _____ 130
  Genus *Glossophaga* Geoffroy _____ 130
  Genus *Leptonycteris* Lydekker _____ 131
  Genus *Lichonycteris* Thomas _____ 132
  Genus *Lonchophylla* Thomas _____ 132
  Genus *Macrotus* Gray _____ 132
  Genus *Micronycteris* Gray _____ 133
  Genus *Mimon* Gray _____ 133
  Genus *Monophyllus* Leach _____ 133
  Genus *Mormoops* Leach _____ 134
  Genus *Phyllonycteris* Gundlach _____ 135
  Genus *Reithronycteris* Miller _____ 135
  Genus *Sturnira* Gray _____ 135
  Genus *Sturnirops* Goodwin _____ 136
  Genus *Tonatia* Gray _____ 136
  Genus *Trachops* Gray _____ 136
  Genus *Uroderma* Peters _____ 136
  Genus *Vampyressa* Thomas _____ 136
  Genus *Vampyrops* Peters _____ 137
  Genus *Vampyrum* Rafinesque _____ 137
 Family Pteropidae: Fruit bats _____ 137
  Genus *Cynopterus* F. Cuvier _____ 137
  Genus *Eonycteris* Dobson _____ 138
  Genus *Harpyionycteris* Thomas _____ 139
  Genus *Pteropus* Brisson _____ 139
 Family Rhinolophidae: Horseshoe bats _____ 143
  Genus *Rhinolophus* Lacépède _____ 143
 Family Thyropteridae: Disk-winged bats _____ 145
  Genus *Thyroptera* Spix _____ 145
 Family Vespertilionidae: Vespertilionid bats _____ 145
  Genus *Antrozous* H. Allen _____ 145
  Genus *Corynorhinus* H. Allen _____ 146
  Genus *Dasypterus* Peters _____ 146

Order CHIROPTERA: Bats—Continued.
    Family Vespertilionidae: Vespertilionid bats—Continued.   Page
        Genus *Eptesicus* Rafinesque 146
        Genus *Kerivoula* Gray 147
        Genus *Lasiurus* Gray 148
        Genus *Miniopterus* Bonaparte 149
        Genus *Murina* Gray 150
        Genus *Myotis* Kaup 150
        Genus *Nycticeius* Rafinesque 159
        Genus *Phoniscus* Miller 159
        Genus *Pipistrellus* Kaup 160
        Genus *Rhogeëssa* H. Allen 162
Order DERMOPTERA: Flying lemurs 162
    Family Galeopithecidae 162
        Genus *Galeopterus* Thomas 162
Order HYRACOIDEA: Hyraxes 164
    Family Procaviidae 164
        Genus *Dendrohyrax* Gray 164
        Genus *Heterohyrax* Gray 165
Order INSECTIVORA: Insect eaters 165
    Family Erinaceidae: Hedgehogs 165
        Genus *Atelerix* Pomel 165
        Genus *Echinosorex* Blainville 165
        Genus *Podogymnura* Mearns 165
    Family Macroscelididae: Jumping shrews 166
        Genus *Cercoctenus* Hollister 166
        Genus *Elephantulus* Thomas and Schwann 166
    Family Nesophontidae: Extinct Antillean insectivores 166
        Genus *Nesophontes* Anthony 166
    Family Soricidae: Shrews 167
        Genus *Blarina* Gray 167
        Genus *Crocidura* Wagler 167
        Genus *Cryptotis* Pomel 175
        Genus *Microsorex* Coues 179
        Genus *Neomys* Kaup 181
        Genus *Notiosorex* Coues 181
        Genus *Sorex* Linnaeus 182
        Genus *Suncus* Ehrenberg 198
        Genus *Surdisorex* Thomas 198
        Genus *Sylvisorex* Thomas 198
    Family Talpidae: Moles 198
        Genus *Dymecodon* True 198
        Genus *Euroscaptor* Miller 199
        Genus *Neürotrichus* Günther 199
        Genus *Scalopus* Geoffroy 200
        Genus *Scapanus* Pomel 200
    Family Tupaiidae: Tree shrews 202
        Genus *Tana* Lyon 202
        Genus *Tupaia* Raffles 203
        Genus *Urogale* Mearns 207
Order LAGOMORPHA: Hares, rabbits, pikas 208
    Family Leporidae: Hares, rabbits 208
        Genus *Brachylagus* Miller 208
        Genus *Lepus* Linnaeus 208

Order LAGOMORPHA: Hares, rabbits, pikas—Continued.
Family Leporidae: Hares, rabbits—Continued.   Page
Genus *Romerolagus* Merriam_____ 215
Genus *Sylvilagus* Gray_____ 215
Family Ochotonidae: Pikas, or conies_____ 224
Genus *Ochotona* Link_____ 224
Order MARSUPIALIA: Marsupials_____ 228
Family Caenolestidae_____ 228
Genus *Lestoros* Oehser_____ 228
Family Didelphiidae: Opossums_____ 228
Genus *Chironectes* Illiger_____ 228
Genus *Didelphis* Linnaeus_____ 228
Genus *Marmosa* Gray_____ 229
Genus *Metachirops* Matschie_____ 231
Genus *Metachirus* Burmeister_____ 232
Genus *Monodelphis* Burnett_____ 232
Genus *Philander* Brisson_____ 232
Family Phalangeridae: Phalangers_____ 232
Genus *Phalanger* Storr_____ 232
Order PERISSODACTYLA: Odd-toed ungulates_____ 232
Family Equidae: Horses_____ 232
Genus *Equus* Linnaeus_____ 232
Family Tapiridae: Tapirs_____ 233
Genus *Tapirella* Palmer_____ 233
Order PINNIPEDIA: Seals, walruses_____ 234
Family Otariidae: Eared seals_____ 234
Genus *Arctocephalus* E. Geoffroy and F. Cuvier_____ 234
Family Phocidae: Hair seals_____ 234
Genus *Mirounga* Gray_____ 234
Genus *Phoca* Linnaeus_____ 234
Order PRIMATES: Lemurs, marmosets, monkeys, apes, men_____ 235
Family Alouattidae: Howler monkeys_____ 235
Genus *Alouatta* Lacépède_____ 235
Family Aotidae: Durukulis, or night monkeys_____ 236
Genus *Aotus* Humboldt_____ 236
Family Callitrichidae: Marmosets_____ 236
Genus *Mystax* Gray_____ 236
Family Cebidae: American monkeys_____ 236
Genus *Ateles* E. Geoffroy_____ 236
Genus *Cebus* Erxleben_____ 237
Family Cercopithecidae: Guenons, macaques, baboons, langurs_____ 237
Genus *Cercopithecus* Brünnich_____ 237
Genus *Colobus* Illiger_____ 239
Genus *Cynopithecus* I. Geoffroy_____ 240
Genus *Erythrocebus* Trouessart_____ 240
Genus *Lyssodes* Gistel_____ 240
Genus *Macaca* Lacépède_____ 240
Genus *Papio* Erxleben_____ 246
Genus *Presbytis* Eschscholtz_____ 247
Genus *Simias* Miller_____ 250
Family Galagidae: Bush babies_____ 250
Genus *Galago* E. Geoffroy_____ 250
Family Hylobatidae: Gibbons_____ 251
Genus *Hylobates* Illiger_____ 251

	Page
Order PRIMATES: Lemurs, marmosets, monkeys, apes, men—Continued.	
Family Lorisidae: Lorises	251
Genus *Nycticebus* Geoffroy	251
Family Tarsiidae: Tarsiers	252
Genus *Tarsius* Storr	252
Order RODENTIA: Rodents	253
Family Aplodontiidae: Mountain-beavers	253
Genus *Aplodontia* Richardson	253
Family Bathyergidae: Sand moles	254
Genus *Heliophobius* Peters	254
Family Castoridae: Beavers	254
Genus *Castor* Linnaeus	254
Family Chinchillidae: Chinchillas	256
Genus *Lagostomus* Brookes	256
Family Cricetidae: Cricetine rats and mice	256
Genus *Akodon* Meyen	256
Genus *Alticola* Blanford	257
Genus *Aschizomys* Miller	258
Genus *Baiomys* True	258
Genus *Chelemys* Thomas	259
Genus *Chraeomys* Thomas	260
Genus *Clethrionomys* Tilesius	260
Genus *Dicrostonyx* Gloger	264
Genus *Euneomys* Coues	265
Genus *Geoxus* Thomas	265
Genus *Gerbillus* Desmarest	265
Genus *Hesperomys* Waterhouse	266
Genus *Hodomys* Merriam	266
Genus *Holochilus* Brandt	266
Genus *Hyperacrius* Miller	266
Genus *Lemmiscus* Gloger	267
Genus *Lemmus* Link	268
Genus *Lophiomys* Depéret	269
Genus *Microtus* Schrank	269
Genus *Myopus* Miller	283
Genus *Neacomys* Thomas	283
Genus *Nectomys* Peters	284
Genus *Nelsonia* Merriam	284
Genus *Neofiber* True	284
Genus *Neotoma* Say and Ord	285
Genus *Neotomodon* Merriam	298
Genus *Nyctomys* Saussure	299
Genus *Ondatra* Link	300
Genus *Onychomys* Baird	301
Genus *Oryzomys* Baird	304
Genus *Ototylomys* Merriam	311
Genus *Peromyscus* Gloger	311
Genus *Phenacomys* Merriam	337
Genus *Phodopus* Miller	339
Genus *Pitymys* McMurtrie	339
Genus *Reithrodon* Waterhouse	340
Genus *Reithrodontomys* Giglioli	341
Genus *Rheomys* Thomas	349
Genus *Rhipidomys* Tschudi	350

Order RODENTIA: Rodents—Continued.
  Family Cricetidae: Cricetine rats and mice—Continued.   **Page**
    Genus *Scotinomys* Thomas_____ 350
    Genus *Sigmodon* Say and Ord_____ 350
    Genus *Synaptomys* Baird_____ 354
    Genus *Tatera* Lataste_____ 356
    Genus *Teanopus* Merriam_____ 356
    Genus *Thallomyscus* Thomas_____ 356
    Genus *Thomasomys* Coues_____ 357
    Genus *Tylomys* Peters_____ 357
    Genus *Xenomys* Merriam_____ 357
    Genus *Zygodontomys* J. A. Allen_____ 358
  Family Cuniculidae: Spotted cavies_____ 358
    Genus *Cuniculus* Brisson_____ 358
  Family Dasyproctidae: Agoutis_____ 358
    Genus *Dasyprocta* Illiger_____ 358
  Family Dipodidae: Jerboas_____ 359
    Genus *Allactaga* F. Cuvier_____ 359
    Genus *Euchoreutes* W. L. Sclater_____ 359
  Family Echimyidae: Spiny rats_____ 360
    Genus *Aphaetreus* Miller_____ 360
    Genus *Boromys* Miller_____ 360
    Genus *Brotomys* Miller_____ 360
    Genus *Capromys* Desmarest_____ 360
    Genus *Ctenomys* Blainville_____ 361
    Genus *Diplomys* Thomas_____ 361
    Genus *Echimys* Cuvier_____ 362
    Genus *Hexolobodon* Miller_____ 362
    Genus *Hoplomys* J. A. Allen_____ 362
    Genus *Isolobodon* J. A. Allen_____ 362
    Genus *Plagiodontia* F. Cuvier_____ 362
    Genus *Proechimys* J. A. Allen_____ 363
    Genus *Quemisia* Miller_____ 363
  Family Erethizontidae: American porcupines_____ 364
    Genus *Erethizon* F. Cuvier_____ 364
  Family Geomyidae: Pocket gophers_____ 364
    Genus *Cratogeomys* Merriam_____ 364
    Genus *Geomys* Rafinesque_____ 368
    Genus *Heterogeomys* Merriam_____ 371
    Genus *Macrogeomys* Merriam_____ 372
    Genus *Orthogeomys* Merriam_____ 372
    Genus *Pappogeomys* Merriam_____ 374
    Genus *Platygeomys* Merriam_____ 375
    Genus *Thomomys* Wied_____ 377
    Genus *Zygogeomys* Merriam_____ 403
  Family Graphiuridae: African dormice_____ 404
    Genus *Claviglis* Jentink_____ 404
  Family Heteromyidae: Kangaroo rats, pocket mice_____ 405
    Genus *Dipodomys* Gray_____ 405
    Genus *Heteromys* Desmarest_____ 416
    Genus *Liomys* Merriam_____ 418
    Genus *Microdipodops* Merriam_____ 421
    Genus *Perognathus* Wied_____ 422

Order RODENTIA: Rodents—Continued.   Page
    Family Hydrochoeridae: Capybaras _____ 437
        Genus *Hydrochoerus* Brisson _____ 437
    Family Hystricidae: Old World porcupines _____ 438
        Genus *Atherurus* F. Cuvier _____ 438
        Genus *Thecurus* Lyon _____ 438
        Genus *Trichys* Günther _____ 439
    Family Idiuridae: African flying squirrels _____ 439
        Genus *Idiurus* Matschie _____ 439
    Family Muridae: Murine rats and mice _____ 439
        Genus *Acomys* Geoffroy _____ 439
        Genus *Aethomys* Thomas _____ 439
        Genus *Apodemus* Kaup _____ 440
        Genus *Apomys* Mearns _____ 441
        Genus *Arvicanthis* Lesson _____ 442
        Genus *Bandicota* Gray _____ 443
        Genus *Batomys* Thomas _____ 443
        Genus *Bullimus* Mearns _____ 443
        Genus *Chiropodomys* Peters _____ 443
        Genus *Cricetomys* Waterhouse _____ 443
        Genus *Dasymys* Peters _____ 444
        Genus *Dendromus* Smith _____ 445
        Genus *Dephomys* Thomas _____ 445
        Genus *Echiothrix* Gray _____ 446
        Genus *Eropeplus* Miller and Hollister _____ 446
        Genus *Grammomys* Thomas _____ 446
        Genus *Hylomyscus* Thomas _____ 446
        Genus *Leggada* Gray _____ 447
        Genus *Lemniscomys* Trouessart _____ 449
        Genus *Lenomys* Thomas _____ 449
        Genus *Lenothrix* Miller _____ 449
        Genus *Limnomys* Mearns _____ 450
        Genus *Lophuromys* Peters _____ 450
        Genus *Mastomys* Thomas _____ 451
        Genus *Melasmothrix* Miller and Hollister _____ 452
        Genus *Mus* Linnaeus _____ 452
        Genus *Mylomys* Thomas _____ 452
        Genus *Myomys* Thomas _____ 453
        Genus *Oenomys* Thomas _____ 453
        Genus *Otomys* Cuvier _____ 453
        Genus *Pelomys* Peters _____ 454
        Genus *Poemys* Thomas _____ 454
        Genus *Praomys* Thomas _____ 454
        Genus *Rattus* G. Fischer _____ 455
        Genus *Saccostomus* Peters _____ 487
        Genus *Steatomys* Peters _____ 488
        Genus *Tarsomys* Mearns _____ 488
        Genus *Thallomys* Thomas _____ 488
        Genus *Tryphomys* Miller _____ 488
        Genus *Typomys* Thomas _____ 489
        Genus *Uranomys* Dollman _____ 489
        Genus *Zelotomys* Osgood _____ 489
    Family Muscardinidae: Dormice _____ 489
        Genus *Eliomys* Wagner _____ 489

Order RODENTIA: Rodents—Continued.   Page
    Family Myocastoridae: Coypus_____ 490
        Genus *Myocastor* Kerr_____ 490
    Family Pedetidae: Cape jumping hares_____ 490
        Genus *Pedetes* Illiger_____ 490
    Family Rhizomyidae: Bamboo rats_____ 490
        Genus *Tachyoryctes* Rüppell_____ 490
    Family Sciuridae: Squirrels_____ 491
        Genus *Callosciurus* Gray_____ 491
        Genus *Citellus* Oken_____ 504
        Genus *Cynomys* Rafinesque_____ 521
        Genus *Dremomys* Heude_____ 522
        Genus *Eutamias* Trouessart_____ 522
        Genus *Glaucomys* Thomas_____ 533
        Genus *Heliosciurus* Trouessart_____ 536
        Genus *Hylopetes* Thomas_____ 537
        Genus *Iomys* Thomas_____ 537
        Genus *Lariscus* Thomas and Wroughton_____ 537
        Genus *Marmota* Blumenbach_____ 538
        Genus *Menetes* Thomas_____ 541
        Genus *Microsciurus* J. A. Allen_____ 541
        Genus *Nannosciurus* Trouessart_____ 542
        Genus *Paraxerus* Forsyth-Major_____ 543
        Genus *Petaurista* Link_____ 543
        Genus *Petinomys* Thomas_____ 544
        Genus *Protoxerus* Forsyth-Major_____ 544
        Genus *Pteromys* G. Cuvier_____ 545
        Genus *Ratufa* Gray_____ 545
        Genus *Sciurus* Linnaeus_____ 551
        Genus *Tamias* Illiger_____ 560
        Genus *Tamiasciurus* J. A. Allen_____ 560
        Genus *Tamiops* J. A. Allen_____ 562
        Genus *Tomeutes* Thomas_____ 562
    Family Spalacidae: Mole rats_____ 566
        Genus *Myospalax* Laxmann_____ 566
        Genus *Spalax* Gueldenstaedt_____ 566
    Family Thryonomyidae: Rush rats_____ 566
        Genus *Thryonomys* Fitzinger_____ 566
    Family Zapodidae: Jumping mice_____ 566
        Genus *Napaeozapus* Preble_____ 566
        Genus *Sicista* Gray_____ 567
        Genus *Zapus* Coues_____ 567
Order XENARTHRA: Edentates_____ 569
    Family Bradypodidae: Three-toed sloths_____ 569
        Genus *Bradypus* Linnaeus_____ 569
    Family Dasypodidae: Armadillos_____ 569
        Genus *Cabassous* McMurtrie_____ 569
        Genus *Dasypus* Linnaeus_____ 570
    Family Megalonychidae: Ground sloths_____ 570
        Genus *Acratocnus* Miller_____ 570
        Genus *Parocnus* Miller_____ 570
    Family Myrmecophagidae: Anteaters_____ 570
        Genus *Cyclopes* Gray_____ 570
        Genus *Myrmecophaga* Linnaeus_____ 571

CONTENTS

	Page
Missing type specimens	571
Geographical guide to type localities	577
Eastern Hemisphere	577
Western Hemisphere	600
Collectors of the type specimens of mammals in the United States National Museum, including the Biological Surveys collection	641
Index	647

CATALOG OF THE TYPE SPECIMENS OF MAMMALS IN THE UNITED STATES NATIONAL MUSEUM, INCLUDING THE BIOLOGICAL SURVEYS COLLECTION

By Arthur J. Poole and Viola S. Schantz

INTRODUCTION

This volume is a second catalog of the type specimens of recent mammals in the United States National Museum, including those now in the collections made by the Fish and Wildlife Service, United States Department of the Interior.[1] These collections are kept in separate but adjoining laboratories in the Natural History Building of the National Museum in Washington. The present list records all the type specimens in both collections at the end of 1940, a total of 2,824, of which 1,409 are new additions since the publication of the first type list in 1909.[2] Of these specimens 1,498 are in the collection of the United States National Museum, and 1,326 are in that of the Fish and Wildlife Service.

As in the preparation of the previous edition of the type list, one author has represented the Fish and Wildlife Service and the other the National Museum. The senior author, A. J. Poole, died suddenly on July 3, 1937, when this manuscript was yet uncompleted.[3]

The joint authorship has had correspondingly the joint direction of Gerrit S. Miller, Jr., curator of mammals of the National Museum, and Dr. Hartley H. T. Jackson, in charge of the section of biological surveys, Division of Wildlife Research, Fish and Wildlife Service.

---

[1] The Bureau of Biological Survey and the Bureau of Fisheries were consolidated on June 30, 1940, under the name Fish and Wildlife Service, as an entity in the United States Department of the Interior.

[2] Lyon, Marcus Ward, Jr., and Osgood, Wilfred Hudson, Catalogue of the type-specimens of mammals in the United States National Museum, including the Biological Survey collection. U. S. Nat. Mus. Bull. 62, 325 pp., 1909.

[3] For obituary see Schantz, Viola S., Journ. Mamm. 19 (2) : 277, 1938.

1

OUTSTANDING AUTHORS AND COLLECTORS OF TYPE SPECIMENS

Among the early mammalogists who have described many of our older types are such well-known men as Audubon, Allen (J. A.), Bachman, Baird, Cassin, Cope, Coues, Elliot, Kennicott, LeConte, Peale, and True. The recent authors equally prominent are Bailey, Goldman (E. A.), Heller, Hollister, Howell (A. H.), Jackson, Lyon, Mearns, Merriam (C. H.), Miller, Nelson, and Osgood. Dr. C. Hart Merriam described 651 of the type specimens listed here, Gerrit S. Miller, Jr., 473, and E. A. Goldman, 277.

The numerous type specimens of Malayan and African mammals have come from two main sources, namely, the Malayan explorations of the late Dr. W. L. Abbott during the years 1897 to 1909 and the Smithsonian and Rainey African expeditions of 1909–1910 and 1911–1912, respectively. No less than 462 type specimens have been designated among the mammals presented to the National Museum by Dr. Abbott. Those in the African collections number about 100.

The older type specimens of North American mammals have also come from two main sources, the collections made by naturalists attached to the many governmental exploring parties sent to the Western United States about the middle of the nineteenth century and those accumulated by the more recent activities of the Biological Survey. Work in Mexico carried on by Dr. E. W. Nelson and E. A. Goldman during the years 1892 to 1906, under the auspices of the Survey, resulted in the enriching of the type collection by no less than 354 specimens. Major Goldman also collected 78 mammal types in Arizona and 49 in Panama. Vernon Bailey collected extensively west of the Mississippi River; 104 of his specimens have been made types. Major E. A. Mearns collected 81 types in the region of the Mexican boundary and among the Philippine Islands.

Most of the types have been described by recent authors, who have worked with large series of specimens and with careful modern methods of technique and discrimination. Nearly every prominent mammalogist is represented here. The majority of the types in the Biological Surveys collection were collected and described by mammalogists on the staff of the Service.

ARRANGEMENT

In this list of type specimens of mammals a strictly alphabetical order of arrangement has been adopted. It is applied alike to orders, families, genera, species, and subspecies.

The name of each genus, subgenus, species, and subspecies is recorded as in the original description, followed by a reference to the place and date of its publication. Whenever changes have been made by subsequent authors references to these are added. The current name is preceded by the sign of equality and followed by a citation of the authority for its use. An author's name is placed in parentheses when the generic name that he used in the original description has been changed.

The citations are followed by: (1) U. S. National Museum catalog number. (2) Nature of specimen, whether skin and skull, or skull only, or skin only, or skeleton, or specimen preserved in alcohol. (3) Age and sex (omission of the sex indicates that it is not known). (4) Locality. (5) Date of collecting (omission of date indicates that it is not known). (6) Name of person by whom collected, or from whom received, or from whom purchased if collector is not known. (7) Original number of specimen, usually the number in the collector's field catalog. Some Biological Survey original specimen numbers are followed by the letter X. This indicates that the specimen is entered in the "X Catalog" of the Fish and Wildlife Service, in which are recorded specimens acquired by exchange or purchase or received from or collected by persons other than members of the permanent staff. (8) Date when specimen was cataloged, when date of collection is unknown. (9) The condition of the specimen at the present time is briefly stated. Skull conditions are graded as follows:

Grade A=Skull showing all essential characters.
Grade B=Skull sufficiently defective to lack some essential characters.
Grade C=Skull lacking most of the essential characters.
Grade D=Skull fragmentary.

Examples of the four grades might be as follows:

Grade A.—Complete, or lacking some unimportant part on one side only.
Grade B—Lacking both zygomas.
Grade C—Lacking posterior or anterior portion of skull.
Grade D—Nothing but fragments.

Finally, the reasons are given for considering a particular specimen as a type when it was not clearly so designated by the original author. In the case of many early descriptions it is difficult to determine whether any individual specimen formed the principal basis of the description. In these cases, where no type was indicated by the writer, preference has been given to specimens that have been figured or to the ones that seem to be the most minutely described or measured among those originally in hand. The views of subsequent writers have also been considered in the selection of the type. In some cases it has been found necessary to regard several specimens as cotypes of a species. In a few cases the evidence for regarding particular specimens as types is very unsatisfactory. Consequently a few of the specimens here listed may not strictly be regarded as types in the present meaning of the word.

251543—42——2

Since a single type sometimes has more than one number, a few words about the cataloging of these specimens seem desirable. In the records of the National Museum two systems of cataloging have been used: First, a "double entry" system, in which all the skulls were entered in one catalog and all skins and alcoholic specimens in another. The complete number of a specimen so cataloged is indicated by a fraction; thus, No. $\frac{1163}{2045}$ on a skin means skin No. 1163, to which belongs skull No. 2045; while $\frac{2045}{1163}$ on a skull means skull No. 2045, to which belongs skin No. 1163. At the suggestion of Frank H. Hitchcock, then a clerk in the Biological Survey, this cumbersome method was abandoned at the end of the year 1892 in favor of a "single entry" system in which each individual is given one number regardless of whether it is preserved as a skin, skull, skeleton, or alcoholic specimen. The new system began with No. 50001 in January 1893. Since that date there have been no separate entries for skins and skulls, one number being used for each entire specimen.

The type specimens have been taken out of the regular study collections and placed in separate storage cases plainly labeled on the outside "Types," where they receive special care and attention.

SUMMARY OF THE LIST OF TYPES

The present catalog includes types, cotypes, lectotypes, and chirotypes, as defined by Thomas (Proc. Zool. Soc. London, 1893, p. 241) and Schuchert (U. S. Nat. Mus. Bull. 53, pt. 1, p. 7, 1895). Appended to the catalog of type specimens now actually in the two collections is a list of those, 21 in number, that should be in these collections, but are now apparently lost or destroyed (p. 571). The number of types, cotypes, lectotypes, or chirotypes in each of the families represented in the two collections is shown in table 1.

EXPLANATION OF SYMBOLS

A dagger (†) is placed before the scientific name of a type in the Biological Surveys collection. An asterisk (*) indicates that the specimen is in the National Museum collection.

TABLE 1.—*Number of type specimens of mammals in the United States National Museum at the end of the year 1940, arranged by order and family*

Order and family	Number of types	Order and family	Number of types
ARTIODACTYLA:		MARSUPIALIA:	
Antilocapridae	3	Caenolestidae	1
Bovidae	41	Didelphiidae	21
Cervidae	40	Phalangeridae	1
Hippopotamidae	2	PERISSODACTYLA:	
Moschidae	1	Equidae	1
Suidae	13	Tapiridae	2
Tayassuidae	10	PINNIPEDIA:	
Tragulidae	40	Otariidae	1
CARNIVORA:		Phocidae	6
Bassariscidae	8	PRIMATES:	
Canidae	62	Alouattidae	2
Felidae	46	Aotidae	1
Hyaenidae	1	Callitrichidae	1
Mustelidae	91	Cebidae	4
Procyonidae	34	Cercopithecidae	66
Protelidae	1	Galagidae	2
Ursidae	86	Hylobatidae	3
Viverridae	41	Lorisidae	3
CETACEA:		Tarsiidae	5
Balaenopteridae	1	RODENTIA:	
Delphinidae	15	Aplodontiidae	5
Iniidae	1	Bathyergidae	1
Kogiidae	2	Castoridae	8
Ziphiidae	5	Chinchillidae	1
CHIROPTERA:		Cricetidae	505
Emballonuridae	9	Cuniculidae	1
Hipposideridae	7	Dasyproctidae	5
Megadermidae	6	Dipodidae	3
Molossidae	24	Echimyidae	19
Natalidae	7	Erethizontidae	2
Noctilionidae	1	Geomyidae	216
Phyllostomidae	56	Graphiuridae	4
Pteropidae	25	Heteromyidae	174
Rhinolophidae	11	Hydrochoeridae	2
Thyropteridae	1	Hystricidae	5
Vespertilionidae	81	Idiuridae	1
DERMOPTERA:		Muridae	254
Galeopithecidae	10	Muscardinidae	1
HYRACOIDEA:		Myocastoridae	1
Procaviidae	2	Pedetidae	3
INSECTIVORA:		Rhizomyidae	1
Erinaceidae	3	Sciuridae	366
Macroscelididae	3	Spalacidae	3
Nesophontidae	3	Thryonomyidae	1
Soricidae	163	Zapodidae	15
Talpidae	17	XENARTHRA:	
Tupaiidae	32	Bradypodidae	1
LAGOMORPHA:		Dasypodidae	2
Leporidae	75	Megalonychidae	2
Ochotonidae	21	Myrmecophagidae	2
		Total	2,824

Order ARTIODACTYLA: Even-toed Ruminants

Family ANTILOCAPRIDAE: Pronghorns

Genus ANTILOCAPRA Ord

†Antilocapra americana mexicana Merriam.

Proc. Biol. Soc. Washington 14: 31, Apr. 5, 1901.

98742. Skin and skull. Young adult male. Sierra en Media, Chihuahua, Mexico. October 4, 1899. Collected by E. W. Nelson and E. A. Goldman. Original number 13989.

Well-made skin in good condition; skull Grade A.

†Antilocapra americana oregona Bailey.

Proc. Biol. Soc. Washington 45: 45, Apr. 2, 1932.

205548. Skin and skull. Adult male. Hart Mountain, Warner Mountains, altitude 5,500 feet, Lake County, Oreg. September 22, 1914. Collected by Luther J. Goldman. Original number 2040.

Tanned skin in good condition; skull Grade A.

†Antilocapra americana peninsularis Nelson.

Proc. Biol. Soc. Washington 25: 107, June 29, 1912.

178445. Skin and skull. Adult male. 45 miles south of Calmalli, Lower California, Mexico. February 4, 1912. Collected by E. W. Funcke. Original number 42 (9074-X).

Well-made skin in good condition; skull Grade A.

Family BOVIDAE: Cattle, Antelope, Sheep, Goats

Genus ADENOTA Gray

*Adenota kob alurae Heller.

Smithsonian Misc. Coll. 61 (7) : 11, July 31, 1913.

164788. Skin and skull. Adult male. Rhino Camp, Lado Enclave, Uganda, Africa. January 14, 1910. Collected by Theodore Roosevelt. Original number (Heller) 590.

Flat skin in good condition: skull Grade A, upper left and right first premolars missing, apparently owing to age. Incisiform teeth removed for safe preservation.

6

Genus ALCELAPHUS Blainville

*Bubalis cokei kongoni Heller.

Smithsonian Misc. Coll. 60 (8) : 5, Nov. 2, 1912.

=*Alcelaphus cokii kongoni* (Heller). See Hollister, U. S. Nat. Mus. Bull. 99 (pt. 3) : 67, June 20, 1924.

162992. Skin and skull. Adult male. Loita Plains, Southern Guaso Nyiro River, British East Africa [=Kenya]. June 19, 1909. Collected by Theodore Roosevelt. Original number (Heller) 139.

Flat skin in good condition; skull Grade B, the entire left half of brain case blown off by impact of bullet, but pieces saved; coronoid process of left mandible missing. Incisiform teeth removed for safe preservation.

*Bubalis lelwel keniae Heller.

Smithsonian Misc. Coll. 61 (17) : 3, Oct. 21, 1913.

=*Alcelaphus lelwel keniae* (Heller). See Hollister, U. S. Nat. Mus. Bull. 99 (pt. 3) : 70, June 20, 1924.

182009. Skin and skull. Adult male. North Kenia Plateau, 20 miles northeast of Nyeri near the Meru road, British East Africa [=Kenya]. June 27, 1911. Collected by Paul J. Rainey. Original number (Heller) 2310.

Flat skin in good condition; skull Grade A. Incisiform teeth removed for safe preservation.

*Bubalis lelwel roosevelti Heller.

Smithsonian Misc. Coll. 60 (8) : 7, Nov. 2, 1912.

=*Alcelaphus lelwel roosevelti* (Heller). See Hollister, U. S. Nat. Mus. Bull. 99 (pt. 3) : 69, June 20, 1924.

164734. Skin and skull. Adult male. Nimule, Uganda, Africa [=Anglo-Egyptian Sudan]. February 15, 1910. Collected by Theodore Roosevelt. Original number (Heller) 643.

Flat skin in good condition; skull Grade A. Left pterygoid, left premaxillary, and nasal region slightly damaged by bullet. Incisiform teeth removed for safe preservation.

*Bubalis nakurae Heller.

Smithsonian Misc. Coll. 60 (8) : 6, Nov. 2, 1912.

=*Alcelaphus cokii nakurae* (Heller). See Hollister, U. S. Nat. Mus. Bull. 99 (pt. 3) : 68, June 20, 1924.

163130. Skin and skull. Adult male. Nakuru, British East Africa [=Kenya]. October 20, 1909. Collected by Kermit Roosevelt. Original number (Heller) 418.

For skin in good condition; skull Grade A. Incisiform teeth removed for safe preservation.

Genus BISON Hamilton Smith

†**Bison bison oregonus** Bailey.

Proc. Biol. Soc. Washington 45: 48, Apr. 2, 1932.

250145. Skull and nearly complete skeleton. Adult male. The dry bed of Malheur Lake, Harney County, Oreg. November 1931. Collected by George M. Benson. Original number 26728-X.

Skull Grade A, except horn-sheaths and incisors missing.

Genus CEPHALOPHUS Hamilton Smith

***Cephalophus monticola musculoides** Heller.

Smithsonian Misc. Coll. 61 (7) : 9, July 31, 1913.

182388. Skin and skull. Adult male. Kagumega Forest, British East Africa [=Kenya]. February 13, 1912. Collected by Edmund Heller. Original number 2709.

Flat skin in good condition except that head had been severed from body and is now sewed on again; skull Grade A. Incisiform teeth removed for safe preservation.

***Cephalophus spadix** True.

Proc. U. S. Nat. Mus. 13: 227, Sept. 16, 1890.

$\frac{18965}{34707}$. Skin and skull. Adult male. In high altitudes, Mount Kilimanjaro, German East Africa [=Tanganyika Territory]. 1889–90. Collected by W. L. Abbott. Original number 21.

Skin in good condition, formerly mounted. In November 1912 it was made into a study skin; skull Grade A.

No type specified, but the entire description is based on one specimen, the above, designated by number.

Genus CONNOCHAETES Lichtenstein

***Gorgon albojubatus mearnsi** Heller.

Smithsonian Misc. Coll. 61 (17) : 1, Oct. 21, 1913.

=*Connochaetes albojubatus mearnsi* (Heller). See Hollister, U. S. Nat. Mus. Bull. 99 (pt. 3) : 77, June 20, 1924.

163020. Skin and skull. Adult male. Loita Plains, British East Africa [=Kenya]. June 28, 1909. Collected by Edgar A. Mearns. Original number 6809.

Flat skin in good condition; skull Grade A. First upper left premolar and all incisors except one missing.

Genus EGOCERUS Desmarest

***Ozanna roosevelti** Heller.

Smithsonian Misc. Coll. 54 (6) : 1, Feb. 28, 1910.

=*Egocerus niger roosevelti* (Heller). See Hollister, U. S. Nat. Mus. Bull. 99 (pt. 3) : 126, June 20, 1924.

163166. Skin and skull. Adult female. Shimba Hills, British East Africa [=Kenya]. December 12, 1909. Collected by Kermit Roosevelt. Original number (Heller) 550.

Flat skin in good condition; skull Grade A. Incisiform teeth removed for safe preservation.

Genus GAZELLA Blainville

*Gazella granti raineyi Heller.

Smithsonian Misc. Coll. 61 (7) : 6, July 31, 1913.

182016. Skin and skull. Adult male. Isiola River, Northern Guaso Nyiro, British East Africa [=Kenya]. June 30, 1911. Collected by Paul J. Rainey. Original number (Heller) 2318.

Flat skin in good condition; skull Grade A. Posterior two-thirds of right mandible, containing entire tooth row, missing. Incisiform teeth removed for safe preservation.

*Gazella granti roosevelti Heller.

Smithsonian Misc. Coll. 61 (7) : 4, July 31, 1913.

162009. Skin and skull. Adult male. Kitanga Farm, Athi Plains, British East Africa [=Kenya]. April 26, 1909. Collected by Theodore Roosevelt. Original number (Heller) 8.

Flat skin in good condition; skull Grade A. Incisiform teeth removed for safe preservation.

*Gazella granti serengetae Heller.

Smithsonian Misc. Coll. 61 (7) : 5, July 31, 1913.

$\frac{18961}{34703}$. Skin and skull. Adult male. Taveta, western edge of the Serengeti Plains, Kilimanjaro district, British East Africa [=Kenya]. Collected by W. L. Abbott. Original number 23. Cataloged June 24, 1890.

Flat skin in good condition; skull Grade B. Lower jaw missing.

Genus KOBUS A. Smith

*Kobus defassa raineyi Heller.

Smithsonian Misc. Coll. 61 (13) : 5, Sept. 16, 1913.

181961. Skin and skull. Adult male. Amala River, British East Africa [=Kenya]. May 14, 1911. Collected by Paul J. Rainey. Original number (Heller) 2203.

Flat skin in good condition; skull Grade A. Incisiform teeth removed for safe preservation.

*Kobus ellipsiprymnus kuru Heller.

Smithsonian Misc. Coll. 61 (13) : 6, Sept. 16, 1913.

$\frac{18950}{34694}$. Skin and skull. Immature male. Taveta, Kilimanjaro district, British East Africa [=Kenya]. 1888. Collected by W. L. Abbott. Original number 27.

Flat skin in good condition; skull Grade A, lower jaw missing. At the time this subspecies was described the skull could not be located. In 1921 it was found in the collection but minus the lower jaw.

Genus NESOTRAGUS von Düben

*Nesotragus moschatus deserticola Heller.

Smithsonian Misc. Coll. 61 (7) : 2, July 31, 1913.

182261. Skin and skull. Old female. Maji-ya-chumvi, British East Africa [=Kenya]. December 9, 1911. Collected by Edmund Heller. Original number 2574.

Flat skin in good condition; skull Grade A. Incisiform teeth removed for safe preservation.

Genus OREOTRAGUS A. Smith

*Oreotragus oreotragus aureus Heller.

Smithsonian Misc. Coll. 61 (13): 7, Sept. 16, 1913.

182149. Skin and skull. Adult female. Summit of Mount Lololokwi, north of the Northern Guaso Nyiro River, British East Africa [=Kenya]. September 15, 1911. Collected by Edmund Heller. Original number 2458.

Flat skin in good condition; skull Grade B, both bullae broken. Incisiform teeth removed for safe preservation.

Genus ORYX Blainville

*Oryx annectens Hollister.

Smithsonian Misc. Coll. 56 (2) : 7, Mar. 31, 1910.

=Oryx beisa annectens Hollister. See Roosevelt, African Game Trails, Amer. ed.: 475, 1910.

155436. Skin only. Vicinity of Guaso Nyiro River, Laikipia Plateau, British East Africa [=Kenya]. August 8, 1908. Collected by John Jay White.

Flat body skin in good condition.

Genus OUREBIA Laurillard

*Ourebia microdon Hollister.

Smithsonian Misc. Coll. 56 (2) : 4, Mar. 31, 1910.

=Ourebia ourebi cottoni Thomas and Wroughton. See Schwarz, Deutsch. Zent.-Afr.-Exped. 1910–11, Erg. 2, 1: 963, 1920.

155422. Skull, without jaws. Adult male. South of the Nzoia River on the Guas Ngishu Plateau, British East Africa [=Kenya]. Summer 1908. Collected by John Jay White.

Skull Grade A.

*Ourebia montana aequatoria Heller.

Smithsonian Misc. Coll. 60 (8) : 12, Nov. 2, 1912.

164713. Skin and skull. Adult male. Rhino Camp, Lado Enclave, Uganda, Africa. January 12, 1910. Collected by Theodore Roosevelt. Original number (Heller) 608.

Flat skin in good condition; skull Grade A. Incisiform teeth removed for safe preservation.

Genus OVIS Linnaeus

*Ovis canadensis auduboni Merriam.

Proc. Biol. Soc. Washington 14: 31, Apr. 5, 1901.

$\frac{1520}{22610}$. Skin (lost) and skull. Young adult male. "Upper Missouri." Probably collected in the Badlands of South Dakota in 1855 by F. V. Hayden. Skin of head cataloged June 21, 1856; skull cataloged April 27, 1887.

Skull and horns, No. 22610, in good condition. Incisiform teeth removed for safe preservation. Catalog calls for skin of the head, No. 1520, which cannot be found.

*Ovis canadensis gaillardi Mearns.

U. S. Nat. Mus. Bull. 56 (pt. 1) : 240, Apr. 13, 1907.

59906. Skin and skull. Immature female. Gila Mountains, between Tinajas Atlas and the Mexican boundary line, in Yuma County, Ariz. February 21, 1894. Collected by Edgar A. Mearns. Original number 3029.

Flat folded skin in good condition; skull Grade B. The first permanent molars are in place above, the second molars are just appearing above the alveoli.

†Ovis canadensis texiana Bailey.

Proc. Biol. Soc. Washington 25: 109, June 29, 1912.

118255. Adult female. Skin and skull. Guadalupe Mountains, western Texas. September 2, 1902. Collected by Vernon Bailey. Original number 7971.

Well-made skin in good condition; skull Grade B.

†Ovis canadensis weemsi Goldman.

Proc. Biol. Soc. Washington 50: 29, Apr. 2, 1937.

261696. Skin and skull. Adult female. Cajon de Tecomaja, Sierra de la Giganta, about 30 miles south of Cerro de la Giganta, southern Lower California, Mexico. April 13, 1936. Collected and presented by F. Carrington Weems. Original number 27590-X.

Tanned skin in good condition except for small perforation on left shoulder and another on left abdominal region; skull Grade A.

†Ovis mexicana Merriam.

Proc. Biol. Soc. Washington 14: 30, Apr. 5, 1901.

99342. Skin and skull. Adult male. Lake Santa Maria, Chihuahua, Mexico. September 16, 1899. Collected by E. W. Nelson and E. A. Goldman. Original number 13974.

Well-made skin in good condition; skull Grade A.

*Ovis montana dalli Nelson.   Cotypes.

Proc. U. S. Nat. Mus. 7: 12, June 3, 1884.

=*Ovis dalli dalli* Nelson. See J. A. Allen, Bull. Amer. Mus. Nat. Hist. 9:112, Apr. 8, 1897.

In the original description, Nelson says: "The types of the new race are two specimens brought me by Mr. L. N. McQuesten, a fur-trader living at Fort Reliance, on the Upper Yukon River, near the point where it crosses the British boundary line. These specimens were killed by the Indians on some mountains south of Fort Yukon, and on the west bank of the river." They were taken in the winter of 1879–80. Cotypes not designated by number in the original description.

$\frac{13265}{20787}$. Skin and lower jaws. Adult female. Original number $\frac{154}{249}$.

Skin in fair condition; lower jaws Grade A. Incisiform teeth have been removed for safe preservation.

$\frac{13266}{20786}$. Skin and skull. Adult male. Original number $\frac{155}{248}$.

Skin in fair condition; skull Grade A; slight injury about foramen magnum. Incisiform teeth have been removed for safe preservation.

Both specimens were mounted by Ward's Natural Science Establishment, of Rochester, N. Y., and were on exhibition for many years. In April 1902 they were made into study skins. Each was then found to contain a wooden skull to which horns were fastened. These wooden skulls with the attached horns are still in the skins. The horns fastened to the wooden skull of the male skin are slightly larger than those that fit the horn cores of the actual skull of the same specimen. This skull was lost for many years, but it was found in the collection January 12, 1905, by Walter L. Hahn and was recognized as a long-lost cotype.

†Ovis nelsoni Merriam.

Proc. Biol. Soc. Washington 11: 218, July 15, 1897.

=*Ovis canadensis nelsoni* Merriam. See Grinnell, Univ. California Publ. Zool. 40 (2) : 210, Sept. 26, 1933.

$\frac{28383}{40487}$. Skin and skull. Adult female. Grapevine Mountains, near lat. 37° N., California-Nevada boundary line. June 4, 1891. Collected by E. W. Nelson. Original number 942.

Well-made skin in good condition; skull Grade A.

*Nemorhoedus palmeri Cragin.

Bull. Geol. Soc. Amer. 11: 611, pl. 57, Oct. 31, 1900.

=*Ovis canadensis canadensis* (Shaw). See Miller, Smithsonian Misc. Coll. 82 (14) : 1, Dec. 22, 1930.

255680.   Right humerus and right metacarpal, one epiphysis of each missing.   Cave on the "Glen Eyrie estate," in a valley or canyon about 5 miles northwest of Colorado Springs, across the mesa, Colorado.   Collected by Gen. William J. Palmer.   Received from E. R. Warren.   Cataloged October 16, 1930.

Specimens in good condition.

†Ovis sheldoni Merriam.

Proc. Biol. Soc. Washington 29 : 130, Sept. 6, 1916.

210585.   Skin and skull.   Adult male.   El Rosario, northern Sonora, Mexico.   March 10, 1916.   Collected and presented by Charles Sheldon.   Original number 14006–X.

Tanned skin in good condition; skull Grade A.

Genus PRODORCAS Pocock

*Procapra altaica Hollister.

Smithsonian Misc. Coll. 60 (19) : 1, Feb. 8, 1913.
=*Prodorcas gutturosa altaica* (Hollister).   See G. M. Allen, Mamm. China and Mongolia 2 : 1215, Sept. 3, 1940.

175179.   Skin and skull.   Adult male.   Suok Plains, near south end of Bain-Chagan Pass, Little Altai, Mongolia.   July 5, 1912. Collected by Theodore Lyman.   Original number (Hollister) 4382.

Well-made skin in good condition, left fore foot and leg to knee missing; skull Grade A.   Incisiform teeth removed for safe preservation.

Genus PSEUDOIS Hodgson

*Pseudois nayaur caesia A. B. Howell.

Proc. Biol. Soc. Washington 41 : 118, June 29, 1928.
=*Pseudois nayaur szechuanensis* (Rothschild).   See G. M. Allen, Mamm. China and Mongolia 2 : 1269, Sept. 3, 1940.

240683.   Skin and skull.   Young adult male.   Archuen, Minshan Mountains, 140 miles south of Lanchow, Kansu, China.   September 14, 1923.   Collected by F. R. Wulsin.   Original number 1129.

Flat skin in good condition; skull Grade A; the three lower right premolars broken off at alveoli.   Incisiform teeth removed for safe preservation.

Genus REDUNCA Hamilton Smith

*Cervicapra chanleri Rothschild.

Novitates Zoologicae 2 : 53, Feb. 1895.
=*Redunca fulvorufula chanleri* (Rothschild).   See Roosevelt, African Game Trails, Amer. ed., p. 475; London ed., p. 487, 1910.

$\frac{61868}{49418}$. Skin formerly mounted, and skeleton, now mounted and on exhibition. Adult male. On the slopes of the Jambine Mountains, about 45 miles north-northeast of Mount Kenia, British East Africa [=Kenya]. (See Sclater and Thomas, Book of Antelopes, 2: 183, March 1897.) 1893. Collected by William Astor Chanler.

Both skin and skeleton are in good condition. In 1912 the skin was dismounted and made into a study specimen.

The specimen was mounted in London by Rowland Ward, Ltd., and while in that establishment it was described by Walter Rothschild, who specifically designated it as the type.

*Redunca redunca tohi Heller.

Smithsonian Misc. Coll. 61 (7) : 10, July 31, 1913.
=*Redunca bohor tohi* Heller. See Hollister, U. S. Nat. Mus. Bull. 99 (pt. 3) : 103, June 20, 1924.

182289. Skin and skull. Adult female. Mariakani, British East Africa [=Kenya]. January 2, 1912. Collected by Edmund Heller. Original number 2603.

Flat skin in good condition; skull Grade A. Incisiform teeth removed for safe preservation.

Genus RHYNCHOTRAGUS Neumann

*Rhynchotragus kirkii nyikae Heller.

Smithsonian Misc. Coll. 61 (7) : 3, July 31, 1913.

182228. Skin and skull. Adult male. Ndi, near Voi, British East Africa [=Kenya]. November 1, 1911. Collected by Edmund Heller. Original number 2541.

Flat skin in good condition; skull Grade A. Incisiform teeth removed for safe preservation.

Genus RUPICAPRA Blainville

*Rupicapra faesula Miller.

Proc. Biol. Soc. Washington 25: 131, July 31, 1912.
=*Rupicapra rupicapra* Linnaeus. See Coutourier, Le Chamois, Grenoble, pt. 1, pp. 326–327, 1938. No chamois occurs in the part of Italy in which Schlüter's specimens were supposed to have been taken.

174943. Skin and skull. Adult male. "Passo Mandrioli, headwaters of the Savio River, Florence, Italy. September 1911." Purchased from Wilhelm Schlüter, of Halle, Germany.

Flat skin in good condition; skull Grade A. Incisiform teeth removed for safe preservation.

Genus STREPSICEROS Frisch

*Ammelaphus imberbis australis Heller.

Smithsonian Misc. Coll. 61 (13) ; 2, Sept. 16, 1913.

=*Strepsiceros imberbis australis* (Heller). See Hollister, U. S. Nat. Mus. Bull. 99 (pt. 3) : 130, June 20, 1924.

182073. Skin and skull. Adult female. Longaya water, Marsabit district, British East Africa [=Kenya]. July 21, 1911. Collected by Marius A. Johnston. Original number (Heller) 2380.

Flat skin in fairly good condition; a rather large piece cut out of right shoulder and considerable sloughing of hair on sides, neck, and forelegs; skull Grade B, both bullae broken. Incisiform teeth removed for safe preservation.

*Strepsiceros strepsiceros bea Heller.

Smithsonian Misc. Coll. 60 (8) : 10, Nov. 2, 1912.

163247. Skin and skull. Adult female. Donyo Gelsha on the escarpment east of Lake Baringo, British East Africa [=Kenya]. October 10, 1909. Collected by Kermit Roosevelt. Original nummer (Heller) 410.

Flat skin in good condition; skull Grade A. Incisiform teeth removed for safe preservation.

Genus SYLVICAPRA Ogilby

*Sylvicapra grimmi altivallis Heller.

Smithsonian Misc. Coll. 61 (13) : 2, Sept. 16, 1913.

164746. Skin and skull. Adult female. Aberdare Range, near Kinanagop Peak (altitude 10,500 feet), British East Africa [=Kenya]. August 10, 1909. Collected by Theodore Roosevelt. Original number (Heller) 295.

Flat skin in good condition; skull Grade A. Incisiform teeth removed for safe preservation.

*Sylvicapra grimmia deserti Heller.

Smithsonian Misc. Coll. 61 (17) : 4, Oct. 21, 1913.

182219. Skin and skull. Adult male. Voi, British East Africa [=Kenya]. October 27, 1911. Collected by Edmund Heller. Original number 2532.

Flat skin in good condition; skull Grade A; the three premolars and third molar on upper right side destroyed by shot, right pterygoid injured. Incisiform teeth removed for safe preservation.

*Sylvicapra grimmi roosevelti Heller.

Smithsonian Misc. Coll. 60 (8) : 9, Nov. 2, 1912.

164664. Skin and skull. Young adult male. Rhino Camp, Lado Enclave, Uganda, Africa. January 25, 1910. Collected by Theodore Roosevelt. Original number (Heller) 616.

Flat skin in good condition except for a rather large cut on right side of rump and some sloughing of hair; skull Grade A; first and third upper left premolars broken off at alveoli, the second one missing. The third lower premolars, both mandibles, and all incisiform teeth somewhat damaged.

Genus TRAGELAPHUS Blainville

*Tragelaphus scriptus olivaceus Heller.

Smithsonian Misc. Coll. 61 (13) : 1, Sept. 16, 1913.

182267. Skin and skull. Adult male. Maji-ya-Chumvi, British East Africa [=Kenya]. December 11, 1911. Collected by Edmund Heller. Original number 2580.

Flat skin in good condition; skull Grade A.

Family CERVIDAE: Deer

Genus ALCES Gray

†Alces americana shirasi Nelson.

Proc. Biol. Soc. Washington 27: 72, Apr. 25, 1914.

202973. Skin and skull. Adult male. Snake River, 4 miles south of Yellowstone Park, Lincoln County, Wyo. December 11, 1913. Collected by John Shive. Original number 10658-X.

Tanned skin in good condition; skull Grade A. The skull with antlers attached is at present hung on the wall of the Biological Surveys office, Room 60, United States National Museum.

*Alces gigas Miller.

Proc. Biol. Soc. Washington 13: 57, May 29, 1899.

86166. Skin and skull. Adult male. North side Tustumena Lake, Kenai Peninsula, Alaska. September 1898. Collected by Dall De Weese. Original number 16.

The skin is a complete tanned hide, folded and in good condition; skull Grade A. The skull, with antlers attached, is hung on the wall in the office of the Division of Mammals, United States National Museum.

Genus CAPREOLUS Gray

*Capreolus melanotis Miller.

Proc. Biol. Soc. Washington 24: 231, Nov. 28, 1911.

=Capreolus bedfordi bedfordi Thomas. See Jacobi, Abh. Ber. Mus. Dresden 16 (1) : 22, Apr. 15, 1923; and G. M. Allen, Mamm. China and Mongolia 2: 1162, 1165, Sept. 3, 1940.

155220. Skin and skull. Immature female. Thirty miles east of Ching-yang-fu, Kansu, China. August 14, 1909. Collected by Arthur deC. Sowerby. Original number 247.

Flat skin in good condition; skull Grade A, incisiform teeth removed for safe preservation.

Genus CERVUS Linnaeus

*Cervus canadensis nelsoni Bailey.

Proc. Biol. Soc. Washington 48: 188, Nov. 15, 1935.

$\frac{49722}{124656}$. Skin, skull, and skeleton. Adult male. Yellowstone National Park, Wyo. Born spring 1896. Sent to National Zoological Park November 1899. Collected by John Pitcher. Died September 21, 1904. Zoo No. 671-1/4.

Tanned skin in good condition; skull and skeleton Grade A; antlers have been removed from the skull.

*Cervus merriami Nelson.

Bull. Amer. Mus. Nat. Hist. 16: 7, Jan. 16, 1902.

111639. Skin and skull. Adult male. Head of Black River, White Mountains, Ariz. August 1886. Collected by E. W. Nelson.

The specimen was in the National Museum for many years without having been entered in the catalogs. The skin had data attached, but the skull was without data, and it was not known to belong with the skin until the summer of 1901. In the spring of 1901 the antlers were sawed off the skull. As both antlers and skull were without number or other data, they were thought to be of little value, and no special care was taken of them with the result that the main part of the skull became misplaced. In the summer of 1901 the antlers, in the velvet, were recognized by Nelson as belonging to the skin that he had collected 15 years before. A search was made for the skull, but only the lower jaw could be found. Nelson described the species without the complete specimen. (Cranial characters were obtained, however, from a skull in the American Museum of Natural History, New York City.) In September 1902 the missing and main part of the skull was found in one of the Museum's storage sheds, where the antlers were originally discovered.

The skin is a tanned pelt, in fair condition, worn summer pelage. The antlers, in velvet, are nearly perfect; one tip is slightly injured. The main part of the skull is perfect. The lower jaw is injured as follows: The crowns of all the incisors and lower canines are broken off, and the ascending ramus of the right half of the mandible is missing.

The skull and antlers are at present hung on the wall of the office of the Division of Mammals, United States National Museum.

†Cervus nannodes Merriam.

Proc. Biol. Soc. Washington 18: 24, Feb. 2, 1905.

135042. Skin and skull. Two-year-old male. Buttonwillow, Kern County, Calif. November 12, 1904. Collected by C. Hart Merriam and E. W. Nelson. Original number 16832 (E. W. N.).

Skin tanned and in good condition; skull Grade A.

†Cervus roosevelti Merriam.

Proc. Biol. Soc. Washington 11: 272, Dec. 17, 1897.
=*Cervus canadensis occidentalis* (Hamilton Smith).   See Lydekker, The Deer of All Lands, London, p. 101, 1898.

91579. Skin and skull. Adult male. Mount Elaine, on ridge between heads of Hoh, Elwah, and Soleduc Rivers, near Mount Olympus, Olympic Mountains, Clallam County, Wash. October 4, 1897. Collected by H. and C. Emmet.

Well-made skin in good condition; skull Grade B, antlers perfect, severed from skull at base.

Genus MAZAMA Rafinesque

†Mazama pandora Merriam.

Proc. Biol. Soc. Washington 14: 105, July 19, 1901.

108273. Skin and skull. Adult male. Tunkas, Yucatan, Mexico. February 15, 1901. Collected by E. W. Nelson and E. A. Goldman. Original number 14544.

Well-made skin in good condition; skull Grade B.

*Mazama tema cerasina Hollister.

Proc. Biol. Soc. Washington 27: 209, Oct. 31, 1914.
=*Mazama sartorii cerasina* Hollister. See J. A. Allen, Bull. Amer. Mus. Nat. Hist. 34: 542, Nov. 2, 1915.

$\frac{12206}{14206}$. Skin and skull. Young male. Talamanca, Costa Rica. 1874. Collected by William M. Gabb. Original number 54.

Fairly well-made skin in good condition; skull Grade A. Right premaxillary bone and all the incisiform teeth missing.

†Mazama tema reperticia Goldman.

Smithsonian Misc. Coll. 60 (22) : 2, Feb. 28, 1913.
=*Mazama sartorii reperticia* Goldman. See J. A. Allen, Bull. Amer. Mus. Nat. Hist. 34: 542, Nov. 2, 1915.

171673. Skin and skull. Adult male. Gatun, Canal Zone, Panama. June 21, 1911. Collected by E. A. Goldman. Original number 21178.

Well-made skin in good condition, except tip of tail missing; skull Grade A.

Genus MUNTIACUS Rafinesque

*Muntiacus bancanus Lyon.

Proc. U. S. Nat. Mus. 31: 582, Dec. 18, 1906.
=*Muntiacus muntjak bancanus* Lyon. See Lydekker, Catalogue of the Ungulate Mammals in the British Museum 4: 115, Apr. 19, 1915.

124726. Skin and skull. Adult female. Tanjong Bedaan, Island of Banka, off east coast of Sumatra. June 7, 1904. Collected by W. L. Abbott. Original number 3296.

Well-made skin in good condition; skull Grade A.

*Muntiacus rubidus Lyon.

Proc. U. S. Nat. Mus. 40: 73, Apr. 25, 1911.

=*Muntiacus muntjak rubidus* Lyon.   See Lydekker, Catalogue of the Ungulate Mammals in the British Museum 4: 16, Apr. 19, 1915.

151863. Skin and skull. Adult male. Pamukang Bay, southeastern Borneo. March 20, 1908. Collected by W. L. Abbott. Original number 5907.

Well-made skin in good condition; skull Grade A. Incisiform teeth removed for safe preservation.

Genus ODOCOILEUS Rafinesque

†Odocoileus cerrosensis Merriam.

Proc. Biol. Soc. Washington 12: 101, Apr. 30, 1898.

=*Odocoileus hemionus cerrosensis* Merriam.   See Lydekker, Catalogue of the Ungulate Mammals in the British Museum 4: 238, 1915.

80782. Skin and skull. Adult male. Cerros Island, off Lower California, Mexico. August 9, 1896. Collected by A. W. Anthony. Original number 113.

Well-made skin in good condition; skull Grade A.

*Cariacus clavatus True.

Proc. U. S. Nat. Mus. 11: 417, July 5, 1889. Preoccupied by *Cervus clavatus* Hamilton Smith (Griffith's Cuvier, Animal Kingdom 5: 315, 1827).

=*Odocoileus truei* (Merriam).   See Merriam (renaming of *clavatus* True), Proc. Biol. Soc. Washington 12: 103, Apr. 30, 1898.

$\frac{16075}{37424}$. Skin and skull. Young adult male. Open pine forests on the Segovia River, about 50 miles from the sea, northern Nicaragua. 1887, probably in July or August. Collected by C. H. Townsend.

Specimen formerly mounted, but now taken down and made into a modern study skin; in good condition. Skull that of a young adult male, with spike antlers. It is slightly injured about the pterygoids, and only small proximal portions of the premaxillae remain. All but two of the lower incisors and canines are lost and the tip of the right coronoid process is missing.

No type designated. The greater part of the description is based on No. 16075 in table on page 423, *loc. cit.* This is the specimen that True said he considered the most typical at the time he described the species and on which had been placed the red type label. It is also the specimen that Miller regarded as the type in 1901 (Proc. Biol. Soc. Washington 14: 37, footnote, Apr. 25, 1901).

†Odocoileus columbianus scaphiotus Merriam.

Proc. Biol. Soc. Washington 12: 101, Apr. 30, 1898.

=*Odocoileus hemionus columbianus* Richardson.   See Cowan, California Fish and Game 22 (3) : 215, July 1936.

251543—42——3

65162. Skin and skull. Adult male. Laguna Ranch, Gabilan Range, San Benito County, Calif. April 24, 1894. Collected by J. E. McLellan. Original number 797.

Well-made skin in good condition; skull Grade A.

†Odocoileus columbianus sitkensis Merriam.

Proc. Biol. Soc. Washington 12: 100, Apr. 30, 1898.

=Odocoileus hemionus sitkensis Merriam. See Cowan, California Fish and Game 22 (3) : 224, July 1936.

74383. Skin and skull. Immature female. Sitka, Alaska. August 8, 1895. Collected by C. P. Streator. Original number 4767.

Well-made skin in good condition; skull Grade A.

*Odocoileus costaricensis Miller.

Proc. Biol. Soc. Washington 14: 35, Apr. 25, 1901.

$\frac{11385}{13039}$. Skin and skull. Young adult male. Talamanca, between the coast and the foot of the Cordilleras, eastern Costa Rica. Latter part of 1872 or early in 1873. Collected by José C. Zeledon. Received from W. M. Gabb. Original number 46.

Specimen has been remade into a modern study skin in good condition. Skull Grade A; all incisiform teeth and the right upper and lower premolars lost.

*Dorcelaphus crooki Mearns.

Preliminary Diagnoses of New Mammals of the Genera Mephitis, Dorcelaphus, and Dicotyles, from the Mexican Border of the United States, p. 2, Feb. 11, 1897. (Reprint: Proc. U. S. Nat. Mus. 20: 468, Dec. 24, 1897.)

=Odocoileus hemionus crooki (Mearns). See Goldman and Kellogg, Journ. Mamm. 20 (4) : 507, Nov. 1939.

$\frac{20572}{35752}$. Skull and parts of skin. Adult female. Summit of Dog Mountains, Grant County, N. Mex. June 9, 1892. Collected by E. A. Mearns and F. X. Holzner. Original number 1873.

Skull Grade A; incisiform teeth injured. The following parts of the skin are present and in good condition: Skin of head, tail, two pieces of body skin, one about 360 by 200 mm., another about 160 by 70 mm., and the hind feet.

†Odocoileus hemionus canus Merriam.

Proc. Washington Acad. Sci. 3: 560, Nov. 29, 1901.

=Odocoileus hemionus crooki (Mearns). See Goldman and Kellogg, Journ. Mamm. 20 (4) : 507, Nov. 1939.

99361. Skin and skull. Adult male. Sierra en Media, Chihuahua, Mexico. October 7, 1899. Collected by E. W. Nelson and E. A. Goldman. Original number 13996.

Well-made skin in good condition; skull Grade B.

*Dorcelaphus hemionus eremicus Mearns.

Preliminary Diagnoses of New Mammals of the Genera *Mephitis, Dorcelaphus,* and *Dicotyles,* from the Mexican Border of the United States, p. 4, Feb. 11, 1897. (Reprint: Proc. U. S. Nat. Mus. 20: 470, Dec. 24, 1897.)

=*Odocoileus hemionus eremicus* (Mearns). See Thompson, Forest and Stream 51: 286, Oct. 8, 1898.

63403. Skin (no skull). Adult male. Sierra Seri, near the Gulf of California, opposite Tiburon Island, in the most arid portion of Sonora, Mexico. December 1895. Collected by W. J. McGee.

This skin is represented by a rug, well made and well preserved, and also by a few small fragments trimmed from the skin before it was made into a rug. Until 1902 the skin was owned by Dr. Anita N. McGee, of Washington, D. C., while the small scraps had been in the National Museum since May 20, 1896. On May 28, 1902, the rug was purchased by the Museum.

No type was designated. Mearns specified three individuals in the original description, namely, skin No. 63403, and two pairs of antlers, Nos. 59910 and 60855. The description is based primarily on the skin, and the antlers are mentioned rather incidentally at the end of the description, prefaced by this statement: "It appears to be a larger animal than the mule deer of the Eastern Desert Tract, and, unless the specimens brought home by our party are abnormal, its horns are heavier," which seems to indicate that the antlers form but a minor part of the description.

†Odocoileus hemionus sheldoni Goldman.

Journ. Mamm. 20 (4) : 496, Nov. 14, 1939.

242322. Skin and skull. Adult female. Tiburon Island, Sonora, Mexico. December 27, 1921. Collected by Charles Sheldon. Original number 22627 X.

Tanned skin in good condition; skull Grade A.

Cervus lewisii Peale. See page 574.

Cervus macrotis californicus Caton. See page 575.

*Odocoileus nelsoni Merriam.

Proc. Biol. Soc. Washington, 12: 103, Apr. 30, 1898.

76201. Skin and skull. Two-year-old male. San Cristobal, highlands of Chiapas, Mexico. October 1, 1895. Collected by E. W. Nelson and E. A. Goldman. Original number 8524.

Well-made skin in good condition; skull Grade A.

*Dorcelaphus texanus Mearns.

Proc. Biol. Soc. Washington 12: 23, Jan. 27, 1898.
=*Odocoileus texanus* (Mearns). See Thompson, Forest and Stream 51: 286, Oct. 8, 1898.

84794.   Skin and skull.   Adult male.   Fort Clark, Kinney County, Tex.   December 25, 1897.   Collected by Edgar A. Mearns. Original number 4288.

Skin in good condition; skull Grade A.   Antlers sawed off, but present. Type designated by the original number.

†Odocoileus thomasi Merriam.

Proc. Biol. Soc. Washington 12: 102, Apr. 30, 1898.

77866.   Skin and skull.   Adult male.   Huehuetan, Chiapas, Mexico. February 22, 1896.   Collected by E. W. Nelson and E. A. Goldman.   Original number 9359.

Well-made skin in good condition; skull Grade A.

†Odocoileus virginianus carminis Goldman and Kellogg.

Proc. Biol. Soc. Washington 53: 81, June 28, 1940.

265224.   Skin and skull.   Adult male.   Botellas Cañon, Sierra del Carmen, altitude 6,500 feet, northern Coahuila, Mexico. October 27, 1939.   Collected by Joseph MacDonald Dealy.   Original number 29148-X.

Tanned skin in good condition, except for perforation on left flank; skull Grade A.

*Cariacus virginianus couesi Coues and Yarrow.

Rep. Explor. and Surv. W. 100th Mer. (Wheeler), vol. 5 (Zool.): 72, 1875.

=Odocoileus couesi Coues and Yarrow.   See Thompson, Forest and Stream 51: 286, Oct. 8, 1898.

$\frac{12400}{38455}$.   Skin and skull.   Young adult male.   Camp Crittenden, Sonoita Creek, near Patagonia, between Santa Rita Mountains and Patagonia Mountains, altitude 4,000 feet, Pima County, Ariz. September 10, 1874.   Collected by J. T. Rothrock.   Original number 657.

Tanned skin in worn summer pelage and in rather poor condition; skull Grade A, except lower jaw missing.

*Odocoileus virginanus dacotensis Goldman and Kellogg.

Proc. Biol. Soc. Washington 53: 82, June 28, 1940.

$\frac{2879}{1837}$.   Skull without antlers, no skin.   Adult male.   White Earth River, Mountrail County, N. Dak.   1856.   Collected by F. V. Hayden, surgeon and naturalist with Lt. G. K. Warren during the exploration of the upper Missouri and Yellowstone Rivers.

Skull Grade B.

*Odocoileus virginianus hiltonensis Goldman and Kellogg.

Proc. Biol Soc. Washington 53 : 83, June 28, 1940.

256015. Skin and skull. Adult male. Hilton Head Island, Beaufort County, S. C. December 9, 1930. Collected by W. L. Brown. Original number 1.

Tanned skin in good condition; skull Grade A.

†Odocoileus virginianus miquihuanensis Goldman and Kellogg.

Proc. Biol. Soc. Washington 53 : 84, June 28, 1940.

94071. Skin and skull. Adult female. Sierra Madre Oriental, altitude 6,500 feet, near Miquihuana, southwestern Tamaulipas, Mexico. June 9, 1898. Collected by E. W. Nelson and E. A. Goldman. Original number 12511.

Flat stuffed skin in good condition; skull Grade B.

†Odocoileus virginianus nigribarbis Goldman and Kellogg.

Proc. Biol. Soc. Washington 53 : 85, June 28, 1940.

265213. Skin and skull (antlers shed). Adult male. Blackbeard Island, McIntosh County, Ga. April 21, 1939. Collected by E. A. Goldman. Original number 24014.

Tanned skin (worn winter pelage) in good condition except for bullet hole on right shoulder and another on middle of back; skull Grade A.

†Odocoileus virginianus oaxacensis Goldman and Kellogg.

Proc. Biol. Soc. Washington 53 : 85, June 28, 1940.

68242. Skin and skull. Adult male. Mountains 15 miles west of Oaxaca, altitude 9,500 feet, Oaxaca, Mexico. September 15, 1894. Collected by E. W. Nelson and E. A. Goldman. Original number 6765.

Flat, stuffed skin in good condition; skull Grade B.

†Odocoileus virginianus ochrourus Bailey.

Proc. Biol. Soc. Washington 45 : 43, Apr. 2, 1932.

159353. Skin and skull. Adult male. Coolin, south end of Priest Lake, Bonner County, Idaho. December 27, 1908. Collected by Frank Lemmer. Original number 7483–X.

Well-made skin in good condition; skull Grade C.

†Odocoileus virginianus seminolus Goldman and Kellogg.

Proc. Biol. Soc. Washington 53 : 86, June 28, 1940.

265557. Skin and skull (antlers in velvet). Adult male. Ten miles northeast of Everglades, Collier County, Fla. April 13, 1940. Collected by R. H. Tabb. Original number 29415–X.

Tanned skin in good condition; skull Grade A.

†**Odocoileus virginianus taurinsulae** Goldman and Kellogg.

Proc. Biol. Soc. Washington 53: 87, June 28, 1940.

265356. Skin and skull. Adult male. Bulls Island, Charleston County, S. C. December 18, 1939. Collected by W. P. Baldwin. Original number 29214–X.

Tanned skin in good condition except for some loss of hair across shoulders and a perforation along upper outer side of right foreleg; skull Grade A.

*****Odocoileus virginianus venatorius** Goldman and Kellogg.

Proc. Biol. Soc. Washington 53: 88, June 28, 1940.

256049. Skin and skull. Young adult male. Hunting Island, Beaufort County, S. C. December 12, 1930. Collected by W. L. Brown.

Tanned skin in good condition; skull Grade A.

†**Odocoileus virginianus veraecrucis** Goldman and Kellogg.

Proc. Biol. Soc. Washington 53: 89, June 28, 1940.

93192. Skin and skull. Adult female. Chijol, altitude 200 feet, northern Veracruz, Mexico. May 10, 1898. Collected by E. W. Nelson and E. A. Goldman. Original number 12363.

Flat stuffed skin in fair condition; skull Grade A.

Genus RANGIFER Hamilton Smith

*****Rangifer excelsifrons** Hollister.

Smithsonian Misc. Coll. 56 (35) : 5, Feb. 7, 1912.
=*Rangifer arcticus stonei* Allen. See Murie, North Amer. Fauna 54: 76, June 1935.

16755. Skull only. Adult male. Meade River, near Point Barrow, Alaska. March 1883. Collected by P. H. Ray. Original number 1496.

Skull Grade A. Atlas and first cervical vertebra saved. All incisiform teeth missing.

*****Rangifer fortidens** Hollister.

Smithsonian Misc. Coll. 56 (35) : 3, Feb. 7, 1912.
=*Rangifer arcticus fortidens* Hollister. See Jacobi, Das Rentier, Erganzungs-band zum Zool. 96: 94, Nov. 1931.

174505. Skin and skull. Adult male. Head of Moose Pass branch of Smoky River, Alberta, Canada. July 29, 1911. Collected by N. Hollister and C. D. Walcott, Jr. Original number 3826.

Flat skin in good condition; skull Grade A. Antlers in the velvet and in good condition.

*Rangifer phylarchus Hollister.

Smithsonian Misc. Coll. 56 (35) : 6, Feb. 7, 1912.

=*Rangifer tarandus phylarchus* Hollister. See Lydekker, Catalogue of the Ungulate Mammals in the British Museum 4: 245, 1915.

21343. Skull only. Adult male. Southeastern Kamchatka, Siberia. 1883. Collected by Leonhard Stejneger. Original number 2709.

Skull Grade B.

Genus RUSA Hamilton Smith

*Rusa nigellus Hollister.

Proc. U. S. Nat. Mus. 46: 332, Dec. 31, 1913.

144711. Skin and skull. Adult male. Mount Malindang, altitude 8,000 feet, Mindanao, Philippine Islands. May 30, 1906. Collected by Edgar A. Mearns. Original number 6193.

Flat, untanned skin in good condition, tips of ears slightly injured; skull Grade B. Incisiform teeth removed for safe preservation.

Family HIPPOPOTAMIDAE: Hippopotamuses

Genus HIPPOPOTAMUS Linnaeus

*Hippopotamus amphibius kiboko Heller.

Smithsonian Misc. Coll. 61 (22) : 1, Jan. 26, 1914.

162979. Skin and skeleton. Adult male. Lake Naivasha, British East Africa [=Kenya]. July 20, 1909. Collected by Theodore Roosevelt. Original number (Heller) 280.

Flat skin in good condition; skull Grade A, a fair-sized bullet hole in cranium.

*Hippopotamus constrictus Miller.

Smithsonian Misc. Coll. 54 (7) : 1, Mar. 28, 1910.

34787. Skull only. Immature male. Angola, Africa. Collected by H. Chatelain. Cataloged August 13, 1890.

Skull Grade A.

Family MOSCHIDAE: Musk Deer

Genus MOSCHUS Linnaeus

*Moschus parvipes Hollister.

Proc. Biol. Soc. Washington 24: 1, Jan. 28, 1911.

=*Moschus moschiferus parvipes* Hollister. See Lydekker, Catalogue of the Ungulate Mammals in the British Museum 4: 8, Apr. 19, 1915.

143184. Skin only. Mountains near Mok-po, South Tscholla Province, Korea. Winter 1902–3. Collected by William Lord Smith.

Flat skin in good condition.

Family SUIDAE: Pigs

Genus PHACOCHOERUS F. Cuvier

*Phacochoerus africanus bufo Heller.

Smithsonian Misc. Coll. 61 (22) : 2, Jan. 26, 1914.
=*Phacochoerus aethiopicus bufo* Heller. See Lydekker, Catalogue of the
Ungulate Mammals in the British Museum 4: 372, Apr. 19, 1915.

164796. Skull only. Immature female. Rhino Camp, Lado Enclave, Uganda, Africa. January 25, 1910. Collected by Edmund Heller. Original number 617.

Skull Grade A.

Genus SUS Linnaeus

*Sus babi Miller.

Proc. U. S. Nat. Mus. 30: 752, June 13, 1906.
=*Sus vittatus babi* Miller. See Lydekker, Catalogue of the Ungulate Mammals in the British Museum 5: 328, Apr. 19, 1915.

114283. Skin and skull. Adult male. Pulo Babi (an island about
halfway between Simalur and Pulo Bangkuru, the outermost
of the Banjak group), off west coast of Sumatra. January 14,
1902. Collected by W. L. Abbott. Original number 1413.

Flat, folded skin in good condition; skull Grade A.

*Sus babi enganus Lyon.

Proc. U. S. Nat. Mus. 52: 454, Dec. 30, 1916.

140959. Skull only. Old female. Engano Island, off west coast
of Sumatra. November 30, 1904. Collected by W. L. Abbott
Original number 3814.

Skull Grade A; the following teeth were lost during life: All upper
left incisors, all lower incisors except one, left pm $^{1-2}$, m ^{1}, right pm ^{1},
m $^{1-2}$, left pm ₁, right pm ₁.

*Sus babi tuancus Lyon.

Proc. U. S. Nat. Mus. 52: 453, Dec. 30, 1916.

114415. Skin and skull. Adult female. Tuanku Island, off west
coast of Sumatra. January 30, 1902. Collected by W. L. Abbott. Original number 1493.

Flat, folded skin in good condition; skull Grade A.

*Sus jubatulus Miller.

Proc. U. S. Nat. Mus. 30: 746, June 13, 1906.
=*Sus cristatus jubatulus* Miller. See Lydekker, Game Animals of India. . .
p. 283, 1907.

123918. Skin and skull. Adult male. Pulo Terutau (also written
Trotau and Trotto), off west coast of Malay Peninsula. November 11, 1903. Collected by W. L. Abbott. Original number
2859.

Flat, folded skin in good condition; skull Grade A.

*Sus jubatus Miller.

Proc. U. S. Nat. Mus. 30: 745, June 13, 1906.
=*Sus cristatus jubatus* Miller. See Lydekker, Game Animals of India . . ., p. 283, 1907.

83518. Skin and skull. Adult male. Trong (or Tarang), Peninsular Siam. 1896. Collected by W. L. Abbott. Original number "B."

Well-made skin in good condition; skull Grade A.

*Sus mimus Miller.

Proc. U. S. Nat. Mus. 30: 753, June 13, 1906.
=*Sus vittatus mimus* Miller. See Lydekker, Catalogue of the Ungulate Mammals in the British Museum, 4: 329, Apr. 19, 1915.

114178. Skin and skull. Adult male. Simalur Island, off west coast of Sumatra. November 25, 1901. Collected by W. L. Abbott. Original number 1353.

Flat, folded skin in good condition; bones of both hind legs and feet; skull Grade A.

*Sus natunensis Miller.

Proc. Washington Acad. Sci. 3: 117, Mar. 26, 1901.
=*Sus cristatus natunensis* Miller. See Chasen, Bull. Raffles Mus. 10: 13, Oct. 1935.

104856. Skin and skull. Adult female. Pulo Laut, Natuna Islands, South China Sea, between Malay Peninsula and Borneo. August 6, 1900. Collected by W. L. Abbott. Original number 609.

Well-made skin in good condition; skull Grade A.

*Sus niadensis Miller.

Proc. U. S. Nat. Mus. 30: 751, June 13, 1906.
=*Sus vittatus niadensis* Miller. See Lydekker, Catalogue of the Ungulate Mammals in the British Museum 4: 328, Apr. 19, 1915.

141167. Skin and skull. Adult female. Nias Island, off west coast of Sumatra. March 30, 1905. Collected by W. L. Abbott. Original number 4155.

Flat, folded skin in good condition; skull Grade A.

*Sus nicobaricus Miller.

Proc. U. S. Nat. Mus. 24: 755, May 28, 1902.
=*Sus vittatus nicobaricus* Miller. See Lydekker, Game Animals of India . . ., p. 284, 1907.

111794. Skin and skull. Young adult male. Great Nicobar Island, Nicobar Islands, Malay Archipelago. March 13, 1901. Collected by W. L. Abbott. Original number 930.

Well-made skin in good condition; skull Grade A.

*Sus oi Miller.

Proc. Biol. Soc. Washington 15: 51, Mar. 5, 1902.

=*Sus verrucosus oi* Miller.   See Schwarz, Journ. Mamm. 21 (1) : 74, Feb. 1940.

113150.   Skin and skull.   Adult male.   Banks of the Indragiri
River, about 30 miles above the mouth, eastern Sumatra.   September 20, 1901.   Collected by W. L. Abbott.   Original number
1319.

Well-made skin in good condition; skull Grade A.

*Sus peninsularis Miller.

Proc. U. S. Nat. Mus. 30: 749, June 13, 1906.

=*Sus vittatus peninsularis* Miller.   See Lydekker, Game Animals of India . . .,
p. 284, 1907.

142470.   Skull only.   Adult female.   Near foot of Gunong Pulai,
southwestern Johore, Federated Malay States.   1905.   Collected
by C. Boden Kloss.

Skull Grade A.

*Sus rhionis Miller.

Proc. U. S. Nat. Mus. 30: 749, June 13, 1906.

=*Sus vittatus rhionis* Miller.   See Lydekker, Catalogue of the Ungulate Mammals in the British Museum 4: 327, Apr. 19, 1915.

122928.   Skin and skull.   Young adult male.   Pulo Ungar, Rhio-
Linga Archipelago.   June 26, 1903.   Collected by W. L. Abbott.
Original number 2555.

Flat, folded skin in good condition; skull Grade A.

Family TAYASSUIDAE: Peccaries

Genus PECARI Reichenbach

†Pecari angulatus bangsi Goldman.

Proc. Biol. Soc. Washington 30: 109, May 23, 1917.

179976.   Skin and skull.   Male.   Boca de Cupe, altitude 250 feet,
eastern Panama.   June 19, 1912.   Collected by E. A. Goldman.
Original number 21790.

Well-made skin in good condition, except for injury to left hindfoot; skull
Grade A.

†Tayassu angulatus crassus Merriam.

Proc. Biol. Soc. Washington 14: 124, July 19, 1901.

=*Pecari angulatus crassus* (Merriam).   See Miller, U. S. Nat. Mus. Bull. 79:
383, Dec. 31, 1912.

92960.   Skin and skull.   Young adult male.   Metlaltoyuca, Puebla,
Mexico.   February 1, 1898.   Collected by E. W. Nelson and E. A.
Goldman.   Original number 12127.

Well-made skin in good condition; skull Grade A.

†**Tayassu angulatus humeralis** Merriam.

Proc. Biol. Soc. Washington 14: 122, July 19, 1901.
=*Pecari angulatus humeralis* (Merriam). See Miller, U. S. Nat. Mus. Bull. 79: 383, Dec. 31, 1912.

$\frac{33238}{45243}$. Skin and skull. Adult male (not female, as in original description). Armeria, Colima, Mexico. February 26, 1892. Collected by E. W. Nelson and E. A. Goldman. Original number 1947.

Well-made skin in good condition; skull Grade A.

†**Pecari angulatus nelsoni** Goldman.

Proc. Biol. Soc. Washington 39: 49, July 30, 1926.

77865. Skin and skull. Adult male. Huehuetan, altitude 500 feet, Chiapas, Mexico. February 24, 1896. Collected by E. W. Nelson and E. A. Goldman. Original number 9381.

Well-made skin in good condition; skull Grade A.

†**Pecari angulatus nigrescens** Goldman.

Proc. Biol. Soc. Washington 39: 49, July 30, 1926.

148735. Skin and skull. Adult female. Chamelecon, Honduras, March 10, 1901. Collected by H. S. Reed. Original number 6416–X.

Well-made skin in good condition; skull Grade A.

***Dicotyles angulatus sonoriensis** Mearns.

Preliminary Diagnoses of New Mammals of the Genera *Mephitis, Dorcelaphus,* and *Dicotyles,* from the Mexican Border of the United States, p. 3, Feb. 11, 1897. (Reprint: Proc. U. S. Nat. Mus., 20: 469, Dec. 24, 1897.)
=*Pecari angulatus sonoriensis* (Mearns). See Miller, U. S. Nat. Mus. Bull. 79: 383, Dec. 31, 1912.

$\frac{20657}{35814}$. Skin and skull. Adult male. San Bernardino River, near monument No. 77, Mexican boundary line, Sonora, Mexico. September 8, 1892. Collected by Edgar A. Mearns and F. X. Holzner. Original number 2099.

Poorly made skin (laid out on side) in good condition; skull Grade A.

†**Tayassu angulatus yucatanensis** Merriam.

Proc. Biol. Soc. Washington 14: 123, July 19, 1901.
=*Pecari angulatus yucatanensis* (Merriam). See Miller, U. S. Nat. Mus. Bull. 79: 383, Dec. 31, 1912.

108282. Skin and skull. Young adult male. Tunkas, Yucatan, Mexico. February 12, 1901. Collected by E. W. Nelson and E. A. Goldman. Original number 14534.

Well-made skin in good condition; skull Grade A.

†**Tayassu nanus** Merriam.

Proc. Biol. Soc. Washington 14: 102, July 19, 1901.
=*Pecari nanus* (Merriam). See Miller, U. S. Nat. Mus. Bull. 79: 384, Dec. 31, 1912.

108516. Skin and skull. Adult male. Cozumel Island, off coast of Quintana Roo, Mexico. April 7, 1901. Collected by E. W. Nelson and E. A. Goldman. Original number 14664.

Well-made skin in good condition; skull Grade A.

Genus TAYASSU Fischer

†**Tayassu albirostris ringens** Merriam.

Proc. Biol. Soc. Washington 14: 121, July 19, 1901.
=*Tayassu pecari ringens* Merriam. See J. A. Allen, Bull. Amer. Mus. Nat. Hist. 16: 166, July 1, 1902.

108279. Skin and skull. Adult female. Apazote, near Yohaltun, Campeche, Mexico. January 1, 1901. Collected by E. W. Nelson and E. A. Goldman. Original number 14383.

Well-made skin in good condition; skull Grade A.

*****Tayassu albirostris spiradens** Goldman.

Proc. Biol. Soc. Washington 25: 189, Dec. 24, 1912.
=*Tayassu pecari spiradens* Goldman. See Goldman, Smithsonian Misc. Coll. 69 (5): 74, Apr. 24, 1920.

$\frac{12085}{14095}$. Skin and skull. Adult. Talamanca, Costa Rica. 1874. Collected by William M. Gabb. Original number 24.

Flat skin in poor condition, numerous large holes on neck, back, and sides, with considerable sloughing of hair at various places; skull Grade A.

Family TRAGULIDAE: Chevrotains, or Mouse Deer

Genus TRAGULUS Brisson

*****Tragulus amoenus** Miller.

Proc. U. S. Nat. Mus. 26: 439, Feb. 3, 1903.
=*Tragulus javanicus amoenus* Miller. See Trouessart, Catalogus Mammalium tam Viventium quam Fossilium, Suppl., p. 689, 1904.

114563. Skin and skull. Adult male. Pulo Mansalar, off Tapanuli Bay, west coast of Sumatra. March 8, 1902. Collected by W. L. Abbott. Original number 1632.

Well-made skin in good condition; skull Grade A.

*****Tragulus bancanus** Lyon.

Proc. U. S. Nat. Mus. 31: 576, Dec. 18, 1906.
=*Tragulus javanicus bancanus* Lyon. See Lydekker, Catalogue of the Ungulate Mammals in the British Museum 4: 275, Apr. 19, 1915.

124714. Skin and skull. Adult female. Tanjong Tedong, island of Banka, off east coast of Sumatra. May 31, 1904. Collected by W. L. Abbott. Original number 3283.

Well-made skin in good condition; skull Grade A.

*Tragulus batuanus Miller.

Smithsonian Misc. Coll. 45: 2, Nov. 6, 1903.
=*Tragulus javanicus batuanus* Miller. See Trouessart, Catalogus Mammalium tam Viventium quam Fossilium, Suppl., p. 689, 1904.

121695. Skin and skull. Adult female. Tana Bala, Batu Islands, off west coast of Sumatra. February 5, 1903. Collected by W. L. Abbott. Original number 2226.

Well-made skin in good condition; skull Grade A.
Type designated as number 121697, a clerical error for 121695.

*Tragulus billitonus Lyon.

Proc. U. S. Nat. Mus. 31: 578, Dec. 18, 1906.
=*Tragulus javanicus billitonus* Lyon. See Lydekker, Catalogue of the Ungulate Mammals in the British Museum 4: 277, Apr. 19, 1915.

124929. Skin and skull. Adult male. Tanjong Batu, Billiton Island, off east coast of Sumatra. July 20, 1904. Collected by W. L. Abbott. Original number 3524.

Well-made skin in good condition; skull Grade A.

*Tragulus borneanus Miller.

Proc. Biol. Soc. Washington 15: 174, Aug. 6, 1902.
=*Tragulus javanicus borneanus* Miller. See Bonhote, Ann. Mag. Nat. Hist. (ser. 7) 11: 296, Mar. 1903.

$\frac{19205}{34924}$. Skin and skull. Adult male. Banks of Suanlamba River, British North Borneo. January 18, 1888. Collected by C. F. Adams. Original number K I=154.

Skin in fair condition; formerly mounted and on exhibition; the original color much injured by pickling fluid and exposure to light; skull Grade A.
When this species was described, the skin could not be found. At that time it was mounted and in storage. In April 1907 it was made into a study skin.

*Tragulus brevipes Miller.

Proc. U. S. Nat. Mus. 26: 443, Feb. 3, 1903.
=*Tragulus kanchil brevipes* Miller. See Trouessart, Catalogus Mammalium tam Viventium quam Fossilium, Suppl., p. 689, 1904.

114326. Skin and skull. Adult female. Pulo Bangkaru, Banjak Islands, off west coast of Sumatra. January 20, 1902. Collected by W. L. Abbott. Original number 1443.

Well-made skin in good condition; skull Grade A.

*Tragulus bunguranensis Miller.

Proc. Washington Acad. Sci. 3: 113, Mar. 26, 1901.
=*Tragulus javanicus bunguranensis* Miller. See Bonhote, Ann. Mag. Nat.
Hist. (ser. 7) 11: 296, Mar. 1903.

104604. Skin and skull. Adult male. Bunguran Island, Natuna
Islands, South China Sea, between Malay Peninsula and Borneo.
July 9, 1900. Collected by W. L. Abbott. Original number 547.

Well-made skin in good condition; skull Grade A.

*Tragulus canescens Miller.

Proc. Biol. Soc. Washington 13: 185, Dec. 21, 1900.
=*Tragulus javanicus napu* (F. Cuvier). See Chasen, Bull. Raffles Mus. 15: 194,
Apr. 1940.

83509. Skin and skull. Adult female. Tyching, Trong (or Tarang), Peninsular Siam. September 7, 1896. Collected by W. L.
Abbott.

Well-made skin in good condition; skull Grade A.

*Tragulus carimatae Miller.

Proc. U. S. Nat. Mus. 31: 55, July 23, 1906.
=*Tragulus kanchil carimatae* Miller. See Lyddeker, Catalogue of the Ungulate Mammals in the British Museum 4: 284, Apr. 19, 1915.

125062. Skin and skull. Young adult female. Telok Pai, Karimata Island, off west coast of Borneo. August 25, 1904. Collected by W. L. Abbott. Original number 3651.

Well-made skin in good condition; skull Grade A.

*Tragulus flavicollis Miller.

Proc. Biol. Soc. Washington 16: 33, Mar. 19, 1903.
=*Tragulus javanicus flavicollis* Miller. See Trouessart, Catalogus Mammalium
tam Viventium quam Fossilium, Suppl., p. 688, 1904.

115505. Skin and skull. Immature female. Pulo Sugi, Rhio-
Linga Archipelago. August 24, 1902. Collected by W. L. Abbott. Original number 1957.

Well-made skin in good condition; skull Grade A.

*Tragulus focalinus Miller.

Proc. Biol. Soc. Washington 16: 35, Mar. 19, 1903.
=*Tragulus kanchil focalinus* Miller. See Chasen, Bull. Raffles Mus. 15:201,
Apr. 1940.

120574. Skin and skull. Adult female. Near Buitenzorg. Java.
October or November 1902. Received from B. S. Rairden,
United States Consul at Batavia.

Well-made skin in good condition; skull Grade A.

*Tragulus formosus Miller.

Proc. Biol. Soc. Washington 16: 34, Mar. 19, 1903.
=*Tragulus javanicus formosus* Miller. See Chasen, Bull. Raffles Mus. 15: 195,
Apr. 1940.

115511. Skin and skull. Adult male. Pulo Bintang, Rhio-Linga Archipelago. August 19, 1902. Collected by W. L. Abbott. Original number 1907.

Well-made skin in good condition; skull Grade A.

*Tragulus fulvicollis Lyon.

Proc. U. S. Nat Mus. 34: 630, Sept. 14, 1908.

=*Tragulus kanchil fulvicollis* Lyon. See Lydekker, Catalogue of the Ungulate Mammals in the British Museum 4: 284, Apr. 19, 1915.

143519. Skin and skull. Adult female. Pulo Bengkalis, off east coast of Sumatra. March 27, 1906. Collected by W. L. Abbott. Original number 4765.

Well-made skin in good condition; skull Grade A.

*Tragulus jugularis Miller.

Proc. U. S. Nat. Mus. 26: 440, Feb. 3, 1903.

=*Tragulus javanicus jugularis* Miller. See Trouessart, Catalogus Mammalium tam Viventium quam fossilium, Suppl., p. 689, 1904.

114574. Skin and skull. Adult male. Pulo Mansalar, off Tapanuli Bay, west coast of Sumatra. March 8, 1902. Collected by W. L. Abbott. Original number 1627.

Well-made skin in good condition; skull Grade A.

*Tragulus kanchil longipes Lyon.

Proc. U. S. Nat. Mus. 34: 628, Sept. 14, 1908.

144141. Skin and skull. Adult male. Little Siak River, eastern Sumatra. November 3, 1906. Collected by W. L. Abbott. Original number 4853.

Well-made skin in good condition; skull Grade A.

*Tragulus lampensis Miller.

Proc. Biol. Soc. Washington 16: 42, Mar. 19, 1903.

=*Tragulus kanchil lampensis* Miller. See Trouessart, Catalogus Mammalium tam Viventium quam Fossilium, Suppl., p. 690, 1904.

104429. Skin and skull. Adult female. Pulo Lampee or Sullivan Island, Mergui Archipelago. February 4, 1900. Collected by W. L. Abbott. Original number 299.

Well-made skin in good condition; skull Grade A.

*Tragulus lancavensis Miller.

Proc. Biol. Soc. Washington 16: 41, Mar. 19, 1903.

=*Tragulus kanchil lancavensis* Miller. See Trouessart, Catalogus Mammalium tam Viventium quam Fossilium, Suppl., p. 690, 1904.

104412. Skin and skull. Adult female. Pulo Langkawi, off west coast of Malay Peninsula (about 75 miles north of Penang). December 7, 1899. Collected by W. L. Abbott. Original number 132.

Well-made skin in good condition; skull Grade A.

*Tragulus luteicollis Lyon.

Proc. U. S. Nat. Mus. 31: 579, Dec. 18, 1906.

=*Tragulus kanchil luteicollis* Lyon.   See Lydekker, Catalogue of the Ungulate Mammals in the British Museum 4 : 282, Apr. 19, 1915.

124733.   Skin and skull.   Adult male.   Tanjong Bedaan, island of Banka, off east coast of Sumatra.   June 12, 1904.   Collected by W. L. Abbott.   Original number 3311.

Well-made skin in good condition; skull Grade A.

*Tragulus lutescens Miller.

Proc. Biol. Soc. Washington 16 : 32, Mar. 19, 1903.

=*Tragulus javanicus lutescens* Miller.   See Trouessart, Catalogus Mammalium tam Viventium quam Fossilium, Suppl. : 688, 1904.

115507.   Skin and skull.   Adult male.   Pulo Sugi Bawa, Rhio-Linga Archipelago.   September 2, 1902.   Collected by W. L. Abbott.   Original number 2011.

Well-made skin in good condition; skull Grade A.

*Tragulus napu niasis Lyon.

Proc. U. S. Nat. Mus. 52 : 455, Dec. 30, 1916.

=*Tragulus javanicus niasis* Lyon.   See Chasen, Bull. Raffles Mus. 15 : 194, Apr. 1940.

141171.   Skin and skull.   Adult male.   Kwala Mojeia, Nias Island, off west coast of Sumatra.   March 4, 1905.   Collected by W. L. Abbott.   Original number 3979.

Well-made skin in good condition; skull Grade A.

*Tragulus natunae Miller.

Proc. Biol. Soc. Washington 16 : 38, Mar. 19, 1903.

=*Tragulus kanchil everetti* Bonhote.   See Lydekker, Catalogue of the Ungulate Mammals in the British Museum 4 : 291, Apr. 19, 1915.

104614.   Skin and skull.   Adult female.   Bunguran Island, Natuna Islands, South China Sea, between Malay Peninsula and Borneo.   July 9, 1900.   Collected by W. L. Abbott.   Original number 555.

Well-made skin in good condition; skull Grade A.

*Tragulus nigricollis Miller.

Proc. Acad. Nat. Sci. Philadelphia 54 : 145, June 11, 1902.

=*Tragulus javanicus nigricollis* Miller.   See Trouessart, Catalogus Mammalium tam Viventium quam Fossilium, Suppl., p. 688, 1904.

113121.   Skin and skull.   Adult male.   Sinkep Island, Rhio-Linga Archipelago.   September 6, 1901.   Collected by W. L. Abbott.   Original number 1292.

Well-made skin in good condition; skull Grade A.

*Tragulus nigrocinctus Miller.

Proc. U. S. Nat. Mus. 31: 250, Sept. 11, 1906.
=*Tragulus javanicus nigrocinctus* Miller. See Lydekker, Catalogue of the Ungulate Mammals in the British Museum 4: 276, Apr. 19, 1915.

122863. Skin and skull. Adult male. Pulo Kundur, Rhio-Linga Archipelago. June 21, 1903. Collected by W. L. Abbott. Original number 2531.

Well-made skin in good condition; skull Grade A.

*Tragulus pallidus Miller.

Proc. Washington Acad. Sci. 3: 116, Mar. 26, 1901.
=*Tragulus kanchil pallidus* Miller. See Bonhote, Ann. Mag. Nat. Hist. (ser. 7) 11: 296, Mar. 1903.

104616. Skin and skull. Adult female. Pulo Laut, Natuna Islands, South China Sea, between Malay Peninsula and Borneo. August 11, 1900. Collected by W. L. Abbott. Original number 625.

Well-made skin in good condition; skull Grade A.

*Tragulus perflavus Miller.

Proc. U. S. Nat. Mus. 31: 251, Sept. 11, 1906.
=*Tragulus javanicus stanleyanus* (Gray). See Chasen, Bull. Raffles Mus. 15: 195, Apr. 1940.

142125. Skin and skull. Adult female. Semimba Bay, Batam Island, Rhio-Linga Archipelago. September 21, 1905. Collected by C. Boden Kloss. Original number 28.

Well-made skin in good condition; skull Grade A.

*Tragulus pinius Lyon.

Proc. U. S. Nat. Mus. 52: 455, Dec. 30, 1916.
=*Tragulus kanchil pinius* Lyon. See Chasen, Bull. Raffles Mus. 15: 200, Apr. 1940.

121837. Skin and skull. Subadult male. Pulo Pinie, off west coast of Sumatra. March 3, 1903. Collected by W. L. Abbott. Original number 2362.

Well-made skin in good condition; skull Grade A.

*Tragulus pretiellus Miller.

Proc. U. S. Nat. Mus. 31: 253, Sept. 11, 1906.
=*Tragulus javanicus pretiellus* Miller. See Lydekker, Catalogue of the Ungulate Mammals in the British Museum 4: 274, Apr. 19, 1915.

122994. Skin and skull. Adult male. Pulo Bakong, Rhio-Linga Archipelago. July 18, 1903. Collected by W. L. Abbott. Original number 2643.

Well-made skin in good condition; skull Grade A.

*Tragulus pretiellus parallelus Miller.

Proc. Biol. Soc. Washington 24: 165, June 16, 1911.

=*Tragulus javanicus parallelus* Miller. See Lydekker, Catalogue of the Ungulate Mammals in the British Museum 4: 274, Apr. 19, 1915.

123051. Skin and skull. Adult male. Pulo Sebang, Rhio-Linga Archipelago. July 30, 1903. Collected by W. L. Abbott. Original number 2694.

Well-made skin in good condition; skull Grade A.

*Tragulus pretiosus Miller.

Proc. Acad. Nat. Sci. Philadelphia 54: 144, June 11, 1902.

=*Tragulus javanicus pretiosus* Miller. See Bonhote, Ann. Mag. Nat. Hist. (ser. 7) 11: 296, Mar. 1903.

113031. Skin and skull. Adult male. Linga Island, Rhio-Linga Archipelago. August 27, 1901. Collected by W. L. Abbott. Original number 1238.

Well-made skin in good condition; skull Grade A.

*Tragulus ravulus Miller.

Proc. Biol. Soc. Washington 16: 41, Mar. 19, 1903.

=*Tragulus kanchil ravulus* Miller. See Trouessart, Catalogus Mammalium tam Viventium quam Fossilium, Suppl., p. 689, 1904.

104417. Skin and skull. Adult female. Pulo Adang, Butang Islands, off west coast of Malay Peninsula. December 16, 1899. Collected by W. L. Abbott. Original number 161.

Well-made skin in good condition; skull Grade A. Type designated by number 104717, which is an error for 104417.

*Tragulus ravus Miller.

Proc. Biol. Soc. Washington 15: 173, Aug. 6, 1902.

=*Tragulus kanchil ravus* Miller. See Chasen, Bull. Raffles Mus. 15:198, Apr. 1940.

83506. Skin and skull. Immature female. Tyching, Trong (or Tarang), Peninsular Siam. September 6, 1896. Collected by W. L. Abbott.

Well-made skin in good condition; skull Grade A. Milk molars in place, much worn; last permanent molars not up.

*Tragulus rubeus Miller.

Proc. Biol. Soc. Washington 16: 40, Mar. 19, 1903.

=*Tragulus kanchil rubeus* Miller. See Trouessart, Catalogus Mammalium tam Viventium quam Fossilium, Suppl., p. 690, 1904.

115522. Skin and skull. Adult female. Pulo Bintang, Rhio-Linga Archipelago. August 20, 1902. Collected by W. L. Abbott. Original number 1914.

Well-made skin in good condition; skull Grade A.

*Tragulus rufulus Miller.

Proc. Washington Acad. Sci. 2: 227, Aug. 20, 1900.
=*Tragulus javanicus rufulus* Miller. See Chasen, Bull. Raffles Mus. 15: 195, Apr. 1940.

101767. Skin and skull. Young adult male. Tioman Island, off southeast coast of Malay Peninsula. September 30, 1899. Collected by W. L. Abbott.

Well-made skin in good condition; skull Grade A.

*Tragulus russeus Miller.

Proc. U. S. Nat. Mus. 26: 444, Feb. 3, 1903.
=*Tragulus kanchil russeus* Miller. See Trouessart, Catalogus Mammalium tam Viventium quam Fossilium, Suppl., p. 689, 1904.

114337. Skin and skull. Adult male. Pulo Tuangku, Banjak Islands, off west coast of Sumatra. February 5, 1902. Collected by W. L. Abbott. Original number 1518.

Well-made skin in good condition; skull Grade A.

*Tragulus russulus Miller.

Smithsonian Misc. Coll. 45: 3, Nov. 6, 1903.
=*Tragulus kanchil russulus* Miller. See Trouessart, Catalogus Mammalium tam Viventium quam Fossilium, Suppl., p. 689, 1904.

121701. Skin and skull. Adult male. Tana Bala, Batu Islands, off west coast of Sumatra. February 8, 1903. Collected by W. L. Abbott. Original number 2249.

Well-made skin in good condition; skull Grade A.

*Tragulus russulus masae Lyon.

Proc. U. S. Nat. Mus. 52: 456, Dec. 30, 1916.
=*Tragulus kanchil russulus* Miller. See Chasen, Bull. Raffles Mus. 15: 200, Apr. 1940.

121813. Skin and skull. Adult female. Tana Masa Island, off west coast of Sumatra. February 18, 1903. Collected by W. L. Abbott. Original number 2306.

Well-made skin in good condition; skull Grade A.

*Tragulus sebucus Lyon.

Proc. U. S. Nat. Mus. 40: 64, Apr. 25, 1911.
=*Tragulus javanicus sebucus* Lyon. See Lydekker, Catalogue of the Ungulate Mammals in the British Museum 4: 277, Apr. 19, 1915.

151810. Skin and skull. Adult male. Pulo Sebuku, off southeastern Borneo. January 4, 1908. Collected by W. L. Abbott. Original number 5736.

Well-made skin in good condition: skull Grade A.

*Tragulus subrufus Miller.

Proc. Biol. Soc. Washington 16: 39, Mar. 19, 1903.
=*Tragulus kanchil subrufus* Miller. See Trouessart, Catalogus Mammalium tam Viventium quam Fossilium, Suppl., p. 690, 1904.

113119. Skin and skull. Adult female. Sinkep Island, Rhio-Linga Achipelago. September 5, 1901. Collected by W. L. Abbott. Original number 1285.

Well-made skin in good condition; skull Grade A.

*Tragulus umbrinus Miller.

Proc. Biol. Soc. Washington 13: 191, Dec. 21, 1900.
=*Tragulus javanicus umbrinus* Miller. See Bonhote, Ann. Mag. Nat. Hist. (ser. 7) 11: 296, Mar. 1903.

104414. Skin and skull. Adult male. Pulo Langkawi, off west coast of Malay Peninsula. December 7, 1899. Collected by W. L. Abbott. Original number 134.

Well-made skin in good condition, except for a break about the left carpal joint; skull Grade A.

*Tragulus virgicollis Miller.

Proc. Biol. Soc. Washington 16: 37, Mar. 19, 1903.
=*Tragulus kanchil hosei* Bonhote. See Lydekker, Catalogue of the Ungulate Mammals in the British Museum 4: 290, Apr. 19, 1915.

83941. Skin and skull. Adult male. Mount Dulit, altitude 3,000 feet, Sarawak, Borneo. June 1895. Collected by Ernest and Charles Hose.

Well-made skin in good condition; skull Grade A.

Order CARNIVORA: Flesh-eaters

Family BASSARISCIDAE: Cacomistles

Genus BASSARISCUS Coues

†Bassariscus astutus arizonensis Goldman.

Proc. Biol. Soc. Washington 45: 87, June 21, 1932.

205388. Skin and skull. Adult male. Cosper Ranch, altitude 5,000 feet, Blue River, about 12 miles south of Blue, Greenlee County, Ariz. September 1, 1914. Collected by E. A. Goldman. Original number 22461.

Well-made skin in good condition; skull Grade A.

†Bassariscus astutus consitus Nelson and Goldman.

Journ. Washington Acad. Sci. 22: 487, Oct. 19, 1932.

126162. Skin and skull. Adult female. La Salada, 40 miles south of Uruapan, Michoacan, Mexico. March 16, 1903. Collected by E. W. Nelson and E. A. Goldman. Original number 16151.

Well-made skin in good condition, except for about two-thirds of tail-fur sloughed off; skull Grade A.

†**Bassariscus astutus insulicola** Nelson and Goldman.

Proc. Biol. Soc. Washington 22: 26, Mar. 10, 1909.

79034. Skin and skull. Adult female. San Jose Island, Lower California, Mexico. August 7, 1895. Collected by J. E. McLellan. Original number 1416.

Well-made skin in good condition; skull Grade A.

***Bassariscus astutus nevadensis** Miller.

Proc. Biol. Soc. Washington 26: 159, June 30, 1913.

174760. Skin and skull. Adult female. Eldorado Canyon, Clark County, Nev. January 8, 1912. Collected by Maximilian Weiss.

Well-made skin in good condition; skull Grade A.

†**Bassariscus astutus palmarius** Nelson and Goldman.

Proc. Biol. Soc. Washington 22: 26, Mar. 10, 1909.

146192. Skin and skull. Adult male. Comondu, altitude 700 feet, Lower California, Mexico. November 8, 1905. Collected by E. W. Nelson and E. A. Goldman. Original number 18500.

Well-made skin in good condition; skull Grade A.

***Bassaris raptor** Baird.

Report U. S. and Mex. Boundary Survey 2 (pt. 2) : 19, Jan. 1859.

=*Bassariscus astutus raptor* (Baird). See Hall, Univ. California Publ. Zool. 30: 39, Sept. 8, 1926.

$\frac{97}{976}$. Skin, skull, and nearly all the disarticulated skeleton (except the leg bones that are usually left in the skin). Killed in a hen roost near Washington, D. C., April 23, 1852. It was supposed to have been brought from California and kept in captivity, whence it escaped. A collar mark shows plainly around the neck.

Specimen has been made into a modern study skin and is in fair condition, although the hair has a dirty yellow color, looking as if the skin had once been preserved in alcohol. The skull is in fair condition. It is somewhat cracked posteriorly, the left jugal is lacking, and the following teeth are missing: Third left upper premolar, all the lower incisors, last right lower molar. All parts of the skeleton are apparently present except the distal bones of the limbs (these apparently inside of the skin).

The collar mark and the original label leave no doubt that this is the specimen Baird had in hand.

Hall (1926) designates "by restriction" Glenn Ellen, Sonoma County, Calif., as the type locality.

†**Bassariscus saxicola** Merriam.

Proc. Biol. Soc. Washington 11: 185, July 1, 1897.

79031. Skin and skull. Adult female. Espiritu Santo Island, Gulf of California, Lower California, Mexico. August 19, 1895. Collected by J. E. McLellan. Original number 1438.

Well-made skin in good condition; skull Grade A.

Genus JENTINKIA Trouessart

†**Jentinkia sumichrasti campechensis** Nelson and Goldman.

Journ. Washington Acad. Sci. 22: 486, Oct. 19, 1932.

108291. Skin and skull. Adult male. Apazote, near Yohaltun, central Campeche, Mexico. January 2, 1901. Collected by E. W. Nelson and E. A. Goldman. Original number 14386.

Well-made skin in good condition; skull Grade C.

Family CANIDAE: Dogs

Genus ALOPEX Kaup

†**Vulpes beringensis** Merriam.

Proc. Biol. Soc. Washington 15: 171, Aug. 6, 1902.
=*Alopex beringensis* (Merriam). See Ognev, Bull. Pacific Sci. Fishery Research Sta., Vladivostok, 2 (pt. 5): 9, 1929.

47109. Skull only. Young adult female. Bering Island, Bering Sea, Siberia, June 3, 1892. Collected by B. W. Evermann. Original number 19.

Skull grade B.

†**Vulpes hallensis** Merriam.

Proc. Washington Acad. Sci. 2: 15, Mar. 14, 1900.
=*Alopex hallensis* (Merriam). See Miller, U. S. Nat. Mus. Bull. 79: 82, Dec. 31, 1912.

98067. Skin and skull. Adult female. Hall Island, Bering Sea, Alaska. July 14, 1899. Collected by C. Hart Merriam. Shot by W. B. Devereux. Original number 2177 (A. K. Fisher).

Well-made skin in good condition; skull Grade A.

†**Vulpes lagopus innuitus** Merriam.

Proc. Biol. Soc. Washington 15: 170, Aug. 6, 1902.
=*Alopex lagopus innuitus* (Merriam). See Miller, U. S. Nat. Mus. Bull. 79: 82, Dec. 31, 1912.

107626. Skin and skull. Adult female. Korogaro River, near Point Barrow, Alaska. June 27, 1898. Collected by E. A. McIlhenny. Original number 831 (2877x).

Well-made skin in good condition; skull Grade A.

*****Vulpes lagopus ungava** Merriam.

Proc. Biol. Soc. Washington 15: 170, Aug. 6, 1902.
=*Alopex lagopus ungava* (Merriam). See Miller, U. S. Nat. Mus. Bull. 79: 82, Dec. 31, 1912.

23195. Skull only. Adult male. Fort Chimo, Labrador Peninsula, Quebec, Canada. Collected by L. M. Turner. Original number 2362. Cataloged January 15, 1889.

Skull Grade A.

†**Vulpes pribilofensis** Merriam.

Proc. Biol. Soc. Washington 15: 171, Aug. 6, 1902.
=*Alopex pribilofensis* (Merriam). See Miller, U. S. Nat. Mus. Bull. 79: 82, Dec. 31, 1912.

$\frac{30651}{42624}$. Skin and skull. Adult male. St. George Island, Pribilof Islands, Alaska. August 10, 1891. Collected by C. Hart Merriam. Original number 8.

Well-made skin in good condition; skull Grade A.

Genus CANIS Linnaeus

*****Thos aureus bea** Heller.

Smithsonian Misc. Coll. 63 (7) : 5, June 24, 1914.
=*Canis aureus bea* (Heller). See Schwarz, Jahrb. Nassauisch. Ver. Naturk. Wiesbaden 68: 62, 1915.

162904. Skin and skull. Adult female. Loita Plains, British East Africa [=Kenya]. July 4, 1909. Collected by Edmund Heller. Original number 200.

Cased skin in good condition; skull Grade A.

†**Canis estor** Merriam.

Proc. Biol. Soc. Washington 11: 31, Mar. 15, 1897.
=*Canis latrans estor* Merriam. See Nelson, Proc. Biol. Soc. Washington 45: 224, Nov. 26, 1932.

57141. Skin and skull. Adult female. Noland Ranch, San Juan River, San Juan County, Utah. November 20, 1893. Collected by J. A. Loring. Original number 1379.

Well-made skin in good condition; skull Grade A.

*****Canis floridanus** Miller.

Proc. Biol. Soc. Washington 25: 95, May 4, 1912.
=*Canis rufus floridanus* Miller. See Goldman, Journ. Mamm. 18: 45, Feb. 14. 1937.

$\frac{19376}{38488}$. Skin and skull. Adult female. Horse Landing, about 12 miles south of Palatka, Putnam County, Fla. August 12, 1890. Collected by W. L. Ralph.

Flat skin in good condition, tip of tail lacking; detached bones of all four legs (toe bones in skin) ; skull Grade A.

*****Canis frustror** Woodhouse.

Proc. Acad. Nat. Sci. Philadelphia 5: 147, recommended for publication Feb. 4, 1851.
=*Canis rufus rufus* Audubon and Bachman. See Goldman, Journ. Mamm. 18: 45, Feb. 14, 1937.

4105. Skin. Young male. Red Fork of Arkansas River probably between 96° and 98° longitude, now Cimarron River, Okla., about 100 miles west of Fort Gibson, Okla. (See Reports of Explorations and Surveys Pacific R. R. 11 : 63, and map, 1859.) August 1850. Collected by S. W. Woodhouse on exploring expedition under command of Capt. Lorenzo Sitgreaves and Lt. I. C. Woodruff, in 1849 and 1850. (See Sitgreaves' Report of an Expedition down the Zuñi and Colorado Rivers, p. 46, 1853.)

Specimen formerly mounted, but now made into a modern study skin. Baird, in Mammals of North America, and Woodhouse, in the original description, speak of skulls that have not yet lost their milk teeth. These skulls cannot now be found, nor is there any record of them in the Museum catalog.

No type designated. The two specimens procured by S. W. Woodhouse, a male and a female, both young, are not mentioned by number in Baird's Mammals, but they (Nos. 4105 and 4106) are undoubtedly the two that Woodhouse described. The entry of 4105 in the Museum catalog reads: "[*Canis latrans* written on line above] ♂ juv., Red Fork of Ark., Aug. 1850, Capt. Sitgreaves, Woodhouse, Type of *C. frustror*," all in Baird's handwriting. The other specimen, 4106 ♀ juv., has the same data but is not marked "Type of *C. frustror*."

Heretofore the type locality of *Canis frustror* has been said to be Fort Gibson, Okla. It is true that this is the only locality mentioned in the original description; but Fort Gibson was merely the place where S. W. Woodhouse "first saw" the animal. He does not tell where the specimens came from. The actual type locality can be found only by consulting the Museum catalog.

†Canis goldmani Merriam.

Proc. Biol. Soc. Washington 17: 157, Oct. 6, 1904.
=*Canis latrans goldmani* Merriam. See Nelson, Proc. Biol. Soc. Washington 45: 224, Nov. 26, 1932.

133204. Skin and skull. Adult female. San Vicente, Chiapas, Mexico, near Guatemala border. April 25, 1904. Collected by E. A. Goldman. Original number 16725.

Well-made skin in good condition; skull Grade A.

†Canis hondurensis Goldman.

Journ. Washington Acad. Sci. 26: 32, Jan. 15, 1936.

251447. Skin and skull. Adult male. Cerro Guinote, northeast of Archaga, on the Talanga road north of Tegucigalpa, Honduras. August 18, 1934. Collected by C. F. Underwood. Original number 27352–X.

Tanned skin in good condition; skull Grade A.

*Canis jamesi C. H. Townsend.

Bull. Amer. Mus. Nat. Hist. 31: 130, June 14, 1912.
=*Canis latrans jamesi* C. H. Townsend. See Nelson, Proc. Biol. Soc. Washington 45: 224, Nov. 26, 1932.

198402. Skin and skull. Adult male. Tiburon Island, Gulf of California, Sonora, Mexico. April 13, 1911. Collected by H. E. Anthony. Original number 147.

Well-made skin in good condition; skull Grade A.

†**Canis lestes** Merriam.

Proc. Biol. Soc. Washington 11: 25, Mar. 15, 1897.

=*Canis latrans lestes* Merriam. See Nelson, Proc. Biol. Soc. Washington 45: 223, Nov. 26, 1932.

$\frac{24552}{32347}$. Skin and skull. Adult male. Toyabe Mountains, near Cloverdale, Nye County, Nev. November 30, 1890. Collected by Vernon Bailey. Original number 2223.

Well-made skin in good condition; skull Grade A.

†**Canis lupus irremotus** Goldman.

Journ. Mamm. 18: 41, Feb. 14, 1937.

214869. Skin and skull. Adult male. Red Lodge, Carbon County, southwestern Montana. April 19, 1916. Collected by M. E. Martin. Original number 16243–X.

Tanned skin in good condition; skull Grade B.

*****Canis lupus labradorius** Goldman.

Journ. Mamm. 18: 38, Feb. 14, 1937.

23136. Skull only. Probably female. Vicinity of Fort Chimo, Labrador Peninsula, Quebec, Canada. 1882 or 1883. Collected by Lucien M. Turner. Original number 2190.

Skull Grade A.

†**Canis lupus ligoni** Goldman.

Journ. Mamm. 18: 39, Feb. 14, 1937.

243323. Skin and skull. Adult male. Head of Duncan Canal, Kupreanof Island, Alexander Archipelago, Alaska. November 7, 1922. Collected by J. Stokley Ligon. Original number 23022–X.

Tanned skin in good condition; skull Grade A.

†**Canis lupus mogollonensis** Goldman.

Journ. Mamm. 18: 43, Feb. 14, 1937.

224548. Skin and skull. Adult male. "S. A." Creek, 10 miles northwest of Luna, Catron County, New Mexico. July 1, 1916. Collected by Bart Burnam. Original number 18119–X.

Tanned skin in good condition; skull Grade A.

†**Canis lupus monstrabilis** Goldman.

Journ. Mamm. 18: 42, Feb. 14, 1937.

209497. Skin and skull. Adult male. 10 miles south of Rankin, Upton County, Tex. September 3, 1915. Collected by W. F. DeLong. Original number 12646X.

Tanned skin in good condition; skull Grade A.

†**Canis lupus youngi** Goldman.

Journ. Mamm. 18 : 40, Feb. 14, 1937.

224001. Skin and skull. Adult male. Harts Draw, north slope of Blue Mountains, 20 miles northwest of Monticello, San Juan County, Utah. December 11, 1916. Collected by Bert B. Turner. Original number 17413–X.

Tanned skin in good condition; skull Grade A.

***Canis mearnsi** Merriam.

Proc. Biol. Soc. Washington 11 : 30, Mar. 15, 1897.

=*Canis latrans mearnsi* Merriam. See Nelson, Proc. Biol. Soc. Washington 45 : 224, Nov. 26, 1932.

59899. Skin and skull. Young adult male. Quitobaquita, Pima County, Ariz. February 5, 1894. Collected by E. A. Mearns and F. X. Holzner. Original number 2925.

Well-made skin in good condition; skull Grade A.

†**Canis microdon** Merriam.

Proc. Biol. Soc. Washington 11 : 29, Mar. 15, 1897.

=*Canis latrans microdon* Merriam. See Nelson, Proc. Biol. Soc. Washington 45 : 224, Nov. 26, 1932.

$\frac{27555}{39654}$. Skin and skull. Adult male. Mier, on the Rio Grande, Tamaulipas, Mexico. April 28, 1891. Collected by W. Lloyd. Original number 478.

Well-made skin in good condition, except for small bare spaces on throat and right forefoot, and small perforation on right side of abdomen; skull Grade A.

†**Canis nebracensis texensis** Bailey.

North Amer. Fauna 25 : 175, Oct. 24, 1905.

=*Canis latrans texensis* Bailey. See Nelson, Proc. Biol. Soc. Washington 45 : 224, Nov. 26, 1932.

116277. Skin and skull. Young adult male. Forty-five miles southwest of Corpus Christi, Nueces County, Tex. December 14, 1901. Collected by J. M. Priour. Original number 3478–X.

Well-made skin in good condition; skull Grade A.

†**Canis nubilus baileyi** Nelson and Goldman.

Journ. Mamm. 10 : 165, May 9, 1929.

=*Canis lupus baileyi* Nelson and Goldman. See Goldman, Journ. Mamm. 18 : 45, Feb. 14, 1937.

98312. Skin and skull. Adult male. Colonia Garcia (about 60 miles southwest of Casas Grandes, altitude 6,700 feet), Chihuahua, Mexico. July 10, 1899. Collected by E. W. Nelson and E. A. Goldman. Original number 13895.

Well-made skin in good condition; skull Grade B.

†**Canis pallidus** Merriam.

Proc. Biol. Soc. Washington 11: 24, Mar. 15, 1897. (Not of Rüppell, 1826.)
=*Canis latrans nebracensis* Merriam. See Nelson, Proc. Biol. Soc. Washington 45: 223, Nov. 26, 1932.

77093. Skin and skull. Young adult male. Johnstown, Brown County, Nebr. March 12, 1896. Collected by E. E. Fast. Original number 5.

Well-made skin in good condition; skull Grade A.

†**Canis peninsulae** Merriam.

Proc. Biol. Soc. Washington 11: 28, Mar. 15, 1897.
=*Canis latrans peninsulae* Merriam. See Nelson, Proc. Biol. Soc. Washington 45: 224, Nov. 26, 1932.

74245. Skin and skull. Adult male. Santa Anita, Cape San Lucas, Lower California, Mexico. May 15, 1895. Collected by J. E. McLellan. Original number 1354.

Well-made skin; pelage ragged; skull Grade A.

†**Canis rufus gregoryi** Goldman.

Journ. Mamm. 18: 44, Feb. 14, 1937.

136731. Skin and skull. Adult male. Macks Bayou, 3 miles east of Tensas River, 18 miles southwest of Tallulah, Madison Parish, La. April 25, 1905. Collected by B. V. Lilly. Original number 5338–X.

Tanned skin in good condition; skull Grade B.

Canis torquatus Baird. See page 576.

*****Canis tundrarum** Miller.

Smithsonian Misc. Coll. 59 (15) : 1, June 8, 1912.
=*Canis lupus tundrarum* Miller. See Goldman, Journ. Mamm. 18: 45, Feb. 14, 1937.

16748. Skull only. Adult male. Point Barrow, Alaska. February 23, 1883. P. H. Ray. Original number 1119.

Skull Grade A.

†**Canis vigilis** Merriam.

Proc. Biol. Soc. Washington 11: 33, Mar. 15, 1897.
=*Canis latrans vigilis* Merriam. See Nelson, Proc. Biol. Soc. Washington 45: 224, Nov. 26, 1932.

$\frac{32627}{44550}$. Skin and skull. Young adult female. Manzanillo, Colima, Mexico. February 6, 1892. Collected by E. W. Nelson. Original number 1840.

Well-made skin in good condition; several small bare spaces on underparts and hind feet; skull Grade A.

Genus ICTICYON Lund

†Icticyon panamensis Goldman.

Smithsonian Misc. Coll. 60 (2) : 14, Sept. 20, 1912.

179046. Skin and skull. Adult female. Head of Rio Limon, Mount Pirri, altitude 5,000 feet, eastern Panama. April 28, 1912. Collected by E. A. Goldman. Original number 21655.

Well-made skin in good condition; skull Grade A.

Genus LUPULELLA Hilzheimer

*Thos mesomelas elgonae Heller.

Smithsonian Misc. Coll. 63 (7) : 6, June 24, 1914.
=Lupulella mesomelas elgonae (Heller). See Hilzheimer, Zool. Beobacht. 47 : 363, 1906.

164699. Skin and skull. Adult male. Guas Ngishu Plateau, altitude 8,000 feet, British East Africa [=Kenya]. November 13, 1909. Collected by Edmund Heller. Original number 466.

Cased skin in good condition; skull Grade A.

*Thos mesomelas mcmillani Heller.

Smithsonian Misc. Coll. 63 (7) : 6, June 24, 1914.

181483. Skin and skull. Adult female. Mtoto Andei, altitude 2,500 feet, British East Africa [=Kenya]. April 5, 1911. Collected by Edmund Heller. Original number 2003.

Cased skin in good condition; skull Grade A.

Genus OTOCYON Müller

*Otocyon virgatus Miller.

Smithsonian Misc. Coll. 52 (4) : 485, Dec. 18, 1909.

162126. Skin and skull. Adult male. Naivasha Station, British East Africa [=Kenya]. August 8, 1909. Collected by J. Alden Loring. Original number 6962.

Well-made skin in good condition; skull Grade A.

Genus SCHAEFFIA Hilzheimer

*Thos adustus bweha Heller.

Smithsonian Misc. Coll. 63 (7) : 3, June 24, 1914.
=Schaeffia adustus bweha (Heller). See Hilzheimer, Zool. Beobacht. 47 : 364, 1906.

182342. Skin and skull. Adult male. Kisumu, British East Africa [=Kenya]. January 20, 1912. Collected by Edmund Heller. Original number 2663.

Cased skin in good condition; skull Grade A.

*Thos adustus notatus Heller.

Smithsonian Misc. Coll. 63 (7) : 4, June 24, 1914.

=*Schaeffia adustus notatus* (Heller). See Hilzheimer, Zool. Beobacht. 47: 364, 1906.

181486. Skin and skull. Young adult male. Loita Plains, British East Africa [=Kenya]. April 16, 1911. Collected by Edmund Heller. Original number 2033.

Cased skin in good condition; skull Grade A.

Genus UROCYON Baird

*Urocyon californicus townsendi Merriam.

North Amer. Fauna 16: 103, Oct. 28, 1899.

=*Urocyon cinereoargenteus townsendi* Merriam. See Grinnell, Univ. California Publ. Zool. 40 (2) : 110, Sept. 26, 1933.

14130. Skin only. Adult. Baird, Shasta County, Calif. November 11, 1893. Collected by C. H. Townsend. Original number 49.

Well-made skin in good condition. Although Townsend collected skulls of gray foxes at Baird, there is no record of a skull for this skin.

†Urocyon catalinae Merriam.

Proc. Biol. Soc. Washington 16: 74, May 29, 1903.

=*Urocyon littoralis catalinae* Merriam. See Grinnell, Univ. California Publ. Zool. 40 (2) : 112, Sept. 26, 1933.

$\frac{33223}{45228}$. Skin and skull. Adult male. Santa Catalina Island, Santa Barbara Islands, Los Angeles County, Calif. April 14, 1892. Collected by C. P. Streator. Original number 1801.

Well-made skin in good condition; skull Grade A.

†Urocyon cinereoargenteus borealis Merriam.

Proc. Biol. Soc. Washington 16: 74, May 29, 1903.

119725. Skin and skull. Adult male. Marlboro, 7 miles from Monadnock, Cheshire County, N. H. November 17, 1902. Collected by A. H. Thayer. Original number 3847–X.

Well-made skin in good condition; skull Grade B.

*Urocyon cinereoargenteus californicus Mearns.

Preliminary Diagnoses of New Mammals of the Genera *Lynx*, *Urocyon*, *Spilogale*, and *Mephitis*, from the Mexican Boundary Line, p. 3, Jan. 12, 1897. (Reprint: Proc. U. S. Nat. Mus. 20: 459, Dec. 24, 1897.)

62873. Skin and skull. Old adult male. San Jacinto Mountains, altitude 8,000 feet, Riverside County, Calif. July 6, 1895. Collected by A. W. Anthony. Original number 41.

Well-made skin in good condition; skull Grade A.

†**Urocyon cinereoargenteus colimensis** Goldman.

Journ. Washington Acad. Sci. 28: 495, Nov. 15, 1938.

$\frac{33519}{45564}$. Skin and skull. Adult male. City of Colima, 3 miles west, altitude 1,700 feet, Colima, Mexico. April 1, 1892. Collected by E. W. Nelson and E. A. Goldman. Original number 2378.

Well-made skin in good condition; skull Grade A.

†**Urocyon cinereoargenteus orinomus** Goldman.

Journ. Washington Acad. Sci. 28: 497, Nov. 15, 1938.

58411. Skin and skull. Adult female. Orizaba, altitude 4,000 feet, Veracruz, Mexico. January 18, 1894. Collected by E. W. Nelson and E. A. Goldman. Original number 5679.

Well-made skin in good condition; skull Grade A.

*****Urocyon cinereoargenteus texensis** Mearns.

Preliminary Diagnoses of New Mammals of the Genera *Lynx*, *Urocyon*, *Spilogale*, and *Mephitis*, from the Mexican Boundary Line, p. 2, Jan. 12, 1897. (Reprint: Proc. U. S. Nat. Mus. 20: 459, Dec. 24, 1897.)

=*Urocyon cinereoargenteus scottii* Mearns. See Goldman, Journ. Washington Acad. Sci. 28: 495, Nov. 15, 1938.

$\frac{130}{1116}$. Skin and skull. Adult. San Pedro, near Eagle Pass, Maverick County, Tex. January 1851. Collected by A. Schott, Mexican Boundary Survey.

Specimen has been made into a modern study skin in good condition; skull Grade C.

†**Urocyon clementae** Merriam.

Proc. Biol. Soc. Washington 16: 75, May 29, 1903.

=*Urocyon littoralis clementae* Merriam. See Grinnell and Linsdale, Proc. Biol. Soc. Washington 43: 154, Sept. 26, 1930.

92034. Skin and skull. Adult male. San Clemente Island, Santa Barbara Islands, Los Angeles County, Calif. June 5, 1897. Collected by H. A. Gaylord. Original number 1163-X.

Well-made skin in good condition; skull Grade A.

†**Urocyon guatemalae** Miller.

Proc. Acad. Nat. Sci. Philadelphia 51: 278, July 26, 1899.

76723. Skin and skull. Adult male. Nenton, Guatemala. December 16, 1895. Collected by E. W. Nelson and E. A. Goldman. Original number 8801.

Well-made skin in good condition; skull Grade A.

*****Vulpes (Urocyon) littoralis** Baird.   Lectotype.

Mammals of North America, p. 143, 1857.

=*Urocyon littoralis* (Baird). See Merriam, Proc. Biol. Soc. Washington 4: 135, Feb. 18, 1888.

$\frac{1351}{2154}$ Skin and skull. Adult. San Miguel Island, Santa Barbara Islands, Santa Barbara County, Calif. January 1856. Collected by W. P. Trowbridge.

Specimen was remade in January 1902 into a modern study skin. It is in good condition except for a few slight imperfections on the head. Skull Grade A.

Baird listed two specimens, each designated by number, the one mentioned above, and No. $\frac{1417}{2275}$, formerly mounted.

Lyon and Osgood, U. S. Nat. Mus. Bull. 62: 212, Jan. 28, 1909, made No. $\frac{1351}{2154}$ the lectotype because this skull was figured on plate 35 of Baird's Mammals of North America.

†Urocyon littoralis santacruzae Merriam.

Proc. Biol. Soc. Washington 16: 75, May 29, 1903.

$\frac{34852}{47117}$. Skin and skull. Adult female. Santa Cruz Island, Santa Barbara Islands, Santa Barbara County, Calif. July 11, 1892. Collected by C. P. Streator. Original number 1914.

Well-made skin in good condition; skull Grade A.

*Urocyon parvidens Miller.

Proc. Acad. Nat. Sci. Philadelphia 51: 276, July 26, 1899.

=Urocyon cinereoargenteus fraterculus Elliot. See Goldman, Journ. Washington Acad. Sci. 28: 495, Nov. 15, 1938.

$\frac{11429}{37762}$. Skin and skull. Young adult male. Merida, Yucatan, Mexico. Collected by A. Schott. Original number 385. Skin cataloged in 1873; skull, May 4, 1899.

Specimen made into a modern study skin and skull removed May 1899. Skin in good condition; skull Grade A.

Genus VULPES Oken

*Vulpes alascensis Merriam.

Proc. Washington Acad. Sci. 2: 668, Dec. 28, 1900.

21420. Skull only. Old male. Andreafski, near mouth of Yukon River, Alaska. February 1880. Collected by E. W. Nelson. Original number 180.

Skull Grade A.

†Vulpes alascensis abietorum Merriam.

Proc. Washington Acad. Sci. 2: 699, Dec. 28, 1900.

71197. Skull only. Adult male. Stuart Lake, British Columbia, Canada. Winter 1893–94. Collected by A. C. Murray.

Skull Grade A.

†Vulpes cascadensis Merriam.

Proc. Washington Acad. Sci. 2: 665, Dec. 28, 1900.

92767. Skin and skull. Young adult male. Trout Lake, south base of Mount Adams, Cascade Mountains, Skamania County, Wash. March 3, 1898. Collected by P. Schmid. Original number 1318-X.

Well-made skin in good condition; skull Grade A.

†Vulpes harrimani Merriam.

Proc. Washington Acad. Sci. 2: 14, Mar. 14, 1900.

99626. Skin only. Adult. Kodiak Island, Alaska. 1899. Collected by C. Hart Merriam.

Cased skin, tanned; in good condition; feet missing.

†Vulpes kenaiensis Merriam.

Proc. Washington Acad. Sci. 2: 670, Dec. 28, 1900.

96145. Skull only. Old male. Kenai Peninsula, Alaska. 1898. Collected by Dall De Weese.

Skull Grade A.

*Vulpes macrotis Merriam.

Proc. Biol. Soc. Washington 4: 136, Feb. 18, 1888.

186449. Skin and skull. Young adult male. Riverside, Riverside County, Calif.; more exactly, on western margin of San Jacinto Plain in vicinity of Box Springs, within 10 miles southeast of Riverside (*fide* F. Stephens). November 1, 1885. Collected by F. Stephens. Merriam collection number $\frac{1792}{2324}$.

Well-made skin in good condition, except for a bare spot on muzzle and another on right forefoot; skull Grade C.

†Vulpes macrotis arizonensis Goldman.

Journ. Washington Acad. Sci. 21: 249, June 4, 1931.

202959. Skin and skull. Adult male. Tule Tanks (2 miles south, near Mexican Boundary), Yuma County, Ariz. December 9, 1913. Collected by E. A. Goldman. Original number 22357.

Well-made skin in good condition; skull Grade A.

†Vulpes macrotis devius Nelson and Goldman.

Proc. Biol. Soc. Washington 22: 25, Mar. 10, 1909.

=*Vulpes macrotis devia* Nelson and Goldman.

147078. Skin and skull. Adult male. Llano de Yrais, opposite Magdalena Island, Lower California, Mexico. December 13, 1905. Collected by E. W. Nelson and E. A. Goldman. Original number 18771.

Well-made skin in good condition; skull Grade A.

†Vulpes macrotis neomexicanus Merriam.

Proc. Biol. Soc. Washington 15: 74, Mar. 22, 1902.
=*Vulpes macrotis neomexicana* Merriam.

98646. Skull only. Adult male. Band's ranch, San Andreas Range, Dona Ana County, N. Mex. (about 50 miles north of El Paso, Tex.). April 4, 1899. Collected by C. M. Barber. Original number 2055-X.

Skull Grade A.

†Vulpes macrotis nevadensis Goldman.

Journ. Washington Acad. Sci. 21: 250, June 4, 1931.

213103. Skin and skull. Adult male. Willow Creek Ranch, near Jungo, Humboldt County, Nev. December 14, 1915. Collected by Mike Gill. Original number 13255-X.

Tanned skin in good condition; skull Grade B.

†Vulpes macrotis tenuirostris Nelson and Goldman.

Journ. Mamm. 12: 302, Aug. 24, 1931.

140394. Skin and skull. Adult male. Trinidad Valley, northwest base of San Pedro Martir Mountains, altitude 2,600 feet, Lower California, Mexico. July 1, 1905. Collected by E. W. Nelson and E. A. Goldman. Original number 17371.

Well-made skin in much-worn summer pelage; skull Grade A.

*Vulpes macroura Baird.

Stansbury's Exploration and Survey of the Valley of the Great Salt Lake of Utah, p. 309, May 1852.

4107. Skin only. Adult. Wasatch Mountains bordering Great Salt Lake, Utah. 1849 or 1850. Collected by Captain Stansbury's Expedition. Original number "A." The specimen was purchased from hunters in the Salt Lake Valley.

Specimen made over into modern study skin in fair condition. The left fore foot is the only foot having claws. The right ear is broken and rather mutilated. It is in an envelope attached to the skin.

In Baird's Mammals of North America, p. 131, 1857, the type is designated by the original number "A."

†Vulpes muticus Merriam.

Proc. Biol. Soc. Washington 15: 74, Mar. 22, 1902.
=*Vulpes macrotis mutica* Merriam. See Grinnell, Univ. California Publ. Zool. 40 (2): 109, Sept. 26, 1933.

75828. Skin and skull. Adult male. Tracy, San Joaquin Valley, San Joaquin County, Calif. November 5, 1895. Collected by G. Leonard. Original number 6.

Well-made skin in good condition; skull Grade B.

251543—42——5

†Vulpes necator Merriam.

Proc. Washington Acad. Sci. 2: 664, Dec. 28, 1900.

=*Vulpes fulva necator* Merriam.   See Grinnell, Univ. California Publ. Zool.
40 (2): 108, Sept. 26, 1933.

$\frac{30735}{42635}$.   Skin and skull.   Young adult female.   Whitney Meadows,
altitude 9,500 feet, near Mount Whitney, Tulare County, Calif.
September 1, 1891.   Collected by A. K. Fisher.   Original number 940.

Well-made skin in good condition; skull Grade C.

†Vulpes regalis Merriam.

Proc. Washington Acad. Sci. 2: 672, Dec. 28, 1900.

$\frac{31697}{43558}$.   Skin and skull.   Adult male.   Elk River, Sherburne County,
Minn.   March 5, 1887.   Collected by Vernon Bailey.   Original
number 659.

Well-made skin in good condition; skull Grade B.

†Vulpes velox hebes Merriam.

Proc. Biol. Soc. Washington 15: 73, Mar. 22, 1902.

108255.   Skin and skull.   Young adult male.   Calgary, Alberta,
Canada.   October 8, 1900.   Collected by W. G. Mackay and G. F.
Dippie.   Original number 560 (2890–X).

Well-made skin in good condition; skull Grade A.

Family FELIDAE: Cats

Genus ACINONYX Brookes

†Acinonyx jubatus raineyi Heller.

Smithsonian Misc. Coll. 61 (19): 9, Nov. 8, 1913.

182321.   Skin and skull.   Adult male.   Ulu, Kapiti Plains, British
East Africa [=Kenya].   October 13, 1911.   Collected by Paul J.
Rainey.   Original number (Heller) 2639.

Flat skin in good condition, a few small bare spots on back where hair
has sloughed; skull Grade A.

†Acinonyx jubatus velox Heller.

Smithsonian Misc. Coll. 61 (19): 7, Nov. 8, 1913.

163096.   Skin and skull.   Adult male.   Loita Plains, British East
Africa [=Kenya].   June 12, 1909.   Collected by Kermit Roosevelt.   Original number (Heller) 107.

Flat skin in good condition; skull Grade A.

Genus FELIS Linnaeus [4]

*Felis aequatorialis Mearns.

Proc. U. S. Nat. Mus. 25: 246, Sept. 17, 1902.

=*Felis pardalis aequatorialis* Mearns.

113267. Skin and skull. Adult female. Paramba, altitude 3,500 feet, northern Ecuador. November 2, 1899. Collected by G. Flemming. Original number 22.

Well-made skin in good condition; skull Grade A.

*Felis apache Mearns.

Proc. Biol. Soc. Washington 14: 150, Aug. 9, 1901.

1373. Skull only. Young adult female. Matamoros, Tamaulipas, Mexico. Collected by J. Louis Berlandier. Cataloged January 25, 1855.

Skull Grade A.

†Felis arundivaga Hollister.

Proc. Biol. Soc. Washington 24: 176, June 16, 1911.

=*Felis concolor coryi* Bangs. See Nelson and Goldman, Journ. Mamm. 10: 347, Nov. 11, 1929.

137122. Skin and skull. Adult male. Twelve miles southwest of Vidalia, Concordia Parish, La. June 17, 1905. Collected by B. V. Lilly. Original number 5431-X.

Tanned skin in good condition; skull Grade A.

†Felis aztecus browni Merriam.

Proc. Biol. Soc. Washington 16: 73, May 29, 1903.

=*Felis concolor browni* Merriam. See Nelson and Goldman, Journ. Mamm. 10: 347, Nov. 11, 1929.

125719. Skull only. Adult male. Lower Colorado River, 12 miles south of Yuma, Yuma County, Ariz. February (?) 1903. Collected by Herbert Brown. Original number 3908-X.

Skull Grade B.

*Felis cacomitli Berlandier.

In Baird, Rep. U. S. and Mexican Boundary Survey 2 (pt. 2) : 12, Jan. 1859.

1426. Skull only. Adult female. Matamoros, Tamaulipas, Mexico. 1840. Collected by J. Louis Berlandier. Received from D. N. Couch.

Skull Grade A.

---

[4] Because of the present lack of agreement on the subject of the generic groups of cats, we have decided to continue to use the name *Felis* for most of the species.

*Felis centralis Mearns.

Proc. Biol. Soc. Washington 14: 139, Aug. 9, 1901.

=*Felis onca centralis* Mearns. See J. A. Allen, Bull. Amer. Mus. Nat. Hist. 28: 107, Apr. 30, 1910.

14177. Skull. Adult, probably male. Talamanca, Costa Rica. Collected by W. M. Gabb. Original number 47. Cataloged November 19, 1874.

Skull Grade A. Catalog calls for a skin, No. 12177, which cannot be found.

†Felis concolor greeni Nelson and Goldman.

Journ. Washington Acad. Sci. 21: 211, May 19, 1931.

249896. Skin and skull. Adult male. Curraes Novos, Rio Grande do Norte, Brazil. November 1930. Collected by Edward C. Green. Original number 26600–X.

Well-made skin in good condition; skull Grade A.

*Felis concolor incarum Nelson and Goldman.

Journ. Mamm. 10: 347, Nov. 11, 1929.

194310. Skin and skull. Adult male. Piscocoucho, altitude 8,700 feet, Rio Urubamba, Department of Cuzco, Peru. July 1915. Collected by Edmund Heller. Original number 566.

Flat skin in good condition. The head and tail had been severed from the body but they are now sewed in place. Skull Grade A.

†Felis concolor kaibabensis Nelson and Goldman.

Journ. Washington Acad. Sci. 21: 209, May 19, 1931.

171186. Skin and skull. Adult male. Powell Plateau, altitude 8,700 feet, Grand Canyon National Park, Ariz. April 15, 1911. Collected by J. T. Owens. Original number 8432–X.

Well-made skin in good condition; skull Grade A.

†Felis concolor mayensis Nelson and Goldman.

Journ. Mamm. 10: 350, Nov. 11, 1929.

244856. Skin and skeleton. Adult male. La Libertad, Department of Peten, Guatemala. August 22, 1923. Collected by Harry Malleis. Original number 465.

Tanned skin in good condition, but lacking nose, mouth, and legs; small perforation in back of neck; skull Grade B.

Felis concolor stanleyana Goldman.

See *Felis concolor youngi* Goldman.

†Felis concolor vancouverensis Nelson and Goldman.

Proc. Biol. Soc. Washington 45: 105, July 15, 1932.

211519. Skull only. Adult male. Campbell Lake, Vancouver Island, British Columbia, Canada. September 13, 1915. Collected by W. R. Kent. Original number 15040-X.

Skull Grade A.

†Felis concolor youngi Goldman.

Proc. Biol. Soc. Washington 49: 137, August 22, 1936.

=*Felis concolor stanleyana* Goldman. See Goldman, Proc. Biol. Soc. Washington 51: 63, Mar. 18, 1938. (Substitute for *F. c. youngi* Goldman, 1936. Not *F. youngi* Pei, 1934.)

251419. Skin and skull. Young adult male. Bruni Ranch, near Bruni, southeastern Webb County, Tex. October 6, 1934. Collected by Ira Wood. Original number 27354-X.

Tanned skin in good condition; skull Grade A.

*Felis costaricensis Mearns.

Proc. U. S. Nat. Mus. 25: 245, Sept. 17, 1902. Preoccupied by *Felis bangsi costaricensis* Merriam, Proc. Washington Acad. Sci. 3: 596, Dec. 11, 1901.

=*Felis pardalis mearnsi* J. A. Allen. See Lyon and Osgood, U. S. Nat. Mus. Bull. 62: 208, Jan. 28, 1909. (Renaming of *costaricensis* Mearns, preoccupied.)

14180. Skull only. Adult (male, *fide* E. A. Mearns). Talamanca, Costa Rica. Collected by W. M. Gabb. Original number 73. Cataloged November 19, 1874.

The catalog calls for a skin, No. 12180, which cannot be found. Skull Grade A.

*Felis fossata Mearns.

Proc. Biol. Soc. Washington 14: 150, Aug. 9, 1901.

7036. Skull only. Adult. Merida, Yucatan, Mexico. Collected by A. Schott. Original number 952. Cataloged July 8, 1866.

Skull Grade A.

†Felis glaucula oaxacensis Nelson and Goldman.

Journ. Mamm. 12 (3) : 303, Aug. 24, 1931.

68169. Skin and skull. Adult male. Cerro San Felipe, altitude 10,000 feet, Oaxaca, Mexico. August 31, 1894. Collected by E. W. Nelson and E. A. Goldman. Original number 6697.

Well-made skin in good condition; skull Grade A.

*Felis glaucula yucatanica Nelson and Goldman.

Journ. Mamm. 12: 304, Aug. 24, 1931.

8612. Skin only. Merida, Yucatan, Mexico. Collected by A. Schott. Cataloged August 4, 1866.

Well-made skin in good condition. The tail was not skinned out when the specimen was made up. The extreme tip of tail is missing, and the hair is now lacking on terminal half of tail.

*Felis hernandesii goldmani Mearns.

Proc. Biol. Soc. Washington 14 : 142, Aug. 9, 1901.
=*Felis onca goldmani* Mearns. See Goldman, Proc. Biol. Soc. Washington
45 : 144, Sept. 9, 1932.

105930. Skin only. Adult. Yohaltun, Campeche, Mexico. January 5, 1901. Received from E. A. Goldman.

The skin is a tanned pelt, without feet, in good condition.

†Felis hippolestes Merriam.

Proc. Biol. Soc. Washington 11 : 219, July 15, 1897.
=*Felis concolor hippolestes* Merriam. See Nelson and Goldman, Journ. Mamm.
10 : 347, Nov. 11, 1929.

57936. Skin and skull. Old male. Wind River Mountains, near head of Big Wind River, Fremont County, Wyo. November 1892. Collected by John Burlingame.

Well-made skin in good condition; skull Grade C.

†Felis hippolestes aztecus Merriam.

Proc. Washington Acad. Sci. 3 : 592, Dec. 11, 1901.
=*Felis concolor azteca* Merriam. See Nelson and Goldman, Journ. Mamm.
10 : 347, Nov. 11, 1929.

99658. Skin and skull. Adult male. Colonia Garcia, Chihuahua, Mexico. October 17, 1899. Collected by H. A. Cluff. Original number 2401–X.

Well-made skin in good condition; skull Grade A.

†Felis hippolestes olympus Merriam.

Proc. Biol. Soc. Washington 11 : 220, July 15, 1897.
=*Felis concolor oregonensis* Merriam. See Nelson and Goldman, Journ.
Mamm. 10 (4) : 347, Nov. 11, 1929.

77973. Skin and skull. Adult male (?). Lake Cushman, Mason County, Olympic Mountains, Wash. April 18, 1896. Collected by Thomas Hayes.

Well-made skin in good condition; skull Grade A.

*Leo leo hollisteri J. A. Allen.

Bull. Amer. Mus. Nat. Hist. 47 : 229, Apr. 11, 1924.
=*Felis leo hollisteri* (J. A. Allen).

181568. Skin and skull. Adult male. Lime Springs, Sotik, British East Africa [=Kenya]. April 18, 1911. Collected by Edmund Heller. Original number 2054.

Flat skin in good condition; skull Grade A.

*Felis leo nyanzae Heller.

Smithsonian Misc. Coll. 61 (19) : 4, Nov. 8, 1913.

164551. Skin and fragments of skull. Adult male. Kampala, Uganda, Africa. December 30, 1909. Gift of European residents to Theodore Roosevelt. Original number (Heller) 580.

Flat skin in good condition, several cuts around shoulder apparently caused in tanning; the premaxillaries, canines, and incisors were the only parts of the skull saved.

*Felis leo roosevelti Heller.

Smithsonian Misc. Coll. 61 (19) : 2, Nov. 8, 1913.

144054. Skin and skull. Old male. Near Addis Ababa, Highlands of Abyssinia [=Ethiopia], Africa. 1904. Presented by King Menelik to President Theodore Roosevelt. Original number, Nat. Zool. Park $\frac{1151}{5307}$.

Flat skin in good condition; skull Grade A.

Hollister, U. S. Nat. Mus. Bull. 99 (pt. 1) : 165, Aug. 16, 1918, points out the fact that the type specimen is an animal raised in captivity and suggests that it may be an individual of *Felis leo massaica*. See also J. A. Allen (Bull. Amer. Mus. Nat. Hist. 47 : 224, Apr. 11, 1924).

†Felis limitis Mearns.

Proc. Biol. Soc. Washington 14 : 146, Aug. 9, 1901.

=*Felis pardalis albescens* Pucheran. See J. A. Allen, Bull. Amer. Mus. Nat. Hist. 22 : 219, July 25, 1906.

$\frac{32679}{44602}$. Skin and skull. Adult made. Brownsville, Cameron County, Tex. March 4, 1892. Collected by F. B. Armstrong. Original number 102.

Well-made skin in good condition; skull Grade A.

*Felis notialis Hollister.

Proc. U. S. Nat. Mus. 48 : 170, Dec. 16, 1914.

=*Felis onca notialis* Hollister. See Barbour, in Gray, Records of North American Big Game, p. 155, Dec. 1932.

4361. Skull only. Adult [male]. San José, Entre Rios, Argentina. August 1860. Collected by T. J. Page.

Skull Grade B.

*Felis ocreata nandae Heller.

Smithsonian Misc. Coll. 61 (13) : 14, Sept. 16, 1913.

182367. Skin and skull. Adult male. Headwaters of the Lukosa River, Nandi escarpment, altitude 7,000 feet, British East Africa [=Kenya]. February 9, 1912. Collected by Edmund Heller. Original number 2688.

Cased skin in good condition; skull Grade A.

*Felis ocreata taitae Heller.

Smithsonian Misc. Coll. 61 (13) : 14, Sept. 16, 1913.

182220. Skin and skull. Adult female. Voi, British East Africa [=Kenya]. October 27, 1911. Collected by Edmund Heller. Original number 2533.

Cased skin in good condition, tip of tail missing; skull Grade A.

†**Felis onca arizonensis** Goldman.

Proc. Biol. Soc. Washington 45: 144, Sept. 9, 1932.

244507.   Skin and skull.   Adult male.   Near Cibecue, Navajo County, Ariz.   April 12, 1924.   Collected by Jack Funk.   Original number 23633–X.

Tanned skin in good condition; skull Grade A.

***Felis onca coxi** Nelson and Goldman.

Journ. Mamm. 14: 225, Aug. 17, 1933.

256388.   Skull only.   Adult female.   North of Rio Doce, Espiritu Santo, Brazil.   1931.   Collected by W. T. Cox.

Skull Grade A.

†**Felis onca paulensis** Nelson and Goldman.

Journ. Mamm. 14: 228, Aug. 17, 1933.

100123.   Skull only.   [Male] adult.   São Paulo region, southeastern Brazil (exact locality undetermined).   June 1900.   Received from Hermann von Ihering.   Original number 2629–X.

Skull Grade B.

†**Felis onca veraecrucis** Nelson and Goldman.

Journ. Mamm. 14: 236, Aug. 17, 1933.

67403.   Skull only.   Adult male.   San Andres Tuxtla, Veracruz, Mexico.   April 24, 1894.   Collected by E. W. Nelson and E. A. Goldman.   Original number 6090.

Skull Grade B.

***Felis paraguensis** Hollister.

Proc. U. S. Nat. Mus. 48: 169, Dec. 16, 1914.
=*Felis onca paraguensis* Hollister.   See Barbour, in Gray, Records of North American Big Game, p. 155, Dec. 1932.

4128.   Skull only.   Adult male.   Paraguay.   Collected by T. J. Page.   Cataloged June 1860.

Skull Grade B.

F. W. Miller, Journ. Mamm. 11: 14, Feb. 11, 1930, proposes a new name, *Felis ramsayi*, as a substitute for *Felis paraguensis* Hollister, which he regards as preoccupied by [*Felis*] *Panthera paragayensis* Oken (1816).   As the names published by Oken and Hollister differ in spelling this change is not required by the International Code, Art. 36, with accompanying recommendation.

Felis pardalis mearnsi J. A. Allen.

See *Felis costaricensis* Mearns.

† **Felis pardalis nelsoni** Goldman.

Journ. Mamm. 6 : 122, May 12, 1925.

$\frac{32642}{44565}$ Skin and skull. Old male. Manzanillo, Colima, Mexico. February 11, 1892. Collected by E. W. Nelson. Original number 1862.

Well-made skin in good condition, except for a few bare spots on left hindleg; skull Grade A.

† **Felis pardalis sonoriensis** Goldman.

Journ. Mamm. 6 : 123, May 12, 1925.

96216. Skin and skull. Adult male. Camoa, Rio Mayo, Sonora, Mexico. December 3, 1898. Collected by E. A. Goldman. Original number 13268.

Well-made skin in good condition, except for small bare spot on abdomen; skull Grade B.

* **Felis pardus chui** Heller.

Smithsonian Misc. Coll. 61 (19) : 6, Nov. 8, 1913.

164764. Skin and skull. Adult male. Gondokoro, northern Uganda, Africa. February 26, 1910. Collected by Edmund Heller. Original number 653.

Flat skin in good condition; skull Grade A.

* **Felis pardus fortis** Heller.

Smithsonian Misc. Coll. 61 (19) : 5, Nov. 8, 1913.

=*Felis (Panthera) pardus fusca* Myer. See Pocock, Proc. Zool. Soc. London, 1932, pt. 1, p. 561, Mar. 1932.

181600. Skin and skull. Adult male. Loita Plains, Southern Guaso Nyiro district, British East Africa [=Kenya]. May 31, 1911. Collected by Paul J. Rainey. Original number (Heller) 2309.

Flat skin in good condition; skull Grade A.

† **Felis pirrensis** Goldman.

Smithsonian Misc. Coll. 63 (5) : 4, Mar. 14, 1914.

179162. Skin and skull. Adult female. Cana, altitude 2,000 feet, eastern Panama. March 22, 1912. Collected by E. A. Goldman. Original number 21559.

Well-made skin in good condition; skull Grade A.

† **Felis puma patagonica** Merriam.

Proc. Washington Acad. Sci. 3 : 598, Dec. 11, 1901.

=*Felis concolor patagonica* Merriam. See Nelson and Goldman, Journ. Mamm. 10 : 346, Nov. 11, 1929.

108693. Skin and skull. Young adult male. East base Andes Mountains (lat. 47°30′ S.), Santa Cruz Territory, Argentina, 1899. Collected by J. B. Hatcher. Original number 3020–X.

Tanned skin in good condition, claws missing; skull Grade A.

*Felis tingia Lyon.

Proc. U. S. Nat. Mus. 34: 658, Sept. 14, 1908.

144325. Skin and skull. Adult female. Pulo Tebing Tinggi, off east coast of Sumatra. January 24, 1907. Collected by W. L. Abbott. Original number 5022.

Well-made skin in good condition; skull Grade A.

Genus LYNX Kerr

*Lynx baileyi Merriam.

North Amer. Fauna 3: 79, Sept. 11, 1890.
=Lynx rufus baileyi Merriam. See Grinnell and Dixon, Univ. California Publ. Zool. 21 (13) : 349, Jan. 24, 1924.

186519. Skin and skull. Adult female. Moccasin Spring, Coconino County, Ariz. December 28, 1888. Collected by Vernon Bailey. Original number 466. Merriam collection No. $\frac{5214}{5909}$.

Well-made skin in good condition; skull Grade A.

†Lynx fasciatus pallescens Merriam.

North Amer. Fauna 16: 104, Oct. 28, 1899.
=Lynx rufus pallescens Merriam. See Grinnell and Dixon, Univ. California Publ. Zool. 21 (13) : 350, Jan. 24, 1924.

76585. Skin and skull. Adult male. South base of Mount Adams, near Trout Lake, Skamania County, Wash. January 10, 1896 (not 1895, as in original description). Collected by D. N. Kaegi. Original number 23.

Well-made skin in good condition; skull Grade A.

*Lynx rufus californicus Mearns.

Preliminary Diagnoses of New Mammals of the Genera Lynx, Urocyon, Spilogale, and Mephitis, from the Mexican Boundary Line, p. 2, Jan. 12, 1897. (Reprint: Proc. U. S. Nat. Mus. 20: 458, Dec. 24, 1897.)

$\frac{1588}{37163}$ Skin and skull. Adult female. San Diego, San Diego County, Calif. February 2, 1856. Collected by J. F. Hammond.

Well-made skin in fair condition, a small bare spot on throat. In 1896 it was made over into its present shape and the skull removed and cleaned. Skull Grade A.

*Lynx rufus eremicus Mearns.

Preliminary Diagnoses of New Mammals of the Genera Lynx, Urocyon, Spilogale, and Mephitis, from the Mexican Boundary Line, p. 1, Jan. 12, 1897. (Reprint: Proc. U. S. Nat. Mus. 20: 457, Dec. 24, 1897.)
=Lynx rufus baileyi Merriam. See Grinnell and Dixon, Univ. California Publ. Zool. 21 (13) : 349, Jan. 24, 1924.

60676.   Skin, skull, and tail vertebrae. Adult male. New River, 6 miles northwest of Laguna station, in the Colorado Desert, Imperial County, Calif. May 5, 1894. Collected by E. A. Mearns. Original number 3506. International Boundary Commission.

Specimen remade in February 1902 into a modern study skin, in good condition; skull Grade A.

†Lynx uinta Merriam.

Proc. Biol. Soc. Washington 15: 71, Mar. 22, 1902.

$\frac{18915}{25648}$.   Skin and skull. Adult male. Bridger Pass, south slope of Uinta Mountains, Carbon County, Wyo. May 11, 1890. Collected by Vernon Bailey. Original number 1156.

Well-made skin in good condition; skull Grade A.

Family HYAENIDAE: Hyaenas
Genus CROCUTA Kaup

*Crocuta crocuta fisi Heller.

Smithsonian Misc. Coll. 61 (22) : 5, Jan. 26, 1914.

182078.   Skin and skull. Adult male. Merille Waterholes, Marsabit Road, British East Africa [=Kenya]. July 23, 1911. Collected by Edmund Heller. Original number 2385.

Flat skin in good condition except for considerable sloughing of hair; skull Grade A.

Family MUSTELIDAE: Weasels, Minks, Martens, Skunks, Otters, Badgers
Genus AONYX Lesson

*Aonyx capensis helios Heller.

Smithsonian Misc. Coll. 61 (19) : 1, Nov. 8, 1913.

175750.   Skin and skull. Adult female. Forty miles southwest of Kericho Station, Sotik District, British East Africa [=Kenya]. October 1912. Collected by H. J. Allen Turner. Original number 1181.

Flat skin in good condition except that the claws are missing; skull Grade A.

Genus CONEPATUS Gray

†Conepatus filipensis Merriam.

Proc. Biol. Soc. Washington 15: 163, Aug. 6, 1902.

68172.   Skin and skull. Adult male. Cerro San Felipe, Oaxaca, Mexico. August 24, 1894. Collected by E. W. Nelson and E. A. Goldman. Original number 6619.

Well-made skin in good condition; skull Grade A.

†**Conepatus leuconotus texensis** Merriam.

Proc. Biol. Soc. Washington 15: 162, Aug. 6, 1902.

$\frac{34857}{47122}$. Skin and skull. Adult male. Brownsville, Cameron County, Tex. July 20, 1892. Collected by F. B. Armstrong. Original number 70.

Well-made skin in good condition; skull Grade A.

***Conepatus mesoleucus mearnsi** Merriam.

Proc. Biol. Soc. Washington 15: 163, Aug. 6, 1902.

186455. Skin and skull. Adult female. Mason, Mason County, Tex. February 20, 1886. Collected by Ira B. Henry. Original number 69. Merriam collection No. $\frac{2154}{2681}$.

Well-made skin in good condition, except most of hair missing from terminal half of tail; skull Grade B.

†**Conepatus mesoleucus nelsoni** Goldman.

Journ. Mamm. 3: 41, Feb. 8, 1922.

$\frac{33252}{35257}$. Skin and skull. Old male. Armeria, altitude 200 feet, near Manzanillo, Colima, Mexico. March 3, 1892. Collected by E. W. Nelson. Original number 2004.

Well-made skin in good condition, except for absence of hair from middle portion of tail; skull Grade A.

†**Conepatus mesoleucus telmalestes** Bailey.

North Amer. Fauna 25: 203, Oct. 24, 1905.

136551. Skin and skull. Adult male. Big Thicket, 7 miles northeast of Sour Lake, Hardin County, Tex. March 17, 1905. Collected by J. H. Gaut. Original number 3485.

Well-made skin in good condition; skull Grade A.

†**Conepatus mesoleucus venaticus** Goldman.

Journ. Mamm. 3: 40, Feb. 8, 1922.

205376. Skin and skull. Old male. Cosper Ranch, altitude 5,000 feet, Blue River, 12 miles south of Blue, Greenlee County, Ariz. September 1, 1914. Collected by E. A. Goldman. Original number 22459.

Well-made skin in good condition; skull Grade A.

†**Conepatus pediculus** Merriam.

Proc. Biol. Soc. Washington 15: 164, Aug. 6, 1902.

116953. Skin and skull. Young adult male. Sierra Guadalupe, Coahuila, Mexico. April 25, 1902. Collected by E. W. Nelson and E. A. Goldman. Original number 15123.

Well-made skin in good condition; skull Grade A.

†Conepatus sonoriensis Merriam.

Proc. Biol. Soc. Washington 15 : 162, Aug. 6, 1902.

95914.   Skin and skull.   Young adult female.   Camoa, Rio Mayo, Sonora, Mexico.   October 29, 1898.   Collected by E. A. Goldman. Original number 13213.

Well-made skin in good condition; skull Grade A.

†Conepatus tropicalis Merriam.

Proc. Biol. Soc. Washington 15 : 164, Aug. 6, 1902.

63650.   Skin and skull.   Adult female (not male as recorded in original description).   Motzorongo, Veracruz, Mexico.   February 26, 1894.   Collected by E. W. Nelson and E. A. Goldman.   Original number 5903.

Well-made skin in good condition; skull Grade A.

Genus ENHYDRA Fleming

†Latax lutris nereis Merriam.

Proc. Biol. Soc. Washington 17 : 159, Oct. 6, 1904.
=*Enhydra lutris nereis* (Merriam).   See Grinnell, Univ. California Publ. Zool. 21 : 316, Jan. 27, 1923.

133508.   Complete disarticulated skeleton.   Adult male.   San Miguel Island, Santa Barbara Islands, Santa Barbara County, Calif. July 2, 1904.   Collected by G. M. McGuire.   Original number 4690–X.

Skull Grade B.

Genus GRISON Oken

†Galictis canaster Nelson.

Proc. Biol. Soc. Washington 14 : 129, Aug. 9, 1901.
=*Grison canaster* (Nelson).   See Miller and Rehn, Proc. Boston Soc. Nat. Hist. 31 : 114, Aug. 24, 1903.

159562.   Skin and skull.   Adult male.   Near Tunkas, Yucatan, Mexico.   Winter 1901.   Captured alive by the Indians and sent to General F. Canton, Governor of Yucatan, who later presented the specimen to the U. S. Biological Survey.   Original number 7622–X.

Well-made skin in good condition, except for two small lacerations on middle of back and over right shoulders; posterior portion of skull including interparietal, supraoccipital, occipital condyles, and small portions of parietals and basioccipital sawed away; zygomata broken.

This type was described from the living specimen while it was in the possession of General Canton.

Genus GULO Pallas

†**Gulo luscus vancouverensis** Goldman.

Proc. Biol. Soc. Washington 48: 177, Nov. 15, 1935.

211499. Skull only. Old adult male. Great Central Lake, Vancouver Island, British Columbia, Canada. March 27, 1913. Collected by W. R. Kent. Original number 14081–X.

Skull Grade A.

Genus ICTONYX Kaup

*Ictonyx capensis albescens Heller.

Smithsonian Misc. Coll. 61 (13) : 13, Sept. 16, 1913.

182724. Skin and skull. Adult male. Summit of Mount Lololokwi, northern Guaso Nyiro district, British East Africa [=Kenya]. September 15, 1911. Collected by Edmund Heller. Original number 4318.

Well-made skin in good condition ; skull Grade A.

Genus LUTRA Brisson

†**Lutra canadensis evexa** Goldman.

Proc. Biol. Soc. Washington 48: 182, Nov. 15, 1935.

47018. Skull only. Adult male. Stuart Lake, near headwaters of Fraser River, British Columbia, Canada. 1892. Collected by W. E. Traill.

Skull Grade A.

*Lutra canadensis extera Goldman.

Proc. Biol. Soc. Washington 48: 181, Nov. 15, 1935.

12485. Skull and parts of skeleton. Adult (probably male). Nagai Island, Shumagin Islands, Alaska. 1872. Collected by W. H. Dall. Original number 641.

Skull Grade A. Parts of skeleton consist of cervical, dorsal and lumbar vertebrae, innominate bones, femora, tibiae, fibulae, and patellae.

†**Lutra canadensis kodiacensis** Goldman.

Proc. Biol. Soc. Washington 48: 180, Nov. 15, 1935.

98142. Skull only. Adult (probably female). Uyak Bay, Kodiak Island, Alaska. July 1899. Collected by C. Hart Merriam (found and presented to Merriam by George Bird Grinnell).

Skull Grade A.

†**Lutra canadensis nexa** Goldman.

Proc. Biol. Soc. Washington 48: 182, Nov. 15, 1935.

210572. Skin and skull. Adult male. Near Deeth, Humboldt River, Elko County, Nev. December 19, 1915. Collected by R. F. Dietz. Original number 13275-X.

Well-made skin in good condition ; skull Grade B.

†Lutra canadensis optiva Goldman.

Proc. Biol. Soc. Washington 48 : 179, Nov. 15, 1935.

137320. Skin and skull. Adult male. Zaikoff Bay, Montague Island, Alaska. 1905. Collected by Charles Sheldon. Original number 5462-X.

Tanned skin in good condition; skull Grade A.

†Lutra canadensis preblei Goldman.

Proc. Biol. Soc. Washington 48 : 178, Nov. 15, 1935.

147413. Skull only. Adult male. Near McTavish Bay, Great Bear Lake (on canoe route from Lake Hardisty), Mackenzie, Canada. August 1903. Collected by E. A. Preble. Original number 4894.

Skull Grade A.

†Lutra canadensis texensis Goldman.

Proc. Biol. Soc. Washington 48 : 184, Nov. 15, 1935.

156849. Skull only. Adult male. 20 miles west of Angleton, Brazoria County, Tex. March 1908. Collected by B. V. Lilly. Original number 7047-X.

Skull Grade A.

*Lutra canadensis yukonensis Goldman.

Proc. Biol. Soc. Washington 48 : 180, Nov. 15, 1935.

21480. Skull only. Adult female. Unalakleet, Norton Sound, Alaska. Fall 1879. Collected by E. W. Nelson. Original number 112.

Skull Grade A.

*Lutra destructor Barnston. Lectotype.

Canadian Nat. and Geol. 8 : 152, 1863.

=*Lutra canadensis canadensis* Schreber. See Goldman, Proc. Biol. Soc. Washington 48 : 176, Nov. 15, 1925.

$\frac{4445}{5128}$. Skin (lost); skull and skeleton. Female. Michipicotan, Lake Superior, Ontario, Canada. Cataloged October 17, 1861. Collected by George Barnston.

Originally entered in catalog as skin with skull and skeleton. The skin cannot be found. Skull and skeleton Grade A.

†Lutra mira Goldman.

Proc. Biol. Soc. Washington 48 : 185, Nov. 15, 1935.

127888. Skull only. Young adult male. Kasaan Bay, Prince of Wales Island, Alaska. May, 1903. Collected by W. H. Osgood. Original number 2290.

Skull Grade A.

†Lutra repanda Goldman.

Smithsonian Misc. Coll. 63 (5) : 3, Mar. 14, 1914.

179974. Skin and skull. Adult male. Cana, altitude 2,000 feet, eastern Panama. May 30, 1912. Collected by E. A. Goldman. Original number 21758.

Well-made skin in good condition; skull Grade A.

*Lutra stejnegeri Goldman.

Journ. Mamm. 17 (2) : 164, May 14, 1936.

49485. Skull and skeleton (not "skull only" as recorded in original description). Subadult, "probably male." Near Petropavlovsk, Kamchatka, Siberia. 1882 or 1883. Collected by Leonhard Stejneger.

Skull and skeleton Grade A.

†Lutra vancouverensis Goldman.

Proc. Biol. Soc. Washington 48: 186, Nov. 15, 1935.

137775. Skull only. Adult male. Quatsino, Vancouver Island, British Columbia, Canada. 1905. Collected by H. O. Bergh. Original number 5517-X.

Skull Grade A.

Genus MARTES Pinel

*Mustela americana abieticola Preble.

North Amer. Fauna 22: 68, Oct. 31, 1902.
=Martes americana abieticola (Preble). See Miller, U. S. Nat. Mus. Bull. 79: 92, Dec. 31, 1912.

$\frac{19256}{34962}$. Skin and skeleton. Adult male. Cumberland House, Saskatchewan, Canada. February 1890. Collected by R. MacFarlane. Original number 54.

Rather poorly made skin, but in good condition. The entire skeleton is present. The digits of the forefeet, the middle and distal phalanges of the digits of the hindfeet, and the last few caudal vertebrae are in the skin; skull Grade A.

*Mustela americana actuosa Osgood.

North Amer. Fauna 19: 43, Oct. 6, 1900.
=Martes americana actuosa (Osgood). See Miller, U. S. Nat. Mus. Bull. 79: 93, Dec. 31, 1912.

6043. Skull. Old adult male. Fort Yukon, Alaska. November 1860. Collected by Robert Kennicott. Original number 1017.

Skull Grade A. The catalog calls for skin No. 6413, but it cannot be found.

*Mustela caurina Merriam.

North Amer. Fauna 4: 27, Oct. 8, 1890.
=Martes caurina caurina (Merriam). See Miller, U. S. Nat. Mus. Bull. 79: 93, Dec. 31, 1912.

186450. Skin and skull. Young adult male. Near Grays Harbor, Chehalis (=Grays Harbor) County, Wash. Feb. 4, 1886. Collected by L. C. Toney. Original number 9. Merriam collection number $\frac{2054}{2578}$.

Well-made skin in good condition; skull Grade B.

*Mustela caurina origenes Rhoads.

Proc. Acad. Nat. Sci. Philadelphia 54 : 458, Sept. 30, 1902.
=*Martes caurina origenes* (Rhoads). See Miller, U. S. Nat. Mus. Bull. 79 : 93, Dec. 31, 1912.

112170. Skin and skull. Young adult female. Marvine Mountain, Garfield County, Colo. September 16, 1901. Collected by Ernest T. Seton.

Well-made skin in good condition; skull Grade A.

†Mustela nesophila Osgood.

North Amer. Fauna 21 : 33, Sept. 26, 1901.
=*Martes nesophila* (Osgood). See Miller, U. S. Nat. Mus. Bull. 79 : 94, Dec. 31, 1912.

78066. Skull only. Adult male. Massett, Graham Island, Queen Charlotte Islands, British Columbia, Canada. Collected by J. H. Keen.

Skull earth- or smoke-stained; Grade B.

†Martes pennanti columbiana Goldman.

Proc. Biol. Soc. Washington 48 : 176, Nov. 15, 1935.

56953. Skull only. Adult male. Stuart Lake, near headwaters of Fraser River, British Columbia, Canada. 1893. Collected by W. E. Traill.

Skull Grade A.

Genus MELLIVORA Storr

*Mellivora abyssinica Hollister.

Smithsonian Misc. Coll. 56 (13) : 1, Oct. 10, 1910.

171876. Skin and skull. Old adult female. Vicinity of Addis Ababa, Abyssinia [=Ethiopia], Africa. 1909. Collected by Hoffman Philip.

Flat skin in good condition; skull Grade B.

*Mellivora sagulata Hollister.

Smithsonian Misc. Coll. 56 (13) : 2, Oct. 10, 1910.
=*Mellivora capensis sagulata* Hollister. See G. M. Allen and Lawrence, Bull. Mus. Comp. Zool. 79 : 57, Jan. 1936.

171875. Skin and skull. Adult male. Mount Kilimanjaro, altitude 5,000 feet, German East Africa [=Tanganyika Territory]. September 1889. Collected by W. L. Abbott.

Flat skin in good condition; skull Grade A.

Genus MEPHITIS Geoffroy and Cuvier

†Mephitis estor Merriam.

North Amer. Fauna 3: 81, Sept. 11, 1890.
=*Mephitis mephitis estor* Merriam. See Hall, Univ. California Publ. Zool. 37: 1, Apr. 10, 1931.

$\frac{17709}{24645}$. Skin and skull. Adult male. San Francisco Mountain, Coconino County, Ariz. August 17, 1889. Collected by Vernon Bailey. Original number 369.

Well-made skin in good condition; skull Grade A.

*Mephitis frontata Coues.

Bull. U. S. Geol. and Geog. Surv. Terr. (ser. 2), No. 1: 7, 1875.
=*Mephitis mephitis nigra* (Peale and Beauvois). See Hall, Carnegie Inst. Washington Publ. 473: 69, Nov. 20, 1936; Miller, Journ. Mamm. 22: 190–192, May 16, 1941.

2232. Skull. Old adult. Dales Cave, 3 miles northwest of Lewisburg, Union County, Pa. Collected by S. F. Baird. Cataloged March 1856.

Skull Grade B.

*Mephitis milleri Mearns.

Preliminary Diagnoses of New Mammals of the Genera *Mephitis*, *Dorcelaphus* and *Dicotyles*, from the Mexican border of the United States, p. 1, Feb. 11, 1897. (Reprint: Proc. U. S. Nat. Mus. 20: 467, Dec. 24, 1897.)
=*Mephitis macroura milleri* Mearns. See J. A. Allen. Bull. Amer. Mus. Nat. Hist. 14: 334, Nov. 12, 1901.

58851. Skin and skull. Adult male. Fort Lowell, near Tucson, Pima County, Ariz. November 13, 1893. Collected by F. X. Holzner. Original number 1109.

Well-made skin in good condition; skull Grade A.

*Mephitis occidentalis Baird.   Lectotype.

Mammals of North America, p. 194, 1857.
=*Mephitis mephitis occidentalis* Baird. See Hall, Carnegie Inst. Washington Publ. 473: 67, Nov. 20, 1936.

2617. Skull. Adult, probably male. Petaluma, Sonoma County, Calif. Collected by E. Samuels. Original number 837. Cataloged December 10, 1856.

Skull Grade A. The skin, No. 1944, that originally accompanied this skull, was, according to the catalog, "destroyed Jan. 8, 1886."

No type designated among the four specimens listed by Baird. Because Baird gave a table of detailed measurements of $\frac{1944}{2617}$, this specimen was made the lectotype by Lyon and Osgood, U. S. Nat. Mus. Bull. 62: 225, January 28, 1909.

†Chincha occidentalis major Howell.

North Amer. Fauna 20: 37, Aug. 31, 1901.

=*Mephitis mephitis major* (Howell). See Hall, Univ. California Publ. Zool. 37: 2, Apr. 10, 1931.

92238. Skin and skull. Adult male. Fort Klamath, Klamath County, Oreg. January 5, 1898. Collected by B. L. Cunningham. Original number 80 (1188–X).

Well-made skin in good condition; skull Grade A.

†Chincha occidentalis notata Howell.

North Amer. Fauna 20: 36, Aug. 31, 1901.

=*Mephitis mephitis notata* (Howell). See Hall, Carnegie Inst. Washington Publ. 473: 67, Nov. 20, 1936.

87043. Skin and skull. Adult male. Trout Lake, Mount Adams, Skamania County, Wash. March 22, 1897. Collected by P. Schmid. Original number 243–X.

Well-made skin in good condition; skull Grade A.

†Chincha platyrhina Howell.

North Amer. Fauna 20: 39, Aug. 31, 1901.

=*Mephitis platyrhina* (Howell). See J. A. Allen, Bull. Amer. Mus. Nat. Hist. 14: 334, Nov. 12, 1901.

$\frac{29284}{41351}$. Skin and skull. Adult male. South Fork of Kern River, 3 miles above Onyx, Kern County, Calif. July 5, 1891. Collected by Vernon Bailey, Original number 2998.

Well-made skin in good condition, except for two slight perforations in middle of back; skull Grade A.

Genus MUSTELA Linnaeus

*Putorius alleni Merriam.

North Amer. Fauna 11: 24, June 30, 1896.

=*Mustela frenata alleni* (Merriam). See Hall, Carnegie Inst. Washington Publ. 473: 106, Nov. 20, 1936.

186451. Skin and skull. Adult male. Custer, Black Hills, Custer County, S. Dak. July 12, 1888. Collected by Vernon Bailey. Original number 90. Merriam collection number $\frac{4485}{5120}$.

Well-made skin in good condition; skull Grade A.

*Putorius arcticus Merriam.

North Amer. Fauna 11: 15, June 30, 1896.

=*Mustela arctica arctica* (Merriam). See Miller, U. S. Nat. Mus. Bull. 79: 97, Dec. 31, 1912.

$\dfrac{14062}{23010}$. Skin and skull. Adult male. Point Barrow, Alaska. July 16, 1883. Collected by John Murdoch. Original number 1672.

Well-made skin in good condition; skull Grade A.

†Putorius arcticus kadiacensis Merriam.

North Amer. Fauna 11 : 16, June 30, 1896.
=*Mustela kadiacensis* (Merriam). See Miller, U. S. Nat. Mus. Bull. 79 : 97, Dec. 31, 1912.

65290. Skin and skull. Young adult male. Kodiak Island, Alaska. April 25, 1894. Collected by B. J. Bretherton. Original number 304.

Well-made skin in good condition; skull Grade C.

†Mustela campestris Jackson.

Proc. Biol. Soc. Washington 26 : 124, May 21, 1913.

171490. Skin and skull. Adult male. Beemer, Cuming County, Nebr. April 18, 1911. Collected by Grover Sharp. Original number 8440X.

Well-made skin in good condition; skull Grade A.

*Mustela costaricensis Goldman.

Proc. Biol. Soc. Washington 25 : 9, Jan. 23, 1912.
=*Mustela frenata costaricensis* Goldman. See Hall, Carnegie Inst. Washington Publ. 473 : 109, Nov. 20, 1936.

$\dfrac{13770}{37149}$. Skin and skull. Young adult. San José, Costa Rica. Collected by C. H. Van Patten. Cataloged June 1883.

Well-made skin in good condition except that distal half of tail is missing; skull Grade A.

*Putorius culbertsoni Coues.   Cotype.

Fur-Bearing Animals, U. S. Geol. Surv. Terr. Misc. Publ. 8: 136, 1877 (from Baird MSS.) ; description of the cotypes on p. 139 gives technical status to name. Regarded by Coues (p. 139) as a MS. synonym of *Putorius longicauda* Baird, 1857, which would become available for Baird's animal should this prove to be different from the original *longicauda* of Richardson, 1839.
=*Mustela culbertsoni* (Coues).

$\dfrac{4320}{37995}$. Skin and skull. Fort Laramie, Laramie County, Wyo. December 1859. Collected by F. V. Hayden. Exploration of headwaters of Missouri and Yellowstone, under Capt. W. F. Reynolds. Original number 75.

Specimen remade into a fairly good study skin in January 1902 and skull removed. Tail lost; rump scorched; skull Grade A.

The other cotype, No. 4325, cannot be found. The entry in the catalog corresponding to that number is "*Putorius culbertsonii* (sic), Ft. Union [now Fort Buford, N. Dak.], Aug. 8, [18] 60, G. H. Trook."

Cotypes designated by number.

†Putorius frenatus goldmani Merriam.

North Amer. Fauna 11: 28, June 30, 1896.
=*Mustela frenata goldmani* (Merriam). See Miller, U. S. Nat. Mus. Bull. 79: 100, Dec. 31, 1912.

77519. Skin and skull. Adult male. Pinabete, altitude about 8,200 feet, Chiapas, Mexico. February 10, 1896. Collected by E. A. Goldman. Original number 9279.

Well-made skin in good condition; skull Grade C.

†Putorius frenatus leucoparia Merriam.

North Amer. Fauna 11: 29, June 30, 1896.
=*Mustela frenata leucoparia* (Merriam). See Miller, U. S. Nat. Mus. Bull. 79: 100, Dec. 31, 1912.

$\frac{34914}{47179}$. Skin and skull. Adult male. Patzcuaro, Michoacan, Mexico. July 27, 1892. Collected by E. W. Nelson. Original number 2960.

Well-made skin in good condition; skull Grade C.

†Mustela frenata panamensis Hall.

Proc. Biol. Soc. Washington 45: 139, Sept. 9, 1932.

170970. Skin and skull. Subadult female. Rio Indio, Canal Zone, near Gatun, Panama. February 17, 1911. Collected by E. A. Goldman. Original number 20897.

Well-made skin in good condition except for worn pelage on left side of neck. Skull Grade A.

†Mustela frenata perotae Hall.

Carnegie Inst. of Washington Publ. 473: 100, Nov. 20, 1936.

54278. Skin and skull. Adult female. Cofre de Perote, Veracruz, Mexico. May 26, 1893. Collected by E. W. Nelson. Original number 4864.

Well-made skin in good condition; skull Grade A.

†Putorius haidarum Preble.

Proc. Biol. Soc. Washington 12: 169, Aug. 10, 1898.
=*Mustela haidarum* (Preble). See Miller, U. S. Nat. Mus. Bull. 79: 97, Dec. 31, 1912.

94430. Skin and skeleton (not skin and skull as recorded in original description). Adult male, Massett, Graham Island, Queen Charlotte Islands, British Columbia, Canada. March 17, 1898. Collected by J. H. Keen. Original number 1800–X.

Well-made skin in good condition; skeleton Grade A.

*Putorius kaneii Baird.

Mammals of North America, p. 172, 1857.
=*Mustela kaneii* (Baird).

$\frac{2330}{37990}$. Skin (summer pelage) and skull. Adult. Arikamtchitchi Island (Arikam Island), Bering Strait (see footnote in Baird's Mammals of North America, p. 173), Tchuktchi Country, Siberia. Collected by W. Stimpson. Original number 358. Skin cataloged March 1857; skull, January 11, 1902.

Specimen was made into a fairly good modern study skin. The skull was removed in January 1902; skull Grade C.

No type specified in the original description. Baird listed two specimens, No. 1458 from Semipalatinsk, Siberia, in winter pelage, received from the Bremen Museum, through G. Hartlaub, and the above, No. 2330. Most of the description appears to be based on the summer pelage.

*Mustela lineiventer Hollister.

Proc. Biol. Soc. Washington 26: 2, Jan. 18, 1913.

175440. Skin and skull. Adult male. Tchegan-Burgazi Pass, altitude 9,000 feet, Little Altai Mountains, Siberia. July 10, 1912. Collected by N. Hollister. Original number 4281.

Well-made skin in good condition, right forefoot slightly injured; skull Grade A.

*Mustela lymani Hollister.

Smithsonian Misc. Coll. 60 (14): 5, Nov. 29, 1912.

175198. Skin and skull. Adult male. Tapucha, Altai Mountains, Siberia. August 10, 1912. Collected by N. Hollister. Original number 4494.

Well-made skin in good condition; skull Grade A.

*Lutreola macrodon Prentiss.

Proc. U. S. Nat. Mus. 26: 887, July 6, 1903.
=*Mustela macrodon* (Prentiss). See Miller, U. S. Nat. Mus. Bull. 79: 101, Dec. 31, 1912.

115178. Fragments of skull. Pre-Columbian shell heaps, Brooklin, Hancock County, Maine. 1897. Collected by F. W. True and D. W. Prentiss, Jr.

"*Condition of type.*—Fragment of skull composed of the superior maxillae, portions of the nasals, right zygoma, and palate extending 6 mm. back of molars. All of the teeth are present on the right side, three incisors and one premolar on the left side. The teeth are in excellent condition except the canine, which is broken at the point, and portions of enamel missing. The bones are very brittle and of a yellowish color on their broken surfaces." Prentiss, p. 888.

*Mustela meridana Hollister.

Proc. Biol. Soc. Washington 27: 143, July 10, 1914.
=*Mustela frenata meridana* Hollister. See Hall, Carnegie Inst. Washington Publ. 473: 110, Nov. 20, 1936.

123341. Skin and skull. Adult male. Sierra de Mérida, altitude 1,630 m., near Mérida, Venezuela. August 14, 1903. Collected by S. Briceño.

Well-made skin in good condition except for slight injury on right side of rump; skull Grade A.

†Mustela peninsulae olivacea Howell.

Proc. Biol. Soc. Washington 26: 139, May 21, 1913.
=*Mustela frenata olivacea* Howell. See Hall, Carnegie Inst. Washington Publ. 473: 105, Nov. 20, 1936.

180802. Skin and skull. Adult male. Autaugaville, Autauga County, Ala. December 22, 1912. Collected by L. S. Golsan. Original number 144 (9988–X).

Well-made skin in good condition; skull Grade A.

†Mustela primulina Jackson.

Proc. Biol. Soc. Washington 26: 123, May 21, 1913.
=*Mustela frenata primulina* Jackson. See Hall, Carnegie Inst. Washington Publ. 473: 104, Nov. 20, 1936.

168006. Skin and skull. Subadult female. Five miles northeast of Avilla, Jasper County, Mo. May 11, 1905. Collected by Hartley H. T. Jackson. Original number 552 (7869–X).

Well-made skin in good condition; skull Grade C.

†Putorius richardsoni alascensis Merriam.

North Amer. Fauna 11: 12, June 30, 1896.
=*Mustela cicognanii alascensis* (Merriam). See Miller, U. S. Nat. Mus. Bull. 79: 96, Dec. 31, 1912.

74423. Skin and skull. Adult male. Juneau, Alaska. August 22, 1895. Collected by C. P. Streator. Original number 4806.

Well-made skin in good condition; skull Grade A.

†Putorius saturatus Merriam.

North Amer. Fauna 11: 21, June 30, 1896.
=*Mustela frenata saturata* (Merriam). See Hall, Carnegie Inst. Washington Publ. 473: 106, Nov. 20, 1936.

65930. Skin and skull. Adult male. Siskiyou, altitude about 4,000 feet, Jackson County, Oreg. June 6, 1894. Collected by C. P. Streator. Original number 3905.

Well-made skin in good condition; skull Grade A.

†Putorius streatori Merriam.

North Amer. Fauna 11: 13, June 30, 1896.
=*Mustela streatori streatori* (Merriam). See Miller, U. S. Nat. Mus. Bull. 79: 96, Dec. 31, 1912.

76646. Skin and skull. Adult male. Mount Vernon, Skagit Valley, Skagit County, Wash. February 29, 1896. Collected by D. H. Luckey. Original number 3.

Well-made skin in good condition; skull Grade A.

†Putorius streatori leptus Merriam.

Proc. Biol. Soc. Washington 16: 76, May 29, 1903.

=*Mustela streatori leptus* (Merriam). See Miller, U. S. Nat. Mus. Bull. 79: 96, Dec. 31, 1912.

56800. Skin and skull. Young adult male. Silverton, San Juan County, Colo. October 20, 1893. Collected by J. A. Loring. Original number 1185.

Well-made skin in good condition; skull Grade A.

*Mustela tiarata Hollister.

Proc. Biol. Soc. Washington 26: 2, Jan. 18, 1913.

=*Mustela larvata tiarata* Hollister. See G. M. Allen, Amer. Mus. Nov. 358: 2, July 10, 1929.

155160. Skin and skull. Immature male. Chui-ning-chow, 150 miles east of Lanchow, Kansu, China. July 24, 1909. Collected by Arthur deC. Sowerby. Original number 196.

Well-made skin in good condition; skull Grade A.

†Putorius tropicalis Merriam.

North Amer. Fauna 11: 30, June 30, 1896.

=*Mustela frenata tropicalis* (Merriam). See Hall, Carnegie Inst. Washington Publ. 473: 109, Nov. 20, 1936.

54994. Skin and skull. Adult male. Jico, altitude 6,000 feet, Vera Cruz, Mexico. July 9, 1893. Collected by E. W. Nelson. Original number 5195.

Well-made skin in good condition; skull Grade B.

†Putorius tropicalis perdus Merriam.

Proc. Biol. Soc. Washington 15: 67, Mar. 22, 1902.

=*Mustela frenata perda* (Merriam). See Hall, Carnegie Inst. Washington Publ. 473: 109, Nov. 20, 1936.

100041. Skin and skull. Adult male. Teapa, Tabasco, Mexico. March 31, 1900. Collected by E. W. Nelson and E. A. Goldman. Original number 14074.

Well-made skin in good condition; skull Grade A.

*Lutreola vison ingens Osgood.

North Amer. Fauna 19: 42, Oct. 6, 1900.

=*Mustela vison ingens* (Osgood). See Miller, U. S. Nat. Mus. Bull. 79: 101, Dec. 31, 1912.

6530. Skull only. Old adult, probably male. Fort Yukon, Alaska. February 15, 1862. Collected by Robert Kennicott. Original number 262.

Skull Grade A.

†Lutreola vison lacustris Preble.

North Amer. Fauna 22: 66, Oct. 31, 1902.

=*Mustela vison lacustris* (Preble). See Miller, U. S. Nat. Mus. Bull. 79: 101, Dec. 31, 1912.

106872. Skin and skull. Young adult male. Echimamish River (near Painted Stone portage), Keewatin, Canada. September 14, 1900. Collected by E. A. and A. E. Preble. Original number 3518.

Well-made skin in good condition; skull Grade A.

*Mustela vison letifera Hollister.

Proc. U. S. Nat. Mus. 44: 475, April 18, 1913.

188305. Skin and skull. Adult male. Elk River, Sherburne County, Minn. November 7, 1885. Collected by Vernon Bailey. Original number 3. Merriam collection number $\frac{1575}{2189}$.

Well-made skin in good condition, except for absence of right hind foot; skull Grade A.

†Putorius washingtoni Merriam.

North Amer. Fauna 11: 18, June 30, 1896.
=*Mustela frenata washingtoni* (Merriam). See Hall, Carnegie Inst. Washington Publ. 473: 106, Nov. 20, 1936.

76322. Skin and skull. Adult male. Trout Lake, south base of Mount Adams, Skamania County, Wash. December 15, 1895. Collected by D. N. Kaegi. Original number 2.

Well-made skin in good condition; skull Grade A.

†Putorius xanthogenys oregonensis Merriam.

North Amer. Fauna 11: 25, June 30, 1896.
=*Mustela frenata oregonensis* (Merriam). See Hall, Carnegie Inst. Washington Publ. 473: 107, Nov. 20, 1936.

$\frac{32019}{43828}$. Skin and skull. Adult female. Grants Pass, Rogue River Valley, Josephine County, Oreg. December 19, 1891. Collected by C. P. Streator. Original number 1404.

Well-made skin in good condition; skull Grade A.

Genus SPILOGALE Gray

*Spilogale ambigua Mearns.

Preliminary Diagnoses of New Mammals of the Genera *Lynx, Urocyon, Spilogale,* and *Mephitis,* from the Mexican Boundary Line, p. 3, Jan. 12, 1897. (Reprint: Proc. U. S. Nat. Mus. 20: 460, Dec. 24, 1897.)

$\frac{20302}{35606}$. Skin and skull. Adult male. Eagle Mountain, Chihuahua, Mexico, about 4 miles south of monument No. 15, Mexican boundary line, lat. 31°47′, long. 30°15′. March 23, 1892. Collected by E. A. Mearns and F. X. Holzner. Original number 1574.

Well-made skin in good condition; skull Grade A.

†**Spilogale angustifrons** Howell.

Proc. Biol. Soc. Washington 15:242, Dec. 16, 1902.

50825. Skin and skull. Adult male. Tlalpam, Federal District, Mexico. December 15, 1892. Collected by E. W. Nelson and E. A. Goldman. Original number 4035.

Well-made skin in good condition; skull Grade A.

†**Spilogale angustifrons elata** Howell.

North Amer. Fauna 26: 27, Nov. 24, 1906.

133186. Skin and skull. Adult male. San Bartolomé, Chiapas, Mexico. March 19, 1904. Collected by E. A. Goldman. Original number 16618.

Well-made skin in good condition; skull Grade A.

†**Spilogale angustifrons tropicalis** Howell.

Proc. Biol. Soc. Washington 15:242, Dec. 16, 1902.

73523. Skin and skull. Adult male. San Mateo del Mar, Oaxaca, Mexico. May 16, 1895. Collected by E. W. Nelson and E. A. Goldman. Original number 7958.

Well-made skin in good condition; skull Grade B.

†**Spilogale gracilis** Merriam.

North Amer. Fauna 3: 83, Sept. 11, 1890.

$\frac{17986}{24897}$ Skin and skull. Adult male. Grand Canyon of the Colorado, altitude 3,500 feet, north of San Francisco Mountain, Coconino County, Ariz. September 12, 1889. Collected by C. Hart Merriam and Vernon Bailey. Original number 451.

Well-made skin in good condition; skull Grade A.

***Spilogale indianola** Merriam.

North Amer. Fauna 4: 10, Oct. 8, 1890.

1621. Skull only. Young adult. Indianola, Matagorda Bay, Matagorda County, Tex. Collected by J. H. Clark. Cataloged February 15, 1855.

Skull Grade A.

***Spilogale leucoparia** Merriam.

North Amer. Fauna 4: 11, Oct. 8, 1890.

186452. Skin and skull. Adult male. Mason, Mason County, Tex. December 2, 1885. Collected by Ira B. Henry. Original number 16. Merriam collection No. $\frac{1701}{2270}$.

Well-made skin in good condition; skull Grade A.

*Spilogale lucasana Merriam.

North Amer. Fauna 4: 11, Oct. 8, 1890.

$\frac{3970}{4219}$. Skin and skull. Adult male. Cape San Lucas, Lower California, Mexico. Collected by John Xantus. Original number $\frac{603}{610}$. Cataloged in October 1860.

Specimen formerly mounted. It is now a well-made study skin in good condition. Some hair is lost from the tail. Skull Grade A.

†Spilogale microdon Howell.

North Amer. Fauna 26: 34, Nov. 24, 1906.

145887. Skin and skull. Adult male. Comondu, Lower California, Mexico. November 8, 1905. Collected by E. W. Nelson and E. A. Goldman. Original number 18501.

Well-made skin in good condition; skull Grade A.

*Spilogale phenax Merriam.

North Amer. Fauna 4: 13, Oct. 8, 1890.

=*Spilogale gracilis phenax* Merriam. See Grinnell, Univ. California Publ. Zool. 40: 105, Sept. 26, 1933.

186453. Skin and skull. Adult male. Nicasio, Marin County, Calif. October 31, 1885. Collected by C. A. Allen. Merriam collection $\frac{1500}{2100}$.

Well-made skin in good condition; skull Grade A.

†Spilogale phenax latifrons Merriam.

North Amer. Fauna 4: 15, Oct. 8, 1890.

=*Spilogale gracilis latifrons* Merriam. See Grinnell, Univ. California Publ. Zool. 40: 106, Sept. 26, 1933.

$\frac{17271}{24200}$. Skin and skull. Old female. Roseburg, Douglas County, Oreg. July 13, 1889. Collected by T. S. Palmer. Original number 216.

Well-made skin in good condition; skull Grade C.

†Spilogale pygmaea australis Hall.

Ann. Mag. Nat. Hist. (ser. 11) 1: 514, May 1938.

70581. Skin and skull. Adult male. Acapulco, Guerrero, Mexico. January 25, 1895. Collected by E. W. Nelson and E. A. Goldman. Original number 7420.

Well-made skin in good condition, except right foot is missing; skull Grade A.

†Spilogale ringens Merriam.

North Amer. Fauna 4: 9, Oct. 8, 1890.

=*Spilogale putorius* (Linnaeus). See Howell, North Amer. Fauna 26: 15, Nov. 24, 1906.

$\frac{23182}{30642}$. Skin and skull. Adult female. Greensboro, Hale County, Ala. August 2, 1890. Collected by C. S. Brimley. Original number 50.

Well-made skin in good condition; skull Grade C.

*Spilogale saxatilis Merriam.

North Amer. Fauna 4: 13, Oct. 8, 1890.
=*Spilogale gracilis saxatilis* Merriam.   See Howell, North Amer. Fauna 26: 23, Nov. 24, 1906.

186454. Skin and skull. Adult male. Provo, Utah County, Utah. November 13, 1888. Collected by Vernon Bailey. Original number 384. Merriam collection No. $\frac{4928}{5675}$.

Well-made skin in good condition; skull Grade A.

†Spilogale tenuis Howell.

Proc. Biol. Soc. Washington 15: 241, Dec. 16, 1902.

99365. Skin and skull. Adult male. Arkins, Larimer County, Colo. November 13, 1899. Collected by R. S. Weldon. Original number 2198-X.

Well-made skin in good condition; skull Grade A.

Genus TAXIDEA Waterhouse

*Taxidea americana neglecta Mearns.

Bull. Amer. Mus. Nat. Hist. 3: 250, June 5, 1891.
=*Taxidea taxus neglecta* Mearns.   See Miller and Rehn, Proc. Boston Soc. Nat. Hist. 30: 218, Dec. 27, 1901.

$\frac{3835}{4191}$. Skin and skull. Adult male. Fort Crook, Shasta County, Calif. March 25, 1859. Collected by John Feilner. Original number 313.

Well-made skin in good condition (skin remade in January 1902) ; skull Grade A.

*Taxidea berlandieri Baird.

Mammals of North America, p. 205, 1857.
=*Taxidea taxus berlandieri* Baird.   See J. A. Allen, Bull. Amer. Mus. Nat. Hist. 7: 256, June 29, 1895.

1710. Skin (no skull). Male. Llano Estacado (now Cochran, Hockley, Yoakum, and Terry Counties), western Texas. May 8, 1855. Received from J. Pope.

Formerly mounted. Made into a fairly good study skin in February 1902.

Baird's description was based on one specimen, designated by number.

†Taxidea taxus sonoriensis Goldman.

Journ. Washington Acad. Sci. 29: 300, July 15, 1939.

96211. Skin and skull. Young adult male. Camoa, Rio Mayo (about 15 miles above Navojoa), Sonora, Mexico. November 29, 1898. Collected by E. A. Goldman. Original number 13263.

Well-made skin in good condition; skull Grade A.

Genus VORMELA Blasius

*Vormela negans Miller.

Proc. U. S. Nat. Mus. 38: 385, Aug. 19, 1910.

155001. Skin only. Adult male. Ordos Desert about 100 miles north of Yuling-fu, altitude 4,000 feet, Shensi, China. November 18, 1908. Collected by Arthur deC. Sowerby. Original number 92.

Well-made skin in good condtition.

Family PROCYONIDAE: Raccoons, Coatis, Kinkajous

Genus BASSARICYON J. A. Allen

*Bassaricyon gabbii J. A. Allen.

Proc. Acad. Nat. Sci. Philadelphia 28: 21, Apr. 18, 1876; *ibid*, 29: 267, 268, pl. 2, 1877 (illustration supposedly representing animal, but actually representing *Nasua narica*).

14214. Skull. Adult. Talamanca, Costa Rica. Collected by W. M. Gabb. Original number 44. Cataloged November 19, 1874.

Skull Grade B.

According to the catalog there should be a skin bearing the number 12237. It has never been found in the Museum collection. In a letter addressed to Dr. M. W. Lyon, dated May 12, 1908, J. A. Allen remarks: "In reference to the type of *Bassaricyon gabbii*, I never saw a skin belonging to the type skull. Through some error in cataloging a skin of *Nasua narica* purported to belong to the skull, and I figured it as such; being at that time unfamiliar with the species of *Nasua*. Careful search was made for the missing skin after the error was discovered, but I am sure it was never found. My knowledge of the external characters of *Bassaricyon* is based on a living specimen of *B. alleni* which I saw some years ago in the London Zoo."

Type designated by number on page 20 of the original description.

†Bassariscyon [sic] gabbi orinomus Goldman.

Smithsonian Misc. Coll, 60 (2) : 16, Sept. 20, 1912.
=*Bassaricyon gabbii orinomus* Goldman.

179157. Skin and skull. Adult male. Cana, altitude 1,800 feet, mountains of eastern Panama. March 10, 1912. Collected by E. A. Goldman. Original number 21474.

Well-made skin in good condition; skull Grade A.

Genus NASUA Storr

†**Nasua narica molaris** Merriam.

Proc. Biol. Soc. Washington 15: 68, Mar. 22, 1902.

$\frac{32630}{44553}$. Skin and skull. Adult male. Manzanillo, Colima, Mexico. February 7, 1892. Collected by E. W. Nelson. Original number 1844.

Well-made skin in good condition; skull Grade B.

†**Nasua narica richmondi** Goldman.

Journ. Washington Acad. Sci. 22: 312, June 4, 1932.

51331. Skin and skull. Adult male. Escondido River, 50 miles above Bluefields, Nicaragua. November 19, 1892. Collected by Charles W. Richmond. Original number 158.

Well-made skin in good condition; skull Grade B.

†**Nasua nelsoni** Merriam.

Proc. Biol. Soc. Washington 14: 100, July 19, 1901.

108520. Skin and skull. Old male. Cozumel Island, off coast of Quintana Roo, Mexico. April 8, 1901. Collected by E. W. Nelson and E. A. Goldman. Original number 14673.

Well-made skin in good condition; skull Grade B.

Genus POTOS Geoffroy and Cuvier

†**Potos flavus arborensis** Goodwin.

Amer. Mus. Nov. 987: 1, May 13, 1938.

250320. Skin and skull. Adult female. El Sauce Peralta, a farm on the Atlantic Railroad less than halfway from San Jose to Limon, altitude about 1,000 feet, Costa Rica. June 4, 1931. Collected by C. F. Underwood. Original number 26850–X.

Well-made skin in good condition; skull Grade A.

†**Potos flavus campechensis** Nelson and Goldman.

Journ. Washington Acad. Sci. 21: 482, Nov. 19, 1931.

181266. Skin and skull. Adult female. La Tuxpeña, Champoton, Campeche, Mexico. February 12, 1913. Collected by Percy W. Shufeldt. Original number 10234–X.

Well-made skin in good condition; skull Grade A.

†**Potos flavus guerrerensis** Goldman.

Proc. Biol. Soc. Washington 28: 133, June 29, 1915.

74683. Skin and skull. Adult male. Near Ometepec, Guerrero, Mexico. February 15, 1895. Collected by E. W. Nelson and E. A. Goldman. Original number 7464.

Well-made skin in good condition; skull Grade A.

†**Potos flavus isthmicus** Goldman.

Smithsonian Misc. Coll. 60 (22) : 14, Feb. 28, 1913.

179042.   Skin and skull.   Adult female.   Near head of Rio Limon, altitude 5,200 feet, Mount Pirri, eastern Panama.   April 21, 1912.   Collected by E. A. Goldman.   Original number 21631.

Well-made skin in good condition; skull Grade A.

Genus PROCYON Storr

†**Euprocyon cancrivorus panamensis** Goldman.

Smithsonian Misc. Coll. 60 (22) : 15, Feb. 28, 1913.
=*Procyon cancrivorus panamensis* (Goldman).   See Miller, U. S. Nat. Mus. Bull. 128 : 108, Apr. 29, 1924.

171669.   Skin and skull.   Adult female.   Gatun, Canal Zone, Panama.   June 21, 1911.   Collected by E. A. Goldman.   Original number 21174.

Well-made skin in good condition; skull Grade B.

***Procyon hernandezii** var. **mexicana** Baird.

Mammals of North America, p. 215, 1857.
=*Procyon lotor mexicanus* Baird.   See Mearns, Proc. Biol. Soc. Washington 27 : 65, Mar. 20, 1914.

$\frac{2018}{1051}$.   Skin (lost) and skull.   Espia, Sonora, Mexico.   April 1855. Collected by C. B. R. Kennerly.   See Baird, Mammals of the Mexican Boundary, p. 24, 1859.

Original description and catalog indicates that there should be a skin and skull.   The skin apparently has been lost, as no trace of it can be found at this time.   Skull Grade A.

†**Procyon insularis vicinus** Nelson and Goldman.

Proc. Biol. Soc. Washington 44 : 20, Feb. 21, 1931.

88982.   Skin and skull.   Adult male.   Maria Magdalena Island, altitude 250 feet, Tres Marias Islands, off coast of State of Nayarit, western Mexico, May 27, 1897.   Collected by E. W. Nelson and E. A. Goldman.   Original number 11064.

Well-made skin in good condition; skull Grade B.

***Procyon lotor auspicatus** Nelson.

Smithsonian Misc. Coll. 82 (8) : 9, July 10, 1930.

255080.   Skin and skull.   Adult male.   Marathon, Key Vaca, Monroe County, Fla.   March 28, 1930.   Collected by E. W. Nelson.

Well-made skin in good condition; skull Grade A.

***Procyon lotor californicus** Mearns.

Proc. Biol. Soc. Washington 27 : 66, Mar. 20, 1914.

60675. Skin and skull. Adult female. Ocean beach near last Mexican Boundary monument (No. 258), San Diego County, Calif. July 16, 1894. Collected by Frank X. Holzner. Original number 1605.

Well-made skin in good condition; skull Grade A.

*Procyon lotor crassidens Hollister.

Proc. Biol. Soc. Washington 27: 142, July 10, 1914.

$\frac{12191}{14191}$. Skin and skull. Adult male. Talamanca, Costa Rica. 1874. Collected by William M. Gabb. Original number 14.

Well-made skin in good condition; skull Grade A.

†Procyon lotor excelsus Nelson and Goldman.

Journ. Mamm. 11: 458, Nov. 11, 1930.

236214. Skin and skull. Old adult male. Owyhee River, Oreg., 10 miles west of Fairylawn, Owyhee County, Idaho. April 15, 1920. Collected by J. W. Fisk. Original number 22424-X (797).

Tanned skin in good condition except for small area on nape of neck where fur is thin; skull Grade A.

*Procyon lotor fuscipes Mearns.

Proc. Biol. Soc. Washington 27: 63, Mar. 20, 1914.

63055. Skin and skull. Adult male. Las Moras Creek, Fort Clark, Kinney County, Tex. February 6, 1893. Collected by Edgar A. Mearns. Original number 2273.

Well-made skin in good condition; skull Grade A.

†Procyon lotor grinnelli Nelson and Goldman.

Journ. Washington Acad. Sci. 20: 82, Mar. 4, 1930.

147181. Skin and skull. Adult male. La Paz, Lower California, Mexico. February 15, 1906. Collected by E. W. Nelson and E. A. Goldman. Original number 19139.

Tanned skin in good condition; skull Grade A.

*Procyon lotor hirtus Nelson and Goldman.

Journ. Mamm. 11: 455, Nov. 11, 1930.

187926. Skin and skull. Adult male. Elk River, Sherburne County, Minn. March 4, 1886. Collected by Vernon Bailey. Original number 161. Merriam collection No. $\frac{2566}{3176}$.

Well-made skin in good condition; skull Grade A.

*Procyon lotor incautus Nelson.

Smithsonian Misc. Coll. 82 (8) : 10, July 10, 1930.

255060. Skin and skull. Adult male. Torch Key, Big Pine Key Group, Monroe County, Fla. March 24, 1930. Collected by E. W. Nelson.

Well-made skin in good condition; skull Grade A.

*Procyon lotor inesperatus Nelson.

Smithsonian Misc. Coll. 82 (8) : 8, July 10, 1930.

255037. Skin and skull. Adult male. Upper Matecumbe Key, Monroe County, Fla. March 19, 1930. Collected by E. W. Nelson.

Flat skin in good condition, left fore foot slightly injured by trap; skull Grade A.

†Procyon lotor insularis Merriam.

Proc. Biol. Soc. Washington 12: 17, Jan. 27, 1898.
=*Procyon insularis insularis* Merriam. See Nelson and Goldman, Proc. Biol. Soc. Washington 44: 20, Feb. 21, 1931.

88978. Skin and skull. Old male. Maria Madre Island, Tres Marias Islands, Nayarit, Mexico. May 10, 1897. Collected by E. W. Nelson and E. A. Goldman. Original number 10985.

Well-made skin in good condition; skull Grade A.

*Procyon lotor litoreus Nelson and Goldman.

Journ. Mamm. 11: 457, Nov. 11, 1930.

2450. Skull only. Adult (probably male). St. Simon Island, Glynn County, Ga. Collected by Samuel W. Wilson. Cataloged August 7, 1856.

Skull Grade A.

*Procyon lotor marinus Nelson.

Smithsonian Misc. Coll. 82 (8) : 7, July 10, 1930.

254989. Skin and skull. Adult male. Near Chokoloskee, Collier County, Fla. February 28, 1930. Collected by E. W. Nelson.

Well-made skin in good condition; skull Grade A.

*Procyon lotor ochraceus Mearns.

Proc. Biol. Soc. Washington 27: 64, Mar. 20, 1914.

59900. Skin and skull. Subadult male. Sonoyta River, near Quitobaquita, Sonora, Mexico. February 7, 1894. Collected by Edgar A. Mearns. Original number 2937.

Well-made skin in good condition; skull Grade A.

†Procyon lotor shufeldti Nelson and Goldman.

Proc. Biol. Soc. Washington 44: 17, Feb. 21, 1931.

177546. Skin and skull. Adult male. La Tuxpeña, Champoton, southeastern Campeche, Mexico. April 20, 1911. Collected by Percy W. Shufeldt. Original number 8575-X.

Well-made skin in good condition; skull Grade B.

*Procyon lotor solutus Nelson and Goldman.

Journ. Mamm. 12: 308, Aug. 24, 1931.

256027. Skin and skull. Adult male. Hilton Head Island, Beaufort County, S. C. December 10, 1930. Collected by William L. Brown.

Well-made skin in good condition; skull Grade A.

†Procyon lotor vancouverensis Nelson and Goldman.

Journ. Mamm. 11: 458, Nov. 11, 1930.

135457. Skull only. Adult male. Quatsino Sound, Vancouver Island, British Columbia, Canada. November 1904. Collected by Charles Sheldon. Original number 5117–X.

Skull Grade A.

†Procyon lotor varius Nelson and Goldman.

Journ. Mamm. 11: 456, Nov. 11, 1930.

158246. Skin and skull. Adult female. Castleberry, Conecuh County, Ala. October 10, 1908. Collected by A. H. Howell. Original number 1359.

Tanned skin in good condition; skull Grade A.

*Procyon minor Miller.

Proc. Biol. Soc. Washington 24: 4, Jan. 28, 1911.

$\frac{38417}{15481}$. Skin and skull. Young male. Pointe-à-Pitre, Guadeloupe, Lesser Antilles. Collected by L. Guesde. Cataloged June 26, 1886.

Poorly made skin in fair condition, terminal third of tail lacking hair; skull Grade A.

†Procyon pallidus Merriam.

Proc. Biol. Soc. Washington 13: 151, June 13, 1900.

=*Procyon lotor pallidus* Merriam. See Nelson and Goldman, Journ. Washington Acad. Sci. 20: 82, Mar. 4, 1930.

99272. Skin and skull. Adult female. New River, Colorado Desert, Imperial County, Calif. October 16, 1899. Collected by F. Stephens. Original number 3022 (2246–X).

Well-made skin in good condition; skull Grade B.

†Procyon psora pacifica Merriam.

North Amer. Fauna 16: 107, Oct. 28, 1899.

=*Procyon lotor pacificus* Merriam. See Nelson and Goldman, Journ. Mamm. 11: 458, Nov. 11, 1930.

93137. Skin and skull. Adult. Keechelus Lake, Kittitas County, Wash. January 15, 1898. Collected by C. Hansen. Original number 1409–X.

Well-made skin in good condition; skull Grade A.

*Procyon pumilus Miller.

Proc. Biol. Soc. Washington 24: 3, Jan. 28, 1911.

171983. Skin and skull. Young adult. Ancon, Panama. 1910. Collected by Allan H. Jennings.

Well-made skin in good condition, some sloughing on hindfeet and mid-section of tail, and tip of left ear missing; skull Grade A.

†Procyon pygmaeus Merriam.

Proc. Biol. Soc. Washington 14: 101, July 19, 1901.

108511. Skin and skull. Young adult male. Cozumel Island, off coast of Quintana Roo, Mexico. April 14, 1901. Collected by E. W. Nelson and E. A. Goldman. Original number 14698.

Well-made skin in good condition; skull Grade A.

Family PROTELIDAE: Aard Wolves
Genus PROTELES Geoffroy

*Proteles cristatus termes Heller.

Smithsonian Misc. Coll. 61 (13): 9, Sept. 16, 1913.

181523. Skin and skull. Adult female. Kabalolot Hill, head-waters of the Amala River, west of the Loita Plains, British East Africa [=Kenya]. May 8, 1911. Collected by Edmund Heller. Original number 2154.

Well-made skin in good condition, slight loss of hair from sloughing on left shoulder and on belly; skull Grade B.

Family URSIDAE: Bears
Genus EUARCTOS Gray

*Ursus amblyceps Baird. Lectotype.

Rep. U. S. and Mex. Bound. Surv. 2 (pt. 2): 29, Jan. 1859.
=*Euarctos americanus amblyceps* (Baird). See Miller, U. S. Nat. Mus. Bull. 128: 91, Apr. 29, 1924.

992. Skull only. Adult male. Old copper mines near the Rio Mimbres, near present location of Georgetown, Grant County, N. Mex. Collected by J. H. Clark. Cataloged November 1, 1852.

Skull Grade A.

When describing this form Professor Baird had three specimens, an old female and two adult males, all collected at "Coppermines," N. Mex. In describing the skull he wrote: "I shall select a middle aged skull to serve as the type of my description." The female, No. 994, is old, having the crowns and incisors considerably worn. The two males are the only ones listed in the table of measurements. Written in ink on skull number 991 are the words "Glossy black, hair, long." On skull No. 992 is written "Brown bear, not fully grown." No. 992 is the only one of the original specimens that is middle aged and brown, the color that Baird considered as the most usual. We therefore designate it as the lectotype.

†**Ursus americanus eremicus** Merriam.

Proc. Biol. Soc. Washington 17 : 154, Oct. 6, 1904.

=*Euarctos americanus eremicus* (Merriam). See Miller, U. S. Nat. Mus. Bull. 128 : 91, Apr. 29, 1924.

116952. Skin and skull. Adult female. Sierra Guadalupe, Coahuila, Mexico. April 21, 1902. Collected by E. W. Nelson and E. A. Goldman. Original number 15111.

Well-made skin in good condition, except for bare spot on abdomen; skull Grade A.

†**Ursus (Euarctos) carlottae** Osgood.

North Amer. Fauna 21 : 30, Sept. 26, 1901.

=*Euarctos carlottae* (Osgood). See Miller, U. S. Nat. Mus. Bull. 128 : 91, Apr. 29, 1924.

87620. Skull only. Adult male. Massett, Graham Island, Queen Charlotte Islands, British Columbia, Canada. November, 1896. Collected by J. H. Keen. Original number 497–X.

Skull Grade A.

*****Ursus floridanus** Merriam.

Proc. Biol. Soc. Washington 10 : 81, Apr. 13, 1896.

=*Euarctos floridanus* (Merriam). See Miller, U. S. Nat. Mus. Bull. 128 : 92, Apr. 29, 1924.

3484. Skull only. Old adult (male, *fide* Merriam). Key Biscayne, Dade County, Fla. May 21, 1858. Collected by G. Würdemann. Original number 4.

Skull Grade B.

Genus SELENARCTOS Heude

*****Selenarctos thibetanus wulsini** A. B. Howell.

Proc. Biol. Soc. Washington 41 : 115, June 29, 1928.

=*Selenarctos thibetanus ussuricus* Heude. See Pocock, Journ. Bombay Nat. Hist. Soc. 36 : 123, Nov. 15, 1932.

=*Euarctos thibetanus thibetanus* (Cuvier). See G. M. Allen, Mamm. China and Mongolia 1 : 333, 1938.

240668. Skin and skull. Adult female. Eastern Tombs area, Chi-li, China. October 15, 1923. Collected by F. R. Wulsin. Original number 1140.

Flat skin in good condition; skull Grade A.

Genus URSUS Linnaeus

†**Ursus absarokus** Merriam.

Proc. Biol. Soc. Washington 27 : 181, Aug. 13, 1914.

67391. Skull only. Adult male. Near head of Little Bighorn River, northern part of Bighorn Mountains, Carbon County, Mont. Purchased May 1893 by J. Alden Loring.

Skull Grade B.

†**Ursus apache** Merriam.

Proc. Biol. Soc. Washington 29: 134, Sept. 6, 1916.

212436. Skull only. Adult male. Whorton Creek, on south slope of White Mountains, a few miles west of Blue, Greenlee County, Ariz. April 3, 1913. Collected by B. V. Lilly. Original number 14110–X.

Skull Grade A.

†**Ursus arizonae** Merriam.

Proc. Biol. Soc. Washington 29: 135, Sept. 6, 1916.

177332. Skull only. Adult male. East side of Escudilla Mountains, Apache County, Ariz. September 3, 1911. Collected by C. H. Shinn. Original number 8516X.

Skull Grade B.

†**Ursus atnarko** Merriam.

North Amer. Fauna 41: 22, Feb. 9, 1918.

211452. Skull only. Adult male. Lonesome Lake, Atnarko River, one of the upper forks of the Bella Coola, British Columbia, Canada. September 1915. Collected by E. H. Edwards. Original number 15048X.

Skull Grade C.

†**Ursus bairdi** Merriam.

Proc. Biol. Soc. Washington 27: 192, Aug. 13, 1914.

=*Ursus horribilis bairdi* Merriam. See Merriam, North Amer. Fauna 41: 19, Feb. 9, 1918.

203805. Skull only. Old male. Blue River, Summit County, Colo. Purchased from E. R. Warren. Cataloged August 10, 1914. X-Catalog number 11238.

Skull Grade B.

*****Ursus californicus tularensis** Merriam.

Proc. Biol. Soc. Washington 27: 188, Aug. 13, 1914.

=*Ursus tularensis* Merriam. See Merriam, North Amer. Fauna 41: 30, Feb. 9, 1918.

3536. Skull only. Old male. Fort Tejon, Tehachapi Mountains, Kern County, Calif. Collected by John Xantus. Original number 1172. Cataloged 1859.

Skull Grade A.

†**Ursus caurinus** Merriam.

Proc. Biol. Soc. Washington 27: 187, Aug. 13, 1914.

176591. Skin and skull. Adult female. Berners Bay, east side of Lynn Canal, southeastern Alaska. June 8, 1911. Collected by A. Hasselborg. Original number 8451X.

Tanned skin in good condition; skull Grade A.

†**Ursus chelan** Merriam.

Proc. Biol. Soc. Washington 29 : 136, Sept. 6, 1916.

205185. Skull only. Old male. T. 30 N., R. 16 E., Willamette
Meridian, Wenatche National Forest, east slope Cascade Moun-
tains, northern Chelan County, Wash. September 1, 1913.
Collected by D. S. Rice. Original number 11612–X.

Skull Grade B.

***Ursus chelidonias** Merriam.

North Amer. Fauna 41 : 21, Feb. 9, 1918.

223133. Skull only. Old male. On river at head of Jervis Inlet,
British Columbia, Canada. 1916. Collected by Forrest and Fred
Johnstone. Original number 16973–X.

Skull Grade C.

***Ursus colusus** Merriam.

Proc. Biol. Soc. Washington 27 : 187, Aug. 13, 1914.

3837. Skull only. Old male. Sacramento River (probably from
between Colusa and Sacramento), Calif. Collected by the U. S.
Exploring Expedition (1838–1842) ; marked "C. P. Ex. 6.16."
Cataloged 1860.

Skull Grade B.

†**Ursus crassodon** Merriam.

North Amer. Fauna 41 : 90, Feb. 9, 1918.

171049. Skull only. Old male. Klappan Creek (Third South Fork,
Stikine River), British Columbia, Canada. September 1907.
Collected by E. P. Richardson. Original number 8421–X.

Skull Grade C.

†**Ursus crassus** Merriam.

North Amer. Fauna 41 : 90, Feb. 9, 1918.

225473. Skin and skull. Adult male. Upper Macmillan River, Yukon, Canada. September 1916. Collected by William Drury.
Original number 19155–X.

Tanned skin in good condition ; skull Grade B.

†**Ursus cressonus** Merriam.

Proc. Biol. Soc. Washington 29 : 137, Sept. 6, 1916.

206529. Skull only (without mandible). Old male. Lakina River,
south slope of Wrangell Range, Alaska. 1914. Collected by J. P.
Hubrick. Original number 12210–X.

Skull Grade C.

†Ursus dalli Merriam.

Proc. Biol. Soc. Washington 10: 71, Apr. 13, 1896.

75048. Skull only. Old male. Yakutat Bay (northwest side), Alaska. September 8, 1895. Collected by chief of Yakutat Indians. Procured through Albin Johnson. Original number 2.

Skull Grade A.

†Ursus dalli gyas Merriam.

Proc. Biol. Soc. Washington 15: 78, Mar. 22, 1902.

=*Ursus gyas* Merriam. See Merriam, North Amer. Fauna 41: 124, Feb. 9, 1918.

91669. Skull only. Adult male. Pavlof Bay, Alaska Peninsula. 1897. Collected by Willie Pavlof. Original number 1052–X.

Skull Grade A.

*Ursus dusorgus Merriam.

North Amer. Fauna 41: 33, Feb. 9, 1918.

217426. Skull only. Old male. Head of Jack Pine River, near Mount Bess, close to British Columbia Boundary, Alberta, Canada. September 4, 1916. Collected by William Rindsfoos.

Skull Grade A.

†Ursus eltonclarki Merriam.

Proc. Biol. Soc. Washington 27: 175, Aug. 13, 1914.

179066. Skin and skull. Adult male. Near Freshwater Bay, Chichagof Island, Alaska. May 19, 1912. Collected and presented by Elton Clark. Original number 9168–X.

Tanned skin in good condition; skull Grade A.

†Ursus eltonclarki insularis Merriam.

Proc. Biol. Soc. Washington 29: 141, Sept. 6, 1916.

=*Ursus insularis* Merriam. See Merriam, North Amer. Fauna 41: 44, Feb. 9, 1918.

205186. Skull only. Old male. Admiralty Island, Alaska. 1914. Purchased from W. H. Case. Original number 11625–X.

Skull Grade B.

†Ursus eulophus Merriam.

Proc. Biol. Soc. Washington 17: 153, Oct. 6, 1904.

81102. Skull only. Adult male. Admiralty Island, Alaska. 1896. Collected by G. T. Emmons. Original number 7.

Skull Grade A.

*Ursus eximius Merriam.

Proc. Biol. Soc. Washington 29: 139, Sept. 6, 1916.

122495. Skin and skull. Adult male. Head of Knik Arm, Cook Inlet, Alaska. 1903. Killed by native. Purchased from G. W. Palmer.

Flat skin in good condition; skull Grade A.

*Ursus henshawi Merriam.

Proc. Biol. Soc. Washington 27: 190, Aug. 13, 1914.

15671. Skull and atlas. Old male. Southern Sierra Nevada, near Havilah, Kern County, Calif. 1875. Collected by J. T. Rothrock and Henry W. Henshaw.

Skull Grade B.

†Ursus holzworthi Merriam.

Proc. Biol. Soc. Washington 42: 173, June 15, 1929.

248691. Skull only. Adult male. Head of Black River, Talkeetna Mountains, Alaska. September 21, 1928 (not September 23, 1928, as in original description). Collected by John M. Holzworth. Original number 25140–X.

Skull Grade A.

†Ursus hoots Merriam.

Proc. Biol. Soc. Washington 29: 140, Sept. 6, 1916.

206136. Skull only. Adult male. Clearwater Creek, a north branch of Stikine River, British Columbia, Canada. 1913. Collected by John Hyland; presented by Lincoln Ellsworth. Original number 11874–X.

Skull Grade A.

†Ursus horriaeus texensis Merriam.

Proc. Biol. Soc. Washington 27: 191, Aug. 13, 1914.

=*Ursus texensis texensis* Merriam. See Merriam, North Amer. Fauna 41: 35, Feb. 9, 1918.

203198. Skull only. Old male. Davis Mountains, Jeff Davis County, Tex. November 2, 1890. Killed by C. O. Finley and John Z. Means. Presented by C. H. Merriam. Original number 10894–X.

Skull Grade B.

†Ursus horribilis alascensis Merriam.   Lectotype

Proc. Biol. Soc. Washington 10: 74, Apr. 13, 1896.

=*Ursus alascensis* Merriam. See Merriam, North Amer. Fauna 41: 94, Feb. 9 1918.

76466. Skull only. Old male. Unalaklik River, Alaska. 1895. Collected by Rudolf Neumann, of Iliuliuk, Alaska. Original number 2.

Skull Grade A.

In the original description no type was designated, but in North American Fauna 41: 94, February 9, 1918, Merriam made skull No. 76466, one of the original specimens, the lectotype.

*Ursus horribilis californicus Merriam. Lectotype.

Proc. Biol. Soc. Washington 10 : 76, Apr. 13, 1896.

=*Ursus californicus* Merriam. See Merriam, Proc. Biol. Soc. Washington 27 : 188, Aug. 13, 1914.

3630. Skull only. Old adult. Monterey, Monterey County, Calif. Collected by A. S. Taylor. Cataloged October 7, 1859.

Skull Grade A.

No type designated, but a skull is figured (fig. 15) in the original description. This skull was made lectotype by Lyon and Osgood, U. S. Nat. Mus. Bull. 62 : 230, January 28, 1909.

*Ursus horribilis horriaeus Baird. Lectotype.

Mammals of North America, p. 224, 1857.

=*Ursus horriaeus* Baird. See Merriam, Proc. Biol. Soc. Washington 10 : 75, Apr. 13, 1896; 27 : 191, Aug. 13, 1914.

990. Skull only. Adult male. Old copper mines near the Rio Mimbres, near the present location of Georgetown, Grant County, N. Mex. Collected by J. H. Clark. Cataloged November 1, 1852.

Skull Grade B.

No type was designated in the original description. The above specimen was designated as "the type," that is, the lectotype, by C. Hart Merriam (Proc. Biol. Soc. Washington 10 : 75, Apr. 13, 1896).

†Ursus horribilis phaeonyx Merriam.

Proc. Biol. Soc. Washington 17 : 154, Oct. 6, 1904.

=*Ursus phaeonyx* Merriam. See Merriam, Proc. Biol. Soc. Washington 27 : 183, Aug. 13, 1914.

133231. Skin and skull. Old female with most of the molariform teeth worn to roots. Glacier Mountain, Tanana Mountains, Alaska (about 2 miles below source of Comet Creek, near Fortymile Creek, between Yukon and Tanana Rivers). July 12, 1903. Collected by W. H. Osgood. Original number 2684.

Tanned skin in good condition; foot pads missing; skull Grade A.

*Ursus idahoensis Merriam.

North Amer. Fauna 41 : 54, Feb. 9, 1918.

187888. Skull only. Old male. North Fork Teton River, Fremont County, Idaho. September 23, 1874. Killed by Richard Leigh. Merriam Collection number 93.

Skull Grade A.

*Ursus imperator Merriam.

Proc. Biol. Soc. Washington 27 : 180, Aug. 13, 1914.

=*Ursus horribilis imperator* Merriam. See Merriam, North Amer. Fauna 41 : 20, Feb. 9, 1918.

176297. Skin and skeleton. Old male. Yellowstone National Park, Wyo. Received at National Zoological Park July 30, 1894, and died there May 1913. Collected by George S. Anderson. Nat. Zool. Park No. 2217.

Flat skin in good condition; skeleton Grade A.

†Ursus innuitus Merriam.

Proc. Biol. Soc. Washington 27: 177, Aug. 13, 1914.

179780. Skull only. Old male. Golofnin Bay, south side of Seward Peninsula, western Alaska. 1886. Collected by Edward F. Ball.

Skull Grade B.

*Vetularctos inopinatus Merriam.

North Amer. Fauna 41: 132, Feb. 9, 1918.

=Ursus inopinatus (Merriam). See Miller, U. S. Nat. Mus. Bull. 128: 106, Apr. 29, 1924.

$\frac{7149}{8706}$. Skin and skeleton. Adult female. Rendezvous Lake, northeast of Fort Anderson, Mackenzie, Canada. June 24, 1864. Collected by R. MacFarlane. Original number 1979.

Flat skin in good condition; skeleton Grade A.

†Ursus kenaiensis Merriam.

Proc. Biol. Soc. Washington 17: 154, Oct. 6, 1904.

128672. Skull only. Adult female. Cape Elizabeth, extreme west end of Kenai Peninsula, Alaska. 1903. Collected by C. A. Lambert. Original number 4205–X.

Skull Grade A.

*Ursus kennerleyi Merriam.

Proc. Biol. Soc. Washington 27: 194, Aug. 13, 1914.

2086. Skull only. Old male. Mountains near Nogales, Sonora, Mexico. June 1855. Collected by C. B. R. Kennerly. Catalog lists a skin, No. 1047, apparently lost.

Skull Grade B.

†Ursus kidderi Merriam.

Proc. Biol. Soc. Washington 15: 78, Mar. 22, 1902.

116562. Skin and skull. Young male (not fully grown). Chinitna Bay, Cook Inlet, Alaska Peninsula, Alaska. June 9, 1901. Collected by James H. Kidder. Original number 3661–X.

Tanned skin in good condition; skull Grade A.

†Ursus kidderi tundrensis Merriam.

Proc. Biol. Soc. Washington 27: 196, Aug. 13, 1914.

76470. Skull only. Adult male. Shaktolik River, Norton Sound, Alaska. September 1894. Collected by natives, and secured through Rudolf Neumann. Original number 6.

Skull Grade A.

†**Ursus klamathensis** Merriam.

Proc. Biol. Soc. Washington 27: 185, Aug. 13, 1914.

178735. Skull only. Adult male. Beswick, near mouth of Shovel Creek, Klamath River, Siskiyou County, Calif. Collected and presented by Charles Farwell Edson. Cataloged May 13, 1912.

Skull Grade B.

†**Ursus kluane** Merriam.

Proc. Biol. Soc. Washington 29: 141, Sept. 6, 1916.

204188. Skull only. Old male. McConnell River, Yukon, Canada. July 15, 1914. Collected by T. Smith and G. Geddis. Original number 11251–X.

Skull Grade A.

†**Ursus kluane impiger** Merriam.

North Amer. Fauna 41: 81, Feb. 9, 1918.

210708. Skull only. Subadult male. Columbia Valley, British Columbia, Canada. April 1914. Collected by W. G. Mackay and G. F. Dippie. Original number 13986–X.

Skull Grade A.

†**Ursus kwakiutl** Merriam.

Proc. Biol. Soc. Washington 29: 143, Sept. 6, 1916.

211748. Skull and skin of head. Adult male. Jervis Inlet, coast of southern British Columbia, Canada. May 17, 1916. Collected by Fred Mansell. Original number 14093–X.

Skin of head in good condition; skull Grade A.

†**Ursus kwakiutl neglectus** Merriam.

Proc. Biol. Soc. Washington 29: 144, Sept. 6, 1916.
=*Ursus neglectus* Merriam. See Merriam, North Amer. Fauna 41: 28, Feb. 9, 1918.

209889. Skull only. Old male. Near Hawk Inlet, Admiralty Island, southeastern Alaska. April 1914. Collected by W. H. Spaulding. Original number 12718–X.

Skull Grade C.

†**Ursus kwakiutl warburtoni** Merriam.

Proc. Biol. Soc. Washington 29: 145, Sept. 6, 1916.
=*Ursus warburtoni* Merriam. See Merriam, North Amer. Fauna 41: 27, Feb. 9, 1918.

210576. Skull only. Old male. Atnarko River, British Columbia, Canada. July 15, 1915. Collected by E. H. Edwards. Original number 13101–X

Skull Grade B.

*Ursus macfarlani Merriam.

North Amer. Fauna 41: 51, Feb. 9, 1918.

6551. Skull and three leg bones. Adult male. On Anderson River, 50 miles below Fort Anderson, Mackenzie, Canada. May 8, 1863. Collected by R. MacFarlane. Original number 551.

Skull Grade A. The catalog indicates that there were originally a skin, skull, and skeleton. All that can now be found is the skull, two humeri, and one ulna. Merriam mentioned the skull only.

*Ursus macrodon Merriam.

North Amer. Fauna 41: 38, Feb. 9, 1918.

$\frac{15707}{12678}$. Skin and skull. Old male. Twin Lakes, Lake County, Colo. July 28, 1876. Collected by C. W. Derry.

Flat skin in good condition; skull Grade A.

†Ursus magister Merriam.

Proc. Biol. Soc. Washington 27: 189, Aug. 13, 1914.

160155. Skull only. Old male. Los Biacitos, head of San Onofre Canyon, Santa Ana Mountains, San Diego County, Calif. August 1900 or 1901. Collected and presented by Henry A. Stewart. Original number 241 (S. E. Piper).

Skull Grade B.

†Ursus mendocinensis Merriam.

Proc. Biol. Soc. Washington 29: 145, Sept. 6, 1916.

206625. Skull only (mandible missing). Old male. Near Long Valley, Mendocino County, Calif. Received April 23, 1915. Collected by Jim Farley. Obtained through Charles J. and Frank T. Hittell. Original number 12229–X.

Weathered skull Grade C.

†Ursus middendorffi Merriam.

Proc. Biol. Soc. Washington 10: 69, April 13, 1896.

54793. Skull only. Adult male. Kodiak Island, Alaska. July 3, 1893. Collected by B. J. Bretherton. Original number 176.

Skull Grade B.

†Ursus mirabilis Merriam.

Proc. Biol. Soc. Washington 29: 146, Sept. 6, 1916.

137471. Skin and skull. Adult male. Admiralty Islands, Alaska. June 26, 1905. Collected by Cyrus Catt. Original number 5468X.

Tanned skin in worn pelage in good condition; skull Grade A.

†Ursus mirus Merriam.

North Amer. Fauna 41: 40, Feb. 9, 1918.

206595. Skull only. Adult male (rather old). Slough Creek, Yellowstone National Park, Wyo. March 27, 1915. Collected by Henry Anderson. Original number 12227–X.

Skull Grade B.

*Ursus navaho Merriam.

Proc. Biol. Soc. Washington 27: 191, Aug. 13, 1914.

=Ursus texensis navaho Merriam. See Merriam, North Amer. Fauna 41: 37, Feb. 9, 1918.

3500. Skull only. Near Fort Defiance, Ariz. Probably killed in 1856 in Chuska Mountains, on boundary between northeastern Arizona and northwestern New Mexico. Collected by H. B. Möllhausen. Cataloged 1859. Catalog lists a skin, No. 3571, apparently lost.

Skull Grade C.

†Ursus nelsoni Merriam.

Proc. Biol. Soc. Washington 27: 190, Aug. 13, 1914.

99657. Skin and skull. Adult female. Colonia Garcia, Chihuahua, Mexico. November 13, 1899. Collected by H. A. Cluff. Original number 2406–X.

Well-made skin in good condition; skull Grade A.

†Ursus nortoni Merriam.

Proc. Biol. Soc. Washington 27: 179, Aug. 13, 1914.

178763. Skull only. Adult female. Yakutat, Alaska. May 15, 1910. Collected and presented by G. Frederick Norton. Original number A5.

Skull Grade A.

†Ursus nuchek Merriam.

Proc. Biol. Soc. Washington 29: 146, Sept. 6, 1916.

146459. Skull only. Old male. Head of Nuchek Bay, Hinchinbrook Island, Prince William Sound, Alaska. September 15, 1905. Collected by C. Swanson. Original number 5791–X.

Skull Grade C.

†**Ursus ophrus** Merriam.

Proc. Biol. Soc. Washington 29 : 148, Sept. 6, 1916.

210252. Skull only. Old male. Eastern British Columbia, Canada (exact locality unknown). 1915. Collected by E. W. Darbey. Original number 12837-X.

Skull Grade C.

†**Ursus orgiloides** Merriam.

North Amer. Fauna 41 : 46, Feb. 9, 1918.

223275. Skull only. Probably male. Italio River, Alaska. November 1916. Purchased from E. M. Axelson. Original number 17075-X.

Skull Grade A.

†**Ursus orgilos** Merriam.

Proc. Biol. Soc. Washington 27 : 176, Aug. 13, 1914.

180280. Skull only. Probably male, rather old. Bartlett Bay, east side Glacier Bay, southeastern Alaska. August 22, 1912. Collected by A. Hasselborg. Original number 9805-X.

Skull Grade B.

†**Ursus oribasus** Merriam.

North Amer. Fauna 41 : 56, Feb. 9, 1918.

223991. Skin and skull. Old male. Upper Liard River, Yukon, Canada, near British Columbia Boundary. Spring 1916. Killed by J. Thompson. Purchased from William Drury. Original number 18284-X.

Tanned skin in good condition ; skull Grade A.

†**Ursus pallasi** Merriam.

Proc. Biol. Soc. Washington 29 : 149, Sept. 6, 1916.

205160. Skull only. Old male. Donjek River, southwestern Yukon, Canada. August 1913. Collected by T. A. Dixon. Original number 11389-X.

Skull Grade A.

†**Ursus pellyensis** Merriam.

North Amer. Fauna 41 : 82, Feb. 9, 1918.

215477. Skull only. Young adult male. Ketza Divide, Pelly Mountains, Yukon, Canada. September 30, 1915. Collected by Fred E. Enevoldsen. Original number 14704-X.

Skull Grade A.

†**Ursus perturbans** Merriam.

North Amer Fauna 41 : 64, Feb. 9, 1918.

222102. Skin and skull. Old male. Near Mount Taylor, Valencia County, N. Mex. July 9, 1916. Collected by Ed. Anderson. Original number 16694–X.

Tanned skin in good condition; skull Grade A.

*Ursus pervagor Merriam.

Proc. Biol. Soc. Washington 27: 186, Aug. 13, 1914.

187887. Skull only. Adult male. Pemberton Lake (now Lillooet Lake), in edge of humid coast strip, British Columbia, Canada. May 1893 (not 1883 as in original description). Collected by John Fannin. Merriam Collection number 6510.

Skull Grade B.

*Ursus phaeonyx latifrons Merriam.

Proc. Biol. Soc. Washington 27: 183, Aug. 13, 1914.
=Ursus latifrons Merriam. See Merriam, North Amer. Fauna, 41: 97, Feb. 9, 1918.

75612. Skull only. Old male. Jasper House, Alberta, Canada. September 15, 1895. Collected by J. A. Loring. Original number 3270.

Skull Grade A.

*Ursus planiceps Merriam.

North Amer. Fauna 41: 37, Feb. 9, 1918.

13289. Skull. (Bones of left fore and hind feet, all terminal phalanges missing, were found in the collection after the species had been described.) Adult male. Colorado, exact locality unknown, but probably in the foothills or on the western edge of the plains. Collected by F. V. Hayden. Cataloged December 1873.

Skull Grade A.

†Ursus pulchellus ereunetes Merriam.

North Amer. Fauna 41: 56, Feb. 9, 1918.

222323. Skull only. Adult male. Beaverfoot Range, Kootenai District, British Columbia, Canada. October 1, 1916. Collected by George Hill. Original number 16712–X.

Skull Grade A.

†Ursus pulchellus pulchellus Merriam.

North Amer. Fauna 41: 55, Feb. 9, 1918.

221599. Skull only. Adult male. Ross River, Yukon, Canada. July 20, 1916. Collected by Fred E. Enevoldsen. Original number 14968–X.

Skull Grade B.

†**Ursus rogersi bisonophagus** Merriam.

North Amer. Fauna 41: 66, Feb. 9, 1918.

181089. Skin and skull. Young-adult male. Bear Lodge, Sundance National Forest, Black Hills, Crook County, Wyo. February 1887. Collected by Paul Kleineidam. Original number 10066–X.

Tanned skin in good condition, except that all the feet are missing; skull Grade C.

†**Ursus rogersi rogersi** Merriam.

North Amer. Fauna 41: 65, Feb. 9, 1918.

222983. Skull only. Adult male. High up on Greybull River, Absaroka Mountains, Wyo. Fall 1890. Collected and presented by Archibald Rogers. Original number 16923–X.

Skull Grade B.

†**Ursus rungiusi rungiusi** Merriam.

North Amer. Fauna 41: 49, Feb. 9, 1918.

179893. Skull only. Young-adult male. Rocky Mountains on headwaters of Athabaska River, Alberta, Canada. September 1910. Collected and presented by Carl Rungius.

Skull Grade A.

†**Ursus rungiusi sagittalis** Merriam.

North Amer. Fauna 41: 50, Feb. 9, 1918.

210705. Skull only. Adult male (rather old). Champagne Landing, southwestern Yukon, Canada. Fall 1915. Purchased from W. G. Mackay and G. F. Dippie. Original number 13983–X.

Skull Grade C.

†**Ursus selkirki** Merriam.

Proc. Biol. Soc. Washington 29: 105, Sept. 6, 1916.
=*Ursus hylodromus* Elliot. See Merriam, North Amer. Fauna 41: 77, Feb. 9, 1918.

205170. Skull only. Old male. Upper Columbia River, Selkirk Mountains, British Columbia, Canada. June 4, 1914. Collected by John Hurst. Original number 11545–X.

Skull Grade B.

†**Ursus sheldoni** Merriam.

Proc. Biol. Soc. Washington 23: 127, Sept. 2, 1910.

137318. Skull only. Adult Male. Montague Island, Prince William Sound, Alaska. May 1905. Collected and presented by Charles Sheldon. Original number 5460–X.

Skull Grade B.

†**Ursus shirasi** Merriam.

Proc. Biol. Soc. Washington 27: 195, Aug. 13, 1914.

203030. Mounted head and right foreleg; left foreleg, about two square feet of skin from back, and skull. Old male. Pybus Bay, Admiralty Island, Alaska. September 16, 1913. Collected and presented by George Shiras, 4th. Original number 10692–X.

Mounted head and right foreleg; tanned left foreleg with claws and about 2 square feet of skin from back in good condition; skull Grade B. The mounted head and right foreleg were presented May 8, 1936.

†**Ursus shoshone** Merriam.

Proc. Biol. Soc. Washington 27: 184, Aug. 13, 1914.

203185. Skull only. Old male. Estes Park, Larimer County, Colo. Collected by Joe Mills. Received April 1914 from J. C. Miles, through C. Hart Merriam. Original number 10809–X.

Skull Grade C.

***Ursus shoshone canadensis** Merriam.

Proc. Biol. Soc. Washington 27: 184, Aug. 13, 1914.
=*Ursus canadensis* Merriam. See Merriam, North Amer. Fauna 41: 52, Feb. 9, 1918.

174511. Skin and skull. Adult male. Moose Pass, near Mount Robson, British Columbia, Canada. July 23, 1911. Collected by N. Hollister and Charles D. Walcott, Jr. Original number (Hollister) 3792.

Flat skin in good condition; skull Grade A.

***Ursus sitkensis** Merriam.

Proc. Biol. Soc. Washington 10: 73, Apr. 13, 1896.

187891. Skull only. Adult male. Near Sitka, Alaska. 1894. Collected by an Indian; purchased and presented by J. Stanley-Brown. Merriam Collection No. 6543.

Skull Grade A.

†**Ursus stikeenensis** Merriam.

Proc. Biol. Soc. Washington 27: 178, Aug. 13, 1914.

202794. Skin and skull. Adult male. Tatletuey Lake, near head of Skeena River, northern British Columbia, Canada. September 23, 1913. Killed and presented by Charles R. Cross, Jr., through E. A. Preble. Original number 5772 (E. A. P.).

Well-made skin in good condition, except that a small patch of fur has sloughed off the face; skull Grade A.

†**Ursus tahltanicus** Merriam.

Proc. Biol. Soc. Washington 27: 181, Aug. 13, 1914.

251543—42——8

179928. Skull only. Old male. Klappan Creek (third south fork of Stikine River), British Columbia, Canada. September 1906. Collected and presented by G. Frederick Norton. Original number 9258-X.

Skull Grade C.

†Ursus toklat Merriam.

Proc. Biol. Soc. Washington 27: 182, Aug. 13, 1914.

158813. Skull only. Adult female. Head of Toklat River, north base of Alaska range, near Mount McKinley, Alaska. May 24, 1908. Collected by Charles Sheldon. Original number 324.

Skull Grade A.

*Ursus townsendi Merriam.

Proc. Biol. Soc. Washington 29: 151, Sept. 6, 1916.

216643. Skull only. Old male. Mainland of southeastern Alaska, probably between Cross Sound and Alsek River delta, but exact locality uncertain. 1889. Purchased by Charles H. Townsend.

Skull Grade A.

†Ursus utahensis Merriam.

Proc. Biol. Soc. Washington 27: 193, Aug. 13, 1914.

180193. Skull only. Old male. North Fork Salina Creek, 10 or 12 miles southeast of Mayfield, Sanpete County, Utah. May 22, 1911. Collected by Mart Martenson. Original number 9314-X.

Skull Grade B.

†Ursus washake Merriam.

Proc. Biol. Soc. Washington 29: 152, Sept. 6, 1916.

213005. Skull only. Adult male (rather old). North Fork Shoshone River, Absaroka Mountains, between Bighorn Basin and Yellowstone National Park, Wyo. September 1913. Collected by J. A. McGuire. Original number 14166-X.

Skull Grade A.

Family VIVERRIDAE: Civets

Genus ARCTICTIS Temminck [5]

*Arctictis niasensis Lyon.

Proc. U. S. Nat. Mus. 52: 443, Dec. 30, 1916.

141230. Imperfect pelt. Nias Island, off west coast of Sumatra. 1905. Collected by W. L. Abbott. Original number 3970.

Flat skin, minus feet and head, but otherwise in good condition.

---

[5] The status of the members of this genus has been discussed by Pocock, Proc. Zool. Soc. London, 1933, pt. 4; 1015–1031, Dec. 1933.

Genus ARCTOGALIDIA Merriam [6]

*Arctogalidia bicolor Miller.

Smithsonian Misc. Coll. 61 (21) : 7, Dec. 29, 1913.

151875. Skin and skull. Adult female. Klumpang Bay, Dutch Southeast Borneo. January 9, 1908. Collected by W. L. Abbott. Original number 5745.

Well-made skin in good condition; skull Grade A.

*Arctogalidia depressa Miller.

Smithsonian Misc. Coll. 61 (21) : 8, Dec. 29, 1913.

115600. Skull only. Adult female. Pulo Bintang, Rhio-Linga Archipelago. August 18, 1902. Collected by W. L. Abbott. Original number 1896.

Skull Grade A.

*Arctogalidia fusca Miller.

Proc. U. S. Nat. Mus. 31: 269, Sept. 11, 1906.

122920. Skin and skull. Adult male. Pulo Kundur, Rhio-Linga Archipelago. June 22, 1903. Collected by W. L. Abbott. Original number 2540.

Well-made skin in good condition; skull Grade A.

*Arctogalidia inornata Miller.

Proc. Washington Acad. Sci. 3: 131, Mar. 26, 1901.

104859. Skin and skull. Old adult male. Bunguran Island, Natuna Islands, South China Sea, between Malay Peninsula and Borneo. June 23, 1900. Collected by W. L. Abbott. Original number 502.

Well-made skin in good condition. Skull Grade A.

*Arctogalidia macra Miller.

Smithsonian Misc. Coll. 61 (21) : 6, Dec. 29, 1913.

124172. Skin and skull. Adult female. Domel Island, Mergui Archipelago. January 26, 1904. Collected by W. L. Abbott. Original number 3075.

Well-made skin in good condition; skull Grade A.

*Arctogalidia major Miller.

Proc. Biol. Soc. Washington 19: 25, Feb. 26, 1906.

83510. Skin and skull. Young (permanent dentition in place, but unworn; sutures of rostrum and brain case plainly visible) adult male. Lay Song Hong, Trong (or Tarang), Peninsular Siam. September 3, 1896. Collected by W. L. Abbott.

Well-made skin in good condition; skull Grade A.

---

[6] The status of the members of this genus has been discussed by Pocock, Proc. Zool. Soc. London, 1933, pt. 4 : 977–999, Dec. 1933.

*Arctogalidia mima Miller.

Smithsonian Misc. Coll. 61 (21) : 7, Dec. 29, 1913.

142153. Skin and skull. Adult female. Semimba Bay, Batam Island, Rhio-Linga Archipelago. September 16, 1905. Collected by C. Boden Kloss. Original number 10.

Well-made skin in good condition; skull Grade A.

*Arctogalidia minor Lyon.

Proc. U. S. Nat. Mus. 31 : 599, Dec. 18, 1906.

124984. Skin and skull. Adult female. Buding Bay, Billiton Island, off east coast of Sumatra. August 3, 1904. Collected by W. L. Abbott. Original number 3532.

Well-made skin in good condition; skull Grade A.

*Arctogalidia simplex Miller.

Proc. Acad. Nat. Sci. Philadelphia 54 : 156, June 11, 1902.

113069. Skin and skull. Adult male. Linga Island, Rhio-Linga Archipelago. August 30, 1901. Collected by W. L. Abbott. Original number 1254.

Well-made skin in good condition; skull Grade A.

*Arctogalidia sumatrana Lyon.

Proc. U. S. Nat. Mus. 34 : 653, Sept. 14, 1908.

144120. Skin and skull. Adult male. Makapan, eastern Sumatra. February 19, 1907. Collected by W. L. Abbott. Original number 5054.

Well-made skin in good condition; skull Grade A.

*Arctogalidia tingia Lyon.

Proc. U. S. Nat. Mus. 34 : 652, Sept. 14, 1908.

144324. Skin and skull. Old male. Pulo Tebing Tinggi, off east coast of Sumatra. January 20, 1907. Collected by W. L. Abbott. Original number 4992.

Well-made skin in good condition; skull Grade A.

Genus ATILAX Geoffroy and Cuvier

*Mungos paludinosus rubescens Hollister.

Proc. Biol. Soc. Washington 25 : 1, Jan. 23, 1912.
=*Atilax paludinosus rubescens* (Hollister). See Hollister, U. S. Nat. Mus. Bull. 99 (pt. 1) : 127, Aug. 16, 1918.

$\frac{19775}{35251}$. Skin and skull. Adult male. Mount Kilimanjaro, altitude 4,000 feet, German East Africa [=Tanganyika Territory]. November 8, 1889. Collected by W. L. Abbott.

Flat skin in good condition; skull Grade A.

Genus BDEOGALE Peters

*Bdeogale crassicauda omnivora Heller.

Smithsonian Misc. Coll. 61 (13) : 12, Sept. 16, 1913.

182275. Skin and skull. Adult female. Mazeras, British East Africa [=Kenya]. December 21, 1911. Collected by Edmund Heller. Original number 2588.

Well-made skin in good condition; skull Grade A.

Genus GENETTA Oken

*Genetta pumila Hollister.

Smithsonian Misc. Coll. 66 (1) : 4, Feb. 10, 1916.

=*Genetta tigrina erlangeri* (Matschie). See Schwarz, Rev. Zool. Bot. Afr. 19 (2) : 278, 1930.

182704. Skin and skull. Adult male. Mount Gargues, North Creek, altitude 6,000 feet, British East Africa [=Kenya]. September 1, 1911. Collected by Edmund Heller. Original number 4193.

Well-made skin in good condition; skull Grade A.

*Helogale undulata affinis Hollister.

Smithsonian Misc. Coll. 66 (1) : 7, Feb. 10, 1916.

=*Genetta tigrina erlangeri* (Matschie). See Schwarz, Rev. Zool. Bot. Afr. 19 (2) : 278, 1930.

182715. Skin and skull. Adult male. Summit of Mount Lololokwi, altitude 6,000 feet, British East Africa [=Kenya]. September 2, 1911. Collected by Edmund Heller. Original number 4296.

Well-made skin in good condition; skull Grade A. "Left mandibular ramus missing when described." N. Hollister.

Genus HEMIGALUS Jourdan [7]

*Hemigale minor Miller.

Smithsonian Misc. Coll. 45: 43, Nov. 6, 1903.

=*Hemigalus derbyanus minor* Miller. See Pocock, Proc. Zool. Soc. London, 1933, pt. 4: 1006, Dec. 1933.

121651. Skin and skull. Adult female. South Pagi Island, off west coast of Sumatra. December 27, 1902. Collected by W. L. Abbott. Original number 2173.

Well-made skin in good condition; skull Grade A.

---

[7] The status of the members of this genus has been discussed by Pocock, Proc. Zool. Soc. London, 1933, pt. 4 : 1000–1009, Dec. 1933.

Genus ICHNEUMIA Geoffroy

*Mungos albicaudus dialeucos Hollister.

Smithsonian Misc. Coll. 66 (1) : 6, Feb. 10, 1916.
=*Ichneumia albicaudus dialeucos* (Hollister).   See Hollister, U. S. Nat. Mus.
Bull. 99, pt. 1 : 131, Aug. 16, 1918.

184794.   Skin and skull.   Adult male.   Mount Lololokwi, British
East Africa [=Kenya].   September 18, 1911.   Collected by Edmund Heller.   Original number 693.

Cased skin in good condition; skull Grade A.

*Mungos albicaudus ferox Heller.

Smithsonian Misc. Coll. 61 (13) : 11, Sept. 16, 1913.
=*Ichneumia albicaudus ibeana* (Thomas).   See Hollister, U. S. Nat. Mus. Bull.
99, pt. 1 : 130, Aug. 16, 1918.

163294.   Skin and skull.   Adult female.   Changamwe, British East
Africa [=Kenya].   November 25, 1909.   Collected by Edgar A.
Mearns.   Original number 7275.

Flat skin in good condition, right hind foot somewhat torn; skull Grade A.

Genus MUNGOS Geoffroy and Cuvier

*Crossarchus fasciatus colonus Heller.

Smithsonian Misc. Coll. 56 (17) : 16, Feb. 28, 1911.
=*Mungos mungo colonus* (Heller).   See G. M. Allen and Lawrence, Bull. Mus.
Comp. Zool. 79 : 65, Jan. 1936.

162132.   Skin and skull.   Adult female.   Southern Guaso Nyiro
River, Sotik District, British East Africa [=Kenya].   June 21,
1909.   Collected by Edmund Heller.   Original number 6396.

Well-made skin in good condition ; skull Grade A.

Genus MYONAX Thomas

*Mungos dentifer Heller.

Smithsonian Misc. Coll. 61 (13) : 10, Sept. 16, 1913.
=*Myonax dentifer* (Heller).   See G. M. Allen, Bull. Mus. Comp. Zool. 83 : 221,
1939.

182732.   Skin and skull.   Adult female.   Maji-ya-Chumvi, British
East Africa [=Kenya].   December 14, 1911.   Collected by Edmund Heller.   Original number 4865.

Well-made skin in good condition; skull Grade A.

*Mungos sanguineus orestes Heller.

Smithsonian Misc. Coll. 56 (17) : 15, Feb. 28, 1911.
=*Myonax sanguineus orestes* (Heller).   See G. M. Allen, Bull. Mus. Comp.
Zool. 83 : 224, 1939.

164152. Skin and skull. Adult male. West slope of Mount Kenia, altitude 8,500 feet, British East Africa [=Kenya]. October 12, 1909. Collected by J. Alden Loring. Original number 7934.

Well-made skin in good condition, right fore foot slightly injured; skull Grade A.

*Mungos sanguineus parvipes Hollister.

Smithsonian Misc. Coll. 66 (1) : 5, Feb. 10, 1916.
=*Myonax sanguineus parvipes* (Hollister).   See G. M. Allen, Bull. Mus. Comp. Zool. 83 : 224, 1939.

182739. Skin and skull. Adult male. Kaimosi, British East Africa [=Kenya]. February 5, 1912. Collected by Edmund Heller. Original number 5601.

Well-made skin in good condition; skull Grade A.

Genus NANDINIA Gray

*Nandinia binotata arborea Heller.

Smithsonian Misc. Coll. 61 (13) : 9, Sept. 16, 1913.

182374. Skin and skull. Adult male. Lukosa River, northeast of Kisumu, British East Africa [=Kenya]. February 11, 1912. Collected by Edmund Heller. Original number 2695.

Cased skin in good condition, claws on all four feet missing; skull Grade A.

Genus PAGUMA Gray [8]

*Paradoxurus robustus Miller.

Proc. Biol. Soc. Washington 19 : 26, Feb. 26, 1906.
=*Paguma larvata robusta* (Miller).   See Robinson and Kloss, Journ. Federated Malay States Mus. 7 (pt. 4) : 244, June 1918.

86796. Skin and skull. Adult female. Khow Sai Dow, altitude 2,000 feet, Trong (or Tarang), Peninsular Siam. February 13, 1899. Collected by W. L. Abbott.

Well-made skin in good condition; skull Grade A.

Genus PARADOXURUS Geoffroy [9]

*Paradoxurus brunneipes Miller.

Proc. U. S. Nat. Mus. 31 : 269, Sept. 11, 1906.

122886. Skin and skull. Adult male. Pulo Kundur, Rhio-Linga Archipelago. June 24, 1903. Collected by W. L. Abbott. Original number 2549.

Well-made skin in good condition; skull Grade A.

---

[8] The status of the members of this genus has been discussed by Pocock, Journ. Bombay Nat. Hist. Soc. 37 : 326–346, Aug. 15, 1934 ; Proc. Zool. Soc. London, 1934, pt. 3 : 665–683, Sept. 1934.
[9] The status of the members of this genus has been discussed by Pocock, Journ. Bombay Nat. Hist. Soc. 36 : 855–877, Dec. 15, 1933 ; *ibid.* 37 : 172–192, Apr. 15, 1934 ; *ibid.* 37 : 314–326, Aug. 15, 1934 ; Proc. Zool. Soc. London, 1934 (pt. 3) : 613–664, Sept. 1934.

*Paradoxurus canescens Lyon.

Proc. U. S. Nat. Mus. 31: 597, Dec. 18, 1906.

124943. Skin and skull. Adult male. Tanjong Batu, Billiton Island, off east coast of Sumatra. July 19, 1904. Collected by W. L. Abbott. Original number 3520.

Well-made skin in good condition; skull Grade A.

*Paradoxurus hermaphroditus canus Miller.

Smithsonian Misc. Coll. 61 (21) : 5, Dec. 29, 1913.

123976. Skin and skull. Adult female. Pulo Terutau, off west coast of Peninsular Siam. April 7, 1904. Collected by W. L. Abbott. Original number 3209.

Well-made skin in good condition; skull Grade A.

*Paradoxurus hermaphroditus enganus Lyon.

Proc. U. S. Nat. Mus. 52: 442, Dec. 30, 1916.

141026. Skin and skull. Adult female. Engano Island, off west coast of Sumatra. November 11, 1904. Collected by W. L. Abbott. Orginal number 3782.

Well-made skin in good condition; skull Grade A.

*Paradoxurus hermaphroditus fuscus Miller.

Smithsonian Misc. Coll. 61 (21) : 3, Dec. 29, 1913.

124075. Skin and skull. Adult female. James Island, Mergui Archipelago. January 2, 1904. Collected by W. L. Abbott. Original number 2982.

Well-made skin in good condition; skull Grade A.

*Paradoxurus hermaphroditus pallens Miller.

Smithsonian Misc. Coll. 61 (21) : 4, Dec. 29, 1913.

124201. Skin and skull. Adult female. Kisseraing Island, Mergui Archipelago. February 4, 1904. Collected by W. L. Abbott. Original number 3106.

Well-made skin in good condition except for slight injury to right hind foot; skull Grade A.

*Paradoxurus hermaphroditus pugnax Miller.

Smithsonian Misc. Coll. 61 (21) : 4, Dec. 29, 1913.

124100. Skin and skull. Adult female. Sullivan Island, Mergui Archipelago. January 5, 1904. Collected by W. L. Abbott. Original number 2999.

Well-made skin in good condition; skull Grade A.

*Paradoxurus hermaphroditus pulcher Miller.

Smithsonian Misc. Coll. 61 (21) : 5, Dec. 29, 1913.

124142. Skin and skull. Adult female. Clara Island, Mergui Archipelago. January 11, 1904. Collected by W. L. Abbott. Original number 3033.

Well-made skin in good condition; skull Grade A.

*Paradoxurus hermaphroditus ravus Miller.

Smithsonian Misc. Coll. 61 (21) : 2, Dec. 29, 1913.

84429. Skin and skull. Adult female. Trong, Peninsular Siam. March 5, 1897. Collected by W. L. Abbott.

Well-made skin in good condition; skull Grade A.

*Paradoxurus hermaphroditus sacer Miller.

Smithsonian Misc. Coll. 61 (21) : 4, Dec. 29, 1913.

124032. Skin and skull. Adult female. St. Matthew Island, Mergui Archipelago. December 27, 1903. Collected by W. L. Abbott. Original number 2934.

Well-made skin in good condition except for slight injury to right fore foot; skull Grade A.

*Paradoxurus hermaproditus [sic] senex Miller.

Smithsonian Misc. Coll. 61 (21) : 3, Dec. 29, 1913.

124171. Skin and skull. Immature male. Domel Island, Mergui Archipelago. January 26, 1904. Collected by W. L. Abbott. Original number 3074.

Well-made skin in good condition; skull Grade A.

*Paradoxurus hermaphroditus simplex Miller.

Smithsonian Misc. Coll. 61 (21) : 6, Dec. 29, 1913.

124902. Skin and skull. Adult male. Klabat Bay, Banka Island, off east coast of Sumatra. June 26, 1904. Collected by W. L. Abbott. Original number 3443.

Well-made skin in good condition except for loss of right half of right fore foot; skull Grade A.

*Paradoxurus lignicolor Miller.

Smithsonian Misc. Coll. 45 : 44, Nov. 6, 1903.

121645. Skin and skull. Adult male. North Pagi Island, off west coast of Sumatra. November 19, 1902. Collected by W. L. Abbott. Original number 2068.

Well-made skin in good condition; skull Grade A.

*Paradoxurus padangus Lyon.

Proc. U. S. Nat. Mus. 34 : 655, Sept. 14, 1908.

143614. Skin and skull. Adult male. Pulo Padang, off east coast of Sumatra. April 1, 1906. Collected by W. L. Abbott. Original number 4791.

Well-made skin in good condition; skull Grade A.

*Paradoxurus parvus Miller.

Smithsonian Misc. Coll. 61 (21) : 1, Dec. 29, 1913.

114175. Skin and skull. Adult male. Simalur Island, off west coast of Sumatra. December 15, 1901. Collected by W. L. Abbott. Original number 1385.

Well-made skin in good condition; skull Grade A.

Genus VIVERRICULA Hodgson [10]

*Viverricula malaccensis thai Kloss.

Journ. Nat. Hist. Soc. Siam 3 : 352, Dec. 31, 1919.

236629. Skin and skull. Adult female. Prapatom, central Siam. November 20, 1916. Collected by C. Boden Kloss. Original number 2449.

Well-made skin in good condition; skull Grade A.

Order CETACEA: Whales, Porpoises

Family BALAENOPTERIDAE: Finbacks

Genus BALAENOPTERA Lacépède

*Balaenoptera davidsoni Scammon.

Proc. California Acad. Sci. 4 : 269, printed in advance, Oct. 4, 1872.

12177. Skull. Adult female. Admiralty Inlet, Puget Sound, Wash. October 1870. Collected by C. M. Scammon.

Skull in good condition.
Type not designated by number. See True, Smithsonian Contrib. Knowl. 33 : 91, 1904.
Not certainly distinct from *Balaenoptera acutorostrata* Lacépède. See Cowan, Journ. Mamm. 20 : 224, May 1939.

Family DELPHINIDAE: Porpoises

Genus DELPHINUS Linnaeus

*Delphinus albimanus Peale.

U. S. Exploring Expedition 8 (Mamm. and Ornith.) : 33, 1848.
=*Delphinus delphis* Linnaeus. See True, U. S. Nat. Mus. Bull. 36 : 45, 1889.

$\frac{3743}{4107}$. Mounted skin and jaw. Female. Off the coast of Chile, lat. 27°16′ S., long. 75°30′ W. Collected by U. S. ship *Peacock*. No. 31, Peale's list of specimens, *op. cit.*, p. 305. Cataloged June 26, 1860. For further information, see True, *op. cit.*, p. 55.

Skin, formerly mounted. In 1910, while it was being moved, this mounted specimen fell and was badly broken. It cannot now be found. From both mandibles the tip and posterior portions have been cut off, and the left mandible is, in addition, broken near the tip.

---

[10] The status of the members of this genus has been discussed by Pocock, Journ. Bombay Nat. Hist. Soc. 34 : 629–656, Aug. 15, 1933.

Delphinus albirostratus Peale. Lost. See page 575.

Delphinus bairdii Dall. Lost. See page 575.

Genus GLOBICEPHALA Lesson

*Globiocephalus scammonii Cope.

> Proc. Acad. Nat. Sci. Philadelphia 21: 21, 1869; Dall, *in* Scammon's Marine Mammals, p. 299, 1874.
> =*Globicephala scammonii* (Cope). See True, U. S. Nat. Mus. Bull. 36: 139, 1889.

9074. Skull. "Coast of Lower California in latitude 31°, land 10 miles distant. December 14, 1862." (Scammon, Marine Mammals, p. 86, 1874.) Collected by C. M. Scammon.

> Skull Grade A.
> For considering this specimen the type, see True, *op cit.*, pp. 139 and 140. Two mandibles, Nos. 9075 and 9076, in the National Museum formed part of the original material. They may be considered as paratypes.

Genus GRAMPIDELPHIS Iredale and Troughton

*Grampus stearnsii Dall.

> Proc. California Acad. Sci. 5: 13, printed in advance, Jan. 29, 1873.
> =*Grampidelphis griseus* (Cuvier). See Iredale and Troughton, Rec. Australian Mus. 19 (1) : 32, Aug. 2, 1933.

13021. Mandible. Monterey, Calif. Collected by C. M. Scammon. Cataloged in 1873.

> Mandible in good condition; second and third teeth of right side missing. "Two jaws of this animal are in my hands for examination." (Dall in Scammon's Marine Mammals, p. 299, 1874.)
> For considering this specimen the type, see True, *op. cit.*, p. 130.

Genus LAGENORHYNCHUS Gray

Phocaena australis Peale. See page 576.

*Lagenorhynchus gubernator Cope.   Cotypes.

> Proc. Acad. Nat. Sci. Philadelphia 28: 138, ordered published June 20, 1876.
> =*Lagenorhynchus acutus* Gray. See True, U. S. Nat. Mus. Bull. 36: 83, 1889.

12305 and 12306. Plaster casts (No. 2) made and colored from a fresh specimen.

> Cope remarks: "This delphinoid was taken by the U. S. Fish Commission at near the same locality as the last" [i. e., near Portland, Maine. "The last, *L. perspicillatus,* was really from Cape Cod, Massachusetts, but *L. gubernator* was from Casco Bay, near Portland, Maine." F. W. True, manuscript note.]
> Casts in good condition.
> Cotypes not designated by numbers.

*Lagenorhynchus obliquidens Gill.   Cotypes.

Proc. Acad. Nat. Sci. Philadelphia 17: 177, ordered published Sept. 26, 1865;
True, U. S. Nat. Mus. Bull. 36: 96, 1889.

1961, 1962, and 1963.   Skulls.   Pacific Ocean, near San Francisco,
Calif.   "Obtained at San Francisco, California."   Collected by
W. P. Trowbridge.   Cataloged October 24, 1855.

Skulls Grade B.

No type designated by T. N. Gill in the original description.   For considering these specimens cotypes, see True, U. S. Nat. Mus. Bull. 36: 98, 1889.

*Phocaena pectoralis Peale.

U. S. Exploring Expedition 8 (Mamm. and Ornith.) : 32, 1848.
=*Lagenorhynchus electra* (Gray).   See True, U. S. Nat. Mus. Bull. 36: 100, 1889.

4108.   Mandible.   Adult.   Hilo Bay, Hawaii.   Collected by U. S.
Exploring Expedition.   No. 32, Peale's list of specimens, *loc. cit.*,
p. 305.   Cataloged June 26, 1860.

Mandible in good condition; teeth much worn.

Type not designated in the original description, but see True, *op. cit.*, p. 101.

*Lagenorhynchus perspicillatus Cope.   Cotypes.

Proc. Acad. Nat. Sci. Philadelphia 28: 136, ordered published June 30, 1876.
=*Lagenorhynchus acutus* (Gray).   See True, U. S. Nat. Mus. Bull. 36: 85, 1889.

"This species is represented in the collections of the Smithsonian Institution by numerous crania, some skeletons and a colored cast of the natural
size, taken by the United States Commission of Fisheries, near Portland,
Maine" (Cope).

"The foregoing locality is, I believe, incorrect.   It should be Woods Hole,
Mass., or else Cape Cod.   I think cast No. 12939, Woods Hole, Mass.
(original No. 3), and the whole series of skulls and mandibles, Nos. 14228 to
14326, 14335 and 14362 to 14373, are to be regarded as cotypes.   No. 14335 is
marked 'Skeleton without a head,' but it is on exhibition and there is a skull
on it now.   This seems to be the only skeleton in the lot."   F. W. True,
manuscript note.

Genus LISSODELPHIS Gloger

Delphinapterus borealis Peale.   Lost.   See page 575.

Genus PHOCAENA Desmarest

*Phocaena lineata Cope.

Proc. Acad. Nat. Sci. Philadelphia 28: 134, ordered published June 29, 1876.

Lyon and Osgood (U. S. Nat. Mus. Bull. 62: 6, 1909) designate the type
of *Phocaena lineata* as "$\frac{12481}{16255}$. Cast of entire animal and skull.   Hudson
River, New York.   Received at the U. S. National Museum, February 22,
1876, from John Wallace.   Cast (no. 19) catalogued January 20, 1876; skull,
April 22, 1879."

A *Delphinus delphis* was taken in the Hudson River on January 20, 1876,
and mounted by John Wallace of New York City.   This stuffed skin was

received by the Smithsonian Institution on February 22, 1876, and from it a plaster replica was made by Joseph Palmer on or about February 23, 1876. Reference to the U. S. National Museum cast book shows that the entry of this specimen by William Palmer made at the time is "February 23, 1876. Long-nosed porpoise, Hudson River, N. Y. John Wallace. Cast no. 19." A cast presumably was part of the Smithsonian exhibit at the exposition held in 1876 at Philadelphia. Cope saw this *Delphinus* specimen either in Philadelphia or Washington, and in addition examined two casts of a small *Phocaena*, two casts of a small *Lagenorhynchus acutus* and a large cast of another individual of same species. He named these last as *L. gubernator* and *L. perspicillatus*.

Cope (Proc. Acad. Nat. Sci. Philadelphia 28: 134, 1876) described all these specimens but somehow got them somewhat mixed. His *Phocaena lineata* is a mixture of a view of one or two small *Phocaena* casts, the stuffed skin of *Delphinus delphis* from the Hudson River at New York, and a *Phocaena* skull from somewhere else. Nevertheless, Cope stated that "this new porpoise is represented by a single specimen, which was taken in the harbor of New York, not many months ago, and sent to the Smithsonian Institution, where the skeleton is now preserved, etc." The skeleton was not forwarded to Washington, only the mounted skin with the skull inside (see True, U. S. Nat. Mus. Bull. 36: 117, 1889).

"As I remember, the stuffed dolphin was destroyed in 1877 by the writer, the skull saved, and the data written on it by Dr. G. B. Goode at the time or shortly afterward. It was the common practice at that time for the writer to take out skulls and clean them and for Dr. Goode to write the data on them in very black ink. The cast of this stuffed skin is still in our storage room, but the skin was destroyed because it was dirty, oily, and unshapely.

"When Cope's paper was published there was no cast of a long *Phocaena* in the museum. There was none until September 30, 1880, when a mould was made from one sent fresh from Cape Cod by A. H. Clark through E. G. Blackford of New York, a cast of which we still have and which was long erroneously supposed to be the type of *Phocaena lineata* Cope.

"Cope evidently saw the stuffed skin of Wallace's *Delphinus* and he must have seen the teeth; but he could not have seen the skull since it was not removed from the skin until just before June 16, 1877, the skull being first entered on that date. The skin number 12481 was entered on January 20, 1876, as a *Phocaena*, subsequently changed to *Delphinus*, and afterward changed to 'Phocaena lineata Cope Type.' The locality and collector are given as New York Bay and John Wallace, respectively, all in several handwritings. The specimen thus has three numbers, 12481 for the skin, 15781 for the skull, and 16255 for the cast. The name painted on the stand for the cast of this long-nosed porpoise is *Delphinus erebennus* Cope." F. W. True, manuscript note.

Phocaena vomerina Gill.   Cotypes.

Proc. Acad. Nat. Sci. Philadelphia 17: 178, ordered published Sept. 26, 1865. =*Phocaena phocoena* Linnaeus. See True, U. S. Nat. Mus. Bull. 36: 118, 1889.

4149.   Rostrum and part of brain case.   Adult.   Puget Sound, Wash. Collected by C. B. R. Kennerly.   Cataloged July 1860.

Skull Grade C.

$\frac{4746}{4402}$.   Skin and skull.   Young.   San Francisco, Calif.   Collected by
William Stimpson.   Cataloged April 20, 1861.

> Well-made skin in fair condition.   The skin has cracked and broken away
> around the mouth and throat.   Skull cannot be found.
>
> Cotypes not designated by number.   The two above specimens are the only
> ones in the collection having the data given by T. N. Gill.

Genus PHOCOENOIDES Andrews

*Phocaena dalli True.

> Proc. U. S. Nat. Mus. 8: 95, May 20, 1885; U. S. Nat. Mus. Bull. 36: 123, 1889.
> =*Phocoenoides dalli* (True).   See Andrews, Bull. Amer. Mus. Nat. Hist. 30:
> 34, May 16, 1911.

21762.   Skull.   Adult male.   Strait west of Adakh Island, Aleutian
Group, Alaska.   August 13, 1873.   Collected by W. H. Dall.
Original number 1554.

> Skull in good condition, but earbones, jugals, and upper teeth lacking and
> one pterygoid broken.
>
> Type not originally designated by number.   On page 98 of the original
> description measurements are given of "the type skull of *Phocaena Dalli.*"
> On page 125, U. S. Nat. Mus. Bull. 36, the same measurements are given and
> the type is indicated as No. 21762.

Genus PSEUDORCA Reinhardt

*Orca destructor Cope.

> Proc. Acad. Nat. Sci. Philadelphia 18: 293, ordered published Oct. 30, 1866.
> =*Pseudorca crassidens* (Owen).   See True, U. S. Nat. Mus. Bull. 36: 143, 1889.

3697.   Beak and mandible.   Pacific Ocean, off Paita, Peru.   Received
from E. Jewett (see Smithsonian Report, 1860, p. 80).

> In good condition.
> Description based on one specimen, designated by number.

Genus SAGMATIAS Cope

*Sagmatias amblodon Cope.

> Proc. Acad. Nat. Sci. Philadelphia 18: 294, ordered published Oct 30, 1866.
> See True, U. S. Nat. Mus. Bull. 36: 106, 1889.

3887.   Skull.   Old adult.   "Caught at sea."   Locality unknown.
(See Cope and True, *loc. cit.*)   Collected by the ship *Vincennes*,
of the U. S. Exploring Expedition (1838–1842).   Cataloged June
20, 1860.

> Skull Grade A.
>
> Type not designated by number.   There was but one specimen taken by
> the ship *Vincennes*.   Locality not known, but probably between Cape Horn
> and Lima, Peru, or Australia, or New Zealand.   This specimen is No. 3887.
> See True, *op. cit.,* p 106, table.

Genus STENELLA Gray

Delphinus lateralis Peale. Lost. See page 576.

*Delphinus longidens Cope.

Proc. Acad. Nat. Sci. Philadelphia 18 : 295, ordered published Oct. 30, 1866.

3886. Skull. Young adult. Locality unknown. Collected by U. S. Exploring Expedition (1838–1842). Cataloged June 20, 1860.

Skull Grade B.
Type not designated by number. Cope had only one specimen, No. 3886.

*Delphinus plagiodon Cope.

Proc. Acad. Nat. Sci. Philadelphia 18 : 296, ordered published Oct. 30, 1866.
=*Stenella plagiodon* (Cope). See Kellogg, Nat. Geogr. Mag. 77(1) : 83, Jan. 1940.

3884. Skull. Youngish. Locality unknown. Received from J. Varden. Cataloged June 20, 1860.

Skull Grade A.
Species based on one specimen, No. 3884, mentioned in the original description.

Genus TURSIOPS Gervais

*Tursiops gillii Dall.

Proc. California Acad. Sci. 5 : 13, printed in advance, Jan 29, 1873; Scammon's Marine Mammals, p. 288, 1874; True, U. S. Nat. Mus. Bull. 36 : 43, 1889.

13022. Mandible (no other portion of specimen known to describer) "and outline of animal drawn by Captain Scammon." Young adult. Monterey, Monterey County, Calif. Collected by C. M. Scammon.

Mandible in good condition; one tooth lacking.
Outline not found.
Type not designated by number. For regarding this specimen as the type, see True, *op. cit.*, p. 43, footnote.

Family INIIDAE: River Dolphins

Genus LIPOTES Miller

*Lipotes vexillifer Miller.

Smithsonian Misc. Coll. 68 (9) : 8, Mar. 30, 1918.

218293. Skull and cervical vertebrae. Adult male. Tung Ting Lake, Hu-nan, China. February 18, 1916. Collected by Charles M. Hoy.

Skull and vertebrae Grade B.
On one of his visits to Washington Hoy told us that the tympanic bones were stolen from the specimen by a Chinese servant.

Family KOGIIDAE: Pigmy Sperm Whales

Genus KOGIA Gray

*Kogia floweri Gill.

Amer. Nat. 4 : 738, Feb. 1871.
=*Kogia breviceps* (Blainville). See True, Proc. U. S. Nat. Mus. 7 : 590, 1885.

8016. Mandible and water-color sketch of entire animal (the "portrait" mentioned by T. N. Gill). Off Mazatlan, Sinaloa, Mexico. 1868. Collected by A. J. Grayson.

> Posterior end of mandible broken and a few teeth lacking. Water-color sketch (188 by 52 mm.) in good condition. (In 1934 water-color sketch could not be located.)
> Type not designated by number. In the original description it is said to be based on "jaw and portrait."

*Kogia goodei True.

U. S. Nat. Mus. Bull. 27 : 630 (table) and 641 (list) 1884. *Nomen nudum.*
=*Kogia breviceps* (Blainville). See True, Report U. S. Fish Commission, 1883 : pl. 8, fig. 22.

$\frac{13738}{20909}$. Cast of entire animal, and skeleton. Adult female. Spring Lake, N. J. Received in the flesh from H. S. Howland, April 27, 1883. Original number of cast 40.

> Cast in good condition; in storage.
> Skeleton in good condition.
> No description of this species has been published. The name occurs in the table and list cited above. Two specimens are mentioned, No. $\frac{13738}{20909}$, and one from Jupiter Inlet, Fla. (collected by E. M. Spencer), represented by "a photograph and the lower jaw" (True, U. S. Nat. Mus. Bull. 27 : 641, 1884).

Family ZIPHIIDAE: Beaked Whales

Genus BERARDIUS Duvernoy

*Berardius bairdii Stejneger.

Proc. U. S. Nat. Mus. 6 : 75, June 22, 1883.

20992. Skull. Immature. Stare Gavan, eastern shore of Bering Island, Bering Sea, Siberia. Autumn of 1882. Collected by L. Stejneger. Original number 1520.

> Skull in good condition, on exhibition.
> Type designated by the original number.
> "There is something wrong about the record of this skull. While it appears correct, the measurements do not agree with Doctor Stejneger's original measurements."—F. W. True, manuscript note.

Genus MESOPLODON Gervais

*Mesoplodon mirum True.

Smithsonian Misc. Coll. 60 (25) : 1, Mar. 14, 1913.

175019. Skull, partial skeleton, cast of entire body and cast of head. Adult female. Beaufort Harbor, N. C. July 26, 1912. Collected by U. S. Bureau of Fisheries.

Skull, partial skeleton, casts of entire body and of head Grade A. The casts of entire animal and of head are at present in the exhibition series.

*Mesoplodon stejnegeri True.

Proc. U. S. Nat. Mus. 8 : 585, Oct. 19, 1885.

21112. Cranium. Young. Bering Island, Bering Sea, Siberia. 1883. Collected by L. Stejneger.

Cranium Grade B.
Description based on one specimen, mentioned by number.

Genus ZIPHIUS G. Cuvier

*Ziphius grebnitzkii Stejneger.

Proc. U. S. Nat. Mus. 6 : 77, June 22, 1883.
=*Ziphius cavirostris* G. Cuvier. See True, U. S. Nat. Mus. Bull. 73 : 30, 1910.

20993. Skull. Bering Island, Bering Sea, Siberia. Autumn of 1882. Collected by L. Stejneger. Original number 1521.

Skull Grade A.
Type designated by Stejneger's original number 1521=Museum number 20993.

*Hyperodon [sic] **semijunctus** Cope.

Proc. Acad. Nat. Sci. Philadelphia 17 : 280, ordered published Dec. 26, 1865. *Hyperaodon* [sic] *semijunctus* Cope. See Cope, Proc. Acad. Nat. Sci. Philadelphia 21 : 31, 1869.
=*Ziphius cavirostris* G. Cuvier. See True, U. S. Nat. Mus. Bull. 73 : 30, 1910.

21975. Skeleton. Young female. Charleston Harbor, S. C., March 1861. Collected by G. E. Manigault.

Skeleton in fair condition, nearly complete.
Type not designated by number. Described while in possession of the Charleston Museum. Acquired by the U. S. National Museum, June 30, 1885.

Order CHIROPTERA: Bats

Family EMBALLONURIDAE: Sheath-tailed Bats

Genus EMBALLONURA Temminck

*Emballonura anambensis Miller.

Proc. Washington Acad. Sci. 2 : 236, Aug. 20, 1900.

251543—42——9

101716. In alcohol (skull removed). Adult female. Pulo Mobur, Anamba Islands, South China Sea, between Malay Peninsula and Borneo. August 26, 1899. Collected by W. L. Abbott.

In good condition; skull Grade A.

*Emballonura peninsularis Miller.

Proc. Acad. Nat. Sci. Philadelphia 50: 323, July 12, 1898.

83575. In alcohol (skull removed). Adult male. Lay Song Hong, Trong (or Tarang), Peninsular Siam. November 1896. Collected by W. L. Abbott.

In good condition; skull Grade B.

*Emballonura pusilla Lyon.

Proc. U. S. Nat. Mus. 40: 132, Apr. 25, 1911.

153940. In alcohol (skull removed). Adult female. Mankol, Kendawangan River, southwestern Borneo. September 29, 1908. Collected by W. L. Abbott. Original number 6223.

In good condition; skull Grade A.

*Vespertilio semicaudatus Peale.

U. S. Exploring Expedition 8 (Mamm. and Ornith.): 23, 1848.
=Emballonura semicaudata (Peale). See Wagner, Suppl. Schreber's Säugethiere 5: 698, 1855.

3727. Mummy, dried from alcohol. No skull. Samoan Islands, Oceania. Collected by the U. S. Exploring Expedition (1838–42).

Skin with wings spread and wing membranes torn in places. Skin of head badly torn and mutilated, probably during a clumsy extraction of the skull, which has been lost. Right ear missing.

There is very little doubt that the above is the type. The description is based upon a single specimen collected by the U. S. Exploring Expedition in the Samoan Islands.

*Emballonura sulcata Miller.

Proc. Biol. Soc. Washington 24: 161, June 16, 1911.

151568. Skin and skull. Adult. Uola Island, Truk Group, Caroline Islands, Oceania. February 16, 1900. Collected by H. F. Moore.

Well-made skin in good condition; skull Grade A.

Genus TAPHONYCTERIS Dobson

*Taphonycteris capito Hollister.

Proc. U. S. Nat. Mus. 46: 308, Dec. 31, 1913.

155149. Skin and skull. Adult female. Pandan, Catanduanes Island, Philippine Islands. 1909. Collected by D. B. Mackie.

Well-made skin in good condition; skull Grade A.

*Taphozous pluto Miller.

Proc. U. S. Nat. Mus. 38: 396, Aug. 19, 1910.

=*Taphonycteris pluto* (Miller). See Hollister, Proc. U. S. Nat. Mus. 46: 307, Dec. 31, 1913.

144812. Skin and skull. Adult female. Mercedes, 9 miles east of Zamboanga, Mindanao, Philippine Islands. March 28, 1906. Collected by Edgar A. Mearns. Original number 6054.

Well-made skin in good condition; skull Grade A.

Genus TAPHOZOUS Geoffroy

*Taphozous cavaticus Hollister.

Proc. Biol. Soc. Washington 26: 157, June 30, 1913.

141092. Skin and skull. Adult female. Moeara Dua, near Emmahaven, south of Padang, West Sumatra. January 15, 1905. Collected by W. L. Abbott. Original number 3944.

Well-made skin in good condition; skull Grade A.

*Taphozous solifer Hollister.

Proc. Biol. Soc. Washington 26: 157, June 30, 1913.

113010. In alcohol. Adult male. Peking [=Peiping], Chi-li, China. March 28, 1901. Collected by M. L. Robb.

Well preserved and in good condition; skull not removed.

Family HIPPOSIDERIDAE: Horseshoe Bats

Genus COELOPS Blyth

*Chilophylla hirsuta Miller.

Proc. U. S. Nat. Mus. 38: 395, Aug. 19, 1910.

=*Coelops* (probably *C. robinsoni* Bonhote). See Miller, Proc. Biol. Soc. Washington 41: 85 (footnote), Mar. 16, 1928.

144821. Skin only. Adult female. Alag River, opposite mouth of Egbert River, Mindoro, Philippine Islands. December 2, 1906. Collected by Edgar A. Mearns. Original number 6337.

Skin in good condition, in alcohol.

*Coelops inflata Miller.

Proc. Biol. Soc. Washington 41: 85, Mar. 16, 1928.

238991. In alcohol (skull removed). Adult male. Near Yenping-fu, altitude 2,000 feet, Fukien, China. April 7, 1922. Collected by Arthur de C. Sowerby. Original number 1277.

In good condition, head nearly severed in removing skull; skull Grade A.

Genus HIPPOSIDEROS Gray

*Hipposideros barbensis Miller.

Proc. Washington Acad. Sci. 2: 233, Aug. 20, 1900.

101625. Skin and skull. Adult male. Ste. Barbe Island, South China Sea, between Sumatra and Borneo. August 1, 1899. Collected by W. L. Abbott.

Well-made skin in good condition; skull Grade A.

*Hipposideros gentilis toala Shamel.

Journ. Mamm. 21: 352, Aug. 12, 1940.

219390. Alcoholic, skull removed. Adult female. Toeare, Celebes. September 16, 1917. Collected by H. C. Raven. Original number 3255.

Alcoholic specimen in good condition; skull Grade A.

*Hipposideros insolens Lyon.

Proc. U. S. Nat. Mus. 40: 129, Apr. 25, 1911.

154389. In alcohol (skull removed). Adult male. Near Lowatsi on the upper Pasir River, southeastern Borneo. December 31, 1908. Collected by W. L. Abbott. Original number 6274.

In good condition; skull Grade A.

*Hipposideros nicobarulae Miller.

Proc. U. S. Nat. Mus. 24: 781, May 28, 1902.

111874. In alcohol (skull removed). Adult male. Little Nicobar, Nicobar Islands, off west coast of Malay Peninsula. March 2, 1901. Collected by W. L. Abbott.

In good condition; skull Grade A.

*Hipposideros pelingensis Shamel.

Journ. Mamm. 21: 353, Aug. 12, 1940.

219433. Alcoholic, skull removed. Adult female. Peling Island, Celebes. May, 1918. Collected by H. C. Raven. Original number 3571.

Alcoholic specimen in good condition; skull Grade A.

Family MEGADERMIDAE: False Vampires

Genus LAVIA Gray

*Lavia rex Miller.

Proc. Biol. Soc. Washington 18: 227, Dec. 9, 1905.
=*Lavia frons frons* Geoffroy. See Andersen and Wroughton, Ann. Mag. Nat. Hist. (ser. 7) 19: 139, Feb. 1907.

$\frac{18993}{38197}$. In alcohol (skull removed). Adult male. Taveta, British East Africa [=Kenya]. 1889. Collected by W. L. Abbott.

In good condition; skull Grade C.

Genus MEGADERMA Geoffroy

*Megaderma carimatae Miller.

Proc. U. S. Nat. Mus. 31: 63, July 23, 1906.

125185. In alcohol (skull removed). Adult female. Tanjong Karimata Tua, Karimata Island, off west coast of Borneo. August 31, 1904. Collected by W. L. Abbott. Original number 3709.

In good condition; skull Grade A.

*Megaderma lasiae Lyon.

Proc. U. S. Nat. Mus. 52: 439, Dec. 30, 1916.

114249. Skin and skull. Adult male. Pulo Lasia, off west coast of Sumatra. January 6, 1902. Collected by W. L. Abbott. Original number 1401.

Well-made skin in good condition; ears, membranes, and feet stained by corrosive sublimate; skull Grade A.

*Megaderma niasense Lyon.

Proc. U. S. Nat. Mus. 52: 440, Dec. 30, 1916.

141305. In alcohol (skull removed). Adult male. Pulo Nias (Mojeia River), off west coast of Sumatra. March 15, 1905. Collected by W. L. Abbott. Original number 4066.

In good condition; skull Grade A.

*Megaderma siumatis Lyon.

Proc. U. S. Nat. Mus. 52: 439, Dec. 30, 1916.

114227. Skin and skull. Adult female. Pulo Siumat, off west coast of Sumatra. December 27, 1901. Collected by W. L. Abbott. Original number 1390.

Well-made skin in good condition; ears, membranes, and feet stained by corrosive sublimate; skull Grade B.

*Megaderma spasma celebensis Shamel.

Journ. Mamm. 21: 352, Aug. 12, 1940.

216945. Skin and skull. Adult male. Likoepang, Celebes. February 26, 1916. Collected by H. C. Raven. Original number 2404.

Well-made skin in good condition; skull Grade A.

Family MOLOSSIDAE: Free-tailed Bats

Genus CHAEREPHON Dobson

*Nyctinomus jobensis Miller.

Proc. Biol. Soc. Washington 15: 246, Dec. 16, 1902.

=*Chaerephon jobensis* (Miller). See Miller, U. S. Nat. Mus. Bull. 57: 245, June 29, 1907.

$\frac{18545}{38035}$. In alcohol (skull removed). Female. Ansus, Island of Jobie, northwestern New Guinea. Collected by Odoardo Beccari. Original number 33. Cataloged May 2, 1890; skull, October 15, 1902.

In good condition; skull Grade A.

*Chaerephon luzonus Hollister.

Proc. U. S. Nat. Mus. 46: 312, Dec. 31, 1913.

144881. In alcohol (skull removed). Adult male. Cagayan, Cagayan Province, Northern Luzon, Philippine Islands. Cataloged November 13, 1907. Collected by Edgar A. Mearns.

In good condition; skull Grade A.

*Chaerephon pumilus naivashae Hollister.

Smithsonian Misc. Coll. 66 (1): 4, Feb. 10, 1916.

166658. In alcohol (skull removed). Adult male. Naivasha Station, British East Africa [=Kenya]. August 7, 1909. Collected by J. Alden Loring. Original number 6955.

In good condition; skull Grade A.

*Nyctinomus pusillus Miller.

Proc. Biol. Soc. Washington 15: 245, Dec. 16, 1902.

=*Chaerephon pusillus* (Miller). See Miller, U. S. Nat. Mus. Bull. 57: 245, June 29, 1907.

$\frac{20991}{37852}$. In alcohol (skull removed). Adult female. Aldabra Island, Indian Ocean, northwest of Madagascar. Collected by W. L. Abbott. Alcoholic cataloged June 30, 1893; skull, February 12, 1900.

In good condition; skull Grade B.

Type designated by No. $\frac{37852}{20997}$, an error for $\frac{20991}{37852}$.

Genus CHEIROMELES Horsfield

*Cheiromeles parvidens Miller and Hollister.

Proc. Biol. Soc. Washington 34: 100, June 30, 1921.

219350. Skin and skull. Adult female. Pinedapa, Middle Celebes. February 20, 1918. Collected by H. C. Raven. Original number 3547.

Well-made skin in good condition; skull Grade A.

Genus EUMOPS Miller

*Molossus californicus Merriam.

North Amer. Fauna 4: 31, Oct. 8, 1890.

=*Eumops perotis californicus* (Merriam). See Sanborn, Journ. Mamm. 13: 351, Nov. 11, 1932.

186448. In alcohol (skull not removed). Adult female. Alhambra, Los Angeles County, Calif. December 14, 1889. Collected by E. C. Thurber. Merriam collection No. 5736.

In good condition; skull not removed.

*Eumops hansae Sanborn.

Journ. Mamm. 13:356, Nov. 2, 1932.

200993. Skin and skull. Adult male. Colonia Hansa, near Joinville, Santa Catherina, Brazil. 1901. Collected by H. Ehrhardt. Original number, Museu Paulista, 1339.

Well-made skin in good condition except for some sloughing of hair on back; skull Grade A.

*Nyctinomus orthotis H. Allen.

Proc. Amer. Philos. Soc. 26: 561, Dec. 18, 1889.

=E[umops] glaucinus (Wagner). See Miller, Proc. Biol. Soc. Washington 19:85, June 4, 1906.

$\frac{9397}{37447}$. Skin (in alcohol) and skull. Spanish Town, Jamaica, Greater Antilles. Probably August 1868. Collected by W. T. March.

In good condition; skull Grade C.

Genus MOLOSSUS E. Geoffroy

*Molossus debilis Miller.

Proc. U. S. Nat. Mus. 46: 90, Aug. 23, 1913.

110935. In alcohol (skull removed). Adult female. St. Kitts, Lesser Antilles. 1901. Collected by W. H. Alexander.

In good condition; skull Grade A.

*Molossus fortis Miller.

Proc. U. S. Nat. Mus. 46: 89, Aug. 23, 1913.

102319. In alcohol (skull removed). Adult male. Luquillo, Puerto Rico, Greater Antilles. March 5, 1900. Collected by L. Stejneger and C. W. Richmond.

In good condition; a small patch of hair has sloughed from back; skull Grade A.

†Molossus nigricans Miller.

Proc. Acad. Nat. Sci. Philadelphia 54: 395, Sept. 12, 1902.

90941. Skin and skull. Adult male. Acaponeta, Nayarit, Mexico. August 2, 1897. Collected by E. W. Nelson and E. A. Goldman. Original number 11433.

Well-made skin in good condition; skull Grade A.

*Molossus pretiosus Miller.

Proc. Acad. Nat. Sci. Philadelphia 54: 396, Sept. 12, 1902.

102761. Skin and skull. Adult male. La Guaira, Venezuela. July 13, 1900. Collected by Wirt Robinson and M. W. Lyon, Jr. Original number 106.

Well-made skin in good condition; skull Grade A.

*Molossus pygmaeus Miller.

Proc. Biol. Soc. Washington 13: 162, Oct. 31, 1900.

102104. In alcohol (skull removed). Adult female. In an attic of a house near Willemstad, Curaçao, off north coast of Venezuela. January 16, 1900. Collected by Leon J. Guthrie.

In good condition; skull Grade A.

Genus PROMOPS Gervais

*Promops pamana Miller.

Proc. Biol. Soc. Washington 26: 33, Feb. 8, 1913.

105528. Skin only (in alcohol). Adult male. Hyutanaham, Upper Purus River, Brazil. March 22, 1901. Collected by J. B. Steere.

In good condition, body has been skinned out.

Genus TADARIDA Rafinesque

*Nyctinomus antillularum Miller.

Proc. Acad. Nat. Sci. Philadelphia 54: 398, Sept. 12, 1902.
=*Tadarida antillularum* (Miller). See Miller, U. S. Nat. Mus. Bull. 128: 85, Apr. 29, 1924.

113188. In alcohol (skull removed). Adult male. Roseau, Dominica, Lesser Antilles. August 5, 1901. Collected by Charles E. Ashcraft, Jr.

In good condition; skull Grade A.

*Dysopes aurispinosus Peale.

U. S. Exploring Expedition 8 (Mamm. and Ornith.): 21, 1848.
=*Tadarida aurispinosa* (Peale). See Shamel, Proc. U. S. Nat. Mus. 78 (19): 11, May 6, 1931.

3726. Skin preserved in alcohol. Adult male. Peale writes: "This remarkable bat flew on board the U. S. ship *Peacock*, off the coast of Brazil, on the 18th of November, when the ship was about one hundred miles from land, south of Cape St. Roque" (*op. cit.*, pp. 22–23). This specimen is undoubtedly No. 3726, cataloged December 20, 1859, as *Molossus aurispinosus* from Brazil. It was recataloged as No. 5476, October 31, 1861. There is no record of a skull in either of the entries. U. S. Exploring Expedition (1838–1842).

The specimen was a dry skin until September 27, 1899, when it was placed in alcohol by Gerrit S. Miller, Jr., who made a note of the color at that time: "Belly wood brown, back between wood brown and russet. 9, 27, '99." It is in good condition.

Type not designted by number, but there is not the slightest doubt that this is the specimen mentioned by Peale.

*Tadarida constanzae Shamel.

Proc. U. S. Nat. Mus. 78 (19) : 10, May 6, 1931.

217205. In alcohol (skull removed.) Adult male. Constanza, Dominican Republic, Greater Antilles. September 26, 1916. Collected by W. L. Abbott.

In good condition; skull Grade A.

*Nycticea cynocephala LeConte.

McMurtrie's Cuvier, Animal Kingdom 1: 432, 1831.
=*Tadarida cynocephala* (LeConte).   See Miller, U. S. Nat. Mus. Bull. 128: 85, Apr. 29, 1924.

4742. Skin with skull inside. Collected by J. E. LeConte, probably on the LeConte plantation, near Riceboro, Ga. Cataloged April 13, 1861.

Skin in good condition, but with wings spread out.

No type designated. The above seems to be an original specimen, and has "*Cynocephalus*" written on two old labels, and is so entered in the catalog.

*Nyctinomus europs H. Allen.   Lectotype.

Proc. Amer. Philos. Soc. 26: 558, Oct. 4, 1889.
=*Tadarida europs* (H. Allen).   See Shamel, Proc. U. S. Nat. Mus. 78 (19) : 14, May 6, 1931.

101498. In alcohol (skull removed). Adult female. Brazil. Collected by Charles F. Hartt. Cataloged December 5, 1899.

In good condition; skull Grade A.

Shamel writes: "Harrison Allen based his description on 20 adult alcoholic specimens from Brazil, without exact locality. Ten of these specimens are in the United States National Museum collection. No. 101498, adult female, is therefore chosen as the lectotype."

*Nyctinomus femorosaccus Merriam.

North Amer. Fauna 2: 23, Oct. 30, 1889.
=*Tadarida femorosacca* (Merriam).   See Miller, U. S. Nat. Mus. Bull. 128: 86, Apr. 29, 1924.

186447. In alcohol (skull not removed). Adult male. Agua Caliente, now Palm Springs, Riverside County, Calif. March 27, 1885. Collected by F. Stephens. Original number 252. Merriam collection No. 2276.

In good condition; skull not removed.

†Tadarida intermedia Shamel.

Proc. U. S. Nat. Mus. 78 (19) : 7, May 6, 1931.

78488. In alcohol (skull removed). Adult male. Valley of Comitan, altitude 5,700 feet, Chiapas, Mexico. December 11, 1895. Collected by E. W. Nelson and E. A. Goldman. Original number 8773.

In good condition; skull Grade A.

*Nyctinomus macrotis nevadensis H. Allen.

U. S. Nat. Mus. Bull. 43: 171, Mar. 14, 1894.
=*Tadarida macrotis* (Gray). See Miller, U. S. Nat. Mus. Bull. 128: 86, Apr. 29, 1924.

15178/36569. In alcohol (skull removed). Immature female. California (exact locality not known). Collected by John Mullan. Alcoholic cataloged August 31, 1885; skull, November 22, 1893.

In fair condition; rather shrunken and skull badly extracted from top of head; skull Grade A.
For regarding the above as type see J. A. Allen, Bull. Amer. Mus. Nat. Hist. 6: 326, footnote, Nov. 7, 1894.

*Nyctinomus mohavensis Merriam.

North Amer. Fauna 2: 25, Oct. 30, 1889.
=*Tadarida mexicana* (Saussure). See Miller, U. S. Nat. Mus. Bull. 128: 86, Apr. 29, 1924.

186446. In alcohol. Adult male. Fort Mohave, Mohave County, Ariz. March 8, 1889. Collected by Vernon Bailey. Original number 643. Merriam collection number 5418.

In good condition; skull not removed.

†Nyctinomops yucatanicus Miller.

Proc. Acad. Nat. Sci. Philadelphia 54: 393, Sept. 12, 1902.
=*Tadarida yucatanica* (Miller). See Miller, U. S. Nat. Mus. Bull. 128: 87, Apr. 29, 1924.

108166. Skin and skull. Adult female. Chichen Itza, Yucatan, Mexico. February 9, 1901. Collected by E. W. Nelson and E. A. Goldman. Original number 14521.

Well-made skin in good condition; skull Grade A.

Family NATALIDAE: Long-legged Bats
Genus CHILONATALUS Miller

*Natalus (Chilonatalus) brevimanus Miller.

Proc. Acad. Nat. Sci. Philadelphia 50: 328, July 12, 1898.
=*Chilonatalus brevimanus* (Miller). See Miller, Proc. Biol. Soc. Washington 16: 119, Sept. 30, 1903.

15835. In alcohol (skull not removed). Adult male. Old Providence Island, Caribbean Sea, off coast of Nicaragua. Collected by C. B. Cory. Cataloged May 25, 1887.

In good condition.

*Chilonatalus macer Miller.

Proc. Biol. Soc. Washington 27: 225, Dec. 29, 1914.

113724. In alcohol (skull removed). Adult female. Baracoa, Cuba, Greater Antilles. February 6, 1902. Collected by William Palmer. Original number 699.

In fair condition; tail membrane and both hind legs have been disconnected from body; skull Grade A.

*Chilonatalus tumidifrons Miller.

Proc. Biol. Soc. Washington 16: 119, Sept. 30, 1903.

122024. In alcohol (skull removed). Adult male. Watling Island, Bahama Islands, West Indies. July 12, 1903. Collected by J. H. Riley. Original number 157.

In good condition; skull Grade A.

Genus NATALUS Gray

*Natalus dominicensis Shamel.

Proc. Biol. Soc. Washington 41: 67, Mar. 16, 1928.

113605. In alcohol (skull removed). Adult male. Island of Dominica, Lesser Antilles. July 18, 1901. Collected by H. Selwyn Branch.

In good condition; skull Grade A.

*Natalus major Miller.

Proc. Acad. Nat. Sci. Philadelphia 54: 398, Sept. 12, 1902.

101395. In alcohol (skull removed). Adult male. Savaneta, Prov. de Santiago, Dominican Republic, Greater Antilles. Collected by W. M. Gabb. 1869–71. Cataloged November 3, 1899. Received in exchange from Academy of Natural Sciences of Philadelphia.

In good condition; skull Grade A.

†Natalus mexicanus Miller.

Proc. Acad. Nat. Sci. Philadelphia 54: 399, Sept. 12, 1902.

96496. In alcohol (skull removed). Adult female. Santa Anita, Lower California, Mexico. July or August 1897. Collected by J. F. Abbott. Original number 1953X.

In good condition; skull Grade A.

Genus PHODOTES Miller

*Natalus tumidirostris Miller.

Proc. Biol. Soc. Washington 13: 160, Oct. 31, 1900.
=*Phodotes tumidirostris* (Miller). See Miller, Proc. Biol. Soc. Washington 19: 85, June 4, 1906.

102106. In alcohol (skull removed). Adult male. In a cave at Hatto, north side of Curaçao, off north coast of Venezuela. May 1, 1900. Collected by Leon J. Guthrie.

In good condition; skull Grade A.

Family NOCTILIONIDAE: Hare-lipped Bats

Genus NOCTILIO Linnaeus

†Noctilio leporinus mexicanus Goldman.

Proc. Biol. Soc. Washington 28: 136, June 29, 1915.

126672. Skin and skull. Papayo, Guerrero, Mexico. April 17, 1903. Collected by E. W. Nelson and E. A. Goldman. Original number 16318.

Well-made skin in good condition; skull Grade A.

Family PHYLLOSTOMIDAE: Leaf-nosed Bats

Genus ARDOPS Miller

*Ardops annectens Miller.

Proc. Biol. Soc. Washington 26: 33, Feb. 8, 1913.

113502. In alcohol (skull removed). Adult female. Island of Guadeloupe. Lesser Antilles. February 1, 1902. Collected by H. Selwyn Branch.

In good condition, hair has sloughed on stomach and on back near tail; skull Grade A.

*Stenoderma luciae Miller.

Proc. Acad. Nat. Sci. Philadelphia 54: 407, Sept. 12, 1902.
=*Ardops luciae* (Miller). See Miller, Proc. Biol. Soc. Washington 19: 84, June 4, 1906.

110921. In alcohol (skull removed). Adult female. Santa Lucia Island, Lesser Antilles. February 4, 1901. Collected by H. Selwyn Branch.

In good condition; skull Grade A.

Genus ARTIBEUS Leach

†Artibeus aztecus Andersen.

Ann. Mag. Nat. Hist. (ser. 7) 18: 422, Dec. 1906.

52050. Skin and skull. Adult male. Tetela del Volcan, Morelos, Mexico. February 12, 1893. Collected by E. W. Nelson. Original number 4332.

Well-made skin in good condition; skull Grade B.

†**Artibeus hirsutus** Andersen.

Ann. Mag. Nat. Hist. (ser. 7) 18: 420, Dec. 1906.

126449. Skin and skull. Adult male. La Salada, Michoacan, Mexico. March 16, 1903. Collected by E. W. Nelson and E. A. Goldman. Original number 16168.

Well-made skin in good condition, except for a perforation of the femoral portion of the right wing membrane; skull Grade A.

*****Artibeus jamaicensis praeceps** Andersen.

Ann. Mag. Nat. Hist. (ser. 7) 18: 421, Dec. 1906.

113503. In alcohol (skull removed). Adult male. Guadeloupe, Lesser Antilles. January 22, 1902. Collected by H. Selwyn Branch.

In good condition; skull Grade A.

†**Dermanura phaeotis** Miller.

Proc. Acad. Nat. Sci. Philadelphia 54: 405, Sept. 12, 1902.
=*Artibeus phaeotis* (Miller). See Miller, U. S. Nat. Mus. Bull. 57: 161, June 29, 1907.

108176. Skin and skull. Adult female. Chichen Itza, Yucatan, Mexico. February 10, 1901. Collected by E. W. Nelson and E. A. Goldman. Original number 14537.

Well-made skin, with epidermis about joints of wings and feet damaged by insects; skull Grade A.

*****Dermanura rava** Miller.

Proc. Acad. Nat. Sci. Philadelphia 54: 404, Sept. 12, 1902.
=*Artibeus ravus* (Miller). See Miller, U. S. Nat. Mus. Bull. 57: 162, June 29, 1907.

113338. Skin and skull. Adult male. San Javier, northern Ecuador. August 10, 1900. Collected by G. Flemming. Original number 12.

Well-made skin in good condition; skull Grade A.

Genus BRACHYPHYLLA Gray

*****Brachyphylla minor** Miller.

Proc. Biol. Soc. Washington 26: 32, Feb. 8, 1913.

101528. In alcohol (skull removed). Adult female. Coles Cave, St. Thomas Parish, Barbados, Lesser Antilles. June 14, 1899. Collected by P. McDonough.

In good condition; skull Grade A.

*Brachyphylla nana Miller.

Proc. Acad. Nat. Sci. Philadelphia 54: 409, Sept. 12, 1902.

103828. Skull. Adult. Taken from pellets of Cuban barn owl, El Guama, Cuba, Greater Antilles. March 10, 1900. Collected by William Palmer and J. H. Riley. Original number 108.

No lower jaw; all teeth missing except the first molar on each side; posterior right part of brain case broken away.

*Brachyphylla pumila Miller.

Proc. Biol. Soc. Washington 31: 39, May 16, 1918.

218354. Skull. Cave known as "Trou de Bon Dieu," near Port de Paix, Haiti, Greater Antilles. Fall 1917. Collected by W. L. Abbott.

Skull lacks roof of brain case and all teeth except pm⁴ and m¹.

Genus CAROLLIA Gray

*Carollia castanea H. Allen.

Proc. Amer. Philos. Soc. 28: 19, Feb. 25, 1890.

$\frac{12914}{36384}$. In alcohol (skull removed). Adult male. Costa Rica. Probably 1876. Collected by José C. Zeledon.

In good condition; skull Grade A.

†Hemiderma subrufum Hahn.

Proc. Biol. Soc. Washington 18: 247, Dec. 9, 1905.

=*Carollia subrufa* (Hahn). See Miller, U. S. Nat. Mus. Bull. 128: 54, Apr. 29, 1924.

75127. Skin and skull. Adult male. Santa Ifigenia, Oaxaca, Mexico. July 29, 1895. Collected by E. W. Nelson and E. A. Goldman. Original number 8235.

Well-made skin in good condition; skull Grade A.

*Hemiderma tricolor Miller.

Proc. Acad. Nat. Sci. Philadelphia 54: 408, Sept. 12, 1902.

=*Hemiderma* [*Carollia*] *perspicillata perspicillata* Linnaeus. See Hahn, Proc. U. S. Nat. Mus. 32: 108, Feb. 8, 1907.

114005. Skin and skull. Adult female. Cave at Sapucay, Paraguay. December 5, 1901. Collected by William T. Foster. Original number 589.

Well-made skin in good condition; skull Grade A.

Genus CENTURIO Gray

*Centurio mcmurtrii H. Allen.

Proc. Acad. Nat. Sci. Philadelphia 13: 360, ordered published Nov. 26, 1861.

=*Centurio senex* Gray. See Rehn, Proc. Acad. Nat. Sci. Philadelphia 53: 297, June 8, 1901.

$\dfrac{8289}{37806}$. In alcohol (skull removed). Adult male. Mirador, Vera-cruz, Mexico. Collected by C. Sartorius. Cataloged in 1865; skull, November 14, 1899.

In good condition; skull Grade A.

Type not designated by number, see Rehn, Proc. Acad. Nat. Sci. Philadelphia 53: 297, June 8, 1901.

Genus CHILONYCTERIS Gray

†Chilonycteris mexicana Miller.

Proc. Acad. Nat. Sci. Philadelphia 54: 401, Sept. 12, 1902.

=Chilonycteris rubiginosa mexicana Miller. See Rehn, Proc. Acad. Nat. Sci. Philadelphia 56: 203, Mar. 26, 1904.

89277. Skin and skull. Adult male. San Blas, Nayarit, Mexico. June 9, 1897. Collected by E. W. Nelson and E. A. Goldman. Original number 11132.

Well-made skin in good condition; skull Grade A.

*Chilonycteris portoricensis Miller.

Proc. Acad. Nat. Sci. Philadelphia 54: 400, Sept. 12, 1902.

=Chilonycteris parnellii portoricensis Miller. See Rehn, Proc. Acad. Nat. Sci. Philadelphia 56: 199, Mar. 26, 1904.

102358. Skin and skull. Adult female. Cave near Pueblo Viejo, Puerto Rico, Greater Antilles. March 19, 1900. Collected by L. Stejneger and C. W. Richmond. Original number "G."

Well-made skin in good condition; skull Grade A.

Genus CHIRODERMA Peters

*Chiroderma isthmicum Miller.

Proc. U. S. Nat. Mus. 42: 25, Mar. 6, 1912.

173834. In alcohol (skull removed). Adult female. Cabima, Panama. May 1911. Collected by August Busck.

In good condition, hair has sloughed on stomach; skull Grade A.

Genus ECTOPHYLLA H. Allen

*Ectophylla alba H. Allen.

Proc. U. S. Nat. Mus. 15: 442, Oct. 26, 1892.

15950. Skin (without skull) preserved in alcohol. Segovia River, northern Nicaragua. July 1, 1887. Collected by C. H. Townsend. Original number 313.

In good condition except for some mutilation about the lower lip.

No type designated. H. Allen had but one specimen, readily seen to be the above from his opening paragraph, where he speaks of its condition, locality, etc. He says, "believed to be from the vicinity of the Segovia River, eastern Honduras." A note written on February 1, 1902, by C. H. Townsend, after referring to No. 313 in his catalog, reads: No.

313 (bat) was killed July 1/88 on Segovia R." Evidently the date '88 is a slip of the pen for '87, as the specimen was cataloged on November 10, 1887.

Genus EROPHYLLA Miller

*Phyllonycteris bombifrons Miller.

Proc. Biol. Soc. Washington 13: 36, May 29, 1899.
=Erophylla bombifrons (Miller). See Miller, Proc. Biol. Soc. Washington 19: 84, June 4, 1906.

86274. In alcohol (skull removed). Adult male. In a limestone cave near Bayamon, San Juan Province, Puerto Rico, Greater Antilles. January 18, 1899. Collected by Paul Beckwith.

In good condition; skull Grade A.

*Phyllonycteris planifrons Miller.

Proc. Biol. Soc. Washington 13: 34, May 29, 1899.
=Erophylla planifrons planifrons (Miller). See Miller, Proc. Biol. Soc. Washington 19: 84, June 4, 1906.

62517. In alcohol (skull removed). Adult male. Nassau, New Providence, Bahama Islands, West Indies. March 18, 1886. Collected by James E. Benedict.

In good condition; skull Grade A.

*Erophylla planifrons mariguanensis Shamel.

Journ. Washington Acad. Sci. 21: 252, June 4, 1931.

255593. In alcohol (skull removed). Adult male. Abraham Hill, Mariguana Island, Bahama Islands, West Indies. July 20, 1930. Collected by Paul Bartsch.

In good condition; skull Grade A.

Genus GLOSSOPHAGA Geoffroy

*Glossophaga elongata Miller.

Proc. Biol. Soc. Washington 13: 124, Apr. 6, 1900.

101871. Skin and skull. Adult female. Willemstad, Curaçao, off north coast of Venezuela. December 4, 1899. Collected by Leon J. Guthrie.

The specimen was originally preserved in formalin. On February 27, 1900 it was made into a study skin, in good condition; skull Grade A.

†Glossophaga mutica Merriam.

Proc. Biol. Soc. Washington 12: 18, Jan. 27, 1898.
=Glossophaga soricina mutica Merriam. See Miller, Proc. U. S. Nat. Mus. 46: 420, Dec. 31, 1913.

89271. Skin and skull. Adult male. Maria Madre Island, Tres Marias Islands, Nayarit, Mexico. May 8, 1897. Collected by E. W. Nelson and E. A. Goldman. Original number 10976.

Well-made skin in good condition; skull Grade A.

*Glossophaga rostrata Miller.

Proc. Biol. Soc. Washington 26: 32, Feb. 8, 1913.
=*Glossophaga longirostris rostrata* Miller. See Miller, Proc. U. S. Nat. Mus. 46: 423, Dec. 31. 1913.

111500. Skin and skull. Adult male. Westerhall Estate, Grenada, Lesser Antilles. August 25, 1900. Collected by Peter Gellineau. Original number 29.

Well-made skin in good condition; skull Grade A.

*Glossophaga soricina microtis Miller.

Proc. U. S. Nat. Mus. 46: 419, Dec. 31, 1913.

115061. In alcohol (skull removed). Adult female. Sapucay, Paraguay. June 1901. Collected by William Foster. Original number 66.

In good condition; skull Grade A.

*Glossophaga villosa H. Allen.

Proc. U. S. Nat. Mus. 18: 779, Oct. 27, 1896. Preoccupied by *Glossophaga villosa* Rengger, Naturgeschichte der Säugethiere von Paraguay, p. 80, 1830.
=*Glossophaga soricina soricina* (Pallas). See Miller, Proc. U. S. Nat. Mus. 46: 418, Dec. 31, 1913.

$\frac{9523}{37388}$. Skin in alcohol, and skull. The specimen has no original label, and bears only a small tag numbered 9523. Under this number the catalog entry is a small bat, "*Vespertilio*," marked as coming from "Guyana, Venezuela." No other data are given. It was cataloged some time between February 12 and March 17, 1870; skull, April 21, 1898. H. Allen, in his description of *Glossophaga villosa*, says that the locality is probably La Guayra, Venezuela. This mistake was probably made by his referring to the copied volume of the original catalog, where the locality is entered as "Guyara, Venezuela." This might be taken to mean La Guayra; but in the original catalog itself the writing is quite plainly "Guyana, Venezuela." Whether the locality in the catalog is meant to be the eastern end of Venezuela bordering on Guiana [in the old spelling, "Guyana"] or whether it means that the specimen came from the general region of Venezuela and Guiana, it is impossible to say. A second specimen, No. 9524, examined by H. Allen has no data whatever. It may or may not have come from the same locality as the type.

In good condition, skull Grade B. The type is designated by number, "9522," an error for 9523.

Genus LEPTONYCTERIS Lydekker

*Leptonycteris curasoae Miller.

Proc. Biol. Soc. Washington 13: 126, Apr. 6, 1900.

101851. In alcohol (skull removed). Adult male. Willemstad, Curaçao, off north coast of Venezuela. November to December 1899. Collected by Leon J. Guthrie.

Considerable hair has sloughed away, and the viscera are soft; skull Grade A.

Genus LICHONYCTERIS Thomas

*Lichonycteris degener Miller.

Journ. Mamm. 12: 411, Nov. 11, 1931.

239520. Skin and skull. Adult female. Para, Brazil. July 22, 1923. Collected by C. R. Aschemeier. Original number 1437.

Well-made skin in good condition; skull Grade B.

Genus LONCHOPHYLLA Thomas

†Lonchophylla concava Goldman.

Smithsonian Misc. Coll. 63 (5) : 2, Mar. 14, 1914.

179621. Skin and skull. Adult male. Cana, altitude 2,000 feet, eastern Panama. May 20, 1912. Collected by E. A. Goldman. Original number 21701.

Well-made skin in good condition; skull Grade A.

*Lonchophylla robusta Miller.

Proc. U. S. Nat. Mus. 42: 23, Mar. 6, 1912.

173854. In alcohol (skull removed). Adult male. In cave on Chilibrillo River, Panama. April 14, 1911. Collected by August Busck.

In good condition; skull Grade A.

Genus MACROTUS Gray

Macrotus californicus Baird. See page 571.

*Macrotus waterhousii compressus Rehn.

Proc. Acad. Nat. Sci. Philadelphia 56: 434, June 30, 1904.

122484. Skin and skull. Adult female. Eleuthera, Bahama Islands, West Indies. July 6, 1903. Collected by S. H. Derickson.

Well-made skin in good condition; skull Grade A.

*Macrotus waterhousii heberfolium Shamel.

Journ. Washington Acad. Sci. 21: 252, June 4, 1931.

255651. In alcohol (skull removed). Adult male. Kingston, Providencialis Island, Bahama Islands, West Indies. July 23, 1930. Collected by Paul Bartsch.

In good condition; skull Grade A.

*Macrotus waterhousii jamaicensis Rehn.

Proc. Acad. Nat. Sci. Philadelphia 56 : 432, June 27, 1904.

$\frac{8553}{37543}$. Skin and skull. Adult female. Spanish Town, Jamaica, Greater Antilles. Cataloged July 3, 1866. Collected by William March.

Well-made skin in good condition ; skull Grade B.

Genus MICRONYCTERIS Gray

†Micronycteris megalotis mexicanus Miller.

Proc. Acad. Nat. Sci. Philadelphia 50 : 329, Aug. 2, 1898.
=*Micronycteris megalotis mexicana* Miller.

52105. In alcohol (skull not removed). Adult female. Plantinar, Jalisco, Mexico. April 4, 1892. Collected by E. W. Nelson. Original number 2389.

In good condition ; skull not removed.

*Micronycteris microtis Miller.

Proc. Acad. Nat. Sci. Philadelphia 50 : 328, July 12, 1898.

$\frac{16366}{23364}$. Skin and skull. Adult male. Greytown, Nicaragua. Collected by L. F. H. Birt. Cataloged February 2, 1889, as an alcoholic ; skull cataloged April 16, 1889. There is no record showing at what time the alcoholic specimen was made into a skin.

Wing membranes considerably torn, but skin otherwise in good condition ; skull Grade A.

Genus MIMON Gray

†Mimon cozumelae Goldman.

Proc. Biol. Soc. Washington 27 : 75, May 11, 1914.

203191. Skin and skull. Cozumel Island, off coast of Quintana Roo, Mexico. Collected by George F. Gaumer. Original number 11030-X. Cataloged May 5, 1914.

Well-made skin in good condition ; skull Grade C.

Genus MONOPHYLLUS Leach

*Monophyllus clinedaphus Miller.

Proc. Washington Acad. Sci. 2 : 36, Mar. 30, 1900.

$\frac{5210}{37405}$. In alcohol (skull removed). Adult male. Specimen with no history. Alcoholic cataloged October 30, 1861 ; skull May 2, 1898.

In good condition ; skull Grade A.

*Monophyllus cubanus Miller.

Proc. Acad. Nat. Sci. Philadelphia, 54 : 410, Sept. 12, 1902.

113674.   Skin and skull.   Adult male.   Baracoa, eastern Cuba, Greater Antilles.   February 6, 1902.   Collected by William Palmer. Original number 645.

Well-made skin in good condition; skull Grade A.

*Monophyllus cubanus ferreus Miller.

Proc. Biol. Soc. Washington 31: 40, May 16, 1918.

219151.   Skin and skull.   Adult male.   In cave near Jérémie, Haiti, Greater Antilles.   December 7, 1917.   Collected by W. L. Abbott.

Well-made skin in good condition; skull Grade A.

*Monophyllus luciae Miller.

Proc. Acad. Nat. Sci. Philadelphia 54: 411, Sept. 12, 1902.

106095.   In alcohol (skull removed).   Adult male.   Santa Lucia Island, Lesser Antilles.   February 4, 1901.   Collected by H. Selwyn Branch.

In good condition; skull Grade A.

*Monophyllus plethodon Miller.

Proc. Washington Acad. Sci. 2: 35, Mar. 30, 1900.

101530.   In alcohol (skull removed).   Adult male.   St. Michaels Parish, Barbados, Lesser Antilles.   August 1899.   Collected by P. McDonough.

In good condition; skull Grade A.

*Monophyllus portoricensis Miller.

Proc. Washington Acad. Sci. 2: 34, Mar. 30, 1900.

86261.   In alcohol (skull removed).   Adult male.   Cave near Bayamon, Puerto Rico, Greater Antilles.   January 18, 1899.   Collected by Paul Beckwith.

In good condition; skull Grade A.

Genus MORMOOPS Leach

*Mormoops intermedia Miller.

Proc. Biol. Soc. Washington 13: 160, Oct. 31, 1900.
=*Mormoops megalophylla intermedia* Miller.   See Rehn, Proc. Acad. Nat. Sci. Philadelphia 54: 170, June 11, 1902.

102174.   In alcohol (skull not removed).   Adult female.   Cave at Hatto, on the north coast of Curaçao, off north coast of Venezuela.   April 29, 1900.   Collected by Leon J. Guthrie.

Specimen is in "brown phase" and in fairly good condition; skin torn on the back over lumbar vertebrae; skull not removed.

*Mormoops megalophylla senicula Rehn.

Proc. Acad. Nat. Sci. Philadelphia 54: 169, June 11, 1902.

84801. Skin and skull. Adult female. Fort Clark, Kinney County, Tex. December 3, 1897. Collected by Edgar A. Mearns. Original number 4273.

Well-made skin in good condition; skull Grade A.

*Mormoops tumidiceps Miller.

Proc. Acad. Nat. Sci. Philadelphia 54: 403, Sept. 12, 1902.

186443. In alcohol (skull removed). Adult male. Point Gourde Caves, Trinidad, off northeast coast of Venezuela. 1889. Collected by William Robinson. Merriam Collection number 5581.

In good condition except for small patch on back where hair has sloughed; skull Grade A.

Genus PHYLLONYCTERIS Gundlach

*Phyllonycteris obtusa Miller.

Smithsonian Misc. Coll. 81 (9) : 10, Mar. 30, 1929.

253095. Imperfect skull. In "crooked cave" near the Atalaye plantation, St. Michel, Haiti, Greater Antilles. March 1925. Collected by Gerrit S. Miller, Jr.

Skull lacking posterior portion of brain case, basioccipital and supraoccipital regions, and all teeth except the molars. No mandible.

Genus REITHRONYCTERIS Miller

*Reithronycteris aphylla Miller.

Proc. Acad. Nat. Sci. Philadelphia 50: 334, Aug. 2, 1898.

255514. In alcohol (skull removed). Jamaica, Greater Antilles.

Well preserved and in good condition; skull Grade A.

Genus STURNIRA Gray

*Sturnira lilium bogotensis Shamel.

Proc. Biol. Soc. Washington 40: 129, Sept. 26, 1927.

251989. Skin and skull. Adult female. Bogota (Estacion "La Uribe"), Colombia. November 1925. Collected by Nicéforo Maria.

Well-made skin in good condition; skull Grade A.

†Sturnira lilium parvidens Goldman.

Proc. Biol. Soc. Washington 30: 116, May 23, 1917.

126555. Skin and skull. Adult female. Papayo (about 25 miles northwest of Acapulco), Guerrero, Mexico. April 17, 1903. Collected by E. W. Nelson and E. A. Goldman. Original number 16313.

Well-made skin in good condition; skull broken into three sections with parts of squamosals, zygomata, left parietal, and the ectotympanics missing.

Genus STURNIROPS Goodwin

*Sturnirops mordax Goodwin.

Amer. Mus. Nov. 976: 1, May 4, 1938.

250310. Skin and skull. Adult male. El Sauce Peralta, a farm on the Atlantic Railroad, less than halfway from San José to Limon, probably about 1,000 feet elevation, Costa Rica. July 14, 1931. Collected by C. F. Underwood. Original number 543 (26881-X).

Well-made skin in good condition; skull Grade A.

Genus TONATIA Gray

*Lophostoma venezuelae Robinson and Lyon.

Proc. U. S. Nat. Mus. 24: 154, Oct. 3, 1901.
=*Tonatia venezuelae* (Robinson and Lyon). See Lyon, Proc. Biol. Soc. Washington 15: 248, Dec. 16, 1902.

102919. In alcohol (skull removed). Adult female. Macuto, 8 miles east of La Guaira, Venezuela. August 4, 1900. Collected by M. W. Lyon, Jr., and Wirt Robinson. Original number 199.

In good condition, except for a small bare patch on back; skull Grade A.

Genus TRACHOPS Gray

†Trachops coffini Goldman.

Proc. Biol. Soc. Washington 38: 23, Mar. 12, 1925.

244266. Skin and skeleton. Adult female. Guyo, Peten, Guatemala. June 30, 1923. Collected by Harry Malleis. Original number 388.

Well-made skin in good condition; skeleton complete.

Genus URODERMA Peters

*Uroderma convexum Lyon.

Proc. Biol. Soc. Washington 15: 83, Apr. 25, 1902.
=*Uroderma bilobatum* Peters. See Andersen, Proc. Zool. Soc. London 1908: 218, Sept. 1908.

111722. In alcohol (skull removed). Young adult female. Colon, Panama. May 28, 1901. Collected by J. W. Humphreys.

In good condition, but rather shrunken from action of formalin and subsequent drying; skull Grade B.

Genus VAMPYRESSA Thomas

*Vampyressa minuta Miller.

Proc. U. S. Nat. Mus. 42: 25, Mar. 6, 1912.

173832. In alcohol (skull removed). Immature female. Cabima, Panama. May 1911. Collected by August Busck.

In good condition; skull Grade A.

Genus VAMPYROPS Peters

*Vampyrops fumosus Miller.

Proc. Acad. Nat. Sci. Philadelphia 54: 405, Sept. 12, 1902.

105530. Skin and skull. Adult female. Hyutanaham, Upper Purus River, Brazil. March 4, 1901. Collected by J. B. Steere. Original number 83.

Well-made skin in good condition; skull Grade C.

Genus VAMPYRUM Rafinesque

†Vampyrus spectrum nelsoni Goldman.

Proc. Biol. Soc. Washington 30: 115, May 23, 1917.

=*Vampyrum spectrum nelsoni* Goldman. See Miller, U. S. Nat. Mus. Bull. 128: 49, Apr. 29, 1924.

78127. In alcohol, skull removed. Adult male. Coatzacoalcos, Vera Cruz, Mexico. May 14, 1896. Collected by E. W. Nelson. Original number 9579.

In good condition, except for some epidermis rubbed off wings while specimen was in an alcohol container during field transit; skull Grade A.

Family PTEROPIDAE: Fruit Bats

Genus CYNOPTERUS F. Cuvier

*Cynopterus angulatus Miller.

Proc. Acad. Nat. Sci. Philadelphia 50: 316, July 25, 1898.

=*Cynopterus brachyotis angulatus* Miller. See Andersen, Catalogue of the Chiroptera in the British Museum 1: 611, 1912.

83569. In alcohol, skull removed. Adult male. Trong (or Tarang), Peninsular Siam. 1896. Collected by W. L. Abbott.

In good condition; skull Grade B.

*Cynopterus babi Lyon.

Proc. U. S. Nat. Mus. 52: 438, Dec. 30, 1916.

114269. Skin and skull. Adult female. Pulo Babi, off west coast of Sumatra. January 8, 1902. Collected by W. L. Abbott. Original number 1411.

Well-made skin in good condition; membranes, ears, and feet stained by corrosive sublimate; skull Grade B.

*Cynopterus major Miller.

Proc. Biol. Soc. Washington 19: 62, May 1, 1906.

141236. Skin and skull. Adult male. Mojeia River, Nias Island, off west coast of Sumatra. March 10, 1905. Collected by W. L. Abbott. Original number 4021.

Well-made skin in good condition; skull Grade A.

*Niadius minor Lyon.

Proc. U. S. Nat. Mus. 34: 665, Sept. 14, 1908.
=*Cynopterus horsfieldi lyoni* Andersen. See Andersen, Catalogue of the Chiroptera in the British Museum 1: 827, 1912.

144264. In alcohol (skull removed). Nearly adult male. Confluence of the Gasip and Siak Rivers, eastern Sumatra. December 14, 1906. Collected by W. L. Abbott. Original number 4951.

In good condition, hair somewhat sloughed on shoulders and lower back; skull Grade A.

*Cynopterus minutus Miller.

Proc. Biol. Soc. Washington 19: 63, May 1, 1906.
=*Cynopterus brachyotis minutus* Miller. See Andersen, Catalogue of the Chiroptera in the British Museum 1: 625, 1912.

141240. Skin and skull. Adult male. Nias Island, off west coast of Sumatra. March 11, 1905. Collected by W. L. Abbott. Original number 4043.

Well-made skin in good condition; skull Grade A.

*Cynopterus pagensis Miller.

Proc. Biol. Soc. Washington 19: 62, May 1, 1906.
=*Cynopterus brachyotis angulatus* Miller. See Andersen, Catalogue of the Chiroptera in the British Museum 1: 612, 1912.

121581. Skin and skull. Adult female. North Pagi Island, off west coast of Sumatra. November 12, 1902. Collected by W. L. Abbott. Original number 2028.

Well-made skin in good condition; skull Grade A.

*Cynopterus princeps Miller.

Proc. Biol. Soc. Washington 19: 61, May 1, 1906.

141235. Skin and skull. Adult female. Mojeia River, Nias Island, off west coast of Sumatra. March 10, 1905. Collected by W. L. Abbott. Original number 4020.

Well-made skin in good condition, except a bare spot over left thigh; skull Grade A.

Genus EONYCTERIS Dobson

*Eonycteris robusta Miller.

Proc. Biol. Soc. Washington 26: 73, Mar. 22, 1913.

175849. In alcohol (skull removed). Adult male. In cave at Montalban, Luzon, Philippine Islands. July 5, 1908. Collected by Paul Bartsch.

In good condition; skull Grade A.

Genus HARPYIONYCTERIS Thomas

*Harpyionycteris celebensis Miller and Hollister.

Proc. Biol. Soc. Washington 34: 99, June 30, 1921.

219349. Skin and skull. Adult female. Gimpoe, Middle Celebes, August 23, 1917. Collected by H. C. Raven. Original number 3176.

Well-made skin in good condition; skull Grade A.

Genus PTEROPUS Brisson

*Pteropus aldabrensis True.   Cotypes.

Description of a New Species of Fruit Bat, *Pteropus aldabrensis*, from Aldabra Island, p. 1, July 14, 1893. (Reprint: Proc. U. S. Nat. Mus. 16: 533, Oct. 21, 1893.)

$\frac{20984}{36053}$ and $\frac{20985}{36054}$. Skins and skulls. Adult males. Aldabra Island, Indian Ocean, northwest of Madagascar. September 26 and October 5, 1892. Collected by W. L. Abbott.

Well-made skins in good condition, except proximal extremities of bones of forearm have been cut off, so that measurements of the forearm cannot be obtained; skulls Grade A.

No type is specified in the original description, but these two specimens are mentioned by number and are therefore regarded as cotypes.

*Pteropus arquatus Miller and Hollister.

Proc. Biol. Soc. Washington 34: 100, June 30, 1921.

218612. Skin and skull. Adult male. Koelawi, Middle Celebes. January 5, 1917. Collected by H. C. Raven. Original number 3067.

Well-made skin in good condition; skull Grade A.

*Pteropus balutus Hollister.

Proc. Biol. Soc. Washington 26: 111, May 3, 1913.

144760. Skin and skull. Adult female. Balut Island, Serangani Group, south of Mindanao, Philippine Islands. January 23, 1906. Collected by Edgar A. Mearns. Original number 6021.

Well-made skin in good condition; skull Grade B.

*Pteropus baveanus Miller.

Proc. Biol. Soc. Washington 19: 63, May 1, 1906.

125482. Skin and skull. Adult male. Bawean Island, Java Sea, Malay Archipelago. July 19, 1904. Collected by W. Grasshoff. Original number 16.

Well-made skin in good condition; skull Grade A.

*Pteropus cagayanus Mearns.

Proc. U. S. Nat. Mus. 28: 433, May 13, 1905.
=*Pteropus hypomelanus cagayanus* Mearns. See Andersen, Catalogue of the
Chiroptera in the British Museum 1: 121, 1912.

125289. Skin and skull. Adult male. Cagayan Sulu Island, near
west side of the Sulu Sea, Philippine Islands. February 25, 1904.
Collected by Edgar A. Mearns. Original number 5755.

Well-made skin in good condition; skull Grade A.

*Pteropus enganus Miller.

Proc. U. S. Nat. Mus. 30: 822, June 4, 1906.
=*Pteropus hypomelanus enganus* Miller. See Andersen, Ann. Mag. Nat. Hist.
(ser. 8) 2: 364, Oct. 1908.

140966. Skin and skull. Adult male. Pulo Dua, Engano Island,
off west coast of Sumatra. November 4, 1904. Collected by
W. L. Abbott. Original number 3774.

Well-made skin in good condition; skull Grade A.

*Pteropus faunulus Miller.

Proc. U. S. Nat. Mus. 24: 785, May 28, 1902.

111730. Skin and skull. Adult male. Car Nicobar, Nicobar
Islands, off west coast of Malay Peninsula. January 23, 1901.
Collected by W. L. Abbott. Original number 864.

Well-made skin in good condition; skull Grade B.

*Pteropus geminorum Miller.

Smithsonian Misc. Coll. 45: 60, Nov. 6, 1903.
=*Pteropus hypomelanus geminorum* Miller. See Andersen, Ann. Mag. Nat.
Hist. (ser. 8) 2: 363, Oct. 1908.

104464. Skin and skull. Adult female. South Twin Island, Mergui Archipelago. January 28, 1900. Collected by W. L. Abbott.
Original number 283.

Well-made skin in good condition; skull Grade A.

*Pteropus lanensis Mearns.

Proc. U. S. Nat. Mus. 28: 432, May 13, 1905.
=*Pteropus vampyrus lanensis* Mearns. See Andersen, Ann. Mag. Nat. Hist.
(ser. 8) 2: 368, Oct. 1908.

123291. Skin and skull. Adult male. Pantar, near Lake Lanao,
altitude 1,907 feet, Mindanao, Philippine Islands. September 7,
1903. Collected by Edgar A. Mearns. Original number 5626.

Well-made skin in good condition; somewhat stained by corrosive sublimate; skull Grade A.

*Pteropus lanigera H. Allen.

Proc. Amer. Philos. Soc. 28: 70, May 10, 1890.

=*Pteropus insularis* Hombron and Jacquinot. See Matschie, Die Fledermäuse des Berliner Museums für Naturkunde, p. 28, 1899; Andersen, Catalogue of the Chiroptera in the British Museum (ed. 2) 1: 297–298, Mar. 23, 1912.

$\frac{19066}{37815}$. Skin and skull. Said to be from the Samoan Islands, but this locality is undoubtedly incorrect. Purchased from Ward's Natural Science Establishment, Rochester, N. Y., bearing No. 4397. Cataloged August 21, 1890; skull, November 14, 1899.

Well-made skin (remade and skull removed in November 1899) in good condition. Skull Grade A.

H. Allen fails to specify the type by number but speaks of only one specimen in his description, and that as being in Ward's Natural Science Establishment. The specimen was purchased from Ward's in August 1890, shortly after H. Allen's description appeared. On the original label is written "*Pteropus lanigera sp. nov.* Samoa Is.," the italicized part being in H. Allen's handwriting.

*Pteropus lepidus Miller.

Proc. Washington Acad. Sci. 2: 237, Aug. 20, 1900.

=*Pteropus hypomelanus lepidus* Miller. See Andersen, Ann. Mag. Nat. Hist. (ser. 8) 2: 361, Oct. 1908.

101670. Skin and skull. Adult female. Kaju Ara, or Saddle Island, Tambelan Islands, South China Sea, between Malay Peninsula and Borneo. August 15, 1899. Collected by W. L. Abbott.

Well-made skin in good condition; skull Grade A.

*Pteropus mearnsi Hollister.

Proc. Biol. Soc. Washington 26: 112, May 3, 1913.

144739. Skin and skull. Adult male. Isabella, Basilan Island, Philippine Islands. January 26, 1906. Collected by Edgar A. Mearns. Original number 6024.

Well-made skin in good condition; skull Grade A.

*Pteropus niadicus Miller.

Proc. Biol. Soc. Washington 19: 64, May 1, 1906.

141233. Skin and skull. Adult male. Teliwaa, Nias Island, off west coast of Sumatra. March 5, 1905. Collected by W. L. Abbott. Original number 3981.

Well-made skin in good condition; skull Grade A.

*Pteropus pumilus Miller.

Proc. U. S. Nat. Mus. 38: 394, Aug. 19, 1910.

144758. Skin and skull. Adult male. Palmas Island, southeast of Mindanao, Philippine Islands. January 21, 1906. Collected by Edgar A. Mearns. Original number 6019.

Well-made skin in good condition; skull Grade A.

*Pteropus samoensis Peale.   Cotypes.

U. S. Exploring Expedition 8 (Mamm. and Ornith.) : 20, 1848.

This species is based on material brought back by the U. S. Exploring Expedition (1838–42). No type is designated, and there is nothing to show that one specimen is more typical than any other. As it is inconvenient to regard all the Samoan *Pteropus* brought back by the Expedition as cotypes, the specimens from Tutuila are here regarded as the cotypes of the species, the following quotation from the original description seeming to justify this selection: "This species was first discovered on the island of Tutuila, and subsequently on all the islands of the Samoan group; we obtained numerous specimens."

The specimens from Tutuila are as follows:

$\frac{8594}{22562}$. Collected by James Gibson. The catalog, under remarks, says: "Specimen turned over to Dept. Comp. Anat. for exhibition." Only the skull can now be found. It has the posterior part of brain-case cut away. Skin cataloged July 30, 1866; skull, February 7, 1887.

$\frac{8596}{37862}$. Female. Original number 14. Recently made into a modern study skin in fair condition and skull removed. Posterior part of brain-case cut off, all molars of upper left hand side broken away, otherwise skull in good condition. Skin cataloged July 30, 1866; skull, February 21, 1900.

$\frac{8597}{37860}$. Collected by W. Elliott. Recently made into a modern study skin, in fair condition, and skull removed. Skull Grade A. Skin cataloged July 30, 1866; skull, February 26, 1900.

*Pteropus vociferus Peale.

U. S. Exploring Expedition 8 (Mamm. and Ornith.) : 19, 1848.

3961. Skin. Adult male. Island of Mangsi, straits of Balabac, between Philippine Islands and British North Borneo. Collected by U. S. Exploring Expedition (1838–1842). Original number 7.

Specimen once mounted and on exhibition, then packed away in storage, but taken out March 31, 1902. It is in fair condition for an old specimen, but evidently bleached. It had no skull inside, nor is there any record of one.

Peale speaks of but one specimen, a male, and unquestionably it is No. 3961, cataloged as *Pteropus macklotii* from Mangsi.

Family RHINOLOPHIDAE: Horseshoe Bats

Genus RHINOLOPHUS Lacépède

*Rhinolophus affinis nesites Andersen.

Proc. Zool. Soc. London, 1905, pt. 2: 104, Oct. 17, 1905.

104753. In alcohol (skull removed). Adult female. Bunguran, Natuna Islands, South China Sea, between Malay Peninsula and Borneo. July 24, 1900. Collected by W. L. Abbott.

In fair condition, slightly mutilated in removing skull and parts of skeleton; right wing and foot detached; skull crushed, grade C.

*Rhinolophus circe Andersen.

Proc. U. S. Nat. Mus. 29: 657, Mar. 7, 1906.

141343. In alcohol (skull removed). Adult male. Pulo Nias, off west coast of Sumatra. March 15, 1905. Collected by W. L. Abbott. Original number 4094.

Skin in good condition; skull Grade A.

*Rhinolophus hirsutus Andersen.

Ann. Mag. Nat. Hist. (ser. 7) 16: 289, Sept. 1905.

105487. In alcohol (skull removed). Adult female. Guimarás Island, Philippine Islands. December 1887. Collected by J. B. Steere.

In fair condition, apparently allowed to dry so that soft parts of body have become somewhat hardened; skull Grade A.

*Rhinolophus inops Andersen.

Ann. Mag. Nat. Hist. (ser. 7) 16: 284, Sept. 1905.

125314. In alcohol (skull removed). Adult male. Todaya, Mount Apo, altitude 4,000 feet, southern Mindanao, Philippine Islands. July 8, 1904. Collected by Edgar A. Mearns. Original number 5713.

In good condition; skull Grade A.

*Rhinolophus keniensis Hollister.

Smithsonian Misc. Coll. 66 (1): 2, Feb. 10, 1916.

166352. In alcohol (skull removed). Adult male. West side of Mount Kenia, altitude 7,000 feet, British East Africa [=Kenya] August 27, 1909. Collected by Edmund Heller. Original number 1154.

In good condition; skull Grade A.

Rhinolophus minutillus Miller.

See *Rhinolophus minutus* Miller.

*Rhinolophus minutus Miller.

Proc. Washington Acad. Sci. 2: 235, Aug. 20, 1900. Preoccupied by *Vespertilio minutus* Montagu applied to the British race of *Rhinolophus hipposideros*. (See Andersen, Proc. Zool. Soc. London 1905, pt. 2: 129.) =*Rhinolophus minutillus* Miller. See Proc. Biol. Soc. Washington 19: 41, Feb. 26, 1906.

101715. In alcohol (skull removed). Adult male. Pulo Siantan, Anambas Islands, South China Sea, between Malay Peninsula and Borneo. September 1899. Collected by W. L. Abbott.

In good condition; skull Grade C.

*Rhinolophus nereis Andersen.

Proc. Zool. Soc. London 1905, pt. 2: 90, Oct. 17, 1905.

101714. In alcohol (skull removed). Adult female. Pulo Siantan, Anambas Islands, South China Sea, between Malay Peninsula and Borneo. September 1899. Collected by W. L. Abbott.

Skin in good condition except for broken right wing; skull Grade C.

*Rhinolophus solitarius Andersen.

Ann. Mag. Nat. Hist. (ser. 7) 16: 250, Aug. 1905.

124767. In alcohol (skull removed). Adult male. Tanjong Pamuja, island of Banka, off east coast of Sumatra. June 18, 1904. Collected by W. L. Abbott. Original number 3415.

Skin in good condition; skull Grade A.

*Rhinolophus spadix Miller.

Proc. Washington Acad. Sci. 3: 136, Mar. 26, 1901.

104752. In alcohol (skull removed). Adult female. Sirhassen Island, Natuna Islands, South China Sea, between Malay Peninsula and Borneo. June 5, 1900. Collected by W. L. Abbott.

In good condition, right forearm broken; skull Grade A.

*Rhinolophus trifoliatus niasensis Andersen.

Proc. U. S. Nat. Mus. 29: 658, Mar. 7, 1906.

141350. In alcohol (skull removed). Adult male. Pulo Nias, off west coast of Sumatra. March 15, 1905. Collected by W. L. Abbott. Original number 4088.

In good condition, wing membranes slightly injured; skull Grade A.

*Rhinolophus virgo Andersen.

Proc. Zool. Soc. London 1905, pt. 2: 88, Oct. 17, 1905.

101966. In alcohol (skull removed). Adult female. Southern coast of Luzon, province of South Camarines, Philippine Islands, 1899–1900. Collected by L. M. McCormick.

In good condition; skull Grade A.

Family THYROPTERIDAE: Disk-winged Bats

Genus THYROPTERA Spix

*Thyroptera discifera major Miller.

Journ. Mamm. 12: 411, Nov. 11, 1931.

105419. Skin and skull. Adult female. San Julian, Venezuela. July 17, 1900. Collected by Wirt Robinson and M. W. Lyon, Jr. Original number 1511.

Well-made skin in good condition; skull Grade A.

Family VESPERTILIONIDAE: Vespertilionid Bats

Genus ANTROZOUS H. Allen

†Antrozous minor Miller.

Proc. Acad. Nat. Sci. Philadelphia 54: 389, Sept. 12, 1902.

79096. Skin and skull. Comondu, Lower California, Mexico. September 20, 1895. Collected by J. E. McLellan.

Well-made skin in good condition, except for slight mutilation of border of interfemoral membrane. Skull lacks entire basal portion of brain case, otherwise perfect.

*Vespertilio pallidus LeConte.

Proc. Acad. Nat. Sci. Philadelphia 7: 437, this paper was reported favorably for publication Dec. 25, 1855.

=*Antrozous pallidus pallidus* (LeConte). See H. Allen, Smithsonian Misc. Coll. 7 (1): 68, June 1864.

152 and 5467. Skin without skull. El Paso, El Paso County, Tex. 1851. Collected by J. H. Clark during the U. S. and Mexican Boundary Survey.

The specimen was twice entered in the Museum catalog. The first entry is dated May 19, 1853, as No. 152, and as having skull No. 1134, which is now lost. This entry was made as a deposit: "Dep." The second entry is under No. 5467, with original number again marked 152 but with no skull number indicated; column for date marked "8–11.34 (?)." Specimen in good condition, recently made into a modern study skin. Harrison Allen, *loc. cit.*, p. 69, in his second table, regarded this specimen as the type. Baird, U. S. and Mexican Boundary Survey Report, 2: 5, 1859, said that "the one described by LeConte was taken at El Paso."

†Antrozous pallidus cantwelli Bailey.

North Amer. Fauna 55: 391, Aug. 29, 1936.

232362. Skin and skull. Adult female. Rogersburg, Asotin County, Wash. May 28, 1918. Collected by George G. Cantwell. Original number 1211.

Well-made skin in good condition; skull Grade A.

†Antrozous pallidus pacificus Merriam.

Proc. Biol. Soc. Washington 11: 180, July 1, 1897.

29815. In alcohol (skull not removed). Adult female. Old Fort Tejon, Tehachapi Mountains, Kern County, Calif. June 28, 1891. Collected by C. Hart Merriam. Original number 208.

In fair condition; hairs on back slipping; skull not removed.

Genus CORYNORHINUS H. Allen

†Corynorhinus macrotis pallescens Miller.

North Amer. Fauna 13: 52, Oct. 16, 1897.
=Corynorhinus rafinesquii pallescens Miller. See Miller, U. S. Nat. Mus. Bull. 128: 82, Apr. 29, 1924.

66534 (not 65534, as in original description). Skin and skull. Adult female. Keam Canyon, Navajo County, Ariz. August 3, 1894. Collected by A. K. Fisher. Original number 1715.

Well-made skin in good condition. Skull Grade C.

†Corynorhinus megalotis mexicanus G. M. Allen.

Bull. Mus. Comp. Zool. 60: 347, Apr. 1916.
=Corynorhinus rafinesquii mexicanus G. M. Allen. See Miller, U. S. Nat. Mus. Bull. 128: 83, Apr. 29, 1924.

98285. Skin and skull. Near Pacheco, Chihuahua, Mexico. August 25, 1899. Collected by E. W. Nelson and E. A. Goldman. Original number 13955.

Well-made skin in good condition; skull Grade A.

Genus DASYPTERUS Peters

*Dasypterus floridanus Miller.

Proc. Acad. Nat. Sci. Philadelphia 54: 392, Sept. 12, 1902.

111379. Skin and skull. Adult female. Lake Kissimmee, Osceola County, Fla. March 28, 1901. Collected by Edgar A. Mearns. Orginal number 5183.

Well-made skin in good condition; skull Grade A.

Lasiurus intermedius H. Allen.

=Dasypterus intermedius (H. Allen). See page 571.

Genus EPTESICUS Rafinesque

†Vespertilio fuscus bahamensis Miller.

North Amer. Fauna 13: 101, Oct. 16, 1897.
=Eptesicus bahamensis (Miller). See Miller, U. S. Nat. Mus. Bull. 79: 61, Dec. 31, 1912.

76537. In alcohol (skull not removed). Adult male. Nassau, New Providence, Bahama Islands, West Indies. Spring 1894. Collected by C. J. Maynard.

In good condition.

*Eptesicus hispaniolae Miller.

Proc. Biol. Soc. Washington 31: 39, May 16, 1918.

217207. In alcohol (skull removed). Adult male. Constanza, Dominican Republic, Greater Antilles. September 22, 1916. Collected by W. L. Abbott.

In good condition; skull Grade A.

*Eptesicus pallidus Young.

Proc. Acad. Nat. Sci. Philadelphia 60: 408, Oct. 14, 1908.

=*Eptesicus fuscus pallidus* Young. See Miller, U. S. Nat. Mus. Bull. 79: 62, Dec. 31, 1912.

142526. Skin and skull. Adult female. Boulder, Boulder County, Colo. July 23, 1903. Collected by R. T. Young. Original number 1315.

Well-made skin in good condition; skull Grade A.

*Eptesicus serotinus pallens Miller.

Proc. Biol. Soc. Washington 24: 53, Feb. 24, 1911.

155156. Skin and skull. Adult male. Ch'eng-yuan-hsien, 70 miles west of Ch'ing-yang-fu, Kansu, China. August 4, 1909. Collected by Arthur deC. Sowerby. Original number 246.

Well-made skin in good condition; skull Grade A.

*Eptesicus ugandae Hollister.

Smithsonian Misc. Coll. 66 (1) : 3, Feb. 10, 1916.

166520. In alcohol (skull removed). Adult female. Ledgus, Uganda, Africa. January 15, 1910. Collected by J. Alden Loring. Original number 9022.

Well preserved and in good condition; skull Grade A.

*Eptesicus wetmorei Jackson.

Proc. Biol. Soc. Washington 29: 37, Feb. 24, 1916.

179142. In alcohol (skull removed). Adult male. Maricao, altitude 1,375 feet, Puerto Rico. May 29, 1912. Collected by Alexander Wetmore. Original number 900.

In good condition; skull Grade B.

Genus KERIVOULA Gray

*Kerivoula bombifrons Lyon.

Proc. U. S. Nat. Mus. 40: 134, Apr. 25, 1911.

145616. In alcohol (skull removed). Adult male. Along Matan River, western Borneo. August 15, 1907. Collected by W. L. Abbott. Original number 5497.

In good condition; skull Grade B.

*Kerivoula depressa Miller.

Proc. Biol. Soc. Washington 19: 64, May 1, 1906.

$\frac{18533}{38194}$. In alcohol (skull removed). Adult female. Biapo, Carin Hills, northeast Toungoo, southern Burma, India. Collected by L. Fea. Original number 29. Cataloged May 2, 1890; skull, February 4, 1904.

In good condition; skull Grade A.

*Kerivoula engana Miller.

Proc. U. S. Nat. Mus. 30: 825, June 4, 1906.

141020. In alcohol (skull removed). Adult male. Pulo Dua, Engano Island, off west coast of Sumatra. November 3, 1904. Collected by W. L. Abbott. Original number 3766.

In good condition; skull Grade A.

*Kerivoula minuta Miller.

Proc. Acad. Nat. Sci. Philadelphia 50: 321, July 25, 1898.

83547. In alcohol (skull removed). Adult male. Lay Song Hong, Trong (or Tarang), Peninsular Siam. September 1896. Collected by W. L. Abbott.

In good condition; skull Grade A.

Genus LASIURUS Gray

†Lasiurus degelidus Miller.

Journ. Mamm. 12: 410, Nov. 11, 1931.

96188. (Not 96187 as in original description.) In alcohol (skull removed). Adult female. Sutton's, District of Vere, Jamaica, Greater Antilles. Received from the Institute of Jamaica in 1898. Original number 1908–X.

In good condition, slight sloughing of hair on both under and upper parts; skull Grade A.

*Lasiurus minor Miller.

Journ. Mamm. 12: 410, Nov. 11, 1931.

256505. Skull with complete set of molariform teeth (but lacking canines, incisors, and mandible). From owl pellets in the "Voute l'Eglise," a cave situated near the Jacmel road a few kilometers north of Trouin, Haiti, Greater Antilles. March 6–7, 1931. Collected by H. W. Krieger.

Skull Grade C.

*Myotis quebecensis Yourans.

Le Naturaliste Canadien 57 (3) : 65, Mar. 1930.

=*Lasiurus borealis borealis* (Müller). See [G. Maheux], Le Naturaliste Canadien 57 (10) : 185–186, Oct. 1930.

255564.   Skin (skull inside).   Adult male.   Anse-à-Wolfe, Quebec,
Canada.   1927.   Collected by Edmund Yourans.

Skin with wings spread and attached to a small board, in good condition; skull inside.

Type originally in Musée de l'Académie Commercial, Quebec, Canada.

*Atalapha semota H. Allen.

Proc. U. S. Nat. Mus. 13: 173, Sept. 9, 1890.

=*Lasiurus semota* (H. Allen).   See Miller, U. S. Nat. Mus. Bull. 57: 222, June
29, 1907.

$\frac{15631}{38983}$.   In alcohol (skull removed).   Adult female.   Sandwich
[=Hawaiian] Islands.   Collected by Valdemar Knudsen of
Kauai.   Cataloged January 4, 1887.

In good condition.

No type designated.   The above specimen is selected as the type, because
a great part of the description is based upon it.   A table of measurements
is given of it; it heads the list of nine specimens, is the first specimen mentioned by H. Allen and the only one that he considered a "perfect adult
specimen."

*Atalapha teliotis H. Allen.

Proc. Amer. Philos. Soc. 29: 5, Apr. 10, 1891.

=*Lasiurus borealis teliotis* (H. Allen).   See Miller, North Amer. Fauna 13: 110,
Oct. 16, 1897.

84555.   In alcohol (skull removed and lost).   Probably from the
southern part of California.   Sent to H. Allen by J. G. Cooper,
of the California Academy of Sciences.   It was not cataloged
until April 27, 1898.

As H. Allen remarks in the original description, the specimen is in poor
condition.   The skin of the head has been split open in order to take out
the skull; most of the hair has sloughed from the back.

No type was designated; but this specimen was unique at the time of the
description.   It bears an original label marked "*Atalapha teliotis*, Cal. Acad.
N. S."

Genus MINIOPTERUS Bonaparte

*Miniopterus natalensis arenarius Heller.

Smithsonian Misc. Coll. 60 (12) : 2, Nov. 4, 1912.

181811.   Skin and skull.   Adult female.   Guaso Nyuki, Northern
Guaso Nyiro River, British East Africa [=Kenya].   October 4,
1911.   Collected by Edmund Heller.   Original number 4413.

Well-made skin in good condition; skull Grade A.

*Miniopterus paululus Hollister.

Proc. U. S. Nat. Mus. 46: 311, Dec. 31, 1913.

105493.   In alcohol (skull removed).   Adult.   Guimarás Island,
Philippine Islands.   December 1887.   Collected by J. B. Steere.

Well preserved; body partially skinned out with portion of skin on underside missing; skull Grade A.

Genus MURINA Gray

*Murina huttoni fuscus Sowerby.

Journ. Mamm. 3: 46, Feb. 8, 1922.

199672. Skin and skull. Adult female. Forest of North Kirin, Imienpo district, Manchuria [=Manchukuo]. September 28, 1914. Arthur deC. Sowerby. Original number 702.

Skin in rather poor condition the entire left half of back, side, and about half of the underpart missing; left wing nearly detached from body; skull Grade A.

Genus MYOTIS Kaup

*Myotis abbotti Lyon.

Proc. U. S. Nat. Mus. 52: 441, Dec. 30, 1916.

121611. In alcohol (skull removed). Adult female. North Pagi Island, off west coast of Sumatra. January 3, 1903. Collected by W. L. Abbott. Original number 2191.

Well preserved and in good condition; skull Grade A.

*Vespertilio affinis H. Allen.

Smithsonian Misc. Coll. 7 (165) : 53, June 1864.
=*Myotis lucifugus lucifugus* (LeConte). See Miller, U. S. Nat. Mus. Bull. 79: 55, Dec. 31, 1912.

5342. In alcohol (skull removed and lost). Adult female. Fort Smith, Sebastian County, Ark. Collected by G. G. Shumard. Cataloged October 30, 1861.

In fair condition; all the hair of belly and lower back has slipped off; skull lost.

Species based on one specimen, the above, designated by number.

*Myotis altifrons Hollister.

Smithsonian Misc. Coll. 56 (26) : 3, Dec. 5, 1911.
=*Myotis volans longicrus* True. See Miller and G. M. Allen, U. S. Nat. Mus. Bull. 144: 140, May 25, 1928.

174133. Skin and skull. Adult male. Henry House, Alberta, Canada. September 5, 1911. Collected by J. H. Riley. Original number 2317.

Well-made skin in good condition; skull Grade A.

†Myotis baileyi Hollister.

Proc. Biol. Soc. Washington 22: 44, Mar. 10, 1909.
=*Myotis occultus* Hollister. See Miller and G. M. Allen, U. S. Nat. Mus. Bull. 144: 97, May 25, 1928.

125787. Skin and skull. Adult female. Base of White Mountains, altitude 7,500 feet, near Ruidoso, Lincoln County, N. Mex.

September 14, 1902. Collected by N. Hollister. Original number 195.

Specimen originally preserved in alcohol, but made into a dry skin on November 7, 1910.
Well-made skin in good condition; skull Grade A.

†Myotis californicus caurinus Miller.

North Amer. Fauna 13: 72, Oct. 16, 1897.

72219. In alcohol (skull removed). Adult male. Massett, Graham Island, Queen Charlotte Islands, British Columbia, Canada. 1895. Collected by J. H. Keen.

In good condition, except for slight injury to abdomen; skull Grade B.

†Myotis californicus pallidus Stephens.

Proc. Biol. Soc. Washington 13: 153, June 13, 1900.

99829. Skin and skull inside. Adult male. Vallecito, San Diego County, Calif. April 1, 1895. Collected by Frank Stephens. Original number 2498.

Well-made skin in good condition; skull not removed.
Lyon and Osgood (p. 291) recorded this specimen as "probably mislaid temporarily." It had been, however, in F. Stephens' private collection and was afterward turned over to the San Diego Society of Natural History. Finally it was returned to the U. S. Biological Survey on February 27, 1929.

†Myotis capitaneus Nelson and Goldman.

Proc. Biol. Soc. Washington 22: 28, Mar. 10, 1909.
=*Myotis volans volans* H. Allen. See Miller and G. M. Allen, U. S. Nat. Mus. Bull. 144: 139, May 25, 1928.

146046. Skin and skull. Adult male. San Jorge, altitude 100 feet, 30 miles southwest of Comondu, Lower California, Mexico. November 12, 1905. Collected by E. W. Nelson and E. A. Goldman. Original number 18526.

Well-made skin in good condition; skull Grade A.

*Myotis carimatae Miller.

Proc. U. S. Nat. Mus. 31: 62, July 23, 1906.
=*Myotis horsfieldi carimatae* Miller. See Thomas, Ann. Mag. Nat. Hist. (ser. 8) 15: 172, Jan. 1915.

125154. In alcohol (skull removed). Adult female. Telok Edar, Karimata Island, off west coast of Borneo. August 28, 1904. Collected by W. L. Abbott. Original number 3673.

In good condition; skull Grade A.

*Vespertilio ciliolabrum Merriam.

Proc. Biol. Soc. Washington 4: 2, Dec. 17, 1886.
=*Myotis subulatus subulatus* (Say). See Miller and G. M. Allen, U. S. Nat. Mus. Bull. 144: 168, May 25, 1928.

186444. In alcohol (skull removed). Adult female. Near Banner, Trego County, Kans. August 1885. Collected by A. B. Baker. Merriam collection number 2797.

In good condition; skull Grade A.

*Myotis dominicensis Miller.

Proc. Biol. Soc. Washington 15: 243, Dec. 16, 1902.
=*Myotis nigricans dominicensis* Miller. See Miller and G. M. Allen, U. S. Nat. Mus. Bull. 144: 183, May 25, 1928.

113564. In alcohol (skull removed). Adult male. Dominica, Lesser Antilles. July 20, 1901. Collected by H. Selwyn Branch.

In good condition; skull Grade A.

*Vespertilio evotis H. Allen.   Lectotype.

Smithsonian Misc. Coll. 7 (165): 48, June 1864.
=*Myotis evotis evotis* (H. Allen). See Miller, North Amer. Fauna 13: 77, Oct. 16, 1897.

$\frac{5391}{38660}$. In alcohol (skull removed). Male. "Puget Sound," Wash. Collected by C. B. R. Kennerly. Cataloged October 31, 1861.

In the original description specimens are mentioned from the upper Missouri River and the Pacific coast from Puget Sound to Cape San Lucas. Miller, North Amer. Fauna 13: 77, Oct. 16, 1897, selected Monterey, Calif., as the type locality, whereby the specimen from that place became, according to Lyon and Osgood (1909), the lectotype.   However, in 1894, H. Allen (p. 90) had described a specimen from Easton, Wash., as representing what he considered "typical *V. evotis* of the Monograph" (1864). Easton lies about 55 miles inland from Puget Sound. Miller and G. M. Allen, U. S. Nat. Mus. Bull. 144, May 25, 1928, in their list of recognized forms of American *Myotis* (p. 10), erroneously gave "Near Colville, Wash." as the type locality, but correctly stated the facts in the body of their text on p. 115, where they show that "Puget Sound" is the true type locality. H. Allen originally had three specimens from this region, all taken at "Puget Sound." As one of these (No. 5391) is still in the National Museum, it may be made the lectotype.

Skin in fair condition; left wing missing; hair has sloughed on left side and at extreme posterior part of body; left leg detached from membrane. Skull Grade D.

†Myotis grisescens Howell.

Proc. Biol. Soc. Washington 22: 46, Mar. 10, 1909.

157517. Skin and skull. Adult male. Nickajack Cave, near Shellmound, Marion County, Tenn. August 31, 1908. Collected by A. H. Howell. Original number 1233.

Well-made skin in good condition; skull Grade A.

*Vespertilio gryphus var. septentrionalis Trouessart.   Lectotype.

Catalogus Mammalium tam Viventium quam Fossilium, p. 131, 1897.
=*Myotis keenii septentrionalis* (Trouessart). See Miller and G. M. Allen, U. S. Nat. Mus. Bull. 144: 105, May 25, 1928.

$\frac{8188}{38663}$. In alcohol (skull removed). Adult female. Halifax, Nova Scotia. Collected by Dr. J. B. Gilpin. Cataloged 1865.

In good condition; skull Grade A.

Lectotype chosen by Miller and G. M. Allen, U. S. Nat. Mus. Bull. 144: 106, May 25, 1928.

*Myotis hirsutus A. B. Howell.

Proc. Biol. Soc. Washington 39: 139, Dec. 27, 1926.

238863. Skin and skull. Adult female. Near Yen-ping-fu, altitude 2,000 feet, Fukien, China. April 7, 1922. Collected by Arthur deC. Sowerby. Original number 1358.

Well-made skin in good condition; skull Grade A.

*Vespertilio longicrus True.

Science 8: 588, Dec. 24, 1886.

=*Myotis volans longicrus* (True). See Miller and G. M. Allen, U. S. Nat. Mus. Bull. 144: 140, May 25, 1928.

$\frac{15623}{22480}$. In alcohol (skull removed). Young adult female. Region of Puget Sound, Wash. Collected by D. S. Jordan. Cataloged December 16, 1886.

The hair has slipped from the lower dorsal and ventral regions, and the skin has been incised along the midventral line to permit removal of skull; skull Grade A.

Type not designated by number. The description implies but a single specimen, unquestionably the above. The word "type" is written in the "Remarks" column of the catalog.

†Myotis longicrus amotus Miller.

Proc. Biol. Soc. Washington 27: 212, Oct. 31, 1914.

=*Myotis volans amotus* Miller. See Miller and G. M. Allen, U. S. Nat. Mus. Bull. 144: 145, May 25, 1928.

54437. Skin and skull. Adult female. Cofre de Perote, altitude 12,500 feet, Veracruz, Mexico. May 27, 1893. Collected by E. W. Nelson. Original number 4873.

Well-made skin in good condition; skull Grade A.

†Myotis longicrus interior Miller.

Proc. Biol. Soc. Washington 27: 211, Oct. 31, 1914.

=*Myotis volans interior* Miller. See Miller and G. M. Allen, U. S. Nat. Mus. Bull. 144: 142, May 25, 1928.

133426. Skin and skull. Adult male. Five miles south of Twining, altitude 11,400 feet, Taos County, N. Mex. July 23, 1904. Collected by Vernon Bailey. Original number 8182.

Well-made skin in good condition, except for torn wing membranes; skull Grade A.

Vespertilio lucifugus Le Conte.

Missing. See page 572.

†Myotis lucifugus alascensis Miller.

North Amer. Fauna 13: 63, Oct. 16, 1897.

77416. In alcohol (skull removed). Adult female. Sitka, Alaska. August 5, 1895. Collected by C. P. Streator. Original number 4754.

In good condition; skull Grade A.

†Myotis lucifugus phasma Miller and G. M. Allen.

U. S. Nat. Mus. Bull. 144: 53, May 25, 1928.

148159. Skin and skull. Adult female. Snake River, south of Sunny Peak, Routt County, Colo. August 28, 1906. Collected by Merritt Cary. Original number 792.

Well-made skin in good condition; skull Grade A.

*Vespertilio macropus H. Allen.

Proc. Acad. Nat. Sci. Philadelphia 18: 288, ordered published Aug. 28, 1866.
=*Myotis yumanensis yumanensis* (H. Allen). See Miller, North Amer. Fauna 13: 66, Oct. 16, 1897.

84549. Skin without skull. Adult male. Colorado River, near Fort Mohave (misspelled "Majaor" in the original description), Mohave County, Ariz. November 1, 1866. Collected by Elliott Coues.

Specimen a flat skin with expanded wings and much of the membrane between the fingers broken out.

The specimen bears the following label: "Private collection. Expl. in Rocky Mts. Elliott Coues U. S. A. [in print] *V. macropus.* Nov. Type [in what seems to be Harrison Allen's handwriting]; Near Fort Mojave, Colorado R., Nov. 1, 1866 [in what may be Coues's handwriting]." Mojave (the Spanish spelling of Mohave) is so written that it resembles Majaor; and thus it was printed in the original description. The above label agrees in every respect with the data given by H. Allen in the original description of the single specimen that he had. It was found in the Museum collection unnumbered, and was cataloged as No. 84549, April 21, 1898.

†Vespertilio melanorhinus Merriam.

North Amer. Fauna 3: 46, Sept. 11, 1890.
=*Myotis subulatus melanorhinus* (Merriam). See Miller and G. M. Allen, U. S. Nat. Mus. Bull. 144: 169, May 25, 1928.

18684. Alcoholic specimen made into skin, skull removed. Adult male. Little Spring, north base of San Francisco Mountain, altitude 8,250 feet, Coconino County, Ariz. August 4, 1889. Collected by C. Hart Merriam and Vernon Bailey. Original number 275.

Skin slightly faded, otherwise in good condition; skull Grade A.

†**Myotis micronyx** Nelson and Goldman.

Proc. Biol. Soc. Washington 22: 28, Mar. 10, 1909.

=*Myotis evotis chrysonotus* (J. A. Allen). See Miller and G. M. Allen, U. S. Nat. Mus. Bull. 144: 116, May 25, 1928.

146044. Skin and skull. Adult male. Comondu, altitude 700 feet, Lower California, Mexico. November 8, 1905. Collected by E. W. Nelson and E. A. Goldman. Original number 18490.

Well-made skin, in good condition; skull Grade C.

Vespertilio mundus H. Allen.

=*Myotis albescens* (E. Geoffroy). Missing. See p. 572.

*****Myotis nesopolus** Miller.

Proc. Biol. Soc. Washington 13: 123, Apr. 6, 1900.

=*Myotis nigricans nesopolus* Miller. See Miller and G. M. Allen, U. S. Nat. Mus. Bull. 144: 182, May 25, 1928.

101849. Skin and skull. Adult male. Punda, Curaçao, off north coast Venezuela. November 4, 1899. Collected by Leon J. Guthrie.

Specimen originally preserved entire in formalin, but made into a dry skin on February 8, 1900.

Well-made skin, in good condition; skull Grade A.

*****Myotis niasensis** Lyon.

Proc. U. S. Nat. Mus. 52: 441, Dec. 30, 1916.

121876. In alcohol (skull removed). Siaba Bay, Nias Island, off west coast of Sumatra. March 20, 1903. Collected by W. L. Abbott. Original number 2402.

Well preserved and in good condition; skull Grade A.

†**Myotis nigricans extremus** Miller and G. M. Allen.

U. S. Nat. Mus. Bull. 144: 181, May 25, 1928.

77670. Skin and skull. Adult female. Huehuetan, altitude 300 feet, Chiapas, Mexico. March 1, 1896. Collected by E. W. Nelson and E. A. Goldman. Original number 9455.

Well-made skin in good condition; skull Grade A.

*****Vespertilio nitidus** H. Allen.

Proc. Acad. Nat. Sci. Philadelphia 14: 247, ordered published Apr. 29, 1862.

=*Myotis californicus californicus* (Audubon and Bachman). See Miller, U. S. Nat. Mus. Bull. 79: 56, Dec. 31, 1912.

$\frac{1981}{5437}$. Skin (skull lost). Monterey, Monterey County, Calif. Collected by W. Hutton. First cataloged December 13, 1856; again cataloged October 31, 1861, as No. 5437.

No type originally designated. Miller, North Amer. Fauna 13: 69, Oct. 16, 1897 selected Monterey, Calif., as the type locality. As H. Allen had but one specimen from Monterey, it automatically became the type. In H. Allen's original list of specimens the one from Monterey was mentioned as alcoholic, whereas the catalog entry, made some time previously, lists it as dry skin.

The skin is in poor condition. The posterior half of upper part and extreme posterior part of under side of body are lacking. Wing and tail membranes in fair condition.

*Vespertilio nitidus henshawii H. Allen.   Cotypes.

U. S. Nat. Mus. Bull. 43 : 103, Mar. 14, 1894.
=*Myotis subulatus melanorhinus* (Merriam). See Miller and G. M. Allen, U. S. Nat. Mus. Bull. 144 : 169, May 25, 1928.

12450. Alcoholic (skull inside). Adult female. Near Fort Wingate, McKinley County, N. Mex. 1872. Collected by H. W. Henshaw.

In good condition, well preserved; viscera removed.

102426. Alcoholic (skull removed, lost). Adult female. Near Fort Wingate, McKinley County, N. Mex. 1872. Collected by H. W. Henshaw.

In good condition, viscera removed; skull lost.

Harrison Allen (1894), mentions two specimens under the single catalog number of 12450. Later one of these specimens was reentered as number 102426. Lyon and Osgood (1909) apparently overlooked these cotypes, but Miller, in his Lists of 1911 and 1923 indicates they were in the Museum collection. In 1928 Miller and G. M. Allen, *loc. cit.*, wrote that the cotypes "appear to be no longer in the National Museum collection." This, happily, is no longer true.

*Vespertilio obscurus H. Allen.

Proc. Acad. Nat. Sci. Philadelphia 18 : 281, ordered published Aug. 26, 1866.
=*Myotis yumanensis yumanensis* (H. Allen). See Goldman Proc. Biol. Soc. Washington 27 : 102, May 11, 1914.

$\frac{8223}{38357}$. In alcohol (skull removed). Adult male. Lower California, Mexico. Collected by John Xantus. Cataloged in 1865.

Left wing entirely lacking and only the bones of the right wing remaining. The rest of the skin is in good condition; skull Grade A.

Lyon and Osgood, U. S. Nat. Mus. Bull. 62 : 272, Jan. 28, 1909, followed Miller, North Amer. Fauna 13 : 69, Oct. 16, 1897, who, without removing the skull, assigned the alcoholic specimen to *Myotis californicus*. Later, however, Goldman, Proc. Biol. Soc. Washington 27 : 102, May 11, 1914, examined the skull and found that the animal was *Myotis yumanensis*.

†Myotis occultus Hollister.

Proc. Biol. Soc. Washington 22 : 43, Mar. 10, 1909.

137098. Skin and skull. Adult male. West side of Colorado River, 10 miles above Needles, San Bernardino County, Calif. May 14, 1905. Collected by N. Hollister. Original number 2237.

Well-made skin in good condition; skull Grade A.

*Vespertilio oregonensis H. Allen.   Cotypes.

Smithsonian Misc. Coll. 7 (165) : 61, June 1864.
=*Myotis californicus californicus* (Audubon and Bachman). See Miller,
North Amer. Fauna 13 : 69, Oct. 16, 1897. Four cotypes. See Miller, *loc.*
cit., p. 33.

5402. Cataloged earlier as No. 4977. In alcohol. Male. Cape San
Lucas, Lower California, Mexico. Collected by John Xantus.
Original number 3895. Cataloged May 31, 1861, and again in
October 1861. Cannot be found.

5405. In alcohol. Female. Fort Yuma, Imperial County, Calif.
Collected by G. H. Thomas in 1855. Cataloged October 31, 1861.
Cannot be found.

5537. In alcohol. Male. Fort Yuma, Imperial County, Calif.
Collected by G. H. Thomas, probably in 1855. Cataloged February 6, 1862. Cannot be found.

$\frac{5512}{37335}$. Cataloged earlier as No. 4740. Labeled "*Vespertilio ore-*
gonensis U. States Major LeConte." Cataloged April 13 and
November 1, 1861; skull, March 2, 1898.

A mummified skin with wings spread out, in rather poor condition.
Skull Grade B.

*Myotis pernox Hollister.

Smithsonian Misc. Coll. 56 (26) : 4, Dec. 5, 1911.
=*Myotis lucifugus alascensis* Miller. See Miller and G. M. Allen, U. S. Nat.
Mus. Bull. 144 : 48, May 25, 1928.

174134. Skin and skull. Adult male. Henry House, Alberta,
Canada. September 6, 1911. Collected by J. H. Riley. Original number 2318.

Well-made skin in good condition; skull Grade A.

*Myotis petax Hollister.

Smithsonian Misc. Coll. 60 (14) : 6, Nov. 29, 1912.

175189. Skin and skull. Adult female. Kosh-Agatch, Chuisaya
Steppe, altitude 7,300 feet, Altai District, Siberia. June 30,
1912. Collected by N. Hollister. Original number 4412.

Well-made skin in good condition; skull Grade A.

*Myotis sowerbyi A. B. Howell.

Proc. Biol. Soc. Washington 39 : 138, Dec. 27, 1926.
=*Myotis laniger* (Peters). See G. M. Allen, Mamm. China and Mongolia 1 : 218,
Sept. 3, 1938.

238869. Skin and skull. Adult female. Near Yen-ping-fu, altitude 2,000 feet, Fukien, China. April 7, 1922. Collected by
Arthur deC. Sowerby. Original number 1366.

Well-made skin in good condition; skull Grade A.

†Vespertilio subulatus keenii Merriam.

Amer. Nat. 29: 860, Sept. 1, 1895.
=*Myotis keenii keenii* (Merriam). See Miller and G. M. Allen, U. S. Nat. Mus. Bull. 144: 104, May 25, 1928.

72922. In alcohol (skull removed). Adult female. Massett, Graham Island, Queen Charlotte Islands, British Columbia, Canada. Summer 1894. Collected by J. H. Keen.

In good condition; skull Grade A.

Vespertilio tenuidorsalis H. Allen.

=*Myotis californicus californicus* (Audubon and Bachman). Lost. See p. 573.

†Myotis thysanodes Miller.

North Amer. Fauna 13: 80, Oct. 16, 1897.

29827. In alcohol (skull removed). Adult female. Fort Tejon, Tehachapi Mountains, Kern County, Calif. July 5, 1891. Collected by T. S. Palmer. Original number 235.

In good condition; skull Grade A.

*Vespertilio volans H. Allen.

Proc. Acad. Nat. Sci. Philadelphia 18: 282, ordered published Aug. 28, 1866.
=*Myotis volans volans* (H. Allen). See Goldman, Proc. Biol. Soc. Washington 27: 102, May 11, 1914; Miller and G. M. Allen, U. S. Nat. Mus. Bull. 144: 139, May 25, 1928.

$\frac{5398}{37326}$. In alcohol (lost), and skull. Cape San Lucas, Lower California, Mexico. Collected by John Xantus. Cataloged October 31, 1861; skull, March 1, 1898.

The alcoholic specimen cannot be found; skull Grade A. H. Allen had only one specimen, designated by number.

†Myotis winnemana Nelson.

Proc. Biol. Soc. Washington 26: 183, Aug. 8, 1913.
=*Myotis subulatus leibii* (Audubon and Bachman). See Miller and G. M. Allen, U. S. Nat. Mus. Bull. 144: 171, May 25, 1928.

150275. Skin and skull. Adult male. Plummers Island, in Potomac River, Montgomery County, Md. August 31, 1907. Collected by A. K. Fisher. Original number 2432.

Well-made skin in good condition; skull Grade A.

Vespertilio yumanensis H. Allen.   Cotypes.

=*Myotis yumanensis yumanensis* (H. Allen). Lost. See p. 573.

†Myotis yumanensis lutosus Miller and G. M. Allen.

U. S. Nat. Mus. Bull. 144: 72, May 25, 1928.

50783. Skin and skull. Adult female. Patzcuaro, Michoacán, Mexico. July 17, 1892. Collected by E. W. Nelson. Original number 2860.

Well-made skin in good condition; skull Grade C.

†Myotis yumanensis saturatus Miller.

North Amer. Fauna 13: 68, Oct. 16, 1897.

$\frac{17399}{24305}$. Skin and skull. Adult male. Hamilton, Skagit County, Wash. September 13, 1889. Collected by T. S. Palmer. Original number 392.

Well-made skin in good condition; skull Grade A.

Genus NYCTICEIUS Rafinesque

*Nyct[icea] crepuscularis LeConte. Cotypes.

McMurtrie's Cuvier, Animal Kingdom 1: 432, 1831.
=*Nycticeius humeralis* (Rafinesque). See Miller, North Amer. Fauna 13: 118, Oct. 16, 1897.

4735 and 4736. Skins with skulls inside. "U. States, Maj. LeConte." Cataloged April 13, 1861.

Specimens in poor condition.

These specimens are regarded as cotypes, more from tradition than anything else. There is nothing in the early description to show that they are cotypes. They were presented to the Museum years ago by Major E. L. LeConte as typical, or perhaps as original specimens. Each bears two old labels, a small paper tag and a standard Smithsonian Institution label. The word "Crepuscularis" is written on each of the paper tags in a handwriting that we cannot identify. The large label on No. 4735 is now so stained as to be illegible, but the one on the other specimen is in good condition. Its inscription: "4736 Vespertilio crepuscularis U. States Maj Leconte" was obviously written by Baird.

Genus PHONISCUS Miller

*Phoniscus atrox Miller.

Proc. Biol. Soc. Washington 18: 230, Dec. 9, 1905.

123141. In alcohol (skull removed). Adult female. Vicinity of the Kateman River, eastern Sumatra. September 9, 1903. Collected by W. L. Abbott. Original number 2781.

In good condition; skull Grade A.

*Phoniscus rapax Miller.

Journ. Mamm. 12: 412, Nov. 11, 1931.

199834. In alcohol (skull removed). Adult male. Palaleh, north coast of northeastern Celebes (about latitude 122°). August 25, 1914. Collected by H. C. Raven. Original number 1670.

In fair condition, some sloughing of hair on both under and upper parts; skull Grade A.

Genus PIPISTRELLUS Kaup

*Pipistrellus aero Heller.

Smithsonian Misc. Coll. 60 (12) : 3, Nov. 4, 1912.

181812. Skin and skull. Adult male. Mount Garguez, Mathews Range, altitude 7,000 feet, British East Africa [=Kenya]. August 26, 1911. Collected by Edmund Heller. Original number 4110.

Well-made skin in good condition; skull Grade A.

*Pipistrellus camortae Miller.

Proc. U. S. Nat. Mus. 24: 779, May 28, 1902.

111897. In alcohol (skull removed). Adult male. Kamorta, Nicobar Islands, Malay Archipelago. February 12, 1901. Collected by W. L. Abbott.

In good condition; skull Grade A.

†Pipistrellus cinnamomeus Miller.

Proc. Acad. Nat. Sci. Philadelphia 54: 390, Sept. 12, 1902.

100231. Skin and skull. Adult female. Montecristo, Tabasco, Mexico. May 4, 1900. Collected by E. W. Nelson and E. A. Goldman. Original number 14136.

Well-made skin in good condition; skull Grade A.

*Pipistrellus curtatus Miller.

Proc. Biol. Soc. Washington 24: 25, Feb. 24, 1911.

141019. In alcohol (skull removed). Adult female. Engano Island, off west coast of Sumatra. December 1, 1904. Collected by W. L. Abbott. Original number 3785.

In good condition; skull Grade A.

*Pipistrellus helios Heller.

Smithsonian Misc. Coll. 60 (12) : 3, Nov. 4, 1912.

181813. Skin and skull. Adult male. Merelle Water, 30 miles south of Mount Marsabit, British East Africa [=Kenya]. July 22, 1911. Collected by Edmund Heller. Original number 3065.

Well-made skin in good condition; skull Grade A.

*Scotophilus hesperus H. Allen.

Smithsonian Misc. Coll. 7 (165) : 43, June 1864.

=*Pipistrellus hesperus* (H. Allen). See Miller, North Amer. Fauna 13: 88, Oct. 16, 1897.

$\frac{5406}{37406}$. In alcohol (skull removed). Adult male. Old Fort Yuma, Imperial County, Calif. 1855. Collected by G. H. Thomas.

Hair on lower back and belly sloughed off; otherwise alcoholic in good condition; skull with central part of each zygoma broken out, right orbital region and right side of rostrum injured.

This may be considered as the type because it is the first one mentioned in Harrison Allen's list of three individuals, and the only alcoholic specimen among them. Furthermore, Miller (North Amer. Fauna 13: 88) definitely chose it as the type. Of the original three specimens, the two others, Nos. 5509 and 5910, came from Poso Creek, Kern County, Calif., and are dry skins.

†Pipistrellus hesperus australis Miller.

North Amer. Fauna 13: 90, Oct. 16, 1897.

52112. In alcohol (skull not removed). Adult female. Barranca Ibarra, Jalisco, Mexico. May 14, 1892. Collected by E. W. Nelson. Original number 2614.

In fair condition; viscera protruding and somewhat mutilated; right humerus broken; skull not removed.

*Vesperugo merriami Dobson.

Ann. Mag. Nat. Hist. (ser. 5) 18: 124, Aug., 1886.
=*Pipistrellus hesperus merriami* (Dobson). See Grinnell, Proc. California Acad. Sci. (ser. 4) 3: 279, Aug. 28, 1913.

186445. In alcohol (skull not removed). Male. Red Bluff, Tehama County, Calif. February 3, 1885. Collected by L. Belding. Original number 11. Merriam collection number 1135.

In fair condition; viscera removed; part of scalp missing; skull not removed.

*Pipistrellus minusculus Miller.

Proc. Washington Acad. Sci. 2: 647, Dec. 28, 1900.
=*Pipistrellus stampflii* Jentink. See G. M. Allen and Coolidge, Mammals of Liberia, p. 578, 1930.

84500. In alcohol (skull removed). Adult female. Mount Coffee, Liberia, West Africa. May 1894. Collected by O. F. Cook.

In good condition except for an area of sloughed hair on back; skull Grade A.

†Pipistrellus subflavus obscurus Miller.

North Amer. Fauna 13: 93, Oct. 16, 1897.

67723. Skin and skull. Adult female. Lake George, Warren County, N. Y. September 6, 1894. Collected by W. K. Fisher. Original number 198.

Well-made skin in good condition; skull Grade A.

*Pipistrellus subulidens Miller.

Proc. Washington Acad. Sci. 3: 134, Mar. 26, 1901.

104758. In alcohol (skull removed). Adult female. Sirhassen Island, Natuna Islands, South China Sea, between Malay Peninsula and Borneo. June 3, 1900. Collected by W. L. Abbott.

In good condition; skull Grade A.

Genus RHOGEËSSA H. Allen

†Rhogeëssa gracilis Miller.

North Amer. Fauna 13 : 126, Oct. 16, 1897.

70694. In alcohol. Adult male. Piaxtla, Puebla, Mexico. November 24, 1894. Collected by E. W. Nelson and E. A. Goldman. Original number 7099.

In fair condition; right humerus and ulna broken; skull attached to body, but separated from skin.

*Rhogeëssa minutilla Miller.

Proc. Biol. Soc. Washington 11 : 139, May 13, 1897.

63216. Skin with skull. Adult male. Margarita Island, off north coast Venezuela. July 8, 1895. Collected by Wirt Robinson. Original number 463.

Skin in good condition. Skull Grade B.

Rhogeëssa parvula H. Allen. See page 571.

*Rhogeëssa tumida H. Allen.

Proc. Acad. Nat. Sci. Philadelphia 18 : 286, ordered published Aug. 28, 1866.

84021. Skull. Adult male. Mirador, Veracruz, Mexico, Collected by A. J. Grayson. Cataloged March 1, 1898.

The skin is said to be in alcohol, but cannot be found; skull Grade A.

The specimen is accompanied by these two notes signed G. S. M.[iller], Jr. :
"In the orig. descr. the number of this sp. is said to be 8195. This is an error. [This number in the Museum catalog does not refer to a bat; it may be an original number.] Specimens recataloged 3.1.98."

"There is no doubt that this is the type skull. It was returned by H. A.[llen] with no. given in orig. descr."

Order DERMOPTERA: Flying Lemurs

Family GALEOPITHECIDAE

Genus GALEOPTERUS Thomas

*Galeopterus abbotti Lyon.

Proc. U. S. Nat. Mus. 40 : 126, Apr. 25, 1911.

145577. Skin and skull. Adult female. Pulo Panebangan, off west coast of Borneo. May 16, 1907. Collected by W. L. Abbott. Original number 5231.

Well-made skin in good condition; skull Grade A.

*Galeopithecus aoris Miller.

Smithsonian Misc. Coll. 45 : 47, Nov. 6, 1903.

=*Galeopterus variegatus aoris* (Miller). See Chasen and Kloss, Bull. Raffles Mus. 2 : 20, July 1929.

112428. Skin and skull. Adult female. Pulo Aor, off coast of Johore, Federated Malay States. June 8, 1901. Collected by W. L. Abbott. Original number 1028.

Well-made skin in good condition, flying membranes slightly cracked; skull Grade A.

*Galeopterus borneanus Lyon.

Proc. U. S. Nat. Mus. 40: 124, Apr. 25, 1911.
=*Galeopterus variegatus borneanus* Lyon. See Chasen and Kloss, Bull. Raffles. Mus. 2: 18, July 1929.

151888. Skin and skull. Adult female. Tjantung, southeastern Borneo. January 30, 1908. Collected by W. L. Abbott. Original number 5775.

Well-made skin in good condition; skull Grade A.

*Galeopterus chombolis Lyon.

Proc. U. S. Nat. Mus. 36: 486, June 1, 1909.
=*Galeopterus variegatus chombolis* Lyon. See Chasen and Kloss, Bull. Raffles Mus. 2: 19, July 1929.

144375. Skin and skull. Adult female. Pulo Jombol, Rhio-Linga Archipelago. March 3, 1907. Collected by W. L. Abbott. Original number 5091.

Well-made skin in good condition; skull Grade A.

*Galeopithecus gracilis Miller.

Smithsonian Misc. Coll. 45: 49, Nov. 6, 1903.
=*Galeopterus variegatus gracilis* (Miller). See Chasen, Bull. Raffles Mus. 10: 24, Oct. 1935.

104601. Skin and skull. Adult female. Sirhassen Island, Natuna Islands, South China Sea, between Malay Peninsula and Borneo. June 7, 1900. Collected by W. L. Abbott. Original number 461.

Well-made skin in good condition; flying membranes cracked; skull Grade A.

*Galeopterus lautensis Lyon.

Proc. U. S. Nat. Mus. 40: 125, Apr. 25, 1911.
=*Galeopterus variegatus lautensis* Lyon. See Chasen, Bull. Raffles Mus. 15: 21, Apr. 1940.

151886. Skin and skull. Adult female. Pulo Laut, off southeastern Borneo. December 23, 1907. Collected by W. L. Abbott. Original number 5679.

Well-made skin in good condition; skull Grade A.

*Galeopithecus natunae Miller.

Smithsonian Misc. Coll. 45: 50, Nov. 6, 1903.
=*Galeopterus variegatus natunae* (Miller). See Chasen and Kloss, Journ. Malay Branch Roy. Asiatic Soc. 6 (pt. 3) : 39, Aug. 1928.

104602. Skin and skull. Adult female. Bunguran, Natuna Islands, South China Sea, between Malay Peninsula and Borneo. July 16, 1900. Collected by W. L. Abbott. Original number 573.

Well-made skin in good condition; skull Grade A.

*Galeopithecus pumilus Miller.

Smithsonian Misc. Coll. 45 : 46, Nov. 6, 1903.
=*Galeopterus variegatus pumilus* (Miller). See Chasen and Kloss, Bull. Raffles Mus. 2 : 20, July 1929.

104448. Skin and skull. Adult male. Pulo Adang, Butang Islands, off west coast of Malay Peninsula. December 17, 1899. Collected by W. L. Abbott. Original number 165.

Well-made skin in good condition; skull Grade A.

*Galeopithecus saturatus Miller.

Smithsonian Misc. Coll. 45 : 51, Nov. 6, 1903.
=*Galeopterus saturatus* (Miller). See Lyon, Proc. U. S. Nat. Mus. 52 : 459, Dec. 30, 1916.

121750. Skin and skull. Adult female. Tana Bala, Batu Islands, off west coast of Sumatra. February 12, 1903. Collected by W. L. Abbott. Original number 2278.

Well-made skin in good condition; skull Grade A.

*Galeopithecus tuancus Miller.

Smithsonian Misc. Coll. 45 : 53, Nov. 6, 1903.
=*Galeopterus variegatus tuancus* (Miller). See Chasen, Bull. Raffles Mus. 15 : 20, Apr. 1940.

114375. Skin and skull. Adult female. Pulo Tuanku, Banjak Islands, off west coast of Sumatra. January 22, 1902. Collected by W. L. Abbott. Original number 1454.

Well-made skin in good condition; skull Grade A.

Order HYRACOIDEA: Hyraxes

Family PROCAVIIDAE

Genus DENDROHYRAX Gray

*Dendrohyrax validus True.

Proc. U. S. Nat. Mus. 13 : 228, Sept. 16, 1890.

$\frac{18986}{34721}$. Skin and skull. Adult male. Mount Kilimanjaro, German East Africa [=Tanganyika Territory]. June 17, 1888. Collected by W. L. Abbott. Original number 8.

Well-made skin in good condition; skull Grade B.

No type designated. Five specimens are listed by number of which $\frac{18986}{34721}$ is here chosen as the type because, first, it heads the list; second, it is the only one of which a table of skull measurements is given; third, it is the only specimen taken on Mount Kilimanjaro, the other four coming from Taveta, and the title of the paper reads, "Description of two new species of mammals from Mt. Kilimanjaro, East Africa."

The designation of the skull as No. 25796 in the original description was due to an error made in the cataloging. It has now been corrected to 34721.

Genus HETEROHYRAX Gray

*Heterohyrax brucei albipes Hollister.

Proc. Biol. Soc. Washington 35: 135, Oct. 17, 1922.

181551. Skin and skull. Adult female. Telek River, Loita Plains, British East Africa [=Kenya]. May 17, 1911. Collected by Edmund Heller. Original number 1816.

Well-made skin in good condition; skull Grade A.

Order INSECTIVORA: Insect Eaters

Family ERINACEIDAE: Hedgehogs

Genus ATELERIX Pomel

*Erinaceus sotikae Heller.

Smithsonian Misc. Coll. 56 (15): 1, Dec. 23, 1910.
=Atelerix albiventris hindei (Thomas). See Cabrera, Genera Mammalium, Insectivora, Galeopithecia, p. 67, 1925.

162112. Skin and skull. Adult male. Southern Guaso Nyiro River, British East Africa [=Kenya]. June 28, 1909. Collected by J. Alden Loring. Original number 6451.

Well-made skin in good condition; skull Grade A.

Genus ECHINOSOREX Blainville

*Gymnura gymnura minor Lyon.

Proc. U. S. Nat. Mus. 36: 453, May 27, 1909.
=Echinosorex gymnura minor (Lyon). See Cabrera, Genera Mammalium, Insectivora, Galeopithecia, p. 59, 1925.

86783. Skin and skull. Adult male. Khow Nok Ram, altitude 2,000 feet, Trong, Peninsular Siam. January 12, 1899. Collected by W. L. Abbott.

Well-made skin in good condition; skull Grade A.

Genus PODOGYMNURA Mearns

*Podogymnura truei Mearns.

Proc. U. S. Nat. Mus. 28: 437, May 13, 1905.

125286. In alcohol (skull removed). Adult female. Mount Apo, at 6,000 feet, southern Mindanao, Philippine Islands. June 25, 1904. Collected by Edgar A. Mearns. Original number 5667.

Alcoholic in good condition; skull Grade C.

Family MACROSCELIDIDAE: Jumping Shrews
Genus CERCOCTENUS Hollister

*Petrodromus sultani sangi Heller.

Smithsonian Misc. Coll. 60 (12) : 12, Nov. 4, 1912.
=*Cercoctenus sultan sangi* (Heller). See Hollister, Smithsonian Misc. Coll.
66 (1) : 2, Feb. 10, 1916.

181822. Skin and skull. Adult male. Summit of Mount Mbololo,
altitude 4,000 feet, Taiti Hills, British East Africa [=Kenya].
Nov. 9, 1911. Collected by Edmund Heller. Original number
4698.

Well-made skin in good condition, distal portion of tail apparently lost
during life; skull Grade A.

Genus ELEPHANTULUS Thomas and Schwann

*Elephantulus phaeus Heller.

Smithsonian Misc. Coll. 56 (15) : 8, Dec. 23, 1910.
=*Elephantulus rufescens phaeus* Heller. See Hollister, U. S. Nat. Mus. Bull.
99 (pt. 1) : 35, Aug. 16, 1918.

162074. Skin and skull. Adult male. Njoro O Solali, Sotik District, British East Africa [=Kenya]. June 26, 1909. Collected
by J. Alden Loring. Original number 6441.

Well-made skin in good condition; skull Grade A.

*Elephantulus rufescens mariakanae Heller.

Smithsonian Misc. Coll. 60 (12) : 10, Nov. 4, 1912.

181821. Skin and skull. Adult female. Mariakani, British East
Africa [=Kenya]. Dec. 31, 1911. Collected by Edmund Heller.
Original number 5072.

Well-made skin in good condition; skull Grade A.

Family NESOPHONTIDAE: Extinct Antillean Insectivores
Genus NESOPHONTES Anthony

*Nesophontes hypomicrus Miller.

Smithsonian Misc. Coll. 81 (9) : 4, Mar. 30, 1929.

253077. Nearly perfect skull (lacking auditory parts, incisors,
canines, and right median premolar). In deep cave near the
Atalaye plantation, 4 miles east of St. Michel, Haiti, Greater
Antilles. March 1925. Collected by Gerrit S. Miller, Jr.

*Nesophontes paramicrus Miller.

Smithsonian Misc. Coll. 81 (9) : 3, Mar. 30, 1929.

253063. Skull, lacking postero-inferior portion of occiput; the following teeth in place: pm², pm⁴, m¹, and m² of right side, m¹ and
m² of left side. In large cave near St. Michel, Haiti, Greater Antilles. March 1925. Collected by Gerrit S. Miller, Jr.

*Nesophontes zamicrus Miller.

Smithsonian Misc. Coll. 81 (9) : 7, Mar. 30, 1929.

253090. Anterior part of skull with complete palate (teeth lacking except pm^2 left and the molariform teeth of both sides). In large cave near St. Michel, Haiti, Greater Antilles. March 1925. Collected by Gerrit S. Miller, Jr.

Family SORICIDAE: Shrews

Genus BLARINA Gray

*Blarina angusticeps Baird.

Mammals of North America, p. 47, 1857.
=*Blarina brevicauda brevicauda* Say. See Merriam, North Amer. Fauna 10: 10, Dec. 31, 1895.

$\frac{1318}{2120}$. Skin and skull. Burlington, Chittenden County, Vt. Collected by Zadock Thompson. Original number 203. Cataloged February 1856.

Skin in fair condition; some hair has sloughed from the sides and belly; skull Grade B.

†Blarina carolinensis peninsulae Merriam.

North Amer. Fauna 10: 14, Dec. 31, 1895.
=*Blarina brevicauda peninsulae* Merriam. Trouessart, Catalogus Mammalium tam Viventium quam Fossilium, pt. 1, p. 188, 1897.

70874. Skin and skull. Adult male. Miami River, Dade County, Fla., Mar. 2, 1895. Collected by J. A. Loring. Original number 2777.

Well-made skin, with small abdominal patch of hair sloughed; skull Grade A.

†Blarina telmalestes Merriam.

North Amer. Fauna 10: 15, Dec. 31, 1895.

71823. Skin and skull. Adult female. Lake Drummond, Dismal Swamp, Norfolk County, Va., June 6, 1895. Collected by A. K. Fisher. Original number 1775.

Well-made skin in good condition; skull Grade A.

Genus CROCIDURA Wagler

*Crocidura alchemillae Heller.

Roosevelt's African Game Trails, Amer. ed., p. 480, 1910.
=*Crocidura fumosa fumosa* Thomas. See Cabrera, Genera Mammalium, Insectivora, Galeopithecia, p. 151, 1925.

163087. Skin and skull. Adult male. Aberdare Range, altitude 10,500 feet, British East Africa [=Kenya]. October 17, 1909. Collected by Edmund Heller. Original number 1177.

Well-made skin in good condition; skull Grade A.

*Crocidura alpina Heller.

Smithsonian Misc. Coll. 56 (9) : 5, July 22, 1910.
=*Crocidura allex alpina* Heller.   See Hollister, U. S. Nat. Mus. Bull. 99 (pt. 1) :
68, Aug. 16, 1918.

163089.   Skin and skull.   Adult female.   West slope of Mount
Kenia, altitude 10,000 feet, British East Africa [=Kenya].
October 4, 1909.   Collected by J. Alden Loring.   Original
number 7728.

Well-made skin in good condition, skull Grade D.

*Crocidura andamanensis Miller.

Proc. U. S. Nat. Mus. 24 : 777, May 28, 1902.

111825.   Skin and skull.   Adult male.   South Andaman Island,
Andaman Islands, Malay Archipelago.   January 16, 1901.   Collected by W. L. Abbott.   Original number 851.

Well-made skin in good condition; skull Grade A.

*Crocidura beatus Miller.

Proc. U. S. Nat. Mus. 38 : 392, Aug. 19, 1910.

144647.   Skin, skull, and skeleton.   Adult male.   Summit of Mount
Bliss, altitude 5,750 feet, Mindanao, Philippine Islands.   May
28, 1906.   Collected by Edgar A. Mearns.   Original number
6173.

Well-made skin in good condition; skeleton Grade A.

*Crocidura caudata Miller.

Proc. Biol. Soc. Washington 14 : 42, Apr. 25, 1901.

103302.   In alcohol (skull removed.)   Young adult female.   Palermo, Sicily.   June 21, 1900.   Collected by Dane Coolidge.
Original number 1365.

Alcoholic in fair condition; intestines have been removed, some hair
has slipped from left leg.   Tip of tail is flattened by some accident;
skull Grade B.

*Crocidura daphnia Hollister.

Smithsonian Misc. Coll. 66 (8) : 1, May 22, 1916.

164898.   Skin and skull.   Adult female.   Gondokoro, Uganda,
Africa.   February 19, 1910.   Collected by J. Alden Loring.
Original number 9009.

Well-made skin in good condition; skull Grade C.

*Crocidura elongata Miller and Hollister.

Proc. Biol. Soc. Washington 34 : 101, June 30, 1921.

217534.   Skin and skull.   Adult male.   Temboan, northeastern
Celebes.   Aug. 1, 1916.   Collected by H. C. Raven.   Original
number 2790.

Well-made skin in good condition; skull Grade A.

*Crocidura grandis Miller.

Proc. U. S. Nat. Mus. 38: 393, Aug. 19, 1910.

144648. Skin and skull. Adult male. Grand Malindang Mountain, altitude 6,100 feet, Mindanao, Philippine Islands. June 3, 1906. Collected by Edgar A. Mearns. Original number 6181.

Well-made skin in good condition except that tip of tail is lacking; skull Grade A.

*Crocidura grisea A. B. Howell.

Proc. Biol. Soc. Washington 39: 137, Dec. 27, 1926.

=*Crocidura attenuata* Milne-Edwards. See G. M. Allen, Mamm. China and Mongolia 1: 122, Sept. 2, 1938.

238229. Skin and skull. Adult female. 75 miles southwest of Yengpingfu, Fukien, China. Nov. 23, 1921. Collected by Arthur deC. Sowerby. Original number 1076.

Well-made skin in good condition; skull Grade A.

*Crocidura grisescens A. B. Howell.

Journ. Mamm. 9: 60, Feb. 9, 1928.

=*Crocidura dracula grisescens* Howell. See A. B. Howell, Proc. U. S. Nat. Mus. 75 (art. 1) : 10, June 7, 1929.

252187. Skin and skull. Adult female. Kuatun, Fukien, China. Cataloged July 1, 1927. Collected by F. T. Smith. Original number 89.

Well-made skin in good condition; skull Grade A.

*Crocidura halconus Miller.

Proc. U. S. Nat. Mus. 38: 391, Aug. 19, 1910.

144652. Skin and skull. Young adult female. Spur of main ridge of Mount Halcon, altitude 6,300 feet, Mindoro, Philippine Islands. November 18, 1906. Collected by Edgar A. Mearns. Original number 6316.

Well-made skin in good condition, slightly sloughed on rump; skull Grade A.

*Crocidura hildegardeae altae Heller.

Smithsonian Misc. Coll. 60 (12) : 9, Nov. 4, 1912.

181819. Skin and skull. Adult male. North Creek, Mount Garguez, Mathews Range, altitude 6,000 feet, British East Africa [=Kenya]. August 31, 1911. Collected by Edmund Heller. Original Number 4190.

Well-made skin in good condition; skull Grade A.

*Crocidura hildegardeae procera Heller.

Smithsonian Misc. Coll. 60 (12) : 10, Nov. 4, 1912.

=*Crocidura hildegardeae hildegardeae* Thomas. See Hollister, U. S. Nat. Mus. Bull. 99 (pt. 1) : 64, Aug. 16, 1918.

181820. Skin and skull. Adult female. Mount Lololokwi, altitude 6,000 feet, British East Africa [=Kenya]. September 9, 1911. Collected by Edmund Heller. Original number 4274.

Well-made skin in good condition; skull Grade A.

*Crocidura lea Miller and Hollister.

Proc. Biol. Soc. Washington 34 : 102, June 30, 1921.

217553. Skin and skull. Adult male. Temboan, northeastern Celebes. August 3, 1916. Collected by H. C. Raven. Original number 2837.

Well-made skin in good condition ; skull Grade A.

*Crocidura lepidura Lyon.

Proc. U. S. Nat. Mus. 34 : 662, Sept. 14, 1908.

123140. Skin and skull. Adult female. Kateman River, eastern Sumatra. September 1, 1903. Collected by W. L. Abbott. Original number 2772.

Well-made skin in good condition ; skull Grade C.

*Crocidura levicula Miller and Hollister.

Proc. Biol. Soc. Washington 34 : 103, June 30, 1921.

219450. Skin and skull. Adult female. Pinedapa, Middle Celebes. February 13, 1918. Collected by H. C. Raven. Original number 3521.

Well-made skin in good condition ; skull Grade A.

*Crocidura lignicolor Miller.

Proc. Washington Acad. Sci. 2 : 39, Mar. 30, 1900.
=Crocidura suaveolens lignicolor Miller. See Ognev, Mamm. Eastern Europe and Northern Asia 1 : 356, 1928.

62180. Skin and skull. Adult female. Jungles east of Maralbashi on the Yarkand River, eastern Turkestan. January 10, 1894. Collected by W. L. Abbott.

Well-made skin in good condition ; skull Grade A.

*Crocidura littoralis Heller.

Smithsonian Misc. Coll. 56 (15) : 5, Dec. 23, 1910.

164642. Skin and skull. Adult male. Butiaba, east shore of Albert Nyanza, Uganda, Africa. January 6, 1910. Collected by J. Alden Loring. Original number 8598.

Well-made skin in good condition ; skull Grade A.

*Crocidura lutrella Heller.

Smithsonian Misc. Coll. 56 (15) : 4, Dec. 23, 1910.

164640. Skin and skull. Adult male. Rhino Camp, Lado Enclave, Uganda, Africa. January 14, 1910. Collected by J. Alden Loring. Original number 8729.

Well-made skin in good condition; skull Grade A.

*Crocidura lutreola Heller.

Smithsonian Misc. Coll. 60 (12) : 8, Nov. 4, 1912.
=*Crocidura hildegardeae hildegardeae* Thomas. See Hollister, U. S. Nat. Mus. Bull. 99 (pt. 1) : 64, Aug. 16, 1918.

181818. Skin and skull. Adult female. Mount Mbololo, Taita Hills, altitude 5,000 feet, British East Africa [=Kenya]. November 6, 1911. Collected by Edmund Heller. Original number 4635.

Well-made skin in good condition ; skull Grade A.

*Crocidura maanjae Heller.

Smithsonian Misc. Coll. 56 (15) : 4, Dec. 23, 1910.
=*Crocidura hildegardeae hildegardeae* Thomas. See Cabrera, Genera Mammalium, Insectivora, Galeopithecia, p. 152, 1925.

164639. Skin and skull. Adult male. Kabula Muliro, Uganda, Africa. December 27, 1909. Collected by J. Alden Loring. Original number 8502.

Well-made skin in good condition ; skull Grade B.

*Crocidura mimula Miller.

Proc. Biol. Soc. Washington 14 : 95, June 27, 1901.
=*Crocidura suaveolens mimula* Miller. See Ognev, Mamm. Eastern Europe and Northern Asia 1 : 356, 1928.

105801. Skin and skull. Adult female. Züberwangen, St. Gallen, Switzerland. December 1, 1900. Collected by Ernst H. Zollikofer. Original number 192.

Well-made skin in good condition; skull Grade A.

*Crocidura mindorus Miller.

Proc. U. S. Nat. Mus. 38 : 392, Aug. 19, 1910.

144654. Skin, skull, and skeleton. Young adult male. Summit main ridge of Mount Halcon, altitude 6,300 feet, Mindoro, Philippine Islands. Nov. 19, 1906. Collected by Edgar A. Mearns. Original number 6321.

Well-made skin in good condition; skull Grade A, skeleton in alcohol.

*Myosorex muricauda Miller.

Proc. Washington Acad. Sci. 2 : 645, Dec. 28, 1900.
=*Crocidura muricauda* (Miller). See Hollister, Bull. Amer. Mus. Nat. Hist. 35 : 669, Oct. 21, 1916.

83809. In alcohol (skull removed). Adult male. Mount Coffee, Liberia, West Africa. April 5, 1897. Collected by R. P. Currie. Original number 32.

Alcoholic, in good condition; skull Grade A.

*Crocidura mutesae Heller.

Smithsonian Misc. Coll. 56 (15) : 3, Dec. 23, 1910.

164636. Skin and skull. Adult female. Kampala, Uganda, Africa. December 22, 1909. Collected by J. Alden Loring. Original number 8430.

Well-made skin in good condition; skull Grade A.

*Crocidura nicobarica Miller.

Proc. U. S. Nat. Mus. 24: 776, May 28, 1902.

111788. In alcohol (skull removed). Adult female. Great Nicobar Island, Nicobar Islands, Malay Archipelago. Mar. 15, 1901. Collected by W. L. Abbott. Original number 931.

Specimen well preserved. It contains a large fetus. Tip of tail, hind feet and ankles, left fore foot and tip of snout have been somewhat nibbled, probably by ants. Skull Grade A.

*Crocidura nigripes Miller and Hollister.

Proc. Biol. Soc. Washington 34: 101, June 30, 1921.

217545. Skin and skull. Adult male. Temboan, northeastern Celebes. Aug. 4, 1916. Collected by H. C. Raven. Original number 2866.

Well-made skin in good condition; skull Grade A.

*Crocidura nigripes lipara Miller and Hollister.

Proc. Biol. Soc. Washington 34: 101, June 30, 1921.

219444. Skin and skull. Adult male. Gimpoe, Middle Celebes. Sept. 2, 1917. Collected by H. C. Raven. Original number 3207.

Well-made skin in good condition; skull Grade A.

*Crocidura nilotica Heller.

Smithsonian Misc. Coll. 56 (15) : 3, Dec. 23, 1910.
=Crocidura turpa nilotica Heller. See Hollister, Bull. Amer. Mus. Nat. Hist. 35: 664, Oct. 21, 1916.

164638. Skin and skull. Adult female. Rhino Camp, Lado Enclave, Uganda, Africa. Jan. 17, 1910. Collected by J. Alden Loring. Original number 8768.

Well-made skin in good condition; skull Grade A.

*Crocidura parvipes nisa Hollister.

Smithsonian Misc. Coll. 66 (8) : 2, May 22, 1916.

182440. Skin and skull. Adult female. Kibabe, Kisumu, British East Africa [=Kenya]. January 20, 1912. Collected by Edmund Heller. Original number 5126.

Well-made skin in good condition; skull Grade A.

*Crocidura pergrisea Miller.

Proc. Biol. Soc. Washington 26: 113, May 3, 1913.

175918. Skin and skull. Adult female. Skoro Loomba, altitude 9,500 feet, Shigar, Baltistan, Kashmir, India. October 16, 1912. Collected by W. L. Abbott. Original number 8036.

Well-made skin in good condition; skull Grade A.

*Crocidura planiceps Heller.

Smithsonian Misc. Coll. 56 (15) : 5, Dec. 23, 1910.

164641. Skin and skull. Adult male. Rhino Camp, Lado Enclave, Uganda, Africa. January 23, 1910. Collected by J. Alden Loring. Original number 8837.

Well-made skin in good condition; skull Grade A.

*Crocidura pullata Miller.

Proc. Biol. Soc. Washington 24: 241, Nov. 28, 1911.

173213. Skin and skull. Adult male. Kotihar, altitude 7,000 feet, Kashmir, India. October 9, 1910. Collected by W. L. Abbott. Original number 7421.

Well-made skin in good condition; skull Grade A.

*Crocidura raineyi Heller.

Smithsonian Misc. Coll. 60 (12) : 7, Nov. 4, 1912.

181817. Skin and skull. Adult male. Mount Garguez, Mathews Range, altitude 6,000 feet, British East Africa [=Kenya]. September 1911. Collected by Edmund Heller. Original number 4195.

Well-made skin in good condition; skull Grade A.

*Crocidura rhoditis Miller and Hollister.

Proc. Biol. Soc. Washington 34: 102, June 30, 1921.

217550. Skin and skull. Adult male. Temboan, northeastern Celebes. Aug. 3, 1916. Collected by H. C. Raven. Original number 2834.

Well-made skin in good condition; skull Grade A.

*Heliosorex roosevelti Heller.

Smithsonian Misc. Coll. 56 (15) : 6, Dec. 23, 1910.

=*Crocidura roosevelti* (Heller). See Hollister, U. S. Nat. Mus. Bull. 99 (pt. 1) : 68, Aug. 16, 1918.

164643. Skin and skull. Adult female. Rhino Camp, Lado Enclave, Uganda, Africa. January 21, 1910. Collected by J. Alden
Loring. Original number 8812.

Well-made skin in good condition; skull Grade B.

*Crocidura shantungensis Miller.

Proc. Biol. Soc. Washington 14: 158, Aug. 9, 1901.

=Crocidura ilensis shantungensis Miller. See G. M. Allen, Mamm. China and
Mongolia 1: 131, Sept. 2, 1938.

86151. Skin and skull. Adult. Chimeh, Shantung, northern
China. June 1898. Collected by Paul D. Bergen.

Well-made skin in good condition. Skull Grade C.

*Crocidura sicula Miller.

Proc. Biol. Soc. Washington 14: 41, Apr. 25, 1901.

=Crocidura mimula sicula Miller. See Cabrera, Genera Mammalium, Insectivora, Galeopithecia, p. 154, 1925.

103301. Skin and skull. Adult male, Palermo, Sicily. June 20,
1900. Collected by Dane Coolidge. Original number 1332.

Well-made skin in good condition; skull Grade A.

*Crocidura simiolus Hollister.

Smithsonian Misc. Coll. 66 (8): 3, May 22, 1916.

197959. Skin and skull. Adult female. Kisumu, British East
Africa [=Kenya]. September 25, 1913. Collected by H. J. A.
Turner. Original number 3.

Well-made skin in good condition; skull Grade A.

*Crocidura suahelae Heller.

Smithsonian Misc. Coll. 60 (12): 6, Nov. 4, 1912.

181815. Skin and skull. Adult male. Mazeras, British East Africa,
[=Kenya]. December 17, 1911. Collected by Edmund Heller.
Original number 4875.

Well-made skin in good condition; skull Grade A.

*Crocidura sururae Heller.

Smithsonian Misc. Coll. 56 (15): 2, Dec. 23, 1910.

164637. Skin and skull. Adult male. Rhino Camp, Lado Enclave,
Uganda, Africa. January 18, 1910. Collected by J. Alden
Loring. Original number 8777.

Well-made skin in good condition; skull Grade A.

*Crocidura turba lakiundae Heller.

Smithsonian Misc. Coll. 60 (12): 6, Nov. 4, 1912.

=Crocidura turba zaodon Osgood. See Hollister, U. S. Nat. Mus. Bull. 99 (pt.
1): 54, Aug. 16, 1918.

181816. Skin and skull. Adult female. Lakiundu River, near its junction with the Northern Guaso Nyiro River, British East Africa [=Kenya]. July 12, 1911. Collected by Edmund Heller. Original number 1986.

Well-made skin in good condition; skull Grade A.

Genus CRYPTOTIS Pomel

†Blarina alticola Merriam.

North Amer. Fauna 10: 27, Dec. 31, 1895.
=*Cryptotis alticola* (Merriam). See Miller, U. S. Nat. Mus. Bull. 79: 27, Dec. 31, 1912.

52047. Skin and skull. Adult male. Mount Popocatepetl, altitude 11,500 feet, State of Mexico, Mexico. February 25, 1893. Collected by E. W. Nelson. Original number 4396.

Well-made skin in good condition; skull Grade A.

*Blarina berlandieri Baird.   Lectotype.

Mammals of North America, p. 53, 1857.
=*Cryptotis berlandieri* (Baird). See Miller, U. S. Nat. Mus. Bull. 79: 25, Dec. 31, 1912.

2159. In alcohol, skull removed April 1936. Vicinity of Matamoros, Tamaulipas, Mexico. Probably collected by J. L. Berlandier. Received from D. N. Couch. Cataloged February 14, 1857.

Body in good condition except for some loss of hair on belly; skull Grade A. Baird's figure of the skull was made from one of the paratypes.

No type was designated by Baird. He listed four specimens of which 2159 was figured on pl. 28. This was made lectotype by Lyon and Osgood, U. S. Nat. Mus. Bull. 62: 237, Jan. 28, 1909.

*Blarina exilipes Baird.   Lectotype.

Mammals of North America, p. 51, 1857.
=*Cryptotis parva* (Say). See Merriam, North Amer. Fauna 10: 17, Dec. 31, 1895.

2157. In alcohol, skull removed April 1936. Washington, Adams County, Miss. Collected by B. L. C. Wailes. Cataloged February 14, 1857.

Specimen rather the worse for loss of hair on the posterior parts of the body; skull Grade B.

Baird's figure of the skull was made from one of the paratypes. No type was designated by Baird. He listed eight specimens, of which No. 2157 was figured on pl. 28. This was made lectotype by Lyon and Osgood, U. S. Nat. Mus. Bull. 62: 237, Jan. 28, 1909.

†Blarina floridana Merriam.

North Amer. Fauna 10: 19, Dec. 31, 1895.
=*Cryptotis floridana* (Merriam). See Miller, U. S. Nat. Mus. Bull. 79: 25, Dec. 31, 1912.

$\frac{16510}{23937}$. In alcohol, skull removed. Chester Shoal, 11 miles north of Cape Canaveral, Brevard County, Fla. April 22, 1889. Collected by M. M. Green. Original number 44.

Specimen in good condition. Skull Grade A.

†Blarina fossor Merriam.

North Amer. Fauna 10: 28, Dec. 31, 1895.
=*Cryptotis fossor* (Merriam). See Miller, U. S. Nat. Mus. Bull. 79: 28, Dec. 31, 1912.

68545. Skin and skull. Adult female. Mount Zempoaltepec, altitude 10,500 feet, Oaxaca, Mexico. July 10, 1894. Collected by E. W. Nelson and E. A. Goldman. Original number 6419.

Well-made skin in good condition; skull Grade A.

*Cryptotis frontalis Miller.

Proc. Biol. Soc. Washington 24: 222, Oct. 31, 1911.

123429. In alcohol, skull removed. Adult female. Near Tehuantepec City, Oaxaca, Mexico. About 1870. Collected by F. Sumichrast.

Specimen in good condition, hair has sloughed on sides and belly; skull Grade A.

†Cryptotis goodwini Jackson.

Proc. Biol. Soc. Washington 46: 81, Apr. 27, 1933.

77074. Skin and skull. Adult male. Calel, altitude 10,200 feet, Tontonicapan, Guatemala. January 13, 1896. Collected by E. W. Nelson and E. A. Goldman. Original number 9073.

Well-made skin in good condition; skull Grade A.

*Cryptotis gracilis Miller.

Proc. Biol. Soc. Washington 24: 221, Oct. 31, 1911.

$\frac{12236}{38471}$. Skin and skull. Adult. Head of Lari River, near base of Pico Blanco, Talamanca, Costa Rica. Collected by Wm. M. Gabb. Cataloged November 19, 1874.

Fairly well-made skin in good condition; skull Grade A.

†Cryptotis griseoventris Jackson.

Proc. Biol. Soc. Washington 46: 80, Apr. 27, 1933.

75894. Skin and skull. Adult male. San Cristobal, altitude 9,500 feet, Chiapas, Mexico. October 4, 1895. Collected by E. W. Nelson and E. A. Goldman. Original number 8545.

Well-made skin in good condition; skull Grade A.

†Cryptotis guerrerensis Jackson.

Proc. Biol. Soc. Washington 46: 80, Apr. 27, 1933.

126895. Skin and skull. Adult female. Omilteme, altitude about 8,000 feet, Guerrero, Mexico. May 17, 1903. Collected by E. W. Nelson and E. A. Goldman. Original number 16429.

Well-made skin in good condition; skull Grade B.

†Blarina magna Merriam.

North Amer. Fauna 10: 28, Dec. 31, 1895.
=*Cryptotis magna* (Merriam). See Miller, U. S. Nat. Mus. Bull. 79: 28, Dec. 31, 1912.

68575. Skin and skull. Adult male. Totontepec, altitude 6,800 feet, Oaxaca, Mexico. July 24, 1894. Collected by E. W. Nelson and E. A. Goldman. Original number 6493.

Well-made skin in good condition; skull Grade A.

†Blarina mayensis Merriam.

Proc. Washington Acad. Sci. 3: 559, Nov. 29, 1901.
=*Cryptotis mayensis* (Merriam). See Miller, U. S. Nat. Mus. Bull. 79: 26, Dec. 31, 1912.

108087. Skin and skull. Adult female. Maya ruin at Chichen Itza, Yucatan, Mexico. February 5, 1901. Collected by E. W. Nelson and E. A. Goldman. Original number 14495.

Well-made skin in good condition; skull Grade A.

†Cryptotis merus Goldman.

Smithsonian Misc. Coll. 60 (2) : 17, Sept. 20, 1912.

178976. Skin and skull. Adult male. Mount Pirri (near head of Rio Limon), altitude 4,500 feet, eastern Panama. May 2, 1912. Collected by E. A. Goldman. Original number 21669.

Well-made skin in good condition, except small patch of fur missing on abdomen; skull Grade A.

*Blarina (Soriciscus) mexicana Coues.

Bull. U. S. Geol. and Geogr. Surv. Terr. 3: 652, May 15, 1877.
=*Cryptotis mexicana mexicana* (Coues). See Miller, Proc. Biol. Soc. Washington 24: 221–222, Oct. 31, 1911.

$\frac{3525}{4438}$. Skin and skull. Jalapa, Veracruz, Mexico. Collected by R. Montes de Oca. Skin cataloged March 18, 1859; skull September 1861.

Skin in fair condition, considering the time at which it was collected; skull Grade A.

†Blarina mexicana goldmani Merriam.

North Amer. Fauna 10: 25, Dec. 31, 1895.
=*Cryptotis mexicana goldmani* (Merriam). See Miller, U. S. Nat. Mus. Bull. 79: 27, Dec. 31, 1912.

70244. Skin and skull. Young adult male. Mountains near Chilpancingo, altitude 9,600 feet, Guerrero, Mexico. December 23, 1894. Collected by E. W. Nelson and E. A. Goldman. Original number 7231.

Well-made skin in good condition; skull Grade A.

†Blarina mexicana machetes Merriam.

North Amer. Fauna 10: 26, Dec. 31, 1895.
=*Cryptotis mexicana machetes* (Merriam). See Miller, U. S. Nat. Mus. Bull. 79: 27, Dec. 31, 1912.

71456. Skin and skull. Adult female. Mountains near Ozolotepec, altitude 10,000 feet, Oaxaca, Mexico. March 26, 1895. Collected by E. W. Nelson and E. A. Goldman. Original number 7723.

Well-made skin in good condition; skull Grade A.

†Blarina mexicana peregrina Merriam.

North Amer. Fauna 10: 24, Dec. 31, 1895.
=*Cryptotis mexicana peregrina* (Merriam). See Miller, Proc. Biol. Soc. Washington 24: 222, Oct. 31, 1911.

68317. Skin and skull. Adult male. Mountains 15 miles west of Oaxaca, altitude 9,500 feet, State of Oaxaca, Mexico. September 12, 1894. Collected by E. W. Nelson and E. A. Goldman. Original number 6748.

Well-made skin in good condition; skull Grade A.

†Blarina nelsoni Merriam.

North Amer. Fauna 10: 26, Dec. 31, 1895.
=*Cryptotis nelsoni* (Merriam). See Miller, U. S. Nat. Mus. Bull. 79: 27, Dec. 31, 1912.

65437. Skin and skull. Adult female. Tuxtla Volcano, altitude 4,800 feet, Vera Cruz, Mexico. May 13, 1894. Collected by E. W. Nelson and E. A. Goldman. Original number 6253.

Well-made skin in good condition; skull Grade A.

†Blarina obscura Merriam.

North Amer. Fauna 10: 23, Dec. 31, 1895.
=*Cryptotis obscura* (Merriam). See Miller, U. S. Nat. Mus. Bull. 79: 26, Dec. 31, 1912.

55634. Skin and skull. Young adult female. Tulancingo, altitude 8,500 feet, Hidalgo, Mexico. August 27, 1893. Collected by E. W. Nelson. Original number 5377.

Well-made skin in good condition; skull Grade A.

*Cryptotis pergracilis macer Miller.

Proc. Biol. Soc. Washington 24: 223, Oct. 31, 1911.
$\frac{15565}{38494}$. In alcohol, skull removed. Near Guanajuato City, Guanajuato, Mexico. Collected by A. Dugés. Original number 103. Cataloged October 19, 1886.

Specimen in good condition; skull Grade A.

†Cryptotis pergracilis nayaritensis Jackson.

Proc. Biol. Soc. Washington 46: 79, Apr. 27, 1933.

88015. Skin and skull. Adult male. Tepic, altitude 3,000 feet, State of Nayarit, Mexico. April 13, 1897. Collected by E. W. Nelson and E. A. Goldman. Original number 10902.

Well-made skin in good condition; skull Grade A.

†Cryptotis pergracilis pueblensis Jackson.

Proc. Biol. Soc. Washington 46: 79, Apr. 27, 1933.

92720. Skin and skull. Adult male. Huachinango, State of Puebla, Mexico. January 6, 1898. Collected by E. A. Goldman. Original number 12014 (Nelson and Goldman catalog).

Well-made skin in good condition; skull Grade A.

†Blarina soricina Merriam.

North Amer. Fauna 10: 22, Dec. 31, 1895.
=*Cryptotis soricina* (Merriam). See Miller, Proc. Biol. Soc. Washington 24: 221, Oct. 31, 1911.

50762. Skin and skull. Adult male. Tlalpam, 10 miles south of the city of Mexico, altitude 7,600 feet, Federal District, Mexico. December 5, 1892. Collected by E. W. Nelson, original number 3989.

Well-made skin in good condition; skull Grade A.

Genus MICROSOREX Coues

†Sorex (Microsorex) alnorum Preble.

North Amer. Fauna 22: 72, Oct. 31, 1902.
=*Microsorex hoyi alnorum* (Preble). See Jackson, Proc. Biol. Soc. Washington 38: 126, Nov. 13, 1925.

107014. Skin and skull. Adult female. Robinson Portage, Manitoba, Canada. June 27, 1900. Collected by Edward A. and Alfred E. Preble. Original number 2662.

Well-made skin in good condition; skull Grade A.

†Sorex (Microsorex) eximius Osgood.

North Amer. Fauna 21: 71, Sept. 26, 1901.
=*Microsorex hoyi eximius* (Osgood). See Jackson, Proc. Biol. Soc. Washington 38: 125, Nov. 13, 1925.

107126. Skin and skull. Adult female. Tyonek, Cook Inlet, Alaska. September 14, 1900. Collected by W. H. Osgood and E. Heller. Original number 1395.

Well-made skin in good condition; skull Grade A.

*Sorex hoyi Baird.   Lectotype.

Mammals of North America, p. 32, 1857.
=*Microsorex hoyi* (Baird). See Elliot, Field Columb. Mus. Publ. 45 (zool. ser. 2) : 377, March 1901.

251543—42——13

$\frac{632}{1783}$.   Skin and skull. Adult male. Racine, Racine County, Wis. Collected by P. R. Hoy. Cataloged April 19, 1855.

No type designated. Two specimens are listed by number in the original description: 1688 and $\frac{632}{1783}$. Lyon and Osgood (U. S. Nat. Mus. Bull. 62: 244, Jan. 28, 1909) regarded No. 1688, an alcoholic specimen with skull inside, as the type. Preble (Proc. Biol. Soc. Washington 23: 102, June 24, 1910) showed that 1688 is a specimen of *Sorex cinereus*. He therefore regarded the skull on which Baird based his description, No. 1783, as the type. In revising the shrews, Jackson, North Amer. Fauna 51: 203, July 24, 1928, formally designated the skin and skull No. $\frac{632}{1783}$ as lectotype.

Skin poorly made and considerably faded. Skull Grade D.

†Microsorex hoyi intervectus Jackson.

Proc. Biol. Soc. Washington 38: 125, Nov. 13, 1925.

226979.   Skin and skull. Adult female. Lakewood, Oconto County, Wis. August 17, 1917. Collected by Hartley H. T. Jackson. Original number 820.

Well-made skin in good condition; skull Grade A.

†Microsorex hoyi washingtoni Jackson.

Proc. Biol. Soc. Washington 38: 125, Nov. 13, 1925.

91007.   Skin and skull. Adult female. Loon Lake, Stevens County, Wash. September 26, 1897. Collected by Vernon Bailey. Original number 6293.

Well-made skin in good condition; skull Grade C.

*Sorex thompsoni Baird.   Lectotype.

Mammals of North America, p. 34, 1857.
=*Microsorex hoyi thompsoni* (Baird). See Jackson, Proc. Biol. Soc. Washington 38: 126, Nov. 13, 1925.

$\frac{1686}{38838}$. In alcohol, skull removed. Burlington, Chittenden County Vt. Collected by Zadock Thompson. Cataloged October 23, 1856.

Specimen in fair condition, upper part of head skin detached from body and much hair lost on the belly; skull Grade C.

No type designated. Three specimens listed: (1) the above, (2) No. 247 from Zanesville, Ohio, and (3) No. 2062 from Halifax, Nova Scotia. As No. 1686 is figured on pl. 27, it was made lectotype by Lyon and Osgood, U. S. Nat. Mus. Bull. 62: 250, Jan. 28, 1909.

†Microsorex winnemana Preble.

Proc. Biol. Soc. Washington 23: 101, June 24, 1910.
=*Microsorex hoyi winnemana* Preble. See Jackson, Proc. Biol. Soc. Washington 38: 126, Nov. 13, 1925.

126320.   Skin and skull. Adult female. Bank of Potomac River near Stubblefield Falls, 4 miles below Great Falls of the Potomac, Fairfax County, Va. April 25, 1903. Collected by Edward A. Preble. Original number 3929–X.

Well-made skin in good condition; skull Grade A.

Genus NEOMYS Kaup

*Neomys fodiens minor Miller.

Proc. Biol. Soc. Washington 14: 45, Apr. 25, 1901.
=*Neomys fodiens fodiens* (Schreber). See Miller, Catalogue of the Mammals
of Western Europe . . ., p. 70, Nov. 23, 1912.

101311. Skin and skull. Adult male. Montréjeau, Haute-Garonne,
France (in foothills of Pyrenees). July 8, 1899. Collected by
Robert T. Young. Original number 641.

Well-made skin in good condition; skull Grade A.

Genus NOTIOSOREX Coues

*Sorex (Notiosorex) crawfordi Coues.

Bull. U. S. Geol. and Geogr. Surv. Terr. 3: 646, May 15, 1877.
=*Notiosorex crawfordi* (Coues). See Merriam, North Amer. Fauna 10: 32,
Dec. 31, 1895.

$\frac{2653}{4437}$. In alcohol, skull removed. Near old Fort Bliss, about 2 miles
above El Paso, El Paso County, Tex. Collected by S. W. Craw-
ford. Alcoholic cataloged April 28, 1857; skull, September 1861.

Body in very poor condition. At some time the alcohol has been
allowed to evaporate, so that the specimen is now hard and shrunken.
Skull Grade A.

*Sorex (Notiosorex) evotis Coues.

Bull. U. S. Geol. and Geogr. Surv. Terr. 3: 652, May 15, 1877.
=*Notiosorex crawfordi evotis* (Coues). See Merriam, North Amer. Fauna 10:
34, Dec. 31, 1895.

9066. Skin (no skull). Along the Rio Mazatlan, Sinaloa, Mexico.
February 1868. Collected by Ferdinand Bischoff.

All parts of skin present but it is poorly made up; tail not skinned
out; left hindfoot and right forefoot present, but broken off from the
skin. The specimen looks as if it had originally been made up with
part of the skull in it. The skull has subsequently been removed and
lost. Coues evidently had the skull, but no mention of it is made in
the Museum catalog.

†Notiosorex gigas Merriam.

Proc. Biol. Soc. Washington 11: 227, July 15, 1897.

88012. Skin and skull. Adult female. Mountains at Milpillas,
altitude 3,800 feet, near San Sebastian, Jalisco, Mexico. March
15, 1897. Collected by E. W. Nelson and E. A. Goldman.
Original number 10706.

Well-made skin in good condition; skull Grade A.

Genus SOREX Linnaeus

†Sorex alascensis shumaginensis Merriam.

Proc. Washington Acad. Sci. 2: 18, Mar. 14, 1900.
=*Sorex obscurus shumaginensis* Merriam. See J. A. Allen, Bull. Amer.
Mus. Nat. Hist. 16: 228, July 12, 1902.

97993. Skin and skull. Adult male. Popof Island, Shumagin
Islands, Alaska. July 17, 1899. Collected by De Alton Saunders. Original number 2210 (A. K. Fisher).

Well-made skin in good condition; skull Grade A.

*Neosorex albibarbis Cope.

Proc. Acad. Nat. Sci. Philadelphia 15: 188, ordered published Apr. 29,
1862.
=*Sorex palustris albibarbis* (Cope). See Rhoads, Mammals of Pennsylvania
and New Jersey, p. 191, 1903.

$\frac{11239}{38743}$. In alcohol, skull removed. Adult female. Profile Lake,
Franconia Mountains, Grafton County, N. H. September 1859.
Collected by E. D. Cope.

Specimen in fair condition; skull Grade A.
No type designated. Cope took two specimens. The above seems to be one
of them. The entry in the original catalog reads: "*Neosorex albi . . . is*
(the omitted letters belong to a word root probably intended to mean
'cheek' instead of 'beard'), Profile Lake, N. H., type." The handwriting
is entirely different from any of the other handwritings in the catalog,
and it is certainly not Cope's.

*Sorex alpinus hercynicus Miller.

Ann. Mag. Nat. Hist. (ser. 8) 3: 417, May 1909.

112928. Skin and skull. Adult male. Mäuseklippe, Bodethal,
Harz Mountains, Germany. October 18, 1901. Collected by
F. L. J. Boettcher. Original number 265.

Well-made skin in good condition; skull Grade A.

†Sorex amoenus Merriam.

North Amer. Fauna 10: 69, Dec. 31, 1895.
=*Sorex vagrans amoenus* Merriam. See Merriam, North Amer. Fauna 16: 87,
Oct. 28, 1899.

$\frac{29784}{41863}$. Skin and skull. Adult male. Near Mammoth, altitude
about 8,000 feet, head of Owens River, east slope of the Sierra
Nevada, Mono County, Calif. July 22, 1891. Collected by
E. W. Nelson. Original number 1129.

Well-made skin in good condition; skull Grade A.

*Sorex araneus alticola Miller.

Proc. Biol. Soc. Washington 14: 43, Apr. 25, 1901.
=*Sorex araneus tetragonurus* Hermann. See Miller, Catalogue of the Mammals of Western Europe . . ., p. 42, Nov. 1912.

85930. Skin and skull. Adult male (not female as in original description). Meiringen, Switzerland. October 17, 1898. Collected by J. A. Loring. Original number 5731 (not 5781, as in original description).

Well-made skin in good condition, except small bare spot on right flank; skull Grade A.

*Sorex araneus bergensis Miller.

Ann. Mag. Nat. Hist. (ser. 8) 3 : 416, May 1909.

84664. Skin and skull. Adult female. Gravin, Hardanger, Norway. June 10, 1898. Collected by Thora Stejneger. Original number 31.

Well-made skin in good condition; skull Grade A.

*Sorex araneus euronotus Miller.

Proc. Biol. Soc. Washington 14 : 44, Apr. 25, 1901.

101321. Skin and skull. Adult male. Montréjeau, Haute-Garonne, France (in foothills of Pyrenees). July 8, 1899. Collected by Robert T. Young. Original number 642.

Well-made skin in good condition; skull Grade A.

*Sorex arcticus laricorum Jackson.

Proc. Biol. Soc. Washington 38 : 127, Nov. 13, 1925.

186837. Skin and skull. Adult male. Elk River, Sherburne County, Minn. Feb. 19, 1886. Collected by Vernon Bailey. Original number 75. Merriam collection number $\frac{2019}{2552}$.

Well-made skin in good condition; skull Grade A.

†Sorex bairdi Merriam.

North Amer. Fauna 10 : 77, Dec. 31, 1895.
=*Sorex obscurus bairdi* Merriam. See Jackson, Proc. Biol. Soc. Washington 31 : 127, Nov. 29, 1918.

$\frac{17414}{24318}$. Skin and skull. Adult female. Astoria, Clatsop County, Oreg. Aug. 2, 1889. Collected by T. S. Palmer. Original number 270.

Well-made skin in good condition; skull Grade A.

*Atophyrax bendirii Merriam.

Trans. Linn. Soc. New York 2 : 217, Aug. 28, 1884.
=*Sorex bendirii* (Merriam). See Dobson, Monograph of the Insectivora, pt. 3, fasc. 1, pl. 23, fig. 17 and explanation, 1890.

186442. Skin and skeleton. Adult male. 18 miles southeast of Fort Klamath, Klamath County, Oreg. August 1, 1882. Collected by Charles E. Bendire. Merriam collection No. $\frac{496}{1200}$.

Skin made from alcoholic specimen. In good condition, except a small patch of fur missing on abdomen. Skeleton imperfect, lacking innominate bones and all the limb bones except the humeri.

†Sorex (Atophyrax) bendirii albiventer Merriam.

North Amer. Fauna 10: 97, Dec. 31, 1895.
=*Sorex bendirii albiventer* Merriam. See Jackson, Journ. Mamm. 7: 58, Feb. 15, 1926.

66198. Skin and skull. Adult male. Lake Cushman, Mason County, Olympic Mountains, Wash. July 7, 1894. Collected by C. P. Streator. Original number 4021.

Well-made skin in good condition; skull Grade A.

†Sorex (Atophyrax) bendirii palmeri Merriam.

North Amer. Fauna 10: 97, Dec. 31, 1895.
=*Sorex bendirii palmeri* Merriam. See Jackson, Journ. Mamm. 7: 58, Feb. 15, 1926.

$\frac{17338}{24263}$. Skin and skull. Adult female. Astoria, Clatsop County, Oreg. July 29, 1889. Collected by T. S. Palmer. Original number 256.

Well-made skin in good condition; skull Grade A.

†Sorex californicus Merriam.

North Amer. Fauna 10: 80, Dec. 31, 1895.
=*Sorex ornatus californicus* Merriam. See Jackson, Journ. Washington Acad. Sci. 12: 264, June 4, 1922.

$\frac{32578}{44426}$. Skin and skull. Adult male. Walnut Creek, Contra Costa County, Calif. February 15, 1892. Collected by C. P. Streator. Original number 1583.

Well-made skin in good condition; skull Grade A.

†Sorex californicus juncensis Nelson and Goldman.

Proc. Biol. Soc. Washington 22: 27, Mar. 10, 1909.
=*Sorex juncensis* Nelson and Goldman. See Jackson, North Amer. Fauna 51: 172, July 24, 1928.

139594. Skin and skull. Young adult (female?). Socorro, 15 miles south of San Quintin, Lower California, Mexico. September 1, 1905. Collected by E. W. Nelson and E. A. Goldman. Original number 17916.

Well-made skin in good condition, except for small patch of skin missing on right side of body; skull Grade A.

†Sorex dobsoni Merriam.

North Amer. Fauna 5: 33, July 30, 1891.
=*Sorex vagrans monticola* Merriam. See Jackson, North Amer. Fauna 51: 110, July 24, 1928.

$\frac{24274}{31678}$. Skin and skull. Adult female. Sawtooth (also called Alturas) Lake, east base of Sawtooth Mountains, altitude about 7,200 feet, Blaine County, Idaho. October 3, 1890. Collected by C. Hart Merriam and Vernon Bailey. Original number 1929.

Well-made skin in good condition; skull Grade C.

†Sorex durangae Jackson.

Proc. Biol. Soc. Washington 38: 127, Nov. 13, 1925.

94540. Skin and skull. Adult male. El Salto, Durango, Mexico. July 19, 1898. Collected by E. W. Nelson and E. A. Goldman. Original number 12774.

Well-made skin in good condition; skull Grade A.

†Sorex emarginatus Jackson.

Proc. Biol. Soc. Washington 38: 129, Nov. 13, 1925.

90847. Skin and skull. Young adult female. Sierra Madre near Bolaños, altitude 7,600 feet, Jalisco, Mexico. September 17, 1897. Collected by E. W. Nelson and E. A. Goldman. Original number 11765.

Well-made skin in good condition; skull Grade A.

*Sorex fimbripes Bachman.

Journ. Acad. Nat. Sci. Philadelphia 7 (pt. 2): 391, 1837.
=Sorex cinereus cinereus Kerr. See Jackson, North Amer. Fauna 51: 40, July 24, 1928.

84556. In alcohol, skull removed. "Was found [by Walter R. Johnson] on the high table-land on a branch of Drury's Run [Pennsylvania], a tributary of the west bank of the Susquehanna River" (Bachman, 1837: 394).

Condition of the specimen poor; most of the hair on the posterior half of body lacking; skull Grade A.

Found in the collection in the early part of 1898 in a bottle with an old-style Museum label, without number, tied around the top, bearing the inscription "Sorex fimbripes (type)." Tied to the specimen itself is an old parchment label that originally bore the words "Sorex fimbripes. Type." The writing was perfectly legible, but very faint, when examined by Lyon and Osgood in 1908. In 1936 only the word "type" remained legible. The parchment has to be dried in order to read it. On April 29, 1898, this specimen was entered in the Museum catalog and given its present number, 84556. No original data accompany the specimen. The hand writing on the old Museum label and on the parchment tag is unidentifiable; both labels were obviously written many years before 1898.

†Sorex fisheri Merriam.

North Amer. Fauna 10: 86, Dec. 31, 1895.
=Sorex longirostris fisheri Merriam. See Jackson, North Amer. Fauna 51: 87, July 24, 1928.

75166. Skin and skull. Adult male. Lake Drummond, Dismal Swamp, Va. October 11, 1895. Collected by A. K. Fisher. Original number 1800.

Well-made skin in good condition; skull Grade B.

*Sorex fontinalis Hollister.

Proc. U. S. Nat. Mus. 40: 378, Apr. 17, 1911.

85439. Skin and skull. Adult female. Cold Spring Swamp, near Beltsville, Prince Georges County, Md. November 6, 1898. Collected by G. S. Miller, Jr.

Well-made skin in good condition, right foreleg detached from body; skull Grade A.

†Sorex fumeus umbrosus Jackson.

Proc. Biol. Soc. Washington 30: 149, July 27, 1917.

150065. Skin and skull. Adult male. James River, Antigonish County, Nova Scotia. July 29, 1907. Collected by W. H. Osgood. Original number 3140.

Well-made skin in good condition, except for small patch of abdominal hairs missing; skull Grade A.

†Sorex glacialis Merriam.

Proc. Washington Acad. Sci. 2: 16, Mar. 14, 1900.
=*Sorex obscurus alascensis* Merriam. See Jackson, North Amer. Fauna 51: 126, July 24, 1928.

97709. Skin and skull. Adult male. Point Gustavus, east side of entrance to Glacier Bay, Alaska. June 12, 1899. Collected by A. K. Fisher. Original number 2056.

Well-made skin in good condition; skull Grade A.

†Sorex godmani Merriam.

Proc. Biol. Soc. Washington 11: 229, July 15, 1897.
=*Sorex saussurei godmani* Merriam. See Jackson, North Amer. Fauna 51: 158, July 24, 1928.

77044. Skin and skull. Adult female. Volcan Santa Maria, altitude 9,000 feet, Quezaltenango, Guatemala. January 28, 1896. Collected by E. W. Nelson and E. A. Goldman. Original number 9239.

Well-made skin in good condition; skull Grade A.

*Sorex haydeni Baird.   Lectotype.

Mammals of North America, p. 29, 1857.
=*Sorex cinereus haydeni* Baird. See Jackson, Journ. Mamm. 6: 56, Feb. 9, 1925.

1685. In alcohol, skull not removed. Fort Union, Nebraska Territory, now Mondak, Mont., near Buford, Williams County, N. Dak. 1856. Collected by F. V. Hayden.

Specimen in fair condition; lips loosened and left cheek cut in order to expose all the teeth.

No type designated. Baird mentioned three specimens, Nos. 1684 and 1685, from Fort Union, and No. 2048 from Fort Pierre, Nebr. Lyon and Osgood, U. S. Nat. Mus. Bull. 62: 244, Jan. 28, 1909, made No. 1685 the lectotype because it was figured on Baird's plate 27.

†Sorex idahoensis Merriam.

North Amer. Fauna 5: 32, July 30, 1891.
=*Sorex cinereus cinereus* Kerr. See Jackson, North Amer. Fauna 51: 41, July 24, 1928.

$\frac{23527}{30945}$. Skin and skull. Adult female. Timber Creek, altitude 8,200 feet, Salmon River Mountains [now Lemhi Mountains], Idaho. August 26, 1890. Collected by C. Hart Merriam and Vernon Bailey. Original number 1674.

Well-made skin in good condition; skull Grade A.

†Sorex lagunae Nelson and Goldman.

Proc. Biol. Soc. Washington 22: 27, Mar. 10, 1909.
=*Sorex ornatus lagunae* Nelson and Goldman. See Jackson, North Amer. Fauna 51: 169, July 24, 1928.

147119. Skin and skull. Adult female. La Laguna, altitude 5,500 feet, Sierra Laguna, Lower California, Mexico. January 29, 1906. Collected by E. W. Nelson and E. A. Goldman. Original number 19036.

Well-made skin in good condition; skull Grade B.

†Sorex leucogenys Osgood.

Proc. Biol. Soc. Washington 22: 52, Apr. 17, 1909.
157952. Skin and skull. Adult female. Mouth of the canyon of Beaver River, about 3 miles east of Beaver, Beaver County, Utah. August 12, 1908. Collected by W. H. Osgood. Original number 3318.

Well-made skin in good condition; skull Grade A.

†Sorex longicauda elassodon Osgood.

North Amer. Fauna 21: 35, Sept. 26, 1901.
=*Sorex obscurus elassodon* Osgood. See Elliot, Field Columb. Mus. Publ. 105 (zool. ser. 6): 450, 1905.

100597. Skin and skull. Adult male. Cumshewa Inlet, near old Indian village of Clew, Moresby Island, Queen Charlotte Islands, British Columbia, Canada. June 13, 1900. Collected by W. H. Osgood and E. Heller. Original number 1030.

Well-made skin in good condition; skull Grade A.

†**Sorex longicauda prevostensis** Osgood.

North Amer. Fauna 21 : 35, Sept. 26, 1901.

100618. Skin and skull. Adult male. North end of Prevost Island, on coast of Houston Stewart Channel, Queen Charlotte Islands, British Columbia, Canada. July 3, 1900. Collected by W. H. Osgood and E. Heller. Original number 1089.

Well-made skin in good condition ; skull Grade A.

†**Sorex macrodon** Merriam.

North Amer. Fauna 10 : 82, Dec. 31, 1895.

58272. Skin and skull. Adult male. Orizaba, altitude 4,200 feet, Veracruz, Mexico. January 26, 1894. Collected by E. W. Nelson and E. A. Goldman. Original number 5759.

Well-made skin in good condition ; skull Grade A.

***Sorex macropygmaeus** Miller.

Proc. Biol. Soc. Washington 14 : 158, Aug. 9, 1901.

84012. Skin and skull. Adult male. Petropaulski, Kamchatka, Siberia. September 23, 1897. Collected by Mrs. Leonhard Stejneger. Original number 8019 (L. Stejneger).

Fairly well-made skin, much contracted posteriorly ; skull Grade A.

***Sorex merriami** Dobson.

Monograph of the Insectivora, pt. 3, fasc. 1, pl. 23, fig. 6, May 1890.

186441. In alcohol, skull removed. Adult female. Fort Custer, Bighorn County, Montana. December 26, 1884. Collected by Charles E. Bendire. Merriam collection number $\frac{1001}{4861}$.

Specimen in good condition ; skull Grade A.

†**Sorex montereyensis** Merriam.

North Amer. Fauna 10 : 79, Dec. 31, 1895.
=*Sorex trowbridgii montereyensis* Merriam. See Jackson, Journ. Washington Acad. Sci. 12 : 264, June 4, 1922.

$\frac{32000}{44810}$. Skin and skull. Adult male. Monterey, Monterey County, Calif. October 1, 1891. Collected by Vernon Bailey. Original number 3336.

Well-made skin in good condition ; skull Grade A.

†**Sorex monticolus** Merriam.

North Amer. Fauna 3 : 43, Sept. 11, 1890.
=*Sorex vagrans monticola* Merriam. See Merriam, North Amer. Fauna 10 : 69, Dec. 31, 1895.

$\frac{17599}{24535}$. Skin and skull. Adult male. San Francisco Mountain, altitude 11,500 feet, Coconino County, Ariz. August 28, 1889. Collected by C. Hart Merriam and Vernon Bailey. Original number 406.

Well-made skin in good condition; skull Grade B.

*Neosorex navigator Baird.

Mammals of North America, p. 11, 1857.
=*Sorex palustris navigator* (Baird). See Merriam, North Amer. Fauna 10: 92, Dec. 31, 1895.

$\frac{629}{1780}$. Skin and skull. Near head of Yakima River, Cascade Mountains, Wash. About August 31, 1853. Collected by J. G. Cooper. Skin in bad condition, almost broken in two in the middle, anterior portion alone showing the hair, left hind leg detached, tail intact but with vertebrae not skinned out; skull Grade A.

Baird designated his single specimen by number.

†Sorex navigator alaskanus Merriam.

Proc. Washington Acad. Sci. 2: 18, Mar. 14, 1900.
=*Sorex alaskanus* Merriam. See Jackson, Journ. Mamm. 7 (1): 58, Feb. 15, 1926.

97713. Skin and skull. Adult male. Point Gustavus, Glacier Bay, Alaska. June 12, 1899. Collected by A. K. Fisher. Original number 2058.

Well-made skin in good condition; skull Grade A.

†Sorex nevadensis Merriam.

North Amer. Fauna 10: 71, Dec. 31, 1895.
=*Sorex vagrans nevadensis* Merriam. See Jackson, North Amer. Fauna 51: 107, July 24, 1928.

$\frac{24891}{32302}$. Skin and skull. Adult male. Reese River at about 6,000 feet at line between Lander and Nye Counties, Nev. November 20, 1890 (not November 24, 1890, as in original description). Collected by Vernon Bailey. Original number 2150.

Well-made skin in good condition; skull Grade A.

Sorex obscurus Merriam.

See *Sorex vagrans similis* Merriam.

†Sorex obscurus alascensis Merriam.

North Amer. Fauna 10: 76, Dec. 31, 1895.
73539. Skin and skull. Adult female. Yakutat, Alaska. July 10, 1895. Collected by C. P. Streator. Original number 4676.
Well-made skin in good condition; skull Grade A.

†**Sorex obscurus isolatus** Jackson.

Journ. Washington Acad. Sci. 12 : 263, June 4, 1922.

177719. Skin and skull. Adult male. Mouth of Millstone Creek, Nanaimo, Vancouver Island, British Columbia, Canada. May 21, 1911. Collected by Alexander Wetmore. Original number 517.

Well-made skin in good condition; skull Grade A.

†**Sorex obscurus longicauda** Merriam.

North Amer. Fauna 10 : 74, Dec. 31, 1895.

74711. Skin and skull. Adult male. Wrangel, Alaska. September 9, 1895. Collected by C. P. Streator. Original number 4891.

Well-made skin in good condition; skull Grade A.

†**Sorex obscurus neomexicanus** Bailey.

Proc. Biol. Soc. Washington 26 : 133, May 21, 1913.

100440. Skin and skull. Old adult male. Cloudcroft, altitude 9,000 feet in the Sacramento Mountains, Otero County, N. Mex. May 29, 1900. Collected by Vernon Bailey. Original number 7383.

Well-made skin in good condition; skull Grade A.

†**Sorex obscurus parvidens** Jackson.

Journ. Mamm. 2 (3) : 161, Aug. 19, 1921.

56561. Skin and skull. Adult male. Spring known as Thurmans Camp, Bluff Lake, altitude about 7,500 feet, San Bernardino Mountains, San Bernardino County, Calif. October 3, 1893. Collected by J. E. McLellan. Original number 242.

Well-made skin in good condition; skull Grade A.

†**Sorex obscurus permiliensis** Jackson.

Proc. Biol. Soc. Washington 31 : 128, Nov. 29, 1918.

91048. Skin and skull. Adult male. Permilia Lake, west base of Mount Jefferson, Cascade Range, Marion County, Oreg. October 2, 1897. Collected by J. A. Loring. Original number 4756.

Well-made skin in good condition; skull Grade A.

†**Sorex obscurus ventralis** Merriam.

North Amer. Fauna 10 : 75, Dec. 31, 1895.

=*Sorex ventralis* Merriam. See Elliot, Field Columb. Mus. Publ. 71 (zool. ser. 3) : 148, 1903.

68341. Skin and skull. Adult male. Cerro San Felipe, altitude 10,000 feet, Oaxaca, Mexico. August 26, 1894. Collected by E. W. Nelson and E. A. Goldman. Original number 6636.

Well-made skin in good condition; skull Grade B.

†Sorex oreopolus Merriam.

Proc. Biol. Soc. Washington 7 : 173, Sept. 29, 1892.

$\frac{33663}{45698}$. Skin and skull. Adult male. North slope of Sierra Nevada de Colima, altitude about 10,000 feet, Jalisco, Mexico. April 22, 1892. Collected by E. W. Nelson. Original number 2517.

Well-made skin in good condition ; skull Grade A.

†Sorex orizabae Merriam.

North Amer. Fauna 10 : 71, Dec. 31, 1895.

=*Sorex vagrans orizabae* Merriam. See Jackson, North Amer. Fauna 51 : 113, July 24, 1928.

53633. Skin and skull. Adult female. Mount Orizaba, altitude 9,500 feet on west slope, Puebla, Mexico. April 24, 1893. Collected by E. W. Nelson. Original number 4733.

Well-made skin in good condition ; skull Grade C.

†Sorex ornatus Merriam.

North Amer. Fauna 10 : 79, Dec. 31, 1895.

$\frac{31333}{43198}$. Skin and skull. Adult male. Head of San Emigdio Canyon, Mount Pinos, Kern County, Calif. October 19, 1891. Collected by E. W. Nelson. Original number 1328.

Well-made skin in good condition ; skull Grade C.

*Sorex pachyurus Baird. Lectotype.

Mammals of North America, p. 20, 1857. (Not of Küster, 1835).

=*Sorex arcticus laricorum* Jackson. See Jackson, North Amer. Fauna 51 : 71, July 24, 1928.

$\frac{1674}{38820}$. Skeleton, formerly in alcohol. Pembina, Pembina County, N. Dak. (not Minn. as stated by Baird). Collected by Charles Cavileer. Cataloged October 23, 1856.

Skeleton in fair condition ; all parts of it seem to be present.

No type designated by Baird, who mentioned three specimens, the above in alcohol at that time, and two skins, 626 from Pembina, and 638 from Ripley, Minn. As No. 1674 was figured by Baird (pl. 27), it was made the lectotype by Lyon and Osgood, U. S. Nat. Mus. Bull. 62 : 247, Jan. 28, 1909.

*Sorex pacificus Coues.

Bull. U. S. Geol. and Geogr. Surv. Terr. 3 : 650, May 15, 1877.

3266. Skin with fragment of skull inside. Fort Umpqua, mouth of Umpqua River, Douglas County, Oreg. Received from E. P. Vollum. Cataloged in March, 1858.

Skin in poor condition ; torn about the mouth so as to expose what teeth are present, the unicuspids only ; no filling ; tail not skinned out ; hair everywhere intact.

†**Sorex palustris hydrobadistes** Jackson.

Journ. Mamm. 7 : 57, Feb. 15, 1926.

229061. Skin and skull. Adult male, Withee, Clark County, Wis. July 23, 1918. Collected by Hartley H. T. Jackson. Original number 1211.

Well-made skin in good condition ; skull Grade A.

†**Sorex personatus arcticus** Merriam.

Proc. Washington Acad. Sci. 2 : 17, Mar. 14, 1900. (Not *Sorex arcticus* Kerr, 1792.)

=*Sorex cinereus hollisteri* Jackson. See Jackson, Journ. Mamm. 6 : 55, Feb. 9, 1925.

99305. Skin and skull. Adult female. St. Michael, Alaska. September 14, 1899. Collected by W. H. Osgood. Original number 910.

Well-made skin in good condition ; skull Grade A.

†**Sorex personatus streatori** Merriam.

North Amer. Fauna 10 : 62, Dec. 31, 1895.

=*Sorex cinereus streatori* Merriam. See Jackson, Journ. Mamm. 6 (1) : 56, Feb. 9, 1925.

73537. Skin and skull. Adult male. Yakutat, Alaska. July 9, 1895. Collected by C. P. Streator. Original number 4674.

Well-made skin in good condition ; skull Grade A.

*****Sorex planiceps** Miller.

Proc. Biol. Soc. Washington 24 : 242, Nov. 28, 1911.

173915. Skin and skull. Adult male. Dachin, altitude 9,000 feet, Khistwar, Kashmir, India. May 30, 1911. Collected by W. L. Abbott. Original number 7714.

Well-made skin in good condition ; skull Grade A.

†**Sorex preblei** Jackson.

Journ. Washington Acad. Sci. 12 : 263, June 4, 1922.

208032. Skin and skull. Adult male. Jordan Valley, altitude 4,200 feet, Malheur County, Oreg. July 3, 1915. Collected by Edward A. Preble. Original number 5972.

Well-made skin in good condition ; skull Grade A.

†**Sorex pribilofensis** Merriam.

North Amer. Fauna 10 : 87, Dec. 31, 1895.

30911. In alcohol. Adult female. St. Paul Island, Pribilof Islands, Alaska. July 29, 1891. Collected by C. Hart Merriam.

Specimen in good condition ; skull not removed, apparently slightly fractured.

*Sorex roboratus Hollister.

Smithsonian Misc. Coll. 60 (24) : 2, Mar. 13, 1913.

175436. Skin and skull. Adult male. Tapucha, Altai Mountains, Siberia. August 7, 1912. Collected by N. Hollister. Original number 4451.

Well-made skin in good condition; skull Grade B.

†Sorex salvini Merriam.

Proc. Biol. Soc. Washington 11 : 229, July 15, 1897.
=*Sorex saussurei salvini* Merriam. See Jackson, North Amer. Fauna 51: 159, July 24, 1928.

77035. Skin and skull. Adult female. Calel, altitude 10,200 feet, Tontonicapan, Guatemala. January 12, 1896. Collected by E. W. Nelson and E. A. Goldman. Original number 9057.

Well-made skin in good condition; skull Grade A.

†Sorex saussurei Merriam.

Proc. Biol. Soc. Washington 7 : 173, Sept. 29, 1892.

$\frac{33667}{45702}$. Skin and skull. Adult female. North slope of Sierra Nevada de Colima, altitude about 8,000 feet, Jalisco, Mexico. April 23, 1892. Collected by E. W. Nelson. Original number 2538.

Well-made skin in good condition, except for absence of right front foot; skull Grade A.

†Sorex saussurei caudatus Merriam.

North Amer. Fauna 10 : 84, Dec. 31, 1895. (Not *Sorex caudatus* Hodgson, 1849, or Horsfield, 1851.)
=*Sorex veraepacis mutabilis* Merriam. See Jackson, Proc. Biol. Soc. Washington 38 : 130, Nov. 13, 1925.

69600. Skin and skull. Young adult female. Reyes (near Cuicatlan), altitude 10,200 feet, Oaxaca, Mexico. October 21, 1894. Collected by E. W. Nelson and E. A. Goldman. Original number 6963.

Well-made skin in good condition; skull Grade A.

†Sorex saussurei cristobalensis Jackson.

Proc. Biol. Soc. Washington 38 : 129, Nov. 13, 1925.

75883. Skin and skull. Adult female. San Cristobal, altitude 8,400 feet, Chiapas, Mexico. September 19, 1895. Collected by E. W. Nelson and E. A. Goldman. Original number 8429.

Well-made skin in good condition; skull Grade A.

†Sorex saussurei oaxacae Jackson.

Proc. Biol. Soc. Washington 38 : 128, Nov. 13, 1925.

71467. Skin and skull. Adult female. Mountains near Ozolotepec, altitude 10,000 feet, Oaxaca, Mexico. March 27, 1895. Collected by E. W. Nelson and E. A. Goldman. Original number 7748.

Well-made skin in good condition; skull Grade B.

†Sorex saussurei veraecrucis Jackson.

Proc. Biol. Soc. Washington 38 : 128, Nov. 13, 1925.

55106. Skin and skull. Adult female. Xico, altitude 6,000 feet, Veracruz, Mexico. July 14, 1893. Collected by E. W. Nelson. Original number 5235.

Well-made skin in good condition; skull Grade A.

†Sorex sclateri Merriam.

Proc. Biol. Soc. Washington 11 : 228, July 15, 1897.

75872. Skin and skull. Adult female. Tumbala, altitude 5,000 feet, Chiapas, Mexico. October 23, 1895. Collected by E. W. Nelson and E. A. Goldman. Original number 8567.

Well-made skin in good condition; skull Grade A.

†Sorex shastensis Merriam.

North Amer. Fauna 16 : 87, Oct. 28, 1899.
=Sorex vagrans amoenus Merriam. See Merriam, North Amer. Fauna 16 : 87, Oct. 28, 1899.

95450. Skin and skull. Adult. Wagon camp, Mount Shasta, altitude 5,700 feet, Siskiyou County, Calif. September 26, 1898. Collected by W. H. Osgood. Original number 317.

Well-made skin, tail complete but detached at base; skull Grade B.

Sorex similis Merriam.

See *Sorex vagrans similis* Merriam.

*Sorex sphagnicola Coues.

Bull. U. S. Geol. and Geogr. Surv. Terr. 3 : 650, May 15, 1877.
=Sorex arcticus arcticus Kerr. See Jackson, North Amer. Fauna 51 : 69, July 24, 1928.

6361. Skin (no skull). Vicinity of Fort Liard, southwestern Mackenzie, Canada. Collected by W. L. Hardisty. Cataloged in April 1863.

Specimen in very poor condition; skin without filling and completely torn in two at the middle; both front feet missing; tail and hind feet present.

†Sorex stizodon Merriam.

North Amer. Fauna 10 : 98, Dec. 31, 1895.

75885. Skin and skull. Adult female. San Cristobal, altitude 9,000 feet, Chiapas, Mexico. September 25, 1895. Collected by E. W. Nelson and E. A. Goldman. Original number 8473.

Well-made skin in good condition except right front foot missing; skull Grade A.

*Sorex suckleyi Baird.   Lectotype.

Mammals of North America, p. 18, 1857.

=*Sorex vagrans vagrans* Baird. See Merriam, North Amer. Fauna 10: 67, Dec. 31, 1895.

1677. In alcohol. Fort Steilacoom, Pierce County, Wash., 1856. Collected by George Suckley. Northern Pacific R. R. Survey.

Specimen is in fair condition; some hair has fallen from the back. The skull has not been removed (and the skull of a paratype is the one probably figured), but the lips have been cut loose and the head skinned out so that all the teeth may be seen.

Baird had seven specimens from four different localities. The description is based upon Nos. 362 and 1677, the second of which was made lectotype by Lyon and Osgood, U. S. Nat. Mus. Bull. 62: 250, Jan. 28, 1909, because it is figured on Baird's plate 27.

†Sorex tenellus Merriam.

North Amer. Fauna 10: 81, Dec. 31, 1895.

$\frac{25083}{32495}$. Skin and skull. Adult, sex undetermined. Along Lone Pine Creek, at upper edge of Alabama Hills at about 5,000 feet, near Lone Pine, Owens Valley, Inyo County, Calif. December 22, 1890. Collected by E. W. Nelson. Original number 131.

Well-made skin in good condition; skull Grade C.

†Sorex tenellus lyelli Merriam.

Proc. Biol. Soc. Washington 15: 75, Mar. 22, 1902.

=*Sorex lyelli* Merriam. See Jackson, North Amer. Fauna 51: 57, July 24, 1928.

109530. Skin and skull. Young adult male. Mount Lyell, Tuolumne County, Calif. August 29, 1901. Collected by W. K. Fisher. Original number 2275.

Well-made skin in good condition; skull Grade A.

†Sorex tenellus myops Merriam.

Proc. Biol. Soc. Washington 15: 76, Mar. 22, 1902.

=*Sorex myops* Merriam. See Jackson, North Amer. Fauna 51: 173, July 24, 1928.

$\frac{29559}{41634}$. Skin and skull. Adult female. Pipers Creek (Cottonwood Creek), near main peak of White Mountain, altitude 9,500 feet, Mono County, Calif. July 13, 1891. Collected by E. W. Nelson. Original number 1101.

Well-made skin; tail complete, but detached at base; skull Grade A.

251543—42——14

†Sorex tenellus nanus Merriam.

North Amer. Fauna 10: 81, Dec. 31, 1895.
=*Sorex nanus* Merriam. See Jackson, North Amer. Fauna 51: 174, July 24, 1928.

73773. Skin and skull. Young adult female. Estes Park, Larimer County, Colo. August 3, 1895. Collected by Edward A. Preble. Original number 567.

Well-made skin in good condition; skull Grade C.

†Sorex trigonirostris Jackson.

Journ. Washington Acad. Sci. 12: 264, June 4, 1922.

203608. Skin and skull. Adult female. Ashland, altitude 1,975 feet, Jackson County, Oreg. May 5, 1914. Collected by Luther J. Goldman. Original number 1308.

Well-made skin in good condition; skull Grade A.

*Sorex trowbridgii Baird.   Lectotype.

Mammals of North America, p. 13, 1857.

$\frac{813}{3088}$. Skin and skull. Astoria, mouth of Columbia River, Clatsop County, Oreg. Collected by James Wayne. Received from W. P. Trowbridge. Skin cataloged July 1855, skull January 1857.

All parts of the skin are present, but it is poorly made up and not in good condition. The skull is badly cleaned and more or less broken about the cranium, and the right half of the mandible is missing.

Baird lists four specimens by number, two from Oregon and two from Steilacoom, Wash. From his remarks on page 15 it is clear that the Oregon specimens form the basis of his description. On plate 26 one of the Oregon specimens is figured (see explanation of plates, p. 742). As No. $\frac{813}{3088}$ consists of both skin and skull, as figured, it is here made the lectotype.

†Sorex trowbridgii humboldtensis Jackson.

Journ. Washington Acad. Sci. 12: 264, June 4, 1922.

97271. Skin and skull. Adult male. Carsons Camp, Mad River, Humboldt Bay, Humboldt County, Calif. June 11, 1899. Collected by Walter K. Fisher. Original number 914.

Well-made skin in good condition; skull Grade A.

†Sorex tundrensis Merriam.

Proc. Washington Acad. Sci. 2: 16, Mar. 14, 1900.

99286. Skin and skull. Adult male. St. Michael, Alaska. September 13, 1899. Collected by W. H. Osgood. Original number 902.

Well-made skin in good condition; skull Grade A.

*Sorex vagrans Baird. Lectotype.

Mammals of North America, p. 15, 1857.

1675. In alcohol. Adult male. Shoalwater Bay, Pacific County, Wash. Received from J. G. Cooper. Cataloged October 23, 1856.

Specimen entirely devoid of hair, otherwise its preservation is good. The skull has not been removed (the skull of a paratype is therefore probably the one that Baird figured), but the lips have been loosened in order to expose the teeth.

No type designated. Baird had seven specimens from four different localities. Specimen 1675 having been figured on Baird's plate 26, Lyon and Osgood, U. S. Nat. Mus. Bull. 62: 251, Jan. 28, 1909, made it the lectotype.

†Sorex vagrans similis Merriam.

North Amer. Fauna 5: 34, July 30, 1891. (Not *Sorex similis* Hensel, 1855.)
=*Sorex obscurus* Merriam. See Merriam, North Amer. Fauna 10: 72, Dec. 31, 1895.

$\frac{23525}{30943}$. Skin and skull. Adult female. Near Timber Creek, altitude 8,200 feet, Salmon River Mountains (now Lemhi Mountains), 10 miles west of Junction, Lemhi County, Idaho. August 26, 1890. Collected by Vernon Bailey and B. H. Dutcher. Original number 1670.

Well-made skin in good condition; skull Grade B.

†Sorex vancouverensis Merriam.

North Amer. Fauna 10: 70, Dec. 31, 1895.
=*Sorex vagrans vancouverensis* Merriam. See Jackson, North Amer. Fauna 51: 106, July 24, 1928.

71913. Skin and skull. Adult male. Goldstream, Vancouver Island, British Columbia, Canada. May 10, 1895. Collected by C. P. Streator. Original number 4592.

Well-made skin in good condition; skull Grade A.

†Sorex veraepacis chiapensis Jackson.

Proc. Biol. Soc. Washington 38: 129, Nov. 13, 1925.

75877. Skin and skull. Adult female. San Cristobal, altitude 9,500 feet, Chiapas, Mexico. October 1, 1895. Collected by E. W. Nelson and E. A. Goldman. Original number 8528.

Well-made skin; skull Grade A.

†Sorex yaquinae Jackson.

Proc. Biol. Soc. Washington 31: 127, Nov. 29, 1918.

73051. Skin and skull. Adult female. Yaquina Bay, Lincoln County, Oreg. July 18, 1895. Collected by B. J. Bretherton. Original number 2031.

Well-made skin in good condition; skull Grade A.

Genus SUNCUS Ehrenberg

*Pachyura lixa aequatoria Heller.

Smithsonian Misc. Coll. 60 (12) : 4, Nov. 4, 1912.

=*Suncus lixus aequatorius* (Heller). See Cabrera, Genera Mammalium, Insectivora, Galeopithecia, p. 146, 1925.

181814. Skin and skull. Adult male. Mount Sagalla, Taita Hills, British East Africa [=Kenya]. November 19, 1911. Collected by Edmund Heller. Original number 4815.

Well-made skin in good condition; skull Grade B.

*Pachyura occultidens Hollister.

Proc. U. S. Nat. Mus. 46: 303, Dec. 31, 1913.

=*Suncus occultidens* (Hollister). See Cabrera, Genera Mammalium, Insectivora, Galeopithecia, p. 146, 1925.

175761. In alcohol (skull removed). Young adult male. Ilo-ilo Panay Island, Philippine Islands. August 1912. Collected by Carroll Fox.

Well preserved and in good condition; skull Grade A.

Genus SURDISOREX Thomas

*Surdisorex polulus Hollister.

Smithsonian Misc. Coll. 66 (1) : 1, Feb. 10, 1916.

163992. Skin and skull. Adult male. West side Mount Kenia, altitude 10,700 feet, British East Africa [=Kenya]. September 30, 1909. Collected by J. Alden Loring. Original number 7562.

Well-made skin in good condition; skull Grade A.

Genus SYLVISOREX Thomas

*Sylvisorex gemmeus Heller.

Smithsonian Misc. Coll. 56 (15) : 7, Dec. 23, 1910.

164644. Skin and skull. Adult male. Rhino Camp, Lado Enclave, Uganda, Africa. January 14, 1910. Collected by J. Alden Loring. Original number 8730.

Well-made skin in good condition; skull Grade A.

Family TALPIDAE: Moles

Genus DYMECODON True

*Dymecodon pilirostris True.

Proc. U. S. Nat. Mus. 9: 97, Sept. 25, 1886.

$\frac{15291}{22139}$. Alcoholic (skull removed). Immature male. Mouth of Yeddo Bay, Yenosima, Japan. Collected by E. S. Morse. Received from the Boston Society of Natural History February 19, 1878.

The body is in rather bad condition. Considerable hair has slipped from the belly. It has been split open from the chin nearly to the anus, to permit the removal of the skull and shoulder girdle; skull Grade C.

The single specimen is referred to by number in the original description.

Genus EUROSCAPTOR Miller

*Talpa parvidens Miller.

Journ. Mamm. 21: 203, May 15, 1940.

=*Euroscaptor parvidens* (Miller). See Miller, Journ. Mamm. 21: 444, Nov. 15, 1940.

258342. Alcoholic, skull removed. Male. In forest at the agricultural station of Blao, "Délégation de Djynrinh," near the upper Donai River, Annam, French Indo-China. June 13, 1933. Collected by E. Poilane.

Alcoholic in fair condition, except nearly all hair sloughed off abdominal region and posterior underparts; skull Grade A.

*Euroscaptor grandis Miller.

Journ. Mamm. 21: 444, Nov. 15, 1940.

255370. Skin and skull. Adult female. Mount Omei, altitude 5,000 feet, Szechwan, China. January 1930. Collected by David C. Graham. Original number 370.

Well-made skin, except that forelegs are partially detached; skull Grade B.

Genus NEÜROTRICHUS Günther

*Urotrichus gibbsii Baird.

Mammals of North America, p. 76, 1857.

=*Nëurotrichus* [sic] *gibbsii* (Baird). See Günther, Proc. Zool. Soc. London, 1880; pl. 42, June 1, 1880.

$\frac{662}{1843}$. Skin and skull. Immature. White River Pass, north of Mount Rainier, Pierce County, Wash. July 15, 1854. Collected by George Gibbs. Original number 15. Received from George Suckley.

Skin in rather poor condition, badly made, and left forefoot detached. Skull Grade C.

Baird had only one specimen, which he designated by number.

†Neürotrichus gibbsi major Merriam.

North Amer. Fauna 16: 88, Oct. 28, 1899.

=*Nëurotrichus gibbsii gibbsii* Baird. See Miller, U. S. Nat. Mus. Bull. 128: 16, April 29, 1924.

65321. Skin and skull. Adult male. Carberry ranch, between Mount Shasta and Mount Lassen, altitude 4,100 feet, Shasta County, Calif. May 18, 1894. Collected by C. P. Streator. Original number 3789.

Well-made skin in good condition; skull Grade A.

Genus SCALOPUS Geoffroy

†Scalopus aquaticus caryi Jackson.

Proc. Biol. Soc. Washington 27: 20, Feb. 2, 1914.

116799. Skin and skull. Young adult male. Neligh, Antelope County, Nebr. September 18, 1901. Collected by Merritt Cary. Original number 3640–X (307).

Well-made skin in good condition; skull Grade A.

†Scalopus aquaticus howelli Jackson.

Proc. Biol. Soc. Washington 27: 19, Feb. 2, 1914.

177931. Skin and skull. Adult male. Autaugaville, Autauga County, Ala. January 4, 1912. Collected by L. S. Golsan. Original number 8877–X.

Well-made skin in good condition, except that tip of tail and a small patch of fur on abdominal region are missing; skull Grade A.

†Scalopus aquaticus machrinoides Jackson.

Proc. Biol. Soc. Washington 27: 19, Feb. 2, 1914.

169717. Skin and skull. Adult male. Manhattan, Riley County, Kans. June 1, 1910. Collected by W. E. Berg. Original number 8139–X.

Well-made skin in good condition; skull Grade B.

†Scalopus aquaticus pulcher Jackson.

Proc. Biol. Soc. Washington 27: 20, Feb. 2, 1914.

170698. Skin and skull. Adult male. Delight, Pike County, Ark. January 20, 1911. Collected by W. G. Savage. Original number 8316–X.

Well-made skin in good condition; skull Grade A.

†Scalopus inflatus Jackson.

Proc. Biol. Soc. Washington 27: 21, Feb. 2, 1914.

52709. Skin and skull. Young adult. Tamaulipas, Mexico, 45 miles from Brownsville, Tex. 1892. Collected by Frank Armstrong. Original number 1.

Well-made skin, pelage ragged and right hind claws missing; skull Grade B.

Genus SCAPANUS Pomel

*Scalops aeneus Cassin.

Proc. Acad. Nat. Sci. Philadelphia 6: 299, reported favorably for publication Feb. 22, 1853.

=Scapanus townsendii (Bachman). See True, Proc. U. S. Nat. Mus. 19: 51, Dec. 21, 1896.

3725. Skin (no skull). Oregon. Collected by the U. S. Exploring Expedition. Cataloged December 20, 1859.

In good state of preservation but rather badly made up. The specimen has every appearance of having been discolored by immersion in some preserving fluid.

The original description says, "A single specimen, apparently fully adult, is in the collection of the Exploring Expedition, labeled as having been obtained in Oregon." No. 3725 is undoubtedly this "single specimen."

†Scapanus alpinus Merriam.

Proc. Biol. Soc. Washington 11 : 102, Apr. 26, 1897.
=*Scapanus latimanus dilatus* True. See Palmer, Journ. Mamm. 18 (3) : 291, Aug. 13, 1937.

79967. Skin and skull. Adult male. Crater Lake, altitude 7,000 feet, Mount Mazama, Klamath County, Oreg. August 18, 1896. Collected by Vernon Bailey. Original number 5784.

Well-made skin in good condition ; skull Grade A.

*Scapanus dilatus True.

Diagnoses of New North American Mammals, p. 2, Apr. 26, 1894. (Reprint: Proc. U. S. Nat. Mus. 17 : 242, Nov. 15, 1894.)
=*Scapanus latimanus dilatus* True. See Jackson, North Amer. Fauna 38 : 72. Sept. 30, 1915.

186628. Skeleton. Adult. Fort Klamath, Klamath County, Oreg. 1883. Collected and presented by Charles E. Bendire. Merriam collection number 1286.

Complete skeleton in good condition.

†Scapanus latimanus sericatus Jackson.

Proc. Biol. Soc. Washington 27 : 55, Mar. 20, 1914.

109548. Skin and skull. Adult female. Yosemite, Yosemite Valley, Mariposa County, Calif. August 20, 1901. Collected by W. K. Fisher. Original number 2227.

Well-made skin in good condition ; skull Grade A.

*Scapanus orarius True.

Proc. U. S. Nat. Mus. 19 : 52, Dec. 21, 1896.

$\frac{1381}{37434}$. Skin and skull. Adult female. Shoalwater Bay, Pacific County, Wash. August 30, 1855. Collected by J. G. Cooper.

Specimen recently made into a good study skin ; skull Grade B.
Type originally designated as number 381, an error for 1381.

†Scapanus orarius schefferi Jackson.

North Amer. Fauna 38 : 63, Sept. 30, 1915.

204997. Skin and skull. Adult male. Walla Walla, Walla Walla County, Washington. August 8, 1914. Collected by Theo. H. Scheffer. Original number 11231X.

Well-made skin in good condition ; skull Grade A.

†**Scapanus truei** Merriam.

Proc. Biol. Soc. Washington 11: 102, Apr. 26, 1897.
=*Scapanus latimanus dilatus* True. See Jackson, North Amer. Fauna 38: 72. Sept. 30, 1915.

79290. Skin and skull. Adult. Lake City, Modoc County, Calif. June 15, 1896. Collected by C. P. Streator. Original number 5289.

Well-made skin in good condition; skull Grade A.

Family TUPAIIDAE: Tree Shrews

Genus TANA Lyon

***Tupaia bunoae** Miller.

Proc. Washington Acad. Sci. 2: 229, Aug. 20, 1900.
=*Tana tana bunoae* (Miller). See Lyon, Proc. U. S. Nat. Mus. 45: 136, Nov. 29, 1913.

101640. Skin and skull. Adult female. Pulo Bunoa, Tambelan Islands, South China Sea, between Malay Peninsula and Borneo. August 5, 1899. Collected by W. L. Abbott.

Well-made skin in good condition; skull Grade A.

***Tupaia cervicalis** Miller.

Smithsonian Misc. Coll. 45: 59, Nov. 6, 1903.
=*Tana cervicalis cervicalis* (Miller). See Lyon, Proc. U. S. Nat. Mus. 45: 136, Nov. 29, 1913.

121754. Skin and skull. Adult male. Tana Bala, Batu Islands, off west coast of Sumatra. February 14, 1903. Collected by W. L. Abbott. Original number 2294.

Well-made skin in good condition; skull Grade A.

***Tana cervicalis masae** Lyon.

Proc. U. S. Nat. Mus. 45: 148, Nov. 29, 1913.

121835. Skin and skull. Adult female. Tana Masa, Batu Islands, off west coast of Sumatra. February 18, 1903. Collected by W. L. Abbott. Original number 2302.

Well-made skin in good condition; skull Grade A.

***Tana lingae** Lyon.

Proc. U. S. Nat. Mus. 45: 145, Nov. 29, 1913.

101597. Skin and skull. Adult male. Linga Island, altitude 2,000 feet, Rhio-Linga Archipelago. July 16, 1899. Collected by W. L. Abbott.

Well-made skin in good condition; skull Grade B.

***Tupaia sirhassenensis** Miller.

Proc. Washington Acad. Sci. 3: 133, Mar. 26, 1901.
=*Tana tana sirhassenensis* (Miller). See Lyon, Proc. U. S. Nat. Mus. 45: 136, Nov. 29, 1913.

104712. Skin and skull. Adult male. Sirhassen Island, Natuna Islands, South China Sea, between Malay Peninsula and Borneo. June 5, 1900. Collected by W. L. Abbott. Original number 442.

Well-made skin in good condition; skull Grade A.

*Tana tana besara Lyon.

Proc. U. S. Nat. Mus. 45: 141, Nov. 29, 1913.

142247. Skin and skull. Adult male. Opposite Pulo Jambu, below Tyan, on north bank of Kapuas River, western Borneo. September 17, 1905. Collected by W. L. Abbott. Original number 4458.

Well-made skin in good condition; skull Grade A.

*Tana tana tuancus Lyon.

Proc. U. S. Nat. Mus. 45: 145, Nov. 29, 1913.

114412. Skin and skull. Adult male. Pulo Tuangku, Banjak Islands, off west coast of Sumatra. January 29, 1902. Collected by W. L. Abbott. Original number 1489.

Well-made skin in good condition; skull Grade A.

Genus TUPAIA Raffles

*Tupaia anambae Lyon.

Proc. U. S. Nat. Mus. 45: 89, Nov. 29, 1913.
=*Tupaia glis anambae* Lyon. See Chasen and Kloss, Journ. Malay Branch Roy. Asiatic Soc. 6 (pt. 3) : 38, Aug. 1928.

101743. Skin and skull. Adult male. Pulo Jimaja, Anamba Islands, South China Sea, between Malay Peninsula and Borneo. September 23, 1899. Collected by W. L. Abbott.

Well-made skin in good condition; skull Grade A.

*Tupaia carimatae Miller.

Proc. U. S. Nat. Mus. 31: 61, July 23, 1906.

125123. Skin and skull. Adult male. Telok Edar, Karimata Island, off west coast of Borneo. September 2, 1904. Collected by W. L. Abbott. Original number 3716.

Well-made skin in good condition; skull Grade A.

*Tupaia castanea Miller.

Smithsonian Misc. Coll. 45: 54, Nov. 6, 1903.
=*Tupaia glis castanea* Miller. See Chasen, Bull. Raffles Mus. 15: 3, Apr. 1940.

115608. Skin and skull. Adult female. Pulo Bintang, Rhio-Linga Archipelago. August 11, 1902. Collected by W. L. Abbott. Original number 1872.

Well-made skin in good condition; skull Grade A.

*Tupaia chrysogaster Miller.

Smithsonian Misc. Coll. 45: 58, Nov. 6, 1903.
=*Tupaia glis chrysogaster* Miller. See Chasen, Bull. Raffles Mus. 15: 3, Apr. 1940.

121572. Skin and skull. Adult female. North Pagi Islands, off west coast of Sumatra. November 21, 1902. Collected by W. L. Abbott. Original number 2078.

Well-made skin in good condition; skull Grade A.

*Tupaia chrysomalla Miller.

Proc. Washington Acad. Sci. 2: 232, Aug. 20, 1900.
=*Tupaia glis chrysomalla* Miller. See Chasen and Kloss, Journ. Malay Branch Roy. Asiatic Soc. 6 (pt. 3) : 38, Aug. 1928.

101710. Skin and skull. Adult female. Pulo Siantan, Anambas Islands, South China Sea, between Malay Peninsula and Borneo. August 24, 1899. Collected by W. L. Abbott.

Well-made skin in good condition; skull Grade A.

*Tupaia cuyonis Miller.

Proc. U. S. Nat. Mus. 38: 393, Aug. 19, 1910.

239182. Skin and skull. Adult male. Island of Cuyo, Philippine Islands. January 15, 1903. Collected by R. C. McGregor and A. Celestino. Original number 26, P. B. S.

Well-made skin in good condition; skull Grade A.

*Tupaia discolor Lyon.

Proc. U. S. Nat. Mus. 31: 602, Dec. 18, 1906.
=*Tupaia glis discolor* Lyon. See Chasen, Bull. Raffles Mus. 15: 3, Apr. 1940.

124703. Skin and skull. Adult female. Tanjong Rengsam, Island of Banka, east of Sumatra. May 24, 1904. Collected by W. L. Abbott. Original number 3262.

Well-made skin in good condition; skull Grade A.

*Tupaia ferruginea batamana Lyon.

Proc. U. S. Nat. Mus. 31: 656, Jan. 16, 1907.
=*Tupaia glis batamana* Lyon. See Lyon, Proc. U. S. Nat. Mus. 45: 46, Nov. 29, 1913.

142151. Skin and skull. Adult female. Semimba Bay, Batam Island, Rhio-Linga Archipelago. September 15, 1905. Collected by C. Boden Kloss. Original number 2.

Well-made skin in good condition; skull Grade A.

*Tupaia glis olivacea Kloss.

Journ. Nat. Hist. Soc. Siam 3: 358, Dec. 31, 1919.

221562. Skin and skull. Adult male. Pak Bu, near Tachin, central Siam. October 23, 1916. Collected by C. Boden Kloss. Original number 2208.

Well-made skin in good condition; skull Grade A.

*Tupaia gracilis edarata Lyon.

Proc. U. S. Nat. Mus. 45: 118, Nov. 29, 1913.

153859. Skin and skull. Young adult female. Telok Edar, Karimata Island, off west coast of Borneo. October 5, 1908. Collected by W. L. Abbott. Original number 6226.

Well-made skin in good condition; skull Grade B.

*Tupaia inflata Lyon.

Proc. U. S. Nat. Mus. 31: 600, Dec. 18, 1906.

=*Tupaia gracilis inflata* Lyon. See Lyon, Proc. U. S. Nat. Mus. 45: 118, Nov. 29, 1913.

124709. Skin and skull. Adult male. Tanjong Rengsam, island of Banka, east of Sumatra. May 20, 1904. Collected by W. L. Abbott. Original number 3241.

Well-made skin in good condition; skull Grade A.

*Tupaia lacernata kohtauensis Shamel.

Journ. Mamm. 11: 71, Feb. 11, 1930.

253446. Skin and skull. Adult male. Island of Koh Tau, off east coast of Malay Peninsula. September 19, 1928. Collected by Hugh M. Smith. Original number 2372.

Well-made skin in good condition; skull Grade A.

*Tupaia longipes salatana Lyon.

Proc. U. S. Nat. Mus. 45: 77, Nov. 29, 1913.

=*Tupaia glis salatana* Lyon. See Chasen, Bull. Raffles Mus. 15: 3, Apr. 1940.

151882. Skin and skull. Adult male. Pangkallahan River, southeastern Borneo. February 11, 1908. Collected by W. L. Abbott. Original number 5785.

Well-made skin in good condition; skull Grade B.

*Tupaia natunae Lyon.

Proc. Biol. Soc. Washington 24: 168, June 16, 1911.

=*Tupaia glis natunae* Lyon. See Chasen, Bull. Raffles Mus. 10: 22, Oct. 1935.

104714. Skin and skull. Adult female. Bunguran, Natuna Islands, South China Sea, between Malay Peninsula and Borneo. June 27, 1900. Collected by W. L. Abbott. Original number 514.

Well-made skin in good condition; skull Grade B.

*Tupaia nicobarica surda Miller.

Proc. U. S. Nat. Mus. 24: 774, May 28, 1902.

111757. Skin and skull. Adult male. Little Nicobar, Nicobar Islands, Malay Archipelago. March 1, 1901. Collected by W. L. Abbott. Original number 899.

Well-made skin in good condition; skull Grade A.

*Tupaia pemangilis Lyon.

Proc. Biol. Soc. Washington 24: 168, June 16, 1911.
=*Tupaia glis pemangilis* Lyon.   See Lyon, Proc. U. S. Nat. Mus. 45: 48, Nov. 29, 1913.

112499.   Skin and skull.   Adult female.   Pulo Pemangil, off east coast Malay Peninsula.   June 12, 1901.   Collected by W. L. Abbott.   Original number 1064.

Well-made skin in good condition; skull Grade A.

*Tupaia phaeura Miller.

Proc. Acad. Nat. Sci. Philadelphia 54: 157, June 11, 1902.
=*Tupaia glis phaeura* Miller.   See Chasen, Bull. Raffles Mus. 15: 3, Apr. 1940.

113148.   Skin and skull.   Adult male.   Sinkep Island, Rhio-Linga Archipelago.   September 4, 1901.   Collected by W. L. Abbott.   Original number 1275.

Well-made skin in good condition; skull Grade A.

*Tupaia pulonis Miller.

Smithsonian Misc. Coll. 45: 56, Nov. 6, 1903.
=*Tupaia glis pulonis* Miller.   See Lyon, Proc. U. S. Nat. Mus. 45: 47, Nov. 29, 1913.

112449.   Skin and skull.   Adult female.   Pulo Aor, off Coast of Johore, Federated Malay States.   June 7, 1901.   Collected by W. L. Abbott.   Original number 1023.

Well-made skin in good condition; skull Grade A.

*Tupaia raviana Lyon.

Proc. Biol. Soc. Washington 24: 167, June 16, 1911.
=*Tupaia glis raviana* Lyon.   See Chasen, Bull. Raffles Mus. 15: 2, Apr. 1940.

104355.   Skin and skull.   Old adult male.   Pulo Rawi, Butang Islands, off west coast of Malay Peninsula.   December 18, 1899.   Collected by W. L. Abbott.   Original number 172.

Well-made skin in good condition; skull Grade A.

*Tupaia riabus Lyon.

Proc. U. S. Nat. Mus. 45: 88, Nov. 29, 1913.
=*Tupaia glis riabus* Lyon.   See Chasen, Bull. Raffles Mus. 15: 4, Apr. 1940.

104881.   Skin and skull.   Adult female.   Pulo Raibu, Anamba Islands, South China Sea, between Malay Peninsula and Borneo.   August 23, 1900.   Collected by W. L. Abbott.   Original number 636.

Well-made skin in good condition; skull Grade A.

*Tupaia siaca Lyon.

Proc. U. S. Nat. Mus. 34: 661, Sept. 14, 1908.

=*Tupaia glis siaca* Lyon. See Chasen, Bull. Raffles Mus. 15: 2, Apr. 1940.

144205. Skin and skull. Adult female. Little Siak River, eastern Sumatra. November 4, 1906. Collected by W. L. Abbott. Original number 4856.

Well-made skin in good condition; skull Grade A.

*Tupaia sincepis Lyon.

Proc. Biol. Soc. Washington 24: 169, June 16, 1911.

=*Tupaia minor sincepis* Lyon. See Lyon, Proc. U. S. Nat. Mus. 45: 115, Nov. 29, 1913.

123105. Skin and skull. Adult male. Pulo Singkep, Rhio-Linga Archipelago. August 8, 1903. Collected by W. L. Abbott. Original number 2732.

Well-made skin in good condition; skull Grade A.

*Tupaia sordida Miller.

Proc. Washington Acad. Sci. 2: 231, Aug. 20, 1900.

=*Tupaia glis sordida* Miller. See Lyon, Proc. U. S. Nat. Mus. 45: 48, Nov. 29, 1913.

101747. Skin and skull. Adult male. Pulo Tioman, off southeast coast of Malay Peninsula. October 2, 1899. Collected by W. L. Abbott.

Well-made skin in good condition; skull Grade A.

*Tupaia tephrura Miller.

Smithsonian Misc. Coll. 45: 57, Nov. 6, 1903.

121752. Skin and skull. Adult female. Tana Bala, Batu Islands, off west coast of Sumatra. February 12, 1903. Collected by W. L. Abbott. Original number 2276.

Well-made skin in good condition; skull Grade A.

Genus UROGALE Mearns

*Urogale cylindrura Mearns.

Proc. U. S. Nat. Mus. 28: 435, May 13, 1905.

=*Urogale everetti* (Thomas). See Hollister, Proc. U. S. Nat. Mus. 46: 304, Dec. 31, 1913.

125287. Skin and skull. Adult male. Mount Apo, at the Bagobo village of Todaya, altitude 4,000 feet, southern Mindanao, Philippine Islands. July 12, 1904. Collected by Edgar A. Mearns. Original number 5727.

Well-made skin in good condition; skull Grade A.

Order LAGOMORPHA: Hares, Rabbits, Pikas

Family LEPORIDAE: Hares, Rabbits

Genus BRACHYLAGUS Miller

†Lepus idahoensis Merriam.

North Amer. Fauna 5: 76, July 30, 1891.
=*Brachylagus idahoensis* (Merriam). See Lyon, Smithsonian Misc. Coll. 45: 323, June 15, 1904.
=*Sylvilagus idahoensis* (Merriam). See Grinnell, Dixon and Linsdale, Univ. California Publ. Zool. 35: 553, Oct. 1930.

$\frac{24045}{31461}$. Skin and skull. Adult male. Pahsimeroi Valley, Custer County, Idaho. September 16, 1890. Collected by Vernon Bailey and B. H. Dutcher. Original number 1816.

Well-made skin in good condition; skull Grade A.

Genus LEPUS Linnaeus

*Lepus alleni tiburonensis Townsend.

Bull. Amer. Mus. Nat. Hist. 31: 120, June 14, 1912.

198403. Skin and skull. Adult male. Tiburon Island, Gulf of California, Sonora, Mexico. April 13, 1911. Collected by H. E. Anthony. Original number 160.

Well-made skin in good condition; skull Grade A.

*Lepus americanus dalli Merriam.

Proc. Washington Acad. Sci. 2: 29, Mar. 14, 1900.

$\frac{8996}{7579}$. Skin and skull. Adult male. Nulato, Alaska. January 27, 1867. Collected by W. H. Dall. Original number 584. Western Union Co.'s Overland International Telegraph Expedition.

Unfilled skin in winter pelage, in rather poor condition; skull Grade A. Type designated by the skull number. Skin was not known to exist at time of publication of description.

*Lepus americanus macfarlani Merriam.

Proc. Washington Acad. Sci. 2: 30, Mar. 14, 1900.

$\frac{7111}{14467}$. Skin (lost) and skull. Adult male. Fort Anderson, Mackenzie, Canada. March 1863. Collected by R. MacFarlane. Original number 319.

Skull Grade A. Catalog calls for skin No. 7111, which cannot now be found.

†Lepus arcticus canus Preble.

North Amer. Fauna 22: 59, Oct. 31, 1902.
=*Lepus arcticus labradorius* Miller. See Howell, Journ. Mamm. 17: 322, Nov. 15, 1936.

106860. Skin and skull. Immature male. Barren grounds near Hubbart Point, about 75 miles north of Fort Churchill, Keewatin, Canada. August 17, 1900. Collected by E. A. Preble. Original number 3347.

Well-made skin in good condition, except head partly torn from body; skull Grade B.

†Lepus arcticus monstrabilis Nelson.

Proc. Biol. Soc. Washington 47: 85, Mar. 8, 1934.

126169. Skin and skull. Adult male. Buchanan Bay, Ellesmere Island, northern Canada. April 24 (not 21 as in original description), 1901. Collected by J. S. Warmbath. Original number 3923–X (54).

Well-made skin in good condition; skull Grade A.

†Lepus arcticus porsildi Nelson.

Proc. Biol. Soc. Washington 47: 83, Mar. 8, 1934.

248723. Skin and skull. Near Julianehaab, lat. 61°20′ N. (not 60°20′ N. as in original description), Greenland. September 5, 1926. Collected by O. Hastrup (not by P. Porsild as in original description). Presented by Morten P. Porsild. Original number 24637–X.

Well-made skin in good condition, except for absence of hind legs; skull Grade A.

*Lepus asellus Miller.

Proc. Acad. Nat. Sci. Philadelphia 51: 380, Sept. 29, 1899.
=Lepus californicus asellus Miller. See Nelson, North Amer. Fauna 29: 150, Aug. 31, 1909.

$\frac{20895}{36009}$. Skin and skull. Adult female. San Luis Potosi, State of San Luis Potosi, Mexico. October 22, 1891. Collected by P. L. Jouy. Original number 270.

Well-made skin in good condition; skull Grade A.

*Lepus aurigineus Hollister.

Proc. Biol. Soc. Washington 25: 181, Dec. 24, 1912.
=Lepus tolai aurigineus Hollister. See G. M. Allen, Amer. Mus. Nov. 284: 9, Sept. 13, 1927.

$\frac{13761}{38173}$. Skin and skull. Adult female. Chiu Keang [=Kiukiang], northern Kiangsi, China. December 27, 1880. Received in December 1881 from D. C. Jansen, Shanghai Museum (R. A. S.), through P. L. Jouy.

Well-made skin in fair condition; tail and a portion of adjoining skin torn; small bare patch between shoulders; skull Grade C.

*Lepus bairdii Hayden.   Cotypes.

Amer. Nat. 3: 115, May 1869.

No type designated. The description is based on specimens collected in the Columbia Valley, Wind River Mountains, near Fremonts Peak, long. 110°, lat. 43°, Fremont County, Wyo., in the first part of June 1860, by F. V. Hayden.

The specimens, excluding three marked young in the catalog, are as follows:

$\frac{4262}{38001}$. Skin and skull. Male. June 2, 1860. Original number 62. Made over into fairly good study skin, March 1902.

Skull Grade B.

$\frac{4263}{4273}$. Skin and skull. June 2, 1860. Original number 63. Originally mounted, made over into a fairly good study skin.

Skull Grade C.

4264. Skin without skull. June 4, 1860. Original number 90.

Skin cannot be found.

*Lepus brachyurus angustidens Hollister.

Proc. Biol. Soc. Washington 25: 183, Dec. 24, 1912.

$\frac{13871}{38514}$. Skin and skull. Adult male. Tate Yama Mountain, Hondo Island, Japan. December 14, 1882. Collected by P. L. Jouy.

Skin, not made up, in good condition; skull Grade A.

†Lepus californicus magdalenae Nelson.

Proc. Biol. Soc. Washington 20: 81, July 22, 1907.

146168. Skin and skull. Adult male. Magdalena Island, Lower California, Mexico. November 26, 1905. Collected by E. W. Nelson and E. A. Goldman. Original number 18638.

Well-made skin in good condition; skull Grade A.

†Lepus campestris sierrae Merriam.

Proc. Biol. Soc. Washington 17: 132, July 14, 1904.

=*Lepus townsendii sierrae* Merriam. See Hollister, Proc. Biol. Soc. Washington 28: 70, Mar. 12, 1915.

67863. Skin and skull. Adult female. Hope Valley, Alpine County, Calif. September 9, 1894. Collected by F. Stephens. Original number 1889.

Well-made skin in good condition; skull Grade B.

*Lepus capensis abbotti Hollister.

Proc. Biol. Soc. Washington 31: 35, May 16, 1918.

$\frac{19014}{34779}$. Skin and skull. Adult female. Plains east of Mount Kilimanjaro, British East Africa [=Kenya]. September 20, 1888. Collected by W. L. Abbott.

Skin, not made up, in good condition; skull Grade A.

*Lepus europaeus cinnamomeus Shamel.

Journ. Mamm. 21 (1): 77, Feb. 14, 1940.

255006. Skin and skeleton. Adult male. Suifu, altitude 1,000 to 2,000 feet, Szechwan, China. December 13, 1929. Collected by D. C. Graham. Original number 321.

Well-made skin in good condition; skeleton complete, excepting 6 ribs missing and part of the leg bones have not been removed from the skin.

†Lepus festinus Nelson.

Proc. Biol. Soc. Washington 17: 108, May 18, 1904.
=Lepus californicus festinus Nelson. See Nelson, North Amer. Fauna, 29: 151, Aug. 31, 1909.

53490. Skin and skull. Adult male. Irolo, Hidalgo, Mexico. March 31, 1893. Collected by E. W. Nelson and E. A. Goldman. Original number 4522.

Well-made skin in good condition; skull Grade A.

*Lepus gaillardi Mearns.

Proc. U. S. Nat. Mus. 18: 560, June 24, 1896.

$\frac{20525}{35714}$. Skin and skull. Adult male. West fork of the Playas Valley, near monument No. 63, Mexican boundary line, Grant County, N. Mex. June 17, 1892. Collected by Edgar A. Mearns and F. X. Holzner. Original number 1885.

Well-made skin in good condition; pelage somewhat worn. Skull Grade A.

*Lepus grahami A. B. Howell.

Proc. Biol. Soc. Washington 41: 143, Oct. 15, 1928.
=Lepus oiostolus grahami A. B. Howell. See G. M. Allen, Mamm. China and Mongolia 1: 577, Sept. 3, 1938.

239875. Skin and skull. Adult female. Ulongkong, south of Tatsienlu, Szechwan, China. July 31, 1923. Collected by D. C. Graham. Original number 8.

Flat skin in fair condition; skull Grade A.

*Lepus kakumegae Heller.

Smithsonian Misc. Coll. 59 (16): 19, July 5, 1912.
=Lepus victoriae kakumegae Heller. See Hollister, U. S. Nat. Mus. Bull. 99 (pt. 2): 169, May 16, 1919.

181809.   Skin and skull.   Adult female.   Ludosa River, Kakumega Forest, British East Africa [=Kenya].   February 12, 1912. Collected by Edmund Heller.   Original number 5644.

Well-made skin in good condition; skull Grade A.

†Lepus klamathensis Merriam.

North Amer. Fauna 16: 100, Oct. 28, 1899.

=*Lepus washingtonii klamathensis* Merriam.   See Nelson, North Amer. Fauna 29: 107, Aug. 31, 1909.

92248.   Skin and skull.   Adult female.   Head of Wood River, near Fort Klamath, Klamath County, Oreg.   January 25, 1898.   Collected by B. L. Cunningham.   Original number 1191–X.

Well-made skin in good condition; skull Grade A.

*Lepus labradorius Miller.   Cotypes.

Proc. Biol. Soc. Washington 13: 39, May 29, 1899.

=*Lepus arcticus labradorius* Miller.   See G. M. Allen and Copeland, Journ. Mamm. 5: 12, Feb. 9, 1924.

$\frac{14149}{37138}$.   Skin and skull.   Adult.   Fort Chimo, Ungava [=Labrador Peninsula, Quebec, Canada].   September 28, 1882.   Collected by Lucien M. Turner.   Original number 1180.

Well-made skin in good condition, pelage somewhat worn; skull Grade C.

23132.   Skull only.   Adult.   Same place and collector as above. Original number 2326.

Both cotypes are designated by number.   There is a typographical error in the skull number.   It should be 23132 instead of 32132.

Skull Grade A.

*Lepus merriami Mearns.

Preliminary Diagnoses of New Mammals from the Mexican Border of the United States, p. 2, Mar. 25, 1896.   (Reprint: Proc. U. S. Nat. Mus. 18: 444, May 23, 1896.)

=*Lepus californicus merriami* Mearns.   See Nelson, North Amer. Fauna 29: 148, Aug. 31, 1909.

83797.   Skin and skull.   Adult female.   Fort Clark, Kinney County, Tex.   April 6, 1893.   Collected by Edgar A. Mearns.   Original number 2317.

Skin well made and preserved but made up on its side instead of belly; skull Grade A.

Type designated by the collector's original number.

†Lepus merriami altamirae Nelson.

Proc. Biol. Soc. Washington 17: 109, May 18, 1904.

=*Lepus altamirae* Nelson.   See Nelson, North Amer. Fauna 29: 124, Aug. 31, 1909.

93691. Skin and skull. Adult male. Alta Mira, Tamaulipas, Mexico. May 16, 1898. Collected by E. W. Nelson and E. A. Goldman. Original number 12365.

Well-made skin in good condition; skull Grade A.

*Lepus othus Merriam.

Proc. Washington Acad. Sci. 2 : 28, Mar. 14, 1900.

15883. Skull, no skin. Adult. St. Michael, Norton Sound, Alaska. February 1877. Collected by Lucien M. Turner. Original number 1418.

Skull Grade B.

*Lepus parnassius Miller.

Proc. Biol. Soc. Washington 16 : 145, Nov. 12, 1903.

122093. Skin and skull. Adult male. Agorianni, north side of Lyakura (Mount Parnassus), Greece. September 10, 1895. Received from Wilhelm Schlüter.

Well-made skin in good condition; skull Grade B.

†Lepus poadromus Merriam.

Proc. Washington Acad. Sci. 2 : 29, Mar. 14, 1900.
=*Lepus othus poadromus* Merriam. See Howell, Journ. Mamm. 17 : 334, Nov. 15, 1936.

98068. Skin and skull. Adult. Stepovak Bay, Alaska Peninsula, Alaska. July 8, 1899. Collected by C. Palache. Original number 2207 (A. K. Fisher).

Well-made skin in good condition, except for absence of left hind foot; skull Grade A.

*Lepus quercerus Hollister.

Proc. Biol. Soc. Washington 25 : 182, Dec. 24, 1912.

175446. Skin and skull. Adult male. Chuisaya Steppe, Altai Mountains, Siberia. July 28, 1912. Collected by N. Hollister. Original number 4405.

Well-made skin in good condition; skull Grade A.

*Lepus raineyi Heller.

Smithsonian Misc. Coll. 59 (16) : 18, July 5, 1912.

181808. Skin and skull. Adult female. Longaya Water, 30 miles south of Mount Marsabit, British East Africa [=Kenya]. July 21, 1911. Collected by Paul J. Rainey. Original number (Heller) 3061.

Well-made skin in good condition; skull Grade A.

†Lepus saliens Osgood.

North Amer. Fauna 19: 39, Oct. 6, 1900.
=*Lepus americanus macfarlani* Merriam. See Nelson, North Amer. Fauna 29: 98. Aug. 31. 1909.

98956. Skin and skull. Adult male. Caribou Crossing, between Lake Bennett and Lake Tagish, Yukon, Canada. June 26, 1899. Collected by W. H. Osgood. Original number 504.

Well-made skin in good condition; skull Grade B.

*Lepus swinhoei sowerbyae Hollister.

Proc. Biol. Soc. Washington 25: 182, Dec. 24, 1912.
=*Lepus tolai filchneri* Matschie. See G. M. Allen, Amer. Mus. Nov. 284: 8, Sept. 13, 1927.

172628. Skin and skull. Adult male. Wu-tsai, altitude 6,000 feet, 20 miles west of Ning-wu-fu, northern Shansi, China. February 5, 1910. Collected by Arthur deC. Sowerby. Original number 365.

Well-made skin in good condition; skull Grade A.

*Lepus texianus griseus Mearns.

Proc. U. S. Nat. Mus. 18: 562, June 24, 1896.
=*Lepus californicus texianus* Waterhouse. See Nelson, North Amer. Fauna 29: 142, Aug. 31, 1909.

$\frac{21068}{36108}$. Skin and skull. Adult female. Fort Hancock, El Paso County, Tex. June 22, 1893. Collected by Edgar A. Mearns. Original number 2353.

Well-made skin in good condition but made up lying on the side instead of belly; skull Grade A.

†Lepus texianus wallawalla Merriam.

Proc. Biol. Soc. Washington 17: 137, July 14, 1904.
=*Lepus californicus wallawalla* Merriam. See Nelson, North Amer. Fauna 29: 132, Aug. 31, 1909.

$\frac{23923}{31328}$ (not $\frac{23923}{21328}$ as in original description). Skin and skull. Adult female. Touchet, Plains of the Columbia, Walla Walla County, Wash. September 18, 1890. Collected by C. P. Streator. Original number 271.

Well-made skin in good condition; skull Grade A.

†Lepus tularensis Merriam.

Proc. Biol. Soc. Washington 17: 136, July 14, 1904.
=*Lepus californicus richardsonii* Bachman. See Nelson, North Amer. Fauna 29: 133, Aug. 31, 1909.

126334. Skin and skull. Adult female. Alila, Tulare County, Calif. October 25, 1900. Collected by L. J. Goldman. Original number 496.

Well-made skin in good condition; skull Grade A.

*Lepus varronis Miller.

Proc. Biol. Soc. Washington 14: 97, June 27, 1901.

=*Lepus timidus varronis* Miller.   See Miller, Mammals of Western Europe, ... p. 528, Oct. 1912.

105832. Skin and skull. Adult male. Heinzenberg, Canton of Graubünden, Switzerland. December 5, 1900. Collected by Ernst H. Zollikofer. Original number 196.

Well-made skin in good condition; skull Grade A.

*Lepus washingtonii Baird.

Proc. Acad. Nat. Sci. Philadelphia 7: 333, favorably reported for publication Apr. 24, 1855.

$\frac{280}{1223}$. Skin and skull. Adult. Steilacoom, Pierce County, Wash.

April 1, 1854. Collected by George Suckley.

Well-made skin in good condition; skull Grade C.

Type not designated by number, but by comparing the measurements in the original description with those in the table on page 585 of Baird's Mammals of North America it is seen that no. $\frac{280}{1223}$ must be regarded as the type.

Genus ROMEROLAGUS Merriam

†Romerolagus nelsoni Merriam.

Proc. Biol. Soc. Washington 10: 173, Dec. 29, 1896.

=*Romerolagus diazi* (Diaz).   See Miller, Proc. Biol. Soc. Washington 24: 228, Oct. 31, 1911.

57949. Skin and skull. Adult male. West slope of Mount Popocatepetl, altitude 11,000 feet, State of Mexico, Mexico. January 6, 1894. Collected by E. W. Nelson and E. A. Goldman. Original number 5639.

Well-made skin in good condition; skull Grade B.

Genus SYLVILAGUS Gray

†Sylvilagus aquaticus littoralis Nelson.

North Amer. Fauna 29: 273, Aug. 31, 1909.

$\frac{33848}{45883}$. Skin and skull. Adult female. Houma, Terrebonne Parish, La. May 4, 1892. Collected by Vernon Bailey. Original number 3581.

Well-made skin in good condition; skull Grade A.

†Lepus arizonae goldmani Nelson.

Proc. Biol. Soc. Washington 17: 107, May 18, 1904.

=*Sylvilagus audubonii goldmani* (Nelson).   See Nelson, North Amer. Fauna 29: 225, Aug. 31, 1909.

96812. Skin and skull. Adult female (not male, as in original description). Culiacan, Sinaloa, Mexico. March 20, 1899. Collected by E. A. Goldman. Original number 13588.

Well-made skin in good condition; skull Grade A.

*Lepus arizonae major Mearns.

Proc. U. S. Nat. Mus. 18: 557, June 24, 1896.

=*Sylvilagus audubonii arizonae* (J. A. Allen). See Nelson, North Amer. Fauna 29: 222, Aug. 31, 1909.

$\frac{18192}{25090}$. Skin and skull. Adult male. Calabasas, Pima County, Ariz. October 23, 1889. Collected by L. Stejneger. Original number 3053.

Well-made skin in good condition; skull Grade A.

*Lepus arizonae minor Mearns.

Proc. U. S. Nat. Mus. 18: 557, June 24, 1896.

=*Sylvilagus audubonii minor* (Mearns). See Nelson, Proc. Biol. Soc. Washington 20: 83, July 22, 1907.

$\frac{20104}{37064}$. Skin and skull. Adult male. El Paso, El Paso County, Tex. February 6, 1892. Collected by Edgar A. Mearns and F. X. Holzner. Original number 1418.

Well-made skin in good condition; skull Grade A.

*Lepus audubonii Baird.

North American Mammals, p. 608, 1857.

=*Sylvilagus audubonii* (Baird). See Nelson, North Amer. Fauna 29: 214, Aug. 31, 1909.

$\frac{1163}{2045}$. Skin (skull lost). San Francisco, San Francisco County, Calif. Received from R. S. Williamson; collected by J. S. Newberry. Cataloged December 31, 1855.

Well-made skin in good condition; skull cannot be found.

No type was designated in the original description, and in the description itself there is nothing to show that Baird had in mind any particular one of his five specimens collected at three localities. The specimens labeled "Presidio" probably came from Monterey, as is seen by reading the original labels and the entry in the catalog. On plate 13, Baird figures the entire animal but does not state which specimen; however, on plate 58 a skull is figured and referred to by number, 2045. As this specimen seems to be mentioned more particularly than any other specimen, it seems well to take it as the type. San Francisco, Calif., is thus made the type locality, in agreement with Miller and Rehn, Proc. Boston Soc. Nat. Hist. 30: 185, Dec. 1901.

†Sylvilagus audubonii cedrophilus Nelson.

Proc. Biol. Soc. Washington 20: 83, July 22, 1907.

148287. Skin and skull. Adult female. Cactus Flat, 20 miles north of Cliff, Grant County, N. Mex. November 6, 1906. Collected by V. Bailey. Original number 8595.

Well-made skin in good condition; skull Grade B.

†**Sylvilagus audubonii neomexicanus** Nelson.

Proc. Biol. Soc. Washington 20: 83, July 22, 1907.

118477. Skin and skull. Adult male. Fort Sumner, Guadalupe County, N. Mex. September 23, 1902. Collected by J. H. Gaut. Original number 506.

Well-made skin in good condition; skull Grade A.

†**Sylvilagus audubonii vallicola** Nelson.

Proc. Biol. Soc. Washington 20: 82, July 22, 1907.

$\frac{31257}{43122}$ Skin and skull. Adult female. San Emigdio Ranch, Kern County, Calif. October 22, 1891. Collected by E. W. Nelson. Original number 1353.

Well-made skin in good condition; skull Grade B.

†**Sylvilagus audubonii warreni** Nelson.

Proc. Biol. Soc. Washington 20: 83, July 22, 1907.

148632. Skin and skull. Adult female. Coventry, Montrose County, Colo. January 4, 1907. Collected by C. H. Smith. Original number 6312–X.

Well-made skin in good condition; skull Grade C.

†**Sylvilagus bachmani exiguus** Nelson.

Proc. Biol. Soc. Washington 20: 84, July 22, 1907.

139607. Skin and skull. Adult male. Yubay, central Lower California, Mexico. September 19, 1905. Collected by E. W. Nelson and E. A. Goldman. Original number 18153.

Well-made skin in good condition; skull Grade A.

*****Lepus bachmani ubericolor** Miller.

Proc. Acad. Nat. Sci. Philadelphia 51: 383, Sept. 29, 1899.

=*Sylvilagus bachmani ubericolor* (Miller). See Lyon, Smithsonian Misc. Coll. 45: 337, June 15, 1904.

$\frac{19964}{35371}$ Skin and skull. Adult male. Beaverton, Washington County, Oreg. February 25, 1890. Collected by A. W. Anthony. Original number 1226.

Well-made skin in good condition; skull Grade A.

†**Lepus baileyi** Merriam.

Proc. Biol. Soc. Washington 11: 148, June 9, 1897.

=*Sylvilagus audubonii baileyi* (Merriam). See Nelson, North Amer. Fauna 29: 232, Aug. 31, 1909.

56016. Skin and skull. Adult female. Spring Creek, east side of Bighorn Basin, Bighorn County, Wyo. September 17, 1893. Collected by C. Hart Merriam and Vernon Bailey. Original number 4372.

Well-made skin in good condition; skull Grade B.

*Lepus brasiliensis gabbi J. A. Allen.   Cotypes.

Monographs of North American Rodentia, p. 349, Aug. 1877.
=*Sylvilagus gabbi gabbi* (Allen). See Lyon, Smithsonian Misc. Coll. 45: 336, June 15, 1904.

$\frac{11371}{37794}$. Skin and skull. Adult male. Talamanca, Costa Rica. Late in 1872 or early in 1873. Received from W. M. Gabb. Collected by J. C. Zeledon. Original number 18.

Specimen has been made over into a modern study skin, in good condition; skull Grade A.

11372. Skin with skull inside; all data as above except original number, which is 19.

As J. A. Allen wrote, this specimen is quite immature and on the whole is a wretched-looking object. It has never been made up into a modern study skin.

Allen based this species on three specimens, all designated by number on page 350, Monographs of North American Rodentia: One (No. 8140) from Chiriqui, received from Fred Hicks, and the others (Nos. 11371 and 11372) from Talamanca, Costa Rica, collected by José Zeledon. No type or cotypes were designated. In order to avoid two type localities for a single species, the two specimens from Talamanca are now designated as cotypes and the Chiriqui specimen as a paratype. This course seems perfectly justifiable, as two-thirds of the specimens upon which the description was based came from Talamanca, and the species was named after their donor.

†Sylvilagus cognatus Nelson.

Proc. Biol. Soc. Washington 20: 82, July 22, 1907.

136569. Skin and skull. Adult. Tajique, near summit of Manzano Mountains, altitude 10,000 feet, Valencia County, N. Mex. February 1905. Collected by A. Rea. Original number 5331-X.

Well-made skin in good condition; skull Grade A.

†Sylvilagus floridanus ammophilus Howell.

Journ. Mamm. 20: 365, Aug. 14, 1939.

70313. Skin and skull. Adult male. "Oak Lodge," on peninsula opposite Micco, Brevard County, Fla. January 22, 1895. Collected by J. Alden Loring. Original number 2672.

Well-made skin in good condition; skull Grade A.

*Lepus floridanus caniclunis Miller.

Proc. Acad. Nat. Sci. Philadelphia 51: 388, Oct. 5, 1899.
=*Sylvilagus floridanus chapmani* (J. A. Allen). See Nelson, North Amer. Fauna 29: 176, Aug. 31, 1909.

63137. Skin and skull. Adult male. Fort Clark, Kinney County, Tex. December 27, 1892. Collected by Edgar A. Mearns. Original number 2172.

Well-made skin in good condition; skull Grade A.

Lepus floridanus chiapensis Nelson.

Proc. Biol. Soc. Washington 17: 106, May 18, 1904.
=*Sylvilagus floridanus chiapensis* (Nelson). See Lyon and Osgood, U. S. Nat. Mus. Bull. 62: 32, Jan. 28, 1909.

75953. Skin and skull. Adult female. San Cristobal, Chiapas, Mexico. September 28, 1895. Collected by E. W. Nelson and E. A. Goldman. Original number 8483.

Well-made skin in good condition; skull Grade A.

†Lepus floridanus connectens Nelson.

Proc. Biol. Soc. Washington 17: 105, May 18, 1904.
=*Sylvilagus floridanus connectens* (Nelson). See Lyon and Osgood, U. S. Nat. Mus. Bull. 62: 32, Jan. 28, 1909.

63660. Skin and skull. Adult male. Chichicaxtle, Veracruz, Mexico. February 15, 1894. Collected by E. W. Nelson and E. A. Goldman. Original number 5849.

Well-made skin in good condition; skull Grade A.

*Sylvilagus floridanus hitchensi Mearns.

Proc. U. S. Nat. Mus. 39: 227, Jan. 9, 1911.

155577. Skin and skull. Adult female. Smiths Island, Northampton County, Va. May 13, 1910. Collected by Edgar A. Mearns. Original number 7419.

Well-made skin in good condition; skull Grade A.

*Sylvilagus floridanus hondurensis Goldman.

Proc. Biol. Soc. Washington 45: 122, July 30, 1932.

257062. Skin and skull. Adult male. Monte Redondo, altitude 5,100 feet, about 30 miles northwest of Tegucigalpa, Honduras. December 3, 1931. Collected by C. F. Underwood. Original number 628.

Well-made skin in good condition; skull Grade A.

†Sylvilagus floridanus restrictus Nelson.

Proc. Biol. Soc. Washington 20: 82, July 22, 1907.

$\frac{33687}{45722}$. Skin and skull. Adult male. Zapotlan, Jalisco, Mexico. April 25, 1892. Collected by E. W. Nelson. Original number 2576.

Well-made skin in good condition; skull Grade B.

*Lepus floridanus sanctidiegi Miller.

Proc. Acad. Nat. Sci. Philadelphia 51 : 389, Oct. 5, 1899.

=*Sylvilagus aubbonii sanctidiegi* (Miller). See Nelson, North Amer. Fauna 29 : 218, Aug. 31, 1909.

60668. Skin and skull. Adult female. Shore of Pacific Ocean, Mexican boundary monument No. 258, San Diego County, Calif. July 10, 1894. Collected by Edgar A. Mearns. Original number 3783.

Well-made skin in good condition; skull Grade A.

†Sylvilagus floridanus similis Nelson.

Proc. Biol. Soc. Washington 20 : 82, July 22, 1907.

69517. Skin and skull. Adult male. Valentine, Cherry County, Nebr. November 10, 1894. Collected by C. P. Streator. Original number 4442.

Well-made skin in good condition; skull Grade A.

*Lepus floridanus subcinctus Miller.

Proc. Acad. Nat. Sci. Philadelphia 51 : 386, Oct. 5, 1899.

=*Sylvilagus floridanus subcinctus* (Miller). See Lyon, Smithsonian Misc. Coll. 45 : 336, June 15, 1904.

$\frac{20435}{35665}$. Skin and skull. Adult female. Hacienda El Molino, near Negrete, Michoacan, Mexico. June 15, 1892. Collected by P. L. Jouy. Original number 415.

Well-made skin in good condition; skull Grade A.

*Lepus floridanus yucatanicus Miller.

Proc. Acad. Nat. Sci. Philadelphia 51 : 384, Sept. 29, 1899.

=*Sylvilagus floridanus yucatanicus* (Miller). See Lyon, Smithsonian Misc. Coll. 45 : 336, June 15, 1904.

$\frac{11441}{37772}$. Skin and skull. Adult female. Merida, Yucatan, Mexico. February 22, 1865. Collected by A. Schott. Original number 207. Comision Cientifica de Yucatan, José Salazar Llarregui.

Specimen recently made over into a modern study skin, well-preserved; skull Grade B.

†Sylvilagus gabbi messorius Goldman.

Smithsonian Misc. Coll. 60 (2) : 13, Sept. 20, 1912.

179569. Skin and skull. Adult male. Cana, altitude 1,800 feet, in the mountains of eastern Panama. May 23, 1912. Collected by E. A. Goldman. Original number 21736.

Well-made skin in good condition; skull Grade B.

*Lepus graysoni J. A. Allen.

Monographs of North American Rodentia, p. 347, August 1877.
=*Sylvilagus graysoni* (Allen). See Lyon, Smithsonian Misc. Coll. 45: 336, June 15, 1904.

8318. Skin, with skull inside. Adult female. Tres Marias Islands, Nayarit, Mexico; probably from Maria Madre Island (see Nelson, North Amer. Fauna 14: 16, Apr. 29, 1899). Collected during "Explorations in N. W. Mexico, Col. A. J. Grayson." Original number 135. Cataloged November 15, 1865.

Wretched skin, in poor condition, with a skull inside.
Type not explicitly designated by number in the original description; but No. 8318 is labeled *"Lepus Graysoni* type" in Allen's handwriting.

†Lepus insonus Nelson.

Proc. Biol. Soc. Washington 17: 103, May 18, 1904.
=*Sylvilagus insonus* (Nelson). See Lyon and Osgood, U. S. Nat. Mus. Bull. 62: 34, Jan. 28, 1909.

126878. Skin and skull. Adult female. Omilteme, Guerrero, Mexico. May 20, 1903. Collected by E. W. Nelson and E. A. Goldman. Original number 16466.

Well-made skin in good condition, except for a small bare spot on the back and slight injury behind left fore leg; skull Grade A.

†Sylvilagus mansuetus Nelson.

Proc. Biol. Soc. Washington 20: 83, July 22, 1907.
79041. Skin and skull. Adult female (not male, as in original description). San José Island, Gulf of California, Lower California, Mexico. August 2, 1895. Collected by J. E. McLellan. Original number 1444.

Well-made skin in good condition; skull Grade B.

*Lepus margaritae Miller.

Proc. Biol. Soc. Washington 12: 97, Apr. 30, 1898.
=*Sylvilagus margaritae* (Miller). See Lyon, Smithsonian Misc. Coll. 45: 336, June 15, 1904.

63217. Skin and skull. Adult male. Margarita Island, off north coast of Venezuela. July 1, 1895. Collected by Wirt Robinson. Original number 369.

Well-made skin in good condition; skull Grade A.

†Lepus orizabae Merriam.

Proc. Biol. Soc. Washington 8: 143, Dec. 29, 1893.
=*Sylvilagus floridanus orizabae* (Merriam). See Nelson, North Amer. Fauna 29: 183, Aug. 31, 1909.

53318. Skin and skull. Adult female. Mount Orizaba, altitude 9,500 feet, Puebla, Mexico. April 24, 1893. Collected by E. W. Nelson. Original number 4730.

Well-made skin in good condition; skull Grade B.

†**Lepus pinetis robustus** Bailey.

North Amer. Fauna 25: 159, Oct. 24, 1905.
=*Sylvilagus robustus* (Bailey). See Nelson, North Amer. Fauna 29: 194, Aug. 31, 1909.

$\frac{18262}{25165}$. Skin and skull. Adult female. Davis Mountains, altitude 6,000 feet, Jeff Davis County, Tex. January 6, 1890. Collected by V. Bailey. Original number 873.

Well-made skin in good condition; skull Grade B.

***Lepus simplicicanus** Miller.

Proc. Biol. Soc. Washington 15: 81, Apr. 25, 1902.
=*Sylvilagus floridanus chapmani* (J. A. Allen). See Nelson, North Amer. Fauna 29: 176, Aug 31, 1909.

$\frac{21805}{36508}$. Skin and skull. Adult female. Brownsville, Cameron County, Tex. October 19, 1891. Collected by F. B. Armstrong. Purchased from C. K. Worthen. Original number 1402.

Well-made skin in good condition; skull Grade C.

***Lepus sylvaticus arizonae** J. A. Allen.

Monographs of North American Rodentia, p. 332, Aug. 1877.
=*Sylvilagus audubonii arizonae* (J. A. Allen). See Nelson, North Amer. Fauna 29: 222, Aug. 31, 1909.

8439. Skin of adult male. No record of skull. Beales Springs, 50 miles west of Fort Whipple, Yavapai County, Ariz. September 8, 1865. Collected by Elliott Coues. Original number 1563.

A flat, poorly preserved skin; one hind leg missing; the other detached from the skin.

Type not explicitly designated by number, but on comparing Allen's remarks, p. 332, *loc. cit.*, with his list of specimens in table 39, p. 340, it is readily seen that No. 8439 is the type.

***Lepus sylvaticus holzneri** Mearns.

Proc. U. S. Nat. Mus. 18: 554, June 24, 1896.
=*Sylvilagus floridanus holzneri* (Mearns). See Lyon, Smithsonian Misc. Coll. 45: 336, June 15, 1904.

58937. Skin and skull. Adult female. In the Douglas Spruce zone, near the summit of the Huachuca Mountains, Cochise County, southern Ariz. August 29, 1893. Collected by Frank X. Holzner. Original number 989.

Well-made skin in good condition; skull Grade A.

***Lepus sylvaticus rigidus** Mearns.

Proc. U. S. Nat. Mus. 18: 555, footnote, June 24, 1896.
=*Sylvilagus floridanus holzneri* (Mearns). See Nelson, North Amer. Fauna 29: 178, Aug. 31, 1909.

$\frac{20336}{35537}$. Skin and skull. Adult male. Carrizalillo Mountains, near Monument No. 31, Mexican boundary line, Grant County, N. Mex. April 21, 1892. Collected by Edgar A. Mearns and F. X. Holzner. Original number 1680.

Well-made skin in good condition; skull Grade B.

*Lepus trowbridgii Baird.   Lectotype.

Proc. Acad. Nat. Sci. Philadelphia 7 : 333, favorably reported for publication Apr. 24, 1855.

=*Sylvilagus* (*Microlagus*) *bachmani* (Waterhouse). See Lyon, Smithsonian Misc. Coll. 45 : 336, June 15, 1904.

$\frac{310}{1235}$. Skin and skull, lectotype, Monterey County, Calif. 1853. Collected by W. P. Trowbridge. The entry in the skull catalog reads, "Monterey? Cal. Perhaps San Diego."

Well-made skin in good condition; skull Grade C.

"No type designated. By referring to Mammals of North America, pages 610–612, it is seen that most of the description is based upon No. 310; moreover, the measurements of 310 agree more nearly with those given in the original description. For these reasons No. $\frac{310}{1235}$ is here chosen as the type" (Lyon and Osgood, U. S. Nat. Mus. Bull. 62 : 37, January 28, 1909).

*Lepus truei J. A. Allen.

Bull. Amer. Mus. Nat. Hist. 3 : 192, Dec. 10, 1890.

=*Sylvilagus gabbi truei* (J. A. Allen). See Nelson, North Amer. Fauna (29) : 262, Aug. 31, 1909.

$\frac{6357}{34878}$. Skin and skull. Adult. Mirador, Veracruz, Mexico. Collected by C. Sartorius. Original mark "e." Skin cataloged April 1863; skull, November 27, 1890.

Skin in poor condition, laid out flat on side. A good deal of the epidermis has slipped from the feet. Skull, formerly in the skin, has the posterior parts more or less damaged by the preservative used on the skin; Grade C.

Type designated by the number $\frac{6357}{25953}$. A large series of skulls in the Museum collection in the twenty-five thousands was misnumbered, and the skull of the present specimen, along with others, had to be reentered. It is now No. 34878, instead of No. 25953.

†Lepus veraecrucis pacificus Nelson.

Proc. Biol. Soc. Washington 17 : 104, May 18, 1904.

=*Sylvilagus cunicularius pacificus* (Nelson). See Lyon and Osgood, U. S. Nat. Mus. Bull. 62 : 35, Jan. 28, 1909.

70622. Skin and skull. Adult male. Acapulco, Guerrero, Mexico, January 9, 1895. Collected by E. W. Nelson and E. A. Goldman. Original number 7340.

Well-made skin in good condition; skull Grade A.

Family OCHOTONIDAE: Pikas, or Conies

Genus OCHOTONA Link

*Ochotona (Pika) alpina argentata A. B. Howell.

Proc. Biol. Soc. Washington 41: 116, June 29, 1928.

240726. Skin, skull, and skeleton. Adult female. 15 miles north-northwest of Ninghsia, northern Kansu, China. May 16, 1923. Collected by F. R. Wulsin. Original number 1059.

Well-made skin in good condition; skull Grade C. Skeleton good.

*Ochotona annectens Miller.

Proc. Biol. Soc. Washington 24: 54, Feb. 24, 1911.
=*Ochotona (Ochotona) dauurica annectens* Miller. See A. B. Howell, Proc. U. S. Nat. Mus. 75 (1): 68, June 7, 1929.

155164. Skin and skull. Adult male. 15 miles northeast of Ching-ning-chow, altitude 6,200 feet, Kansu, China. July 27, 1909. Collected by Arthur deC. Sowerby. Original number 225.

Well-made skin in good condition; skull Grade A.

*Ochotona cansus Lyon.

Smithsonian Misc. Coll. 50: 136, July 9, 1907.

144030. Skin and skull. Adult male. Taocheo, Province of Kansu, China. June 8, 1906. Collected by W. W. Simpson. Original number 13.

Well-made skin in good condition; skull Grade A.

*Lagomys collaris Nelson.

Proc. Biol. Soc. Washington 8: 117, Dec. 21, 1893.
=*Ochotona collaris* (Nelson). See Trouessart, Catalogus Mammalium tam Viventium quam Fossilium, p. 648, 1897.

$\frac{14384}{36297}$. Skin and skull. Adult. Near the head of the Tanana River. about 200 miles south of Fort Yukon, Alaska. Summer of 1880. Collected by E. W. Nelson. Original number 164.

Skin fairly well preserved, but badly made up; no wire in legs. Skull Grade B.

*Ochotona (Ochotona) erythrotis vulpina A. B. Howell.

Proc. Biol. Soc. Washington 41: 117, June 29, 1928.

240723. Skin and skull. Adult male. 30 miles west of Sining, Kansu, China. August 12, 1927. Collected by F. R. Wulsin. Original number 1103.

Well-made skin in good condition; skull Grade A.

†Ochotona fenisex brunnescens Howell.

Proc. Biol. Soc. Washington 32: 108, May 20, 1919.
=*Ochotona princeps brunnescens* Howell. See Howell, North Amer. Fauna 47: 31, Aug. 21, 1924.

227259. Skin and skull. Subadult male. Keechelus, Kittitas County, Wash. August 23, 1917. Collected by George G. Cantwell. Original number 38 (19568X).

Well-made skin in good condition; skull Grade A.

†Ochotona fenisex fumosa Howell.

Proc. Biol. Soc. Washington 32: 109, May 20, 1919.

=Ochotona princeps fumosa Howell. See Howell, North Amer. Fauna 47: 33, Aug. 21, 1924.

91144. Skin and skull. Adult male. Permilia Lake, west base Mt. Jefferson, Linn County, Oreg. October 4, 1897. Collected by J. Alden Loring. Original number 4799.

Well-made skin in good condition; skull Grade A.

*Ochotona levis Hollister.

Proc. Biol. Soc. Washington 25: 57, Apr. 13, 1912.

=Ochotona princeps levis Hollister. See Howell, North Amer. Fauna 47: 16, Aug. 21, 1924.

$\frac{12000}{22241}$. Skin and skull. Adult female. Chief Mountain Lake [=Waterton Lake], Alberta, Canada. August 24, 1874. Collected by Elliott Coues. Original number 4593.

Well-made skin in good condition; skull Grade A.

†Ochotona nigrescens Bailey.

Proc. Biol. Soc. Washington 26: 133, May 21, 1913.

=Ochotona princeps nigrescens Bailey. See Howell, North Amer. Fauna 47: 26, Aug. 21, 1924.

147976. Skin and skull. Adult male. Jemez Mountains, altitude 10,000 feet, Bernalillo County, N. Mex. August 28, 1906. Collected by Vernon Bailey. Original number 8447.

Well-made skin in good condition; skull Grade A.

*Ochotona nitida Hollister.

Smithsonian Misc. Coll. 60 (14) : 4, Nov. 29, 1912.

175390. Skin and skull. Adult female. Tchegan-Burgazi Pass, Altai Mountains (near Mongolian border, south of Kosh-Agatch), Siberia. July 8, 1912. Collected by N. Hollister. Original number 4257.

Well-made skin in good condition; skull Grade A.

†Ochotona princeps brooksi Howell.

North Amer. Fauna 47: 30, Aug. 21, 1924.

69275. Skin and skull. Adult male. Sicammous, British Columbia, Canada. September 24, 1894. Collected by Clark P. Streator. Original number 4319.

Well-made skin in good condition; skull Grade B.

†**Ochotona princeps lutescens** Howell.

Proc. Biol. Soc. Washington 32: 105, May 20, 1919.

108650. Skin and skull. Adult male. Mount Inglesmaldie, near Banff, altitude about 8,000 feet, Alberta, Canada. July 26, 1899. Collected by G. F. Dippie. Original number 193 (2973–X).

Well-made skin in good condition; skull Grade B.

†**Ochotona saxatilis incana** Howell.

Proc. Biol. Soc. Washington 32: 107, May 20, 1919.
=*Ochotona princeps incana* Howell. See Howell, North Amer. Fauna 47: 25, Aug. 21, 1924.

128914. Skin and skull. Adult female. Pecos Baldy, altitude 12,000 feet, Santa Fe County, N. Mex. Aug. 10, 1903. Collected by Vernon Bailey. Original number 8079.

Well-made skin in good condition; skull Grade A.

*****Lagomys schisticeps** Merriam.

North Amer. Fauna 2: 11, Oct. 30, 1889.
=*Ochotona schisticeps schisticeps* (Merriam). See Merriam, Mazama 1: 223, Oct. 1897.

186517 (not 186518 as in North Amer. Fauna 47: 38, Aug. 21, 1924). Skin and skull. Adult male. Donner, Placer County, Calif. June 9, 1888. Collected by Charles A. Allen. Merriam collection number $\frac{4725}{5376}$.

Well-made skin in good condition; skull Grade B.

†**Ochotona schisticeps fuscipes** Howell.

Proc. Biol. Soc. Washington 32: 110, May 20, 1919.

158094. Skin and skull. Adult male. Brian Head, Parowan Mountains, Iron County, Utah. September 7, 1908. Collected by W. H. Osgood. Original number 3475.

Well-made skin in good condition; skull Grade A.

†**Ochotona schisticeps goldmani** Howell.

North Amer. Fauna 47: 40, Aug. 21, 1924.
=*Ochotona princeps goldmani* Howell. See Hall and Bowlus, Univ. California Publ. Zool. 42: 337, Oct. 12, 1938.

236408. Skin and skull. Adult male. Echo Crater, Snake River Desert, 20 miles southwest of Arco, Butte County, Idaho. June 18, 1921. Collected by Luther J. Goldman. Original number 2754.

Well-made skin in good condition; skull Grade B.

†**Ochotona schisticeps jewetti** Howell.

Proc. Biol. Soc. Washington 32: 109. May 20. 1919.

208352. Skin and skull. Adult male. Head of Pine Creek, near Cornucopia, south slope of Wallowa Mountains, Baker County, Oreg. September 3, 1915. Collected by Stanley G. Jewett. Original number 2362.

Well-made skin in good condition; skull Grade A.

*Ochotona uinta Hollister.

Proc. Biol. Soc. Washington 25: 58, Apr. 13, 1912.

=*Ochotona princeps uinta* Hollister. See Howell, North Amer. Fauna 47: 19, Aug. 21, 1924.

9750. Skin only. Adult. Uinta Mountains, near head of east fork of Bear River, Utah. September 28, 1870. Collected by F. V. Hayden. Original number 567.

Fairly well-made skin in good condition.

†Ochotona uinta lemhi Howell.

Proc. Biol. Soc. Washington 32: 106, May 20, 1919.

=*Ochotona princeps lemhi* Howell. See Howell, North Amer. Fauna 47: 16, Aug. 21, 1924.

$\frac{23543}{30961}$. Skin and skull. Adult female. Lemhi Mountains, 10 miles west of Junction, Lemhi County, Idaho. August 19, 1890. Collected by Clark P. Streator. Original number 174.

Well-made skin in good condition; skull Grade A.

†Ochotona uinta nevadensis Howell.

Proc. Biol. Soc. Washington 32: 107, May 20, 1919.

=*Ochotona princeps nevadensis* Howell. See Howell, North Amer. Fauna 47: 21, Aug. 21, 1924.

94213. Skin and skull. Adult female. Ruby Mountains, altitude 10,500 feet, southwest of Ruby Valley P. O., Elko County, Nev. June 21, 1898. Collected by Vernon Bailey. Original number 6580.

Well-made skin in good condition; skull Grade B.

†Ochotona uinta ventorum Howell.

Proc. Biol. Soc. Washington 32: 106, May 20, 1919.

=*Ochotona princeps ventorum* Howell. See Howell, North Amer. Fauna 47: 18, Aug. 21, 1924.

176778. Skin and skull. Adult male. Fremont Peak, altitude 11,500 feet, Wind River Mountains, Fremont County, Wyo. July 19, 1911. Collected by H. E. Anthony. Original number 395.

Well-made skin in good condition; skull Grade A.

251543—42——16

Order MARSUPIALIA: Marsupials

Family CAENOLESTIDAE

Genus LESTOROS Oehser

*Orolestes inca Thomas.

Smithsonian Misc. Coll. 68 (4) : 3, Apr. 10, 1917.
=*Lestoros inca* (Thomas). See Oehser, Journ. Mamm. 15: 240, Aug. 11, 1934.

194401. Skin and skeleton. Adult male. Torontoy, altitude 14,000 feet, Peru. May 14, 1915. Collected by Edmund Heller. Original number 248.

Well-made skin in good condition; skull Grade A. Skeleton (trunk) appears to be complete and in good condition.

Family DIDELPHIIDAE: Opossums

Genus CHIRONECTES Illiger

†Chironectes panamensis Goldman.

Smithsonian Misc. Coll. 63 (5) : 1, Mar. 14, 1914.

179164. Skin and skull. Old male. Cana, altitude 2,000 feet, mountains of eastern Panama. March 23, 1912. Collected by E. A. Goldman. Original number 21562.

Well-made skin in good condition; skull Grade A.

Genus DIDELPHIS Linnaeus

†Didelphis marsupialis tabascensis J. A. Allen.

Bull. Amer. Mus. Nat. Hist. 14: 172, June 15, 1901.
=*Didelphis mesamericana tabascensis* J. A. Allen. See J. A. Allen, Bull. Amer. Mus. Nat. Hist. 16: 257, Aug. 18, 1902.

100512. Skin and skull. Adult male. Teapa, Tabasco, Mexico. April 7, 1900. Collected by E. W. Nelson and E. A. Goldman. Original number 14118.

Well-made skin in good condition; skull Grade B.

†Didelphis marsupialis texensis J. A. Allen.

Bull. Amer. Mus. Nat. Hist. 14: 172, June 15, 1901.
=*Didelphis mesamericana texensis* J. A. Allen. See J. A. Allen, Bull. Amer. Mus. Nat. Hist. 16: 256, Aug. 18, 1902.

$\frac{33133}{45137}$. Skin and skull. Adult male. Brownsville, Cameron County, Tex. April 13, 1892. Collected by F. B. Armstrong. Original number 12.

Well-made skin in good condition; skull Grade B.

†Didelphis richmondi J. A. Allen.

Bull. Amer. Mus. Nat. Hist. 14 : 175, June 15, 1901.

$\frac{33136}{45140}$. Skin and skull. Adult female. Greytown, Nicaragua. February 10, 1892 (not February 7, as in original description). Collected by C. W. Richmond. Original number 16.

Well-made skin in good condition; skull Grade A.

†Didelphis yucatanensis J. A. Allen.

Bull. Amer. Mus. Nat. Hist. 14 : 178, June 15, 1901.

108299 (not 100299, as in original description). Skin and skull. Adult male. Chichen Itza, Yucatan, Mexico. February 1, 1901 (not January 29, 1901, as in original description.) Collected by E. W. Nelson and E. A. Goldman. Original number 14468.

Well-made skin in good condition, with a small bare spot on right shoulder and injured toes on right hind foot; skull Grade A.

†Didelphis yucatanensis cozumelae Merriam.

Proc. Biol. Soc. Washington 14 : 101, July 19, 1901.

108498. Skin and skull. Adult male. Cozumel Island, off coast of Quintana Roo, Mexico. April 16, 1901. Collected by E. W. Nelson and E. A. Goldman. Original number 14700.

Well-made skin in good condition; skull Grade A.

Genus MARMOSA Gray

*Marmosa caucae albiventris Tate.

Bull. Amer. Mus. Nat. Hist. 66 : 182, Aug. 10, 1933.

194378. Skin and skull. Adult male. Torontoy, near Cuzco, altitude 8,000 feet, Peru. April 30, 1915. Collected by E. Heller. Original number 129.

Well-made skin in good condition; skull Grade A.

†Marmosa demararae meridae Tate.

Amer. Mus. Nov. 493 : 3, Sept. 26, 1931.

137510. Skin and skull. Old male. "Cafetos de Mérida," Mérida, 1,630 meters, Venezuela. June 14, 1904. Collected by Briceño Gabaldon. Original number 5393–X.

Fairly well-made specimen in good condition; skull Grade A.

Marmosa formosa Shamel.

See *Marmosa muscula* Shamel.

†Marmosa insularis Merriam.

Proc. Biol. Soc. Washington 12 : 14, Jan. 27, 1898.

=*Marmosa canescens insularis* Merriam. See Tate, Bull. Amer. Mus. Nat. Hist. 66 : 144, Aug. 10, 1933.

89215. Skin and skull.   Adult male.   Maria Madre Island, Tres Marias Islands, Nayarit, Mexico.   May 16, 1897.   Collected by E. W. Nelson and E. A. Goldman.   Original number 11028.

Well-made skin in good condition; skull Grade A.

†Marmosa invicta Goldman.

Smithsonian Misc. Coll. 60 (2) : 3, Sept. 20, 1912.

178708.   Skin and skull.   Adult male.   Cana, altitude 2,000 feet, in the mountains of eastern Panama.   March 14, 1912.   Collected by E. A. Goldman.   Original number 21517.

Well-made specimen in good condition except for slightly injured ears; skull Grade B.

†Marmosa isthmica Goldman.

Smithsonian Misc. Coll. 56 (36) : 1, Feb. 19, 1912.
=*Marmosa ruatanica isthmica* Goldman.   See Tate, Bull. Amer. Mus. Nat. Hist. 66: 125, Aug. 10, 1933.

170969.   Skin and skull.   Adult male.   Rio Indio, near Gatun, Canal Zone, Panama.   February 16, 1911.   Collected by E. A. Goldman.   Original number 20889.

Well-made skin in good condition; skull Grade A.

†Marmosa murina mexicana Merriam.

Proc. Biol. Soc. Washington 11 : 44, March 16, 1897.
=*Marmosa mexicana mexicana* Merriam.   See Bangs, Bull. Mus. Comp. Zool. 39: 19, April, 1902.

71526.   Skin and skull.   Immature male.   Juquila, Oaxaca, Mexico. February 28, 1895.   Collected by E. W. Nelson and E. A. Goldman.   Original number 7571.

Well-made skin in good condition; skull Grade A.

*Marmosa muscula Shamel.

Journ. Washington Acad. Sci. 20 : 83, Mar. 4, 1930.
=*Marmosa formosa* Shamel, Journ. Mamm. 11: 311, Aug. 9, 1930.   (Renaming of *Marmosa muscula*, preoccupied.)

236330.   Skin and skull.   Adult male.   Riacho Pilago, 10 miles northwest of Kilometro 182, Formosa, Argentina.   August 9, 1920.   Collected by Alexander Wetmore.   Original number 1081.

Well-made skin in good condition; skull Grade A.

†Marmosa oaxacae Merriam.

Proc. Biol. Soc. Washington 11 : 43, Mar. 16, 1897.
=*Marmosa canescens oaxacae* Merriam.   See Tate, Bull. Amer. Mus. Nat. Hist. 66 : 143, Aug. 10, 1933.

68240. Skin and skull. Adult female. City of Oaxaca, State of Oaxaca, Mexico. August 14, 1894. Collected by E. W. Nelson and E. A. Goldman. Original number 6571.

Well-made skin in good condition, except for a bare spot on the rump; skull Grade A.

*Marmosa purui Miller.

Proc. Biol. Soc. Washington 26:31, Feb. 8, 1913.
=*Marmosa caucae purui* Miller. See Tate, Bull. Amer. Mus. Nat. Hist. 66:184, Aug. 10, 1933.

105543. Skin in alcohol, skull removed. Adult male. Hyutana-ham, upper Purus River, Brazil. March 1901. Collected by J. B. Steere.

Skin well-preserved and in good condition; skull Grade B.

*Marmosa ruatanica Goldman.

Proc. Biol. Soc. Washington 24:237, Nov. 28, 1911.

$\frac{7785}{37700}$. Skin and skull. Adult. Ruatan Island, off north coast of Honduras. Collected by J. Akhurst. Cataloged February 4, 1865.

Well-made skin in good condition; skull Grade B.

*Marmosa zeledoni Goldman.

Proc. Biol. Soc. Washington 24:238, Nov. 28, 1911.
=*Marmosa mexicana zeledoni* Goldman. See Cabrera, Genera Mammalium, Monotremata, Marsupialia, p. 37, 1919.

$\frac{12885}{37133}$. Skin and skull. Adult male. Navarro, Costa Rica, March 1, 1878. Collected by Juan Cooper for José C. Zeledon. Original number 119.

Well-made skin in good condition except for small bare patch on left side of rump; skull Grade A.

Genus METACHIROPS Matschie

†Metachirus fuscogriseus pallidus J. A. Allen.

Bull. Amer. Mus. Nat. Hist. 14: 215, July 3, 1901.
=*Metachirops opossum pallidus* (J. A. Allen). See Miller, U. S. Nat. Mus. Bull. 128: 7, Apr. 29, 1924.

58158. Skin and skull. Adult male. Orizaba, Veracruz, Mexico. January 24, 1894 (not June 24, 1894, as in original description). Collected by E. W. Nelson and E. A. Goldman. Original number 5740.

Well-made skin in good condition; skull Grade A.

Genus METACHIRUS Burmeister

†Metachirus nudicaudatus dentaneus Goldman.

Smithsonian Misc. Coll. 56 (36) : 2, Feb. 19, 1912.

172732. Skin and skull. Adult male. Gatun, Canal Zone, Panama. January 12, 1911. Collected by E. A. Goldman. Original number 20837.

Well-made skin in good condition; skull Grade A.

Genus MONODELPHIS Burnett

†Peramys melanops Goldman.

Smithsonian Misc. Coll. 60 (2) : 2, Sept. 20, 1912.
=Monodelphis melanops (Goldman). See Miller, U. S. Nat. Mus. Bull. 128: 7, Apr. 29, 1924.

179609. Skin and skull. Adult male. Cana, altitude 2,800 feet (not 2,000 feet as in original description), in the mountains of eastern Panama. May 23, 1912. Collected by E. A. Goldman. Original number 21737.

Well-made skin in good condition; skull Grade C.

Genus PHILANDER Brisson

*Philander centralis Hollister.

Proc. Biol. Soc. Washington 27: 103, May 11, 1914.

$\frac{12218}{38522}$. Skin and skull. Adult female. Talamanca, Costa Rica.

Collected by William Gabb. Cataloged November 19, 1874.

Well-made skin in good condition; skull Grade A.

Family PHALANGERIDAE: Phalangers

Genus PHALANGER Storr

*Phalanger furvus Miller and Hollister.

Proc. Biol. Soc. Washington 35: 115, Oct. 17, 1922.

219473. Skin and skull. Adult male. Rano Rano, Middle Celebes. January 5, 1918. Collected by H. C. Raven. Original number 3369.

Flat skin in good condition; skull Grade A.

Order PERISSODACTYLA: Odd-toed Ungulates

Family EQUIDAE: Horses

Genus EQUUS Linnaeus

*Equus quagga cuninghamei Heller.

Smithsonian Misc. Coll. 61 (22) : 3, Jan. 26, 1914.

182157. Skin and skull. Young adult male. Archers Post, Northern Guaso Nyiro River, British East Africa [=Kenya]. September 23, 1911. Collected by Edmund Heller. Original number 2466.

Flat skin in good condition; skull Grade A.

Family TAPIRIDAE: Tapirs

Genus TAPIRELLA Palmer

*Elasmognathus bairdii Gill.

Proc. Acad. Nat. Sci. Philadelphia 17: 183, presented at meeting of Oct. 10, 1865.

=*Tapirella bairdii* (*Gill*). See Elliot, Field Columb. Mus. Publ. 95 (zool. ser. 4, pt. 1) : 87, 1904.

6019. Skull, no skin. Isthmus of Panama. Collected by W. T. White. Cataloged April 9, 1863.

Skull Grade B.

Gill designated no type specimen. His description was based on two skulls, adult and young, collected on the Isthmus of Panama by W. S. White. Two such specimens, adult and immature, are now in the National Museum, cataloged April 9, 1863. The adult should be regarded as the type. In the original description, Gill speaks of the vomer and the nasal septum, both of which are lacking in the younger specimen (No. 6020) but well developed in the adult.

*Elasmognathus dowii Gill.

Amer. Journ. Sci. and Arts (ser. 2) 50: 142, 1870.

=*Tapirella dowii* (Gill). See Elliot, Field Columb. Mus. Publ. 95 (zool. ser. 4, pt. 1) : 88, 1904.

11278. Skull, no skin. Nearly adult. Guatemala. Collected by J. M. Dow. Original number 1. Cataloged July 19, 1870.

Skull Grade B.

Type not designated by number. The original description refers to skulls of four adults and one young in the Smithsonian collection, all obtained by John M. Dow. These five specimens are catalog Nos. 11278-9, 11280-1-2, bearing the original numbers 1, 2, 3, 4, and 5. The title of Gill's article is "A New Species of Tapir, from Guatemala." However only one of the skulls came from Guatemala, namely, the first, No. 11278, and that one shows the reduced fused nasals emphasized in the description better than any of the others. This specimen is plainly marked "Guatemala" in old lettering on the skull. The four others are marked "Salvador, C. A." In the catalog its locality was first entered as "Salvador, C. Am."; but the word "Salvador" now has a line drawn through it and "Guatemala" written above it. The other four are marked "Salvador." There is no doubt, therefore, that No. 11278 must be regarded as the type.

Order PINNIPEDIA: Seals, Walruses

Family OTARIIDAE: Eared Seals

Genus ARCTOCEPHALUS E. Geoffroy and F. Cuvier

*Arctocephalus townsendi Merriam.

Proc. Biol. Soc. Washington 11: 178, July 1, 1897.

83617. Skull. Adult male. Collected on the beach on the west side of Guadelupe Island, Lower California, Mexico, by C. H. Townsend, May 22, 1892.

Skull is an old weather-worn specimen, without teeth, and with no lower jaw; Grade C.

Family PHOCIDAE: Hair Seals

Genus MIROUNGA Gray

*Macrorhinus angustirostris Gill.   Lectotype.

Proc. Essex Inst. 5: 13, 1866–1867 (communicated Oct. 16, 1865; separates issued Apr. 7, 1866); Proc. Chicago Acad. Sci. 1: 33, Apr. 1866.

=*Mirounga angustirostris* (Gill). See Elliot, Field Columb. Mus. Publ. 95 (zool. ser. 4, pt. 2): 545, 1904.

4704. Skull. Immature female. St. Bartholomews Bay, Lower California, Mexico. 1857. Collected by W. O. Ayres. Skull has the following legend on it in old, much-faded writing: "Macrorhinus/ * * * * Bartholemew Bay/ L. California/ Sea Elephant/ * * posited Dr. Ayre /A/," and number 4704.

Skull Grade B. Type not designated by the original describer. This is the only specimen in the Museum answering to the locality and dimensions published by T. N. Gill. It was figured by J. A. Allen (History of North American Pinnipeds, figs. 57, 58, 59, 60, 1880), who designated it as the type (=lectotype) on p. 748, footnote to table.

Genus PHOCA Linnaeus

*Halichoerus antarcticus Peale.

U. S. Exploring Expedition 8 (Mamm. and Ornith.): 30; woodcut, 31, 1848.

=*Phoca pealii* Gill, Proc. Essex Inst. 5: 4, footnote, 1866–67. J. A. Allen, History of North American Pinnipeds, U. S. Geol. Surv., Misc. Pub. 12: 561, 580–582, 1880.

=*Phoca richardii richardii* (Gray). See J. A. Allen, Bull. Amer. Mus. Nat. Hist. 16: 491, Dec. 12, 1902; see also pp. 463, 466, and 467.

3648. Skull only. Young adult. Said to have been collected by the United States Exploring Expedition at Deception Island, South Shetland Islands, October 10. Cataloged January 10, 1860. Gill and Allen (see references above) strongly and rightly question the locality given by Peale.

The skull has evidently been injured in recent years; Grade B. There should be a skin, No. 3741, which cannot be found.

Type not designated by number, but a consideration of Allen's "Pinnipeds," pp. 580–582, leaves no doubt that this specimen is the type.

*Phoca ochotensis macrodens J. A. Allen.

Bull. Amer. Mus. Nat. Hist. 16: 483, Dec. 12, 1902.

83447. Skull only. Young adult (male *fide* Allen). Avatcha Bay, Kamchatka, Siberia, 1896. Collected by L. Stejneger.

Skull Grade A.

†Phoca richardii geronimensis J. A. Allen.

Bull. Amer. Mus. Nat. Hist. 16: 495, Dec. 12, 1902.

81520. Skin and skull (skin not examined by describer and not mentioned in original description). Adult male. San Geronimo Island, Lower California, Mexico. September 13, 1896. Collected by A. W. Anthony. Original number 209.

Well-made skin in good condition; skull Grade A.

*Phoca richardii pribilofensis J. A. Allen.

Bull. Amer. Mus. Nat. Hist. 16: 495, Dec. 12, 1902.

$\frac{83223}{49550}$. Skin and skeleton. Adult female. St. Paul Island, Pribilof Islands, Alaska. Collected by C. H. Townsend. Cataloged November 28, 1896.

Well-made skin in good condition; skeleton Grade A.

In writing the original description, J. A. Allen seems to have been unaware that this skin, 83223, pertains to the same individual as skull and skeleton 49550.

*Phoca stejnegeri J. A. Allen.

Bull. Amer. Mus. Nat. Hist. 16: 485, Dec. 12, 1902.

21310. Skull only. Adult male. Bering Island, Bering Sea, Siberia. April 16, 1883. Collected by L. Stejneger. Original number 1973.

Skull Grade A.

Order PRIMATES: Lemurs, Marmosets, Monkeys, Apes, Men

Family ALOUATTIDAE: Howler Monkeys

Genus ALOUATTA Lacépède

†Alouatta palliata inconsonans Goldman.

Smithsonian Misc. Coll. 60 (22) : 17, Feb. 28, 1913.
=*Alouatta palliata aequatorialis* Festa. See Lawrence, Bull. Mus. Comp. Zool. 75: 322, Nov 1933.

171068. Skin and skull. Adult male. Cerro Azul, altitude 2,500 feet, near headwaters of the Chagres River, Panama. March 23, 1911. Collected by E. A. Goldman. Original number 20995.

Well-made skin in good condition; skull Grade A.

†Alouatta palliata mexicana Merriam.

Proc. Biol. Soc. Washington 15: 67, Mar. 22, 1902.

79398. Skin and skull. Adult male. Minatitlan, Veracruz, Mexico, April 23, 1896. Collected by E. W. Nelson and E. A. Goldman. Original number 9551.

Well-made skin in good condition; skull Grade A.

Family AOTIDAE: Durukulis, or Night Monkeys

Genus AOTUS Humboldt

†Aotus zonalis Goldman.

Smithsonian Misc. Coll. 63 (5) : 6, Mar. 14, 1914.

171231. Skin and skull. Adult female. Gatun, altitude 100 feet, Canal Zone, Panama. April 29, 1911. Collected by E. A. Goldman. Original number 21101.

Well-made skin in good condition; skull Grade A.

Family CALLITRICHIDAE: Marmosets

Genus MYSTAX Gray

*Midas elegantulus Slack.

Proc. Acad. Nat. Sci. Philadelphia 13: 463, ordered printed Dec. 31, 1861. =*Mystax rufiventer* (Gray). See Thomas, Ann. Mag. Nat. Hist. (ser. 9) 9: 198, Feb. 1922.

$\frac{5132}{37870}$. Skin and skull. Adult male. "Amazon River and its tributaries." 1851. Collected by W. L. Herndon.

Skin with terminal two-thirds of tail missing, otherwise in good condition; skull Grade A.

Type not designated by number.

Family CEBIDAE: American Monkeys

Genus ATELES E. Geoffroy

†Ateles dariensis Goldman.

Proc. Biol. Soc. Washington 28: 101, Apr. 13, 1915.

179044. Skin and skull. Adult female. Near head of Rio Limon, altitude 5,200 feet, Mount Pirri, eastern Panama. April 29, 1912. Collected by E. A. Goldman. Original number 21664.

Well-made skin in good condition; skull Grade A.

*Ateles tricolor Hollister.

Proc. Biol. Soc. Washington 27 : 141, July 10, 1914.

=*Ateles neglectus* Reinhardt. See Hollister, Proc. Biol. Soc. Washington 28 : 142, June 29, 1915.

$\frac{9427}{8972}$. Skin and skull. Adult female. Santa Efigenia, Oaxaca, Mexico. January 14, 1869. Collected by F. Sumichrast. Original number 42.

Well-made skin in good condition; skull Grade A.

Genus CEBUS Erxleben

*Cebus capucinus limitaneus Hollister.

Proc. Biol. Soc. Washington 27 : 105, May 11, 1914.

$\frac{16084}{22845}$. Skin and skull. Adult male. Segovia River, northern Nicaragua. 1887. Collected by C. H. Townsend.

Well-made skin in good condition, some loss of hair on left fore and right hind foot; skull Grade A.

*Cebus margaritae Hollister.

Proc. Biol. Soc. Washington 27 : 105, May 11, 1914.

63219. Skin and skull. Old adult female. Margarita Island, off north coast of Venezuela. July 13, 1895. Collected by Wirt Robinson. Original number 520.

Well-made skin in good condition; skull Grade A.

Family CERCOPITHECIDAE: Guenons

Genus CERCOPITHECUS Brünnich [12]

*Lasiopyga albogularis kima Heller.

Smithsonian Misc. Coll. 61 (17) : 9, Oct. 21, 1913.

=*Cercopithecus mitis kibonotensis* (Lönnberg). See G. M. Allen, Bull. Mus. Comp. Zool. 83 : 147, Feb. 1939.

182242. Skin and skull. Adult male. Mount Mbololo, Taita District, British East Africa [=Kenya]. November 6, 1911. Collected by Edmund Heller. Original number 2555.

Flat skin in good condition; skull Grade A.

*Lasiopyga albogularis maritima Heller.

Smithsonian Misc. Coll. 61 (17) : 8, Oct. 21, 1913.

=*Cercopithecus mitis kibonotensis* (Lönnberg). See G. M. Allen, Bull. Mus. Comp. Zool. 83 : 147, Feb. 1939.

---

[12] For use of this name in place of *Lasiopyga* Illiger see Opinions rendered by the International Commission on Zoological Nomenclature, Opinion 104, Smithsonian Misc. Coll. 73 (5) : 26, 28, Sept. 19, 1928.

182272. Skin and skull. Adult female. Mazeras, British East Africa [=Kenya]. December 17, 1911. Collected by Edmund Heller. Original number 2585.

Flat skin in good condition; skull Grade A.

*Lasiopyga ascanius kaimosae Heller.

Smithsonian Misc. Coll. 61 (17) : 10, Oct. 21, 1913.

=Cercopithecus nictitans schmidti (Matschie). See Schwarz, Ann. Mag. Nat. Hist. (ser. 10) 1 : 662, June 1928.

182371. Skin and skull. Adult male. Upper Lukosa River, near the mission station of Kaimosi, British East Africa [=Kenya]. February 10, 1912. Collected by Edmund Heller. Original number 2692.

Flat skin in good condition; skull Grade A.

*Cercopithecus centralis luteus Elliot.

Smithsonian Misc. Coll. 56 (7) : 1, June 11, 1910.

=Cercopithecus aethiops johnstoni Pocock. See Schwarz, Zeitschr. für Säugetierkunde 1 (1) : 40, Aug. 31, 1926.

163086. Skin and skull. Adult female. Wambugu, southwest of Mount Kenia, British East Africa [=Kenya]. September 12, 1909. Collected by J. Alden Loring. Original number 7190.

Well-made skin in good condition; skull Grade A.

*Lasiopyga leucampax [sic.] mauae Heller.

Smithsonian Misc. Coll. 61 (17) : 7, Oct. 21, 1913.

=Cercopithecus mitis neumanni Matschie. See G. M. Allen, Bull. Mus. Comp. Zool. 83 : 148, Feb. 1939.

173002. Skin and skull. Adult male. Summit of Mau Escarpment, between Londiani and Sirgoit, British East Africa [=Kenya]. November 1, 1910. Collected by John Jay White.

Well-made skin in good condition except for slight breaking of the skin on both hips. Skull Grade A.

*Lasiopyga pygerythra arenaria Heller.

Smithsonian Misc. Coll. 61 (17) : 11, Oct. 21, 1913.

=Cercopithecus aethiops arenaria (Heller). See Schwarz, Zeitschr. für Säugetierkunde 1 (1) : 44, Aug. 31, 1926.

182201. Skin and skull. Adult male. Merille waterholes, Marsabit road, British East Africa [=Kenya]. July 25, 1911. Edmund Heller. Original number 387.

Flat skin in good condition except for the loss of left fore leg; skull Grade A.

*Lasiopyga pygerythra callida Hollister.

Smithsonian Misc. Coll. 59 (3) : 1, Mar. 2, 1912.

=Cercopithecus aethiops callidus (Hollister). See Schwarz, Zeitschr. für Säugetierkunde 1 (1) : 41, Aug. 31, 1926.

162843. Skin and skull. Adult male. South side of Lake Naivasha, British East Africa [=Kenya]. July 21, 1909. Collected by Edgar A. Mearns. Original number 6859.

Flat skin in good condition; skull Grade A.

*Lasiopyga pygerythra contigua Hollister.

Smithsonian Misc. Coll 72 (2) : 2, Jan. 22, 1920.
=*Cercopithecus aethiops johnstoni* Pocock. See Schwarz, Zeitschr. für Säugetierkunde 1 (1) : 40, Aug. 31, 1926.

163327. Skin and skull. Adult male. Changamwe, 6 miles inland from Mombasa, British East Africa [=Kenya]. November 30, 1909. Collected by Edgar A. Mearns. Original number 7321.

Flat skin in good condition; skull Grade A.

*Lasiopyga pygerythra tumbili Heller.

Smithsonian Misc. Coll. 61 (17) : 10, Oct. 21, 1913.
=*Cercopithecus aethiops johnstoni* Pocock. See Schwarz, Zeitschr. für Säugetierkunde 1 (1) : 40, Aug. 31, 1926.

182229. Skin and skull. Adult male. Ndi, Taita District, British East Africa [=Kenya]. November 1, 1911. Collected by Edmund Heller. Original number 2542.

Flat skin in good condition; skull Grade A.

Genus COLOBUS Illiger

*Colobus abyssinicus percivali Heller.

Smithsonian Misc. Coll. 61 (17) : 6, Oct. 21, 1913.
=*Colobus polykomos percivali* Heller. See Schwarz, Proc. Zool. Soc. London 3 : 593, 1929.

182138. Skin and skull. Adult male. Mount Gargues, British East Africa [=Kenya]. August 22, 1911. Collected by Edmund Heller. Original number 2447.

Flat skin in good condition; skull Grade A.

*Colobus abyssinicus roosevelti Heller.

Smithsonian Misc. Coll. 61 (17) : 5, Oct. 21, 1913.
=*Colobus polykomos matschiei* O. Neumann. See Schwarz, Proc. Zool. Soc. London 3 : 592, 1929.

163261. Skin and skull. Adult male. Mau forest near Enjoro, British East Africa [=Kenya]. December 6, 1909. Collected by Theodore Roosevelt. Original number (Heller) 513.

Flat skin in good condition; skull Grade A.

*Colobus abyssinicus terrestris Heller.

Smithsonian Misc. Coll. 61 (17) : 7, Oct. 21, 1913.
=*Colobus polykomos uellensis* Matschie. See Schwarz, Proc. Zool. Soc. London 3 : 591, 1929.

164756. Skin and skull. Adult female. Rhino Camp, Lado Enclave, Uganda, Africa. January 20, 1910. Collected by Kermit Roosevelt. Original number (Heller) 623.

Flat skin in good condition; skull Grade A.

Genus CYNOPITHECUS I. Geoffroy

*Cynopithecus lembicus Miller.

Journ. Mamm. 12 (4) : 413, Nov. 11, 1931.

217573. Skull only. Adult male. Pulo Lembeh, northeastern Celebes. May 30, 1916. Collected by H. C. Raven. Original number 2471.

Skull Grade A.

Genus ERYTHROCEBUS Trouessart

*Erythrocebus whitei Hollister.

Smithsonian Misc. Coll. 56 (2) : 11, Mar. 31, 1910.
=Erythrocebus patas pyrronotus Hemprich and Ehrenberg. See Schwarz, Sitz.–Ber. Ges. naturf. Freunde, Berlin, Nos. 1–10, p. 31, Feb. 9, 1926.

155440. Skin and skull. Adult male. Nzoia River, Guas Ngishu Plateau, British East Africa [=Kenya]. September 30, 1908. Collected by John Jay White.

Flat skin in good condition; skull Grade A.

Genus LYSSODES Gistel

*Pithecus pullus A. B. Howell.

Proc. Biol. Soc. Washington 41: 41, Mar. 16, 1928.
=Lyssodes speciosus melli (Matschie). See G. M. Allen, Amer. Mus. Nov. 429: 4, Sept. 8, 1930.

252157. Skin and skull. Young adult male. Kuatun, Fukien, China. Collected by F. T. Smith. Cataloged July 1, 1927.

Well-made skin in good condition; skull Grade A.

Genus MACACA Lacépède [13]

*Macaca adusta Miller.

Proc. U. S. Nat. Mus. 29: 559, Feb. 3, 1906.
=Macaca nemestrina andamanensis Bartlett. See Pocock, Journ. Bombay Nat. Hist. Soc. 35: 303, Oct. 15, 1931.

124023. Skin and skull. Adult male. Champang, Tenasserim, Malay Peninsula. December 22, 1903. Collected by W. L. Abbott. Original number 2929.

Well-made skin in good condition; skull Grade A.

---

[13] Until a revision of this group is made and exact limits of genera are established, we prefer to use this name for all the macaques except Lyssodes.

*Pithecus agnatus Elliot.[14]

Proc. U. S. Nat. Mus. 38: 344, Aug. 6, 1910.

=*Macaca irus irus* (F. Cuvier). See Chasen, Bull. Raffles Mus. 15 : 66, Apr. 1940.

114409. Skin and skull. Adult male. Pulo Tuangku, Banjak Islands, off west coast of Sumatra. January 26, 1902. Collected by W. L. Abbott. Original number 1471.

Well-made skin in good condition; skull Grade A.

*Pithecus baweanus Elliot.

Proc. U. S. Nat. Mus. 38 : 347, Aug. 6, 1910.

=*Macaca irus baweana* (Elliot). See Chasen, Bull. Raffles Mus. 15 : 70, Apr. 1940.

151829. Skin and skull. Adult male. Bawean Island, Java Sea, Malay Archipelago. November 24, 1907. Collected by W. L. Abbott. Original number 5565.

Well-made skin in good condition; skull Grade A.

*Macaca broca Miller.

Proc. U. S. Nat. Mus. 29 : 558, Feb. 3, 1906.

=*Macaca nemestrina nemestrina* Linnaeus. See Chasen, Bull. Raffles Mus. 15 : 65, Apr. 1940.

$\frac{19211}{34930}$. Skin and skull. Adult male. Along the Sapagaya River, northeastern Borneo. November 21, 1887. Collected by C. F. Adams.

Well-made skin in good condition; skull Grade A.

*Cynomolgus cagayanus Mearns.

Proc. U. S. Nat. Mus. 28 : 431, May 13, 1905.

=*Macaca cagayana* (Mearns). Lyon and Osgood, U. S. Nat. Mus. Bull. 62 : 283, Jan. 28, 1909.

125325. Skin and skull. Adult male. Cagayan Sulu Island, Sulu Sea, Philippine Islands. February 25, 1904. Collected by Edgar A. Mearns. Original number 5771.

Well-made skin in fair condition; several bare spots on arms and legs and on belly; originally preserved for some months in alcohol, but now a dry skin. (See under heading "Color" in the original description.) Skull Grade A.

*Pithecus capitalis Elliot.

Proc. U. S. Nat. Mus. 38 : 350, Aug. 6, 1910.

=*Macaca irus capitalis* (Elliot). See Chasen, Bull. Raffles Mus. 15 : 69, Apr. 1940.

83271. Skin and skull. Adult male. Trong, or Tarang, Peninsular Siam. March 7, 1896. Collected by W. L. Abbott.

Well-made skin in good condition except for sloughing of hair from arms and legs; skull Grade A.

---

[14] The name *Pithecus* as used by Elliot has been suppressed by the International Commission on Zoological Nomenclature, Opinion 114, Smithsonian Misc. Coll. 73 (6) : 25, June 8, 1929, and is, therefore, discarded from use in zoology.

*Pithecus carimatae Elliot.

Proc. U. S. Nat. Mus. 38 : 346, Aug. 6, 1910.
=*Macaca irus irus* (F. Cuvier). See Chasen, Bull. Raffles Mus. 15 : 66, Apr. 1940.

125101. Skin and skull. Adult male. Telok Pai, Karimata Islands, off west coast of Borneo. August 24, 1904. Collected by W. L. Abbott. Original number 3646.

Well-made skin in good condition; skull Grade A.

*Pithecus cupidus Elliot.

Proc. U. S. Nat. Mus. 38 : 348, Aug. 6, 1910.
=*Macaca irus cupida* (Elliot). See Chasen, Bull. Raffles Mus. 15 : 70, Apr. 1940.

151831. Skin and skull. Adult male. Pulo Mata Siri, 44 miles from Pulo Laut, Java Sea, Malay Archipelago. December 8, 1907. Collected by W. L. Abbott. Original number 5584.

Well-made skin in good condition; skull Grade A.

*Macacus fuscus Miller.

Proc. U. S. Nat. Mus. 26 : 476, Feb. 3, 1903.
=*Macaca irus fusca* Miller. See Chasen, Bull. Raffles Mus. 15 : 69, Apr. 1940.

114164. Skin and skull. Old male. Simaur Island off northwestern coast of Sumatra. November 20, 1901. Collected by W. L. Abbott. Original number 1348.

Well-made skin in good condition; skull Grade A.

*Pithecus fuscus lasiae Lyon.

Proc. U. S. Nat. Mus. 52 : 453, Dec. 30, 1916.
=*Macaca irus lasiae* (Lyon). See Chasen, Bull. Raffles Mus. 15 : 69, Apr. 1940.

114248. Skin and skull. Adult male. Pulo Lasia, off west coast of Sumatra. January 5, 1902. Collected by W. L. Abbott. Original number 1398.

Well-made skin in good condition; skull Grade A.

*Pithecus impudens Elliot.

Proc. U. S. Nat. Mus. 38 : 350, Aug. 6, 1910.
=*Macaca irus irus* (F. Cuvier). See Chasen, Bull. Raffles Mus. 15 : 66, Apr. 1940.

115675. Skin and skull. Adult male. Pulo Sugi, Rhio-Linga Archipelago. August 24, 1902. Collected by W. L. Abbott. Original number 1956.

Well-made skin in good condition; skull Grade A.

*Macaca insulana Miller.

Proc. U. S. Nat. Mus. 29 : 560, Feb. 3, 1906.
=*Macaca nemestrina andamanensis* Bartlett. See Pocock, Journ. Bombay Nat. Hist. Soc. 35 : 303, Oct. 15, 1931.

104441. Skin and skull. Adult male. Chance Island, Mergui Archipelago. January 1, 1900. Collected by W. L. Abbott. Original number 199.

Well-made skin in good condition; skull Grade A.

*Macaca irus atriceps Kloss.

Journ. Nat. Hist. Soc. Siam **3**: 347, Dec. 31, 1919.

236622. Skin and skull. Adult male. Koh Kram Island, near Cape Liant, Southeast Siam. October 30, 1916. Collected by C. Boden Kloss. Original number 2283.

Well-made skin in good condition; skull Grade A.

*Pithecus lapsus Elliot.

Proc. U. S. Nat. Mus. **38**: 343, Aug. 6, 1910.
=*Macaca irus irus* (F. Cuvier). See Chasen, Bull. Raffles Mus. **15**: 66, Apr. 1940.

124863. Skin and skull. Adult male. Tanjong Pamuja, Banka Island, off east coast of Sumatra. June 19, 1904. Collected by W. L. Abbott. Original number 3418.

Well-made skin in good condition: skull Grade A.

*Pithecus lautensis Elliot.

Proc. U. S. Nat. Mus. **38**: 345, Aug. 6, 1910.
=*Macaca irus pumila* Miller. See Chasen, Bull. Raffles Mus. **15**: 69, Apr. 1940.

104854. Skin and skull. Adult male. Pulo Laut, Natuna Islands, South China Sea, between Malay Peninsula and Borneo. August 9, 1900. Collected by W. L. Abbott. Original number 614.

Well-made skin in good condition; skull Grade A.

*Pithecus lingae Elliot.

Proc. U. S. Nat. Mus. **38**: 349, Aug. 6, 1910.
=*Macaca irus irus* (F. Cuvier). See Chasen, Bull. Raffles Mus. **15**: 66, Apr. 1940.

101603. Skin and skull. Adult male. Linga Island, Rhio-Linga Archipelago. July 23, 1899. Collected by W. L. Abbott.

Well-made skin in good condition; small bare spots on face and legs; skull Grade A.

*Pithecus lingungensis Elliot.

Proc. U. S. Nat. Mus. **38**: 344, Aug. 6, 1910.
=*Macaca irus pumila* Miller. See Chasen, Bull. Raffles Mus. **15**: 69, Apr. 1940.

104853. Skin and skull. Adult male. Pulo Lingung, Natuna Islands, South China Sea, between Malay Peninsula and Borneo. June 19, 1900. Collected by W. L. Abbott. Original number 492.

Well-made skin in good condition; skull Grade A.

251543—42——17

*Pithecus mandibularis Elliot.

Proc. U. S. Nat. Mus. 38: 347, Aug. 6, 1910.
=*Macaca irus irus* (F. Cuvier). See Chasen, Bull. Raffles Mus. 15: 66, Apr. 1940.

142225. Skin and skull. Adult male. Sungei Sama, near Pontianak, Borneo. June 18, 1905. Collected by W. L. Abbott. Original number 4196.

Well-made skin in good condition; skull Grade B.

*Pithecus mansalaris Lyon.

Proc. U. S. Nat. Mus. 52: 452, Dec. 30, 1916.
=*Macaca irus irus* (F. Cuvier). See Chasen, Bull. Raffles Mus. 15: 66, Apr. 1940.

114560. Skin and skull. Adult male. Mansalar Island, off west coast of Sumatra. March 10, 1902. Collected by W. L. Abbott. Original number 1639.

Well-made skin in good condition; skull Grade A.

*Cynomolgus mindanensis Mearns.

Proc. U. S. Nat. Mus. 28: 428, May 13, 1905.
=*Macaca mindanensis* (Mearns). See Lyon and Osgood, U. S. Nat. Mus. Bull. 62: 284, Jan. 28, 1909.

123450. Skin and skull. Adult male. Pantar, altitude 1,900 feet, Mindanao, Philippine Islands. August 26, 1903. Collected by E. A. Mearns. Original number 5620.

Well-made skin in fair condition; bare spots on forehead and arms; skull Grade A.

*Cynomolgus mindanensis apoensis Mearns.

Proc. U. S. Nat. Mus. 28: 429, May 13, 1905.
=Individual variety of *Macaca mindanensis*. See Taylor, Philippine Land Mamm., Monogr. Bur. Sci. 30: 341, June 30, 1934.

125321. Skin and skull. Adult female. Mount Apo, altitude 6,500 feet, southern Mindanao, Philippine Islands. June 25, 1904. Collected by E. A. Mearns. Original number 5670.

Well-made skin in good condition; skull Grade A.

*Pithecus mindorus Hollister.

Proc. U. S. Nat. Mus. 46: 328, Dec. 31, 1913.
=*Macaca mindorus* (Hollister).

144674. Skin and skull. Adult male. Alag River, Mindoro, Philippine Islands. November 1906. Collected by E. A. Mearns. Original number 6301.

Fairly well-made skin in good condition; skull Grade A.

*Macaca nemestrina indochinensis Kloss.

Journ. Nat. Hist. Soc. Siam 3 (4): 343, Dec. 31, 1919.
=*Macaca nemestrina andamanensis* Bartlett. See Pocock, Journ. Bombay Nat. Hist. Soc. 35: 303, Oct. 15, 1931.

236628. Skin and skull. Adult male. Lat Bua Kao, East Siam. October 12, 1916. Collected by C. Boden Kloss. Original number 2148.

Well-made skin in good condition; skull Grade A.

*Macacus pagensis Miller.

Smithsonian Misc. Coll. 45: 61, Nov. 6, 1903.
=*Macaca nemestrinus pagensis* Miller. See Chasen, Bull. Raffles Mus. 15: 66, Apr. 1940.

121653. Skin and skull. Adult female. South Pagi Island, off west coast of Sumatra. November 17, 1902. Collected by W. L. Abbott. Original number 2053.

Well-made skin in good condition; skull Grade A.

*Macacus phaeura Miller.

Smithsonian Misc. Coll. 45: 63, Nov. 6, 1903.
=*Macaca irus phaeura* Miller. See Chasen, Bull. Raffles Mus. 15: 69, Apr. 1940.

121870. Skin and skull. Adult male. Siaba Bay, Nias Island, off west coast of Sumatra. March 20, 1903. Collected by W. L. Abbott. Original number 2399.

Well-made skin in good condition; skull Grade A.

*Macacus pumilus Miller.

Proc. Washington Acad. Sci. 2: 241, Aug. 20, 1900.
=*Macaca irus pumila* Miller. See Chasen and Kloss, Journ. Malay Branch Roy. Asiatic Soc. 6 (pt. 3): 30, Aug. 1928.

101639. Skin and skull. Old adult male. Pulo Bunoa, Tambelan Islands, South China Sea, between Malay Peninsula and Borneo. August 6, 1899. Collected by W. L. Abbott.

Well-made skin in good condition; skull Grade A.

*Macacus rhesus villosus True.

Proc. U. S. Nat. Mus. 17: 2, May 8, 1894.
=*Macaca mulatta villosa* True. See Pocock, Journ. Bombay Nat. Hist. Soc. 35: 539, Feb. 15, 1932.

$\frac{20120}{35485}$ Skin and skull. Adult male. Lolab, Kashmir, India. September 8, 1891. Collected by W. L. Abbott.

Well-made skin in good condition; skull Grade A.

*Pithecus sirhassenensis Elliot.

Proc. U. S. Nat. Mus. 38: 345, Aug. 6, 1910.
=*Macaca irus pumila* Miller. See Chasen, Bull. Raffles Mus. 15: 69, Apr. 1940.

104852. Skin and skull. Adult male. Sirhassen Island, Natuna Islands, South China Sea, between Malay Peninsula and Borneo. June 8, 1900. Collected by W. L. Abbott. Original number 468.

Well-made skin in good condition; skull Grade B.

*Cynomolgus suluensis Mearns.

Proc. U. S. Nat. Mus. 28 : 430, May 13, 1905.
=*Macaca suluensis* (Mearns). See Lyon and Osgood, U. S. Nat. Mus. Bull. 62 : 284, Jan. 28, 1909.

125324. Skull (no skin). Adult male. Foot of Crater Lake Mountain, island of Sulu, Philippine Islands. November 16, 1903. Collected by E. A. Mearns. Original number 5750.

Skull Grade A.

*Macacus umbrosus Miller.

Proc. U. S. Nat. Mus. 24 : 789, May 28, 1902.
=*Macaca umbrosa* Miller.

111795. Skin and skull. Adult male. Little Nicobar, Nicobar Islands, Malay Archipelago. February 25, 1901. Collected by W. L. Abbott. Original number 888.

Well-made skin in good condition ; skull Grade A.

*Pithecus vitiis Elliot.

Proc. U. S. Nat. Mus. 38 : 346, Aug. 6, 1910.
=*Macaca vitiis* (Elliot).

124176. Skin and skull. Adult male. Domel Island, Mergui Archipelago. January 26, 1904. Collected by W. L. Abbott. Original number 3076.

Well-made skin in good condition ; skull Grade A.

Genus PAPIO Erxleben

*Papio anubis lestes Heller.

Smithsonian Misc. Coll. 61 (19) : 10, Nov. 8, 1913.
=*Papio lestes* Heller. See Hollister, U. S. Nat. Mus. Bull. 99 (pt. 3) : 19, June 20, 1924.

164633. Skin and skull. Adult male. Ulukenia Hills, Athi Plains, British East Africa [=Kenya]. November 19, 1909. Collected by J. Alden Loring. Original number 8234.

Flat skin in good condition ; skull Grade A.

*Papio anubis vigilis Heller.

Smithsonian Misc. Coll. 61 (19) : 11, Nov. 8, 1913.
=*Papio vigilis* Heller. See Hollister, U. S. Nat. Mus. Bull. 99 (pt. 3) : 18, June 20, 1924.

182033. Skin and skull. Old male. Lakiundu River near its junction with the Northern Guaso Nyiro, British East Africa [=Kenya]. July 10, 1911. Collected by Edmund Heller. Original number 2337.

Flat skin in good condition ; skull Grade A.

Genus PRESBYTIS [15] Eschscholtz

*Presbytis argentea Kloss. Cotypes.

Journ. Nat. Hist. Soc. Siam 3 : 338, Dec. 31, 1919.

=*Trachypithecus phayrei* (Blyth), according to Pocock, Proc. Zool. Soc. London, 1934 (pt. 4) : 950, Jan. 1935.

236624. Skin and skull. Adult female. Lat Bua Kao, East Siam (="30 miles W. of Korat, some 100 miles N. E. of Bangkok in S. W. Siam, not in E. Siam"; Pocock, *loc. cit.*). October 8, 1916. Collected by C. Boden Kloss. Original number 2127.

Well-made skin in good condition ; skull Grade A.

236625. Skin and skull. Adult male. Lat Bua Kao, East Siam. October 11, 1916. Collected by C. Boden Kloss. Original number 2144.

Well-made skin in good condition ; skull Grade A.

*Presbytis arwasca Miller.

Journ. Mamm. 15 : 126, May 15, 1934.

=*Presbytis chrysomelas* Müller. See Pocock, Proc. Zool. Soc. London, 1934 (pt. 4) : 910, Jan. 1935.

83953. Skin and skull. Young adult male. Miri, Sarawak, Borneo. August 1894. Collected by E. and C. Hose.

Well-made skin in good condition; skull Grade A.

*Presbytis australis Miller.

Smithsonian Misc. Coll. 61 (21) : 28, Dec. 29, 1913.

=*Presbytis femoralis* Martin. See Pocock, Proc. Zool. Soc. London, 1934 (pt. 4) : 901, Jan. 1935.

112709. Skin and skull. Adult male. Jambu Luang, east coast of Johore, Federated Malay States. July 31, 1901. Collected by W. L. Abbott. Original number 1196.

Well-made skin in good condition; skull Grade A.

*Presbytes batuanus Miller.

Smithsonian Misc. Coll. 45 : 65, Nov. 6, 1903.

=*Presbytis melalophus* Raffles. See Pocock, Proc. Zool. Soc. London, 1934 (pt. 4) : 912, Jan. 1935.

121810. Skin and skull. Adult male. Pulo Pinie, Batu Islands, off west coast of Sumatra. March 4, 1903. Collected by W. L. Abbott. Original number 2369.

Well-made skin in good condition; skull Grade A.

*Presbytis cana Miller.

Proc. U. S. Nat. Mus. 31 : 275, Sept. 11, 1906.

=*Presbytis femoralis* Martin. See Pocock, Proc. Zool. Soc. London, 1934 (pt. 4) : 901, Jan. 1935.

---

[15] *Trachypithecus* is not here treated as a separate genus. *Pithecus* suppressed ; see Smithsonian Misc. Coll. 73 (6) : 25–26, June 8, 1929.

122915. Skin and skull. Adult male. Pulo Kundur, Rhio-Linga Archipelago. June 28, 1903. Collected by W. L. Abbott. Original number 2558.

Well-made skin in good condition; skull Grade A.

*Presbytis canicrus Miller.

Proc. Biol. Soc. Washington 47: 15, Feb. 9, 1934.
=*Presbytis hosei* Thomas. See Pocock, Proc. Zool. Soc. London, 1934 (pt. 4) : 920, Jan. 1935.

198282. Skin and skull. Young adult female. Karangan River, Dutch Northeast Borneo. November 25, 1913. Collected by H. C. Raven. Original number 1137.

Well-made skin in good condition; skull Grade A.

*Presbytis carimatae Miller.

Proc. U. S. Nat. Mus. 31: 65, July 23, 1906.
=*Presbytis rubicunda* Müller. See Pocock, Proc. Zool. Soc. London, 1934 (pt. 4) : 923, Jan. 1935.

125157. Skin and skull. Adult female. Telok Adar, Karimata Island, off west coast of Borneo. September 2, 1904. Collected by W. L. Abbott. Original number 3717.

Well-made skin in good condition; skull Grade A.
Type wrongly designated as No. 125158 instead of No. 125157.

*Presbytis catemana Lyon.

Proc. U. S. Nat. Mus. 34: 672, Sept. 14, 1908.
=*Presbytis femoralis* Martin. See Pocock, Proc. Zool. Soc. London, 1934 (pt. 4) : 901, Jan. 1935.

123149. Skin and skull. Adult female. Kateman River, eastern Sumatra. August 23, 1903. Collected by W. L. Abbott. Original number 2762.

Well-made skin in good condition; skull Grade A.

*Presbytis corvus Miller.

Smithsonian Misc. Coll. 61 (21) : 27, Dec. 29, 1913.
=*Trachypithecus obscurus carbo* (Thomas and Wroughton), according to Pocock, Proc. Zool. Soc. London, 1934 (pt. 4) : 947, Jan. 1935.

123993. Skin and skull. Adult male. Pulo Terutau, off west coast of Malay Peninsula. November 10, 1903. Collected by W. L. Abbott. Original number 2852.

Well-made skin in good condition; skull Grade A.

*Presbytis cristata koratensis Kloss.

Journ. Nat. Hist. Soc. Siam 3 (4) : 340, Dec. 31, 1919.
=*Trachypithecus pyrrhus germani* Milne-Edwards, according to Pocock, Proc. Zool. Soc. London, 1934 (pt. 4) : 937, Jan. 1935.

236627. Skin and skull. Adult female. Lat Bua Kao, East Siam
(=Southwest Siam. See Pocock, Proc. Zool. Soc. London, 1934
(4) : 950, Jan. 1935). October 10, 1916. Collected by C. Boden
Kloss. Original number 2136.

Well-made skin in good condition; skull Grade A.

*Pygathrix flavicauda Elliot.

Proc. U. S. Nat. Mus. 38: 352, Aug. 6, 1910.
=*Trachypithecus obscurus flavicauda* (Elliot), according to Pocock, Proc. Zool.
Soc. London, 1934 (pt. 4) : 942, Jan. 1935.

83259. Skin and skull. Adult female. Trong (or Tarang), Peninsular Siam, March 27, 1896. Collected by W. L. Abbott.

Well-made skin in good condition; skull Grade A.

*Presbytis percura Lyon.

Proc. U. S. Nat. Mus. 34: 671, Sept. 14, 1908.
=*Presbytis melalophus* Raffles. See Pocock, Proc. Zool. Soc. London, 1934
(pt. 4) : 912, Jan. 1935.

144088. Skin and skull. Adult male. Kompei, eastern Sumatra.
February 26, 1907. Collected by W. L. Abbott. Original number 5083.

.Well-made skin in good condition; skull Grade A.

*Presbytes rhionis Miller.

Smithsonian Misc. Coll. 45: 64, Nov. 6, 1903.
=*Presbytis femoralis* Martin. See Pocock, Proc. Zool. Soc. London, 1934 (pt. 4) :
901, Jan. 1935.

115665. Skin and skull. Adult female. Telok Pemudong, Pulo
Bintang, Rhio-Linga Archipelago. August 15, 1902. Collected
by W. L. Abbott. Original number 1888.

Well-made skin in good condition; skull Grade A.

*Pygathrix rubicunda rubida Lyon.

Proc. U. S. Nat. Mus. 40: 139, Apr. 25, 1911.
=*Presbytis rubicunda* (Müller). See Pocock, Proc. Zool. Soc. London, 1934
(pt. 4) : 923, Jan. 1935.

153790. Skin and skeleton. Adult female. Batu Jurong, southwestern Borneo. June 18, 1908. Collected by W. L. Abbott.
Original number 5979.

Well-made skin in good condition; skull Grade A; skeleton, trunk complete, leg and arm bones remain in the skin.

*Pygathrix sanctorum Elliot.

Proc. U. S. Nat. Mus. 38: 351, Aug. 6, 1910.
=*Trachypithecus obscurus flavicauda* Elliot, according to Pocock, Proc. Zool.
Soc. London, 1934 (pt. 4) : 944, Jan. 1935.

104446. Skin and skull. Adult female. St. Matthew Island, Mergui Archipelago. June 16, 1900. Collected by W. L. Abbott. Original number 235.

Well-made skin in good condition; skull Grade A.

*Pygathrix ultima Elliot.

Proc. U. S. Nat. Mus. 38: 351, Aug. 6, 1910.
=*Trachypithecus pyrrhus cristatus* Raffles, according to Pocock, Proc. Zool. Soc. London, 1934 (pt. 4) : 935, Jan. 1935.

83949. Skin and skull. Adult male. Mount Dulit, altitude 3,000 feet, Borneo. June 1895. Collected by E. and C. Hose.

Well-made skin in good condition; skull Grade A.

*Presbytis vigilans Miller.

Smithsonian Misc. Coll. 61 (21) : 29, Dec. 29, 1913.
=*Trachypithecus pyrrhus cristatus* Raffles, according to Pocock, Proc. Zool. Soc. London, 1934 (pt. 4) : 934, Jan. 1935.

104840. Skull only. Adult female. Sirhassen Island, Natuna Islands, South China Sea, between Malay Peninsula and Borneo. June 2, 1900. Collected by W. L. Abbott. Original number 422.

Skull Grade A. Slight injury to right mandible; all lower incisors lost in life.

Genus SIMIAS Miller

*Simias concolor Miller.

Smithsonian Misc. Coll. 45: 67, Nov. 6, 1903.

121659. Skin and skull. Adult male. South Pagi Island, off west coast of Sumatra. December 3, 1902. Collected by W. L. Abbott. Original number 2103.

Well-made skin in good condition; skull Grade A.

Family GALAGIDAE: Bush Babies

Genus GALAGO E. Geoffroy

*Galago moholi cocos Heller.

Smithsonian Misc. Coll. 60 (12) : 1, Nov. 4, 1912.
=*Galago senegalensis zanzibaricus* Matschie. See Schwarz, Ann. Mag. Nat. Hist. (ser. 10) 7: 55, Jan. 1931.

181810. Skin and skull. Adult male. Mazeras, British East Africa [=Kenya]. December 16, 1911. Collected by Edmund Heller. Original number 4870.

Well-made skin in good condition; skull Grade A.

*Galago sotikae Hollister.

Smithsonian Misc. Coll. 72 (2) : 1, Jan. 22, 1920.
=*Galago senegalensis sotikae* Hollister. See Schwarz, Ann. Mag. Nat. Hist. (ser. 10) 7 : 55, Jan. 1931.

184205. Skin and skull. Adult male. Telek River, Sotik, British East Africa [=Kenya]. May 22, 1911. Collected by Edmund Heller. Original number 1830.

Well-made skin in good condition; skull Grade A.

Family HYLOBATIDAE: Gibbons
Genus HYLOBATES Illiger

*Hylobates cinereus abbotti Kloss.

Proc. Zool. Soc. London, 1929 (pt. 1) : 119, Apr. 1929.

142172. Skin and skull. Adult male. Sungei Nya (or Naja), Landak River, Pontianak, southwest Borneo. June 29, 1905. Collected by W. L. Abbott. Original number 4252.

Well-made skin in good condition; skull Grade A.

*Symphalangus klossii Miller.

Smithsonian Misc. Coll. 45 : 70, Nov. 6, 1903.
=Hylobates (Brachytanites) klossii (Miller). See Schultz, Journ. Mamm. 13 (4) : 369, Nov. 11, 1932.

121678. Skin and skull. Adult male. South Pagi Island, off west coast of Sumatra. November 13, 1902. Collected by W. L. Abbott. Original number 2032.

Well-made skin in good condition; skull Grade A.

*Hylobates mülleri albibarbis Lyon.

Proc. U. S. Nat. Mus. 40 : 142, Apr. 25, 1911.

145327. Skin and skull. Adult male. Along Matan River, a tributary to the Sempang River, west Borneo. August 16, 1907. Collected by W. L. Abbott. Original number 5501.

Well-made skin in good condition; skull Grade A.

Family LORISIDAE: Lorises
Genus NYCTICEBUS Geoffroy

*Nycticebus bancanus Lyon.

Proc. U. S. Nat. Mus. 31 : 536, Nov. 9, 1906.
=Nycticebus coucang bancanus Lyon. See Chasen. Bull. Raffles Mus. 15 : 89, Apr. 1940.

124907. Skin and skull. Adult female. Klabat Bay, island of Banka, east of Sumatra. June 24, 1904. Collected by W. L. Abbott. Original number 3432.

Well-made skin in good condition; skull Grade A.

*Nycticebus borneanus Lyon.

Proc. U. S. Nat. Mus. 31 : 535, Nov. 9, 1906.
=Nycticebus coucang borneanus Lyon. See Chasen, Bull. Raffles Mus. 15 : 89, April, 1940.

142234. Skin and skull. Adult male. Along the Sakaiam River, a tributary of the Kapuas River, Sanggau district, western Borneo. August 15, 1905. Collected by W. L. Abbott. Original number 4322.

Well-made skin in good condition; skull Grade A.

*Nycticebus coucang natunae Stone and Rehn.

Proc. Acad. Nat. Sci. Philadelphia 54: 140, June 4, 1902.
=*Nycticebus coucang natunae* Stone and Rehn. See Chasen, Bull. Raffles Mus. 15: 89, April, 1940.

104599. Skin and skull. Adult male. Bunguran, Natuna Islands, South China Sea, between Malay Peninsula and Borneo. July 28, 1900. Collected by W. L. Abbott. Original number 602.

Well-made skin in good condition; skull Grade A.

Family TARSIIDAE: Tarsiers

Genus TARSIUS Storr

*Tarsius borneanus Elliot.

Bull. Amer. Mus. Nat. Hist. 28: 153, May 27, 1910.
=*Tarsius tarsier borneanus* Elliot. See Chasen, Bull. Raffles Mus. 15: 86, Apr. 1940.

142242. Skin and skull. Young adult female. Landak River, West Borneo. July 10, 1905. Collected by W. L. Abbott. Original number 4259.

Well-made skin in good condition; skull Grade A.

*Tarsius fraterculus Miller.

Proc. U. S. Nat. Mus. 38: 404, Aug. 19, 1910.

239250. Skin and skeleton. Adult female. Sevilla, Bohol Island, Philippine Islands. April 9, 1906. Collected by A. Celestino and M. Canton. Original number 94, Philippine Bureau Science.

Well-made skin in good condition; skeleton Grade A.

*Tarsius fuscus dentatus Miller and Hollister.

Proc. Biol. Soc. Washington 34: 103, June 30, 1921.

218071. Skin and skull. Adult male. Laboea Sore (north of Parigi), Celebes. November 15, 1916. Collected by H. C. Raven. Original number 2956.

Well-made skin in good condition; skull Grade A.

*Tarsius pumilus Miller and Hollister.

Proc. Biol. Soc. Washington 34: 103, June 30, 1921.

219454. Skin and skull. Adult female. Rano Rano, Middle Celebes. December 31, 1917. Collected by H. C. Raven. Original number 3366.

Well-made skin in good condition; skull Grade A.

*Tarsius saltator Elliot.

Bull. Amer. Mus. Nat. Hist. 28: 152, May 27, 1910.
=*Tarsius tarsier saltator* Elliot. See Chasen, Bull. Raffles Mus. 15: 86, Apr. 1940.

124992. Skin and skull. Adult female. Buding Kampong, Billiton Island, off east coast of Sumatra. August 7, 1904. Collected by W. L. Abbott. Original number 3544.

Well-made skin in good condition; skull Grade A.

Order RODENTIA: Rodents

Family APLODONTIIDAE: Mountain-beavers

Genus APLODONTIA Richardson

*Aplodontia major Merriam.   Lectotype.

Ann. New York Acad. Sci. 3: 316, May 1886.
=*Aplodontia rufa californica* Peters. See Taylor, Univ. California Publ. Zool. 17: 473, May 29, 1918.

186473. Skin and skeleton. Adult male. Blue Canyon, Placer County, Calif. October 7, 1885. Collected by C. A. Allen. Merriam collection number $\frac{1501}{2101}$.

Well-made skin in good condition: skeleton perfect, except for absence of first upper premolars and part of left scapula broken away.

†Aplodontia major rainieri Merriam.

Proc. Biol. Soc. Washington 13: 21, Jan. 31, 1899.
=*Aplodontia rufa rainieri* Merriam. See Taylor, Univ. California Publ. Zool. 17: 465, May 29, 1918.

90144. Skin and skull. Adult male. Paradise Creek, south side of Mount Rainier, altitude, 5,200 feet, Lewis County, Wash. August 6, 1897. Collected by Vernon Bailey. Original number 6122.

Well-made skin in good condition; skull Grade A.

†Aplodontia olympica Merriam.

Proc. Biol. Soc. Washington 13: 20, Jan. 31, 1899.
=*Aplodontia rufa olympica* Merriam. See Taylor, Univ. California Publ. Zool. 17: 460, May 29, 1918.

89549. Skin and skull. Young adult male. Quiniault Lake, Olympic Mountains, Chehalis County, Wash. July 24, 1897. Collected by R. T. Young. Original number 309.

Well-made skin in good condition; skull Grade A.

†Aplodontia pacifica Merriam.

Proc. Biol. Soc. Washington 13: 19, Jan. 31, 1899.
=*Aplodontia rufa pacifica* Merriam. See Taylor, Univ. California Publ. Zool. 17: 467, May 29, 1918.

77372. Skin and skull. Adult female. Newport, mouth of Yaquina Bay, Lincoln County, Oreg. March 26, 1896 (not March 20, as in original description). Collected by B. J. Bretherton. Original number 2219.

Well-made skin in good condition; skull Grade A.

*Aplodontia phaea Merriam.

Proc. Biol. Soc. Washington 13 : 20, Jan. 31, 1899.
=*Aplodontia rufa phaea* Merriam. See Taylor, Univ. California Publ. Zool. 17 : 480, May 29, 1918.

186475. Skin and skull. Adult male. Point Reyes, Marin County, Calif. August 1, 1886. Collected by C. A. Allen. Original number 142. Merriam collection number $\frac{2645}{3273}$.

Well-made skin in good condition; skull Grade A.

Family BATHYERGIDAE: Sand Moles
Genus HELIOPHOBIUS Peters

*Georychus kapiti Heller.

Smithsonian Misc. Coll. 52 (4) : 469, Sept. 24, 1909.
=*Heliophobius kapiti* (Heller). See Thomas, Ann. Mag. Nat. Hist. (ser. 8) 6 : 315, Sept. 1910.

161708. Skin and skull. Adult female. Potha, Kapiti Plains, British East Africa [=Kenya]. May 3, 1909. Collected by J. Alden Loring. Original number 6027.

Well-made skin in good condition; skull Grade A.

Family CASTORIDAE: Beavers
Genus CASTOR Linnaeus

†Castor canadensis baileyi Nelson.

Proc. Biol. Soc. Washington 40 : 125, Sept. 26, 1927.

228006. Skin and skull. Adult male. Humboldt River, 4 miles above Winnemucca, Humboldt County, Nev. October 13, 1917. Collected by J. R. Bunch. Original number 19885–X.

Well-made skin in good condition; skull Grade B.

*Castor canadensis frondator Mearns.

Preliminary Diagnoses of New Mammals of the Genera *Sciurus, Castor, Neotoma*, and *Sigmodon*, from the Mexican Border of the United States, p. 2, Mar. 5, 1897. (Reprint: Proc. U. S. Nat. Mus. 20: 502, Jan. 19, 1898.)

$\frac{20750}{35883}$. Skin and skull. Adult male. San Pedro River, Sonora, Mexico, near monument No. 98 of the Mexican boundary line.

October 24, 1892. Collected by E. A. Mearns and F. X. Holzner. Original number 2151. International Boundary Commission.

Well-made skin, but rather overstuffed, in good condition; skull Grade A.

†Castor canadensis mexicanus Bailey.

Proc. Biol. Soc. Washington 26 : 191, Oct. 23, 1913.

96522. Skin and skull. Adult female. Ruidoso Creek, 6 miles below Ruidoso, Lincoln County, N. Mex. September 29, 1898. Collected by C. Barber. Original number 83; 1991–X.

Well-made skin in good condition, except for injury to left forefoot; skull Grade A.

†Castor canadensis michiganensis Bailey.

Proc. Biol. Soc. Washington 26 : 192, Oct. 23, 1913.

170561. Skin and skull. Adult female. Tahquamenaw River, 5 miles above falls, Luce County, Mich. September 20, 1910. Collected by C. Birdseye. Original number 1270.

Well-made skin in good condition; skull Grade A.

†Castor canadensis missouriensis Bailey.

Journ. Mamm. 1 : 32, Nov. 28, 1919.

205763. Skin and skull. Immature male. Apple Creek, 7 miles east of Bismarck, Burleigh County, N. Dak. September 1, 1914. Collected by Vernon Bailey. Original number 9703.

Well-made skin in good condition; skull Grade A.

†Castor canadensis repentinus Goldman.

Journ. Mamm. 13 (3) : 266, Aug. 9, 1932.

161613. Skin and skull. Adult female. Bright Angel Creek, altitude 4,000 feet, Grand Canyon of the Colorado River, Ariz. September 14, 1909. Collected by C. Birdseye. Original number 723.

Well-made skin in good condition; skull Grade A.

†Castor canadensis texensis Bailey.

North Amer. Fauna 25 : 122, Oct. 24, 1905.

135744. Skin and skull. Cummings Creek, Colorado County, Tex. December 25, 1900. Collected by F. Brune. Kept in captivity until January 10, 1901. Original number 5139–X.

Skin folded and flattened, having been made . over after mounting; rump, underparts, and nose largely bare or with scattered patches of underfur; right fore leg missing; nails of hind toes mostly broken or absent; skull Grade B.

†**Castor subauratus shastensis** Taylor.

Univ. California Publ. Zool. 12 : 433, Mar. 20, 1916.
=*Castor canadensis shastensis* Taylor. See Grinnell, Univ. California Publ. Zool. 40 : 166, Sept. 26, 1933.

50978. Skull only. Adult male. Cassel, Pit River, Shasta County, Calif. January 3, 1893. Collected by H. E. Williams.

Skull Grade A.

Family CHINCHILLIDAE: Chinchillas

Genus LAGOSTOMUS Brookes

*Lagostomus maximus petilidens** Hollister.

Proc. Biol. Soc. Washington 27 : 58, Mar. 20, 1914.

172801. Skull only. Adult [male]. 8 miles north of Carmen de Patagones, Rio Negro Terr., Argentina. 1910. Collected by Aleš Hrdlička.

Skull Grade A.

Family CRICETIDAE: Cricetine Rats, Mice

Genus AKODON Meyen

*Akodon chacoensis** Shamel.

Journ. Washington Acad. Sci. 21 : 427, Oct. 19, 1931.

236239. Skin and skull. Adult male. Las Palmas, Chaco, Argentina. July 20, 1920. Collected by Alexander Wetmore. Original number 1059.

Well-made skin in good condition; skull Grade A.

*Akodon surdus** Thomas.

Smithsonian Misc. Coll. 68 (4) : 2, Apr. 10, 1917.

194663. Skin and skull. Adult male. Huadquina, altitude 5,000 feet, Peru. October 28, 1915. Collected by Edmund Heller. Original number 835.

Well-made skin in good condition except for small bare spot on belly; skull Grade A.

*Microxus torques** Thomas.

Smithsonian Misc. Coll. 68 (4) : 3, Apr. 10, 1917.
=*Akodon torques* (Thomas). See Thomas, Ann. Mag. Nat. Hist (ser. 9) 19 : 370, Mar. 1927.

194607. Skin and skull. Adult male. Matchu Picchu, altitude 12,000 feet, Peru. May 28, 1915. Collected by Edmund Heller. Original number 276.

Well-made skin in good condition; skull Grade A.

Genus ALTICOLA Blanford

*Alticola acmaeus Schwarz.

Proc. Zool. Soc. London (ser. B) 108 (pt. 4) : 665, Jan. 26, 1939.

198530. Skin and skull. Adult male. Mrobuk, Phyang Nullah, northwest of Leh, Ladak, India. October 18, 1913. Collected by W. L. Abbott. Original number 8282.

Well-made skin in good condition; skull Grade A.

*Microtus acrophilus Miller.

Proc. Acad. Nat. Sci. Philadelphia 51 : 296, Aug. 9, 1899.
=*Alticola acrophilus* (Miller). See Hinton, Monograph of the Voles and Lemmings 1 : 324, 1926.
=*Alticola stoliczkanus* Blanford. See Schwarz, Proc. Zool. Soc. London 108 : 663, 1938.

62162. Skin and skull. Adult female. On the Ladak side of the Kara Korum Pass, altitude 17,000 feet, Kashmir, India. July 25, 1893. Collected by W. L. Abbott.

Well-made skin in good condition; skull Grade A.

*Arvicola albicauda True.

Proc. U. S. Nat Mus. 17 : 12, May 8, 1894.
=*Alticola albicauda* (True). See Hinton, Monograph of the Voles and Lemmings 1 : 314, 1926.

$\frac{20393}{36816}$. Skin and skull. Adult female. Braldu Valley, altitude 11,000 feet. Baltistan, Kashmir, India. December 19, 1891. Collected by W. L. Abbott.

Well-made skin in good condition; skull Grade A.

*Microtus cricetulus Miller.

Proc. Acad. Nat. Sci. Philadelphia 51 : 294, Aug. 9, 1899.
=*Alticola stracheyi* (Thomas). See Hinton, Monograph of the Voles and Lemmings 1 : 321, 1926.
=*Alticola stoliczkanus* Blanford. See Schwarz, Proc. Zool. Soc. London 108 : 663, 1938.

84043. Skin and skull. Adult male. Banks of the Tso Kyun, altitude 16,000 feet, Ladak, India. August 11, 1897. Collected by W. L. Abbott.

Well-made skin in good condition: skull Grade A.

*Alticola glacialis Miller.

Proc. Biol. Soc. Washington 26 : 197, Oct. 23, 1913.

176071. Skin and skull. Adult female. Chogo Lungma Glacier, altitude 11,000 feet, Baltistan, Kashmir, India. August 23, 1912. Collected by W. L. Abbott. Original number 7841.

Well-made skin in good condition; skull Grade A.

*Arvicola montosa True.

Proc. U. S. Nat. Mus. 17: 11, May 8, 1894.

=*Alticola montosa* (True). See Hinton, Monograph of the Voles and Lemmings 1: 315, 1926.

$\frac{20145}{35508}$. Skin and skull. Half-grown male. Central Kashmir, altitude 11,000 feet, India. October 4, 1891. Collected by W. L. Abbott.

Well-made skin in good condition; skull Grade A.

Genus ASCHIZOMYS Miller

*Aschizomys lemminus Miller.

Proc. Acad. Nat. Sci. Philadelphia 50: 369, Oct. 15, 1898.

=*Clethrionomys* near *C. rufocanus* Sundevall. See Hinton, Monograph of the Voles and Lemmings 1: 43, 1926; Miller, Journ. Mamm. 21: 94, Feb. 14, 1940.

$\frac{9911}{37299}$. Skin and skull and dried body. Adult male. Kelsey Station, Plover Bay, Bering Strait, northeastern Siberia. Collected by G. W. Baxter, Western Union Co.'s Overland International Telegraph Expedition. Original number 423. Skin cataloged January, 1872; skull, April 29, 1897.

Well-made skin in good condition; skull Grade A. The dried-up body is also present. The specimen was originally preserved in alcohol and made into a study skin many years later.

Genus BAIOMYS True

†Peromyscus allex Osgood.

Proc. Biol. Soc. Washington 17: 76, Mar. 21, 1904.

=*Baiomys taylori paulus* (J. A. Allen). See Miller, U. S. Nat. Mus. Bull. 79: 137, Dec. 31, 1912.

$\frac{33429}{45452}$. Skin and skull. Adult male. Colima, State of Colima, Mexico. March 7, 1892. Collected by E. W. Nelson. Original number 2029.

Well-made skin in good condition; skull Grade A.

†Sitomys musculus Merriam.

Proc. Biol. Soc. Washington 7: 170, Sept. 29, 1892.

=*Baiomys musculus musculus* (Merriam). See Mearns, U. S. Nat. Mus. Bull. 56 (pt. 1): 381, Apr. 13, 1907.

$\frac{33437}{45460}$. Skin and skull. Adult female. Colima, State of Colima, Mexico. March 9, 1892. Collected by E. W. Nelson. Original number 2055.

Well-made skin in good condition; skull Grade A.

*Baiomys musculus grisescens Goldman.

Proc. Biol. Soc. Washington 45: 121, July 30, 1932.

257083. Skin and skull. Adult female. Comayabuela, altitude 3,100 feet, just south of Tegucigalpa, Honduras. March 6, 1932. Collected by C. F. Underwood. Original number 838.

Well-made skin in good condition; skull Grade A.

†Peromyscus musculus nigrescens Osgood.

Proc. Biol. Soc. Washington 17: 76, Mar. 21, 1904.
=*Baiomys musculus nigrescens* (Osgood). See Miller, U. S. Nat. Mus. Bull. 79: 137, Dec. 31, 1912.

76827. Skin and skull. Adult female. Valley of Comitan, Chiapas, Mexico. December 9, 1895. Collected by E. W. Nelson and E. A. Goldman. Original number 8719.

Well-made skin in good condition; skull Grade A.

†Peromyscus taylori analogus Osgood.

North Amer. Fauna 28: 256, Apr. 17, 1909.
=*Baiomys taylori analogus* (Osgood). See Miller, U. S. Nat. Mus. Bull. 79: 137, Dec. 31, 1912.

120261. Skin and skull. Adult male. Zamora, Michoacan, Mexico. January 15, 1903. Collected by E. W. Nelson and E. A. Goldman. Original number 15764.

Well-made skin in good condition; skull Grade A.

†Peromyscus taylori subater Bailey.

North Amer. Fauna 25: 102, Oct. 24, 1905.
=*Baiomys taylori subater* (Bailey). See Miller, U. S. Nat. Mus. Bull. 79: 137, Dec. 31, 1912.

$\frac{32616}{44539}$. Skin and skull. Adult female. Bernard Creek, near Columbia, Brazoria County, Tex. February 25, 1892. Collected by W. Lloyd. Original number 1122.

Well-made skin in good condition; skull Grade A.

Genus CHELEMYS Thomas

*Notiomys vestitus alleni Osgood.

Field Mus. Nat. Hist. Publ. 229, zool. ser. 12: 124, Oct. 26, 1925.
=*Chelemys vestitus alleni* (Osgood). See Thomas, Ann. Mag. Nat. Hist. (ser. 9) 19: 656, June 1927; and Gyldenstolpe, Kungl. Svenska Vet.-Akad. Handl. 11: 127, 1932.

84227. Skin and skull. Adult male. Upper Rio Chico, Santa Cruz, southern Argentina. February 8, 1897. Collected by O. A. Peterson. Original number 372.

Well-made skin in good condition, underpart of tail slightly damaged; skull Grade A.

Genus CHRAEOMYS Thomas

*Chraeomys inornatus Thomas.

Smithsonian Misc. Coll. 68 (4) : 2, Apr. 10, 1917.

194685. Skin and skull. Adult female. Ollantaytambo, altitude 13,000 feet, Peru. July 20, 1915. Collected by Edmund Heller. Original number 457.

Well-made skin in good condition except that terminal third of tail is missing; skull Grade A.

Genus CLETHRIONOMYS [16] Tilesius

*Evotomys alascensis Miller.

Proc. Acad. Nat. Sci. Philadelphia 50: 364, Oct. 15, 1898.

=*Clethrionomys dawsoni dawsoni* (Merriam). Placed in synonymy by Osgood, North Amer. Fauna 24: 34, Nov. 23, 1904.

$\frac{14359}{22226}$. Skin and skull. Adult male. St. Michael, Norton Sound, Alaska. October 26, 1879. Collected by E. W. Nelson. Original number 96.

Skin in good condition; skull Grade A.

†Evotomys californicus Merriam.

North Amer. Fauna 4: 26, Oct. 8, 1890.

=*Clethrionomys californicus* (Merriam). See Grinnell, Univ. California Publ. Zool. 40: 185, Sept. 26, 1933.

$\frac{17011}{23920}$. Skin and skull. Adult male. Eureka, Humboldt County, Calif. June 3, 1889. Collected by T. S. Palmer. Original number 110.

Well-made skin in good condition; skull Grade A.

*Evotomys carolinensis Merriam.

Amer. Journ. Sci. (ser. 3) 36: 460, Dec. 1888.

=*Clethrionomys carolinensis* (Merriam). See Kellogg, Proc. U. S. Nat. Mus. 84: 467, Oct. 7, 1937.

186490. In alcohol. Adult female. Roan Mountain, altitude 6,000 feet, Mitchell County, N. C. August 11, 1887. Collected by C. Hart Merriam. Merriam collection number 3660.

Alcoholic in good condition.

†Evotomys caurinus Bailey.

Proc. Biol. Soc. Washington 12: 21, Jan. 27, 1898.

=*Clethrionomys caurinus* (Bailey).

---

[16] *Evotomys=Clethrionomys.* See T. S. Palmer, Proc. Biol. Soc. Washington 41: 87, Mar. 16, 1928.

89460. Skin and skull. Adult male. Lund, Malaspina Inlet, British Columbia, Canada. July 18, 1897. Collected by E. A. Preble. Original number 2147.

Well-made skin in good condition; skull Grade A.

*Evotomys galei Merriam.

North Amer. Fauna 4: 23, Oct. 8, 1890.
=*Clethrionomys gapperi galei* (Merriam). See Hall, Univ. California Publ. Zool. 37: 6, Apr. 10, 1931.

186491. Skin and skull. Adult female. Ward, altitude 9,500 feet, Boulder County, Colo. July 13, 1889. Collected by Denis Gale. Merriam collection No. $\frac{5685}{6352}$.

Well-made skin in good condition; skull Grade C.

"The type locality was given in the original description as Gold Hill. It has since been learned that the type specimen came from Ward, about 6 miles above Gold Hill" (Bailey, Proc. Biol. Soc. Washington 11: 126, May 13, 1897).

†Evotomys gapperi athabascae Preble.

North Amer. Fauna 27: 178, Oct. 26, 1908.
=*Clethrionomys gapperi athabascae* (Preble). See Hall, Univ. California Publ. Zool. 40: 376, Nov. 5, 1934.

109945. Skin and skull. Adult male. Fort Smith, Slave River, Mackenzie, Canada. June 27, 1901. Collected by Edward A. and Alfred E. Preble. Original number 4235.

Well-made skin in good condition; skull Grade A.

*Evotomys gapperi brevicaudus Merriam.

North Amer. Fauna 5: 119, July 30, 1891.
=*Clethrionomys brevicaudus* (Merriam).

186489. Skin and skull. Adult male. Three miles north of Custer, Black Hills, Custer County, S. Dak. July 21, 1888. Collected by Vernon Bailey. Original number 111. Merriam collection No. $\frac{4507}{5142}$.

Well-made skin in good condition; skull Grade B.

†Evotomys gapperi loringi Bailey.

Proc. Biol. Soc. Washington 11: 125, May 13, 1897.
=*Clethrionomys gapperi loringi* (Bailey).

75795. Skin and skull. Adult male. Portland, Traill County, N. Dak. November 22, 1895. Collected by J. A. Loring. Original number 3438.

Well-made skin in good condition; skull Grade A.

*Clethrionomys gapperi maurus Kellogg.

Proc. Biol. Soc. Washington 52: 37, Mar. 11, 1939.

267826. Skin and skull. Adult female. Black Mountains, 4½ miles southeast of Lynch, altitude 4,100 feet, Harlan County, Ky. June 23, 1938. Collected by Watson M. Perrygo and H. J. Cole.

Well-made skin in good condition; skull Grade A.

*Evotomys hercynicus suecicus Miller.

Proc. Washington Acad. Sci. 2: 101, July 26, 1900.
=*Clethrionomys glareolus suecicus* (Miller).

85046. Skin and skull. Adult female. Uppsala, Sweden. August 6, 1898. Collected by J. A. Loring. Original number 5009.

Well-made skin in good condition; skull Grade B.

†Evotomys idahoensis Merriam.

North Amer. Fauna 5: 66, July 30, 1891.
=*Clethrionomys idahoensis* (Merriam). See Hall, Univ. California Publ. Zool. 40: 376, Nov. 5, 1934.

$\frac{24283}{31687}$. Skin and skull. Adult female. Sawtooth (or Alturas) Lake, east base of Sawtooth Mountains, altitude 7,200 feet, Blaine County, Idaho. October 4, 1890. Collected by C. Hart Merriam and Vernon Bailey. Original number 1936.

Well-made skin in good condition; skull Grade A.

†Evotomys limitis Bailey.

Proc. Biol. Soc. Washington 26: 133, May 21, 1913.
=*Clethrionomys limitis* (Bailey). See Bailey, North Amer. Fauna 53: 193, Dec. 1, 1931.

148335. Skin and skull. Adult male. Willow Creek, altitude 8,500 feet, a branch of the Gilita, Mogollon Mountains, Socorro County, N. Mex. October 27, 1906. Collected by Vernon Bailey. Original number 8572.

Well-made skin in good condition; skull Grade A.

†Evotomys mazama Merriam.

Proc. Biol. Soc. Washington 11: 71, Apr. 21, 1897.
=*Clethrionomys mazama mazama* (Merriam). See Grinnell, Univ. California Publ. Zool. 40: 184, Sept. 26, 1933.

79913. Skin and skull. Adult male. Crater Lake, Mount Mazama, altitude 7,000 feet, Klamath County, Oreg. August 15, 1896. Collected by C. Hart Merriam and Vernon Bailey. Original number 5765.

Well-made skin in good condition; skull Grade A.

†Evotomys nivarius Bailey.

Proc. Biol. Soc. Washington 11: 136, May 13, 1897.
=*Clethrionomys nivarius* (Bailey). See Svihla, Murrelet 12: 54, May, 1931.

66203. Skin and skull. Adult female. Mount Ellinor, altitude 4,000 feet, Olympic Mountains, Mason County, Wash. July 9, 1894. Collected by C. P. Streator. Original number 4025.

Well-made skin in good condition; skull Grade A.

*Evotomys norvegicus Miller.

Proc. Washington Acad. Sci. 2: 93, July 26, 1900.
=*Clethrionomys nageri norvegicus* (Miller). See Barrett-Hamilton, History of British Mammals 15: 421, 1914, for subspecific status.

84674. Skin and skull. Adult female. Bergen, Norway. May 13, 1898. Collected by Thora Stejneger. Original number 20.

Well-made skin in good condition; skull Grade A.

†Evotomys obscurus Merriam.

Proc. Biol. Soc. Washington 11: 72, April 21, 1897.
=*Clethrionomys mazama obscurus* (Merriam). See Grinnell, Univ. California Publ. Zool. 40: 185, Sept. 26, 1933.

80413. Skin and skull. Adult male. Prospect, Rogue River Valley, Jackson County, Oreg. August 29, 1896. Collected by E. A. Preble. Original number 1455.

Well-made skin in good condition; skull Grade A.

†Evotomys occidentalis Merriam.

North Amer. Fauna 4: 25, Oct. 8, 1890.
=*Clethrionomys occidentalis* (Merriam).

$\frac{17447}{24351}$. Skin and skull. Adult male. Aberdeen, Chehalis (now Grays Harbor) County, Wash. August 16, 1889. Collected by T. S. Palmer. Original number 308.

Well-made skin in good condition; skull Grade A.

†Evotomys orca Merriam.

Proc. Washington Acad. Sci. 2: 24, Mar. 14, 1900.
=*Clethrionomys orca* (Merriam).

98028. Skin and skull. Adult female. Orca, Prince William Sound, Alaska. June 28, 1899. Collected by A. K. Fisher. Original number 2139.

Well-made skin in good condition; skull Grade A.

*Evotomys ungava Bailey.

Proc. Biol. Soc. Washington 11: 130, May 13, 1897.
=*Clethrionomys ungava* (Bailey).

186492. Skin and skull. Adult male. Fort Chimo, Ungava [=Labrador Peninsula, Quebec], Canada. May 12, 1883. Collected by L. M. Turner. Original number 317. Merriam collection No. $\frac{5471}{6158}$.

Well-made skin in good condition; skull Grade A.

*Evotomys vasconiae Miller.

Proc. Washington Acad. Sci. 2:96, July 26, 1900.
=*Clethrionomys nageri vasconiae* (Miller).

86994. Skin and skull. Adult male. Montréjeau, Haute-Garonne, France. July 4, 1899. Collected by Robert T. Young. Original number 625.

Well-made skin in good condition; skull Grade A.

†Evotomys wrangeli Bailey.

Proc. Biol. Soc. Washington 11:120, May 13, 1897.
=*Clethrionomys wrangeli* (Bailey).

74724. Skin and skull. Adult female. Wrangell, Alaska. September 1, 1895. Collected by C. P. Streator. Original number 4835.

Well-made skin in good condition; skull Grade A.

Genus DICROSTONYX Gloger

*Dicrostonyx nelsoni Merriam.

Proc. Washington Acad. Sci. 2:25, Mar. 14, 1900.
=*Dicrostonyx rubricatus rubricatus* Richardson. See G. M. Allen, Bull. Mus. Comp. Zool. 62:518, Feb. 1919.

186500. Skin and skull, originally an alcoholic. Young adult female. St. Michael, Norton Sound, Alaska. February 14, 1891. Collected by E. W. Nelson. Original number 448. Merriam collection No. $\frac{5488}{6163}$.

Well-made skin in fair condition, except for bare spot and perforation on right side and small bare spot on left side of abdomen; skull Grade A.

*Dicrostonyx richardsoni Merriam.

Proc. Washington Acad. Sci. 2:26, Mar. 14, 1900.
=*Dicrostonyx rubricatus richardsoni* Merriam. See G. M. Allen, Bull. Mus. Comp. Zool. 62:525, Feb. 1919.

186501. In alcohol, skull removed. Adult male. Fort Churchill, Hudson Bay, Keewatin, Canada. July 1859. Collected by W. MacTavish. Merriam collection No. $\frac{5489}{6164}$. Originally cataloged as U.S.N.M. No. 7756.

Alcoholic in fair condition, except for an area of sloughed hair on back and abdominal region; skull Grade C.

†Dicrostonyx unalascensis Merriam.

Proc. Washington Acad. Sci. 2:25, Mar. 14, 1900.

99622. Skull only. Adult. Unalaska, Alaska. July 8, 1899. Collected by C. Hart Merriam.

Skull from owl pellet; Grade B.

Regarded by Glover M. Allen (Bull. Mus. Comp. Zool. 62: 530, Feb. 1919) as a subspecies of *D. rubricatus*.

Regarded by E. W. Nelson (Proc. Biol. Soc. Washington 42: 143, Mar. 30, 1929), as a valid species.

†Dicrostonyx unalascensis stevensoni Nelson.

Proc. Biol. Soc. Washington 42: 145, Mar. 30, 1929.

235552. Skin and skull. Adult female. Umnak Island, Aleutian Islands, Alaska. December 14, 1920. Collected by D. H. Stevenson. Original number 9.

Well-made skin in good condition; skull Grade A.

Genus EUNEOMYS Coues

*Euneomys petersoni J. A. Allen.

Bull. Amer. Mus. Nat. Hist. 19: 192, May 9, 1903.

=*Euneomys chinchilloides* Waterhouse. See Gyldenstolpe, Kungl. Svenska Vet.-Akad. Handl. 11 (3): 93, 1932.

84198. Skin and skull. Adult female. Upper Rio Chico de Santa Cruz, near the Cordilleras, Santa Cruz Territory, Argentina. February 10, 1897. Collected by O. A. Peterson. Original number 390.

Well-made skin in good condition; skull Grade B.

Genus GEOXUS Thomas [17]

*Oxymycterus microtus J. A. Allen.

Bull. Amer. Mus. Nat. Hist. 19: 189, May 9, 1903.

=*Geoxus michaelseni* (Matschie). See Gyldenstolpe, Kungl. Svenska Vet.-Akad. Handl. 11 (3): 125, 1932.

84234. Skin and skull. Adult male. Pacific slope of the Cordilleras near the head of the Rio Chico de Santa Cruz, Santa Cruz Terr., Argentina. March 7, 1897. Collected by O. A. Peterson. Original number 570.

Well-made skin in good condition; skull Grade A.

Genus GERBILLUS Desmarest

*Gerbillus arenicolor Miller.

Proc. Biol. Soc. Washington 13: 163, Oct 31, 1900.

62153. Skin and skull. Adult male. In jungle on Yarkand River, east of Maralbashi, Eastern Turkestan. February 9, 1894. Collected by W. L. Abbott.

Well-made skin in good condition; skull Grade A.

Type designated by number, given as 62143, an error for 62153.

---

[17] For further references regarding this genus see Osgood, Field. Mus. Nat. Hist. Publ. 229 (zool. ser. 12): 113, 119, Oct. 26, 1925; Thomas, Ann. Mag. Nat. Hist. (ser. 9) 19: 656, June 1927; and Tate, Amer. Mus. Nov. 582: 1 (footnote) and 28–29, Nov. 14, 1932.

Genus HESPEROMYS Waterhouse

*Hesperomys frida Thomas.

Smithsonian Misc. Coll. 68 (4) : 1, Apr. 10, 1917.

194779. Skin and skull. Female. Chospyoc, altitude 10,000 feet, Peru. April 14, 1915. Collected by Edmund Heller. Original number 96.

Well-made skin in good condition; skull Grade A.

Genus HODOMYS Merriam

†Neotoma alleni Merriam.

Proc. Biol. Soc. Washington 7 : 168, Sept. 29, 1892.
=*Hodomys alleni* (Merriam). See Merriam, Proc. Acad. Nat. Sci. Philadelphia 46 : 235, Sept. 24, 1894.

$\frac{32709}{44632}$. Skin and skull. Adult made. Manzanillo, Colima, Mexico. January 26, 1892. Collected by E. W. Nelson. Original number 1796.

Well-made skin in good condition; skull Grade A.

†Hodomys alleni guerrerensis Goldman.

Journ. Washington Acad. Sci. 28 : 498, Nov. 15, 1938.

70574. Skin and skull. Adult male. Acapulco (sea level), Guerrero, Mexico. January 6, 1895. Collected by E. W. Nelson and E. A. Goldman. Original number 7321.

Well-made skin in good condition; skull Grade A.

†Hodomys vetulus Merriam.

Proc. Acad. Nat. Sci. Philadelphia 46 : 236, Sept. 24, 1894.

53656. Skin and skull. Adult male. Tehuacan, Puebla, Mexico. May 8, 1893. Collected by E. W. Nelson. Original number 4784.

Well-made skin in good condition; skull Grade B.

Genus HOLOCHILUS Brandt

*Holochilus incarum Thomas.

Proc. U. S. Nat. Mus. 58 : 226, Nov. 10, 1920.

194915. Skin and skull. Female. Santa Ana, Cuzco, Peru. December 22, 1914. Collected by E. C. Erdis. Original number 581.

Poorly made skin, tail with vertebrae left in, most of skin on underparts lacking, all four legs in poor condition; skull Grade A.

Genus HYPERACRIUS Miller

*Microtus brachelix Miller.

Proc. Acad. Nat. Sci. Philadelphia 51 : 290, Aug. 9, 1899.
=*Hyperacrius fertilis brachylix* (Miller). See Hinton, Monograph of the Voles and Lemmings 1 : 335, 1926.

63445. Skin and skull. Young adult female. Nagmarg, altitude 9,000 feet, Kashmir, India. November 15, 1895. Collected by W. L. Abbott.

Well-made skin in good condition; skull Grade A.

*Arvicola fertilis True.

Proc. U. S. Nat. Mus. 17: 10, May 8, 1894.

=*Hyperacrius fertilis fertilis* (True). See Hinton, Monograph of the Voles and Lemmings 1: 334, 1926.

$\frac{20147}{35510}$. Skin and skull. Adult female. Pir Panjal Range, altitude 8,500 feet, Kashmir, India. August 30, 1891. Collected by W. L. Abbott.

Well-made skin in good condition; skull Grade A.

Genus LEMMISCUS Thomas [17a]

*Arvicola curtata Cope.

Proc. Acad. Nat. Sci. Philadelphia 20: 2, presented at meeting of Jan. 21, 1868.

=*Lagurus* (*Lemmiscus*) *curtatus* (Cope). See Thomas, Ann. Mag. Nat. Hist. ser. 8) 9: 401, Apr. 1912.

$\frac{10267}{37419}$. Fragments of skull and feet. Collected by W. M. Gabb at Pigeon Spring, Mount Magruder, Nev., near boundary between Inyo County, Calif., and Esmeralda County, Nev. Skin cataloged October 15, 1872; skull, May 5, 1898.

The following is an inventory of the fragments: (1) Both hind feet, one of them with tibia attached; (2) both forefeet, one of them with radius and ulna attached, the other with radius and ulna detached; a portion of each humerus present; (3) a few small, almost unidentifiable fragments of the skull; (4) all the upper molars, glued to a good-sized fragment of the palate, the free ends of the incisors in small parts of the premaxillaries; (5) all of the lower jaw teeth except the last molar of the left side; the two other molars of that side are attached to a piece of the mandible; incisors rather fragmentary.

Type not designated by number. In the catalog, in the handwriting of the original entry, the specimen is marked "Cope's type." The present specimen is indicated as the type of Coues in Monographs of North American Rodentia, pages 215 to 217, where it appears that the specimen was in as bad condition in 1877 as it is now. One of Coues's labels, reading "No. 10267, Type of *Arvicola curtata* Cope," is still attached to the specimen.

*Arvicola (Chilotus) pallidus Merriam.

Amer. Nat. 22: 704, Aug. 1888.

=*Lemmiscus pallidus* (Merriam).

[17a] For use of *Lemmiscus* for American short-tailed microtines related to *Lagurus* Gloger, see Davis, Recent Mammals of Idaho: 325–327, Apr. 5, 1939.

186498. Skin and skull. Adult female. Fort Buford, Williams County, N. Dak. September 10, 1887. Collected by Vernon Bailey. Original number 226. Merriam collection number $\frac{3852}{4431}$.

Well-made skin in good condition; skull Grade A.

*Arvicola pauperrima Cooper.

Amer. Nat. 2: 535, Dec. 1868.

=*Lemmiscus pauperrimus* (Cooper). See Davis, Recent Mammals of Idaho: 327, Apr. 5, 1939.

$\frac{10268}{35071}$. Skin and skull. Adult male. Plains of the Columbia, near the Snake River, southwestern Wash. October 9, 1860. Collected by J. G. Cooper. Original number 126.

Skin in poor condition; parts about head and shoulders glued to a cotton filling. Posterior upper parts good for color; all the feet present, also the tail; skull Grade D.

Type designated by the original number.

Genus LEMMUS Link

*Lemmus alascensis Merriam.

Proc. Washington Acad. Sci. 2: 26, Mar. 14, 1900.

186499. In alcohol, skull removed. Adult female. Point Barrow, Alaska. June 11, 1883. Collected by John Murdock. Point Barrow Expedition, Signal Corps, War Department. Original number 102. Merriam collection No. $\frac{5491}{6166}$.

Viscera removed; an area of sloughed hair on back and another on left abdominal region; skull Grade A.

†Lemmus minusculus Osgood.

North Amer. Fauna 24: 36, Nov. 23, 1904.

119612. Skin and skull. Adult male. Kakhtul River, near mouth of Malchatna River, Alaska. September 1, 1902. Collected by W. H. Osgood and A. G. Maddren. Original number 1903.

Well-made skin in good condition; skull Grade A.

*Myodes nigripes True.

Diagnosis of New North American Mammals, p. 2, Apr. 26, 1894. (Reprinted in Proc. U. S. Nat. Mus. 17: 242, Nov. 15, 1894.)

=*Lemmus nigripes* (True). See Miller, North Amer. Fauna 12: 37, July 23, 1896.

59152. Skin and skull. Adult male. St. George Island, Pribilof Islands, Alaska. August 18, 1892 (or 1893). Collected by C. H. Townsend.

Well-made skin in good condition; skull Grade A.

†**Lemmus yukonensis** Merriam.

Proc. Washington Acad. Sci. 2: 27, Mar. 14, 1900.

98849.   Skin and skull.   Young adult female.   Charlie Creek, Yukon River, Alaska.   August 9, 1899.   Collected by W. H. Osgood. Original number 769.

Well-made skin in good condition; skull Grade A.

Genus LOPHIOMYS Depéret

***Lophiomys thomasi** Heller.

Smithsonian Misc. Coll. 59 (16) : 4, July 5, 1912.

181789.   Skin and skull.   Adult male.   Mount Gargues (Uaragess), altitude 6,000 feet, Mathews Range, British East Africa [=Kenya].   September 1, 1911.   Collected by Edmund Heller.   Original number 4206.

Well-made skin in good condition; skull Grade A.

Genus MICROTUS Schrank

***Microtus abbreviatus** Miller.

Proc. Biol. Soc. Washington 13 : 13, Jan. 31, 1899.

$\frac{15540}{22429}$.   Skin and skull.   Young adult female.   Hall Island, Bering Sea, Alaska.   September 8, 1885.   Collected by C. H. Townsend.

Considering its history, the skin is in good condition.   It has been remade into a modern study skin.   Miller (*loc. cit.*) writes: "Mr. Townsend tells me that the specimen was preserved dry.   It was received at the National Museum in September 1886, and its subsequent history is not known.   It was found in a bottle of alcohol in October, 1898."   Skull Grade B.

†**Microtus abbreviatus fisheri** Merriam.

Proc. Washington Acad. Sci. 2: 23, Mar. 14, 1900.

97976.   Skin and skull.   Adult male.   St. Matthew Island, Bering Sea, Alaska.   July 15, 1899.   Collected by A. K. Fisher.   Original number 2189.

Well-made skin in good condition; skull Grade A.

†**Arvicola (Mynomes) alticolus** Merriam.

North Amer. Fauna 3 : 67, Sept. 4, 1890.
=*Microtus longicaudus alticola* (Merriam).   See Goldman, Journ. Mamm. 19 : 491, Nov. 14, 1938.

$\frac{17615}{24551}$.   Skin and skull.   Adult female.   Little Spring, San Francisco Mountain, altitude 8,200 feet, Coconino County, Ariz.   July 31, 1889.   Collected by C. Hart Merriam and Vernon Bailey.   Original number 243.

Well-made skin in good condition; skull Grade B.

†**Microtus amakensis** Murie.

Journ. Mamm. 11: 74, Feb. 11, 1930.

246449. Skin and skull. Adult male. Amak Island, Aleutian Islands, Alaska. July 8, 1925. Collected by Donald H. Stevenson. Original number 80.

Well-made skin in good condition; skull Grade A.

†**Microtus angusticeps** Bailey.

Proc. Biol. Soc. Washington 12: 86, Apr. 30, 1898.

=*Microtus longicaudus angusticeps* Bailey. See Goldman, Journ. Mamm. 19: 491, Nov. 14, 1938.

$\frac{17087}{24008}$. Skin and skull. Adult male. Crescent City, Del Norte County, Calif. June 16, 1889. Collected by T. S. Palmer. Original number 151.

Well-made skin in good condition; skull Grade A.

†**Microtus aphorodemus** Preble.

North Amer. Fauna 22: 52, Oct. 31, 1902.

106422. Skin and skull. Adult female. West shore Hudson Bay, on barren grounds, about 50 miles south of Cape Eskimo, near mouth of Thlewiaza River, Keewatin, Canada. August 5, 1900. Collected by E. A. Preble. Original number 3208.

Well-made skin in good condition; skull Grade A.

***Microtus arvalis duplicatus** Miller.

Catalogue of the Mammals of Western Europe . . . , p. 686, 1912.

112213. Skin and skull. Adult male. Tenkitten, near Königsberg, Germany, 1901. Collected by F. L. J. Boettcher. Original number 11. Type specimen selected by F. H. van der Brink.

Well-made skin in good condition; skull Grade A.
See van der Brink, Zeitschr. für Säugetierkunde 4: 251, Oct. 2, 1930, who regards Miller as the first writer to apply the name *duplicatus* to a subspecies and not to the mere individual type of tooth structure so designated by Rörig and Börner, Arb. kais. biol. Anst. Land und Forstwirtsch, Berlin 5 (2) : pl. 5, fig. 88, 1905.

***Arvicola austerus** LeConte.

Proc. Acad. Nat. Sci. Philadelphia 6: 405, favorably reported for publication Oct. 25, 1853.

=*Microtus ochrogaster* (Wagner). See J. A. Allen, Bull. Amer. Mus. Nat. Hist. 10: 459, Nov. 10, 1898; Osgood, Proc. Biol. Soc. Washington 20: 48, Apr. 18, 1907.

2249. Skin (no record of a skull). Racine, Racine County, Wis. Collected by P. R. Hoy. Original number 950. Cataloged February 28, 1857.

Poorly made skin, right hindleg nearly detached, but specimen well preserved.

Type not designated by number. The specimen bears one old label inscribed "*Arvicola austerus* Racine, Wisc." on the obverse, and on the reverse "Type of species." In the "Remarks" column in the old original catalog is written "Type of Maj. LeConte." On pages 210 and 214 of Monographs of North American Rodentia, Coues speaks of No. 2249 as the type of *Arvicola austerus*.

*Arvicola austerus minor Merriam.

Amer. Nat. 22: 600, July, 1888.
=*Microtus minor* (Merriam). See Bailey, North Amer. Fauna 17: 75, June 6, 1900.

186493. Skin and skull. Male. Bottineau, at base of Turtle Mountains, Bottineau County, N. Dak. August 27, 1887. Collected by Vernon Bailey. Original number 210. Merriam collection No. $\frac{3827}{4406}$.

Well-made skin in good condition; skull Grade C.

†Microtus bairdi Merriam.

Proc. Biol. Soc. Washington 11: 74, Apr. 21, 1897.
=*Microtus oregoni bairdi* Merriam. See Hatfield and Hooper, Murrelet 16: 34, May 1935.

79906. Skin and skull. Adult female. Glacier Peak, Crater Lake, altitude 7,800 feet, Klamath County, Oreg. August 24, 1896. Collected by C. Hart Merriam and Vernon Bailey. Original number 5813.

Well-made skin in good condition; skull Grade B.

*Arvicola breweri Baird.   Cotypes.

Mammals of North America, p. 525, 1857.
=*Microtus breweri* (Baird). See Miller, Proc. Boston Soc. Nat. Hist. 27: 83, June, 1896.

No particular specimen was designated by Baird as the type and there is nothing to show that any one of the six specimens given in his list should be taken as such. Consequently all six listed become cotypes. They were collected in July 1856, on Muskeget Island, off Nantucket, Mass., by T. M. Brewer. The specimens are as follows:

2828. Adult male in alcohol; in good condition.

2829. Adult male in alcohol; cannot be found.

$\frac{2830}{3213}$. Adult female. Skin and skull.

Skin poorly made, but well preserved, except for two spots devoid of hair on side. Skull Grade A.

$\frac{2831}{3214}$. Adult male. Skin and skull.

Skin poorly made, but well preserved. Skull Grade A.

$\frac{2832}{3220}$.   Immature male. Skin and skull.

Skin cannot now be found. Skull Grade C. Two extra molars present, perhaps belonging to the missing lower jaws of the two preceding.

2833. Specimen in alcohol; cannot now be found.

*Arvicola californica Peale.

U. S. Exploring Expedition 8 (Mamm. and Ornith.), p. 46, 1848.
=[*Microtus*] *californicus* (Peale). See Trouessart, Catalogus Mammalium tam Viventium quam Fossilium, p. 563, 1897.

$\frac{10082}{4156}$. Skin and skull. Vicinity of San Francisco Bay, probably at San Francisquito Creek, near Palo Alto, Santa Clara County, Calif. Collected by T. R. Peale, October 26, 1841. U. S. Exploring Expedition (1838 to 1842).

Skin poorly made up; vertebrae left in tail. It looks rather discolored. The catalog entry says "Dry," but the specimen looks as if it had been in alcohol at one time. An old parchment label further bears out this view; skull Grade B.

Type not designated by number. In the entry of the skin in 1872 (12 years after entry of the skull [18]) under the remarks column of the catalog is written in the same handwriting as that of the original entry "type of *californicus*." The old parchment label on the specimen is marked "*Arvicola Californica* Peale." One of Coues's labels is attached, marked "Monographs of American Muridae. Elliott Coues, U. S. A., No. 10082. Type of Arvicola 'californica'." On page 534 of his Mammals of North America, Baird speaks of having the original specimen. In the table on page 173, Monographs of North American Rodentia, Coues has No. 10082 marked as the type of "*californicus*."

†Microtus californicus constrictus Bailey.

North Amer. Fauna 17: 36, June 6, 1900.

98347. Skin and skull. Adult male. Cape Mendocino, Humboldt County, Calif. September 6, 1899. Collected by Vernon Bailey. Original number 7174.

Well-made skin in good condition; skull Grade A.

†Microtus californicus vallicola Bailey.

Proc. Biol. Soc. Washington 12: 89, Apr. 30, 1898.

$\frac{25393}{32806}$. Skin and skull. Adult female. Lone Pine, Inyo County, Calif. December 23, 1890. Collected by E. W. Nelson. Original number 149.

Well-made skin in good condition; skull Grade A.

---

[18] Bailey (North Amer. Fauna 17: 35, 1900) thinks the skull is abnormal or never came from the same animal as the skin. The lapse of time between the two entries tends to substantiate this view.

†Microtus canicaudus Miller.

Proc. Biol. Soc. Washington 11: 67, Apr. 21, 1897.

75841. Skin and skull. Adult male. McCoy, Willamette Valley, Polk County, Oreg. December 1, 1895. Collected by B. J. Bretherton. Original number 219.

Well-made skin in good condition; skull Grade A.

*Arvicola (Pedomys) cinnamomea Baird.

Mammals of North America, p. 541, 1857.

=*Microtus ochrogaster* (Wagner). See Osgood, Proc. Biol. Soc. Washington 20: 48, Apr. 18, 1907.

$\frac{591}{1714}$. Skin (lost) and skull. Adult male. Pembina(?), Pembina County, N. Dak. Collected by C. Cavileer. Original number 23. Cataloged March 19, 1855.

The skin, number 591, according to a note in the catalog, was misplaced before 1890. It has not been found since. Skull Grade A.

Baird had but one specimen, the above, designated by number.

Bailey, North Amer. Fauna 17: 74, 1900, says, "Except for a slightly abnormal tooth pattern, Baird's type of *cinnamomea* is a large specimen of typical *austerus*. I cannot believe that it ever came from Pembina."

†Microtus dutcheri Bailey.

Proc. Biol. Soc. Washington 12: 85, Apr. 30, 1898.

=*Microtus montanus dutcheri* Bailey. See Grinnell, Proc. California Acad. Sci. (ser. 4) 3: 317, Aug. 28, 1913.

$\frac{29769}{41848}$. Skin and skull. Collected by J. L. LeConte. California, near Mount Whitney, altitude 10,000 feet, Tulare County, Calif. July 10, 1891. Collected by B. H. Dutcher. Original number 69.

Well-made skin in good condition; skull Grade A.

*Arvicola edax LeConte.

Proc. Acad. Nat. Sci. Philadelphia 6: 405, favorably reported for publication Oct. 25, 1853.

=*Microtus californicus californicus* (LeConte). See Trouessart, Catalogus Mammalium tam Viventium quam Fossilium, p. 563, 1897.

$\frac{4721}{37298}$. Skin and skull. Collected by J. L. LeConte. California, south of San Francisco (probably Monterey, according to R. Kellogg, Univ. California Publ. Zool. 21: 18, Dec. 28, 1918). Skin cataloged April 13, 1861; skull April 27, 1897.

Specimen made into a modern study skin and skull in the early part of 1897. Skull Grade C.

Major LeConte did not designate a type. The present specimen is the one that Baird alludes to as "the orginal of the species as described by Major LeConte." Mammals of North America, p. 532, 1857.

†**Microtus elymocetes** Osgood.

Proc. Biol. Soc. Washington 19: May 1, 1906.

137323. Skin and skull. Adult male. East side of Montague Island, Prince William Sound, Alaska. May 12, 1905. Collected by C. Sheldon. Original number 8 (5448–X).

Well-made skin in good condition; skull Grade A.

†**Microtus fulviventer** Merriam.

Proc. Biol. Soc. Washington 12: 106, Apr. 30, 1898.

68250. Skin and skull. Adult male. Cerro San Felipe, altitude 10,200 feet, Oaxaca, Mexico. August 22, 1894. Collected by E. W. Nelson and E. A. Goldman. Original number 6601.

Well-made skin in good condition; skull Grade B.

†**Microtus guatemalensis** Merriam.

Proc. Biol. Soc. Washington 12: 108, Apr. 30, 1898.

76777. Skin and skull. Adult male. Todos Santos, altitude 10,000 feet, Huehuetenango, Guatemala. December 30, 1895. Collected by E. W. Nelson and E. A. Goldman. Original number 8960.

Well-made skin in good condition; skull Grade A.

***Arvicola (Pedomys) haydenii** Baird.

Mammals of North America, p. 543, 1857.
=*Microtus ochrogaster haydenii* (Baird). See Osgood, Proc. Biol. Soc. Washington 20: 48, Apr. 18, 1907.

$\frac{699}{1862}$. Skin and skull. Adult male. Collected in 1854 by F. V. Hayden at Fort Pierre, then in "Nebraska," now in Stanley County, S. Dak.

Skin badly made up, legs spreading, vertebrae not removed from tail; a small patch on each side of body without hair; general condition of pelage good. Skull Grade A.

This was Baird's only specimen and was designated by number.

†**Microtus innuitus** Merriam.

Proc. Washington Acad. Sci. 2: 21, Mar. 14, 1900.

99373. Skull only. Adult. St. Lawrence Island, Bering Sea, Alaska. July 13, 1899. Collected by C. Hart Merriam.

Skull obtained from an owl pellet; Grade B.

***Microtus insularis** Bailey.

Proc. Biol. Soc. Washington 12: 86, Apr. 30, 1898. (Not of Nilsson, 1844.)
=*Microtus nesophilus* Bailey. See Bailey, Science (new ser.) 8: 783, Dec. 2, 1898. (Substitute for *insularis* Bailey.)

186494. Skin and skull. Immature male. Great Gull Island, off eastern extremity of Long Island, Suffolk County, N. Y. August 6, 1888. Collected by B. H. Dutcher. Merriam collection number $\frac{4952}{5706}$.

Well-made skin in good condition; skull Grade C.

†Microtus kadiacensis Merriam.

Proc Biol. Soc. Washington 11: 222, July 15, 1897.
=*Microtus operarius kadiacensis* Merriam. See Osgood, North Amer. Fauna 21: 64, Sept. 26, 1901.

65827. Skin and skull. Young adult female. Kodiak Island, Alaska. September 12, 1893. Collected by B. J. Bretherton. Original number 213.

Well-made skin in good condition; skull Grade B.

*Arvicola (Mynomes) longicaudus Merriam.

Amer. Nat. 22: 934, Oct. 1888.
=*Microtus longicaudus* (Merriam). See J. A. Allen, Bull. Amer. Mus. Nat. Hist. 7: 266, Aug. 21, 1895.

186496. Adult female. Custer, Black Hills, altitude 5,500 feet, Custer County, S. Dak. July 19, 1888 (not 1887 as in original description). Collected by V. Bailey. Original number 105. Merriam collection number $\frac{4509}{5144}$.

Well-made skin in good condition; skull Grade A.

†Microtus longicaudus baileyi Goldman.

Journ. Mamm. 19: 492, Nov. 14, 1938.

248924. Skin and skull. Adult male. Greenland Spring, head of Bright Angel Creek, altitude 8,000 feet, Grand Canyon National Park, Coconino County, Ariz. July 13, 1929. Collected by Vernon Bailey. Original number 10731.

Well-made skin in good condition; skull Grade B.

*Arvicola longirostris Baird.

Mammals of North America, p. 530, 1857.
=*Microtus montanus montanus* (Peale). See Bailey, North Amer. Fauna 17: 27, June 6, 1900.

$\frac{1268}{2220}$. Mounted skin and fragmentary skull. Adult female. Upper Pit River, northern California. September 1855. Collected by J. S. Newberry.

Mounted specimen in fair condition; a little hair gone from the right side. Skull Grade D.

Baird had but one specimen, the above, which he designated by number.

251543—42——19

†**Microtus ludovicianus** Bailey.

North Amer. Fauna 17: 74, June 6, 1900.

96624. Skin and skull. Adult male. Iowa, Calcasieu Parish, La. April 7, 1899. Collected by Vernon Bailey. Original number 6767.

Well-made skin in good condition; skull Grade A.

***Microtus macfarlani** Merriam.

Proc. Washington Acad. Sci. 2: 24, Mar. 14, 1900.

9155. Skin and skull. Fort Anderson, Anderson River, Mackenzie, 37347 Canada. 1865. Collected by R. MacFarlane. Original number 3179.

Specimen remade into a modern study skin and the skull removed and cleaned in March 1898. The skin is well preserved and in good condition save for some apparent lengthwise stretching. Skull Grade A.

†**Arvicola (Mynomes) macropus** Merriam.

North Amer. Fauna 5: 60, July 30, 1891.

=*Microtus richardsoni macropus* (Merriam). See Bailey, North Amer. Fauna 17: 61, June 6, 1900.

23887. Skin and skull. Adult female. Pahsimeroi Mountains, alti- 31291 tude about 9,700 feet, Custer County, Idaho. September 16, 1890. Collected by C. Hart Merriam and Vernon Bailey. Original number 1803.

Well-made skin in good condition; skull Grade A.

†**Microtus macrurus** Merriam.

Proc. Acad. Nat. Sci. Philadelphia 50: 353, Oct. 4, 1898.

=*Microtus longicaudus macrurus* Merriam. See Goldman, Journ. Mamm. 19: 491, Nov. 14, 1938.

66151. Skin and skull. Adult female. Lake Cushman, Olympic Mountains, Mason County, Wash. June 26, 1894. Collected by C. P. Streator. Original number 3975.

Well-made skin in good condition; skull Grade B.

†**Microtus mexicanus guadalupensis** Bailey.

Proc. Biol. Soc. Washington 15: 118, June 2, 1902.

109191. Skin and skull. Adult male. Guadalupe Mountains, alti- tude 7,800 feet, El Paso County, Tex. August 21, 1901. Collected by Vernon Bailey. Original number 7807.

Well-made skin in good condition; skull Grade A.

†**Microtus mexicanus hualpaiensis** Goldman.

Journ. Mamm. 19: 493, Nov. 14, 1938.

244108. Skin and skull. Adult female. Hualpai Peak, Hualpai Mountains, altitude 8,400 feet, Mohave County, Ariz. October 1, 1923. Collected by E. A. Goldman. Original number 23554.

Well-made skin in good condition; skull Grade B.

†Microtus mexicanus madrensis Goldman.

Journ. Mamm. 19: 493, Nov. 14, 1938.

98172. Skin and skull. Adult male. Gavilan River, 5 miles west of Colonia Garcia, about 60 miles southwest of Casas Grandes, altitude 6,700 feet, Chihuahua, Mexico. July 2, 1899. Collected by E. W. Nelson and E. A. Goldman. Original number 13870.

Well-made skin in good condition; skull Grade A.

†Microtus mexicanus subsimus Goldman.

Journ. Mamm. 19: 494, Nov. 14, 1938.

116918. Skin and skull. Adult male. Sierra Guadalupe, southeastern Coahuila, Mexico. May 3, 1902. Collected by E. W. Nelson and E. A. Goldman. Original number 15195.

Well-made skin in good condition; skull Grade A.

†Microtus miurus Osgood.

North Amer. Fauna 21: 64, Sept. 26, 1901.

107175. Skin and skull. Adult male. Head of Bear Creek, in mountains near Hope, Turnagain Arm, Cook Inlet, Alaska. September 4, 1900. Collected by W. H. Osgood and E. Heller. Original number 1349.

Well-made skin in good condition; skull Grade A.

†Microtus miurus oreas Osgood.

Proc. Biol. Soc. Washington 20: 61, Apr. 18, 1907.

148596. Skin and skull. Adult male. Head of Toklat River, Alaskan Range, Alaska. August 8, 1906. Collected by C. Sheldon. Original number 47 (6289–X).

Well-made skin in good condition; skull Grade B.

*Arvicola modesta Baird.

Mammals of North America, p. 535, 1857.
=*Microtus pennsylvanicus modestus* (Baird). See Bailey, North Amer. Fauna 17: 20, June 6, 1900.

$\frac{594}{1717}$. Skin and skull. Immature. Sawatch Pass [=Saguache Pass, Cochetopa Hills], Saguache County, Colo. August–September, 1853. Collected by Kreutzfeldt. Original number 16.

Skin very fragmentary and dilapidated. Right forefoot still attached. Two other feet loose and also tip of tail. Skull Grade C.

Of Baird's two specimens, both designated by numbers, the above is the only one that he refers with certainty to *modesta*.

Arvicola montana Peale.   See page 573.

†Microtus montanus arizonensis Bailey.

Proc. Biol. Soc. Washington 12: 88, Apr. 30, 1898.

$\frac{24778}{32179}$. Skin and skull. Adult male. Springerville, Apache County, Ariz. November 7, 1890. Collected by E. W. Nelson. Original number 153.

Well-made skin in good condition; skull Grade A.

†Microtus montanus caryi Bailey.

Proc. Biol. Soc. Washington 30: 29, Feb. 21, 1917.

168670. Skin and skull. Adult male. Milford, Fremont County, Wyo. May 8, 1910. Collected by Merritt Cary. Original number 1912.

Well-made skin in good condition; skull Grade A.

†Arvicola (Mynomes) mordax Merriam.

North Amer. Fauna 5: 61, July 30, 1891.
=*Microtus longicaudus mordax* (Merriam). See Goldman, Journ. Mamm. 19: 491, Nov. 14, 1938.

$\frac{24231}{31635}$. Skin and skull. Adult male. Sawtooth (or Alturas) Lake, east base of Sawtooth Mountains, altitude 7,200 feet, Blaine County, Idaho. September 29, 1890. Collected by C. Hart Merriam and Vernon Bailey. Original number 1903.

Well-made skin in good condition; skull Grade A.

†Microtus mordax bernardinus Merriam.

Proc. Biol. Soc. Washington 21: 145, June 9, 1908.
=*Microtus longicaudus bernardinus* Merriam. See Goldman, Journ. Mamm. 19: 492, Nov. 14, 1938.

150632. Skin and skull. Adult male. Dry Lake, San Bernardino Mountains, altitude 9,000 feet, at north base San Gorgonio Peak, San Bernardino County, Calif. August 21, 1907. Collected by Vernon Bailey. Original number 8749.

Well-made skin in good condition; skull Grade A.

†Microtus muriei Nelson.

Journ. Mamm. 12: 311, Aug. 24, 1931.

243482. Skin and skull. Adult female. Kutuk River, tributary of Alatna River, Endicott Mountains, Alaska. March 7, 1923. Collected by O. J. Murie. Original number 1737.

Well-made skin in good condition; skull Grade A.

†Arvicola (Mynomes) nanus Merriam.

North Amer. Fauna 5: 63, July 30, 1891.
=*Microtus montanus nanus* (Merriam). See Hall, Proc. Biol. Soc. Washington 51: 133, Aug. 23, 1938.

$\frac{23853}{31253}$ Skin and skull. Adult female (not male, as in orginal description). Pahsimeroi Mountains, altitude 9,350 feet, Custer County, Idaho. September 16, 1890. Collected by C. Hart Merriam and Vernon Bailey. Original number 1809.

Well-made skin in good condition; skull Grade A.

†Microtus nanus canescens Bailey.

Proc. Biol. Soc. Washington 12: 87, Apr. 30, 1898.
=*Microtus montanus canescens* Bailey. See Hall, Proc. Biol. Soc. Washington 51: 133, Aug. 23, 1938.

90577. Skin and skull. Adult male. Conconully, Okanogan County, Wash. September 12, 1897. Collected by J. A. Loring. Original number 4654.

Well-made skin in good condition; skull Grade C.

Microtus nesophilus Bailey.

See *Microtus insularis* Bailey.

†Microtus nevadensis Bailey.

Proc. Biol. Soc. Washington 12: 86, Apr. 30, 1898.
=*Microtus montanus nevadensis* Bailey. See Hall, Univ. California Publ. Zool. 40: 423, Oct. 25, 1935.

$\frac{26877}{34291}$ Skin and skull. Adult male (not female, as in original description). Ash Meadows, Nye County, Nev. March 2, 1891. Collected by E. W. Nelson. Original number 577.

Well-made skin in good condition; skull Grade B.

*Microtus nevadensis rivularis Bailey.

Proc. Biol. Soc. Washington 12: 87, Apr. 30, 1898.
=*Microtus montanus rivularis* Bailey. See Bailey, North Amer. Fauna 17: 29, June 6, 1900.

186497. Adult male. St. George, Washington County, Utah. January 6, 1889. Collected by Vernon Bailey. Original number 493. Merriam collection number $\frac{5172}{5867}$.

Well-made skin in good condition; skull Grade A.

*Arvicola occidentalis Peale.

U. S. Exploring Expedition 8 (Mamm. and Ornith.), p. 45, 1848.
=*Microtus townsendii* (Bachman). See Bailey, North Amer. Fauna 17: 46, June 6, 1900.

$\frac{10083}{4157}$ Skin and skull. Puget Sound, Wash. U. S. Exploring Expedition (1838 to 1842). Collected by T. R. Peale. Skin cataloged 1872; skull, 1860.

Poorly made skin, tail not skinned out. It has somewhat the look of having been in alcohol at one time. Some of the hair has slipped from each side, especially the right; skull Grade A.

Type not designated by number. In the entry of the skin in 1872 (12 years after the skull was entered in the catalog) the remarks column contains, in the same handwriting as the original entry, the note: "type of *occidentalis*." On page 535 of Mammals of North America, Baird speaks of having the original specimen. One of Coues's labels is attached marked "Monograph of American Muridae. Dr. Elliott Coues, U. S. A. No. 10083. Type of *Arvicola 'occidentalis'* Peale." In the table on page 173, Monographs of North American Rodentia, Coues has No. 10083 marked as the type of "*occidentalis*."

*Arvicola operarius Nelson.

Proc. Biol. Soc. Washington 8: 139, Dec. 28, 1893.
=[*Microtus*] *operarius* (Nelson). See Trouessart, Catalogus Mammalium tam Viventium quam Fossilium, p. 564, 1897.

$\frac{14379}{22225}$. Skin and skull. Adult. St. Michael, Norton Sound, Alaska. November 1879. Collected by E. W. Nelson. Original number 122.

Skin well preserved, but poorly made up, and right foreleg missing. Skull Grade A.

†Microtus operarius endoecus Osgood.

North Amer. Fauna 30: 23, Oct. 7, 1909.

128327. Skin and skull. Adult male. Mouth of Charlie Creek, Yukon River, about 50 miles above Circle, Alaska. June 21, 1903. Collected by W. H. Osgood. Original number 2366.

Well-made skin in good condition; skull Grade A.

†Microtus oregoni adocetus Merriam.

Proc. Biol. Soc. Washington 21: 145, June 9, 1908.

137995. Skin and skull. Adult male. South Yolla Bolly Mountain, Tehama County, Calif. July 30, 1905. Collected by A. S. Bunnell. Original number 135.

Well-made skin in good condition; skull Grade A.

†Microtus oregoni cantwelli Taylor.

Journ. Mamm. 1 (4) : 180, Aug. 24, 1920.

232814. Skin and skull. Adult male. Glacier Basin, altitude 5,935 feet, Mount Rainier, Pierce County, Wash. August 13, 1919. Collected by George G. Cantwell. Original number 1487.

Well-made skin in good condition; skull Grade C.

*Microtus pamirensis Miller.

Proc. Acad. Nat. Sci. Philadelphia 51: 287, Aug. 9, 1899.

62161. Skin and skull. Adult male. Tagdumbash, altitude 12,000 feet, Pamir, Central Asia. June 18, 1894. Collected by W. L. Abbott.

Well-made skin in good condition; skull Grade A.

*Microtus pennsylvanicus labradorius Bailey.

Proc. Biol. Soc. Washington 12: 88, Apr. 30, 1898.

186945. Skin and skull. Adult female. Fort Chimo, Ungava (=Labrador Peninsula, Quebec), Canada. November 15, 1882. Collected by L. M. Turner. Original number 296. Merriam collection number $\frac{5481}{6566}$.

Specimen, originally in alcohol, is now a well-made skin in good condition, except that the color was much changed by the action of the alcohol; skull Grade B.

†Microtus pennsylvanicus wahema Bailey.

Journ. Mamm. 1: 72, Mar. 2, 1920.

212370. Skin and skull. Adult male. Glendive, Dawson County, Mont. May 8, 1916. Collected by Remington Kellogg. Original number 425.

Well-made skin in good condition; skull Grade A.

†Arvicola phaeus Merriam.

Proc. Biol. Soc. Washington 7: 171, Sept. 29, 1892.

=*Microtus mexicanus phaeus* (Merriam). See Bailey, North Amer. Fauna 17: 54, June 6, 1900.

$\frac{33605}{45640}$. Skin and skull. Adult female. North slope Sierra Nevada de Colima, altitude 10,000 feet, Jalisco, Mexico. April 21, 1892. Collected by E. W. Nelson. Original number 2516.

Well-made skin in good condition; skull Grade B.

*Microtus pullus Miller.

Proc. Biol. Soc. Washington 24: 53, Feb. 24, 1911.

=*Microtus mandarinus* (A. Milne-Edwards). See G. M. Allen, Mamm. China and Mongolia 2: 881, Sept. 3, 1940.

155047. Skin and skull. Adult male. Chiao Ch'eng Shan, altitude 7,000 feet, 90 miles west of Tai Yuan Fu, Shansi, China. October 11, 1908. Collected by Arthur deC. Sowerby. Original number 32.

Well-made skin in good condition; skull Grade A.

*Microtus ravidulus Miller.

Proc. Acad. Nat. Sci. Philadelphia 51: 284, Aug. 9, 1899.

62159. Skin and skull. Adult female. Okchi, valley of the Aksai, altitude 7,000 feet, eastern Turkestan, central Asia. November 7, 1893. Collected by W. L. Abbott.

Well-made skin in good condition; skull Grade A.

†Microtus scirpensis Bailey.

North Amer. Fauna 17: 15, June 6, 1900.

=*Microtus californicus scirpensis* Bailey. See Kellogg, Univ. California Publ. Zool. 21: 24, Dec. 28, 1918.

$\frac{25979}{33385}$. Skin and skull. Adult female. Amargosa River (near Nevada line [spring near Shoshone, altitude 1,560 feet]), Inyo County, Calif. February 26, 1891. Collected by Vernon Bailey. Original number 2520.

Well-made skin in good condition; skull Grade A.

†Microtus serpens Merriam.

Proc. Biol. Soc. Washington 11: 75, Apr. 21, 1897.

=*Microtus oregoni serpens* Merriam. See Hatfield and Hooper, Murrelet 16: 34, May 1935.

76303. Skin and skull. Adult male. Agassiz, British Columbia, Canada. December 2, 1895. Collected by C. P. Streator. Original number 5068.

Well-made skin in good condition; skull Grade A.

†Microtus sitkensis Merriam.

Proc. Biol. Soc. Washington 11: 221, July 15, 1897.

73839. Skin and skull. Young adult male. Sitka, Alaska. August 3, 1895. Collected by C. P. Streator. Original number 4745.

Well-made skin in good condition; skull Grade A.

*Arvicola trowbridgii Baird.

Mammals of North America, p. 529, 1857.

=*Microtus californicus* (Peale). See Bailey, North Amer. Fauna 17: 35, June 6, 1900.

$\frac{370}{1284}$. Mounted specimen and skull. Monterey, Monterey County, Calif. Collected by W. P. Trowbridge. Cataloged January 4, 1855.

The mounted specimen is a poor-looking object, with patches devoid of hair on each side. Skull Grade A.

*Microtus tshuktshorum Miller.

Proc. Biol. Soc. Washington 13: 11, Jan. 31, 1899.

$\frac{8419}{37610}$. In alcohol, skull removed. Adult female. Plover Bay, Bering Strait, northeastern Siberia. 1865. Collected by John Davison. Cataloged January 12, 1866; skull, November 10, 1898.

Specimen is fairly well preserved; hair rather loose; a considerable bare patch on right side; skull Grade A.

†Microtus umbrosus Merriam.

Proc. Biol. Soc. Washington 12: 107, Apr. 30, 1898.

68480. Skin and skull. Adult female. Mount Zempoaltepec, altitude 8,200 feet, Oaxaca, Mexico. July 10, 1894. Collected by E. W. Nelson and E. A. Goldman. Original number 6412.

Well-made skin in good condition; skull Grade A.

†Microtus unalascensis Merriam.

Proc. Biol. Soc. Washington 11 : 222, July 15, 1897.

$\frac{30772}{42672}$. Skin and skull. Immature female. Unalaska, Alaska. August 13, 1891. Collected by C. Hart Merriam.

Well-made skin in good condition; skull Grade A.

†Microtus unalascensis popofensis Merriam.

Proc. Washington Acad. Sci. 2 : 22, Mar. 14, 1900.

97956. Skin and skull. Adult male. Popof Island, Shumagin Islands, Alaska. July 16, 1899. Collected by W. E. Ritter. Original number 2200 (A. K. Fisher).

Well-made skin in good condition; skull Grade A.

*Microtus warringtoni Miller.

Smithsonian Misc. Coll. 60 (28) : 1, Mar. 31, 1913.
=*Microtus* (*Phaiomys*) *brandti* (Radde). See G. M. Allen, Amer. Mus. Nov. 133 : 7, Sept. 30, 1924.

175861. Skin and skull. Adult male. Tabool, altitude 4,000 feet, Mongolia, 100 miles north of Kalgan, Chi-li, China. August 13, 1912. Collected by Arthur deC. Sowerby. Original number 508.

Well-made skin in good condition; skull Grade A.

†Microtus yakutatensis Merriam.

Proc. Washington Acad. Sci. 2 : 22, Mar. 14, 1900.

98005. Skin and skull. Adult male. North shore Yakutat Bay, Alaska. June 19, 1899. Collected by C. Hart Merriam. Original number 2101. (A. K. Fisher).

Well-made skin in good condition; skull Grade A.

Genus MYOPUS Miller

*Myopus morulus Hollister.

Smithsonian Misc. Coll. 60 (14) : 1, Nov. 29, 1912.

175197. Skin and skull. Adult male. Tapucha, altitude 6,875 feet, 125 miles southeast of Biisk, Altai Mountains, Siberia. August 6, 1912. Collected by N. Hollister. Original number 4437.

Well-made skin in good condition; skull Grade C.

Genus NEACOMYS Thomas

†Neacomys pictus Goldman.

Smithsonian Misc. Coll. 60 (2) : 6, Sept. 20, 1912.

178717. Skin and skull. Adult male. Cana, altitude 1,800 feet, in the mountains of eastern Panama. March 13, 1912. Collected by E. A. Goldman. Original number 21512.

Well-made skin in good condition, except for a small sewed laceration on right side of abdomen; skull Grade A.

Genus NECTOMYS Peters

†Nectomys alfari efficax Goldman.

Smithsonian Misc. Coll. 60 (22) : 7, Feb. 28, 1913.

178627. Skin and skull. Adult male. Cana, altitude 1,800 feet, eastern Panama. March 12, 1912. Collected by E. A. Goldman. Original number 21498.

Well-made skin in good condition ; skull Grade A.

*Nectomys squamipes pollens Hollister.

Proc. Biol. Soc. Washington 27 : 104, May 11, 1914.

121399. Skin and skull. Adult male. Sapucay, Paraguay. July 27, 1902. Collected by Wm. Foster. Original number 800.

Well-made skin in good condition ; skull Grade A.

Genus NELSONIA Merriam

†Nelsonia goldmani Merriam.

Proc. Biol Soc. Washington 16 : 80, May 29, 1903.

125818. Skin and skull. Adult male. Mount Tancitaro, Michoacan, Mexico. February 25, 1903. Collected by E. W. Nelson and E. A. Goldman. Original number 16021.

Well-made skin in good condition ; skull Grade A.

†Nelsonia neotomodon Merriam.

Proc. Biol. Soc. Washington 11 : 278, Dec. 17, 1897.

90891. Skin and skull. Adult male. Mountains near Plateado, altitude 8,500 feet, Zacatecas, Mexico. September 3, 1897. Collected by E. W. Nelson and E. A. Goldman. Original number 11625.

Well-made skin in good condition ; skull Grade A.

Genus NEOFIBER True

*Neofiber alleni True.

Science 4 : 34, July 11, 1884.

$\frac{14065}{21948}$. Skin, viscera in alcohol, and skeleton. Adult male. Georgiana, Brevard County, Fla. Collected by William Wittfeld. Received December 24, 1883.

The whole specimen was originally in alcohol. It was then skinned, mounted, and placed on exhibition. The skeleton was prepared and the viscera put in alcohol. The mounted specimen has since been taken down and prepared as a study skin, which is well made and in good condition except for a small naked spot on the right hip and the loss of many toenails. Its color is much lighter than normal, from exposure to light and probably from the effects of alcohol. The skeleton is in excellent condition. The viscera, both abdominal and thoracic, are well preserved.

Type not designated by number in the original description. The above specimen was said by F. W. True and F. A. Lucas to be the original specimen, which was unique at the time of describing.

†Neofiber alleni nigrescens Howell.

Journ. Mamm. 1: 79, Mar. 2, 1920.

228392. Skin and skull. Adult male. Ritta, south shore of Lake Okeechobee, Palm Beach County, Fla. March 2, 1918. Collected by A. H. Howell. Original number 2269.

Well-made skin in good condition; skull Grade A.

Genus NEOTOMA Say and Ord

†Neotoma albigula mearnsi Goldman.

Proc. Biol. Soc. Washington 28 : 135, June 29, 1915.

202981. Skin and skull. Adult male. Tinajas Altas, altitude about 1,400 feet, Gila Mountains, near international boundary, Yuma County, Ariz. November 21, 1913. Collected by E. A. Goldman. Original number 22300.

Well-made skin in good condition; skull Grade A.

*Neotoma albigula seri Townsend.

Bull. Amer. Mus. Nat. Hist. 31 : 125, June 14, 1912.

198404. Skin and skull. Male. Tiburon Island, Gulf of California, Sonora, Mexico. April 13, 1911. Collected by H. E. Anthony. Original number 157.

Well-made skin in good condition; skull Grade A.

†Neotoma albigula sheldoni Goldman.

Proc. Biol. Soc. Washington 28 : 136, June 29, 1915.

206812. Skin and skull. Adult male. Pinacate Mountains (Papago Tanks), Sonora, Mexico. 1915. Collected by Charles Sheldon. Original number 19 (11956X).

Well-made skin in good condition, except for small bare spot on throat; skull Grade A.

†Neotoma albigula warreni Merriam.

Proc. Biol. Soc. Washington 21 : 143, June 9, 1908.

151051. Skin and skull. Adult male. Gaume's Ranch, altitude 4,600 feet, northwest corner of Baca County, Colo. November 28, 1907. Collected by Merritt Cary. Original number 1271.

Well-made skin in good condition; skull Grade A.

*Neotoma arizonae Merriam.

Proc. Biol. Soc. Washington 8 : 110, July 31, 1893.

=*Neotoma cinerea arizonae* Merriam. See Goldman, North Amer. Fauna 31 : 106, Oct. 19, 1910.

186482. Skin and skull. Adult female. Keam Canyon, Apache County, Ariz. May 21, 1888. Collected by J. Sullivan. Merriam collection number $\frac{4289}{4980}$.

Well-made skin in good condition, except for small bare spot on rump, and left forefoot is attached to skin with wire; skull Grade A.

*Neotoma baileyi Merriam.

Proc. Biol. Soc. Washington 9: 123, July 2, 1894.
=Neotoma floridana baileyi Merriam. See Bailey, North Amer. Fauna 25: 109, Oct. 24, 1905.

186483. Skin and skull. Adult female. Valentine, Cherry County, Nebr. June 16, 1888. Collected by Vernon Bailey. Original number 41, Merriam collection number $\frac{4311}{5034}$.

Well-made skin in good condition; skull Grade A.

*Neotoma bryanti Merriam.

Amer. Nat. 21: 191, Feb. 1887.

186481. Skin in alcohol, skull removed. Immature male. Cerros Island, altitude 2,000 feet, lat. 28°12′ N., Lower California, Mexico. January 11, 1885. Collected by Walter E. Bryant. Merriam collection number $\frac{2838}{1833}$.

Alcoholic skin in poor condition, fur scorched and sloughed; skull Grade B.

†Neotoma cinerea lucida Goldman.

Proc. Biol. Soc. Washington 30: 111, May 23, 1917.

208968. Skin and skull. Adult female. Charleston Peak, Charleston Mountains, Clark County, Nev. July 1, 1915. Collected by L. J. Goldman. Original number 2282.

Well-made skin in good condition; skull Grade A.

*Neotoma cumulator Mearns.

Preliminary Diagnoses of New Mammals of the genera Sciurus, Castor, Neotoma, and Sigmodon, from the Mexican border of the United States, p. 3, Mar. 5, 1897. (Reprint: Proc. U. S. Nat. Mus. 20: 503, Jan. 19, 1898.)
=Neotoma albigula venusta True. See Goldman, North Amer. Fauna 31: 34, Oct. 19, 1910.

60348. Skin and skull. Adult male. Old Fort Yuma, Imperial County, Calif. April 2, 1894. Collected by E. A. Mearns and F. X. Holzner. Original number 3473. International Boundary Commission.

Well-made skin in good condition; skull Grade A.

†Neotoma desertorum Merriam.

Proc. Biol. Soc. Washington 9: 125, July 2, 1894.
=Neotoma lepida lepida Thomas. See Goldman, Journ. Mamm. 13: 61, Feb. 9, 1932.

$\frac{25739}{33139}$. Skin and skull. Adult male. Furnace Creek, Death Valley, Inyo County, Calif. January 31, 1891. Collected by T. S. Palmer. Original number 43.

Well-made skin in good condition; skull Grade A.

†Neotoma desertorum sola Merriam.

Proc. Biol. Soc. Washington 9: 126, July 2, 1894.
=*Neotoma lepida gilva* Rhoads. See Goldman, Journ. Mamm. 13: 63, Feb. 9, 1932.

$\frac{31516}{43381}$. Skin and skull. Adult male. San Emigdio, Kern County, Calif. October 24, 1891. Collected by E. W. Nelson. Original number 1369.

Well-made skin in good condition; skull Grade A.

"Through transposition, probably while in the hands of the skull cleaner, the skull of a southern member of the *fuscipes* group was numbered to correspond with a skin of *gilva*, and the composite specimen later became the type of *sola*" (Goldman, North Amer. Fauna 31: 45, Oct. 19, 1910).

*Neotoma fallax Merriam.

Proc. Biol. Soc. Washington 9: 123, July 2, 1894.
=*Neotoma mexicana fallax* Merriam. See Goldman, North Amer. Fauna 31: 56, Oct. 19, 1910.

186484. Skin and skull. Adult male. Gold Hill, Boulder County, Colo. November 1, 1889. Collected by Denis Gale. Merriam collection number $\frac{5678}{6345}$.

Well-made skin in good condition; skull Grade A.

†Neotoma ferruginea chamula Goldman.

Proc. Biol. Soc. Washington 22: 141, June 25, 1909.

76061. Skin and skull. Adult female. Mountains near San Cristobal, altitude 9,500 feet (not 8,400 feet as in original description), Chiapas, Mexico. September 29, 1895. Collected by E. W. Nelson and E. A. Goldman. Original number 8489.

Well-made skin in good condition; skull Grade A.

†Neotoma ferruginea ochracea Goldman.

Proc. Biol. Soc. Washington 18: 30, Feb. 2, 1905.

$\frac{34142}{46219}$. Skin and skull. Nearly adult male. Atemajac, altitude about 4,500 feet, near Guadalajara, Jalisco, Mexico. May 21, 1892. Collected by E. W. Nelson. Original number 2653.

Well-made skin in good condition; skull Grade A.

†Neotoma ferruginea solitaria Goldman.

Proc. Biol. Soc. Washington 18: 31, Feb. 2, 1905.

76908. Skin and skull. Adult male. Nenton, altitude 3,500 feet, Guatemala. December 17, 1895. Collected by E. W. Nelson and E. A. Goldman. Original number 8813.

Well-made skin in good condition; skull Grade A.

†Neotoma floridana illinoensis Howell.

Proc. Biol. Soc. Washington 23: 28, Mar. 23 1910.

167752. Skin and skull. Adult female. Wolf Lake, Union County, Ill. January 12, 1910. Collected by John Johnson. Original number 7778–X.

Well-made skin in good condition; skull Grade A.

†Neotoma fulviventer Merriam.

Proc. Biol. Soc. Washington 9: 121, July 2, 1894.
=Neotoma torquata Ward. See Goldman, North Amer. Fauna 31: 63, Oct. 19, 1910.

50165. Skin and skull. Adult female. Toluca Valley, State of Mexico, Mexico. November 5, 1892. Collected by E. W. Nelson. Original number 3744.

Well-made skin in good condition, except for a small bare space on abdomen; skull Grade A.

*Neotoma fuscipes Baird.

Mammals of North America, p. 495, 1857.

22026. Skeleton. Adult male. Petaluma, Sonoma County, Calif. February 1856. Collected by Emanuel Samuels.

The original specimen was No. 2679, preserved in alcohol, but about 1885 it was prepared as a skeleton, No. 22026. In good condition. Skeleton cataloged March 9, 1885; original specimen April 10, 1857.

The description immediately following the brief diagnosis reads "(2679, ♂), This animal * * *." For that reason the specimen bearing this number is considered the type.

†Neotoma fuscipes dispar Merriam.

Proc. Biol. Soc. Washington 9: 124, July 2, 1894.
=Neotoma fuscipes simplex True. See Goldman, North Amer. Fauna 31: 91, Oct. 19, 1910.

$\frac{25391}{32804}$. Skin and skull. Adult male. Lone Pine, Inyo County, Calif. December 25, 1890. Collected by Vernon Bailey. Original number 2310.

Well-made skin in good condition; skull Grade A.

†Neotoma fuscipes streatori Merriam.

Proc. Biol. Soc. Washington 9: 124, July 2, 1894.

64439. Skin and skull. Adult male. Carbondale, Amador County, Calif. April 4, 1894. Collected by C. P. Streator. Original number 3685.

Well-made skin in good condition; skull Grade A.

†Neotoma goldmani Merriam.

Proc. Biol. Soc. Washington 16 : 48, Mar. 19, 1903.

116894. Skin and skull. Young adult male. Saltillo, altitude 5,000 feet, Coahuila, Mexico. April 18, 1902. Collected by E. W. Nelson and E. A. Goldman. Original number 15101.

Well-made skin in good condition; skull Grade A.

*Neotoma insularis Townsend.

Bull. Amer. Mus. Nat. Hist. 31 : 125, June 14, 1912.

198405. Skin and skull. Female. Angel de la Guardia Island, Gulf of California, Lower California, Mexico. April 11, 1911. Collected by H. E. Anthony. Original number 136.

Well-made skin in good condition, terminal third of tail missing; skull Grade A.

*Neotoma intermedia angusticeps Merriam.

Proc. Biol. Soc. Washington 9 : 127, July 2, 1894.

=Neotoma albigula albigula Hartley. See Goldman, North Amer. Fauna 31 : 31, Oct. 19, 1910.

186485. Skin and skull. Adult male. Southwest corner of Grant County, 5 miles from Mexican boundary, N. Mex. April 12, 1886. Collected by A. W. Anthony. Original number 62. Merriam collection No. $\frac{2325}{2833}$.

Well-made skin in good condition, except for broken tail and a bare spot on throat; skull Grade A.

†Neotoma intermedia devia Goldman.

Proc. Biol. Soc. Washington 40 : 205, Dec. 2, 1927.

=Neotoma lepida devia Goldman. See Goldman, Journ. Mamm. 13 : 62, Feb. 9, 1932.

226376. Skin and skull. Adult female. Tanner Tank, altitude 5,200 feet, Painted Desert, Ariz. July 27, 1917. Collected by E. A. Goldman. Original number 23152.

Well-made skin in good condition; skull Grade A.

†Neotoma intermedia melanura Merriam.

Proc. Biol. Soc. Washington 9 : 126, July 2, 1894.

=Neotoma albigula melanura Merriam. See Goldman, North Amer. Fauna 31 : 35. Oct. 19, 1910.

$\frac{17819}{24756}$. Skin and skull. Young adult male. Ortiz, Sonora, Mexico. November 13, 1889. Collected by Vernon Bailey. Original number 671.

Well-made skin in good condition; skull Grade A.

†**Neotoma intermedia notia** Nelson and Goldman.

Proc. Biol. Soc. Washington 44: 108, Oct. 17, 1931.
=*Neotoma lepida notia* Nelson and Goldman. See Goldman, Journ. Mamm.
13: 65, Feb. 9, 1932.

146794. Skin and skull. Adult male. La Laguna, altitude 5,500
feet, Sierra de la Victoria, southern Lower California, Mexico.
January 27, 1906. Collected by E. W. Nelson and E. A. Goldman. Original number 19017.

Well-made skin in good condition; skull Grade A.

†**Neotoma intermedia perpallida** Goldman.

Proc. Biol. Soc. Washington 22: 139, June 25, 1909.
=*Neotoma lepida perpallida* Goldman. See Goldman, Journ. Mamm. 13: 65, Feb.
9, 1932.

79061. Skin and skull. Young adult male. San Jose Island, Gulf
of California, Lower California, Mexico. August 4, 1895. Collected by J. E. McLellan. Original number 1449.

Well-made skin in good condition, except for broken tail; skull Grade D.

†**Neotoma intermedia pretiosa** Goldman.

Proc. Biol. Soc. Washington 22: 139, June 25, 1909.
=*Neotoma lepida pretiosa* Goldman. See Goldman, Journ. Mamm. 13: 64,
Feb. 9, 1932.

146123. Skin and skull. Adult male. Matancita (also called Sole-
dad), altitude 100 feet, 50 miles north of Magdalena Bay, Lower
California, Mexico. November 17, 1905. Collected by E. W.
Nelson and E. A. Goldman. Original number 18589.

Well-made skin in good condition, except for an injury to tip of tail;
skull Grade A.

†**Neotoma intermedia ravida** Nelson and Goldman.

Proc. Biol. Soc. Washington 44: 107, Oct. 17, 1931.
=*Neotoma lepida ravida* Nelson and Goldman. See Goldman, Journ. Mamm.
13: 64, Feb. 9, 1932.

140692. Skin and skull. Adult male. Comondu, altitude 700 feet,
southern Lower California, Mexico. November 7, 1905. Collected by E. W. Nelson and E. A. Goldman. Original number
18476.

Well-made skin in good condition; skull Grade A.

†**Neotoma intermedia vicina** Goldman.

Proc. Biol. Soc. Washington 22: 140, June 25, 1909.
=*Neotoma lepida vicina* Goldman. See Goldman, Journ. Mamm. 13: 65,
Feb. 9, 1932.

146803. Skin and skull. Adult male. Espiritu Santo Island, Gulf
of California, Lower California, Mexico. February 9, 1906.
Collected by E. W. Nelson and E. A. Goldman. Original number 19082.

Well-made skin in good condition; skull Grade A.

†Neotoma isthmica Goldman.

Proc. Biol. Soc. Washington 17: 80, Mar. 21, 1904.
=*Neotoma ferruginea isthmica* Goldman.   See Goldman, North Amer. Fauna 31: 71, Oct. 19, 1910.

73187. Skin and skull. Adult female. Huilotepec, 8 miles south of Tehuantepec, altitude 100 feet, Oaxaca, Mexico. May 5, 1895. Collected by E. W. Nelson and E. A. Goldman. Original number 7843.

Well-made skin in good condition except for small perforation behind left ear; skull Grade A.

†Neotoma latifrons Merriam.

Proc. Biol. Soc. Washington 9: 121, July 2, 1894.

50135. Skin and skull. 'Adult male. Querendaro, Michoacan, Mexico. August 8, 1892. Collected by E. W. Nelson. Original number 3058.

Well-made skin in good condition; skull Grade A.

†Neotoma lepida marshalli Goldman.

Journ. Mamm. 20: 357, Aug. 14, 1939.

263984. Skin and skull. Adult female. Carrington Island, Great Salt Lake, altitude about 4,250 feet, Utah. July 2, 1938. Collected by William H. Marshall. Original number 216.

Well-made skin in good condition; skull Grade A.

†Neotoma lepida monstrabilis Goldman.

Journ. Mamm. 13: 62, Feb. 9, 1932.

243123. Skin and skull. Adult male. Ryan, altitude 6,000 feet, Kaibab National Forest, Coconino County, Ariz. October 10, 1922. Collected by E. A. Goldman. Original number 23379.

Well-made skin in good condition; skull Grade A.

†Neotoma leucodon Merriam.

Proc. Biol. Soc. Washington 9: 120, July 2, 1894.
=*Neotoma albigula leucodon* Merriam.   See Goldman, North Amer. Fauna 31: 36, Oct. 19, 1910.

50137. Skin and skull. Adult male. San Luis Potosi, State of San Luis Potosi, Mexico. August 14, 1892. Collected by E. W. Nelson. Original number 3076.

Well-made skin in good condition, except for a bare space on throat; skull Grade C.

†Neotoma leucodon zacatecae Goldman.

Proc. Biol. Soc. Washington 18: 30, Feb. 2, 1905.
=*Neotoma albigula zacatecae* Goldman.   See Goldman, North Amer. Fauna 31: 38, Oct. 19, 1910.

90957. Skin and skull. Adult female. Plateado, altitude 7,600 feet, Zacatecas, Mexico. September 4, 1897. Collected by E. W. Nelson and E. A. Goldman. Original number 11641.

Well-made skin in good condition; skull Grade C.

*Neotoma macrotis simplex True.

Diagnoses of Some Undescribed Wood Rats (genus *Neotoma*) in the National Museum, p. 2, June 27, 1894. (Reprint: Proc. U. S. Nat. Mus. 17: 354, Nov. 15, 1894.)

=*Neotoma fuscipes simplex* True.   See Miller and Rehn, Proc. Boston Soc. Nat. Hist. 30: 105, Dec. 27, 1901.

$\frac{3651}{3597}$. Skin and skull. Adult male. Old Fort Tejon, Tehachapi Mountains, Kern County, Calif. 1857–58. Collected by J. Xantus. Original number $\frac{785}{786}$. Cataloged March 24, 1859.

Well-made skin in fair condition; skull Grade A.

*Neotoma magister Baird.   Cotypes.

Mammals of North America, pp. 486, 498, 1857.

For remarks concerning the relations of this species with existing forms of *Neotoma* see E. L. Poole, Journ. Mamm. 21: 316–318, Aug. 14, 1940; Miller, Journ. Mamm. 21: 321, Aug. 14, 1940.

The cotypes are as follows, all collected in a cave near Carlisle, Pa., by S. F. Baird. They were not entered in the Museum catalog until October 24, 1872.

12206. Left half of mandible; complete, except for coronoid process.

12207. Right half of mandible; all molar teeth and angular process missing.

12208. Right half of mandible; last molar, angular, condyloid, and coronoid processes missing.

12209. Right half of mandible; all teeth, angular, condyloid, and coronoid processes missing.

12210. Left half of mandible; all molars, angular, coronoid, and condyloid processes missing. [Not found in 1940.]

12211. Middle portion of left half of mandible, containing last two molars and root of incisor.

12212. Left half of mandible; all the teeth, angular, condyloid, and coronoid processes missing.

12213. Anterior portion of right half of mandible, containing only the incisor.

12214. Fragment of left premaxilla, containing the incisor.

Cotypes not designated by number. The above are the only specimens known in the Museum and are unquestionably the ones upon which Baird based his description.

†**Neotoma martinensis** Goldman.

Proc. Biol. Soc. Washington 18: 28, Feb. 2, 1905.

81074. Skin and skull. Adult female. San Martin Island, Lower California, Mexico. July 17, 1896. Collected by A. W. Anthony. Original number 39.

Well-made skin in good condition; skull Grade A.

***Neotoma mexicana** Baird.

Proc. Acad. Nat. Sci. Philadelphia 7: 333, favorably reported for publication Apr. 24, 1855.

$\frac{289}{1674}$. Skin (lost) and skull. Adult. Mountains near Chihuahua, Chihuahua, Mexico. Collected by John Potts. Skin cataloged July 6, 1854; skull, March 10, 1855.

Skull Grade B. Skin lost.

Type not designated by number. In the original description it is said: "Collected near Chihuahua by John Potts, esq." Reference to Baird's Mammals of North America, page 942, shows that No. $\frac{289}{1674}$ is the only one to which that remark applies. It is therefore regarded as the type. Unfortunately it was without a tail, and that is undoubtedly the reason why the measurements of another specimen, No. 565, are given in the original description.

†**Neotoma mexicana bullata** Merriam.

Proc. Biol. Soc. Washington 9: 122, July 2, 1894.

$\frac{16863}{23774}$. Skin and skull. Adult male. Santa Catalina Mountains, Pima County, Ariz. June 1, 1889. Collected by Vernon Bailey. Original number 114.

Well-made skin in good condition; skull Grade A.

†**Neotoma mexicana inopinata** Goldman.

Journ. Washington Acad. Sci. 23: 471, Oct. 15, 1933.

158395. Skin and skull. Adult male. Chuska Mountains, altitude 8,800 feet northwestern N. Mex. October 3, 1908. Collected by Clarence Birdseye. Original number 246.

Well-made skin in good condition; skull Grade A.

†**Neotoma mexicana inornata** Goldman.

Proc. Biol. Soc. Washington 51: 60, Mar. 18, 1938.

263386. Skin and skull. Adult male. Carmen Mountains, altitude 6,100 feet, Coahuila, Mexico. September 22, 1937. Collected by R. S. Sturgis. Original number 28074–X (79).

Well-made skin in good condition; skull Grade A.

†**Neotoma mexicana madrensis** Goldman.

Proc. Biol. Soc. Washington 18: 31, Feb. 2, 1905.

95244. Skin and skull. Adult female. Sierra Madre, near Guadalupe y Calvo, altitude 7,000 feet, Chihuahua, Mexico. August 26, 1898. Collected by E. W. Nelson and E. A. Goldman. Original number 12918.

Well-made skin in good condition; skull Grade A.

*Neotoma micropus Baird.

Proc. Acad. Nat. Sci. Philadelphia 7: 333, favorably reported for publication Apr. 24, 1855.

1676. Skull. Adult male. Charco Escondido, Tamaulipas, Mexico. March 1853. Collected by D. N. Couch. There should be a skin, No. 554, but it cannot be found.

Skull Grade B.

Type not designated by number, but by referring to Baird's Mammals of North America, 1857, page 493, it is seen that the measurements given in the original description apply to No. 554 only, with corresponding skull number 1676. This, consequently, is considered the type.

†Neotoma micropus leucophaea Goldman.

Journ. Washington Acad. Sci. 23: 472, Oct. 15, 1933.

251057. Skin and skull. Adult male. White Sands, 10 miles west of Point of Sands, White Sands National Monument, altitude 4,100 feet, Otero County, N. Mex. May 6, 1933. Collected by Walter P. Taylor. Original number A204.

Well-made skin in good condition; skull Grade A.

†Neotoma micropus littoralis Goldman.

Proc. Biol. Soc. Washington 18: 31, Feb. 2, 1905.

92952. Skin and skull. Adult male. Alta Mira, altitude about 75 feet, Tamaulipas, Mexico. April 10, 1898. Collected by E. A. Goldman. Original number 12281.

Well-made skin in good condition; skull Grade B.

†Neotoma micropus planiceps Goldman.

Proc. Biol. Soc. Washington 18: 32, Feb. 2, 1905.

82105. Skin and skull. Adult male. Rio Verde, altitude about 3,000 feet, San Luis Potosi, Mexico. January 16, 1897. Collected by E. W. Nelson and E. A. Goldman. Original number 10461.

Well-made skin in good condition; skull Grade A.

†Neotoma montezumae Goldman.

Proc. Biol. Soc. Washington 18: 29, Feb. 2, 1905.

81426. Skin and skull. Adult male. Zimapan, altitude 6,200 feet, Hidalgo, Mexico. October 17, 1896. Collected by E. W. Nelson and E. A. Goldman. Original number 10275.

Well-made skin in good condition except that distal half of tail is missing; right hindfoot attached to body with wire; skull Grade A.

†Neotoma navus Merriam.

Proc. Biol. Soc. Washington 16: 47, Mar. 19, 1903.

116895. Skin and skull. Adult female. Sierra Guadalupe, Coahuila, Mexico. April 26, 1902. Collected by E. W. Nelson and E. A. Goldman. Original number 15130.

Well-made skin in good condition; skull Grade A.

†Neotoma nelsoni Goldman.

Proc. Biol. Soc. Washington 18: 29, Feb. 2, 1905.

54320. Skin and skull. Adult female. Perote, altitude 7,800 feet, Veracruz, Mexico. June 3, 1893. Collected by E. W. Nelson. Original number 4935.

Well-made skin in good condition; skull Grade A.

†Neotoma nudicauda Goldman.

Proc. Biol. Soc. Washington 18: 28, Feb. 2, 1905.

79073. Skin and skull. Young adult female. Carmen Island, Gulf of California, Lower California, Mexico. October 14, 1895. Collected by J. E. McLellan. Original number 1517.

Well-made skin in good condition; skull Grade C.

*Neotoma occidentalis Baird.

Proc. Acad. Nat. Sci. Philadelphia 7: 335, favorably reported for publication Apr. 24, 1855.

=Neotoma cinerea occidentalis Baird. See Merriam, North Amer. Fauna 5: 58, July 30, 1891.

572. Skin, formerly mounted; no record of a skull. Adult male. Shoalwater Bay, Pacific County, Wash. 1854, probably June. Collected by J. G. Cooper. Original number 16. Northern Pacific Railroad Survey.

According to the records this specimen has been mounted. It has now been prepared as a well-made study skin, which has the appearance of being considerably bleached and discolored by age and exposure. The ears are somewhat ragged, and a small spot on nose, another on crown, and one on throat have the hair and epidermis missing.

Type not designated by number. It is indicated as coming from Shoalwater Bay and collected by Cooper. In the original description the dimensions are "Head and body 10 inches. Tail vertebrae $8\frac{5}{12}$ inches." By referring to Baird's Mammals of North America, page 497, where detailed measurements of the only three specimens from Shoalwater Bay are given, it is seen that the above figures belong to No. 572 only, which is therefore considered the type.

*Neotoma occidentalis fusca True.

Diagnoses of Some Undescribed Wood Rats (Genus Neotoma) in the National Museum, p. 2, June 27, 1894. (Reprint: Proc. U. S. Nat. Mus. 17: 354, Nov. 15, 1894.)

=[Neotoma cinerea] fusca True. See Trouessart, Catalogus Mammalium tam Viventium quam Fossilium, p. 544, 1897.

3370. Skin without skull. Fort Umpqua, Douglas County, Oreg. Collected by E. P. Vollum. Cataloged in 1859, about February 25.

Specimen remade into a modern study skin, February 1902; a considerable bare spot on the left side, a smaller one on the right side, another on the belly, and a fourth on the face.

†**Neotoma orizabae** Merriam.

Proc. Biol. Soc. Washington 9 : 122, July 2, 1894.
=*Neotoma torquata* Ward. See Goldman, North Amer. Fauna 31 : 63, Oct. 19, 1910.

53653. Skin and skull. Adult male. Mount Orizaba, Puebla, Mexico. April 20, 1893. Collected by E. W. Nelson. Original number 4674.

Well-made skin in good condition; skull Grade B.

†**Neotoma orolestes** Merriam.

Proc. Biol. Soc. Washington 9 : 128, July 2, 1894.
=*Neotoma cinerea orolestes* Merriam. See Goldman, North Amer. Fauna 31 : 104, Oct. 19, 1910.

$\frac{35906}{48215}$. Skin and skull. Adult male. Saguache Valley, 20 miles west of Saguache, Saguache County, Colo. August 13, 1892. Collected by J. A. Loring. Original number 482.

Well-made skin in good condition, except for slightly injured ears; skull grade B.

†**Neotoma palatina** Goldman.

Proc. Biol. Soc. Washington 18 : 27, Feb. 2, 1905.

90959. Skin and skull. Adult male. Bolaños, altitude 2,800 feet, Jalisco, Mexico. September 12, 1897. Collected by E. W. Nelson and E. A. Goldman. Original number 11710.

Well-made skin in fair condition; distal three-fourths of tail missing; skull Grade A.

†**Neotoma parvidens** Goldman.

Proc. Biol. Soc. Washington 17 : 81, Mar. 21, 1904.

71586. Skin and skull. Adult female. Juquila, altitude 5,000 feet, Oaxaca, Mexico. March 2, 1895. Collected by E. W. Nelson and E. A. Goldman. Original number 7587.

Well-made skin in good condition; skull Grade B.

†**Neotoma picta** Goldman.

Proc. Biol. Soc. Washington 17 : 79, Mar. 21, 1904.
=*Neotoma ferruginea picta* Goldman. See Goldman, North Amer. Fauna, 31 : 72, Oct. 19, 1910.

70050. Skin and skull. Adult male. Mountains near Chilpancingo, Guerrero, Mexico. December 20, 1894. Collected by E. W. Nelson and E. A. Goldman. Original number 7179.

Well-made skin in good condition; skull Grade A.

†**Neotoma pinetorum** Merriam.

Proc. Biol. Soc. Washington 8 : 111, July 31, 1893.
=*Neotoma mexicana pinetorum* Merriam.   See Goldman, North Amer. Fauna 31 : 58, Oct. 19, 1910.

$\frac{17692}{24628}$.   Skin and skull.   Adult female.   San Francisco Mountain, Coconino County, Ariz.   August 16, 1889.   Collected by Vernon Bailey.   Original number 366.

Well-made skin in good condition; skull Grade A.

†**Neotoma saxamans** Osgood.

North Amer. Fauna 19 : 33, Oct. 6, 1900.
=*Neotoma cinera saxamans* Osgood.   See Allen, Bull. Amer. Mus. Nat. Hist. 19 : 544, Oct. 10. 1903.

98923.   Skin and skull.   Adult male.   Bennett, head of Lake Bennett, British Columbia, Canada.   June 19, 1899.   Collected by W. H. Osgood.   Original number 462.

Well-made skin in good condition; skull Grade A.

***Neotoma splendens** True.

Diagnoses of Some Undescribed Wood Rats (Genus *Neotoma*) in the National Museum, p. 1, June 27, 1894.   (Reprint: Proc. U. S. Nat. Mus. 17 : 353, Nov. 15, 1894.)
=*Neotoma fuscipes monochroura* Rhoads.   See Hooper, Univ. California Publ. Zool. 42 : 217, Mar. 1, 1938.

19693.   Skin; no record of a skull.   Adult male.   Marin County, Calif.   November 25, 1887.   Purchased from C. K. Worthen.   Original number 211.

Well-made skin in good condition.

†**Neotoma stephensi** Goldman.

Proc. Biol. Soc. Washington 18 : 32, Feb. 2, 1905.
=*Neotoma stephensi stephensi* Goldman.   See Goldman, Journ. Mamm. 13 : 66, Feb. 9, 1932.

117466.   Skin and skull.   Adult female.   Hualpai Mountains, altitude 6,300 feet, Mohave County, Ariz.   July 1, 1902.   Collected by Frank Stephens.   Original number 4192.

Well-made skin in good condition; skull Grade A.

†**Neotoma stephensi relicta** Goldman.

Journ. Mamm. 13 (1) : 66, Feb. 9, 1932.

67780.   Skin and skull.   Adult female.   Keam Canyon, Navajo County, Ariz.   July 22, 1894.   Collected by A. K. Fisher.   Original number 1649.

Well-made skin in good condition; skull Grade A.

†Neotoma tenuicauda Merriam.

Proc. Biol. Soc. Washington 7: 169, Sept. 29, 1892.
=*Neotoma ferruginea tenuicauda* Merriam.   See Goldman, North. Amer. Fauna
    31: 73, Oct. 19, 1910.

$\frac{33594}{45629}$. Skin and skull. Adult female (not "male" as in original
description). North slope Sierra Nevada de Colima, altitude
12,000 feet, Jalisco, Mexico. April 13, 1892. Collected by E. W.
Nelson. Original number 2446.

Well-made skin in good condition; skull Grade A.

†Neotoma tropicalis Goldman.

Proc. Biol. Soc. Washington 17: 81, Mar. 21, 1904.

68593. Skin and skull. Adult male. Totontepec, altitude 6,500
feet, Oaxaca, Mexico. July 17, 1894. Collected by E. W. Nelson
and E. A. Goldman. Original number 6468.

Well-made skin in good condition, but with a small perforation on rump;
skull Grade A.

*Neotoma venusta True.

Diagnoses of Some Undescribed Wood Rats (Genus *Neotoma*) in the
    National Museum, p. 2, June 27, 1894. (Reprint: Proc. U. S. Nat. Mus.
    17: 354, Nov. 15, 1894.)
=*Neotoma albigula venusta* True.   See Goldman, North Amer. Fauna 31: 33,
    Oct. 19, 1910.

$\frac{21696}{36400}$. Skin and skull. Adult male. Carrizo Creek, Imperial
County, Calif. November 30, 1891. Collected by Frank
Stephens. Original number 1800. Purchased from C. K.
Worthen.

Well-made skin in good condition; skull Grade A.

Genus NEOTOMODON Merriam

†Neotomodon alstoni Merriam.

Proc. Biol. Soc. Washington 12: 128, Apr. 30, 1898.

50534. Skin and skull. Old male. Nahuatzin, altitude 8,500 feet,
Michoacan, Mexico. October 12, 1892. Collected by E. W.
Nelson. Original number 3580.

Well-made skin in good condition; skull Grade A.

†Neotomodon orizabae Merriam.

Proc. Biol. Soc. Washington 12: 129, Apr. 30, 1898.

53486. Skin and skull. Old male. Mount Orizaba, altitude 9,500
feet, Puebla, Mexico. April 26, 1893. Collected by E. W. Nelson. Original number 4747.

Well-made skin in good condition; skull Grade C.

†Neotomodon perotensis Merriam.

Proc. Biol. Soc. Washington 12: 129, Apr. 30, 1898.

54398. Skin and skull. Adult female. Cofre de Perote, altitude 9,500 feet, Veracruz, Mexico. May 29, 1893. Collected by E. W. Nelson. Original number 4897.

Well-made skin in good condition; skull Grade B.

Genus NYCTOMYS Saussure

*Sitomys (Rhipidomys) decolorus True.

Proc. U. S. Nat. Mus. 16: 689, Feb. 5. 1894.

=*Nyctomys sumichrasti decolorus* (True). See Goldman, Proc. Biol. Soc. Washington 29: 155, Sept. 6, 1916.

$\frac{21092}{36129}$. Skin and skull. Young adult female. Rio de las Piedras, Honduras. November 17, 1890. (Not Dec. 11, 1890, as recorded in original description. The original label is marked thus: "17.11.90." The "7" is rather blotted, but scarcely looks like a "2.") Collected by Erich Wittkügel. Original number 9.

Well-made skin in good condition; skull Grade A.

Type not designated as such by number, but the single specimen is referred to by number.

†Nyctomys sumichrasti costaricensis Goldman.

Journ. Washington Acad. Sci. 27: 422, Oct. 15, 1937.

250331. Skin and skull. Adult male. From San Geronimo de Pirris, hamlet on the main road to Pirris before reaching Jabillo (altitude about 100 feet), about 2 miles before the abrupt descent to the lowlands of Pozo Axul and about 12 miles inland from Pirris, near the west coast of Costa Rica. April 12, 1931. Collected by C. F. Underwood. Original number 26896–X.

Well-made skin in good condition; skull Grade A.

†Nyctomys sumichrasti pallidulus Goldman.

Journ. Washington Acad. Sci. 27: 420. Oct. 15, 1937.

73302. Skin and skull. Adult male. Santo Domingo, 8 miles west of Lagunas, (altitude 900 feet), Isthmus of Tehuantepec, Oaxaca, Mexico. June 13, 1895. Collected by E. W. Nelson and E. A. Goldman. Original number 8079.

Well-made skin in good condition; skull Grade A.

†Nyctomys sumichrasti venustulus Goldman.

Proc. Biol. Soc. Washington 29: 155, Sept. 6, 1916.

$\frac{33149}{45153}$. Skin and skull. Adult female. Greytown, Nicaragua. February 10, 1892. Collected by C. W. Richmond. Original number 17.

Well-made skin in good condition except tip of tail broken off; skull Grade A.

Genus ONDATRA Link

†**Fiber macrodon** Merriam.

Proc. Biol. Soc. Washington 11 : 143, May 13, 1897.
=*Ondatra zibethica macrodon* (Merriam). See Miller, U. S. Nat. Mus. Bull.
79 : 230, Dec. 31, 1912.

75940. Skin and skull. Adult female. Lake Drummond, Dismal
Swamp, Norfolk County, Va. October 9, 1895. Collected by
A. K. Fisher. Original number 1788.

Well-made skin in good condition ; skull Grade A.

†**Fiber spatulatus** Osgood.

North Amer. Fauna 19 : 36, Oct. 6, 1900.
=*Ondatra zibethica spatulata* (Osgood). See Miller, U. S. Nat. Mus. Bull. 79 :
231, Dec. 31, 1912.

98567. Skin and skull. Young adult female. Lake Marsh,
Yukon, Canada. July 3, 1899. Collected by W. H. Osgood.
Original number 552.

Well-made skin in good condition, except for absence of tip of tail ; left
fore foot detached ; skull Grade A.

†**Ondatra zibethica bernardi** Goldman.

Proc. Biol. Soc. Washington 45 : 93, June 21, 1932.

250454. Skin and skull. Adult male. Four miles south of Gadsden,
Yuma County, Ariz. November 12, 1931. Collected by Bernard
Bailey. Original number A4372; X–catalog number 27010.

Well-made skin in good condition ; skull Grade A.

*****Fiber zibethicus cinnamominus** Hollister.

Proc. Biol. Soc. Washington 23 : 125, Sept. 2, 1910.
=*Ondatra zibethica cinnamomina* (Hollister). See Miller, U. S. Nat. Mus.
Bull. 79 : 232, Dec. 31, 1912.

186518. Skin and skull. Adult male. Wakeeney, Trego County,
Kans. January 14, 1887. Collected by A. B. Baker. Merriam
collection number $\frac{3084}{3724}$.

Well-made skin in good condition ; skull Grade A.

†**Fiber zibethicus hudsonius** Preble.

North Amer. Fauna 22 : 53, Oct. 31, 1902.
=*Ondatra zibethica alba* (Sabine). See Miller, U. S. Nat. Mus. Bull. 79 :
231, Dec. 31, 1912.

106881. Skin and skull. Adult male. Fort Churchill, Keewatin,
Canada. August 9, 1900. Collected by A. E. Preble. Original
number 3081 (E. A. Preble).

Well-made skin in good condition ; skull Grade A.

†**Fiber zibethicus mergens** Hollister.

Proc. Biol. Soc. Washington 23 : 1, Feb. 2, 1910.
=*Ondatra zibethica mergens* (Hollister). See Miller, U. S. Nat. Mus. Bull. 79 : 231, Dec. 31, 1912.

156880. Skin and skull. Adult female. Fallon, Churchill County, Nev. April 3, 1908. Collected by S. E. Piper. Original number 143.

Well-made skin in good condition ; skull Grade A.

†**Fiber zibethicus ripensis** Bailey.

Proc. Biol. Soc. Washington 15 : 119, June 2, 1902.
=*Ondatra zibethica ripensis* (Bailey). See Miller, U. S. Nat. Mus. Bull. 79 : 232, Dec. 31, 1912.

109012. Skin and skull. Adult male. Carlsbad (Eddy), Pecos River, Eddy County, N. Mex. July 26, 1901 (not July 25, as recorded in the original description). Collected by Vernon Bailey. Original number 7757.

Well-made skin in good condition ; left forefoot injured by insects and hanging by a thread of skin ; skull Grade A.

†**Fiber zibethicus zalophus** Hollister.

Proc. Biol. Soc. Washington 23 : 1, Feb. 2, 1910.
=*Ondatra zibethica zalopha* (Hollister). See Miller, U. S. Nat. Mus. Bull. 79 : 231, Dec. 31, 1912.

131488. Skin and skull. Becharof Lake, Alaska Peninsula, Alaska. October 1903. Collected by A. G. Maddren. Original number 21 (4285–X).

Well-made skin in good condition ; skull Grade A.

Genus ONYCHOMYS Baird

†**Onychomys fuliginosus** Merriam.

North Amer. Fauna 3 : 59, Sept. 11, 1890.
=*Onychomys leucogaster fuliginosus* Merriam. See Hollister, Proc. Biol. Soc. Washington 26 : 216, Dec. 20, 1913.

$\frac{17997}{24908}$. Skin and skull. Adult female. Black Tank lava beds, northeast of San Francisco Mountain, Coconino County, Ariz. September 27, 1889. Collected by C. Hart Merriam and Vernon Bailey. Original number 547.

Well-made skin in good condition ; skull Grade A.

†**Onychomys leucogaster albescens** Merriam.

Proc. Biol. Soc. Washington 17 : 124, June 9, 1904.

50040. Skin and skull. Adult female. Samalayuca, Chihuahua, Mexico. December 12, 1892. Collected by C. P. Streator. Original number 2399.

Well-made skin in good condition ; skull Grade A.

*Onychomys leucogaster breviauritus Hollister.

Proc. Biol. Soc. Washington 26: 216, Dec. 20, 1913.

$\frac{19144}{34872}$. Skin and skull. Adult female. Fort Reno, Canadian County, Okla. February 16, 1890. Collected by J. C. Merrill. Original number 18.

Well-made skin in good condition; skull Grade A.

†Onychomys leucogaster brevicaudus Merriam.

North Amer. Fauna 5: 52, July 30, 1891.

$\frac{23086}{30532}$. Skin and skull. Adult male. Blackfoot, Bingham County, Idaho. July 15, 1890. Collected by Vernon Bailey and B. H. Dutcher. Original number 1442.

Well-made skin in good condition; skull Grade C.

†Onychomys leucogaster capitulatus Hollister.

Proc. Biol. Soc. Washington 26: 215, Dec. 20, 1913.

202612. Skin and skull. Adult male. Lower end of Prospect Valley, altitude 4,500 feet, Hualpai Indian Reservation, Grand Canyon, Ariz. September 26, 1913. Collected by E. A. Goldman. Original number 22234.

Well-made skin in good condition; skull Grade A.

*Onychomys leucogaster melanophrys Merriam.

North Amer. Fauna 2: 2, Oct. 30, 1889.

186477. Skin and skull. Adult male. Kanab, Kane County, Utah. December 22, 1888. Collected by Vernon Bailey. Original number 458. Merriam collection No. $\frac{5199}{5894}$.

Well-made skin in good condition; skull Grade A.

†Onychomys leucogaster utahensis Goldman.

Journ. Mamm. 20: 354, Aug. 14, 1939.

263955. Skin and skull. Adult female. South end of Stansbury Island, Great Salt Lake, altitude 4,250 feet, Utah. June 22, 1938. Collected by William H. Marshall. Original number 96.

Well-made skin in good condition; skull Grade A.

*Onychomys longicaudus Merriam.

North Amer. Fauna 2: 2, Oct. 30, 1889.

=*Onychomys torridus longicaudus* Merriam. See Merriam, Proc. Biol. Soc. Washington 17: 123, June 9, 1904.

186476. Skin and skull. Adult male. St. George, Washington County, Utah. January 4, 1889. Collected by Vernon Bailey. Original number 476. Merriam collection number $\frac{5201}{5896}$.

Well-made skin in good condition; skull Grade A.

*Onychomys longipes Merriam.

North Amer. Fauna 2 : 1, Oct. 30, 1889.
=*Onychomys leucogaster longipes* Merriam.   See Hollister, Proc. Biol. Soc. Washington 26 : 216, Dec. 20, 1913.

186478. Skin and skull. Adult female. Concho County, Tex. March 11, 1887. Collected by William Lloyd. Original number 3. Merriam collection No. $\frac{3207}{3839}$.

Well-made skin in good condition, except for bare spot on abdomen; skull Grade A.

*Onychomys melanophrys pallescens Merriam.

North Amer. Fauna 3 : 61, Sept. 11, 1890.
=*Onychomys leucogaster melanophrys* Merriam.   See Hollister, Proc. U. S. Nat. Mus. 47 : 444, Oct. 29, 1914.

186479. Skin and skull. Adult male. Moki Pueblos, Navajo County, Ariz. May 18, 1888. Collected by Jere Sullivan. Original number 11. Merriam collection No. $\frac{4252}{4983}$.

Well-made skin in good condition; skull Grade A.

*Hesperomys (Onychomys) torridus Coues.

Proc. Acad. Nat. Sci. Philadelphia 26 : 183, Dec. 15, 1874.
=*Onychomys torridus torridus* (Coues).   See Hollister, Proc. U. S. Nat. Mus. 47 : 456, Oct. 29, 1914.

9886. Skin without skull. Camp Grant, Graham County, Ariz. June 10, 1867. Collected by E. Palmer.

Skin taken out of alcohol (according to Coues), well preserved but poorly made up. No record of a skull.

*Onychomys torridus arenicola Mearns.

Preliminary Diagnoses of New Mammals from the Mexican Border of the United States, p. 3, May 25, 1896. (Reprint: Proc. U. S. Nat. Mus. 19 : 139, Dec. 21, 1896.)
=*Onychomys torridus torridus* (Coues).   See Hollister, Proc. U. S. Nat. Mus. 47 : 456, Oct. 29, 1914.

$\frac{20081}{35483}$. Skin and skull. Adult male. Rio Grande, about 6 miles above El Paso, El Paso County, Tex. February 29, 1892. Collected by E. A. Mearns and F. X. Holzner. Original number 1528.

Well-made skin in good condition; skull Grade A.

†Onychomys torridus canus Merriam.

Proc. Biol. Soc. Washington 17 : 124, June 9, 1904.

90843. Skin and skull. Adult female. San Juan Capistrano, Zacatecas, Mexico. August 23, 1897. Collected by E. W. Nelson and E. A. Goldman. Original number 11574.

Well-made skin in good condition, except for bare patch on abdomen; skull Grade A.

†**Onychomys torridus clarus** Hollister.

Proc. Biol. Soc. Washington 26: 215, Dec. 20, 1913.

$\frac{25453}{32867}$. Skin and skull. Adult male. Keeler, east shore of Owens Lake, Inyo County, Calif. December 30, 1890. Collected by Vernon Bailey. Original number 2314.

Well-made skin in good condition; skull Grade A.

*****Onychomys torridus perpallidus** Mearns.

Preliminary Diagnoses of New Mammals from the Mexican Border of the United States, p. 4, May 25, 1896. (Reprint: Proc. U. S. Nat. Mus. 19: 140, Dec. 21, 1896.)

60174. Skin and skull. Adult female. Left bank of the Colorado River, at monument 204, Mexican boundary line, Yuma County, Ariz. March 27, 1894. Collected by E. A. Mearns and F. X. Holzner. Original number 3301.

Well-made skin in good condition; skull Grade A.

†**Onychomys torridus surrufus** Hollister.

Proc. U. S. Nat. Mus. 47: 472, Oct. 29, 1914.

93839. Skin and skull. Adult female. Miquihuana, Tamaulipas, Mexico. June 8, 1898. Collected by E. W. Nelson and E. A. Goldman. Original number 12484.

Well-made skin in good condition; skull Grade B.

†**Onychomys torridus tularensis** Merriam.

Proc. Biol. Soc. Washington 17: 123, June 9, 1904.

$\frac{29711}{41786}$. Skin and skull. Adult female. Bakersfield, Kern County, Calif. July 19, 1891. Collected by A. K. Fisher. Original number 792.

Well-made skin in good condition; skull Grade A.

†**Onychomys torridus yakiensis** Merriam.

Proc. Biol. Soc. Washington 17: 124, June 9, 1904.

95855. Skin and skull. Adult female. Camoa, Rio Mayo, southern Sonora, Mexico. October 28, 1898. Collected by E. A. Goldman. Original number 13158.

Well-made skin in good condition; skull Grade A.

Genus ORYZOMYS Baird

†**Oryzomys albiventer** Merriam.

Proc. Washington Acad. Sci. 3: 279, July 26, 1901.

=*Oryzomys couesi albiventer* Merriam. See Goldman, North Amer. Fauna 43: 38, Sept. 23, 1918.

82236. Skin and skull. Adult male. Ameca, altitude 4,000 feet, Jalisco, Mexico. February 6, 1897. Collected by E. W. Nelson and E. A. Goldman. Original number 10478.

Well-made skin in good condition; skull Grade A.

†Oryzomys alfaroi dariensis Goldman.

Proc. Biol. Soc. Washington 28 : 128, June 29, 1915.

178660. Skin and skull. Adult female. Cana, altitude 2,000 feet, eastern Panama. March 4, 1912. Collected by E. A. Goldman. Original number 21453.

Well-made skin in good condition; skull Grade A.

†Oryzomys angusticeps Merriam.

Proc. Washington Acad. Sci. 3 : 292, July 26, 1901.
=*Oryzomys alfaroi angusticeps* Merriam. See Goldman, North Amer. Fauna 43 : 62, Sept. 23, 1918.

76816. Skin and skull. Adult male. Volcan Santa Maria, altitude 9,000 feet, Guatemala. January 22, 1896. Collected by E. W. Nelson and E. A. Goldman. Original number 9190.

Well-made skin in good condition; skull Grade A.

†Oryzomys bombycinus Goldman.

Smithsonian Misc. Coll. 56 (36) : 6, Feb. 19, 1912.

171105. Skin and skull. Adult male. Cerro Azul, altitude 2,500 feet, near headwaters of the Chagres River, Panama. March 26, 1911. Collected by E. A. Goldman. Original number 21009.

Well-made skin in good condition; skull Grade C.

†Oryzomys chapmani caudatus Merriam.

Proc. Washington Acad. Sci. 3 : 289, July 26, 1901
=*Oryzomys alfaroi caudatus* Merriam. See Goldman, North Amer. Fauna 43 : 64, Sept. 23, 1918.

68641. Skin and skull. Adult male. Comaltepec, Oaxaca, Mexico, July 31, 1894. Collected by E. W. Nelson and E. A. Goldman. Original number 6516.

Well-made skin in good condition; skull Grade A.

†Oryzomys chapmani dilutior Merriam.

Proc. Washington Acad. Sci. 3 : 290, July 26, 1901.
=*Oryzomys alfaroi dilutior* Merriam. See Goldman, North Amer. Fauna 43 : 68, Sept. 23, 1918.

93124. Skin and skull. Adult male. Huauchinango, Puebla, Mexico. January 10, 1898. Collected by E. W. Nelson and E. A. Goldman. Original number 12040.

Well-made skin in good condition; skull Grade A.

†**Oryzomys chapmani saturatior** Merriam.

Proc. Washington Acad. Sci. 3 : 290, July 26, 1901.
=*Oryzomys alfaroi saturatior* Merriam.   See Goldman, North Amer. Fauna 43 :
68, Sept. 23, 1918.

76183.   Skin and skull.   Adult female.   Tumbala, Chiapas, Mexico.
October 23, 1895.   Collected by E. W. Nelson and E. A. Goldman.
Original number 8574.

Well-made skin in good condition ; skull Grade B.

†**Oryzomys couesi regillus** Goldman.

Proc. Biol. Soc. Washington 28 : 129, June 29, 1915.

125945.   Skin and skull.   Adult male.   Los Reyes, Michoacan, Mexico.   February 17, 1903.   Collected by E. W. Nelson and E. A.
Goldman.   Original number 15962.

Well-made skin in good condition ; skull Grade A.

†**Oryzomys cozumelae** Merriam.

Proc. Biol. Soc. Washington 14 : 103, July 19, 1901 ; Proc. Washington Acad.
Sci. 3 : 280, July 26, 1901.

108462.   Skin and skull.   Adult male.   Cozumel Island, off coast of
Quintana Roo, Mexico.   April 8, 1901.   Collected by E. W. Nelson
and E. A. Goldman.   Original number 14666.

Well-made skin in good condition ; skull Grade A.

†**Oryzomys crinitus** Merriam.

Proc. Washington Acad. Sci. 3 : 281, July 26, 1901.
=*Oryzomys couesi crinitus* Merriam.   See Goldman, North Amer. Fauna 43 :
36, Sept. 23, 1918.

50182.   Skin and skull.   Adult male.   Tlalpam, Federal District,
Mexico.   November 30, 1892.   Collected by E. W. Nelson and
E. A. Goldman.   Original number 3905.

Well-made skin in good condition ; skull Grade A.

†**Oryzomys crinitus aztecus** Merriam.

Proc. Washington Acad. Sci. 3 : 282, July 26, 1901.
=*Oryzomys couesi aztecus* Merriam.   See Goldman, North Amer. Fauna 43 :
35, Sept. 23, 1918.

51173.   Skin and skull.   Adult male.   Yautepec, Morelos, Mexico.
January 16, 1893.   Collected by E. W. Nelson and E. A. Goldman.
Original number 4290.

Well-made skin in good condition ; skull Grade C.

†**Oryzomys frontalis** Goldman.

Smithsonian Misc. Coll. 56 (36) : 6, Feb. 19, 1912.
=*Oryzomys tectus frontalis* Goldman.   See Goldman, North Amer. Fauna 43 :
85, Sept. 23, 1918.

171531. Skin and skull. Adult female. Corozal, Canal Zone, Panama. June 20, 1911. Collected by E. A. Goldman. Original number 21172.

Well-made skin in good condition; skull Grade A.

†Oryzomys fulvescens lenis Goldman.

Proc. Biol. Soc. Washington 28: 130, June 29, 1915.

125941. Skin and skull. Adult male. Los Reyes, Michoacan, Mexico. February 14, 1903. Collected by E. W. Nelson and E. A. Goldman. Original number 15948.

Well-made skin in good condition; skull Grade A.

†Oryzomys fulvescens mayensis Goldman.

North Amer. Fauna 43: 92, Sept. 23, 1918.

107979. Skin and skull. Adult male. Apazote, near Yohaltum, altitude 200 feet, Campeche, Mexico. January 5, 1901. Collected by E. W. Nelson and E. A. Goldman. Original number 14405.

Well-made skin in good condition; skull Grade A.

†Oryzomys gatunensis Goldman.

Smithsonian Misc. Coll. 56 (36): 7, Feb. 19, 1912.

171034. Skin and skull. Young male, about two-thirds grown. Gatun, Canal Zone, Panama. March 7, 1911. Collected by E. A. Goldman. Original number 20967.

Well-made skin in good condition; skull Grade A.

†Oryzomys goldmani Merriam.

Proc. Washington Acad. Sci. 3: 228, July 26, 1901.
= Oryzomys couesi couesi Alston. See Goldman, North Amer. Fauna 43: 29, Sept. 23, 1918.

78110. Skin and skull. Adult female. Coatzacoalcos, Veracruz, Mexico. April 11, 1896. Collected by E. W. Nelson and E. A. Goldman. Original number 9511.

Well-made skin in good condition; skull Grade A.

†Oryzomys guerrerensis Goldman.

Proc. Biol. Soc. Washington 28: 127, June 29, 1915.

127517. Skin and skull. Adult male. Omilteme, altitude 8,000 feet, Guerrero, Mexico. May 20, 1903. Collected by E. W. Nelson and E. A. Goldman. Original number 16454.

Well-made skin in good condition; skull Grade A.

†Oryzomys hylocetes Merriam.

Proc. Washington Acad. Sci. 3: 291, July 26, 1901.

77605. Skin and skull. Old male. Chicharras, Chiapas, Mexico. February 14, 1896. Collected by E. W. Nelson and E. A. Goldman. Original number 9306.

Well-made skin in good condition; skull Grade A.

†Oryzomys idoneus Goldman.

Smithsonian Misc. Coll. 56 (36) : 5, Feb. 19, 1912.
=*Oryzomys caliginosus idoneus* Goldman. See Goldman, North Amer. Fauna 43: 96, Sept. 23, 1918.

171106. Skin and skull. Adult female. Cerro Azul, altitude 2,500 feet, near headwaters of Chagres River, Panama. March 26, 1911. Collected by E. A. Goldman. Original number 21010.

The skin lacks tail, ears, and right forefoot; toes of hindfeet are broken; two sewed lacerations extend across face and head, specimen in good condition otherwise; skull Grade A.

†Oryzomys jalapae rufinus Merriam.

Proc. Washington Acad. Sci. 3 : 285, July 26, 1901.
=*Oryzomys couesi couesi* Alston. See Goldman, North Amer. Fauna 43: 29, Sept. 23, 1918.

65499. Skin and skull. Adult female. Catemaco, Veracruz, Mexico. April 27, 1894. Collected by E. W. Nelson and E. A. Goldman. Original number 6112.

Well-made skin in good condition; skull Grade A.

*Oryzomys medius Robinson and Lyon.

Proc. U. S. Nat. Mus. 24: 142, Oct. 3, 1901.

105405. Skin and skull. Young adult male. San Julian, 8 miles east of La Guaira, Venezuela. August 8, 1900. Collected by Wirt Robinson. Original number 1655.

Well-made skin in good condition, except for small loss of hair on nape and right ear broken loose from skin; skull Grade A.

†Oryzomys melanotis colimensis Goldman.

North Amer. Fauna 43 : 51, Sept. 23, 1918.

$\frac{33289}{45317}$. Skin and skull. Adult female. Armeria, altitude about 100 feet, Colima, Mexico. March 2, 1892. Collected by E. W. Nelson. Original number 1987.

Well-made skin in good condition; skull Grade A.

†Oryzomys mexicanus peragrus Merriam.

Proc. Washington Acad. Sci. 3 : 283, July 26, 1901.
=*Oryzomys couesi peragrus* Merriam. See Goldman, North Amer. Fauna 43: 39, Sept. 23, 1918.

82119. Skin and skull. Young adult male. Rio Verde, San Luis Potosi, Mexico. January 8, 1897. Collected by E. W. Nelson and E. A. Goldman. Original number 10398.

Well-made skin in good condition; skull Grade A.

†**Oryzomys natator floridanus** Merriam.

Proc. Washington Acad. Sci. 3: 277, July 26, 1901.
=*Oryzomys palustris coloratus* Bangs. See Rhoads, Amer. Nat. 36: 633, Aug. 1902.

71349. Skin and skull. Adult male. Everglades, Collier County, Fla. March 29, 1895. Collected by J. A. Loring. Original number 2819.

Well-made skin in good condition; skull Grade C.

†**Oryzomys nelsoni** Merriam.

Proc. Biol. Soc. Washington 12: 15, Jan. 27, 1898.

89200. Skin and skull. Adult male. Maria Madre Island, Tres Marias Islands, Nayarit, Mexico. May 13, 1897. Collected by E. W. Nelson and E. A. Goldman. Original number 11022.

Well-made skin in good condition; skull Grade A.

†**Oryzomys palatinus** Merriam.

Proc. Washington Acad. Sci. 3: 290, July 26, 1901.
=*Oryzomys alfaroi palatinus* Merriam. See Goldman, North Amer. Fauna 43: 65, Sept. 23, 1918.

99977. Skin and skull. Adult female. Teapa, Tabasco, Mexico. April 1, 1900. Collected by E. W. Nelson and E. A. Goldman. Original number 14080.

Well-made skin in good condition; skull Grade A.

†**Oryzomys pirrensis** Goldman.

Smithsonian Misc. Coll. 60 (22) : 5, Feb. 28, 1913.

178993. Skin and skull. Adult male. Near head of Rio Limon, Mount Pirri, altitude 4,500 feet, eastern Panama. April 29, 1912. Collected by E. A. Goldman. Original number 21662.

Well-made skin in good condition; skull Grade B.

†**Oryzomys rhabdops** Merriam.

Proc. Washington Acad. Sci. 3: 291, July 26, 1901.
=*Oryzomys alfaroi rhabdops* Merriam. See Goldman, North. Amer. Fauna 43: 63, Sept. 23, 1918.

76813. Skin and skull. Adult male. Calel, altitude 10,000 feet, Guatemala. January 15, 1896. Collected by E. W. Nelson and E. A. Goldman. Original number 9135.

Well-made skin in good condition; skull Grade A.

†**Oryzomys richmondi** Merriam.

Proc. Washington Acad. Sci. 3: 284, July 26, 1901.
=*Oryzomys couesi richmondi* Merriam. See Goldman, North Amer. Fauna 43: 32, Sept. 23, 1918.

$\frac{36340}{48705}$. Skin and skull. Adult male. Escondido River, 50 miles above Bluefields, Nicaragua. June 21, 1892. Collected by C. W. Richmond. Original number 63.

Well-made skin in good condition; skull Grade A.

†Oryzomys rostratus Merriam.

Proc. Washington Acad. Sci. 3: 293, July 26, 1901.

93112. Skin and skull. Old male. Metlaltoyuca, Puebla, Mexico. February 5, 1898. Collected by E. W. Nelson and E. A. Goldman. Original number 12130.

Well-made skin in good condition; skull Grade A.

†Oryzomys rostratus megadon Merriam.

Proc. Washington Acad. Sci. 3: 294, July 26, 1901.

99978. Skin and skull. Old male. Teapa, Tabasco, Mexico. March 24, 1900. Collected by E. W. Nelson and E. A. Goldman. Original number 14062.

Well-made skin in good condition; skull Grade A.

†Oryzomys rufus Merriam.

Proc. Washington Acad. Sci. 3: 287, July 26, 1901.
=Oryzomys couesi mexicanus J. A. Allen. See Goldman, North Amer. Fauna 43: 33, Sept. 23, 1918.

91404. Skin and skull. Old female. Santiago, Nayarit, Mexico. June 20, 1897. Collected by E. W. Nelson and E. A. Goldman. Original number 11232.

Well-made skin in good condition; skull Grade C.

*Oryzomys talamancae J. A. Allen.

Proc. U. S. Nat. Mus. 14: 193, July 24, 1891.

$\frac{12222}{22742}$. Skin and skull. Adult male. Talamanca, Costa Rica. 1874. Collected by W. M. Gabb. Original number 99.

Specimen in good state of preservation; in February 1902 made into a fair study skin. Left hindleg missing; tail not skinned out, the epidermis slipped from 2 to 3 cm. of the tip. Skull Grade A. In the original description Allen remarks that there is no lower jaw. The present lower jaw was found in the same vial with the rest of the skull. It was not numbered, however, so there may be some doubt as to its being a part of the type specimen.

†Oryzomys teapensis Merriam.

Proc. Washington Acad. Sci. 3: 286, July 26, 1901.
=Oryzomys couesi couesi Alston. See Goldman, North Amer. Fauna 43: 29, Sept. 23, 1918.

99973. Skin and skull. Young adult male. Teapa, Tabasco, Mexico. April 4, 1900. Collected by E. W. Nelson and E. A. Goldman. Original number 14100.

Well-made skin in good condition; skull Grade B.

†Oryzomys yucatanensis Merriam.

Proc. Washington Acad. Sci. 3: 294, July 26, 1901.
=*Oryzomys rostratus yucatanensis* Merriam. See Goldman, North Amer. Fauna 43: 55, Sept. 23, 1918.

108139. Skin and skull. Young adult male. Chichen Itza, Yucatan, Mexico. February 9, 1901. Collected by E. W. Nelson and E. A. Goldman. Original number 14527.

Well-made skin in good condition; skull Grade A.

†Oryzomys zygomaticus Merriam.

Proc. Washington Acad. Sci. 3: 285, July 26, 1901.
=*Oryzomys couesi zygomaticus* Merriam. See Goldman, North Amer. Fauna 43: 32, Sept. 23, 1918.

76794. Skin and skull. Adult male. Nenton, Guatemala. December 15, 1895. Collected by E. W. Nelson and E. A. Goldman. Original number 8798.

Well-made skin in good condition; skull Grade A.

Genus OTOTYLOMYS Merriam

†Ototylomys phyllotis Merriam.

Proc. Washington Acad. Sci. 3: 562, Nov. 29, 1901.

108099. Skin and skull. Old male. Tunkas, Yucatan, Mexico. February 17, 1901. Collected by E. W. Nelson and E. A. Goldman. Original number 14551.

Well-made skin in good condition; skull Grade A.

†Ototylomys phyllotis phaeus Merriam.

Proc. Washington Acad. Sci. 3: 563, Nov. 29, 1901.

107940. Skin and skull. Adult female. Apazote, near Yohaltun, Campeche, Mexico. December 28, 1900. Collected by E. W. Nelson and E. A. Goldman. Original number 14369.

Well-made skin in good condition, except for bare space on left shoulder; left ear attached to skin with thread; skull Grade A.

Genus PEROMYSCUS Gloger

*Hesperomys (Vesperimus) affinis J. A. Allen.

Proc. U. S. Nat. Mus. 14: 195, July 24, 1891.
=*Peromyscus leucopus affinis* (Allen). See Osgood, North Amer. Fauna 28: 133, Apr. 17, 1909.

$\dfrac{9382}{8665}$. Skin and skull. Adult female. Barrio, Oaxaca, Mexico. October 30, 1868. Collected by F. Sumichrast. Original number 23.

Skin fairly well preserved, rather poorly made up; tail not skinned out; right foot present, but broken off from the leg. Skull Grade A. Type designated by number. In the original description the skin number is wrongly given as 7382.

†Peromyscus allophylus Osgood.

Proc. Biol. Soc. Washington 17: 71, Mar. 21, 1904.

77657. Skin and skull. Adult female. Huehuetan, altitude 500 feet, Chiapas, Mexico. February 21, 1896. Collected by E. W. Nelson and E. A. Goldman. Original number 9352.

Well-made skin in good condition; skull Grade A.

†Peromyscus altilaneus Osgood.

Proc. Biol. Soc. Washington 17: 74, Mar. 21, 1904.

76856. Skin and skull. Adult male. Todos Santos, altitude 10,000 feet, Guatemala. December 30, 1895. Collected by E. W. Nelson and E. A. Goldman. Original number 8942.

Well-made skin in good condition; skull Grade A.

†Peromyscus amplus Osgood.

Proc. Biol. Soc. Washington 17: 62, Mar. 21, 1904.
=*Peromyscus difficilis amplus* Osgood. See Osgood, North Amer. Fauna 28: 181, Apr. 17, 1909.

70158. Skin and skull. Adult female. Coixtlahuaca, Oaxaca, Mexico. November 12, 1894. Collected by E. W. Nelson and E. A. Goldman. Original number 7033.

Well-made skin in good condition; skull Grade A.

*Hesperomys (Vesperimus) anthonyi Merriam.

Proc. Biol. Soc. Washington 4: 5, Apr. 15, 1887.
=*Peromyscus eremicus anthonyi* (Merriam). See Mearns, U. S. Nat. Mus. Bull. 56: 438, Apr. 13, 1907.

186480. Skin and skull. Immature male. Camp Apache, Big Hachita Mountains, Grant County, N. Mex. May 10, 1886. Collected by A. W. Anthony. Merriam collection No. $\dfrac{2333}{2841}$.

Well-made skin in good condition; skull Grade A.

*[Hesperomys] articus [sic] Coues.

Monographs of North American Rodentia, p. 61, 1877.
=*Peromyscus maniculatus maniculatus* (Wagner). See Miller, U. S. Nat. Mus. Bull. 79: 142, Dec. 31, 1912.

3924. Skin, skull inside. Labrador, Canada. Received from H. de Saussure, Geneva Museum. Original number 2. Cataloged May 14, 1860.

Skin well preserved and in good condition, but poorly made up; tail not skinned out. Skull inside of skin.

†Peromyscus attwateri eremicoides Osgood.

Proc. Biol. Soc. Washington 17 : 60, Mar. 21, 1904.
=*Peromyscus pectoralis eremicoides* Osgood. See Lyon and Osgood, U. S. Nat. Mus. Bull. 62 : 128, Jan. 28, 1909.

57729. Skin and skull. Adult male. Mapimi, Durango, Mexico. December 15, 1893. Collected by E. A. Goldman. Original number 235.

Well-made skin in good condition; skull Grade B.

†Peromyscus attwateri pectoralis Osgood.

Proc. Biol. Soc. Washington 17 : 59, Mar. 21, 1904.
=[*Peromyscus*] *pectoralis* Osgood. See Bailey, Proc. Biol. Soc. Washington 19 : 57, May 1, 1906.

81236. Skin and skull. Adult male. Jalpan, Queretaro, Mexico August 30, 1896. Collected by E. W. Nelson and E. A. Goldman. Original number 10095.

Well-made skin in good condition; skull Grade B.

†Peromyscus auritus Merriam.

Proc. Biol. Soc. Washington 12 : 119, Apr. 30, 1898.
=*Peromyscus megalops auritus* Merriam. See Osgood, North Amer. Fauna 28 : 214, Apr. 17, 1909.

68438. Skin and skull. Old female. Mountains 15 miles west of Oaxaca, altitude 9,300 feet, Oaxaca, Mexico. September 17, 1894. Collected by E. W. Nelson and E. A. Goldman. Original number 6795.

Well-made skin in good condition ; skull Grade A.

*Hesperomys austerus Baird. Lectotype.

Proc. Acad Nat. Sci. Philadelphia 7 : 336, reported favorably for publication Apr. 24, 1855.
=*Peromyscus maniculatus austerus* (Baird). See Osgood, North Amer. Fauna 28 : 63, Apr. 17, 1909.

$\frac{1278}{364}$. Skin (lost) and skull. Young adult. Old Fort Steilacoom, Pierce County, Wash. Probably January 20, 1854. Collected by George Suckley.

Skin said to have been mounted ; cannot be found. Skull much broken ; most of mandible present, and most of rostrum, both of the upper tooth rows, and a small portion of the cranium. Parts of the skull have a charred appearance.

No type designated. Baird (Mammals of North America, p. 467, 1857) lists eight specimens as positively *austerus:* No. 229 from Spokane Plain and

Nos. 363, 364, 365, 371, 916, 1964, and 2576 from Steilacoom, Wash. Since Steilacoom is the first locality mentioned in the original description, and since seven-eighths of the specimens came from there, Steilacoom should be chosen as the type locality. (See J. A. Allen, Bull. Amer. Mus. Nat. Hist. 5: 192, 1893.) Miller and Rehn (Proc. Boston Soc. Nat. Hist. 30: 69, Dec. 27, 1901) erroneously give Spokane Plain as the type locality. Of the specimens coming from Steilacoom only the first five were cataloged at the time the original description appeared. The other three were cataloged later in the same year or in the next year. Evidently they were not in Baird's hands when the original description was prepared and they cannot be considered as part of the original material. Of the first four, No. 364, as measured by Baird in 1857, agrees very closely (hindfoot identical) with the measurements given in the original description. Therefore we now make it the lectotype. All these four specimens are represented in the collection by imperfect skulls only. The skins are said to have been mounted. They could not be found in 1893. (See Allen, *loc. cit.*)

*[Hesperomys] bairdii Coues.

Monographs of North American Rodentia, p. 61, 1877.
=*Peromyscus maniculatus maniculatus* (Wagner). See Miller, U. S. Nat. Mus. Bull. 79: 142, Dec. 31, 1912.

3925. Skin, (skull inside?). Labrador, Canada. Received from H. de Saussure, Geneva, Switzerland. Cataloged May 14, 1860.

Specimen should be in the Museum. Osgood, in his revision of the genus *Peromyscus*, North Amer. Fauna 28, 1909, does not mention this type.

†Peromyscus banderanus angelensis Osgood.

Proc. Biol. Soc. Washington 17: 69, Mar. 21, 1904.

71442. Skin and skull. Adult female. Puerto Angel, Oaxaca, Mexico. March 13, 1895. Collected by E. W. Nelson and E. A. Goldman. Original number 7642.

Well-made skin in good condition; skull Grade A.

†Peromyscus banderanus vicinior Osgood.

Proc. Biol. Soc. Washington 17: 68, Mar 21, 1904.

126503. Skin and skull. Adult male. La Salada, Michoacan, Mexico. March 23, 1903. Collected by E. W. Nelson and E. A. Goldman. Original number 16216.

Well-made skin in good condition; skull Grade A.

†Peromyscus boylei laceyi Bailey.

North Amer. Fauna 25: 99, Oct 24, 1905.
=*Peromyscus boylii attwateri* J. A. Allen. See Bailey, Proc. Biol. Soc. Washington 19: 57, May 1, 1906.

92746. Skin and skull. Adult male. Turtle Creek, Kerr County, Tex. December 4, 1897. Collected by H. P. Attwater. Original number 1372-X.

Well-made skin in good condition, except left forefoot missing; skull Grade A.

*Hesperomys boylii Baird.

Proc. Acad. Nat. Sci. Philadelphia 7: 335, reported favorably for publication Apr. 24, 1855.

=*Peromyscus boylii boylii* (Baird). See Mearns, Preliminary Diagnoses of New Mammals from the Mexican Border of the United States, p. 3, May 25, 1896. (Reprinted in Proc. U. S. Nat. Mus. 19: 139, Dec. 21 1896.)

$\frac{356}{1270}$. Mounted skin, and skull and tail vertebrae. Middle fork of the American River, near present town of Auburn, Eldorado County, Calif. Collected by C. C. Boyle. Skin cataloged January 4, 1855; skull, December 20, 1854.

Skin mounted and in wretched condition; skull Grade A.

Type not designated by number. It is referred to in the original description as "collected on the middle fork of the American River, Calif., C. C. Boyle." In the list of specimens of *Hesperomys boylii* in Baird's Mammals, No. $\frac{356}{1270}$ is the only one with the above data. It is consequently to be taken as the type.

*Peromyscus boylii penicillatus Mearns.

Preliminary Diagnoses of New Mammals from the Mexican Border of the United States, p. 2, May 25, 1896. (Reprint: Proc. U. S. Nat. Mus. 19: 139, Dec. 21, 1896.)

=*Peromyscus boylii rowleyi* J. A. Allen. See Bailey, North. Amer. Fauna 25: 98, Oct. 24, 1905.

$\frac{20034}{35426}$. Skin and skull. Adult female. Franklin Mountains near El Paso, El Paso County, Tex. February 19, 1892. Collected by E. A. Mearns and F. X. Holzner. Original number 1463.

Well-made skin in good condition; skull Grade A.

†Peromyscus bullatus Osgood.

Proc. Biol. Soc. Washington 17: 63, Mar. 21, 1904.

54405. Skin and skull. Adult female. Perote, Veracruz, Mexico. June 3, 1893. Collected by E. W. Nelson and E. A. Goldman. Original number 4932.

Well-made skin in good condition; skull Grade A.

*Hesperomys campestris LeConte.

Proc. Acad. Nat. Sci. Philadelphia 6: 413, reported favorably for publication Oct. 25, 1853.

=*Peromyscus leucopus noveboracensis* (Fischer). See Osgood, North Amer. Fauna 28: 117, Apr. 17, 1909.

4726. Skin (no history of a skull). Immature. New Jersey. Collected by J. E. LeConte. Cataloged April 13, 1861.

Skin in very bad condition. LeConte's original specimens were in alcohol, and this skin is evidently an attempt at making a dry preparation from one of them. Large areas of hair have slipped from the back and belly.

Type not designated by number. Coues is the only authority for considering it the type. On page 51 of Monographs of North American Rodentia he refers to it as the type, and again on page 62. In addition, the specimen is entered in the Museum catalog as *"Hesperomys campestris"* and as coming from LeConte April 13, 1861. One of the old labels on the specimen has written on the back "Type of the species as described Pr. A. N. S., VI, 1853, 413."

*Peromyscus canus Mearns.

Preliminary Diagnoses of New Mammals from the Mexican Border of the United States, p. 3, Mar. 25, 1896. (Reprint: Proc. U. S. Nat. Mus. 18: 445, May 23, 1896.)

=*Peromyscus leucopus texanus* Woodhouse. See Osgood, North Amer. Fauna 28: 127, Apr. 17, 1909.

$\frac{21109}{37096}$. Skin and skull. Adult female. Fort Clark, Kinney County, Tex. January 13, 1893. Collected by E. A. Mearns. Original number 2208.

Well-made skin in good condition; skull Grade A.

*Hesperomys cognatus LeConte.   Cotypes.

Proc. Acad. Nat Sci. Philadelphia 7: 442, reported favorably for publication Dec. 25, 1855.

=*Peromyscus gossypinus* (LeConte). See Osgood, North Amer. Fauna 28: 136, Apr. 17, 1909.

4708 and 4709. Poorly made skins but well preserved; skulls inside. Collected by J. E. LeConte. The locality given in the original description is Georgia and South Carolina. Cataloged April 13, 1861.

The specimens are considered cotypes on the authority of Coues, Monographs of North American Rodentia, p. 51, 1877.

†Peromyscus comptus Merriam.

Proc. Biol. Soc. Washington 12: 120, Apr. 30, 1898.

=*Peromyscus megalops auritus* Merriam. See Osgood, North Amer. Fauna 28: 214, Apr. 17, 1909.

70191. Skin and skull. Adult male. Mountains near Chilpancingo, Guerrero, Mexico. December 24, 1894. Collected by E. W. Nelson and E. A. Goldman. Original number 7266.

Well-made skin in good condition; skull Grade B.

†Peromyscus cozumelae Merriam.

Proc. Biol. Soc. Washington 14: 103, July 19, 1901.

=*Peromyscus leucopus cozumelae* Merriam. See Osgood, North Amer. Fauna 28: 135, Apr. 17, 1909.

108449. Skin and skull. Adult male. Cozumel Island, off coast of Quintana Roo, Mexico. April 11, 1901. Collected by E. W. Nelson and E. A. Goldman. Original number 14686.

Well-made skin in good condition; skull Grade A.

†Hesperomys crinitus Merriam.

North Amer. Fauna 5: 53, July 30, 1891.
=*Peromyscus crinitus* (Merriam). See Bangs, Proc. New England Zool. Club 1: 67, July 31, 1899.

$\frac{24255}{31659}$. Skin and skull. Adult male. Shoshone Falls, Snake River, Lincoln County, Idaho. October 10, 1890. Collected by C. Hart Merriam and Vernon Bailey. Original number 1945.

Well-made skin in good condition; skull Grade A.

†Peromyscus crinitus disparilis Goldman.

Proc. Biol. Soc. Washington 45: 90, June 21, 1932.

202989. Skin and skull. Adult male. Tinajas Altas, altitude 2,000 feet, Gila Mountains, Yuma County, Ariz. November 22, 1913. Collected by E. A. Goldman. Original number 22304.

Well-made skin in good condition; skull Grade A.

†Peromyscus crinitus pergracilis Goldman.

Journ. Mamm. 20: 356, Aug. 14, 1939.

264022. Skin and skull. Sex undetermined. South end of Stansbury Island, Great Salt Lake, altitude 4,250 feet, Utah. June 22, 1938. Collected by William H. Marshall. Original number 100.

Well-made skin in good condition; skull Grade A.

†Peromyscus crinitus peridoneus Goldman.

Journ. Mamm. 18: 92, Feb. 14, 1937.

202424. Skin and skull. Adult male. Bright Angel Trail, altitude 4,800 feet, south side of Grand Canyon, Coconino County, Ariz. August 19, 1913. Collected by E. A. Goldman. Original number 22145.

Well-made skin in good condition; skull Grade A.

*Hesperomys eremicus Baird. Cotypes.

Mammals of North America, p. 479, 1857.
=*Peromyscus eremicus* (Baird). See Allen, Bull. Amer. Mus. Nat. Hist. 7: 226, June 29, 1895.

$\frac{1581}{2410}$. Skin (lost) and skull. Male. 1855. Old Fort Yuma, Imperial County, Calif., on west side of Colorado River, opposite Yuma, Ariz. Received from G. H. Thomas.

Both halves of mandible present: left with m_1, right with m_1 and m_2; also a fragment of left maxilla with m^1.

2574. Data as above, preserved in alcohol; specimen lost.

$\frac{2575}{38003}$. In alcohol; skull removed. Female. Data as above. Specimen in good condition except for some shedding of hair about the flanks. The skull was removed in May 1902; Grade A.

Baird's description is based on six specimens, three from Fort Yuma, Calif., and three from "Colorado bottom, Calif." There is nothing to indicate that any one specimen was regarded as more typical than any of the others. It now seems best to regard as cotypes only the three that came from Fort Yuma, since this is a definite locality. The three specimens from "Colorado bottom" are here treated as paratypes. Much of the description is based on details of the soles of the feet, which could be seen more readily in alcoholic specimens. Two of the Fort Yuma specimens were in alcohol, while all the "Colorado bottom" specimens were skins.

*Peromyscus eremicus arenarius Mearns.

Preliminary Diagnoses of New Mammals from the Mexican Border of the United States, p. 2, May 25, 1896. (Reprint: Proc. U. S. Nat. Mus. 19: 138, Dec. 21, 1896.)

=*Peromyscus eremicus* Baird. See Osgood, North Amer. Fauna 28: 239, Apr. 17, 1909.

$\frac{20018}{35413}$. Skin and skull. Adult male. Rio Grande, about 6 miles from El Paso, El Paso County, Tex. February 25, 1892. Collected by E. A. Mearns and F. X. Holzner. Original number 1513.

Well-made skin in good condition; skull Grade A.

†Peromyscus eremicus avius Osgood.

North Amer. Fauna, 28: 247, Apr. 17, 1909.

147024. Skin and skull. Adult female. Ceralbo Island, off east coast of southern Lower California, Mexico. February 13, 1906. Collected by E. W. Nelson and E. A. Goldman. Original number 19125.

Well-made skin in good condition; skull Grade B.

*Peromyscus eremicus carmeni Townsend.

Bull. Amer. Mus. Nat. Hist. 31: 126, June 14, 1912.

198408. Skin and skull. Male. Carmen Island, Gulf of California, Lower California, Mexico. April 3, 1911. Collected by H. E. Anthony. Original number 109.

Well-made skin in good condition; skull Grade A.

†Peromyscus eremicus insulicola Osgood.

North Amer. Fauna 28: 246, Apr. 17, 1909.

147010. Skin and skull. Adult male. Espiritu Santo Island, off east coast of southern Lower California, Mexico. February 9, 1906. Collected by E. W. Nelson and E. A. Goldman. Original number 19077.

Well-made skin in good condition; skull Grade A.

†Peromyscus eremicus papagensis Goldman.

Proc. Biol. Soc. Washington 30: 110, May 23, 1917.

210698. Skin and skull. Adult female. Pinacate Mountains, Sonora, Mexico. February 1915. Collected by Charles Sheldon. Original number 11962–X.

Well-made skin in good condition except for sewed laceration below left ear; skull Grade B.

†Peromyscus eremicus phaeurus Osgood.

Proc. Biol. Soc. Washington 17: 75, Mar. 21, 1904.

50438. Skin and skull. Adult female. Hacienda La Parada, San Luis Potosi, Mexico. August 20, 1892. Collected by E. W. Nelson. Original number 3227.

Well-made skin in good condition; skull Grade B.

†Peromyscus eremicus polypolius Osgood.

North Amer. Fauna 28: 248, Apr. 17, 1909.

146074. Skin and skull. Adult male. Margarita Island, off west coast of southern Lower California, Mexico. November 30, 1905. Collected by E. W. Nelson and E. A. Goldman. Original number 18676.

Well-made skin in good condition; skull Grade A.

†Peromyscus felipensis Merriam.

Proc. Biol. Soc. Washington 12: 122, Apr. 30, 1898.
=Peromyscus difficilis felipensis Merriam. See Osgood, North Amer. Fauna 28: 182, Apr. 17, 1909.

68409. Skin and skull. Adult male. Cerro San Felipe, altitude 10,200 feet, Oaxaca, Mexico. August 22, 1894. Collected by E. W. Nelson and E. A. Goldman. Original number 6611.

Well-made skin in good condition; skull Grade A.

*Hesperomys gambelii Baird.
Cotypes.

Mammals of North America, p. 464, 1857.
=Peromyscus maniculatus gambelii (Baird). See Osgood, North Amer. Fauna 28: 182, Apr. 17, 1909.

$\frac{368}{1282}$. Skin and skull, and tail vertebrae.

$\frac{369}{1283}$. Skin (lost) and skull, and tail vertebrae. 1853. Monterey, Monterey County, Calif. Collected by W. P. Trowbridge. Skins cataloged January 4, 1853; skulls, January 6, 1855.

J. A. Allen discusses the status of the type of this species in Bull. Amer. Mus. Nat. Hist. 5: 190–191, 1893. He says: "*Hesperomys gambellii* Baird was based primarily on two mounted specimens (Nos. $\frac{368}{1282}$ and $\frac{369}{1283}$) from Monterey, Calif., of which No. 369 should probably be regarded as the type, as it is the only specimen specifically mentioned in the original account of the species. This specimen, F. W. True informs me (in a letter dated June 8, 1893), is not now extant, and has not been in the collection for many years. No. 368, which may be considered as a cotype, is, through the kindness of Mr. True, now before me. It is, however, almost valueless for purposes of comparison, having become greatly faded from long exposure to light as a mounted specimen; it has also lost its ears and is in a sad plight generally. This is the only skin extant positively referred to by Baird in his original account of the species of *H. gambelii*."

In a footnote on page 191, *op. cit.*, Allen skillfully eliminates from his cotypes a large number of specimens from various localities that Baird lists in the original description.

Skin No. 368 is in very poor condition, much faded and without ears; No. 369 cannot be found. Skull No. 1282, Grade A; No. 1283, Grade A.

†Peromyscus goldmani Osgood.

Proc. Biol. Soc. Washington 17: 75, Mar. 21, 1904.

96340. Skin and skull. Adult female. Alamos, Sonora, Mexico. December 19, 1898. Collected by E. A. Goldman. Original number 13306.

Well-made skin in good condition; skull Grade A.

*Hesperomys gossypinus LeConte.   Cotype.

Proc. Acad. Nat. Sci. Philadelphia 6: 411, this paper was reported favorably for publication Oct. 25, 1853.

=*Peromyscus gossypinus* (LeConte). See Rhoads, Proc. Acad. Nat. Sci. Philadelphia, 1896, p. 189, Apr. 21, 1896.

546. Skin. Male. Georgia; probably the LeConte plantation, near Riceboro, Liberty County. September 13, 1847. Collected by J. E. LeConte. It cannot be found.

4704. Skin, skull inside. Georgia; probably the LeConte plantation, near Riceboro, Liberty County. Collected by J. E. LeConte. Cataloged April 13, 1861.

Skin in fair condition, but bones left in tail; skull still in the skin.

As this is the only one of LeConte's original specimens extant in the National Museum, it is perhaps well to treat it as a cotype.

No. 546 is the only specimen from Georgia listed in Baird's Mammals of North America. Later, other specimens from LeConte, taken in Georgia, came into the collection—4704, 4705, and 4711. Of these, 4704 is the only one that can be found. The published measurements of 546, both in Baird's Mammals of North America, page 469, and in Coues's Monographs of North American Rodentia, page 78, more nearly agree with the measurements of the original description than the measurements of any of the others.

†Peromyscus gossypinus restrictus Howell.

Journ. Mamm. 20: 364, Aug. 14, 1939.

263539. Skin and skull. Adult female. On Chadwick Beach, near Englewood, Sarasota County, Fla. March 13, 1938. Collected by Luther C. Goldman. Original number 479.

Well-made skin in good condition; skull Grade A.

*Hesperomys gracilis LeConte.

Proc. Acad. Nat. Sci. Philadelphia 7: 442, ordered published at meeting of Dec. 25, 1855.

=*Peromyscus maniculatus gracilis* (Le Conte). See Osgood, North Amer. Fauna 28: 42, Apr. 17, 1909.

$\frac{10292}{38002}$. Skin and skull. Michigan. Received from J. E. LeConte.

Skin cataloged October 15, 1872; skull, May 26, 1902.

The skin is in very poor condition. The left hindleg is the only one present. The skull, removed in May 1902, is somewhat more serviceable. The posterior half of the brain-case has been cut away; the left zygoma is missing. The right half of the mandible is perfect, while the ascending portion of the left half is broken off.

Attached to the specimen are three labels reading as follows:

(1) "Monograph of American Muridae. Elliott Coues, U. S. A. No. 10292. Type of *Hesperomys gracilis=leucopus.*"

(2) "*Hesp. 'gracilis'* LeConte type specimen Wisconsin? Ohio? Michigan?" pasted on the reverse side of this label is "*gracilis.*"

(3) "Monograph of American Muridae. Elliott Coues, U. S. A. No. 10292. *Hesperomys leucopus.*"

There is little in the original description to indicate that this specimen is the type. The entry in the catalog for 10292 reads "Dry type of *gracilis.*" On page 51, Monographs of North American Rodentia, under the synonymy of *Hesperomys leucopus,* Coues gives "*Hesperomys gracilis,* LeConte, Proc. Acad. Nat. Sci. Philadelphia, vol. 7, p. 442, 1855 (Ohio or Michigan and Wisconsin; types Nos. —, 4710, Mus. Smiths.)." The dash may refer to the above specimen; the other specimen, 4710, is one not quite so poor. There is nothing about its labels or catalog entry to indicate that it is a type or cotype.

†Peromyscus gratus Merriam.

Proc. Biol. Soc. Washington 12: 123, Apr. 30, 1898.

=*Peromyscus truei gratus* Merriam. See Osgood, North Amer. Fauna 28: 173, Apr. 17, 1909.

50619. Skin and skull. Adult female. Tlalpam, Federal District, Mexico. November 30, 1892. Collected by E. W. Nelson. Original number 3927.

Well-made skin in good condition; skull Grade A.

†Peromyscus gratus gentilis Osgood.

Proc. Biol. Soc. Washington 17: 61, Mar. 21, 1904.

=*Peromyscus truei gentilis* Osgood. See Osgood, North Amer. Fauna 28: 175, Apr. 17, 1909.

78937. Skin and skull. Adult male. Lagos, Jalisco, Mexico. June 27, 1896. Collected by E. W. Nelson and E. A. Goldman. Original number 9702.

Well-made skin in good condition; skull Grade A.

*Peromyscus guardia Townsend.

Bull. Amer. Mus. Nat. Hist. 31: 126, June 14, 1912.

198406. Skin and skull. Female. Angel de la Guardia Island, Gulf of California, Lower California, Mexico. April 11, 1911. Collected by H. E. Anthony. Original number 135.

Well-made skin in good condition; skull Grade A.

†Peromyscus guatemalensis Merriam.

Proc. Biol. Soc. Washington 12: 118, Apr. 30, 1898.

76861. Skin and skull. Adult male. Todos Santos, altitude 10,000 feet, Guatemala. December 31, 1895. Collected by E. W. Nelson and E. A. Goldman. Original number 8991.

Well-made skin in good condition; skull Grade A.

†Peromyscus hylaeus Osgood.

Proc. Biol. Soc. Washington 21: 141, June 9, 1908.

=Peromyscus maniculatus hylaeus Osgood. See Osgood, North Amer. Fauna 28: 53, Apr. 17, 1909.

127038. Skin and skull. Adult male. Hollis, Kasaan Bay, Prince of Wales Island, Alaska. May 15, 1903. Collected by W. H. Osgood. Original number 2234.

Well-made skin in good condition; skull Grade B.

†Peromyscus hylocetes Merriam.

Proc. Biol. Soc. Washington 12: 124, Apr. 30, 1898.

50423. Skin and skull. Adult female. Patzcuaro, altitude 8,000 feet, Michoacan, Mexico. July 27, 1892. Collected by E. W. Nelson and E. A. Goldman. Original number 2961.

Well-made skin in good condition; skull Grade A.

†Peromyscus lepturus Merriam.

Proc. Biol. Soc. Washington, 12: 118, Apr. 30, 1898.

68612. Skin and skull. Adult male. Mount Zempoaltepec, altitude 8,200 feet, Oaxaca, Mexico. July 8, 1894. Collected by E. W. Nelson and E. A. Goldman. Original number 6381.

Well-made skin in good condition; skull Grade A.

†Peromyscus leucocephalus Howell.

Journ. Mamm. 1: 239, Dec. 4, 1920.

234358. Skin and skull. Adult female. Santa Rosa Island, opposite Camp Walton, Santa Rosa County, Fla. February 26, 1920. Collected by A. H. Howell. Original number 2392.

Well-made skin in good condition; skull Grade A.

†Peromyscus leucopus aridulus Osgood.

North Amer. Fauna 28: 122, Apr. 17, 1909.

75704. Skin and skull. Adult female. Fort Custer, Yellowstone County, Mont. November 12, 1895. Collected by J. A. Loring. Original number 3378.

Well-made skin in good condition; skull Grade B.

*Peromyscus leucopus minnesotae Mearns.

Proc. Biol. Soc. Washington 14: 154, Aug. 9, 1901.
=*Peromyscus leucopus noveboracensis* Fischer. See Osgood, North Amer. Fauna 28: 117, Apr. 17, 1909.

82717. Skin and skull. Adult female. Fort Snelling, Hennepin County, Minn. November 30, 1890. Collected by E. A. Mearns. Original number 1181.

Well-made skin in good condition; skull Grade A.

†Peromyscus leucopus ochraceus Osgood.

North Amer. Fauna 28: 124, Apr. 17, 1909.

53301. Skin and, skull. Adult male. Winslow, Navajo County, Ariz. April 30, 1893. Collected by C. P. Streator. Original number 2674.

Well-made skin in good condition; skull Grade A.

†Hesperomys leucopus rufinus Merriam.

North Amer. Fauna 3: 65, Sept. 11, 1890.
=*Peromyscus maniculatus rufinus* (Merriam). See Osgood, North Amer. Fauna 28: 72, Apr. 17, 1909.

$\frac{17646}{24582}$. Skin and skull. Adult female. San Francisco Mountain, altitude 9,000 feet, Coconino County, Ariz. August 22, 1889. Collected by C. Hart Merriam and Vernon Bailey. Original number 401.

Well-made skin in good condition, except for a bare spot on left side of body; skull Grade A.

†Peromyscus levipes Merriam.

Proc. Biol. Soc. Washington 12: 123, Apr. 30, 1898.
=*Peromyscus boylii levipes* Merriam. See Osgood, North Amer. Fauna 28: 153, Apr. 17, 1909.

53673. Skin and skull. Adult male. Mount Malinche, altitude 8,400 feet, Tlaxcala, Mexico. May 12, 1893. Collected by E. W. Nelson. Original number 4799.

Well-made skin in good condition; skull Grade A.

†Peromyscus lophurus Osgood.

Proc. Biol. Soc. Washington 17: 72, Mar. 21, 1904.

77219. Skin and skull. Adult male. Todos Santos, altitude 10,000 feet, Guatemala. December 30, 1895. Collected by E. W. Nelson and E. A. Goldman. Original number 8956.

Well-made skin in good condition; skull Grade A.

† **Peromyscus luteus** Osgood.

Proc. Biol. Soc. Washington 18 : 77, Feb. 21, 1905.

=*Peromyscus maniculatus nebrascensis* Coues. See Mearns, Proc. Biol. Soc. Washington 24 : 102, May 15, 1911.

$\frac{18658}{25447}$. Skin and skull. Adult female. Kennedy, Cherry County, Nebr. April 23, 1890. Collected by Vernon Bailey. Original number 1079.

Well-made skin in good condition ; skull Grade A.

† **Hesperomys macropus** Merriam.

North Amer. Fauna 4 : 53, Oct. 8, 1890.

=[*Peromyscus*] *floridanus* (Chapman). Placed in synonymy by Chapman, Bull. Amer. Mus. Nat. Hist. 6 : 336, Nov. 30, 1894. See Trouessart, Catalogus Mammalium tam Viventium quam Fossilum, p. 516, 1897.

$\frac{16582}{23513}$. Skin and skull. Adult male. Lake Worth, Palm Beach County, Fla. May 5, 1889. Collected by M. M. Green. Original number 72.

Well-made skin in good condition ; skull Grade A.

† **Peromyscus madrensis** Merriam.

Proc. Biol. Soc. Washington 12 : 16, Jan. 27, 1898.

=*Peromyscus boylii madrensis* Merriam. See Osgood, North Amer. Fauna 28 : 152, Apr. 17, 1909.

89223. Skin and skull. Adult male. Maria Madre Island, Tres Marias Islands, Nayarit, Mexico. May 18, 1897. Collected by E. W. Nelson and E. A. Goldman. Original number 11040.

Well-made skin in good condition ; skull Grade A.

† **Peromyscus maniculatus algidus** Osgood.

North Amer. Fauna 28 : 56, Apr. 17, 1909.

130013. Skin and skull. Adult male. Head of Lake Bennett (site of old Bennett City), British Columbia, Canada. September 17, 1903. Collected by W. H. Osgood. Original number 2690.

Well-made skin in good condition ; skull Grade A.

† **Peromyscus maniculatus assimilis** Nelson and Goldman.

Journ. Mamm. 12 : 305, Aug. 24, 1931.

77939. Skin and skull. Adult male. Coronados Island, off northwest coast of Lower California, Mexico. April 24, 1896. Collected by A. W. Anthony. Original number 13.

Well-made skin in good condition ; skull Grade A.

† **Peromyscus maniculatus dorsalis** Nelson and Goldman.

Journ. Washington Acad. Sci. 21 : 535, Dec. 19, 1931.

80857. Skin and skull. Adult female. Natividad Island, off west coast of Lower California, Mexico. August 4, 1896. Collected by A. W. Anthony. Original number 96.

Well-made skin in good condition; skull Grade A.

†Peromyscus maniculatus elusus Nelson and Goldman.

Journ. Washington Acad. Sci. 21: 533, Dec. 19, 1931.

92049. Skin and skull. Adult male. Santa Barbara Island, Santa Barbara Islands, Los Angeles County, Calif. May 16, 1897. Collected by H. A. Gaylord. Original number 1095X.

Well-made skin in good condition; skull Grade A.

†Peromyscus maniculatus eremus Osgood.

North Amer. Fauna 28: 47, Apr. 17, 1909.

150223. Skin and skull. Adult female. Pleasant Bay, Grindstone Island, Magdalen Islands, Quebec, Canada. August 9, 1907. Collected by W. H. Osgood. Original number 3197.

Well-made skin in good condition, except tip of tail missing; skull Grade A.

†Peromyscus maniculatus exterus Nelson and Goldman.

Journ. Washington Acad. Sci. 21: 532, Dec. 19, 1931.

92098. Skin and skull. Old adult female. San Nicolas Island, Santa Barbara Islands, Los Angeles County, Calif. May 23, 1897. Collected by H. A. Gaylord. Original number 1121–X.

Well-made skin in good condition; skull Grade B.

†Peromyscus maniculatus gunnisoni Goldman.

Proc. Biol. Soc. Washington 50: 224, Dec. 28, 1937.

262845. Skin and skull. Adult female. Gunnison Island, altitude about 4,300 feet, Great Salt Lake, Utah. June 1, 1937. Collected by Alfred M. Bailey and Robert J. Niedrach. Original number 28019–X. (3010). Presented by Colorado Museum of Natural History.

Well-made skin in good condition; skull Grade A.

†Peromyscus maniculatus hollisteri Osgood.

North Amer. Fauna 28: 62, Apr. 17, 1909.

130316. Skin and skull. Adult male. Friday Harbor, San Juan Island, San Juan County, Wash. October 23, 1903. Collected by N. Hollister. Original number 832.

Well-made skin in good condition; skull Grade A.

†Peromyscus maniculatus inclarus Goldman.

Journ. Mamm. 20: 355, Aug. 14, 1939.

264119. Skin and skull. Adult male. Fremont Island, Great Salt Lake, altitude 4,250 feet, Utah. August 7, 1938. Collected by William H. Marshall. Original number 276.

Well-made skin in good condition; skull Grade A.

†Peromyscus maniculatus magdalenae Osgood.

North Amer. Fauna 28: 101, Apr. 17, 1909.

146971. Skin and skull. Old male. Magdalena Island, off west coast of southern Lower California, Mexico. December 3, 1905. Collected by E. W. Nelson and E. A. Goldman. Original number 18749.

Well-made skin in good condition; skull Grade B.

†Peromyscus maniculatus margaritae Osgood.

North Amer. Fauna 28: 95, Apr. 17, 1909.

146958. Skin and skull. Adult female. Margarita Island, off west coast of southern Lower California, Mexico. December 1, 1905. Collected by E. W. Nelson and E. A. Goldman. Original number 18726.

Well-made skin in good condition; skull Grade B.

†Peromyscus maniculatus martinensis Nelson and Goldman.

Journ. Washington Acad. Sci. 21: 534, Dec. 19, 1931.
=*Peromyscus maniculatus exiguus* J. A. Allen: See Nelson and Goldman, Journ. Mamm. 13: 370, Nov. 2, 1932.

138979. Skin and skull. Adult female. San Martin Island, off west coast of Lower California, Mexico. August 13, 1905. Collected by E. W. Nelson and E. A. Goldman. Original number 17726.

Well-made skin in good condition; skull Grade A.

†Peromyscus maniculatus santacruzae Nelson and Goldman.

Journ. Washington Acad. Sci. 21: 532, Dec. 19, 1931.

$\frac{35184}{47449}$. Skin and skull. Old adult male. Santa Cruz Island, Santa Barbara Islands, Santa Barbara County, Calif. July 13, 1892. Collected by C. P. Streator. Original number 1923.

Well-made skin in good condition, except for underparts partly sloughed off; skull Grade A.

†Peromyscus maniculatus streatori Nelson and Goldman.

Journ. Washington Acad. Sci. 21: 531, Dec. 19, 1931.

$\frac{34631}{46716}$. Skin and skull. Old adult male. San Miguel Island, Santa Barbara Islands, Santa Barbara County, Calif. June 24, 1892. Collected by C. P. Streator. Original number 1861.

Well-made skin in good condition; skull Grade A.

†Peromyscus megalops Merriam.

Proc. Biol. Soc. Washington 12: 119, Apr. 30, 1898.

71592. Skin and skull. Old male. Mountains near Ozolotepec, Oaxaca, Mexico. March 26, 1895. Collected by E. W. Nelson and E. A. Goldman. Original number 7733.

Well-made skin in good condition; skull Grade C.

†Peromyscus megalops melanurus Osgood.

North Amer. Fauna 28: 215, Apr. 17, 1909.

71385. Skin and skull. Adult male. Pluma, altitude 3,000 feet, Oaxaca, Mexico. March 20, 1895. Collected by E. W. Nelson and E. A. Goldman. Original number 7703.

Well-made skin in good condition; skull Grade B.

†Hesperomys megalotis Merriam.

North Amer. Fauna 3: 63, Sept. 11, 1890.
=*Peromyscus truei* (Shufeldt). See Osgood, North Amer. Fauna 28: 165, Apr. 17, 1909.

$\frac{17943}{24854}$. Skin and skull. Adult male. Black Tank, Little Colorado Desert, Coconino County, Ariz. September 21, 1889. Collected by C. Hart Merriam and V. Bailey. Original number 502.

Well-made skin in good condition; skull Grade A.

†Peromyscus mekisturus Merriam.

Proc. Biol. Soc. Washington 12: 124, Apr. 30, 1898.

64108. Skin and skull. Adult female. Chalchicomula, altitude 8,400 feet, Puebla, Mexico. March 16, 1894. Collected by E. W. Nelson and E. A. Goldman. Original number 5951.

Well-made skin in good condition; skull Grade A.

†Peromyscus melanocarpus Osgood.

Proc. Biol. Soc. Washington 17: 73, Mar. 21, 1904.

68610. Skin and skull. Young adult female. Mount Zempoal-tepec, altitude 8,000 feet, Oaxaca, Mexico. July 8, 1894. Collected by E. W. Nelson and E. A. Goldman. Original number 6379.

Well-made skin in good condition; skull Grade A.

*Hesperomys (Vesperimus) melanophrys Coues.

Proc. Acad. Nat. Sci. Philadelphia 26: 181, Dec. 15, 1874.
=*P*[*eromyscus*] *melanophrys* (Coues). See Allen, Bull. Amer. Mus. Nat. Hist. 9: 51, Mar. 15, 1897.

$\frac{10183}{12453}$. Skin and skull. Adult. Santa Efigenia, Oaxaca, Mexico. July 11, 1871. Collected by F. Sumichrast. Original number 2.

The skin is in good condition and fairly well made up, except that tail has never been skinned out; skull Grade C.

The original label bears the following legible measurements: "Lg. tot. 245 mill.—tip of snout to tail (below) 11 centim.—tail 135 mill.—from tip of nose to eye 15 mill.—ditto to ear 25.—ear, exteriorly 20 mill., interiorly 22 mill."

†Peromyscus melanophrys consobrinus Osgood.

Proc. Biol. Soc. Washington 17: 66, Mar. 21, 1904.

79626. Skin and skull. Adult female. Berriozabal, Zacatecas, Mexico. July 10, 1896. Collected by E. W. Nelson and E. A. Goldman. Original number 9818.

Well-made skin in good condition; skull Grade B.

†Peromyscus melanophrys zamorae Osgood.

Proc. Biol. Soc. Washington 17: 65, Mar. 21, 1904.

120288. Skin and skull. Adult female (not male as recorded in original description). Zamora, Michoacan, Mexico. January 20, 1903. Collected by E. W. Nelson and E. A. Goldman. Original number 15783.

Well-made skin in good condition; skull Grade A.

†Peromyscus melanotis zamelas Osgood.

Proc. Biol. Soc. Washington 17: 59, Mar. 21, 1904.
=*Peromyscus melanotis* J. A. Allen and Chapman. See Osgood, North Amer. Fauna 28: 109, Apr. 17, 1909.

98197. Skin and skull. Adult female. Colonia Garcia, Chihuahua, Mexico. July 24, 1899 (not July 23, 1899, as printed in original description). Collected by E. W. Nelson and E. A. Goldman. Original number 13915.

Well-made skin in good condition; skull Grade A.

*Peromyscus merriami Mearns.

Preliminary Diagnoses of New Mammals from the Mexican Border of the United States, p. 2, May 25, 1896. (Reprint: Proc. U. S. Nat. Mus. 19: 138, Dec. 21, 1896.)
=*Peromyscus eremicus* (Baird). See Osgood, North Amer. Fauna 28: 239, Apr. 17, 1909.

59234. Skin and skull. Adult female. Sonoyta, Sonora, Mexico. January 21, 1894. Collected by E. A. Mearns and F. X. Holzner. Original number 2815.

Well-made skin in good condition; skull Grade A.

†Peromyscus mexicanus orizabae Merriam.

Proc. Biol. Soc. Washington 12: 121, Apr. 30, 1898.
=*Peromyscus mexicanus totontepecus* Merriam. See Osgood, North Amer. Fauna 28: 202, Apr. 17, 1909.

58197. Skin and skull. Adult male. Orizaba, Veracruz, Mexico. January 29, 1894. Collected by E. W. Nelson and E. A. Goldman. Original number 5787.

Well-made skin in good condition; skull Grade A.

†Peromyscus mexicanus saxatilis Merriam.

Proc. Biol. Soc. Washington 12: 121, Apr. 30, 1898.

77296. Skin and skull. Adult male. Jacaltenango, altitude 5,400 feet, Huehuetenango, Guatemala. December 19, 1895. Collected by E. W. Nelson and E. A. Goldman. Original number 8824.

Well-made skin in good condition; skull Grade A.

†Peromyscus mexicanus teapensis Osgood.

Proc. Biol. Soc. Washington 17: 69, Mar. 21, 1904.

100022. Skin and skull. Adult female. Teapa, Tabasco, Mexico. March 25, 1900. Collected by E. W. Nelson and E. A. Goldman. Original number 14067.

Well-made skin in good condition, a bare spot on abdomen; skull Grade A.

†Peromyscus mexicanus totontepecus Merriam.

Proc. Biol. Soc. Washington 12: 120, Apr. 30, 1898.

68624. Skin and skull. Adult female. Totontepec, Oaxaca, Mexico. July 16, 1894. Collected by E. W. Nelson and E. A. Goldman. Original number 6465.

Well-made skin in good condition; skull Grade B.

†Peromyscus musculoides Merriam.

Proc. Biol. Soc. Washington 12: 124, Apr. 30, 1898.
=Peromyscus leucopus affinis J. A. Allen. See Osgood, North Amer. Fauna 28: 133, Apr. 17, 1909.

69661. Skin and skull. Old male. Cuicatlan, Oaxaca, Mexico. October 14, 1894. Collected by E. W. Nelson and E. A. Goldman. Original number 6892.

Well-made skin in good condition; skull Grade A.

†Peromyscus (Megadontomys) nelsoni Merriam.

Proc. Biol. Soc. Washington 12: 116, Apr. 30, 1898.
=Peromyscus nelsoni Merriam. See Osgood, North Amer. Fauna 28: 221, Apr. 17, 1909.

55024. Skin and skull. Adult female. Jico, altitude 6,000 feet, Veracruz, Mexico. July 10, 1893. Collected by E. W. Nelson. Original number 5202.

Well-made skin in good condition; skull Grade B.

†Peromyscus nuttalli lewisi Howell.

Journ. Mamm. 20: 498, Nov. 14, 1939.

262415. Skin and skull. Adult female. Amelia Court House, Va. January 30, 1936. Collected by John B. Lewis. Original number 15(27823–X).

Well-made skin in good condition; skull Grade A.

†Peromyscus oaxacensis Merriam.

Proc. Biol. Soc. Washington 12: 122, Apr. 30, 1898.

68426. Skin and skull. Young adult male. Cerro San Felipe, altitude 9,000 feet, Oaxaca, Mexico. September 1, 1894. Collected by E. W. Nelson and E. A. Goldman. Original number 6700.

Well-made skin in good condition; skull Grade A.

†Peromyscus oreas rubidus Osgood.

Proc. Biol. Soc. Washington 14: 193, Dec. 12, 1901.
=*Peromyscus maniculatus rubidus* Osgood. See Osgood, North Amer. Fauna 28: 65, Apr. 17, 1909.

91650. Skin and skull. Young adult female. Mendocino City, Mendocino County, Calif. November 17, 1897. Collected by J. A. Loring. Original number 4925.

Well-made skin in good condition; skull Grade A.

*[Hesperomys] parasiticus Baird.   Lectotype.

Mammals of North America, p. 479, 1857.
=*Peromyscus californicus parasiticus* (Baird). See Grinnell and Orr, Journ. Mamm. 15: 213, Aug. 11, 1934.

1156. Skin (mounted). Male. "Santa Clara Valley" [probably near Mountain View], Santa Clara County, Calif. November 1855. Collected by J. G. Cooper.

Skin mounted and on exhibition for many years. In good condition. Removed from exhibition series in 1934 and is now in type collection. No record of a skull.
Lectotype selected by Grinnell and Orr, loc. cit.

†Peromyscus pectoralis laceianus Bailey.

Proc. Biol. Soc. Washington 19: 57, May 1, 1906.

97063. Skin and skull. Adult male. Ranch of Howard Lacey, Turtle Creek, near Kerrville, Kerr County, Tex. May 3, 1899. Collected by Vernon Bailey. Original number 6860.

Well-made skin in good condition; skull Grade A.

†Peromyscus pirrensis Goldman.

Smithsonian Misc. Coll. 60 (2) : 5, Sept. 20, 1912.

178997. Skin and skull. Adult male. Near head of Rio Limon, altitude 4,500 feet, Mount Pirri, eastern Panama. May 3, 1912. Collected by E. A. Goldman. Original number 21675.

Well-made skin in good condition, except for several bare spots on abdomen; skull Grade A.

†Peromyscus polionotus decoloratus Howell.

Journ. Mamm. 20: 363, Aug. 14, 1939.

245780. Skin and skull. Adult male. Ponce Park, near Mosquito Inlet, Volusia County, Florida. May 25, 1925. Collected by Arthur H. Howell. Original number 2448.

Well-made skin in good condition; skull Grade A.

†Peromyscus polius Osgood.

Proc. Biol. Soc. Washington 17: 61, Mar. 21, 1904.

98226. Skin and skull. Adult female. Colonia Garcia, Chihuahua, Mexico. June 26, 1899. Collected by E. W. Nelson and E. A. Goldman. Original number 13846.

Well-made skin in good condition; skull Grade A.

†Peromyscus prevostensis Osgood.

North Amer. Fauna 21: 29, Sept. 26, 1901.
=*Peromyscus sitkensis prevostensis* Osgood. See Osgood, North Amer. Fauna 28: 102, Apr. 17, 1909.

100818. Skin and skull. Adult female. Prevost Island, Queen Charlotte Islands, British Columbia, Canada. July 5, 1900. Collected by W. H. Osgood and E. Heller. Original number 1135.

Well-made skin in good condition; skull Grade A.

†Peromyscus simulatus Osgood.

Proc. Biol. Soc. Washington 17: 72, Mar. 21, 1904.

55028. Skin and skull. Adult female. Near Jico, altitude 6,000 feet, Veracruz, Mexico. July 12, 1893. Collected by E. W. Nelson. Original number 5224.

Well-made skin in good condition; skull Grade A.

†Peromyscus sitkensis Merriam.

Proc. Biol. Soc. Washington 11: 223, July 15, 1897.

73809. Skin and skull. Adult male. Sitka, Alaska. July 30, 1895. Collected by C. P. Streator. Original number 4720.

Well-made skin in good condition; skull Grade A.

*Hesperomys sonoriensis LeConte.

Proc. Acad. Nat. Sci. Philadelphia 6: 413, reported favorably for publication Oct. 25, 1853.
=*Peromyscus maniculatus sonoriensis* (LeConte). See Osgood, North Amer. Fauna 28: 89, Apr. 17, 1909.

$\frac{146}{1128}$. Skin and skull. Young. Santa Cruz, Sonora, Mexico. Sept. 24–28, 1851. Collected by J. H. Clark, United States and Mexican Boundary Survey.

The skin is well made up, probably remade, but the specimen has a worn and dirty look about it; skull Grade B.

Type not designated by number, but it is mentioned as one "collected by the Boundary Commission under Major Graham." Referring to Baird's Mammals of North America, page 476, there are found to be three specimens collected by that commission namely, Nos. 144, 146, and 147. The measurements of No. 146 agree very closely with the measurements given by LeConte; No. 144 does not agree with them at all; and of No. 147 no measurements are given, and the specimen itself cannot be found. No. 146 is evidently the type. It was so considered and marked by Coues in 1877.

†Peromyscus sonoriensis blandus Osgood.

Proc. Biol. Soc. Washington 17 : 56, Mar. 21, 1904.
=*Peromyscus maniculatus blandus* Osgood. See Osgood, North Amer. Fauna 28 : 84, Apr. 17, 1909.

57635. Skin and skull. Adult female. Escalon, Chihuahua, Mexico. November 27, 1893. Collected by E. A. Goldman. Original number 166.

Well-made skin in good condition; skull Grade A.

†Peromyscus sonoriensis fulvus Osgood.

Proc. Biol. Soc. Washington 17 : 57, Mar. 21, 1904.
=*Peromyscus maniculatus fulvus* Osgood. See Osgood, North Amer. Fauna 28 : 86, April 17, 1909.

68655. Skin and skull. Adult male. Oaxaca, State of Oaxaca, Mexico. June 12, 1894. Collected by E. W. Nelson and E. A. Goldman. Original number 6277.

Well-made skin in good condition; skull Grade A.

†Peromyscus spicilegus evides Osgood.

Proc. Biol. Soc. Washington 17 : 64, Mar. 21, 1904.
=*Peromyscus boylii evides* Osgood. See Osgood, North Amer. Fauna 28 : 152, Apr. 17, 1909.

71426. Skin and skull. Adult male. Juquila, Oaxaca, Mexico. February 28, 1895. Collected by E. W. Nelson and E. A. Goldman. Original number 7572.

Well-made skin in good condition; skull Grade A.

†Peromyscus spicilegus simulus Osgood.

Proc. Biol. Soc. Washington 17 : 64, Mar. 21, 1904.
=*Peromyscus boylii simulus* Osgood. See Osgood, North Amer. Fauna 28 : 151, Apr. 17, 1909.

88088. Skin and skull. Adult male. San Blas, Nayarit, Mexico. April 18, 1897. Collected by E. W. Nelson and E. A. Goldman. Original number 10933.

Well-made skin in good condition; skull Grade A.

*Peromyscus stephani Townsend.

Bull. Amer. Mus. Nat. Hist. 31: 126, June 14, 1912.

198407. Skin and skull. Male. San Esteban Island, Gulf of California, Lower California, Mexico. April 14, 1911. Collected by H. E. Anthony. Original number 162.

Well-made skin in good condition; skull Grade B.

*Peromyscus stephensi Mearns.

Proc. U. S. Nat. Mus. 19: 721, July 30, 1897.
=*Peromyscus crinitus stephensi* Mearns. See Osgood, North Amer. Fauna 28: 232, Apr. 17, 1909.

61026. Skin and skull. Adult female. Three miles east of Mountain Spring, Imperial County, Calif. May 9, 1894. Collected by E. A. Mearns. Original number 3512.

Well-made skin in good condition; skull Grade A.

†Peromyscus tehuantepecus Merriam.

Proc. Biol. Soc. Washington 12: 122, Apr. 30, 1898.
=*Peromyscus mexicanus mexicanus* Saussure. See Osgood, North Amer. Fauna 28: 199, Apr. 17, 1909.

75302. Skin and skull. Adult female (not male as recorded in original description). Tehuantepec, Oaxaca, Mexico. May 23, 1895. Collected by E. W. Nelson and E. A. Goldman. Original number 7980.

Well-made skin in good condition; skull Grade A.

*Hesperomys texanus Woodhouse.

Proc. Acad. Nat. Sci. Philadelphia 6: 242, reported favorably for publication Feb. 22, 1853.
=*Peromyscus leucopus texanus* (Woodhouse). See Osgood, North Amer. Fauna 28: 127, Apr. 17, 1909.

$\frac{2559}{37026}$. Skin preserved in alcohol; fragments of skull. Probably from vicinity of Mason, Mason County, Tex. Collected by S. W. Woodhouse. Probably autumn of 1852.

Skin in alcohol, a miserable looking affair, much discolored. Feet and leg bones complete and perfect; skull Grade D.

Type not designated by number. In the description but one specimen is implied, and in Baird's Mammals, under list of specimens, 2559 is the only one having the data of Woodhouse's specimen. Another specimen. No. $\frac{4748}{37155}$, labeled "*Hesperomys texana* W. Texas, Dr. Woodhouse," is in the Museum, but this was not mentioned by Baird and has never been regarded as a type, although it may have been in the hands of Woodhouse when the description was written.

†**Peromyscus texanus castaneus** Osgood.

> Proc. Biol. Soc. Washington 17: 58, Mar. 21, 1904.
> =*Peromyscus leucopus castaneus* Osgood.   See Osgood, North Amer. Fauna 28: 133, Apr. 17, 1909.

107980.   Skin and skull.   Adult male.   Yohaltun, Campeche, Mexico.   December 19, 1900.   Collected by E. W. Nelson and E. A. Goldman.   Original number 14283.

> Well-made skin in good condition; skull Grade A.

***Peromyscus texanus clementis** Mearns.

> Preliminary Diagnoses of New Mammals from the Mexican Border of the United States, p. 4, Mar. 25, 1896.   (Reprint: Proc. U. S. Nat. Mus. 18: 446, May 23, 1896.)
> =*Peromyscus maniculatus clementis* Mearns.   See Osgood, North Amer. Fauna 28: 96, Apr. 17, 1909.

61117.   Skin and skull.   Adult male.   San Clemente Island, Santa Barbara Islands, Los Angeles County, Calif.   August 27, 1894.   Collected by E. A. Mearns.   Original number 3819.

> Well-made skin in good condition; skull Grade A.

***Peromyscus texanus medius** Mearns.

> Preliminary Diagnoses of New Mammals from the Mexican Border of the United States, p. 4, Mar. 25, 1896.   (Reprint: Proc. U. S. Nat. Mus. 18: 446, May 23, 1896.)
> =*Peromyscus maniculatus gambelii* Baird.   See Osgood, North Amer. Fauna 28: 67, Apr. 17, 1909.

61059.   Skin and skull.   Adult male.   Nachoguero Valley, near monument No. 238, Mexican boundary line, Lower California, Mexico.   June 4, 1894.   Collected by E. A. Mearns.   Original number 3623.

> Well-made skin in good condition; skull Grade A.

†**Peromyscus texanus mesomelas** Osgood.

> Proc. Biol. Soc. Washington 17: 57, Mar. 21, 1904.
> =*Peromyscus leucopus mesomelas* Osgood.   See Osgood, North Amer. Fauna 28: 132, Apr. 17, 1909.

58210.   Skin and skull.   Adult male.   Orizaba, Veracruz, Mexico.   January 20, 1894.   Collected by E. W. Nelson and E. A. Goldman.   Original number 5705.

> Well-made skin in good condition; skull Grade A.

†**Peromyscus (Megadontomys) thomasi** Merriam.

> Proc. Biol. Soc. Washington 12: 116, Apr. 30, 1898.
> =*Peromyscus thomasi* Merriam.   See Osgood, North Amer. Fauna 28: 219, Apr. 17, 1909.

70142. Skin and skull. Old male. Mountains near Chilpancingo, altitude 9,700 feet, Guerrero, Mexico. December 24, 1894. Collected by E. W. Nelson and E. A. Goldman. Original number 7250.

Well-made skin in good condition; skull Grade A.

*Peromyscus tiburonensis Mearns.

Proc. U. S. Nat. Mus. 19: 720, July 30, 1897.
=*Peromyscus eremicus tiburonensis* Mearns. See Osgood, North Amer. Fauna 28: 250, Apr. 17, 1909.

63186. Skin and skull. Adult male. Tiburon Island, Gulf of California, Sonora, Mexico. December 25, 1895. Collected by J. W. Mitchell. Original number 1.

Skin in fair condition, recently made into a modern study skin, a small area on the left flank without hair; skull Grade A.

*Peromyscus tornillo Mearns.

Preliminary Diagnoses of New Mammals from the Mexican Border of the United States, p. 3, Mar. 25, 1926. (Reprint: Proc. U. S. Nat. Mus. 18: 445, May 23, 1896.)
=*Peromyscus leucopus tornillo* Mearns. See Osgood, North Amer. Fauna 28: 125, Apr. 17, 1909.

$\frac{20225}{35420}$. Skin and skull. Adult male. About 6 miles north of El Paso, on the Rio Grande, El Paso County, Tex. February 18, 1892. Collected by E. A. Mearns and F. X. Holzner. Original number 1458.

Well-made skin in good condition; skull Grade A.

*Hesperomys truei Shufeldt.

Proc. U. S. Nat. Mus. 8: 405, Sept. 14, 1885.
=*P*[*eromyscus*] *truei* (Shufeldt). See Thomas, Ann. Mag. Nat. Hist. (ser. 6) 14: 365, Nov. 1894.

$\frac{14954}{35108}$. Skin, skull, and skeleton. Adult male. Fort Wingate, McKinley County, N. Mex. March 14, 1885. Collected by R. W. Shufeldt.

Fairly well-made skin in good condition. Right foreleg and left hindleg used for the skeleton; skull Grade B. Greater part of skeleton seems to be present but mostly disarticulated.

Type designated by number on page 405 of the original description, where it reads "14904," evidently a mistake for 14954, as 14904 refers in the Museum catalog to a *Neotoma* collected by Shufeldt at Fort Wingate.

†Peromyscus truei lagunae Osgood.

North Amer. Fauna 28: 172, Apr. 17, 1909.

147004. Skin and skull. Adult female. La Laguna, Laguna Mountains, Lower California, Mexico. January 26, 1906. Collected by E. W. Nelson and E. A. Goldman. Original number 19012.

Well-made skin in good condition; skull Grade A.

†**Peromyscus truei preblei** Bailey.

North Amer. Fauna 55: 188, Aug. 29, 1936.

78660. Skin and skull. Adult male. Crooked River, 20 miles southeast of Prineville, Oreg. June 28, 1896. Collected by E. A. Preble. Original number 1079.

Well-made skin in good condition; skull Grade A.

†**Peromyscus xenurus** Osgood.

Proc. Biol. Soc. Washington 17: 67, Mar. 21, 1904.

94518. Skin and skull. Adult female. Durango, State of Durango, Mexico. July 1, 1898. Collected by E. W. Nelson and E. A. Goldman. Original number 12677.

Well-made skin in good condition; skull Grade B.

†**Peromyscus yucatanicus badius** Osgood.

Proc. Biol. Soc. Washington 17: 70, Mar. 21, 1904.

108016. Skin and skull. Adult female. Apazote, Campeche, Mexico. December 28, 1900. Collected by E. W. Nelson and E. A. Goldman. Original number 14377.

Well-made skin in good condition; skull Grade A.

†**Peromyscus zarhynchus** Merriam.

Proc. Biol. Soc. Washington 12: 117, Apr. 30, 1898.

76119. Skin and skull. Adult female. Tumbala, altitude 5,000 feet, Chiapas, Mexico. October 26, 1895. Collected by E. W. Nelson and E. A. Goldman. Original number 8606.

Well-made skin in good condition; skull Grade A.

†**Peromyscus zarhynchus cristobalensis** Merriam.

Proc. Biol. Soc. Washington 12: 117, Apr. 30, 1898.
=*Peromyscus zarhynchus* Merriam. See Osgood, North Amer. Fauna 28: 217, Apr. 17, 1909.

76109. Skin and skull. Adult female. San Cristobal, Chiapas, Mexico. October 2, 1895. Collected by E. W. Nelson and E. A. Goldman. Original number 8536.

Well-made skin in good condition; skull Grade A.

†**Peromyscus zelotes** Osgood.

Proc. Biol. Soc. Washington 17: 67, Mar. 21, 1904.
=*Peromyscus truei gratus* Merriam. See Osgood, North Amer. Fauna 28: 173, Apr. 17, 1909.

50430. Skin and skull. Adult female. Querendaro, Michoacan, Mexico. August 8, 1892. Collected by E. W. Nelson. Original number 3056.

Well-made skin in good condition; skull Grade B.

Genus PHENACOMYS Merriam

†Phenacomys albipes Merriam.

Proc. Biol. Soc. Washington 14: 125, July 19, 1901.

97236. Skin and skull. Adult male. Redwoods near Arcata, Humboldt Bay, Humboldt County, Calif. May 24, 1899. Collected by W. K. Fisher. Original number 821.

Well-made skin in good condition; skull Grade A.

*Phenacomys celatus Merriam.

North Amer. Fauna 2: 33, Oct. 30, 1889.
=*Phenacomys ungava ungava* Merriam. See Miller, Proc. Biol. Soc. Washington 11: 84, Apr. 21, 1897.

186486. Skin and skull, originally an alcoholic specimen. Adult male. Godbout, Quebec, Canada. June 10, 1886. Collected by N. A. Comeau. Merriam collection No. $\frac{2851}{5988}$.

Well-made skin in good condition; skull Grade B.

†Phenacomys intermedius celsus A. B. Howell.

Proc. Biol. Soc. Washington 36: 158, May 1, 1923.

109103. Skin and skull. Adult male. Muir Meadow, altitude 9,300 feet, Tuolumne Meadows, Yosemite National Park, Calif. August 13, 1901. Collected by James H. Gaut. Original number 250.

Well-made skin in good condition; skull Grade B.

†Phenacomys intermedius levis A. B. Howell.

Proc. Biol. Soc. Washington 36: 157, May 1, 1923.

72405. Skin and skull. Adult male. St. Marys Lake, Teton County, Mont. May 23, 1895. Collected by A. H. Howell. Original number 13.

Well-made skin in good condition; skull Grade A.

*Phenacomys latimanus Merriam.

North Amer. Fauna 2: 34, Oct. 30, 1889.
=*Phenacomys ungava ungava* Merriam. See A. B. Howell, North Amer. Fauna 48: 25, Oct. 12, 1926.

186487. Skin and skull. Young adult male. Fort Chimo, Ungava, [=Labrador Peninsula, Quebec], Canada. February 4, 1883. Collected by L. M. Turner. Original number 300. Merriam collection No. $\frac{5484}{6159}$.

Specimen originally in alcohol, now made up as a skin, in good condition; skull Grade B.

*Phenacomys longicaudus True.

Proc. U. S. Nat. Mus. 13: 303, Nov. 15, 1890.

$\frac{19071}{34808}$. Skin and skull. Marshfield, Coos County, Oreg. August 1890. Collected by Aurelius Todd.

Recently made over into a fair study skin, vertebrae left in tail; skull Grade D.

†Phenacomys mackenzii Preble.

Proc. Biol. Soc. Washington 15: 182, Aug. 6, 1902.

110625. Skin and skull. Adult male. Fort Smith, Slave River, Mackenzie, Canada. June 29, 1901. Collected by E. A. Preble. Original number 4271.

Well-made skin in good condition; skull Grade A.

†Phenacomys orophilus Merriam.

North Amer. Fauna 5: 65, July 30, 1891.
=*Phenacomys intermedius intermedius* Merriam. See A. B. Howell, North Amer. Fauna 48: 15, Oct. 12, 1926.

$\frac{23856}{31256}$. Skin and skull. Subadult female. Lemhi Mountains [="Salmon River Mountains"], near head of Timber Creek, Lemhi County, Idaho. August 28, 1890. Collected by C. Hart Merriam and Vernon Bailey. Original number 1710.

Well-made skin in good condition; skull Grade B.

†Phenacomys preblei Merriam.

Proc. Biol. Soc. Washington 11: 45, Mar. 16, 1897.
=*Phenacomys intermedius intermedius* Merriam. See A. B. Howell, North Amer. Fauna 48: 15, Oct. 12, 1926.

74513. Skin and skull. Subadult male. Longs Peak, altitude about 9,000 feet, Larimer County, Colo. August 12, 1895. Collected by E. A. Preble. Original number 647.

Well-made skin in good condition; skull Grade A.

*Phenacomys truei J. A. Allen.

Bull. Amer. Mus. Nat. Hist. 6: 331, Nov. 7, 1894.
=*Phenacomys intermedius intermedius* Merriam. See A. B. Howell, North Amer. Fauna 48: 15, Oct. 12, 1926.

$\frac{3056}{36884}$. Skin and skull. Adult. "Black Hills," now Laramie Mountains, Wyo. August 10, 1857. Collected by W. A. Hammond. Original number 109. Wagon road to Bridgers Pass, Rocky Mountains.

Skin in poor condition, the much-torn anterior parts glued to a cotton filling. Right foreleg missing. Color apparently normal; skull Grade D.

*Phenacomys ungava Merriam.

North Amer. Fauna 2: 35, Oct. 30, 1889.

186488. Skin and skull, orginally an alcoholic specimen. Adult male. Fort Chimo, Ungava, [=Labrador Peninsula, Quebec], Canada. Spring 1884. Collected by L. M. Turner. Original number 525. Merriam collection No. $\frac{5468}{6155}$.

Well-made skin with two large bare spots, one on each side of body; skull Grade B.

Genus PHODOPUS Miller

*Phodopus crepidatus Hollister.

Smithsonian Misc. Coll. 56 (14) : 3, Nov. 29, 1912.

175480. Skin and skull. Adult male. Chuisaya Steppe (8 miles south of Kosh-Agatch), altitude 7,300 feet, Altai district, Siberia. July 28, 1912. Collected by N. Hollister. Original number 4393.

Well-made skin in good condition; skull Grade A.

Genus PITYMYS McMurtrie

*Arvicola apella LeConte.

Proc. Acad. Nat. Sci. Philadelphia 6 : 405, favorably reported for publication Oct. 25, 1853.

=Pitymys pinetorum scalopsoides (Audubon and Bachman). See Miller, U. S. Nat. Mus. Bull. 79 : 228, Dec. 31, 1912.

4714. Skin with skull inside. Pennsylvania. From J. E. LeConte's collection. Cataloged April 13, 1861.

Skin poorly made up, but well preserved.

This specimen was not designated by number as a type. It bears two old labels each marked "apella," as well as one of Coues's labels calling it the type. In Monographs of North American Rodentia, pages 223 and 224, Coues refers to No. 4714 as the type of Arvicola apella LeConte.

†Pitymys parvulus Howell.

Proc. Biol. Soc. Washington 29 : 83, Apr. 4, 1916.

210485. Skin and skull. Adult female. Ocala, Marion County, Fla. December 15, 1915. Collected by R. T. Jackson. Original number 13149–X.

Well-made skin in good condition; skull Grade A.

†Microtus pinetorum auricularis Bailey.

Proc. Biol. Soc. Washington 12 : 90, Apr. 30, 1898.

=Pitymys pinetorum auricularis (Bailey). See Miller, U. S. Nat. Mus. Bull. 79 : 229, Dec. 31, 1912.

$\frac{34062}{46139}$. Skin and skull. Adult male. Washington, Adams County, Miss. May 26, 1892. Collected by Vernon Bailey. Original number 3649.

Well-made skin in good condition; skull Grade A.

†Microtus pinetorum nemoralis Bailey.

Proc. Biol. Soc. Washington 12: 89, Apr. 30, 1898.
=*Pitymys nemoralis* (Bailey). See Miller, U. S. Nat. Mus. Bull. 79: 229,
Dec. 31, 1912.

87246. Skin and skull. Adult female. Stilwell, Boston Mountains,
Adair County, Okla. April 7, 1897. Collected by J. A. Loring.
Original number 3905.

Well-made skin in good condition; skull Grade A.

Arvicola (Pitymys) pinetorum quasiater Coues. See page 573.

*Arvicola scalopsoides Audubon and Bachman.

Proc. Acad. Nat. Sci. Philadelphia 1: 97, submitted for publication Oct.
5, 1841.
=*Pitymys pinetorum scalopsoides* (Audubon and Bachman). See Miller, U. S.
Nat. Mus. Bull. 79: 229, Dec. 31, 1912.

10264. Skin, skull inside. Long Island, N. Y. Collected by
J. E. LeConte. Cataloged October 15, 1872. Evidently the specimen was acquired by the National Museum long after the original
description was issued.

Skin in rather poor condition. It has somewhat the appearance of having
been made up out of alcohol. The left forefoot and right hindfoot are
missing. On the left side there is a considerable patch without hair.

Type not designated by number. "Type of *scalopsoides*" is written in
the remarks column of the catalog in the handwriting of the original
entry. In the table on page 224 of Monographs of North American Rodentia
Coues calls this specimen, 10264, "Type of '*scalopsoides*' Le C." The
specimen also bears a label reading "Monograph of American Muridae,
Elliott Coues, U. S. A., No. 10264. Type of *A.* '*scalopsoides*' apud Le Conte
(=*pinetorum*) Long Island."

Genus REITHRODON Waterhouse

*Reithrodon hatcheri J. A. Allen.

Bull. Amer. Mus. Nat. Hist. 19: 191, May 9, 1903.
=*Reithrodon cuniculoides hatcheri* J. A. Allen. See Gyldenstolpe, Kungl.
Svenska Vet.-Akad. Handl. (ser. 3) 11 (3): 78, 1932.

84210. Skin and skull. Adult male. Pacific slope of the Cordilleras, head of the Rio Chico de Santa Cruz, Santa Cruz Territory,
Argentina. March 11, 1897. Collected by O. A. Peterson. Original number 600.

Well-made skin in good condition, but lacks left fore and right hindlegs.
[It was Mr. Peterson's custom to save a good many skeletons of the animals he had skinned or to make up the skins of the animals he had saved
for skeletons.] The skeleton of this individual was probably saved, but
there is no record of its having been in the Museum. Skull Grade A.

Genus REITHRODONTOMYS Giglioli

†Reithrodontomys albescens Cary.

Proc. Biol. Soc. Washington 16: 53, May 6, 1903.
=*Reithrodontomys montanus albescens* Cary. See Benson, Journ. Mamm. 16: 141, May 15, 1935.

116358. Skin and skull. Adult male. Eighteen miles northwest of Kennedy, Cherry County, Nebr. October 31, 1901. Collected by Merritt Cary. Original number 411 (3431–X).

Well-made skin in good condition; skull Grade A.

†Reithrodontomys alleni Howell.

North Amer. Fauna 36: 59, June 5, 1914.

71563. Skin and skull. Adult male. Mountains near Ozolotepec, altitude 10,000 feet, Oaxaca, Mexico. March 27, 1895. Collected by E. W. Nelson and E. A. Goldman. Original number 7749.

Well-made skin in good condition except for missing left foreleg and skin of shoulder and underparts adjoining it; skull Grade C.

†Reithrodontomys amoles Howell.

North Amer. Fauna 36: 40, June 5, 1914.

81234. Skin and skull. Adult female. Pinal de Amoles, Queretaro, Mexico. September 20, 1896. Collected by E. W. Nelson and E. A. Goldman. Original number 10169.

Well-made skin in good condition, except left ear is torn away, right ear is slightly injured, and underparts are slightly soiled and torn; skull Grade A.

†Reithrodontomys chrysopsis Merriam.

Proc. Biol. Soc. Washington 13: 152, June 13, 1900.

52031. Skin and skull. Adult male. Mount Popocatepetl, State of Mexico, Mexico. February 25, 1893. Collected by E. W. Nelson and E. A. Goldman. Original number 4405.

Well-made skin in good condition; skull Grade A.

†Reithrodontomys chrysopsis tolucae Merriam.

Proc. Washington Acad. Sci. 3: 549, Nov. 29, 1901.

55895. Skin and skull. Adult female. North slope Volcan Toluca, altitude 11,500 feet, State of Mexico, Mexico. September 10, 1893. Collected by E. W. Nelson and E. A. Goldman. Original number 5454.

Well-made skin in good condition; skull Grade A.

†Reithrodontomys colimae Merriam.

Proc. Washington Acad. Sci. 3: 551, Nov. 29, 1901.

$\frac{33671}{45706}$. Skin and skull. Adult male. Sierra Nevada de Colima, altitude 12,000 feet, Jalisco, Mexico. April 13, 1892 (not April 21, 1892, as recorded in the original description). Collected by E. W. Nelson and E. A. Goldman. Original number 2447.

Well-made skin in good condition; skull Grade B.

†Reithrodontomys colimae nerterus Merriam.

Proc. Washington Acad. Sci. 3: 551, Nov. 29, 1901.

$\frac{33680}{45715}$. Skin and skull. Adult female. Foothill region of Sierra Nevada de Colima, altitude 6,500 feet, Jalisco, Mexico. April 21, 1892. Collected by E. W. Nelson and E. A. Goldman. Original number 2514.

Well-made skin in good condition, but right hind foot severed from skin; skull Grade A.

†Reithrodontomys costaricensis jalapae Merriam.

Proc. Washington Acad. Sci. 3: 552, Nov. 29, 1901.
=*Reithrodontomys mexicanus mexicanus* Saussure. See Howell, North Amer. Fauna 36: 70, June 5, 1914.

108538. Skin and skull. Adult male. Jalapa, altitude 4,000 feet, Veracruz, Mexico. May 10, 1901. Collected by E. W. Nelson and E. A. Goldman. Original number 14712.

Well-made skin in good condition; skull Grade A.

†Reithrodontomys difficilis Merriam.

Proc. Washington Acad. Sci. 3: 556, Nov. 29, 1901.
=*Reithrodontomys mexicanus mexicanus* Saussure. See Howell, North Amer. Fauna 36: 50, June 5, 1914.

63735. Skin and skull. Adult male. Orizaba, altitude 4,200 feet, Veracruz, Mexico. February 20, 1894. Collected by E. W. Nelson and E. A. Goldman. Original number 5868.

Well-made skin in good condition; skull Grade A.

†Reithrodontomys dorsalis Merriam.

Proc. Washington Acad. Sci. 3: 557, Nov. 29, 1901.

77009. Skin and skull. Adult male. Calel, Guatemala. January 14, 1896. Collected by E. W. Nelson and E. A. Goldman. Original number 9112.

Well-made skin in good condition, but tip of tail absent, skull Grade B.

†Reithrodontomys dychei nebrascensis J. A. Allen.

Bull. Amer. Mus. Nat. Hist. 7: 122, May 21, 1895.
=*Reithrodontomys megalotis dychei* Allen. See Howell, North Amer. Fauna 36: 30, June 5, 1914.

$\frac{18624}{25426}$. Skin and skull. Adult male. Kennedy, Cherry County, Nebr. April 19, 1890. Collected by Vernon Bailey. Original number 1042.

Well-made skin in good condition; skull Grade A.

†Reithrodontomys fulvescens chiapensis Howell.

North Amer. Fauna 36: 53, June 5, 1914.

132865. Skin and skull. Adult male. Canjob, Chiapas, Mexico. May 2, 1904. Collected by E. W. Nelson and E. A. Goldman. Original number 16741.

Well-made skin in good condition, except for slightly soiled underparts; skull Grade A.

†Reithrodontomys fulvescens mustelinus Howell.

North Amer. Fauna 36: 54, June 5, 1914.

71549. Skin and skull. Adult female. Llano Grande, Oaxaca, Mexico. February 18, 1895. Collected by E. W. Nelson and E. A. Goldman. Original number 7483.

Well-made skin in good condition, except for loss of the right ear, left ear torn, and left forefoot broken; skull Grade B.

†Reithrodontomys fulvescens nelsoni Howell.

North Amer. Fauna 36: 53, June 5, 1914.

$\frac{33409}{45432}$. Skin and skull. Adult female. Colima, State of Colima, Mexico. March 9, 1892. Collected by E. W. Nelson. Original number 2050.

Well-made skin in good condition; skull Grade A.

†Reithrodontomys goldmani Merriam.

Proc. Washington Acad. Sci. 3: 552, Nov. 29, 1901.
=Reithrodontomys mexicanus goldmani Merriam. See Howell, North Amer. Fauna 36: 72, June 5, 1914.

93096. Skin and skull. Adult female. Metlaltoyuca, altitude 800 feet, Puebla, Mexico. February 12, 1898. Collected by E. A. Goldman. Original number 12153.

Well-made skin in good condition; skull Grade A.

†Reithrodontomys griseoflavus Merriam.

Proc. Washington Acad. Sci. 3: 553, Nov. 29, 1901.
=Reithrodontomys fulvescens tenuis J. A. Allen. See Howell, North Amer. Fauna 36: 45, June 5, 1914.

82196. Skin and skull. Adult male. Ameca, altitude 4,000 feet, Jalisco, Mexico. February 9, 1897. Collected by E. W. Nelson and E. A. Goldman. Original number 10501.

Well-made skin in good condition; skull Grade A.

†Reithrodontomys griseoflavus helvolus Merriam.

Proc. Washington Acad. Sci. 3 : 554, Nov. 29, 1901.
=*Reithrodontomys fulvescens helvolus* Merriam.   See Howell, North Amer. Fauna 36 : 52, June 5, 1914.

68387.   Skin and skull.   Adult female.   Oaxaca, State of Oaxaca, Mexico.   August 14, 1894.   Collected by E. W. Nelson and E. A. Goldman.   Original number 6576.

Well-made skin in good condition; skull Grade A.

†Reithrodontomys griseus Bailey.

North Amer. Fauna 25 : 106, Oct. 24, 1905.
=*Reithrodontomys montanus griseus* Bailey.   See Benson, Journ. Mamm. 16 : 141, May 15, 1935.

87852.   Skin and skull.   Adult male.   San Antonio, Bexar County, Tex.   March 4, 1897.   Collected by H. P. Attwater.   Original number 1068.   (371-X).

Well-made skin in good condition; skull Grade A.

†Reithrodontomys hirsutus Merriam.

Proc. Washington Acad. Sci. 3 : 553, Nov. 29, 1901.

82200.   Skin and skull.   Old male.   Ameca, altitude 5,500 feet, Jalisco, Mexico.   February 15, 1897.   Collected by E. W. Nelson and E. A. Goldman.   Original number 10537.

Well-made skin in good condition; skull Grade A.

‡Reithrodontomys humulis virginianus Howell.

Journ. Mamm. 21 : 346, Aug. 12, 1940.

263815.   Skin and skull.   Adult male.   Amelia, Va.   February 15, 1938.   Collected by John B. Lewis.   Original number 28258-X (158).

Well-made skin in good condition; skull Grade A.

†Reithrodontomys klamathensis Merriam.

North Amer. Fauna 16 : 93, Oct. 28, 1899.
=*Reithrodontomys megalotis longicaudus* Baird.   See Grinnell, Proc. California Acad. Sci. (ser. 4) 3 : 303, Aug. 28, 1913.

95444.   Skin and skull.   Adult male.   Big Spring (or Mayten), Shasta Valley, Siskiyou County, Calif.   September 18, 1898. Collected by W. H. Osgood.   Original number 281.

Well-made skin in good condition; skull Grade A.

†Reithrodontomys levipes Merriam.

Proc. Washington Acad. Sci. 3 : 554, Nov. 29, 1901.

88057.   Skin and skull.   Adult male.   San Sebastian, altitude 3,000 feet, Jalisco, Mexico.   March 30, 1897.   Collected by E. W. Nelson and E. A. Goldman.   Original number 10839.

Well-made skin in good condition; skull Grade A.

†Reithrodontomys levipes otus Merriam.

Proc. Washington Acad. Sci. 3: 555, Nov. 29, 1901.
=*Reithrodontomys otus* Merriam. See Howell, North Amer. Fauna 36: 55, June 5, 1914.

$\frac{33670}{45705}$. Skin and skull. Adult female. Foothill region of Sierra Nevada de Colima, altitude 6,500 feet, Jalisco, Mexico. April 11, 1892. Collected by E. W. Nelson and E. A. Goldman. Original number 2439.

Well-made skin in good condition; skull Grade A.

†Reithrodontomys levipes toltecus Merriam.

Proc. Washington Acad. Sci. 3: 555, Nov. 29, 1901.
=*Reithrodontomys fulvescens toltecus* Merriam. See Howell, North Amer. Fauna 36: 51, June 5, 1914.

50746. Skin and skull. Adult female. Tlalpam, Federal District, Mexico. December 1, 1892. Collected by E. W. Nelson and E. A. Goldman. Original number 3935.

Well-made skin in good condition, except for a small injury above base of tail; skull Grade A.

*Reithrodon longicauda Baird. Cotypes.

Mammals of North America, p. 451, 1857.
=*Reithrodontomys megalotis longicaudus* (Baird). See Grinnell, Proc. California Acad. Sci. (ser 4) 3: 303, Aug. 28, 1913.

$\frac{1418}{2282}$. Skin and skull. Female. Original number 231.

$\frac{1419}{2283}$. Skin and skull. Male. Original number 232.

$\frac{1583}{2411}$. Skin and skull. Male. Original number 239.

2581 to 2591, both inclusive, alcoholics.

All collected at Petaluma, Sonoma County, Calif., by E. Samuels. Nos. $\frac{1418}{2282}$ and $\frac{1419}{2283}$ cataloged April 24, 1865; $\frac{1583}{2411}$ June 24, 1856; the alcoholics, April 1857; 2582, 2584, and 2588 are recorded in the catalog as "Distributed to C. E. Aiken, June 1872."

Of these 14 specimens all that can now be found is the skull of No. $\frac{1418}{2282}$. Skull Grade B.

No type is designated, and there is absolutely nothing by which any one of Baird's 15 specimens can be picked out as a type. Fourteen of the specimens came from Petaluma, Calif., and a single one from San Francisco. The former are regarded as cotypes and the type locality fixed at Petaluma. (See Miller and Rehn, Proc. Boston Soc. Nat. Hist. 30: 97, Dec. 27, 1901.)

*Reithrodon megalotis Baird.

Mammals of North America, p. 451, 1857.
=*Reithrodontomys megalotis* (Baird). See J. A. Allen, Bull. Amer. Mus. Nat. Hist. 5: 79, Apr. 28, 1893.

2281.   Skull.   Between Janos, Chihuahua, and San Luis Springs, Grant County, N. Mex.   Collected by C. B. R. Kennerly.   Cataloged November 1855.

Skull Grade A.   There should be a skin, No. 1039, but it cannot be found.

No type specified, but Baird's description is evidently based on the above specimen, designated by number.   The skull is figured.   He had one other specimen, in alcohol, now lost.   His brief diagnosis says, "Hind foot near .70."   No. 1039, in the table of measurements, is put down as .68, while 1040, the alcoholic, is .50.   Evidently the diagnosis was based on No. 1039.   In Report United States and Mexican Boundary Survey, pt. 2, page 43, 1859, No. 1039 is alone spoken of.

†Reithrodontomys megalotis caryi Howell.

Journ. Mamm. 16: 143, May 16, 1935.

150714.   Skin and skull.   Adult female.   Medano Ranch, 15 miles northeast Mosca, Alamosa County, Colo.   November 4, 1907. Collected by Merritt Cary.   Original number 1232.

Well-made skin in good condition; skull Grade A.

†Reithrodontomys megalotis deserti J. A. Allen.

Bull. Amer. Mus. Nat. Hist. 7: 127, May 21, 1895.
=Reithrodontomys megalotis megalotis (Baird).   See Howell, North Amer. Fauna 36: 26, June 5, 1914.

$\frac{27720}{39819}$.   Skin and skull.   Adult female.   Oasis Valley, Nye County, Nev.   March 16, 1891.   Collected by Frank Stephens.   Original number 149.

Well-made skin in good condition; skull Grade C.

†Reithrodontomys megalotis nigrescens Howell.

North Amer. Fauna 36: 32, June 5, 1914.

201616.   Skin and skull.   Adult male.   Payette, Canyon County, Idaho.   June 9, 1913.   Collected by L. E. Wyman.   Original number 98.

Well-made skin in good condition; skull Grade A.

†Reithrodontomys megalotis obscurus Merriam.

Proc. Washington Acad. Sci. 3: 558, Nov. 29, 1901.
=Reithrodontomys megalotis zacatecae Merriam.   See Howell, North Amer. Fauna 36: 39, June 5, 1914.

95277.   Skin and skull.   Adult male.   Sierra Madre, near Guadalupe y Calvo, Chihuahua, Mexico.   August 26, 1898.   Collected by E. W. Nelson and E. A. Goldman.   Original number 12900.

Well-made skin in good condition; skull Grade A.

†Reithrodontomys megalotis ravus Goldman.

Journ. Mamm. 20: 355, Aug. 14, 1939.

263963. Skin and skull. Adult male. North end of Stansbury Island (sandbar at spring on lake shore), Great Salt Lake, altitude 4,250 feet, Utah. June 26, 1938. Collected by William H. Marshall. Original number 161.

Well-made skin in good condition; skull Grade C.

†Reithrodontomys megalotis zacatecae Merriam.

Proc. Washington Acad. Sci. 3: 557, Nov. 29, 1901.

91910. Skin and skull. Adult female. Valparaiso Mountains, Zacatecas, Mexico. December 6, 1897. Collected by E. W. Nelson and E. A. Goldman. Original number 11859.

Well-made skin in good condition; skull Grade A.

†Reithrodontomys merriami J. A. Allen.

Bull. Amer. Mus. Nat. Hist. 7: 119, May 21, 1895.
=*Reithrodontomys humulis merriami* Allen. See Howell, North Amer. Fauna 36: 21, June 5, 1914.

$\frac{32832}{44853}$. Skin and skull. Adult male. Austin Bayou, near Alvin, Brazoria County, Tex. March 15, 1892. Collected by W. Lloyd. Original number 1162.

Well-made skin in good condition; skull Grade C.

†Reithrodontomys mexicanus aurantius J. A. Allen.

Bull. Amer. Mus. Nat. Hist. 7: 137, May 21, 1895.
=*Reithrodontomys fulvescens aurantius* Allen. See Howell, North Amer. Fauna 36: 48, June 5, 1914.

$\frac{33963}{45998}$. Skin and skull. Adult male. Lafayette, Lafayette Parish, La. May 24, 1892. Collected by R. J. Thompson. Original number 174.

Well-made skin in good condition; skull Grade A.

*Reithrodontomys mexicanus lucifrons Howell.

Proc. Biol. Soc. Washington 45: 125, July 30, 1932.

257086. Skin and skull. Adult female. Cerro Cantoral, Honduras. February 7, 1932. Collected by C. F. Underwood. Original number 709.

Well-made skin in good condition; skull Grade A.

*Reithrodontomys mexicanus minusculus Howell.

Proc. Biol. Soc. Washington 45: 125, July 30, 1932.

257087. Skin and skull. Adult male. Comayabuela, just south of Tegucigalpa, Honduras. February 27, 1932. Collected by C. F. Underwood. Original number 797.

Well-made skin in good condition, a small spot on right side has sloughed; skull Grade A.

†**Reithrodontomys microdon** Merriam.

Proc. Washington Acad. Sci. 3: 548, Nov. 29, 1901.

76923. Skin and skull. Adult female. Todos Santos, altitude 10,000 feet, Guatemala. December 31, 1895. Collected by E. W. Nelson and E. A. Goldman. Original number 8977.

Well-made skin in good condition; skull Grade A.

†**Reithrodontomys microdon albilabris** Merriam.

Proc. Washington Acad. Sci. 3: 549, Nov. 29, 1901.

68393. Skin and skull. Adult female. Cerro San Felipe, altitude 10,000 feet, Oaxaca, Mexico. August 25, 1894. Collected by E. W. Nelson and E. A. Goldman. Original number 6629.

Well-made skin in good condition; skull Grade A.

Reithrodon montanus Baird.

Proc. Acad. Nat. Sci. Philadelphia 7: 335, reported favorably for publication Apr. 24, 1855.

=*Reithrodontomys montanus montanus* (Baird). See Benson, Journ. Mamm. 16: 139–142, May 15, 1935.

$\frac{441}{1306}$. Mounted skin, and skull. Probably near the upper end of the San Luis Valley, Saguache County, Colo. August 29 or 30, 1853. Collected by F. Kreutzfeldt, on Capt. J. W. Gunnison's expedition from Westport, Mo., to the Pacific coast in 1853–54. (These data are taken from J. A. Allen, Bull. Amer. Mus. Nat. Hist. 7: 124, 125, May 21, 1895.)

Mounted skin in rather poor condition; body doubled up; both forelegs missing. Both hindlegs present, but one is detached from the body; tail also detached, but present. Skull Grade A.

Type not designated by number in the original description, but the single specimen is referred to by number in Baird's Mammals of North America, p. 450.

†**Reithrodontomys orizabae** Merriam.

Proc. Washington Acad. Sci. 3: 550, Nov. 29, 1901.

=*Reithrodontomys chrysopsis orizabae* Merriam. See Howell, North Amer. Fauna 36: 69, June 5, 1914.

53626. Skin and skull. Adult male. Mount Orizaba, altitude 9,500 feet, Puebla, Mexico. April 24, 1893. Collected by E. W. Nelson and E. A. Goldman. Original number 4734.

Well-made skin in good condition; skull Grade D.

†**Reithrodontomys perotensis** Merriam.

Proc. Washington Acad. Sci. 3: 550, Nov. 29, 1901.

54424. Skin and skull. Adult male. Cofre de Perote, altitude 9,500 feet, Veracruz, Mexico. May 31, 1893. Collected by E. W. Nelson and E. A. Goldman. Original number 4912.

Well-made skin in good condition; skull Grade A.

†Reithrodontomys rufescens luteolus Howell.

North Amer. Fauna 36: 57, June 5, 1914.

71558. Skin and skull. Adult female. Juquila, altitude 5,000 feet, Oaxaca, Mexico. February 28, 1895. Collected by E. W. Nelson and E. A. Goldman. Original number 7579.

Well-made skin in good condition; skull Grade A.

†Reithrodontomys saturatus alticolus Merriam.

Proc. Washington Acad. Sci. 3: 556, Nov. 29, 1901.
=*Reithrodontomys megalotis alticola* Merriam. See Howell, North Amer. Fauna 36: 37, June 5, 1914.

68392. Skin and skull. Old male. Cerro San Felipe, altitude 10,000 feet, Oaxaca, Mexico. August 24, 1894. Collected by E. W. Nelson and E. A. Goldman. Original number 6623.

Well-made skin in good condition; skull Grade A.

†Reithrodontomys saturatus cinereus Merriam.

Proc. Washington Acad. Sci. 3: 556, Nov. 29, 1901.
=*Reithrodontomys megalotis cinereus* Merriam. See Howell, North Amer. Fauna 36: 35, June 5, 1914.

53623. Skin and skull. Adult male. Chalchicomula, Puebla, Mexico. April 13, 1893. Collected by E. W. Nelson and E. A. Goldman. Original number 4659.

Well-made skin in good condition; skull Grade A.

†Reithrodontomys tenuirostris Merriam.

Proc. Washington Acad. Sci. 3: 547, Nov. 29, 1901.

76919. Skin and skull. Adult male. Todos Santos, altitude 10,000 feet, Guatemala. December 29, 1895. Collected by E. W. Nelson and E. A. Goldman. Original number 8917.

Well-made skin in good condition; skull Grade A.

†Reithrodontomys tenuirostris aureus Merriam.

Proc. Washington Acad. Sci. 3: 548, Nov. 29, 1901.

76939. Skin and skull. Adult female. Calel, altitude 10,200 feet, Guatemala. January 15, 1896. Collected by E. W. Nelson and E. A. Goldman. Original number 9140.

Well-made skin in good condition; skull Grade A.

Genus RHEOMYS Thomas

†Rheomys raptor Goldman.

Smithsonian Misc. Coll. 60 (2): 7, Sept. 20, 1912.

179028. Skin and skull. Adult male. Near head of Rio Limon, altitude 4,500 feet, Mount Pirri, eastern Panama. April 28, 1912. Collected by E. A. Goldman. Original number 21658.

Well-made skin in good condition; skull Grade C.

Genus RHIPIDOMYS Tschudi

†Rhipidomys scandens Goldman.

Smithsonian Misc. Coll. 60 (22) : 8, Feb. 28, 1913.

178987 (not 178937 as recorded in original description). Skin and skull. Old adult female. Near head of Rio Limon, altitude 5,000 feet, Mount Pirri, eastern Panama. April 25, 1912. Collected by E. A. Goldman. Original number 21640.

Well-made skin in good condition, except for grease stain across right shoulder; skull Grade C.

Genus SCOTINOMYS Thomas

†Scotinomys teguina subnubilis Goldman.

Proc. Biol. Soc. Washington 48 : 141, Aug. 22, 1935.

76353. Skin and skull. Adult male. Ocuilapa, 10 miles northwest of Ocozucuautla and about 25 miles west of Tuxtla Gutierrez, altitude 3,500 feet, Chiapas, Mexico. August 22, 1895. Collected by E. W. Nelson and E. A. Goldman. Original number 8371.

Well-made skin in good condition; skull Grade A.

Genus SIGMODON Say and Ord

†Sigmodon alleni Bailey.

Proc. Biol. Soc. Washington 15 : 112, June 2, 1902.

88227. Skin and skull. Adult male. San Sebastian, Mascota, Jalisco, Mexico. March 15, 1897. Collected by E. W. Nelson and E. A. Goldman. Original number 10708.

Well-made skin in good condition; skull Grade A.

†Sigmodon alticola Bailey.

Proc. Biol. Soc. Washington 15 : 116, June 2, 1902.

68231. Skin and skull. Adult male. Cerro San Felipe, altitude 10,000 feet, Oaxaca, Mexico. August 24, 1894. Collected by E. W. Nelson and E. A. Goldman. Original number 6624.

Well-made skin in good condition; skull Grade A.

†Sigmodon alticola amoles Bailey.

Proc. Biol. Soc. Washington 15 : 116, June 2, 1902.

81430. Skin and skull. Adult male. Pinal de Amoles, altitude 7,000 feet, Queretaro, Mexico. September 18, 1896 (not 1898, as given in original description). Collected by E. W. Nelson and E. A. Goldman. Original number 10161.

Well-made skin in good condition except that the ears have been badly damaged by insects; skull Grade C.

*Sigmodon berlandieri Baird.

Proc. Acad. Nat. Sci. Philadelphia 7:333, reported favorably for publication Apr. 24, 1855.

=*Sigmodon hispidus berlandieri* Baird. See Bailey, Proc. Biol. Soc. Washington 15:106, June 2, 1902.

$\frac{566}{1687}$. Skin (lost) and skull. Adult female. Rio Nasas, Coahuila, Mexico. 1853. Collected by D. N. Couch.

According to the Museum catalogs this specimen, originally preserved entire in alcohol, was skinned in 1855. The body was left in alcohol. At present neither skin nor body can be found; only the injured skull is left. Skull Grade C.

Type not designated by number in the original description; but by referring to Baird's Mammals of North America, 505, it can be seen that the description is based on the present specimen, designated by number 566.

†Sigmodon guerrerensis Nelson and Goldman.

Proc. Biol. Soc. Washington 46: 196, Oct. 26, 1933.

126936. Skin and skull. Adult female. Omilteme, altitude 8,000 feet, Guerrero, Mexico. May 21, 1903. Collected by E. W. Nelson and E. A. Goldman. Original number 16467.

Well-made skin in good condition; skull Grade A.

†Sigmodon hispidus confinis Goldman.

Proc. Biol. Soc. Washington 31: 21, May 16, 1918.

204241. Skin and skull. Adult male. Safford, altitude 2,900 feet, Graham County, Ariz. July 27, 1914. Collected by J. L. Peters. Original number 77.

Well-made skin in good condition; skull Grade A.

*Sigmodon hispidus eremicus Mearns.

Preliminary Diagnoses of New Mammals of the Genera *Sciurus, Castor, Neotoma,* and *Sigmodon,* from the Mexican Border of the United States, p. 4, Mar. 5, 1897. (Reprint: Proc. U. S. Nat. Mus. 20:504, Jan. 19, 1898.)

60319. Skin and skull. Adult male. Cienega well, 30 miles south of monument No. 204, Mexican boundary line, on the left bank of the Colorado River, Sonora, Mexico. March 24, 1894. Collected by E. A. Mearns and F. X. Holzner. Original number 3367. International Boundary Commission.

Well-made skin in good condition; skull Grade A.

†Sigmodon hispidus jacksoni Goldman.

Proc. Biol. Soc. Washington 31: 22, May 16, 1918.

214121. Skin and skull. Subadult male. Three miles north of Fort Whipple, altitude 5,000 feet, near Prescott, Yavapai County, Ariz. July 8, 1916. Collected by H. H. T. Jackson. Original number 456.

Well-made skin in good condition; skull Grade A.

†**Sigmodon hispidus major** Bailey.

Proc. Biol. Soc. Washington 15: 109, June 2, 1902.

96275. Skin and skull. Adult male. Sierra de Choix, 50 miles northeast of Choix, Sinaloa, Mexico. October 20, 1898. Collected by E. W. Nelson and E. A. Goldman. Original number 13154.

Well-made skin in good condition; skull Grade A.

†**Sigmodon hispidus microdon** Bailey.

Proc. Biol. Soc. Washington 15: 111, June 2, 1902.

108467. Skin and skull. Adult male. Puerto Morelos, Yucatan, Mexico. March 13, 1901. Collected by E. W. Nelson and E. A. Goldman. Original number 14581.

Well-made skin in good condition; skull Grade A.

*****Sigmodon hispidus pallidus** Mearns.

Preliminary Diagnoses of New Mammals of the Genera *Sciurus, Castor, Neotoma,* and *Sigmodon,* from the Mexican Border of the United States, p. 4, Mar. 5, 1897. (Reprint: Proc. U. S. Nat. Mus. 20: 504, Jan. 19, 1898.) =*Sigmodon hispidus berlandieri* Baird. See Bailey, Proc. Biol. Soc. Washington 15: 106, June 2, 1902.

$\frac{20103}{35464}$. Skin and skull. Adult male. Left bank of the Rio Grande, about 6 miles above El Paso, El Paso County, Tex. February 19, 1892. Collected by E. A. Mearns and F. X. Holzner. Original number 1461. International Boundary Commission.

Well-made skin in good condition; skull Grade C.

†**Sigmodon hispidus plenus** Goldman.

Proc. Biol. Soc. Washington 41: 205, Dec. 18, 1928.

181086. Skin and skull. Adult male. Parker, altitude 350 feet, Yuma County, Ariz. February 2, 1913. Collected by E. A. Goldman. Original number 21819.

Well-made skin in good condition; skull Grade A.

†**Sigmodon hispidus saturatus** Bailey.

Proc. Biol. Soc. Washington 15: 111, June 2, 1902.

99998. Skin and skull. Adult male. Teapa, Tabasco, Mexico. April 5, 1900. Collected by E. W. Nelson and E. A. Goldman. Original number 14108.

Well-made skin in good condition; skull Grade A.

†**Sigmodon hispidus tonalensis** Bailey.

Proc. Biol. Soc. Washington 15: 109, June 2, 1902.

75144. Skin and skull. Adult male. Tonala, Chiapas, Mexico. August 9, 1895. Collected by E. W. Nelson and E. A. Goldman. Original number 8312.

Well-made skin in good condition; skull Grade A.

†Sigmodon leucotis Bailey.

Proc. Biol. Soc. Washington 15: 115, June 2, 1902.

92001. Skin and skull. Adult female. Valparaiso Mountains, altitude 8,700 feet, Zacatecas, Mexico. December 2, 1897. Collected by E. W. Nelson and E. A. Goldman. Original number 11812.

Well-made skin in good condition; skull Grade A.

†Sigmodon melanotis Bailey.

Proc. Biol. Soc. Washington 15: 114, June 2, 1902.

50190. Skin and skull. Adult female. Patzcuaro, altitude 7,000 feet, Michoacan, Mexico. July 15, 1892. Collected by E. W. Nelson. Original number 2834.

Well-made skin in good condition; skull Grade A.

*Sigmodon minima Mearns.

Proc. U. S. Nat. Mus. 17: 130, July 19, 1894.

$\frac{21187}{37291}$. Skin and skull. Adult male. Upper corner monument, Grant County, N. Mex., on the Mexican boundary line 100 miles west of the initial monument on the west bank of the Rio Grande. April 26, 1892. Collected by E. A. Mearns and F. X. Holzner. Original number 1704. International Boundary Commission.

Fairly well-made skin in good condition; extreme tip of tail missing and belly a little soiled and torn. Skull Grade A.

†Sigmodon minimus goldmani Bailey.

Proc. Biol. Soc. Washington 26: 132, May 21, 1913.

167625. Skin and skull. Young adult female. Seven miles north of Las Palomas, altitude 4,200 feet, Quay County, N. Mex. October 28, 1909. Collected by E. A. Goldman. Original number 20695.

Well-made skin in good condition; skull Grade A.

†Sigmodon ochrognathus Bailey.

Proc. Biol. Soc. Washington 15: 115, June 2, 1902.

110333. Skin and skull. Adult female. Chisos Mountains, altitude 8,000 feet, Brewster County, Tex. June 13, 1901. Collected by Vernon Bailey. Original number 7681.

Well-made skin in good condition, but right ear imperfect; skull Grade A.

†Sigmodon planifrons Nelson and Goldman.

Proc. Biol. Soc. Washington 46: 197, Oct. 26, 1933.

71918. Skin and skull. Adult female. Juquila, altitude 5,000 feet, southwestern Oaxaca, Mexico. February 28, 1895. Collected by E. W. Nelson and E. A. Goldman. Original number 7569.

Well-made skin in good condition; skull Grade A.

Genus SYNAPTOMYS Baird

†Synaptomys (Mictomys) bullatus Preble.

Proc. Biol. Soc. Washington 15 : 181, Aug. 6, 1902.
=*Synaptomys borealis borealis* Richardson. See A. B. Howell, North Amer.
Fauna 50 : 22, June 30 [=Aug. 5], 1927.

110632. Skin and skull. Adult male. Trout Rock, 25 miles south
of Fort Rae, Great Slave Lake, Mackenzie, Canada. July 17, 1901
(not August 17, 1901, as given in original description). Collected
by E. A. Preble. Original number 4511.

Well-made skin in good condition; skull Grade A.

*Synaptomys cooperi Baird.

Mammals of North America, p. 556, 1857.

$\frac{1367}{3230}$. Skin and skull. Received from William Cooper, of Hoboken,
N. J. Skin cataloged February 26, 1856; skull, June 1857. Locality unknown.

Baird says, "No locality was assigned, but the animal is undoubtedly
North American, probably from the New England States or New York;
possibly from Iowa or Minnesota." According to A. B. Howell (North
Amer. Fauna 50 : 13, June 30 [=Aug. 5], 1927, the type locality "may well
be considered as situated somewhere in the northern or western portion of
the New England States, or in western New York." The skin is little
more than a ball of fur. Head, legs (except one foreleg detached), and
tail are lacking. Skull Grade C.
Type designated by number on page 556 of the original description.

†Synaptomys (Mictomys) dalli Merriam.

Proc. Biol. Soc. Washington 10 : 62, Mar. 19, 1896.
=*Synaptomys borealis dalli* Merriam. See A. B. Howell, North Amer. Fauna
50 : 24, June 30 [=Aug. 5], 1927.

49373. Skeleton made from alcoholic specimen No. 10957, no other
trace of which can now be found. Adult male. Nulato, Yukon
River, Alaska. February 1867. Collected by W. H. Dall.

All of the skeleton is present and in good condition; skull Grade A.

†Arvicola (Synaptomys) gossii Coues.   Lectotype.

Monographs of North American Rodentia, p. 235, 1877.
=*Synaptomys cooperi gossii* (Coues). See Rhoads, Proc. Acad. Nat. Sci. Philadelphia 49 : 307, June 1897.

6915. Skull. (No record of a skin.) Adult male. Neosho Falls,
Woodson County, Kans. 1866. Collected by B. F. Goss.

In the original manuscript Coues did not designate a type specimen.
In 1896 Merriam (Proc. Biol. Soc. Washington 10 : 60) made No. 6915, a
skull, the lectotype. There are now in the Museum collection five paratypes, three skins (Nos. 8508, 8510, 8514) and two skulls (Nos. 6916, 37605) ;
type skull Grade A.

†Synaptomys helaletes Merriam.

Proc. Biol. Soc. Washington 10: 59, Mar. 19, 1896.
=*Synaptomys cooperi helaletes* Merriam. See A. B. Howell, North Amer.
Fauna 50: 17, June 30 [=Aug. 5], 1927.

75172. Skin and skull. Adult female. Dismal Swamp, Norfolk County, Va. October 14, 1895. Collected by A. K. Fisher. Original number 1818.

Well-made skin in good condition; skull Grade A.

*Mictomys innuitus True.

Diagnoses of New North American Mammals, p 3, Apr. 26, 1894. (Reprint: Proc. U. S. Nat. Mus. 17: 243, Nov. 15, 1894.)
=*Synaptomys borealis innuitus* (True). See A. B. Howell, North Amer. Fauna 50: 28, June 30 [=Aug. 5], 1927.

$\frac{14838}{24729}$. In alcohol; skull removed. Adult male. Fort Chimo, Ungava [=Labrador Peninsula, Quebec], Canada. Spring of 1886. Collected by L. M. Turner. Original number 506.

Specimen in good state of preservation, but unnecessarily opened up, in order to remove the skull; skull Grade A.

†Synaptomys (Mictomys) sphagnicola Preble.

Proc. Biol. Soc. Washington 13: 43, May 29, 1899.
=*Synaptomys borealis sphagnicola* Preble. See A. B. Howell, North Amer. Fauna 50: 30, June 30 [=Aug. 5], 1927.

96543. Skin and skull. Adult male. Fabyans, near base of Mount Washington, N. H. June 29, 1898. Collected by E. A. Preble. Original number 2402.

Well-made skin in good condition; skull Grade A.

*Synaptomys (Mictomys) truei Merriam.

Proc. Biol. Soc. Washington 10: 62, Mar. 19, 1896.
=*Synaptomys borealis wrangeli* Merriam. See A. B. Howell, North Amer. Fauna 50: 26, June 30 [=Aug. 5], 1927.

$\frac{3798}{12101}$. Skin and skull. Young adult. Skagit Valley, Skagit County, Wash. August 6, 1859. Collected by C. B. R. Kennerly. Original number 304. Northwestern Boundary Survey.

Skin a mere flat pelt glued on a piece of cloth with the right foreleg attached; the three other legs are detached; skull Grade D.

†Synaptomys (Mictomys) wrangeli Merriam.

Proc. Biol. Soc. Washington 10: 63, Mar. 19, 1896.
=*Synaptomys borealis wrangeli* Merriam. See A. B. Howell, North Amer. Fauna 50: 26, June 30 [=Aug. 5], 1927.

74720. Skin and skull. Adult male. Wrangell, Alaska. September 6, 1895. Collected by C. P. Streator. Original number 4871.

Well-made skin in good condition; skull Grade B.

251543—42——24

Genus TATERA Lataste

*Tatera nigricauda percivali Heller.

Smithsonian Misc. Coll. 63 (7) : 8, June 24, 1914.

183945. Skin and skull. Adult female. Lorian Swamp, altitude 700 feet, British East Africa [=Kenya]. September 9, 1911. Collected by A. V. Percival. Original number 792.

Well-made skin in good condition; skull Grade A.

*Tatera pothae Heller.

Smithsonian Misc. Coll. 56 (9) : 2, July 22, 1910.
=*Tatera vicina pothae* Heller. See Hollister, U. S. Nat. Mus. Bull. 99 (pt. 2) : 29, May 16, 1919.

161716. Skin and skull. Adult female. Potha, Kapiti Plains, British East Africa [=Kenya]. April 30, 1909. Collected by J. Alden Loring. Original number 6013.

Well-made skin in good condition; skull Grade A.

*Tatera varia Heller.

Smithsonian Misc. Coll. 56 (9) : 1, July 22, 1910.
=*Tatera bohmi varia* Heller. See Hollister U. S. Nat. Mus. Bull. 99 (pt 2) : 36, May 16, 1919.

162249. Skin and skull. Adult male. Loletai Plains, Southern Guaso Nyiro River, Sotik District, British East Africa [=Kenya]. June 15, 1909. Collected by J. Alden Loring. Original number 6338.

Well-made skin in good condition; skull Grade A.

Genus TEANOPUS Merriam

†Teanopus phenax Merriam.

Proc. Biol. Soc. Washington 16 : 81, May 29, 1903.

95841. Skin and skull. Adult female. Camoa, Rio Mayo, Sonora, Mexico. November 4, 1898. Collected by E. A. Goldman. Original number 13258.

Well-made skin in good condition; skull Grade A.

Genus THALLOMYSCUS Thomas

*Oryzomys (Microryzomys) aurillus Thomas.

Smithsonian Misc. Coll. 68 (4) : 1, Apr. 10, 1917.
=*Thallomyscus aurillus* (Thomas). See Thomas, Ann. Mag. Nat. Hist. (ser. 9) 17 : 613, May 1926.

194795. Skin and skull. Female. Torontoy, altitude 14,000 feet, Peru. May 15, 1915. Collected by Edmund Heller. Original number 255.

Well-made skin in good condition; skull Grade A.

Genus THOMASOMYS Coues

*Thomasomys daphne Thomas.

Smithsonian Misc. Coll. 68 (4) : 2, Apr. 10, 1917.

194902. Skin and skull. Female. Ocobamba Valley, altitude 9,100 feet, Peru. July 29, 1915. Collected by Edmund Heller. Original number 521.

Well-made skin in good condition; skull Grade A.

*Thomasomys gracilis Thomas.

Smithsonian Misc. Coll. 68 (4) : 2, Apr. 10, 1917.

194816. Skin and skull. Male. Matchu Picchu, altitude 12,000 feet, Peru. June 8, 1915. Collected by Edmund Heller. Original number 321.

Well-made skin in good condition; skull Grade A.

*Thomasomys notatus Thomas.

Smithsonian Misc. Coll. 68 (4) : 2, Apr. 10, 1917.

194548. Skin and skull. Male. Torontoy, altitude, 9,500 feet, Peru. May 5, 1915. Collected by Edmund Heller. Original number 173.

Well-made skin in good condition; skull Grade A.

Genus TYLOMYS Peters

†Tylomys bullaris Merriam.

Proc. Washington Acad. Sci. 3: 561, Nov. 29, 1901.

76058. Skin and skull. Immature male. Tuxtla, Chiapas, Mexico. September 7, 1895. Collected by E. W. Nelson and E. A. Goldman. Original number 8406.

Well-made skin in good condition; skull Grade B.

†Tylomys tumbalensis Merriam.

Proc. Washington Acad. Sci. 3: 560, Nov. 29, 1901.

76059. Skin and skull. Young adult male. Tumbala, Chiapas, Mexico. October 23, 1895. Collected by E. W. Nelson and E. A. Goldman. Original number 8568.

Well-made skin in good condition; skull Grade A.

Genus XENOMYS Merriam

†Xenomys nelsoni Merriam.

Proc. Biol. Soc. Washington, 7: 161, Sept. 29, 1892.

$\frac{33281}{45286}$. Skin and skull. Adult male. Hacienda Magdalena, altitude about 1,500 feet, Colima, Mexico. March 21, 1892. Collected by E. W. Nelson. Original number 2288.

Well-made skin in good condition; skull Grade A.

Genus ZYGODONTOMYS J. A. Allen

†Zygodontomys cherriei ventriosus Goldman.

Smithsonian Misc. Coll. 56 (36) : 8, Feb. 19, 1912.

171098. Skin and skull. Adult male. Tabernilla, Canal Zone, Panama. March 12, 1911. Collected by E. A. Goldman. Original number 20975.

Well-made skin in good condition; skull Grade A.

Family CUNICULIDAE: Spotted Cavies

Genus CUNICULUS Brisson

†Agouti paca nelsoni Goldman.

Smithsonian Misc. Coll. 60 (22) : 9, Feb. 28, 1913.
=*Cuniculus paca nelsoni* (Goldman). See Hollister, Proc. Biol. Soc. Washington 26: 79, Mar. 22, 1913.

65952. Skin and skull. Adult male. Catemaco, southern Veracruz, Mexico. April 30, 1894. Collected by E. W. Nelson and E. A. Goldman. Original number 6135.

Well-made skin in fair condition; skull Grade A.

Family DASYPROCTIDAE: Agoutis

Genus DASYPROCTA Illiger

†Dasyprocta punctata chiapensis Goldman.

Smithsonian Misc. Coll. 60 (22) : 13, Feb. 28, 1913.

77997. Skin and skull. Adult female. Huehuetan, southern Chiapas, Mexico. February 26, 1896. Collected by E. W. Nelson and E. A. Goldman. Original number 9430.

Well-made skin in good condition, except for absence of tail and bare spot on left side of abdomen; skull Grade A.

†Dasyprocta punctata dariensis Goldman.

Smithsonian Misc. Coll. 60 (22) : 11, Feb. 28, 1913.

179056. Skin and skull. Adult female. Near head of Rio Limon, altitude 5,200 feet, Mount Pirri, eastern Panama. April 24, 1912. Collected by E. A. Goldman. Original number 21637.

Well-made skin in good condition; skull Grade A.

†Dasyprocta punctata richmondi Goldman.

Proc. Biol. Soc. Washington 30: 114, May 23, 1917.

51333. Skin and skull. Adult female. Escondido River, 50 miles above Bluefields, Nicaragua. November 16, 1892. Collected by C. W. Richmond. Original number 156.

Well-made skin in good condition; skull Grade A.

*Dasyprocta punctata underwoodi Goldman.

Journ. Washington Acad. Sci. 21: 481, Nov. 19, 1931.

256459. Skin and skull. Adult male. San Geronimo, Pirris, western Costa Rica. June 1, 1931. Collected by C. F. Underwood. Original number 478.

Well-made skin in good condition; skull Grade A.

†Dasyprocta punctata yucatanica Goldman.

Smithsonian Misc. Coll. 60 (22) : 12, Feb. 28, 1913.

108293. Skin and skull. Adult male. Apazote, near Yohaltun, Campeche, Mexico. December 22, 1900. Collected by E. W. Nelson and E. A. Goldman. Original number 14347.

Well-made skin in good condition; skull Grade A.

Family DIPODIDAE: Jerboas

Genus ALLACTAGA F. Cuvier

*Allactaga grisescens Hollister.

Smithsonian Misc. Coll. 60 (14) : 2, Nov. 29, 1912.

=*Allactaga saliens* (Shaw). See Chaworth-Musters, Ann. Mag. Nat. Hist. (ser. 10) 14: 556, Nov. 1934.

175494. Skin and skull. Adult female. Chuisaya Steppe, 8 miles south of Kosh-Agatch, Siberia. July 28, 1912. Collected by N. Hollister. Original number 4395.

Well-made skin in good condition; skull Grade A.

*Allactaga mongolica longior Miller.

Proc. Biol. Soc. Washington 24: 54, Feb. 24, 1911.

=*Allactaga saliens* (Shaw). See Chaworth-Musters, Ann. Mag. Nat. Hist. (ser. 10) 14: 556, Nov. 1934.

155183. Skin and skull. Adult female. 15 miles northeast of Chingning-chow, altitude 6,200 feet, Kansu, China. July 26, 1909. Collected by Arthur deC. Sowerby. Original number 204.

Well-made skin in good condition; skull Grade A.

Genus EUCHOREUTES W. L. Sclater

*Euchoreutes naso alashanicus A. B. Howell.

Proc. Biol. Soc. Washington 41: 42, Mar. 16, 1928.

240764. Skin, skull, and skeleton. Adult female. Alashan Desert, Inner Mongolia, 100 miles north-northwest of Ninghsia, Kansu, China. April 26, 1923. Collected by F. R. Wulsin. Original number 1054.

Skin in fair condition, hair has sloughed under left ear and in spots on under surface of body; skull Grade C. Skeleton disarticulated.

Family ECHIMYIDAE: Spiny Rats

Genus APHAETREUS Miller

*Aphaetreus montanus Miller.

Smithsonian Misc. Coll. 74 (3) : 4, Oct. 16, 1922.

10733 (Paleontology number). Mandible with full set of cheek teeth. In large cave near the Atalaye plantation, St. Michel, Haiti, Greater Antilles. March 1921. Collected by J. S. Brown and W. S. Burbank.

Genus BOROMYS Miller

*Boromys offella Miller.

Smithsonian Misc. Coll. 66 (12) : 8, Dec. 7, 1916.

217138. Anterior half of skull (lacking the nasal bones, interorbital region and posterior termination of palate). In village site at Maisi, Baracoa, Cuba, Greater Antilles. Collected by M. R. Harrington. Cataloged November 9, 1916.

Genus BROTOMYS Miller

*Brotomys (?) contractus Miller.

Smithsonian Misc. Coll. 81 (9) : 13, Mar. 30, 1929.

253100. Anterior portion of skull (lacking zygomata, nasals, and teeth). In small cave near St. Michel, Haiti, Greater Antilles. March 1925. Collected by Gerrit S. Miller, Jr.

*Brotomys voratus Miller.

Smithsonian Misc. Coll. 66 (12) : 7, Dec. 7, 1916.

217177. Anterior half of skull (lacking the nasal bones and second and third molars). In kitchen midden at San Pedro de Macoris, Dominican Republic, Greater Antilles. Collected by Theodoor de Booy. Cataloged October 23, 1916.

Genus CAPROMYS Desmarest

*Capromys brachyurus thoracatus True.

Proc. U. S. Nat. Mus. 11: 469, Sept. 3, 1889.

=Capromys thoracatus True. See Chapman, Bull. Amer. Mus. Nat. Hist. 14: 321, Nov. 12, 1901.

$\frac{15897}{22691}$. Skin and skull. Adult male. Little Swan Island, Caribbean Sea, off coast of Honduras. March 6, 1887. Collected by C. H. Townsend.

Skin well preserved, but not well made up; skull Grade A.

Type not designated by number, but of the two original specimens True personally selected the above as the type and placed a red label on it.

*Capromys prehensilis gundlachi Chapman.

Bull. Amer. Mus. Nat. Hist. 14: 317, Nov. 12, 1901.

103905. Skin and skull. Adult male. Nueva Gerona, Isle of Pines, Cuba, Greater Antilles. July 4, 1900. Collected by William Palmer and J. H. Riley. Original number 505.

Well-made skin in good condition; skull Grade A.

Genus CTENOMYS Blainville

*Ctenomys robustus J. A. Allen.

Bull. Amer. Mus. Nat. Hist. 19: 185, May 9, 1903. Preoccupied by *Ctenomys robustus* Philippi (Anal. Mus. Nac. Chile, zool. entr., 13: 11, 1896).
=*Ctenomys osgoodi* J. A. Allen. See Allen, Princeton Exped. to Patagonia 3 (Mamm.): 191, 1905.

84149. Skin and skull. Adult male. Rio Chico de Santa Cruz, near the Cordilleras, Santa Cruz Territory, Argentina. February 20, 1897. Collected by O. A. Peterson. Original number 485.

Well-made skin in good condition; skull Grade A.

Type designated as No. 84194, an error for 84149. No. 84194 is a specimen of *C. sericeus*. The measurements of No. 84149 agree with those given by J. A. Allen as belonging to the type, and the specimen itself bears Allen's type label.

*Ctenomys sericeus J. A. Allen.

Bull. Amer. Mus. Nat. Hist. 19: 187, May 9, 1903.

84189. Skin and skull. Adult male. Upper Rio Chico de Santa Cruz, Cordilleras, Santa Cruz Territory, Argentina. February 5, 1897. Collected by O. A. Peterson. Original number 331.

Well-made skin in good condition; skull Grade A.

Type designated as No. 84191, which is an error for No. 84189. The measurements of the skin and skull ascribed by Allen to the type are those of 84189 and do not agree with those of 84191, a smaller individual. To indicate further that No. 84189 is the type, Allen tied to the specimen the standard red type label of the American Museum of Natural History, with the italicized words crossed out and the words "U. S. Nat." added, as well as the name *Ctenomys sericeus* Allen.

Genus DIPLOMYS Thomas

†Isothrix darlingi Goldman.

Smithsonian Misc. Coll. 60 (2): 12, Sept. 20, 1912.
=*D*[*iplomys*] *darlingi* (Goldman). See Thomas, Ann. Mag. Nat. Hist. (ser. 8) 18: 296, Sept. 1916.

179577. Skin and skull. Young female. Marraganti, near Real de Santa Maria, on the Rio Tuyra, eastern Panama. May 11, 1912. Collected by E. A. Goldman. Original number 21739.

Well-made skin in good condition; skull Grade A.

Genus ECHIMYS Cuvier

*Loncheres flavidus Hollister.

Proc. Biol. Soc. Washington 27: 143, July 10, 1914.

=*Echimys flavidus* (Hollister). See Thomas, Ann. Mag. Nat. Hist. (ser. 8) 18: 71, July 1916.

63218. Skin and skull. Adult male. El Valle, Margarita Island, off north coast of Venezuela. July 9, 1895. Collected by Wirt Robinson. Original number 479.

Well-made skin in fair condition, sections of skin on face, head, and back of neck, together with entire tail missing; skull Grade B.

Genus HEXOLOBODON Miller

*Hexolobodon phenax Miller.

Smithsonian Misc. Coll. 81 (9) : 20, Mar. 30, 1929.

253118. Palate with complete dentition of immature individual (m^3 with only anterior half of crown worn flat). In small cave near St. Michel, Haiti, Greater Antilles. March 1925. Collected by Gerrit S. Miller, Jr.

Genus HOPLOMYS J. A. Allen

† **Hoplomys goethalsi** Goldman.

Smithsonian Misc. Coll. 56 (36) : 10, Feb. 19, 1912.

170972. Skin and skull. Young female. Rio Indio, near Gatun, Canal Zone, Panama. February 16, 1911. Collected by E. A. Goldman. Original number 20888.

Well-made skin in good condition, except that a portion of the skin is missing from the left forefoot; skull Grade A.

Genus ISOLOBODON J. A. Allen

*Ithydontia levir Miller.

Smithsonian Misc. Coll. 74 (3) : 5, Oct. 16, 1922.

=*Isolobodon levir* (Miller). See Miller, Smithsonian Misc. Coll. 81 (9) : 14, Mar. 30, 1929.

10735 (Paleontology number). "A right mandibular tooth, probably m_1 or m_2." (actually left pm^4, Miller, Smithsonian Misc. Coll. 81 (9) : 14, Mar. 30, 1929). In large cave near St. Michel, Haiti, Greater Antilles. March 1921. Collected by J. S. Brown and W. S. Burbank.

Genus PLAGIODONTIA F. Cuvier

*Plagiodontia hylaeum Miller.

Proc. U. S. Nat. Mus. 72 (art. 16) : 4, Sept. 30, 1927.

239887.   Skin and skeleton.   Young adult male.   Guarabo, 10 miles east of Jovero, Samana Province, Dominican Republic, Greater Antilles.   November 23, 1923.   Collected by W. L. Abbott.

Well-made skin in good condition; skeleton Grade A.

*Plagiodontia spelaeum Miller.

Smithsonian Misc. Coll. 81 (9) : 18, Mar. 30, 1929.

253160.   Right mandible of young adult (incisor and posterior portion of mandible missing).   In crooked cave near the Atalaye plantation, St. Michel, Haiti, Greater Antilles.   March 1925. Collected by Gerrit S. Miller, Jr.

Genus PROECHIMYS J. A. Allen

*Proechimys guairae Thomas.

Proc. Biol. Soc. Washington 14: 27, Apr. 2, 1901.

102731.   Skin and skull.   Adult male.   La Guaira, Venezuela.   July 8, 1900.   Collected by Wirt Robinson and M. W. Lyon, Jr.   Original number 81.

Fairly well-made skin in fair condition; skull Grade A.

*Proechimys rubellus Hollister.

Proc. Biol. Soc. Washington 27: 57, Mar. 20, 1914.

=*Proechimys semispinosus rubellus* Hollister.   See Goldman, Smithsonian Misc. Coll. 69 (5) : 120, Apr. 24, 1920.

$\frac{12901}{38587}$.   Skin and skull.   Adult [male].   Angostura Valley, Costa Rica.   Collected by José C. Zeledón.   Cataloged June 23, 1878.

Poorly made skin.   Tail with vertebrae removed but without wire for support; has been broken off at base and then sewed to skin; its tip missing. Skull Grade C.

*Proechimys steerei Goldman.

Proc. Biol. Soc. Washington 24: 238, Nov. 28, 1911.

105535.   Adult male.   Rio Purus, a southern tributary of the Amazon, in northwestern Brazil.   1901.   Collected by J. B. Steere.

Well-made skin in good condition, tail not skinned out; skull Grade A.

Genus QUEMISIA Miller

*Quemisia gravis Miller.

Smithsonian Misc. Coll. 81 (9) : 23, Mar. 30, 1929.

253175.   Mandible of immature individual (m^3 with crown not yet in place).   In crooked cave near the Atalaye Plantation, St. Michel, Haiti, Greater Antilles.   March 1925.   Collected by Gerrit S. Miller, Jr.

Family ERETHIZONTIDAE: American Porcupines

Genus ERETHIZON F. Cuvier

*Erethizon epixanthum couesi Mearns.

Proc. U. S. Nat. Mus. 19: 723, July 30, 1897.

$\frac{7814}{6501}$. Skin and skull; both femurs; left scapula and humerus. Not quite adult. Fort Whipple, Yavapai County, Ariz. Collected by Elliott Coues. Cataloged February 19, 1865.

Skin well preserved; skull Grade B.

*Erethizon epixanthum myops Merriam.

Proc. Washington Acad. Sci. 2: 27, Mar. 14, 1900.

59140. Skin and skull. Old adult female. Portage Bay, Alaska Peninsula, Alaska. September 1893. Collected by C. H. Townsend.

Well-made skin in good condition, rather greasy; skull Grade A.

Family GEOMYIDAE: Pocket Gophers

Genus CRATOGEOMYS Merriam

*Pseudostoma castanops Baird.

Report Stansbury's Expedition to Great Salt Lake, p. 313, June 1852.
=*Cratogeomys castanops* (Baird). See Merriam, North Amer. Fauna 8: 159, Jan. 31, 1895.

$\frac{4007}{3861}$. Skin and skull. "Collected by Lieutenant Abert along the prairie road to Bent's Fort," near the present town of Las Animas, on the Arkansas River, Bent County, Colo. 1845. Cataloged June 18, 1860.

The specimen, formerly mounted, has been made over into a modern study skin, but it is bleached and otherwise in very poor condition. Skull Grade C.

Type not designated by number, but Baird, in the Mammals of North America, p. 385, says there was only one specimen collected by Abert at the above locality.

†Cratogeomys castanops angusticeps Nelson and Goldman.

Proc. Biol. Soc. Washington 47: 139, June 13, 1934.

$\frac{24503}{31908}$. Skin and skull. Adult male. Eagle Pass, Tex. November 11, 1890. Collected by Clark P. Streator. Original number 434.

Well-made skin in good condition; skull Grade B.

†Cratogeomys castanops consitus Nelson and Goldman.

Proc. Biol. Soc. Washington 47: 140, June 13, 1934.

50924. Skin and skull. Young adult male. Gallego, altitude 5,500 feet, Chihuahua, Mexico. December 16, 1892. Collected by Clark P. Streator. Original number 2416.

Well-made skin in good condition; skull Grade A.

†**Cratogeomys castanops convexus** Nelson and Goldman.

Proc. Biol. Soc. Washington 47 : 142, June 13, 1934.

127356. Skin and skull. Adult female. Seven miles east of Las Vacas, Rio Grande Valley, Coahuila, Mexico (opposite Del Rio, Tex.). June 9, 1903. Collected by James H. Gaut. Original number 1469.

Well-made skin in good condition; skull Grade A.

†**Cratogeomys castanops excelsus** Nelson and Goldman.

Proc. Biol. Soc. Washington 47 : 143, June 13, 1934.

246533. Skin and skull. Adult male. San Pedro, 10 miles west of Laguna de Mayran, Coahuila, Mexico. March 28, 1926. Collected by E. A. Goldman. Original number 23561.

Well-made skin in good condition; skull Grade A.

†**Cratogeomys castanops goldmani** Merriam.

North Amer. Fauna 8 : 160, Jan. 31, 1895.

57965. Skin and skull. Young adult female. Canitas, Zacatecas, Mexico. December 24, 1893. Collected by E. A. Goldman. Original number 286.

Well-made skin in good condition; skull Grade A.

†**Cratogeomys castanops hirtus** Nelson and Goldman.

Proc. Biol. Soc. Washington 47 : 138, June 13, 1934.

58325. Skin and skull. Adult male. Albuquerque, altitude 5,000 feet, N. Mex. January 17, 1894. Collected by J. A. Loring. Original number 1558.

Well-made skin in good condition; skull Grade A.

†**Cratogeomys castanops lacrimalis** Nelson and Goldman.

Proc. Biol. Soc. Washington 47 : 137, June 13, 1934.

119071. Skin and skull. Adult male. Roswell, altitude 3,500 feet, Chaves County, N. Mex. September 13, 1902. Collected by James H. Gaut. Original number 476.

Well-made skin in good condition; skull Grade A.

†**Cratogeomys castanops peridoneus** Nelson and Goldman.

Proc. Biol. Soc. Washington 47 : 148, June 13, 1934.

82049. Skin and skull. Adult male. Rio Verde, altitude 3,000 feet, San Luis Potosi, Mexico. January 10, 1897. Collected by E. W. Nelson and E. A. Goldman. Original number 10423.

Well-made skin in good condition; skull Grade A.

† **Cratogeomys castanops perplanus** Nelson and Goldman.

Proc. Biol. Soc. Washington 47: 136, June 13, 1934.

97171. Skin and skull. Adult male. Tascosa, altitude 3,000 feet, Oldham County, Tex. June 5, 1899. Collected by Vernon Bailey. Original number 6941.

Well-made skin in good condition; skull Grade A.

† **Cratogeomys castanops planifrons** Nelson and Goldman.

Proc. Biol. Soc. Washington 47: 146, June 13, 1934.

93942. Skin and skull. Adult male. Miquihuana, altitude 5,000 feet, southern Tamaulipas (not Nuevo Leon as given in original description), Mexico. June 9, 1898. Collected by E. W. Nelson and E. A. Goldman. Original number 12527.

Well-made skin in good condition; skull Grade A.

† **Cratogeomys castanops subnubilus** Nelson and Goldman.

Proc. Biol. Soc. Washington 47: 145, June 13, 1934.

79482. Skin and skull. Adult male. Carneros, altitude 6,800 feet, Coahuila, Mexico. August 12, 1896. Collected by E. W. Nelson and E. A. Goldman. Original number 10018.

Well-made skin in good condition; skull Grade A.

† **Cratogeomys castanops subsimus** Nelson and Goldman.

Proc. Biol. Soc. Washington 47: 144, June 13, 1934.

51048. Skin and skull. Adult male. Jaral, southeastern Coahuila, Mexico. January 14, 1893. Collected by Clark P. Streator. Original number 2555.

Well-made skin in good condition; skull Grade A.

† **Cratogeomys castanops tamaulipensis** Nelson and Goldman.

Proc. Biol. Soc. Washington 47: 141, June 13, 1934.

116535. Skin and skull. Adult female. Matamoras, Tamaulipas, Mexico. February 8, 1902. Collected by E. W. Nelson and E. A. Goldman. Original number 14885.

Well-made skin in good condition; skull Grade A.

* **Geomys clarkii** Baird.

Proc. Acad. Nat. Sci. Philadelphia 7: 332, favorably reported for publication Apr. 24, 1855.

=*Cratogeomys castanops clarkii* (Baird). See Nelson and Goldman, Proc. Biol. Soc. Washington 47: 140, June 13, 1934.

$\frac{6}{1624}$. Skin, skull, and parts of skeleton. Presidio del Norte, on the Rio Grande, Chihuahua, Mexico. Collected by J. H. Clark, United States and Mexican Boundary Survey. Skin cataloged February 12, 1852; skull, February 15, 1855.

Skin was formerly mounted but was made into a modern study skin in August 1898. It is not in first-class condition and appears much bleached. Skull Grade B. Practically all the skeleton is present, but some bones are in the feet of the skin.

Type not designated by number in the original description. By referring to Baird's Mammals of North America, page 381, it is seen that only two specimens came from Presidio del Norte. One of them is a skull only, not mentioned in the first account. The measurements of No. 6 are exactly the same as those given in the original description.

†Cratogeomys estor Merriam.

North Amer. Fauna 8: 155, Jan. 31, 1895.
=*Cratogeomys perotensis estor* Merriam. See Nelson and Goldman, Proc. Biol. Soc. Washington 47: 151, June 13, 1934.

54308. Skin and skull. Adult male. Las Vigas, altitude 8,000 feet, Veracruz, Mexico. June 12, 1893. Collected by E. W. Nelson. Original number 5005.

Well-made skin in good condition; skull Grade A.

†Cratogeomys fulvescens Merriam.

North Amer. Fauna 8: 161, Jan. 31, 1895.

58168. Skin and skull. Adult male. Chalchicomula, Puebla, Mexico. January 15, 1894. Collected by E. W. Nelson and E. A. Goldman. Original number 5651.

Well-made skin in good condition; skull Grade A.

†Cratogeomys fulvescens subluteus Nelson and Goldman.

Proc. Biol. Soc. Washington 47: 152, June 13, 1934.

54300. Skin and skull. Adult male. Perote, altitude 7,800 feet, Veracruz, Mexico. June 3, 1893. Collected by E. W. Nelson and E. A. Goldman. Original number 4929.

Well-made skin in good condition; skull Grade B.

†Cratogeomys merriami irolonis Nelson and Goldman.

Proc. Biol. Soc. Washington 47: 150, June 13, 1934.

53494. Skin and skull. Adult female. Irolo, altitude 7,600 feet, Hidalgo, Mexico. March 30, 1893. Collected by E. W. Nelson and E. A. Goldman. Original number 4520.

Well-made skin in good condition; skull Grade A.

†Cratogeomys merriami saccharalis Nelson and Goldman.

Proc. Biol. Soc. Washington 47: 149, June 13, 1934.

55347. Skin and skull. Adult male. Atlixco, altitude 5,400 feet, Puebla, Mexico. July 29, 1893. Collected by E. W. Nelson and E. A. Goldman. Original number 5279.

Well-made skin in good condition; skull Grade A.

†Cratogeomys oreocetes Merriam.

North Amer. Fauna 8: 156, Jan. 31, 1895.
=*Cratogeomys merriami oreocetes* Merriam. See Nelson and Goldman, Proc. Biol. Soc. Washington 47: 149, June 13, 1934.

57963. Skin and skull. Young adult female. Mount Popocatepetl, State of Mexico, Mexico. January 7, 1894. Collected by E. W. Nelson and E. A. Goldman. Original number 5647.

Well-made skin in good condition; skull Grade A.

†Cratogeomys peregrinus Merriam.

North Amer. Fauna 8: 158, Jan. 31, 1895.
=*Cratogeomys merriami peregrinus* Merriam. See Nelson and Goldman, Proc. Biol. Soc. Washington 47: 149, June 13, 1934.

57964. Skin and skull. Old female. Mount Iztaccihuatl, altitude 11,500 feet, State of Mexico, Mexico. January 9, 1894. Collected by E. W. Nelson and E. A. Goldman. Original number 5650.

Well-made skin in good condition; skull Grade A.

†Cratogeomys perotensis Merriam.

North Amer. Fauna 8: 154, Jan. 31, 1895.

54299. Skin and skull. Adult female. Cofre de Perote, Veracruz, Mexico. May 28, 1893. Collected by E. W. Nelson. Original number 4889.

Well-made skin in good condition; skull Grade A.

Genus GEOMYS Rafinesque

†Geomys arenarius Merriam.

North Amer. Fauna 8: 139, Jan. 31, 1895.

$\frac{18117}{25015}$ Skin and skull. Adult male. El Paso, El Paso County, Tex. December 14, 1899 (not December 13, 1899, as given in original description). Collected by Vernon Bailey. Original number 798.

Well-made skin in good condition; skull Grade A.

*Geomys breviceps Baird.

Proc. Acad. Nat. Sci. Philadelphia 7: 335, reported favorably for publication Apr. 24, 1855.

$\frac{156}{1138}$ Skin and skull. Adult female. Prairie Mer Rouge, Morehouse Parish, La. 1852. Collected by James Fairie.

Skin well preserved. It has somewhat the appearance of having been in alcohol at one time; rather badly made up. Skull Grade B.

Type not designated by number; but the measurements published in the original description are the same as those of No. 156 in Baird's Mammals of North America (tables on pages 379 and 380).

†Geomys breviceps ammophilus Davis.

Texas Agr. Exp. Stat. Bull. 590: 16, Oct. 23, 1940.

97010. Skin and skull. Adult female. Cuero, De Witt County, Tex. April 26, 1899. Collected by Vernon Bailey. Original number 6841.

Well-made skin in good condition; skull Grade A.

†Geomys breviceps attwateri Merriam.

North Amer. Fauna 8: 135, Jan. 31, 1895.

51382. Skin and skull. Adult male. Rockport, Aransas County, Tex. November 18, 1892. Collected by H. H. Keays. Original number 36.

Well-made skin in good condition; skull Grade A.

†Geomys breviceps dutcheri Davis.

Texas Agr. Exp. Stat. Bull. 590: 12, Oct. 23, 1940.

64591. Skin and skull. Adult female. Fort Gibson, Muskogee County, Okla. April 27, 1894. Collected by B. H. Dutcher. Original number 584.

Well-made skin in good condition; skull Grade A.

†Geomys breviceps llanensis Bailey.

North Amer. Fauna 25: 129, Oct. 24, 1905.

97086. Skin and skull. Adult male. Llano, Llano County, Tex. May 15, 1899. Collected by Vernon Bailey. Original number 6912.

Well-made skin in good condition; skull Grade A.

†Geomys breviceps sagittalis Merriam.

North Amer. Fauna 8: 134, Jan. 31, 1895.

$\frac{32936}{44957}$. Skin and skull. Adult male. Clear Creek, Galveston Bay, Galveston County, Tex. March 28, 1892. Collected by W. Lloyd. Original number 1181.

Well-made skin in good condition; skull Grade A.

†Geomys bursarius lutescens Merriam.

North Amer. Fauna 4: 51, Oct. 8, 1890.
=Geomys lutescens Merriam. See Merriam, North Amer. Fauna 8: 127, Jan. 31, 1895.

$\frac{16677}{23595}$. Skin and skull. Adult male (not female, as recorded in original description). Sandhills on Birdwood Creek, Lincoln County, Nebr. May 27, 1889. Collected by A. B. Baker. Original number 11.

Well-made skin in good condition; skull Grade A.

*Geomys personatus True.   Cotypes.

Proc. U. S. Nat. Mus. 11: 159, Jan. 5, 1889.

$\frac{19667}{37999}$. Skin and skull. Adult male.

$\frac{19668}{38000}$. Skin and skull. Adult female.

Padre Island, Cameron County, Tex. April 11, 1888. Purchased from C. K. Worthen.

No type designated. Description based equally upon the above two specimens indicated by numbers. Well-made skins in fair condition, hair on top of head and on underside of neck of both animals has sloughed, probably when skulls were removed in February 1902. Skulls Grade C, the lower jaws are fairly good, but the rest of each skull is represented by the rostrum and tooth-bearing parts only.

†Geomys personatus fallax Merriam.

North Amer. Fauna 8: 144, Jan. 31, 1895.

$\frac{32031}{43845}$. Skin and skull. Adult male. South side of Nueces Bay, Cameron County, Tex. November 30, 1891. Collected by W. Lloyd. Original number 949.

Well-made skin in good condition; skull Grade B.

†Geomys personatus tropicalis Goldman.

Proc. Biol. Soc. Washington 28: 134, June 29, 1915.

92946. Skin and skull. Adult male. Alta Mira, Tamaulipas, Mexico. April 18, 1898. Collected by E. A. Goldman. Original number 12320.

Well-made skin in good condition; skull Grade A.

*Geomys texensis Merriam.

North Amer. Fauna 8: 137, Jan. 31, 1895.

186502. Skin and skull. Adult female. Mason, Mason County, Tex. December 17, 1885. Collected by Ira B. Henry. Merriam collection number $\frac{1690}{2259}$.

Well-made skin in good condition; skull Grade A.

†Geomys tuza mobilensis Merriam.

North Amer. Fauna 8: 119, Jan. 31, 1895.

$\frac{33988}{46023}$. Skin and skull. Adult male. Mobile Bay, Baldwin County, Ala. April 26, 1892. Collected by R. J. Thompson. Original number 50.

Well-made skin in good condition; skull Grade B.

Genus HETEROGEOMYS Merriam

†Heterogeomys hispidus chiapensis Nelson and Goldman.

Proc. Biol. Soc. Washington 42 : 151, Mar. 30, 1929.

76737. Skin and skull. Adult female. Tenejapa, altitude 7,800 feet, about 16 miles northeast of San Cristobal, Chiapas, Mexico. November 28, 1895. Collected by E. W. Nelson and E. A. Goldman. Original number 8682.

Well-made skin in good condition; skull Grade A.

†Heterogeomys hispidus concavus Nelson and Goldman.

Proc. Biol. Soc. Washington 42 : 148, Mar. 30, 1929.

81227. Skin and skull. Adult male. Pinal de Amoles, altitude 5,500 feet, Queretaro, Mexico. September 9, 1896. Collected by E. W. Nelson and E. A. Goldman. Original number 10130.

Well-made skin in good condition; skull Grade A.

†Heterogeomys hispidus isthmicus Nelson and Goldman.

Proc. Biol. Soc. Washington 42 : 149, Mar. 30, 1929.

78062. Skin and skull. Adult male. Jaltipan, altitude 100 feet, Veracruz, Mexico. May 2, 1896. Collected by E. W. Nelson and E. A. Goldman. Original number 9574.

Well-made skin in good condition; skull Grade A.

†Heterogeomys hispidus teapensis Goldman.

Journ. Washington Acad. Sci. 29 : 176, Apr. 15, 1939.

100035. Skin and skull. Adult female. Teapa, Tabasco, Mexico. March 23, 1900. Collected by E. W. Nelson and E. A. Goldman. Original number 14056.

Well-made skin in good condition; skull Grade A.

†Heterogeomys hispidus tehuantepecus Goldman.

Journ. Washington Acad. Sci. 29 : 175, Apr. 15, 1939.

73434. Skin and skull. Adult male. Mountains 12 miles northwest of Santo Domingo and about 60 miles north of Tehuantepec City, altitude 1,600 feet, Oaxaca, Mexico. June 18, 1895. Collected by E. W. Nelson and E. A. Goldman. Original number 8092.

Well-made skin in good condition; skull Grade A.

†Heterogeomys hispidus yucatanensis Nelson and Goldman.

Proc. Biol. Soc. Washington 42 : 150, Mar. 30, 1929.

100344. Skin and skull. Adult male. Campeche, altitude 50 feet, Campeche, Mexico. June 7, 1900. Collected by E. W. Nelson and E. A. Goldman. Original number 14233.

Well-made skin in good condition, except for small bare spot on middle of back and small perforation of left hindleg; skull Grade A.

† Heterogeomys torridus Merriam.

North Amer. Fauna 8: 183, Jan. 31, 1895.

= *Heterogeomys hispidus torridus* Merriam.   See Nelson and Goldman, Proc. Biol. Soc. Washington 42: 147, Mar. 30, 1929.

63629. Skin and skull. Adult female. Chichicaxtle, Veracruz, Mexico. February 15, 1894. Collected by E. W. Nelson. Original number 5850.

Well-made skin in good condition; skull Grade A.

Genus MACROGEOMYS Merriam

*Macrogeomys costaricensis Merriam.

North Amer. Fauna 8: 192, Jan. 31, 1895.

$\frac{12911}{22551}$. Skin and skull. Young. Pacuare, Costa Rica. 1876. Collected by Juan Cooper. Original number 96.

Well-made skin in good condition; a little hair gone from the occiput; skull Grade A.

† Macrogeomys dariensis Goldman.

Smithsonian Misc. Coll. 60 (2) : 8, Sept. 20, 1912.

179587. Skin and skull. Adult male. Cana, altitude 2,000 feet, mountains of eastern Panama. May 31, 1912. Collected by E. A. Goldman. Original number 21760.

Well-made skin in good condition; skull Grade A.

*Macrogeomys dolichocephalus Merriam.

North Amer. Fauna 8: 189, Jan. 31, 1895.

$\frac{8627}{36295}$. Skin and skull. Adult male. San José, Costa Rica. January 1866. Collected by José C. Zeledon. Explorations in Costa Rica under A. von Frantzius.

Skin not very well made up, but apparently in good condition; skull Grade A.

Genus ORTHOGEOMYS Merriam

† Orthogeomys grandis alleni Nelson and Goldman.

Journ. Mamm. 11: 156, May 9, 1930.

70586. Skin and skull. Adult male. Near Acapulco, altitude 2,000 feet, Guerrero, Mexico. January 21, 1895. Collected by E. W. Nelson and E. A. Goldman. Original number 7409.

Right leg injured by trap, epidermis of tail and left hindleg partly removed; skull Grade A.

† Orthogeomys grandis annexus Nelson and Goldman.

Proc. Biol. Soc. Washington 46: 195, Oct. 26, 1933.

75949. Skin and skull. Adult female. Tuxtla Gutierrez, altitude 2,600 feet, Chiapas, Mexico. September 11, 1895. Collected by E. W. Nelson and E. A. Goldman. Original number 8418.

Well-made skin in good condition; skull Grade A.

†Orthogeomys grandis felipensis Nelson and Goldman.

Journ. Mamm. 11: 157, May 9, 1930.

67030. Skin and skull. Adult male. Cerro San Felipe, altitude 10,000 feet, 10 miles north of Oaxaca, Oaxaca, Mexico. August 28, 1894. Collected by E. W. Nelson and E. A. Goldman. Original number 6669.

Well-made skin in good condition; skull Grade A.

†Orthogeomys grandis guerrerensis Nelson and Goldman.

Journ. Mamm. 11: 158, May 9, 1930.

126536. Skin and skull. Adult female. El Limon, in the valley of the Rio de las Balsas, about 20 miles northwest of La Union, Guerrero, Mexico. April 2, 1903. Collected by E. W. Nelson and E. A. Goldman. Original number 16286.

Pelage on head, neck, and rump removed by ants in the field; skull Grade A.

†Orthogeomys grandis vulcani Nelson and Goldman.

Proc. Biol. Soc. Washington 44: 105, Oct. 17, 1931.

76745. Skin and skull. Adult male. Volcan Santa Maria, altitude 9,000 feet, Quezaltenango, Guatemala. January 28, 1896. Collected by E. W. Nelson and E. A. Goldman. Original number 9243.

Well-made skin in good condition; skull Grade A.

*Orthogeomys latifrons Merriam.

North Amer. Fauna 8: 178, Jan. 31, 1895.
=Orthogeomys grandis latifrons Merriam. See Nelson and Goldman, Journ. Mamm. 11: 156, May 9, 1930.

61239. Skin and skull. Adult. Guatemala (without definite locality, but probably lowlands near Pacific coast). From World's Columbian Exposition (Chicago, 1893), Exhibit of Guatemala, No. 2. Cataloged November 19, 1894.

Well-made skin in good condition, except for a little epidermis about the ears; skull Grade B.

Type designated by the original number 2. Specimen evidently not entered in catalog at time the description was written.

†Orthogeomys nelsoni Merriam.

North Amer. Fauna 8: 176, Jan. 31, 1895.
=Orthogeomys grandis nelsoni Merriam. See Nelson and Goldman, Journ. Mamm. 11: 156, May 9, 1930.

66751. Skin and skull. Adult male. Mount Zempoaltepec, altitude 8,000 feet, Oaxaca, Mexico. July 8, 1894. Collected by E. W. Nelson and E. A. Goldman. Original number 6376.

Well-made skin in good condition; skull Grade A.

Genus PAPPOGEOMYS Merriam

†Pappogeomys albinasus Merriam.

North Amer. Fauna 8: 149, Jan. 31, 1895.

=*Pappogeomys bulleri albinasus* Merriam. See Goldman, Journ. Mamm. 20: 94, Feb. 14, 1939.

$\frac{34138}{46215}$. Skin and skull. Adult male. Altemajac, a suburb of Guadalajara, Jalisco, Mexico. May 21, 1892. Collected by E. W. Nelson. Original number 2654.

Well-made skin in good condition; skull Grade A.

†Pappogeomys bulleri amecensis Goldman.

Journ. Mamm. 20: 97, Feb. 14, 1939.

82189. Skin and skull. Adult male. Mountains near Ameca, altitude 6,500 feet, Jalisco, Mexico. February 20, 1897. Collected by E W. Nelson and E. A. Goldman. Original number 10554.

Well-made skin in good condition; skull Grade A.

†Pappogeomys bulleri flammeus Goldman.

Journ. Mamm. 20: 95, Feb. 14, 1939.

88117. Skin and skull. Adult male. Milpillas, 5 miles southwest of San Sebastian, altitude 3,800 feet, northwestern Jalisco, Mexico. March 15, 1897. Collected by E. W. Nelson and E. A. Goldman. Original number 10716.

Well-made skin in good condition; skull Grade A.

†Pappogeomys bulleri lagunensis Goldman.

Journ. Mamm. 20: 96, Feb. 14, 1939.

88121. Skin and skull. Adult male. La Laguna, Sierra de Juanacatlan, altitude 6,500 feet, northwestern Jalisco, Mexico. March 24, 1897. Collected by E. W. Nelson and E. A. Goldman. Original number 10802.

Well-made skin in good condition; skull Grade A.

†Pappogeomys bulleri nayaritensis Goldman.

Journ. Mamm. 20: 94, Feb. 14, 1939.

88124. Skin and skull. Adult male. Jalisco, about 10 miles south of Tepic, altitude 5,000 feet, Nayarit, Mexico. April 10, 1897. Collected by E. W. Nelson and E. A. Goldman. Original number 10886.

Well-made skin in good condition; skull Grade A.

†Geomys nelsoni Merriam.

Proc. Biol. Soc. Washington 7: 164, Sept. 29, 1892.

=*Pappogeomys bulleri nelsoni* (Merriam). See Goldman, Journ. Mamm. 20: 94, Feb. 14, 1939.

$\frac{33587}{45622}$. Skin and skull. Old male. North slope Sierra Nevada de Colima, altitude 6,500 feet, Jalisco, Mexico. April 11, 1892. Collected by E. W. Nelson. Original number 2436.

Well-made skin in good condition; skull Grade A.

Genus PLATYGEOMYS Merriam

†Geomys fumosus Merriam.

Proc. Biol. Soc. Washington 7: 165, Sept. 29, 1892.

=*Platygeomys fumosus* (Merriam). See Merriam, North Amer. Fauna 8: 170, Jan. 31, 1895.

$\frac{33202}{45207}$. Skin and skull. Adult male. Colima, Colima, Mexico. March 27, 1892. Collected by E. W. Nelson. Original number 2338.

Well-made skin in good condition; skull Grade A.

†Geomys gymnurus Merriam.

Proc. Biol. Soc. Washington 7: 166, Sept. 29, 1892.

=*Platygeomys gymnurus* (Merriam). See Merriam, North Amer. Fauna 8: 164, Jan. 31, 1895.

$\frac{33579}{45614}$. Skin and skull. Adult female. Zapotlan, Jalisco, Mexico. April 16, 1892. Collected by E. W. Nelson. Original number 2460.

Well-made skin in good condition; skull Grade A.

†Platygeomys gymnurus imparilis Goldman.

Journ. Mamm. 20: 89, Feb. 14, 1939.

$\frac{34918}{47183}$. Skin and skull. Adult male. Patzcuaro, altitude 7,000 feet, Michoacan, Mexico. July 23, 1892. Collected by E. W. Nelson and E. A. Goldman. Original number 2918.

Well-made skin in good condition; skull Grade A.

†Platygeomys gymnurus inclarus Goldman.

Journ. Mamm. 20: 88, Feb. 14, 1939.

$\frac{33582}{45617}$. Skin and skull. Young female. North slope Sierra Nevada de Colima, altitude 10,000 feet, Jalisco, Mexico. April 22, 1892. Collected by E. W. Nelson and E. A. Goldman. Original number 2532.

Well-made skin in good condition; skull Grade B.

†**Platygeomys neglectus** Merriam.

Proc. Biol. Soc. Washington 15: 68, Mar. 22, 1902.

81218. Skin and skull. Adult male. Cerro de la Calentura, altitude 9,500 feet, about 8 miles northwest of Pinal de Amoles, Queretaro, Mexico. September 14, 1896 (not September 4, as given in original description). Collected by E. A. Goldman. Original number 10142.

Well-made skin in good condition; skull Grade A.

†**Platygeomys planiceps** Merriam.

North Amer. Fauna 8: 168, Jan. 31, 1895.

55906. Skin and skull. Adult male. North slope Volcan Toluca, State of Mexico, Mexico. September 12, 1893. Collected by E. W. Nelson. Original number 5466.

Well-made skin in good condition; skull Grade A.

†**Platygeomys tylorhinus** Merriam.

North Amer. Fauna 8: 167, Jan. 31, 1895.

51883. Skin and skull. Adult male. Tula, Hidalgo, Mexico. March 13, 1893. Collected by E. W. Nelson. Original number 4442.

Well-made skin in good condition; skull Grade A.

†**Platygeomys tylorhinus angustirostris** Merriam.

Proc. Biol. Soc. Washington 16: 81, May 29, 1903.
=*Platygeomys angustirostris* Merriam. See Goldman, Journ. Mamm. 20: 90, Feb. 14, 1939.

125688. Skin and skull. Adult female. Patamban, Michoacan, Mexico. February 2, 1903. Collected by E. W. Nelson and E. A. Goldman. Original number 15850.

Well-made skin in good condition; skull Grade A.

†**Platygeomys varius** Goldman.

Journ. Mamm. 20: 90, Feb. 14, 1939.

126144. Skin and skull. Adult male. Uruapan, altitude about 6,000 feet, Michoacan, Mexico. March 8, 1903. Collected by E. W. Nelson and E. A. Goldman. Original number 16105.

Well-made skin in good condition; skull Grade A.

†**Platygeomys zinseri** Goldman.

Journ. Mamm. 20: 91, Feb. 14, 1939.

78971. Skin and skull. Adult male. Lagos, altitude 6,150 feet, Jalisco, Mexico. June 29, 1896. Collected by E. W. Nelson and E. A. Goldman. Original number 9718.

Well-made skin in good condition; skull Grade A.

Genus THOMOMYS Wied

†Thomomys alexandrae Goldman.

Journ. Washington Acad. Sci. 23 : 464, Oct. 15, 1933.

250969. Skin and skull. Adult male. Plain 5 miles southeast of Rainbow Lodge, altitude 6,200 feet, near Navajo Mountain, Coconino County, Ariz. June 16, 1933. Collected by E. A. Goldman. Original number 23613.

Well-made skin in good condition; skull Grade A.

†Thomomys alpinus Merriam.

Proc. Biol. Soc. Washington 11 : 216, July 15, 1897.
=*Thomomys bottae alpinus* Merriam. See Goldman, Proc. Biol. Soc. Washington 48 : 154, Oct. 31, 1935.

$\frac{30528}{42512}$. Skin and skull. Adult male. Big Cottonwood Meadows, near Mount Whitney, altitude 10,000 feet, Tulare County, Calif. August 6, 1891. Collected by B. H. Dutcher. Original number 167.

Well-made skin in good condition; skull Grade A.

†Thomomys alpinus awahnee Merriam.

Proc. Biol. Soc. Washington 21 : 146, June 9, 1908.
=*Thomomys bottae awahnee* Merriam. See Goldman, Proc. Biol. Soc. Washington 48 : 154, Oct. 31, 1935.

133076. Skin and skull. Adult female. Yosemite Valley, Mariposa County, Calif. June 14, 1904. Collected by N. Hollister. Original number 870.

Well-made skin in good condition; skull Grade A.

†Thomomys angularis Merriam.

Proc. Biol. Soc. Washington 11 : 214, July 15, 1897.
=*Thomomys bottae angularis* Merriam. See Bailey, North Amer. Fauna 39 : 53, Nov. 15, 1915.

58123. Skin and skull. Adult male. Los Banos, Merced County, Calif. January 1, 1894. Collected by J. E. McLellan. Original number 418.

Well-made skin in good condition; skull Grade A.

†Thomomys angularis pascalis Merriam.

Proc. Biol. Soc. Washington 14 : 111, July 19, 1901.
=*Thomomys bottae pascalis* Merriam. See Bailey, North Amer. Fauna 39 : 54, Nov. 15, 1915.

$\frac{32779}{44702}$. Skin and skull. Adult male. Fresno, San Joaquin Valley, Fresno County, Calif. March 4, 1892 (not May 4, 1892, as recorded in original description). Collected by C. P. Streator. Original number 1634.

Well-made skin in good condition; skull Grade A.

†Thomomys apache Bailey.

Proc. Biol. Soc. Washington 23 : 79, May 4, 1910.

=*Thomomys bottae apache* Bailey.   See Goldman, Proc. Biol. Soc. Washington 48 : 157, Oct. 31, 1935.

135366.   Skin and skull.   Adult male.   La Jara Lake, altitude 7,500 feet, on the Jicarilla Apache Indian Reservation, N. Mex.   September 19, 1904.   Collected by James H. Gaut.   Original number 3289.

Well-made skin in good condition; skull Grade A.

†Thomomys aureus lachuguilla Bailey.

Proc. Biol. Soc. Washington 15 : 120, June 2, 1902.

=*Thomomys bottae lachuguilla* Bailey.   See Goldman, Proc. Biol. Soc. Washington 51 : 55, March 18, 1938.

110336.   Skin and skull.   Adult male.   Foothills near El Paso, El Paso County, Tex.   September 24, 1901.   Collected by Vernon Bailey.   Original number 7858.

Well-made skin in good condition; skull Grade A.

†Thomomys aureus perpes Merriam.

Proc. Biol. Soc. Washington 14 : 111, July 19, 1901.

=*Thomomys bottae perpes* Merriam.   See Goldman, Proc. Biol. Soc. Washington 48 : 155, Oct. 31, 1935.

$\frac{25091}{32503}$.   Skin and skull.   Adult male.   Lone Pine, Owens Valley, Inyo County, Calif.   December 23, 1890.   Collected by E. W. Nelson.   Original number 145.

Well-made skin in good condition; skull Grade A.

†Thomomys aureus pervagus Merriam.

Proc. Biol. Soc. Washington 14 : 110, July 19, 1901.

=*Thomomys bottae pervagus* Merriam.   See Goldman, Proc. Biol. Soc. Washington 48 : 157, Oct. 31, 1935.

58293.   Skin and skull.   Adult male.   Espanola, Rio Arriba County, N. Mex.   January 4, 1894.   Collected by J. A. Loring.   Original number 1548.

Well-made skin in good condition; skull Grade A.

†Thomomys baileyi Merriam.

Proc. Biol. Soc. Washington 14 : 109, July 19, 1901.

$\frac{18256}{25159}$.   Skin and skull.   Adult female.   Sierra Blanca, El Paso County, Tex.   December 28, 1889.   Collected by Vernon Bailey.   Original number 870.

Well-made skin in good condition; skull Grade A.

†Thomomys baileyi spatiosus Goldman.

Proc. Biol. Soc. Washington 51: 58, Mar. 18, 1938.

100427. Skin and skull. Adult male. Alpine, altitude 4,500 feet, Brewster County, Texas. May 26, 1900. Collected by Vernon Bailey. Original number 7368.

Well-made skin in good condition; skull Grade A.

†Thomomys bottae alienus Goldman.

Journ. Washington Acad. Sci. 28: 338, July 15, 1938.

261926. Skin and skull. Adult male. Mammoth, altitude 2,400 feet, San Pedro River, Pinal County, Ariz. November 4, 1936. Collected by E. A. Goldman. Original number 23746.

Well-made skin in good condition; skull Grade A.

†Thomomys bottae birdseyei Goldman.

Proc. Biol. Soc. Washington 50: 134, Sept. 10, 1937.

161654. Skin and skull. Adult male. Pine Valley Mountains, altitude 8,300 feet, 5 miles east of Pine Valley, Washington County, Utah. October 10, 1909. Collected by Clarence Birdseye. Original number 861.

Well-made skin in good condition; skull Grade A.

†Thomomys bottae convergens Nelson and Goldman.

Journ. Mamm. 15: 123, May 15, 1934.

250894. Skin and skull. Adult male. Costa Rica Ranch, delta of Sonora River, southwest of Hermosillo, Sonora, Mexico. December 13, 1932. Collected by Vernon Bailey and Frederic Winthrop. Original number 11280.

Well-made skin in good condition; skull Grade A.

†Thomomys bottae desitus Goldman.

Journ. Washington Acad. Sci. 26: 113, Mar. 15, 1936.

227802. Skin and skull. Adult male. Big Sandy River, near Owen, altitude 2,000 feet, Mohave County, Arizona. September 21, 1917. Collected by E. A. Goldman. Original number 23332.

Well-made skin in good condition; skull Grade A.

†Thomomys bottae divergens Nelson and Goldman.

Journ. Mamm. 15: 122, May 15, 1934.

250892. Skin and skull. Adult male. Four miles west of Huachinera, altitude 4,000 feet, Bavispe River, northeastern Sonora, Mexico. November 8, 1932. Collected by Vernon Bailey and Frederic Winthrop. Original number 11098.

Well-made skin in good condition; skull Grade A.

†Thomomys bottae extenuatus Goldman.

Proc. Biol. Soc. Washington 48: 149, Oct. 31, 1935.

17872/24809. Skin and skull. Adult male. Willcox, altitude 4,000 feet, Cochise County, Arizona. November 27, 1889. Collected by Vernon Bailey. Original number 712.

Well-made skin in good condition; skull Grade A.

†Thomomys bottae guadalupensis Goldman.

Journ. Washington Acad. Sci. 26: 117, Mar. 15, 1936.

109225. Skin and skull. Adult male. McKittrick Canyon, Guadalupe Mountains, altitude 7,800 feet, Texas. August 22, 1901. Collected by Vernon Bailey. Original number 7821.

Well-made skin in good condition; skull Grade B.

†Thomomys bottae howelli Goldman.

Journ. Washington Acad. Sci. 26: 116, Mar. 15, 1936.

75684. Skin and skull. Adult female. Grand Junction, altitude 4,600 feet, Mesa County, Colorado. November 7, 1895. Collected by Arthur H. Howell. Original number 493.

Well-made skin in good condition; skull Grade A.

†Thomomys bottae hualpaiensis Goldman.

Journ. Washington Acad. Sci. 26: 114, Mar. 15, 1936.

227796. Skin and skull. Adult male. Hualpai Peak, Hualpai Mountains, altitude 7,000 feet, Mohave County, Ariz. October 6, 1917. Collected by E. A. Goldman. Original number 23351.

Well-made skin in good condition; skull Grade A.

†Thomomys bottae imitabilis Goldman.

Proc. Biol. Soc. Washington 52: 30, Mar. 11, 1939.

146839. Skin and skull. Adult male. La Paz, southern Lower California, Mexico. February 16, 1906. Collected by E. W. Nelson and E. A. Goldman. Original number 19163.

Well-made skin in good condition; skull Grade A.

†Thomomys bottae incomptus Goldman.

Proc. Biol. Soc. Washington 52: 29, Mar. 11, 1939.

140671. Skin and skull. Adult male. San Jorge, near Pacific coast west of Pozo Grande and about 25 miles southwest of Comondu, altitude 50 feet, southern Lower California, Mexico. November 12, 1905. Collected by E. W. Nelson and E. A. Goldman. Original number 18546.

Well-made skin in good condition; skull Grade A.

†**Thomomys bottae internatus** Goldman.

Journ. Washington Acad. Sci. 26: 115, Mar. 15, 1936.

150997. Skin and skull. Adult male. Salida, altitude 7,000 feet, Chaffee County, Colo. November 10, 1907. Collected by Merritt Cary. Original number 1247.

Well-made skin in good condition; skull Grade A.

†**Thomomys bottae minimus** Durrant.

Proc. Biol. Soc. Washington 52: 161, Oct. 11, 1939.

263942. Skin and skull. Adult male. Stansbury Island, Great Salt Lake, Tooele County, Utah. June 25, 1938. Collected by W. H. Marshall. Original number 141.

Well-made skin in good condition; skull Grade B.

†**Thomomys bottae minor** Bailey.

Proc. Biol. Soc. Washington 27: 116, July 10, 1914.

146463. Skin and skull. Adult male. Fort Bragg, Mendocino County, Calif. November 30, 1905. Collected by James H. Gaut. Original number 4187.

Well-made skin in good condition; skull Grade A.

†**Thomomys bottae nicholi** Goldman.

Journ. Washington Acad. Sci. 28: 337, July 15, 1938.

262864. Skin and skull. Adult male. Twenty miles south of Wolf Hole (road to Parashonts), altitude 5,000 feet, Shivwits Plateau, Mohave County, Ariz. August 6, 1937. Collected by Luther C. Goldman. Original number 363.

Well-made skin in good condition; skull Grade A.

†**Thomomys bottae optabilis** Goldman.

Journ. Washington Acad. Sci. 26: 116, Mar. 15, 1936.

149962. Skin and skull. Adult male. Coventry, Naturita Creek Valley, altitude 6,500 feet, Montrose County, Colo. July 31, 1907. Collected by Merritt Cary. Original number 1105.

Well-made skin in good condition; skull Grade A.

†**Thomomys bottae opulentus** Goldman.

Proc. Biol. Soc. Washington 48: 150, Oct. 31, 1935.

167318. Skin and skull. Adult female. Las Palomas, on the Rio Grande, Sierra County, N. Mex. October 24, 1909. Collected by E. A. Goldman. Original number 20675.

Well-made skin in good condition; skull Grade A.

†**Thomomys bottae parvulus** Goldman.

Journ. Washington Acad. Sci. 28: 339, July 15, 1938.

262813. Skin and skull. Adult male. Pass between Santa Catalina and Rincon Mountains, altitude 4,500 feet, Pima County, Ariz. June 5, 1937. Collected by Luther C. Goldman. Original number 213.

Well-made skin in good condition; skull Grade A.

†Thomomys bottae patulus Goldman.

Journ. Washington Acad. Sci. 28: 341, July 15, 1938.

262899. Skin and skull. Adult male. Bottomland along Hassa-yampa River, altitude 2,000 feet, 2 miles below Wickenburg, Maricopa County, Ariz. September 16, 1937. Collected by Luther C. Goldman. Original number 460.

Well-made skin in good condition; skull Grade A.

†Thomomys bottae pervarius Goldman.

Proc. Biol. Soc. Washington 51: 57, Mar. 18, 1938.

$\frac{18201}{25105}$. Skin and skull. Young adult male. Lloyd Ranch, 35 miles south of Marfa, altitude 4,200 feet, Presidio County, Tex. January 20, 1890. Collected by Vernon Bailey. Original number 900.

Well-made skin in good condition; skull Grade A.

†Thomomys bottae pinalensis Goldman.

Journ. Washington Acad. Sci. 28: 342, July 15, 1938.

245709. Skin and skull. Adult female. Oak Flat, 5 miles east of Superior, Pinal Mountains, Ariz. May 22, 1924. Collected by Walter P. Taylor. Original number 1667.

Well-made skin in good condition except for tail injury; skull Grade A.

†Thomomys bottae russeolus Nelson and Goldman.

Proc. Biol. Soc. Washington 22: 25, Mar. 10, 1909.

139920. Skin and skull. Young adult male. San Angel, 100 feet below sea level, 30 miles west of San Ignacio, Lower California, Mexico. October 15, 1905. Collected by E. W. Nelson and E. A. Goldman. Original number 18355.

Well-made skin in good condition; skull Grade A.

†Thomomys bottae virgineus Goldman.

Proc. Biol. Soc. Washington 50: 133, Sept. 10, 1937.

262016. Skin and skull. Adult male. Beaverdam Creek, near confluence with Virgin River, at Littlefield, altitude 1,500 feet, Mohave County, northwestern Arizona. October 16, 1936. Collected by Luther C. Goldman. Original number 67.

Well-made skin in good condition; skull Grade A.

†Thomomys bottae winthropi Nelson and Goldman.

Journ. Mamm. 15: 122, May 15, 1934.

251028. Skin and skull. Adult male. Hermosillo, Sonora, Mexico. December 21, 1932. Collected by Frederic Winthrop and Bernard Bailey. Original number 27203–X.

Well-made skin in good condition; skull Grade A.

†Thomomys bridgeri Merriam.

Proc. Biol. Soc. Washington 14: 113, July 19, 1901.
=*Thomomys talpoides bridgeri* Merriam. See Goldman, Journ. Mamm. 20: 234, May 14, 1939.

$\frac{18858}{25592}$. Skin and skull. Adult male. Six miles southwest of Old Fort Bridger, Uinta County, Wyo. May 27, 1890. Collected by Vernon Bailey. Original number 1207.

Well-made skin in good condition; skull Grade A.

†Thomomys cabezonae Merriam.

Proc. Biol. Soc. Washington 14: 110, July 19, 1901.
=*Thomomys bottae cabezonae* Merriam. See Goldman, Proc. Biol. Soc. Washington 48: 155, Oct. 31, 1935.

53987. Skin and skull. Adult male. Cabezon, San Gorgonio Pass, Riverside County, Calif. June 3, 1893. Collected by C. P. Streator. Original number 2906.

Well-made skin in good condition; skull Grade A.

†Thomomys canus Bailey.

Proc. Biol. Soc. Washington 23: 79, May 4, 1910.
=*Thomomys bottae canus* Bailey. See Goldman, Proc. Biol. Soc. Washington 48: 155, Oct. 31, 1935.

78365. Skin and skull. Adult male. Deep Hole, at north end of Smoke Creek Desert, Washoe County, Nev. May 14, 1896. Collected by Clark P. Streator. Original number 5169.

Well-made skin in good condition; skull Grade A.

*Thomomys clusius Coues.

Proc. Acad. Nat. Sci. Philadelphia 27: 138, June 15, 1875.
=*Thomomys talpoides clusius* Coues. See Bailey, North Amer. Fauna 39: 100, Nov. 15, 1915.

$\frac{3051}{36805}$. Skin and skull. Adult female. Bridger Pass, 18 miles southwest of Rawlins, Carbon County, Wyo. July 28, 1857. Collected by W. A. Hammond. Original number 88.

Well-made skin in good condition. It has evidently been made over and the skull removed, probably in 1894. Skull Grade B.

†Thomomys clusius fuscus Merriam.

North Amer. Fauna 5: 69, July 30, 1891.
=*Thomomys talpoides fuscus* Merriam. See Goldman, Journ. Mamm. 20: 234, May 14, 1939.

24267. Skin and skull. Adult female. Mountains at Head of Big
31671
Lost River, Custer County, Idaho. September 23, 1890. Collected by B. H. Dutcher. Original number 1847.

Well-made skin in good condition; skull Grade B.

†Thomomys clusius ocius Merriam.

Proc. Biol. Soc. Washington 14: 114, July 19, 1901.
=*Thomomys ocius* Merriam. See Bailey, North Amer. Fauna 39: 107, Nov. 15,
1915.

18852. Skin and skull. Adult male. Six miles southwest of Old
25586
Fort Bridger, Uinta County, Wyo. May 24, 1890. Collected by
Vernon Bailey. Original number 1194.

Well-made skin in good condition; skull Grade A.

*Thomomys desertorum Merriam.

Proc. Biol. Soc. Washington 14: 114, July 19, 1901.
=*Thomomys bottae desertorum* Merriam. See Goldman, Proc. Biol. Soc. Washington 48: 156, Oct. 31, 1935.

186523. Skin and skull. Adult male. Mud Spring, Detrital Valley, Ariz. February 21, 1889. Collected by Vernon Bailey.
Original number 598. Merriam collection No. $\frac{5387}{6082}$.

Well-made skin in good condition; skull Grade A.

†Thomomys douglasii oregonus Merriam.

Proc. Biol. Soc. Washington 14: 115, July 19, 1901.

56939. Skin and skull. Adult male. Ely, near Oregon City, Willamette Valley, Clackamas County, Oreg. October 24, 1893.
Collected by C. P. Streator. Original number 3340.

Well-made skin in good condition; skull Grade A.

†Thomomys douglasii shawi Taylor.

Proc. Biol. Soc. Washington 34: 121, June 30, 1921.
=*Thomomys talpoides shawi* Taylor. See Goldman, Journ. Mamm. 20: 235,
May 14, 1939.

232807. Skin and skull. Adult male. Owyhigh Lakes, altitude
5,100 feet, Mount Rainier, Pierce County, Wash. August 9, 1919.
Collected by George G. Cantwell. Original number 1464.

Well-made skin in good condition; skull Grade A.

†Thomomys douglasii tacomensis Taylor.

Proc. Biol. Soc. Washington 32: 169, Sept. 30, 1919.
=*Thomomys talpoides tacomensis* Taylor. See Goldman, Journ. Mamm. 20:
235, May 14, 1939.

231096.   Skin and skull.   Young adult female.   Six miles south of Tacoma, Pierce County, Wash.   December 24, 1918.   Collected by George G. Cantwell.   Original number 857.

Well-made skin in good condition; skull Grade A.

†Thomomys douglasii yelmensis Merriam.

Proc. Biol. Soc. Washington 13: 21, Jan. 31, 1899.
=*Thomomys talpoides yelmensis* Merriam.   See Goldman, Journ. Mamm. 20: 235, May 14, 1939.

$\frac{31916}{43777}$.   Skin and skull.   Adult male.   Tenino, Yelm Prairie, Thurston County, Wash.   October 24, 1891.   Collected by C. P. Streator. Original number 1385.

Well-made skin in good condition; skull Grade A.

†Thomomys fossor kaibabensis Goldman.

Journ. Washington Acad. Sci. 28: 333, July 15, 1938.
=*Thomomys talpoides kaibabensis* Goldman.   See Goldman, Journ. Mamm. 20: 234, May 14, 1939.

262891.   Skin and skull.   Adult male.   De Motte Park, altitude 9,000 feet, Kaibab Plateau, Coconino County, Ariz.   September 10, 1937. Collected by Luther C. Goldman.   Original number 443.

Well-made skin in good condition; skull Grade A.

†Thomomys fossor levis Goldman.

Journ. Washington Acad. Sci. 28: 336, July 15, 1938.
=*Thomomys talpoides levis* Goldman.   See Goldman, Journ. Mamm. 20: 234, May 14, 1939.

158079.   Skin and skull.   Adult female.   Seven Mile Flat, altitude 10,000 feet, 5 miles north of Fish Lake, Fish Lake Plateau, Sevier County, Utah.   October 1, 1908.   Collected by W. H. Osgood. Original number 3616.

Well-made skin in good condition; skull Grade A.

†Thomomys fossor moorei Goldman.

Journ. Washington Acad. Sci. 28: 335, July 15, 1938.
=*Thomomys talpoides moorei* Goldman.   See Goldman, Journ. Mamm. 20: 234, May 14, 1939.

248222.   Skin and skull.   Adult male.   One mile south of Fairview, altitude 6,000 feet, Sanpete County, Utah.   February 19, 1928. Collected by A. W. Moore.   Original number 24799–X.

Well-made skin in good condition; skull Grade A.

†Thomomys fossor parowanensis Goldman.

Journ. Washington Acad. Sci. 28: 334, July 15, 1938.
=*Thomomys talpoides parowanensis* Goldman.   See Goldman, Journ. Mamm. 20: 234, May 14, 1939.

158072. Skin and skull. Adult male. Brian Head, altitude 11,000 feet, Parowan Mountains, Iron County, Utah. September 8, 1908. Collected by W. H. Osgood. Original number 3483.

Well-made skin in good condition; skull Grade A.

*Geomys fulvus Woodhouse.

Proc. Acad. Nat. Sci. Philadelphia 6: 201, presented at meeting of Dec. 28, 1852.

=*Thomomys bottae fulvus* (Woodhouse). See Goldman, Proc. Biol. Soc. Washington 48: 156, Oct. 31, 1935.

2674. Mounted skin with no skull. San Francisco Mountain, Coconino County, Ariz. October 1851. Collected by S. W. Woodhouse on expedition under command of Capt. L. Sitgreaves.

Specimen in good condition, considering its age and the length of time during which it was on exhibition. It is probably much faded.

Type not designated by number. Woodhouse speaks of but one specimen, giving careful measurements. Reference to Baird's Mammals of North America shows the above specimen to have been the basis of the original description.

†Thomomys fulvus catalinae Goldman.

Journ. Washington Acad. Sci. 21: 419, Oct. 19, 1931.

=*Thomomys bottae catalinae* Goldman. See Goldman, Proc. Biol. Soc. Washington 48: 157, Oct. 31, 1935.

244081. Skin and skull. Adult male. Summerhaven, Santa Catalina Mountains, altitude 7,500 feet, Pima County, Ariz. August 6, 1923. Collected by E. A. Goldman. Original number 23517.

Well-made skin in summer pelage, and in good condition; skull Grade A.

†Thomomys fulvus collinus Goldman.

Journ. Washington Acad. Sci. 21: 421, Oct. 19, 1931.

=*Thomomys bottae collinus* Goldman. See Goldman, Proc. Biol. Soc. Washington 48: 157, Oct. 31, 1935.

66053. Skin and skull. Adult male. Fly Park, altitude 9,000 feet, Chiricahua Mountains, Cochise County, Ariz. June 10, 1894. Collected by A. K. Fisher. Original number 1527.

Well-made skin in good condition; skull Grade B.

†Thomomys fulvus emotus Goldman.

Proc. Biol. Soc. Washington 46: 76, Apr. 27, 1933.

=*Thomomys umbrinus emotus* Goldman. See Nelson and Goldman, Journ. Mamm. 15: 116, May 15, 1934.

157005. Skin and skull. Adult male. Animas Peak, altitude 8,000 feet, Animas Mountains, Hidalgo County, southwestern New Mexico. August 3, 1908. Collected by E. A. Goldman. Original number 19929.

Well-made skin in worn summer pelage; skull Grade B.

†**Thomomys fulvus flavidus** Goldman.

Journ. Washington Acad. Sci. 21: 417, Oct. 19, 1931.
=*Thomomys bottae chrysonotus* Grinnell. See Goldman, Proc. Biol. Soc.
Washington 48: 156, Oct. 31, 1935.

181065. Skin and skull. Adult male. Parker, altitude 350 feet,
Yuma County, Ariz. February 1, 1913. Collected by E. A.
Goldman. Original number 21810.

Well-made skin in good condition; skull Grade A.

†**Thomomys fulvus grahamensis** Goldman.

Journ. Washington Acad. Sci. 21: 420, Oct. 19, 1931.
=*Thomomys bottae grahamensis* Goldman. See Goldman, Proc. Biol. Soc.
Washington 48: 157, Oct. 31, 1935.

204313. Skin and skull. Adult male. Graham Mountains (Pina-
leno Mountains on some maps), altitude 9,200 feet, Graham
County, Ariz. June 7, 1914. Collected by E. G. Holt. Original number 269.

Well-made skin in good condition; skull Grade A.

***Thomomys fulvus intermedius** Mearns.

Proc. U. S. Nat. Mus. 19: 719, July 30, 1897.
=*Thomomys umbrinus intermedius* Mearns. See Nelson and Goldman, Journ.
Mamm. 15: 117, May 15, 1934.

$\frac{21473}{36697}$. Skin and skull. Adult male. Aspen and spruce zone at
the summit of the Huachuca Mountains, altitude 9,000 feet,
southern Arizona. September 6, 1893. Collected by F. X.
Holžner. International Boundary Commission. O r i g i n a l
number 1013.

Well-made skin in good condition; skull Grade A.

***Thomomys fulvus modicus** Goldman.

Journ. Washington Acad. Sci. 21: 418, Oct. 19, 1931.
=*Thomomys bottae modicus* Goldman. Proc. Biol. Soc. Washington 48: 156,
Oct. 31, 1935.

59203. Skin and skull. Adult male. La Osa (near Mexican
boundary), southern end of Altar Valley, Pima County, Ariz.
December 14, 1893. Collected by Edgar A. Mearns and F. X.
Holzner. Original number 2681.

Well-made skin in good condition; skull Grade A.

†**Thomomys fulvus mutabilis** Goldman.

Proc. Biol. Soc. Washington 46: 75, Apr. 27, 1933.
=*Thomomys bottae mutabilis* Goldman. See Goldman, Proc. Biol. Soc. Washington 48: 156, Oct. 31, 1935.

214611. Skin and skull. Adult male. Camp Verde, altitude 3,200
feet, Yavapai County, Ariz. July 25, 1916. Collected by W.
P. Taylor. Original number 269.

Well-made skin in good condition; skull Grade A.

†Thomomys fulvus peramplus Goldman.

Journ. Washington Acad. Sci. 21: 423, Oct. 19, 1931.
=*Thomomys bottae peramplus* Goldman. See Goldman, Proc. Biol. Soc. Washington 48: 157, Oct. 31, 1935.

247632. Skin and skull. Adult male. Wheatfield Creek, west slope of Tunicha Mountains, altitude 7,000 feet, Apache County, northeastern Arizona. June 23, 1927. Collected by Paul Trapier. Original number 720.

Well-made skin in good condition; skull Grade A.

†Thomomys fulvus phasma Goldman.

Proc. Biol. Soc. Washington 46: 72, Apr. 27, 1933.
=*Thomomys bottae phasma* Goldman. See Goldman, Proc. Biol. Soc. Washington 48: 157, Oct. 31, 1935.

203026. Skin and skull. Adult female. Two miles south of Tule Tank, Tule Desert, near Mexican boundary, Yuma County, Ariz. December 8, 1913. Collected by E. A. Goldman. Original number 22355.

Well-made skin in good condition; skull Grade A.

†Thomomys fulvus pusillus Goldman.

Journ. Washington Acad. Sci. 21: 422, Oct. 19, 1931.
=*Thomomys bottae pusillus* Goldman. See Goldman, Proc. Biol. Soc. Washington 48: 157, Oct. 31, 1935.

209290. Skin and skull. Adult female. Coyote Mountains, altitude 3,000 feet, Pima County, Ariz. September 4, 1915. Collected by E. A. Goldman. Original number 22722.

Well-made skin in good condition; skull Grade A.

†Thomomys fulvus suboles Goldman.

Proc. Biol. Soc. Washington 41: 203, Dec. 18, 1928.
=*Thomomys suboles* Goldman. See Goldman, Proc. Biol. Soc. Washington 48: 157, Oct. 31, 1935.

244163. Skin and skull. Adult male. Old Searchlight Ferry, Colorado River, altitude 1,000 feet, northwest of Kingman, Ariz. September 26, 1923. Collected by Luther C. Goldman. Original number 17; 23428–X.

Well-made skin in good condition; skull Grade B.

†Thomomys fulvus subsimilis Goldman.

Proc. Biol. Soc. Washington 46: 74, Apr. 27, 1933.
=*Thomomys bottae subsimilis* Goldman. Proc. Biol. Soc. Washington 48: 156, Oct. 31, 1935.

227803. Skin and skull. Adult female. Harquahala Mountains, altitude 3,000 feet, Yuma County, Ariz. October 14, 1917. Collected by E. A. Goldman. Original number 23356.

Well-made skin in good condition; skull Grade A.

†Thomomys fulvus texensis Bailey.

Proc. Biol. Soc. Washington 15: 119, June 2, 1902.
=*Thomomys bottae texensis* Bailey. See Goldman, Proc. Biol. Soc. Washington 48: 157, Oct. 31, 1935.

$\frac{22511}{31408}$ (not 2251 as given in original description). Skin and skull. Adult male. Head of Limpia Creek, altitude 5,500 feet, Davis Mountains, Jeff Davis County, Tex. January 7, 1890. Collected by Vernon Bailey. Original number 876.

Well-made skin in good condition; skull Grade A.

†Thomomys fuscus columbianus Bailey.

Proc. Biol. Soc. Washington 27: 117, July 10, 1914.
=*Thomomys talpoides columbianus* Bailey. See Goldman, Journ. Mamm. 20: 234, May 14, 1939.

$\frac{23722}{31117}$. Skin and skull. Adult male. Touchet, Walla Walla County, Wash. September 10, 1890. Collected by C. P. Streator. Original number 234.

Well-made skin in good condition; skull Grade A.

†Thomomys fuscus fisheri Merriam.

Proc. Biol. Soc. Washington 14: 111, July 19, 1901.
=*Thomomys talpoides fisheri* Merriam. See Goldman, Journ. Mamm. 20: 234, May 14, 1939.

101238. Skin and skull. Young adult male. Beckwith, Sierra Valley, Plumas County, Calif. August 3, 1900. Collected by W. K. Fisher. Original number 1547.

Well-made skin in good condition; skull Grade A.

†Thomomys fuscus loringi Bailey.

Proc. Biol. Soc. Washington 27: 118, July 10, 1914.
=*Thomomys talpoides loringi* Bailey. See Goldman, Journ. Mamm. 20: 234, May 14, 1939.

68746. Skin and skull. Adult male. South Edmonton, Alberta, Canada. September 23, 1894. Collected by J. A. Loring. Original number 2437.

Well-made skin in good condition; skull Grade A.

†Thomomys fuscus saturatus Bailey.

Proc. Biol. Soc. Washington 27: 117, July 10, 1914.
=*Thomomys talpoides saturatus* Bailey. See Goldman, Journ. Mamm. 20: 234, May 14, 1939.

$\frac{28781}{40885}$. Skin and skull. Adult male. Silver, altitude 4,300 feet, near Saltese, Coeur d'Alene Mountains, Missoula County, Mont. June 20, 1891. Collected by C. P. Streator. Original number 979.

Well-made skin in good condition; skull Grade A.

†Thomomys goldmani Merriam.

Proc. Biol. Soc. Washington 14: 108, July 19, 1901.

=*Thomomys umbrinus goldmani* Merriam. See Nelson and Goldman, Journ. Mamm. 15: 115, May 15, 1934.

58075. Skin and skull. Adult male. Mapimi, Durango, Mexico. December 15, 1893. Collected by E. A. Goldman. Original number 240.

Well-made skin in good condition; skull Grade A.

†Thomomys hesperus Merriam.

Proc. Biol. Soc. Washington 14: 116, July 19, 1901.

69825. Skin and skull. Adult female. Tillamook, Tillamook County, Oreg. November 9, 1894. Collected by J. E. McLellan. Original number 1189.

Well-made skin in good condition; skull Grade A.

†Thomomys idahoensis Merriam.

Proc. Biol. Soc. Washington 14: 114, July 19, 1901.

=*Thomomys talpoides idahoensis* Merriam. See Davis, Recent Mammals of Idaho: 71, 251, Apr. 5, 1939.

$\frac{23482}{30900}$. Skin and skull. Adult male. Birch Creek, Fremont County, Idaho. August 8, 1890. Collected by C. P. Streator. Original number 129.

Well-made skin in good condition; skull Grade A.

†Thomomys lachuguilla confinalis Goldman.

Journ. Washington Acad. Sci. 26: 119, Mar. 15, 1936.

117571. Skin and skull. Subadult male. Edwards County, Tex.; 35 miles east of Rock Springs (altitude 2,450 feet). July 11, 1902. Collected by Vernon Bailey. Original number 7910.

Well-made skin in good condition; skull Grade A.

†Thomomys lachuguilla limitaris Goldman.

Journ. Washington Acad. Sci. 26: 118, Mar. 15, 1936.

110339. Skin and skull. Adult male. Four miles west of Boquillas, Brewster County, Tex. May 28, 1901. Collected by Vernon Bailey. Original number 7659.

Well-made skin in good condition; skull Grade A.

*Thomomys laticeps Baird.

Proc. Acad. Nat. Sci. Philadelphia 7: 335, reported favorably for publication Apr. 24, 1855.

=*Thomomys bottae laticeps* Baird. See Bailey, North Amer. Fauna 39: 46, Nov. 15, 1915.

$\frac{513}{1648}$. Skin and skull. Humboldt Bay, Humboldt County, Calif. Collected by W. P. Trowbridge. Cataloged February 21, 1855.

Badly made skin in rather poor condition; legs sprawling, tail not skinned out. A naked patch on left side. It has the appearance of having once been in alcohol. Skull Grade C.

Type not designated by number in the original description; but in Mammals of North America it is seen that Baird had only the one specimen referred to by number.

†Thomomys latirostris Merriam.

Proc. Biol. Soc. Washington 14: 107, July 19, 1901.
=*Thomomys bottae aureus* Allen. See Goldman, Proc. Biol. Soc. Washington 48: 156, Oct. 31, 1935.

$\frac{18003}{24914}$. Skin and skull. Adult male. Little Colorado River, Painted Desert, Coconino County, Ariz. September 22, 1899. Collected by Vernon Bailey. Original number 504.

Well-made skin in good condition; skull Grade A.

†Thomomys leucodon Merriam.

Proc. Biol. Soc. Washington 11: 215, July 15, 1897.
=*Thomomys bottae leucodon* Merriam. See Bailey, North Amer. Fauna 39: 47, Nov. 15, 1915.

$\frac{32034}{43848}$. Skin and skull. Adult male. Grants Pass, Rogue River Valley, Oreg. December 17, 1891. Collected by C. P. Streator. Original number 1394.

Well-made skin in good condition; skull Grade A.

†Thomomys leucodon navus Merriam.

Proc. Biol. Soc. Washington 14: 112, July 19, 1901.
=*Thomomys bottae navus* Merriam. See Bailey, North Amer. Fauna 39: 49, Nov. 15, 1915.

57791. Skin and skull. Adult male. Red Bluff, Tehama County, Calif. December 26, 1893. Collected by C. P. Streator. Original number 3462.

Well-made skin in good condition; skull Grade A.

†Thomomys limosus Merriam.

Proc. Biol. Soc. Washington 14: 116, July 19, 1901.
=*Thomomys talpoides limosus* Merriam. See Goldman, Journ. Mamm. 20: 235, May 14, 1939.

89724. Skin and skull. Adult male. White Salmon, gorge of the Columbia, Klickitat County, Wash. June 26, 1897. Collected by J. A. Loring. Original number 4382.

Well-made skin with hairs of underparts somewhat matted and soiled; tip of tail slightly injured; skull Grade A.

†**Thomomys magdalenae** Nelson and Goldman.

Proc. Biol. Soc. Washington 22: 24, Mar. 10, 1909.

146832. Skin and skull. Adult male. Magdalena Island, near west coast of Lower California, Mexico. December 3, 1905. Collected by E. W. Nelson and E. A. Goldman. Original number 18743.

Well-made skin in good condition; skull Grade A.

†**Thomomys mazama** Merriam.

Proc. Biol. Soc. Washington 11: 214, July 15, 1897.
=*Thomomys monticola mazama* Merriam. See Bailey, North Amer. Fauna 39: 123, Nov. 15, 1915.

80502. Skin and skull. Adult male. Anna Creek, near Crater Lake, Mount Mazama, altitude 6,000 feet, Klamath County, Oreg. September 3, 1896. Collected by E. A. Preble. Original number 1485.

Well-made skin in good condition; skull Grade A.

†**Thomomys mearnsi** Bailey.

Proc. Biol. Soc. Washington 27: 117, July 10, 1914.
=*Thomomys baileyi mearnsi* Bailey. See Nelson and Goldman, Journ. Mamm. 15 (2) : 124, May 15, 1934.

157008. Skin and skull. Adult male. Gray's Ranch, altitude 5,000 feet, Animas Valley, southwest corner of Grant County, N. Mex. August 10, 1908. Collected by E. A. Goldman. Original number 19939.

Well-made skin in good condition, except for small perforation across shoulders; skull Grade A.

†**Thomomys melanops** Merriam.

Proc. Biol. Soc. Washington 13: 21, Jan. 31, 1899.
=*Thomomys talpoides melanops* Merriam. See Goldman, Journ. Mamm. 20: 235, May 14, 1939.

90630. Skin and skull. Adult female. Timberline at head of Sole duck River, Olympic Mountains, Clallam County, Wash. August 28, 1897. Collected by Vernon Bailey. Original number 6219.

Well-made skin in good condition; skull Grade A.

†**Thomomys mewa** Merriam.

Proc. Biol. Soc. Washington 21: 146, June 9, 1908.
=*Thomomys bottae mewa* Merriam. See Bailey, North Amer. Fauna 39: 50, Nov. 15, 1915.

133183. Skin and skull. Adult male. Raymond, Madera County, Calif. June 28, 1904. Collected by N. Hollister. Original number 908.

Well-made skin in good condition; skull Grade A.

†**Thomomys monticola pinetorum** Merriam.

North Amer. Fauna 16: 97, Oct. 28, 1899.

95152. Skin and skull. Adult male. Sisson, Siskiyou County, Calif. September 4, 1898. Collected by R. T. Fisher. Original number 173.

Well-made skin in good condition; skull Grade A.

†Thomomys muralis Goldman.

Journ. Washington Acad. Sci. 26: 112, Mar. 15, 1936.

202580. Skin and skull. Adult male. Lower end of Prospect Valley, Grand Canyon, altitude 4,500 feet, Hualpai Indian Reservation, Ariz. October 3, 1913. Collected by E. A. Goldman. Original number 22264.

Well-made skin in good condition; skull Grade A.

†Thomomys myops Merriam.

Proc. Biol. Soc. Washington 14: 112, July 19, 1901.
=*Thomomys talpoides myops* Merriam. See Goldman, Journ. Mamm. 20: 234, May 14, 1939.

91066. Skin and skull. Adult female. Conconully, east base Cascade Mountains, Okanogan County, Wash. September 11, 1897. Collected by J. A. Loring. Original number 4650.

Well-made skin in good condition; skull Grade A.

†Thomomys nasicus Merriam.

Proc. Biol. Soc. Washington 11: 216, July 15, 1897.
=*Thomomys monticola nasicus* Merriam. See Bailey, North Amer. Fauna 39: 125, Nov. 15, 1915.

79815. Skin and skull. Adult male. Farewell Bend (=Bend), Des Chutes River, Crook County, Oreg. August 4, 1896. Collected by E. A. Preble. Original number 1274.

Well-made skin in good condition; skull Grade A.

†Thomomys neglectus Bailey.

Proc. Biol. Soc. Washington 27: 117, July 10, 1914.
=*Thomomys bottae neglectus* Bailey. See Goldman, Proc. Biol. Soc. Washington 48: 155, Oct. 31, 1935.

137869. Skin and skull. Adult male. San Antonio Peak, Bear Flat Meadows at 6,400 feet altitude, San Gabriel Mountains, Los Angeles County, Calif. July 23, 1905. James H. Gaut. Original number 3719.

Well-made skin in good condition; skull Grade A.

†Thomomys nelsoni Merriam.

Proc. Biol. Soc. Washington 14: 109, July 19, 1901.
=*Thomomys baileyi nelsoni* Merriam. See Nelson and Goldman, Journ. Mamm. 15: 124, May 15, 1934.

96541. Skin and skull. Adult male. Parral, Chihuahua, Mexico. September 18, 1898. Collected by E. W. Nelson and E. A. Goldman. Original number 13035.

Well-made skin in good condition; skull Grade A.

†Thomomys nevadensis Merriam.

Proc. Biol. Soc. Washington 11: 213, July 15, 1897.
=*Thomomys townsendii nevadensis* Merriam. See Bailey, North Amer. Fauna 39: 44, Nov. 15, 1915.

$\frac{25001}{32413}$. Skin and skull. Young adult male. Austin, Lander County, Nev. November 11, 1890. Collected by Vernon Bailey. Original number 2097.

Well-made skin in good condition; skull Grade A.

†Thomomys nevadensis atrogriseus Bailey.

Proc. Biol. Soc. Washington 27: 118, July 10, 1914.
=*Thomomys townsendii townsendii* Bachman. See Miller, U. S. Nat. Mus. Bull. 128: 236, Apr. 29, 1924.

181196. Skin and skull. Adult male. Nampa, Canyon County, Idaho. March 15, 1913. Collected by L. E. Wyman. Original number 10181–X.

Well-made skin in good condition; skull Grade A.

†Thomomys niger Merriam.

Proc. Biol. Soc. Washington 14: 117, July 19, 1901.

69407. Skin and skull. Adult male. Seaton, near mouth of Umpqua River, Douglas County, Oreg. October 6, 1894. Collected by J. E. McLellan. Original number 1147.

Well-made skin in good condition; skull Grade B.

†Thomomys operarius Merriam.

Proc. Biol. Soc. Washington 11: 215, July 15, 1897.
=*Thomomys bottae operarius* Merriam. See Goldman, Proc. Biol. Soc. Washington 48: 155, Oct. 31, 1935.

$\frac{25054}{32466}$. Skin and skull. Adult male. Keeler, east side of Owens Lake, Inyo County, Calif. November 29, 1890. Collected by E. W. Nelson. Original number 1.

Well-made skin in good condition; skull Grade A.

†Thomomys orizabae Merriam.

Proc. Biol. Soc. Washington 8: 145, Dec. 29, 1893.
=*Thomomys umbrinus orizabae* Merriam. See Bailey, North Amer. Fauna 39: 90, Nov. 15, 1915.

53616. Skin and skull. Adult female. Mount Orizaba, altitude 9,500 feet, Puebla, Mexico. April 25, 1893. Collected by E. W. Nelson. Original number 4744.

Well-made skin in good condition; skull Grade A.

†**Thomomys pectoralis** Goldman.

Journ. Washington Acad. Sci. 26: 120, Mar. 15, 1936.

244372. Adult male. Vicinity of Carlsbad Cave, Carlsbad Cave National Monument, Eddy County, N. Mex. March 17, 1924. Collected by Vernon Bailey. Original number 10222.

Well-made skin in good condition; skull Grade A.

†**Thomomys perditus** Merriam.

Proc. Biol. Soc. Washington 14: 108, July 19, 1901.
=*Thomomys umbrinus perditus* Merriam. See Nelson and Goldman, Journ. Mamm. 15: 115, May 15, 1934.

$\frac{25605}{32998}$. Skin and skull. Adult male. Lampazos, Nuevo Leon, Mexico. January 22, 1891. Collected by C. P. Streator. Original number 512.

Well-made skin in good condition; skull Grade A.

†**Thomomys peregrinus** Merriam.

Proc. Biol. Soc. Washington 8: 146, Dec. 29, 1893.
=*Thomomys umbrinus peregrinus* Merriam. See Bailey, North Amer. Fauna 39: 91, Nov. 15, 1915.

50130. Skin and skull. Young adult female. Salazar, State of Mexico, Mexico. October 24, 1892 (not October 23, 1892 as recorded in original description). Collected by E. W. Nelson. Original number 3668.

Well-made skin in good condition; skull Grade A.

†**Thomomys perpallidus absonus** Goldman.

Journ. Washington Acad. Sci. 21 (17) : 425, Oct. 19, 1931.
=*Thomomys bottae absonus* Goldman. See Goldman, Proc. Biol. Soc. Washington 48: 156, Oct. 31, 1935.

250016. Skin and skull. Adult male. Jacob's Pools, altitude 4,000 feet, Houserock Valley, Coconino County, northern Arizona. June 7, 1931. Collected by E. A. Goldman. Original number 23569.

Well-made skin in good condition; skull Grade A.

†**Thomomys perpallidus dissimilis** Goldman.

Journ. Washington Acad. Sci. 21 (17) : 425, Oct. 19, 1931.
=*Thomomys bottae dissimilis* Goldman. See Goldman, Proc. Biol. Soc. Washington 48: 156, Oct. 31, 1935.

158526. Skin and skull. Adult female. East slope of Mount Ellen, altitude 8,000 feet, Henry Mountains, Garfield County, Utah. October 20, 1908. Collected by W. H. Osgood. Original number 3677.

Well-made skin in good condition; skull Grade A.

†Thomomys perpallidus osgoodi Goldman.

=*Thomomys bottee osgoodi* Goodman.   See Goodman, Proc. Biol. Soc. Wash-
Journ. Washington Acad. Sci. 21 (17) : 424, Oct. 19, 1931.
ington 48: 156, Oct. 31, 1935.

158530.   Skin and skull.   Adult male.   Hanksville, Wayne County,
Utah.   October 20, 1908.   Collected by W. H. Osgood.   Original
number 3701.

Well-made skin in good condition; skull Grade A.

†Thomomys pryori Bailey.

Proc. Biol. Soc. Washington 27: 116, July 10, 1914.

=*Thomomys talpoides pryori* Bailey.   See Bailey, North Amer. Fauna 39:
104, Nov. 15, 1915.

66469.   Skin and skull.   Adult male.   Head of Sage Creek, altitude
6,000 feet, Pryor Mountains, Carbon County, Mont.   July 16,
1894.   Collected by Vernon Bailey.   Original number 4646.

Well-made skin in good condition; skull Grade A.

†Thomomys pygmaeus Merriam.

Proc. Biol. Soc. Washington 14: 115, July 19, 1901.

=*Thomomys talpoides pygmaeus* Merriam.   See Davis, Recent Mammals of
Idaho : 71, 252, Apr. 5, 1939.

55271.   Skin and skull.   Adult male.   Montpelier Creek, about 10
miles northeast of Montpelier, altitude 6,700 feet, Bear Lake
County, Idaho.   July 29, 1893.   Collected by Vernon Bailey.
Original number 4150.

Well-made skin in good condition; skull Grade A.

†Thomomys quadratus Merriam.

Proc. Biol. Soc. Washington 11: 214, July 15, 1897.

=*Thomomys talpoides quadratus* Merriam.   See Goldman, Journ. Mamm. 20:
234, May 14, 1939.

57134.   Skin and skull.   Adult male.   The Dalles, Wasco County,
Oreg.   November 2, 1893.   Collected by C. P. Streator.   Original
number 3359.

Well-made skin in good condition; skull Grade A.

†Thomomys sheldoni Bailey.

North Amer. Fauna 39: 93, Nov. 15, 1915.

=*Thomomys umbrinus sheldoni* Bailey.   See Nelson and Goldman, Journ.
Mamm. 15: 113, May 15, 1934.

90819.   Skin and skull.   Adult male.   Santa Teresa, altitude 6,800
feet, Nayarit, Mexico.   August 10, 1897.   Collected by E. W.
Nelson and E. A. Goldman.   Original number 11443.

Well-made skin in good condition; skull Grade A.

†Thomomys simulus Nelson and Goldman.

Journ. Mamm. 15: 120, May 15, 1934.

96463. Skin and skull. Adult male. Alamos, altitude 1,200 feet, southern Sonora, Mexico. December 29, 1898. Collected by E. A. Goldman. Original number 13339.

Well-made skin in good condition; skull Grade A.

†Thomomys simulus parviceps Nelson and Goldman.

Journ. Mamm. 15: 121, May 15, 1934.

96743. Skin and skull. Young adult female. Chacala, altitude 3,000 feet, western Durango, Mexico. March 6, 1899. Collected by E. A. Goldman. Original number 13485.

Well-made skin in good condition; skull Grade A.

†Thomomys sinaloae Merriam.

Proc. Biol. Soc. Washington 14: 108, July 19, 1901.
=*Thomomys bottae sinaloae* Merriam. See Nelson and Goldman, Journ. Mamm. 15: 124, May 15, 1934.

96745. Skin and skull. Adult male. Altata, Sinaloa, Mexico. March 28, 1899. Collected by E. A. Goldman. Original number 13607.

Well-made skin in good condition; skull Grade A.

†Thomomys sturgisi Goldman.

Proc. Biol. Soc. Washington 51: 56, Mar. 18, 1938.

263376. Skin and skull. Adult female. Carmen Mountains, altitude 6,000 feet, Coahuila, Mexico. September 21, 1937. Collected by R. S. Sturgis. Original number 28064–X (74).

Well-made skin in good condition; skull Grade A.

†Thomomys talpoides agrestis Merriam.

Proc. Biol. Soc. Washington 21: 144, June 9, 1908.

150725. Skin and skull. Adult female. Medano Ranch, San Luis Valley, Colo. October 29, 1907. Collected by M. Cary. Original number 1205.

Well-made skin in good condition; skull Grade A.

†Thomomys talpoides andersoni Goldman.

Journ. Mamm. 20: 235, May 14, 1939.

69001. Skin and skull. Adult male. Medicine Hat, on the South Saskatchewan River, Alberta, Canada. October 14, 1894. Collected by J. A. Loring. Original number 2567.

Well-made skin in good condition; skull Grade B.

†**Thomomys talpoides badius** Goldman.

Journ. Mamm. 20: 242, May 14, 1939.

91073.   Skin and skull.   Adult male.   Wenatchee, Chelan County, Wash.   September 19, 1897.   Collected by J. A. Loring.   Original number 4695.

Well-made skin in good condition; skull Grade A.

†**Thomomys talpoides bullatus** Bailey.

Proc. Biol. Soc. Washington 27: 115, July 10, 1914.

55159 (not 55795 as in original description).   Adult male.   Powderville, Custer County, Mont.   July 21, 1893.   Collected by A. K. Fisher.   Original number 1402.

Well-made skin in good condition; skull Grade A.

†**Thomomys talpoides caryi** Bailey.

Proc. Biol. Soc. Washington 27: 115, July 10, 1914.

168946.   Skin and skull.   Adult female.   Head of Trapper Creek, altitude 9,500 feet, Bighorn Mountains, Bighorn County, Wyo.   June 10, 1910.   Collected by Merritt Cary.   Original number 1993.

Well-made skin in good condition; skull Grade B.

†**Thomomys talpoides couchi** Goldman.

Journ. Mamm. 20: 243, May 14, 1939.

243092.   Skin and skull.   Adult male.   Four miles north of Shelton, Mason County, Wash.   June 27, 1922.   Collected by Leo K. Couch.   Original number 22896–X (15).

Well-made skin in good condition; skull Grade B.

†**Thomomys talpoides ericaeus** Goldman.

Journ. Mamm. 20: 243, May 14, 1939.

242445.   Skin and skull.   Adult male.   Badger Mountains, altitude 3,000 feet, 8 miles southwest of Waterville, Douglas County, Wash.   November 8, 1921.   Collected by G. G. Cantwell.   Original number 2813.

Well-made skin in good condition; skull Grade A.

†**Thomomys talpoides incensus** Goldman.

Journ. Mamm. 20: 240, May 14, 1939.

67096.   Skin and skull.   Adult female.   Shuswap, Yale District, British Columbia, Canada.   September 1, 1894.   Collected by Clark P. Streator.   Original number 4228.

Well-made skin in good condition; skull Grade A.

†**Thomomys talpoides kelloggi** Goldman.

Journ. Mamm. 20: 237, May 14, 1939.

225907. Skin and skull. Adult male. West Boulder Creek, Absaroka Mountain, 18 miles southeast of Livingston, Park County, Mont. June 29, 1917. Collected by Remington Kellogg. Original number 964.

Well-made skin in good condition; skull Grade A.

†**Thomomys talpoides medius** Goldman.

Journ. Mamm. 20: 241, May 14, 1939.

66653. Skin and skull. Adult female. Silver King Mine, summit of Toad Mountain, 6 miles south of Nelson, Kootenay District, British Columbia, Canada. July 23, 1894. Collected by J. A. Loring. Original number 2042.

Well-made skin in good condition; skull Grade A.

†**Thomomys talpoides nebulosus** Bailey.

Proc. Biol. Soc. Washington 27: 116, July 10, 1914.

202495. Skin and skull. Jack Boyden's Ranch, Sand Creek Canyon, 5 miles above mouth, altitude 3,750 feet, Black Hills, Crook County, Wyo. August 25, 1913. Collected by Vernon Bailey. Original number 9508.

Well-made skin in good condition, except claws missing on hindfeet; skull Grade A.

***Thomomys talpoides perpallidus** Merriam.   Lectotype.

Science 8: 588, Dec. 24, 1886.

=*Thomomys bottae perpallidus* Merriam.   See Goldman, Proc. Biol. Soc. Washington 48: 155, Oct. 31, 1935.

191935. Skin and skull. Adult male. Palm Springs, 6 miles south of Palm Springs Station, at sea level on the edge of the Colorado Desert, Riverside County, Calif. March 22, 1886. Collected by Frank Stephens. Merriam collection No. $\frac{2218}{2734}$.

Well-made skin in good condition; skull Grade B.

In the original description no type was designated by number. The above specimen was made a lectotype by Vernon Bailey, North Amer. Fauna 39: 68, Nov. 15, 1915.

†**Thomomys talpoides relicinus** Goldman.

Journ. Mamm. 20: 239, May 14, 1939.

243549. Skin and skull. Adult female. Twin Springs, 20 miles north of Minidoka, Snake River Desert, Idaho. April 22, 1923. Collected by L. J. Goldman. Original number 2841.

Well-made skin in good condition; skull Grade A.

†Thomomys talpoides tenellus Goldman.

Journ. Mamm. 20: 238, May 14, 1939.

169753. Skin and skull. Adult female. Whirlwind Peak, Absaroka Range, altitude 10,500 feet, Park County, Wyo. August 3, 1910. Collected by Merritt Cary. Original number 2114.

Well-made skin in good condition; skull Grade A.

†Thomomys talpoides trivialis Goldman.

Journ. Mamm. 20: 236, May 14, 1939.

225918. Skin and skull. Adult male. Near head of Big Timber Creek, altitude 5,200 feet (aneroid reading), Crazy Mountains, Mont. June 20, 1917. Collected by M. A. Hanna. Original number 349.

Well-made skin in good condition; skull Grade A.

†Thomomys uinta Merriam.

Proc. Biol. Soc. Washington 14: 112, July 19, 1901.
=*Thomomys talpoides uinta* Merriam. See Goldman, Journ. Mamm. 20: 234, May 14, 1939.

$\frac{22501}{30051}$. Skin and skull. Adult male. Uinta Mountains, north base of Gilbert Peak, altitude 10,000 feet, Summit County, Utah. June 6, 1890. Collected by Vernon Bailey. Original number 1262.

Well-made skin in good condition; skull Grade A.

†Thomomys umbrinus albigularis Nelson and Goldman.

Journ. Mamm. 15: 106, May 15, 1934.

51888. Skin and skull. Adult female. El Chico, altitude 9,800 feet, Sierra de Pachuca, Hidalgo, Mexico. March 27, 1893 (not 1896 as given in original description). Collected by E. W. Nelson and E. A. Goldman. Original number 4505.

Well-made skin in good condition; skull Grade A.

†Thomomys umbrinus analogus Goldman.

Proc. Biol. Soc. Washington 51: 59, March 18, 1938.

116994. Skin and skull. Adult male. Sierra Guadalupe, southeastern Coahuila, Mexico. April 25, 1902. Collected by E. W. Nelson and E. A. Goldman. Original number 15117.

Well-made skin in good condition; skull Grade A.

†Thomomys umbrinus caliginosus Nelson and Goldman.

Journ. Mamm. 15: 116, May 15, 1934.

250887. Skin and skull. Adult male. Eight miles west of Altamirano, altitude 8,000 feet, Sierra Madre, northwestern Chihuahua,

Mexico, near Sonora boundary west of Casas Grandes. November 3, 1932. Collected by Vernon Bailey and Frederic Winthrop. Original number 11071.

Well-made skin in good condition; skull Grade A.

†Thomomys umbrinus chihuahuae Nelson and Goldman.

Journ. Mamm. 15: 114, May 15, 1934.

96452. Skin and skull. Adult male. Sierra Madre, altitude 7,000 feet, about 65 miles east of Batopilas, Chihuahua, Mexico. October 1, 1898. Collected by E. A. Goldman. Original number 13076.

Well-made skin in good condition; skull Grade A.

†Thomomys umbrinus chiricahuae Nelson and Goldman.

Journ. Mamm. 15: 117, May 15, 1934.

247828. Skin and skull. Adult male. Pinery Canyon, altitude 7,500 feet, west slope of Chiricahua Mountains, Ariz. April 28, 1927. Collected by George G. Cantwell. Original number 2918.

Well-made skin in good condition; skull Grade A.

†Thomomys umbrinus crassidens Nelson and Goldman.

Journ. Mamm. 15: 113, May 15, 1934.

91986. Skin and skull. Adult male. Sierra de Valparaiso, altitude 8,700 feet, western Zacatecas, Mexico. November 30, 1897. Collected by E. W. Nelson and E. A. Goldman. Original number 11793.

Well-made skin in good condition; skull Grade A.

†Thomomys umbrinus durangi Nelson and Goldman.

Journ. Mamm. 15: 114, May 15, 1934.

94603. Skin and skull. Adult male. Durango, State of Durango, Mexico. June 28, 1898. Collected by E. W. Nelson and E. A. Goldman. Original number 12656.

Well-made skin in good condition; skull Grade A.

†Thomomys umbrinus enixus Nelson and Goldman.

Journ. Mamm. 15: 112, May 15, 1934.

90834. Skin and skull. Adult male. Sierra Moroni, altitude 8,500 feet, near Plateado, Zacatecas, Mexico. September 2, 1897. Collected by E. W. Nelson and E. A. Goldman. Original number 11606.

Well-made skin in good condition; skull Grade A.

†Thomomys umbrinus eximius Nelson and Goldman.

Journ. Mamm. 15: 118, May 15, 1934.

96458. Skin and skull. Adult male. Sierra de Choix, altitude 5,000 feet, about 20 miles northeast of Choix, Sinaloa, Mexico. October 19, 1898. Collected by E. A. Goldman. Original number 13137.

Well-made skin in good condition; skull Grade A.

†Thomomys umbrinus extimus Nelson and Goldman.

Journ. Mamm. 15: 119, May 15, 1934.

88131. Skin and skull. Adult male. Colomo, altitude 600 feet, southern Nayarit, Mexico. April 5, 1897 (not 1898 as recorded in original description). Collected by E. W. Nelson and E. A. Goldman. Original number 10878.

Well-made skin in good condition; skull Grade A.

†Thomomys umbrinus madrensis Nelson and Goldman.

Journ. Mamm. 15: 115, May 15, 1934.

98203. Skin and skull. Adult male. Pilares Canyon, altitude 6,400 feet, 10 miles northeast of Colonia Garcia, and about 25 miles southwest of Casas Grandes, Chihuahua, Mexico. June 23, 1899. Collected by E. W. Nelson and E. A. Goldman. Original number 13810.

Well-made skin in good condition; skull Grade A.

†Thomomys umbrinus martinensis Nelson and Goldman.

Journ. Mamm. 15: 108, May 15, 1934.

55622. Skin and skull. Adult female. San Martin Texmelucan, Puebla, Mexico. August 13, 1893. Collected by E. W. Nelson and E. A. Goldman. Original number 5305.

Well-made skin in good condition; skull Grade A.

†Thomomys umbrinus musculus Nelson and Goldman.

Journ. Mamm. 15: 119, May 15, 1934.

90818. Skin and skull. Adult male. Pedro Pablo, altitude 3,500 feet, about 22 miles east of Acaponeta, Sierra de Teponahuaxtla, Nayarit, Mexico. August 3, 1897. Collected by E. W. Nelson and E. A. Goldman. Original number 11440.

Well-made skin in good condition; skull Grade A.

†Thomomys umbrinus potosinus Nelson and Goldman.

Journ. Mamm. 15: 111, May 15, 1934.

82057. Skin and skull. Adult male. La Tinaja, altitude 6,000 feet, about 20 miles northeast of San Luis Potosi, State of San Luis Potosi, Mexico. January 22, 1897. Collected by E. W. Nelson and E. A. Goldman. Original number 10469.

Well-made skin in good condition; skull Grade A.

†Thomomys umbrinus sonoriensis Nelson and Goldman.

Journ. Mamm. 15: 118, May 15, 1934.

250893.   Skin and skull.   Old adult female (not male as recorded in original description).   10 miles east of Chinapa, altitude 3,000 feet, Sonora River Valley, northern Sonora, Mexico.   November 21, 1932.   Collected by Vernon Bailey and Frederic Winthrop. Original number 11135.

Well-made skin in good condition; skull Grade A.

†Thomomys umbrinus supernus Nelson and Goldman.

Journ. Mamm. 15: 110, May 15, 1934.

81687.   Skin and skull.   Adult male.   Santa Rosa, altitude between 8,500 (not 9,500 as recorded in original description) and 10,000 feet, about 7 miles northeast of Guanajuato, State of Guanajuato, Mexico.   November 15, 1896.   Collected by E. W. Nelson and E. A. Goldman.   Original number 10353.

Well-made skin in good condition; skull Grade A.

†Thomomys umbrinus tolucae Nelson and Goldman.

Journ. Mamm. 15: 109, May 15, 1934.

55908.   Skin and skull.   Adult male.   Volcano of Toluca, north slope, altitude 9,500 feet, State of Mexico, Mexico.   September 5, 1893.   Collected by E. W. Nelson and E. A. Goldman.   Original number 5385.

Well-made skin in good condition; skull Grade A.

†Thomomys umbrinus vulcanius Nelson and Goldman.

Journ. Mamm. 15: 109, May 15, 1934.

51885.   Skin and skull.   Adult female.   Volcano of Popocatepetl, altitude 12,900 feet, State of Mexico, Mexico.   February 27, 1893. Collected by E. W. Nelson and E. A. Goldman.   Original number 4407.

Well-made skin in good condition; skull Grade A.

†Thomomys umbrinus zacatecae Nelson and Goldman.

Journ. Mamm. 15: 112, May 15, 1934.

57972.   Skin and skull.   Adult male.   Berriozabal, altitude 6,600 feet, Zacatecas, Mexico.   December 29, 1893.   Collected by E. W. Nelson and E. A. Goldman.   Original number 5607.

Well-made skin in good condition; skull Grade A.

Genus ZYGOGEOMYS Merriam

†Zygogeomys trichopus Merriam.

North Amer. Fauna 8: 196, Jan. 31, 1895.

251543—42——27

50107. Skin and skull. Adult male. Nahuatzin, Michoacan, Mexico. October 11, 1892. Collected by E. W. Nelson. Original number 3571.

Well-made skin in good condition; skull Grade A.

†Zygogeomys trichopus tarascensis Goldman.

Proc. Biol. Soc. Washington 51: 211, Dec. 23, 1938.

$\frac{34922}{47187}$. Skin and skull. Adult female. Mountains 6 miles southeast of Patzcuaro, altitude 8,000 feet, Michoacan, Mexico. July 24, 1892. Collected by E. W. Nelson and E. A. Goldman. Original number 2943.

Well-made skin in good condition; skull Grade B.

Family GRAPHIURIDAE: African Dormice

Genus CLAVIGLIS Jentink

*Graphiurus murinus isolatus Heller.

Smithsonian Misc. Coll. 59 (16) : 3, July 5, 1912.
=Claviglis murinus isolatus (Heller). See G. M. Allen, Bull. Mus. Comp. Zool. 83: 309, Feb. 1939.

181788. Skin, skull lost. Adult female. Mount Umengo, Taita Mountains, British East Africa [=Kenya]. November 11, 1911. Collected by Edmund Heller. Original number 4719.

Well-made skin in good condition. A note in Heller's handwriting in skull vial containing type label says "skull lost".

*Graphiurus murinus johnstoni Heller.

Smithsonian Misc. Coll. 59 (16) : 2, July 5, 1912.
=Claviglis murinus griseus (G. M. Allen). See G. M. Allen, Bull. Mus. Comp. Zool. 83: 309, Feb. 1939.

181787. Skin and skull. Adult male. Mount Gargues, Mathews Range, altitude 7,000 feet, British East Africa [=Kenya]. August 26, 1911. Collected by Edmund Heller. Original number 4114.

Well-made skin in good condition; skull Grade A.

*Eliomys parvus True.

Proc. U. S. Nat. Mus. 16: 601, Oct. 25, 1893.
=Claviglis parvus parvus (True). See G. M. Allen, Bull. Mus. Comp. Zool. 83: 310, Feb. 1939.

$\frac{21005}{36056}$. Skin and skull. Adult female. Along the Tana River, between the coast and Hameye, British East Africa [=Kenya]. November 1892. Collected by William Astor Chanler and Ludwig von Höhnel.

The specimen was originally in alcohol, but at the time the species was described it was made into a modern study skin, in good condition; skull Grade. A.

*Graphiurus personatus Heller.

Smithsonian Misc. Coll. 56 (17) : 2, Feb. 28, 1911.
=*Claviglis personatus* (Heller). See G. M. Allen, Bull. Mus. Comp. Zool. 83: 310, Feb. 1939.

164827. Skin and skull. Adult female. Rhino Camp, Lado Enclave, Uganda, Africa. January 11, 1910. Collected by J. Alden Loring. Original number 8644.

Well-made skin in good condition; skull Grade A.

Family HETEROMYIDAE: Kangaroo Rats, Pocket Mice

Genus DIPODOMYS Gray

†Perodipus agilis tularensis Merriam.

Proc. Biol. Soc. Washington 17 : 143, July 14, 1904.
=*Dipodomys heermanni tularensis* (Merriam). See Grinnell, Journ. Mamm. 2 : 95, May 2, 1921.

127158. Skin and skull. Adult female. Alila, now Earlimart, Tulare County, Calif. June 23, 1903. Collected by L. J. Goldman. Original number 563.

Well-made skin in good condition; skull Grade B.

†Dipodomys ambiguus Merriam.

North Amer. Fauna 4 : 42, Oct. 8, 1890.
=*Dipodomys merriami ambiguus* Merriam. See Merriam, Science (new ser.) 7 : 31, Jan. 7, 1898.

$\frac{18147}{25045}$. Skin and skull. Adult male. El Paso, El Paso County, Tex. December 13, 1889. Collected by Vernon Bailey. Original number 782.

Well-made skin in good condition; skull Grade A.

†Perodipus cabezonae Merriam.

Proc. Biol. Soc. Washington 17 : 144, July 14, 1904.
=*Dipodomys agilis cabezonae* (Merriam). See Grinnell, Journ. Mamm. 2 : 96, May 2, 1921.

54055. Skin and skull. Adult female. Cabezon, Colorado Desert, San Gorgonio Pass, Riverside County, Calif. May 31, 1893. Collected by C. P. Streator. Original number 2859.

Well-made skin in good condition; skull Grade A.

†Dipodomys californicus Merriam.

North Amer. Fauna 4 : 49, Oct. 8, 1890.
=*Dipodomys heermanni californicus* Merriam. See Grinnell, Journ. Mamm. 2 : 95, May 2, 1921.

$\frac{16618}{23544}$. Skin and skull. Adult male. Ukiah, Mendocino County, Calif. May 4, 1889. Collected by T. S. Palmer. Original number 46.

Well-made skin in good condition; skull Grade A.

*Dipodomys compactus True.

Proc. U. S. Nat. Mus. 11: 160, Jan. 5, 1889.

$\frac{19665}{35227}$. Skin only (skull lost). Adult female. Padre Island, Cameron County, Tex. April 3, 1888. Purchased from C. K. Worthen.

Skin rather carelessly made up. Some epidermis has slipped from about the nose. A sewed-up cut along the throat looks as if the specimen had been made up with a skull inside and that the latter had afterward been removed. This skull cannot be found at present.

Type not designated. The description was based on one specimen only. The data, including three measurements of the above specimen, agree in every respect with those given in the original description.

*Dipodomys deserti Stephens.

Amer. Nat. 21: 42, Jan., 1887.

$\frac{15629}{22522}$. Skin and skull. Adult female. Mohave River, San Bernardino County, Calif. June 29, 1886. Collected by Frank Stephens. Original number 314.

Well-made skin in good condition; skull Grade A.
Type designated by the original number.

†Dipodomys deserti sonoriensis Goldman.

Proc. Biol. Soc. Washington 36: 139, May 1, 1923.

242306. Skin and skull. Adult male. La Libertad Ranch, 30 miles east of Sierra Seri, Sonora, Mexico. January 3, 1922. Collected by Charles Sheldon. Original number 22611–X.

Well-made skin in good condition, except tail wire pushed through tip of tail; skull Grade A.

†Dipodomys elator Merriam.

Proc. Biol. Soc. Washington 9: 109, June 21, 1894.

64802. Skin and skull. Adult male. Henrietta, Clay County, Tex. April 13, 1894. Collected by J. A. Loring. Original number 1804.

Well-made skin in good condition; skull Grade A.

†Perodipus goldmani Merriam.

Proc. Biol. Soc. Washington 17: 143, July 14, 1904.

=Dipodomys heermanni goldmani (Merriam). See Grinnell, Journ. Mamm. 2: 95, May 2, 1921.

118924. Skin and skull. Adult male. Salinas, mouth of Salinas Valley, Monterey County, Calif. September 4, 1902. Collected by L. J. Goldman. Original number 431.

Well-made skin in good condition; skull Grade A.

†Dipodomys heermanni gabrielsoni Goldman.

Proc. Biol. Soc. Washington 38 : 33, Mar. 12, 1925.

244514. Skin and skull. Adult male. Brownsboro, Jackson County, Oreg. June 21, 1924. Collected by Ira N. Gabrielson. Original number 23625–X.

Well-made skin in good condition, except for injury on left hind leg and bare spot (with scab) on middle of back; skull Grade A.

†Perodipus ingens Merriam.

Proc. Biol. Soc. Washington 17 : 141, July 14, 1904.
=*Dipodomys ingens* (Merriam). See Grinnell, Journ. Mamm. 2 : 95, May 2, 1921.

128805. Skin and skull. Adult male. Painted Rock, 20 miles southeast of Simmler, Carrizo Plain, San Luis Obispo County, Calif. August 6, 1903. Collected by L. J. Goldman. Original number 777.

Well-made skin in good condition; skull Grade A.

†Dipodomys insularis Merriam.

Proc. Biol. Soc. Washington 20 : 77, July 22, 1907.

79053. Skin and skull. Adult female. San José Island, Gulf of California, Lower California, Mexico. August 6, 1895. Collected by J. E. McLellan. Original number 1457.

Well-made skin in good condition; skull Grade B.

†Dipodops longipes Merriam.

North Amer. Fauna 3 : 72, Sept. 11, 1890.
=*Dipodomys ordii longipes* (Merriam). See Grinnell, Journ. Mamm. 2 : 96, May 2, 1921.

$\frac{17703}{24639}$. Skin and skull. Young adult male. Foot of Echo Cliffs, Painted Desert, Coconino County, Ariz. September 22, 1889. Collected by C. Hart Merriam. Original number 512.

Well-made skin in good condition; skull Grade B.

†Dipodomys margaritae Merriam.

Proc. Biol. Soc. Washington 20 : 76, July 22, 1907.

146058. Skin and skull. Young adult male. Margarita Island, Lower California, Mexico. December 1, 1905. Collected by E. W. Nelson and E. A. Goldman. Original number 18711.

Well-made skin in good condition; skull Grade A.

†Dipodomys merriami atronasus Merriam.

Proc. Biol. Soc. Washington 9: 113, June 21, 1894.

50276. Skin and skull. Adult male. Hacienda La Parada, about 25 miles northwest of the city of San Luis Potosi, State of San Luis Potosi, Mexico. August 20, 1892. Collected by E. W. Nelson. Original number 3229.

Well-made skin in good condition; skull Grade C.

†Dipodomys merriami exilis Merriam.

Proc. Biol. Soc. Washington 9: 113, June 21, 1894.
=Dipodomys nitratoides exilis Merriam. See Grinnell, Journ. Mamm. 2: 96, May 2, 1921.

$\frac{34843}{43823}$. Skin and skull. Young adult male. Fresno, San Joaquin Valley, Fresno County, Calif. September 23, 1891. Collected by Vernon Bailey. Original number 3277.

Well-made skin in good condition; skull Grade A.

†Dipodomys merriami kernensis Merriam.

Proc. Biol. Soc. Washington 20: 77, July 22, 1907.
=Dipodomys merriami merriami Mearns. See Grinnell, Journ. Mamm. 2: 97, May 2, 1921.

108884. Skin and skull. Adult male. Onyx, west end of Walker Pass, Kern County, Calif. July 25, 1901. Collected by W. K. Fisher. Original number 2106.

Well-made skin in good condition, except for a small bare spot in middle of back; skull Grade B.

†Dipodomys merriami mayensis Goldman.

Proc. Biol. Soc. Washington 41: 141, Oct. 15, 1928.

96437. Skin and skull. Adult male. Alamos, Sonora, Mexico. December 19, 1898. Collected by E. A. Goldman. Original number 13302.

Well-made skin in good condition; skull Grade A.

†Dipodomys merriami nevadensis Merriam.

Proc. Biol. Soc. Washington 9: 111, June 21, 1894.
=Dipodomys merriami merriami Mearns. See Grinnell, Journ. Mamm. 2: 97, May 2, 1921.

54552. Skin and skull. Adult female. Pyramid Lake, Washoe County, Nev. June 26, 1893. Collected by Vernon Bailey. Original number 3990.

Well-made skin in good condition; skull Grade B.

†Dipodomys merriami nitratoides Merriam.

Proc. Biol. Soc. Washington 9: 112, June 21, 1894.
=Dipodomys nitratoides nitratoides Merriam. See Grinnell, Journ. Mamm. 2: 96, May 2, 1921.

54674.   Skin and skull.   Adult male.   Tipton, San Joaquin Valley, Tulare County, Calif.   June 25, 1893.   Collected by C. P. Streator.   Original number 2978.

Well-made skin in good condition; skull Grade B.

†Dipodomys merriami nitratus Merriam.

Proc. Biol. Soc. Washington 9: 112, June 21, 1894.

=*Dipodomys merriami merriami* Mearns.   See Grinnell, Journ. Mamm. 2: 97, May 2, 1921.

$\frac{25359}{32772}$.   Skin and skull.   Adult male.   Keeler, east side of Owens Lake, Inyo County, Calif.   December 29, 1890.   Collected by E. W. Nelson.   Original number 160.

Well-made skin in good condition, except for injured left hindleg; skull Grade A.

†Dipodomys merriami regillus Goldman.

Proc. Biol. Soc. Washington 50: 75, June 22, 1937.

203017.   Skin and skull.   Young adult male.   Tule Well, Tule Desert between Cabeza Prieta Mountains and Tule Mountains, altitude 1,000 feet, Yuma County, Ariz.   December 4, 1913. Collected by E. A. Goldman.   Original number 22345.

Well-made skin in good condition; skull Grade A.

†Perodipus microps Merriam.

Proc. Biol. Soc. Washington 17: 145, July 14, 1904.

=*Dipodomys microps microps* (Merriam).   See Grinnell, Journ. Mamm. 2: 96, May 2, 1921.

$\frac{25288}{32701}$.   Skin and skull.   Adult male.   Lone Pine, Owens Valley, Inyo County, Calif.   December 22, 1890.   Collected by E. W. Nelson.   Original number 138.

Well-made skin in good condition; skull Grade A.

†Dipodomys microps alfredi Goldman.

Proc. Biol. Soc. Washington 50: 221, Dec. 28, 1937.

262846.   Skin and skull.   Adult female.   Gunnison Island, altitude about 4,300 feet, Great Salt Lake, Utah.   June 1, 1937.   Collected by Alfred M. Bailey and Robert J. Niedrach.   Original number 28020–X (2994).   Presented by Colorado Museum of Natural History.

Well-made skin in good condition; skull Grade A.

†Dipodomys microps bonnevillei Goldman.

Proc. Biol. Soc. Washington 50: 222, Dec. 28, 1937.

$\frac{31894}{43755}$.   Skin and skull.   Adult female.   Kelton, altitude about 4,300 feet, Box Elder County, Utah.   November 7, 1891.   Collected by Vernon Bailey.   Original number 3490.

Well-made skin in good condition; skull Grade A.

†**Dipodomys microps celsus** Goldman.

Journ. Washington Acad. Sci. 14 : 372, Sept. 19, 1924.

243101. Skin and skull. Adult male. Six miles north of Wolf Hole, Coconino County, Ariz., altitude 3,500 feet. October 16, 1922. Collected by E. A. Goldman. Original number 23411.

Well-made skin in good condition; skull Grade A.

†**Dipodomys microps leucotis** Goldman.

Proc. Biol. Soc. Washington 44 : 135, Oct. 17, 1931.

250036. Skin and skull. Adult male. Six miles west of Colorado River Bridge, Houserock Valley, altitude 3,700 feet, north side of Marble Canyon of Colorado River, Ariz. June 8, 1931. Collected by E. A. Goldman. Original number 23570.

Well-made skin in good condition; skull Grade A.

†**Perodipus microps levipes** Merriam.

Proc. Biol. Soc. Washington 17 : 145, July 14, 1904.

=*Dipodomys microps levipes* (Merriam). See Grinnell, Univ. California Publ. Zool. 40 : 165, Sept. 26, 1933.

$\frac{27176}{34575}$. Skin and skull. Adult male. Perognathus Flat, altitude 5,200 feet, Emigrant Gap, Panamint Mountains, Inyo County, Calif. April 16, 1891. Collected by Vernon Bailey. Original number 2668.

Well-made skin in good condition; skull Grade A.

†**Perodipus microps preblei** Goldman.

Journ. Mamm. 2 : 233, Nov. 29, 1921.

=*Dipodomys microps preblei* (Goldman). See Miller, U. S. Nat. Mus. Bull. 128 : 297, Apr. 29, 1924.

79340. Skin and skull. Adult female. Narrows, Malheur Lake, Harney County, Oreg. July 23, 1896. Collected by E. A. Preble. Original number 1201.

Well-made skin in good condition; skull Grade B.

†**Dipodomys microps russeolus** Goldman.

Journ. Mamm. 20 : 353, Aug. 14, 1939.

263895. Skin and skull. Adult male. Dolphin Island, Great Salt Lake, altitude 4,250 feet, Utah. June 5, 1938. Collected by William H. Marshall. Original number 65.

Well-made skin in good condition; skull Grade A.

†**Dipodomys microps subtenuis** Goldman.

Journ. Mamm. 20 : 354, Aug. 14, 1939.

263917. Skin and skull. Adult female. Carrington Island, Great Salt Lake, altitude 4,250 feet, Utah. June 30, 1938. Collected by William H. Marshall. Original number 182.

Well-made skin in good condition; skull Grade A.

*Dipodomys mitchelli Mearns.

Proc. U. S. Nat. Mus. 19: 719, July 30, 1897.

63188. Skin and skull. Adult female. Tiburon Island, Gulf of California, Sonora, Mexico. December 23, 1895. Collected by J. W. Mitchell. Original number 3.

Well-made skin in good condition; tail has never been skinned out, but is braced with wire. Skull Grade A.

*Dipodomys montanus Baird.

Proc. Acad. Nat. Sci. Philadelphia 7: 334, reported favorably for publication Apr. 24, 1855.

=*Dipodomys ordii montanus* Baird. See Grinnell, Journ. Mamm. 2: 96, May 2, 1921.

$\frac{490}{1631}$. Skin and skull. Near Fort Massachusetts (now Fort Garland), Costilla County, Colo. 1853. Collected by F. Kreutzfeld (Pacific Railroad Survey).

Skin badly made up, but well-preserved; skull Grade B.

Type not designated by number in the original description; but in Baird's Mammals of North America, p. 412, a footnote to the list of specimens makes 490 the type.

†Perodipus montanus utahensis Merriam.

Proc. Biol. Soc. Washington 17: 143, July 14, 1904.

=*Dipodomys ordii utahensis* (Merriam). See Grinnell, Journ. Mamm. 2: 96, May 2, 1921.

55115. Skin and skull. Adult male. Ogden, Weber County, Utah. July 15, 1893. Collected by Vernon Bailey. Original number 4085.

Well-made skin in good condition; skull Grade A.

†Perodipus morroensis Merriam.

Proc. Biol. Soc. Washington 20: 78, July 22, 1907.

=*Dipodomys morroensis* (Merriam). See Grinnell, Journ. Mamm. 2: 95, May 2, 1921.

$\frac{31626}{43499}$. Skin and skull. Adult female. Morro, San Luis Obispo County, Calif. November 11, 1891. Collected by E. W. Nelson. Original number 1464.

Well-made skin in good condition; skull Grade A.

†Dipodomys nelsoni Merriam.

Proc. Biol. Soc. Washington 20: 75, July 22, 1907.

79439. Skin and skull. Adult male. La Ventura, Coahuila, Mexico. August 10, 1896. Collected by E. W. Nelson and E. A. Goldman. Original number 9998.

Well-made skin in good condition; skull Grade A.

†**Dipodomys oklahomae** Trowbridge and Whitaker.

Journ. Mamm. 21: 343, Aug. 12, 1940.

265454. Skin and skull. Young adult female. North bank of the South Canadian River, 2¼ miles south of Norman, Cleveland County, Okla. March 16, 1934. Collected by H. L. Whitaker. Presented by University of Oklahoma. Original number 29312-X.

Well-made skin in good condition; skull Grade A.

†**Dipodomys ordii cineraceus** Goldman.

Journ. Mamm. 20: 352, Aug. 14, 1939.

263890. Skin and skull. Adult male. Dolphin Island, Great Salt Lake, altitude 4,250 feet, Utah. June 4, 1938. Collected by William H. Marshall. Original number 57.

Well-made skin in good condition; skull Grade A.

†**Dipodomys ordii cleomophila** Goldman.

Journ. Washington Acad. Sci. 23: 469, Oct. 15, 1933.

226348. Skin and skull. Adult female. Five miles northeast of Winona, Coconino County, Ariz. July 16, 1917. Collected by E. A. Goldman. Original number 23101.

Well-made skin in good condition; skull Grade A.

†**Perodipus ordii columbianus** Merriam.

Proc. Biol. Soc. Washington 9: 115, June 21, 1894.

=*Dipodomys ordii columbianus* (Merriam). See Grinnell, Journ. Mamm. 2: 96, May 2, 1921.

$\frac{24181}{31594}$. Skin and skull. Adult female. Umatilla, at mouth of Umatilla River, Plains of Columbia, Umatilla County, Oreg. October 18, 1890. Collected by C. P. Streator. Original number 386.

Well-made skin in good condition; skull Grade A.

†**Dipodomys ordii cupidineus** Goldman.

Journ. Washington Acad. Sci. 14: 372, Sept. 19, 1924.

243093. Skin and skull. Kanab Wash, at southern boundary of Kaibab Indian Reservation, Ariz. October 12, 1922. Collected by E. A. Goldman. Original number 23384.

Well-made skin in good condition; skull Grade A.

†**Dipodomys ordii evexus** Goldman.

Journ. Washington Acad. Sci. 23: 468, Oct. 15, 1933.

150990. Skin and skull. Adult male. Salida, altitude 7,000 feet, Chaffee County, Colo. November 10, 1907. Collected by Merritt Cary. Original number 1245.

Well-made skin in good condition; skull Grade A.

†Perodipus ordii luteolus Goldman.

Proc. Biol. Soc. Washington 30: 112, May 23, 1917.
=*Dipodomys ordii luteolus* (Goldman). See Grinnell, Journ. Mamm. 2: 96, May 2, 1921.

160408. Skin and skull. Adult male. Casper, Natrona County, Wyo. September 2, 1909. Collected by Merritt Cary. Original number 1690.

Well-made skin in good condition; skull Grade A.

†Dipodomys ordii marshalli Goldman.

Proc. Biol. Soc. Washington 50: 223, Dec. 28, 1937.

262655. Skin and skull. Adult female. Bird Island, altitude 4,300 feet, Great Salt Lake, Utah. June 22, 1937. Collected by W. H. Marshall. Original number 27969–X.

Well-made skin in good condition; skull Grade A.

†Dipodomys ordii nexilis Goldman.

Journ. Washington Acad. Sci. 23: 470, Oct. 15, 1933.

149938. Skin and skull. Adult male. Five miles west of Naturita, Montrose County, Colo. July 20, 1907. Collected by Merritt Cary. Original number 1068.

Well-made skin in good condition; skull Grade A.

†Dipodomys ornatus Merriam.

Proc. Biol. Soc. Washington 9: 110, June 21, 1894.

57990. Skin and skull. Adult female. Berriozabal, Zacatecas, Mexico. December 29, 1893. Collected by E. A. Goldman. Original number 5613.

Well-made skin in good condition; skull Grade B.

†Perodipus panamintinus Merriam.

Proc. Biol. Soc. Washington 9: 114, June 21, 1894.
=*Dipodomys panamintinus* (Merriam). See Grinnell, Journ. Mamm. 2: 95, May 2, 1921.

$\frac{28566}{40670}$. Skin and skull. Adult male. Head of Willow Creek, Panamint Mountains, Inyo County, Calif. May 12, 1891. Collected by E. W. Nelson. Original number 853.

Well-made skin in good condition; skull Grade A.

†Dipodomys perotensis Merriam.

Proc. Biol. Soc. Washington 9: 111, June 21, 1894.

54285. Skin and skull. Adult female. Perote, Veracruz, Mexico. May 21, 1893. Collected by E. W. Nelson. Original number 4840.

Well-made skin in good condition; skull Grade A.

†**Perodipus perplexus** Merriam.

Proc. Biol. Soc. Washington 20: 79, July 22, 1907.

=*Dipodomys agilis perplexus* (Merriam). See Grinnell, Journ. Mamm. 2: 96, May 2, 1921.

$\frac{29261}{41328}$. Skin and skull. Adult male. Walker Basin, Kern County, Calif. July 15, 1891. Collected by Vernon Bailey. Original number 3053.

Well-made skin in good condition; skull Grade B.

†**Dipodomys platycephalus** Merriam.

Proc. Biol. Soc. Washington 20: 76, July 22, 1907.

139882. Skin and skull. Adult male. Calmalli, Lower California, Mexico. October 1, 1905. Collected by E. W. Nelson and E. A. Goldman. Original number 18248.

Well-made skin in good condition; skull Grade A.

†**Perodipus simulans peninsularis** Merriam.

Proc. Biol. Soc. Washington 20: 79, July 22, 1907.

=*Dipodomys agilis peninsularis* (Merriam). See Grinnell, Journ. Mamm. 2 (2) : 96, May 2, 1921.

139872. Skin and skull. Young adult male. Santo Domingo, Lower California, Mexico. September 27, 1905. Collected by E. W. Nelson and E. A. Goldman. Original number 18215.

Well-made skin in good condition; skull Grade A.

†**Dipodomys spectabilis** Merriam.

North Amer. Fauna 4: 46, Oct. 8, 1890.

$\frac{17886}{24823}$. Skin and skull. Adult male. Dos Cabezos, Cochise County, Ariz. November 22, 1889. Collected by Vernon Bailey. Original number 695.

Well-made skin in good condition; skull Grade A.

†**Dipodomys spectabilis baileyi** Goldman.

Proc. Biol. Soc. Washington 36: 140, May 1, 1923.

97185. Skin and skull. Adult male. Forty miles west of Roswell, Chaves County, N. Mex. June 13, 1899. Collected by Vernon Bailey. Original number 6961.

Well-made skin in good condition, except for injury to right hindfoot; skull Grade A.

†**Dipodomys spectabilis clarencei** Goldman.

Journ. Washington Acad. Sci. 23: 467, Oct. 15, 1933.

158824. Skin and skull. Adult male. Blanco, San Juan County, N. Mex. November 19, 1908. Collected by Clarence Birdseye. Original number 443.

Well-made skin in good condition; skull Grade A.

†**Dipodomys spectabilis cratodon** Merriam.

Proc. Biol. Soc. Washington 20: 75, July 22, 1907.

78953. Skin and skull. Adult male. Chicalote, Aguas Calientes, Mexico. July 2, 1896. Collected by E. W. Nelson and E. A. Goldman. Original number 9734.

Well-made skin in good condition; skull Grade A.

†**Dipodomys spectabilis perblandus** Goldman.

Journ. Washington Acad. Sci. 23: 466, Oct. 15, 1933.

$\frac{17748}{24689}$. Skin and skull. Adult female. Calabasas, altitude about 3,500 feet, Santa Cruz County, Ariz. October 27, 1889. Collected by Vernon Bailey. Original number 611.

Well-made skin in good condition; skull Grade A.

†**Dipodomys spectabilis zygomaticus** Goldman.

Proc. Biol. Soc. Washington 36: 140, May 1, 1923.

96432. Skin and skull. Adult male. Parral, southern Chihuahua, Mexico. September 17, 1898. Collected by E. A. Goldman. Original number 13030.

Well-made skin in good condition, except for injured right hindfoot and small patch of abdominal hair matted and soiled; skull Grade A.

***Perodipus stephensi** Merriam.

Proc. Biol. Soc. Washington 20: 78, July 22, 1907.
=*Dipodomys stephensi* (Merriam). See Grinnell, Journ. Mamm. 2 (2): 95, May 2, 1921.

186503. Skin and skull. Adult male. San Jacinto Valley, Riverside County, Calif. November 27, 1885. Collected by Frank Stephens. Merriam collection number $\frac{1808}{2340}$.

Well-made skin in good condition; skull Grade B.

†**Perodipus streatori** Merriam.

Proc. Biol. Soc. Washington 9: 113, June 21, 1894.
=*Dipodomys heermanni heermanni* (LeConte). See Grinnell, Journ. Mamm. 2: 97, May 2, 1921.

64310. Skin and skull. Adult female. Carbondale, Amador County, Calif. April 3, 1894. Collected by C. P. Streator. Original number 3673.

Well-made skin in good condition; skull Grade B.

†**Perodipus streatori simulans** Merriam.

Proc. Biol. Soc. Washington 17: 144, July 14, 1904.
=*Dipodomys agilis simulans* (Merriam). See Grinnell, Journ. Mamm. 2: 96, May 2, 1921.

$\frac{33105}{45103}$. Skin and skull. Adult female. Dulzura, San Diego County, Calif. November 24, 1891. Collected by C. H. Marsh. Original number 255.

Well-made skin in good condition, except for injured right hindleg; skull Grade B.

†Perodipus venustus Merriam.

Proc. Biol. Soc. Washington 17: 142, July 14, 1904.

=*Dipodomys venustus venustus* (Merriam). See Grinnell, Proc. Biol. Soc. Washington 32: 204, Dec. 31, 1919.

51852. Skin and skull. Adult male. Santa Cruz, Santa Cruz County, Calif. March 12, 1893. Collected by G. B. Badger. Original number 46.

Well-made skin in good condition; skull Grade A.

Genus HETEROMYS Desmarest

†Heteromys australis conscius Goldman.

Smithsonian Misc. Coll. 60 (22) : 8, Feb. 28, 1913.

=*Heteromys desmarestianus conscius* Goldman. See Goldman, Smithsonian Misc. Coll. 69 (5) : 114, Apr. 24, 1920.

178699. Skin and skull. Adult male. Cana, altitude 2,000 feet, mountains of eastern Panama. March 8, 1912. Collected by E. A. Goldman. Original number 21468.

Well-made skin in good condition, except tail slightly damaged; skull Grade A.

†Heteromys crassirostris Goldman.

Smithsonian Misc. Coll. 60 (2) : 10, Sept. 20, 1912.

=*Heteromys desmarestianus crassirostris* Goldman. See Goldman, Smithsonian Misc. Coll. 69 (5) : 117, Apr. 24, 1920.

179016. Skin and skull. Adult male. Mount Pirri, altitude 5,000 feet, near head of Rio Limon, Panama. April 26, 1912. Collected by E. A. Goldman. Original number 21649.

Well-made skin in good condition, except for slightly damaged tail; skull Grade A.

†Heteromys desmarestianus planifrons Goldman.

Journ. Washington Acad. Sci. 27: 418, Oct. 15, 1937.

250348. Skin and skull. Adult female. San Geronimo, Pirris, western Costa Rica. April 10 (not 12 as given in original description), 1931. Collected by C. F. Underwood. Original number 26913–X (not 26914–X as misprinted in original description).

Well-made skin in good condition; skull Grade A.

*Heteromys desmarestianus subaffinis Goldman.

Journ. Washington Acad. Sci. 27: 420, Oct. 15, 1937.

$\frac{12904}{38591}$. Skin and skull. Adult male. Angostura (altitude about 1,980 feet), southern side of Rio Reventazon, opposite Turrialba, Costa Rica. May 1876. Collected by José C. Zeledon. Original number 98.

Well-made skin in good condition, except for tip of tail broken off; skull Grade B.

†Heteromys goldmani Merriam.

Proc. Biol. Soc. Washington 15: 41, Mar. 5, 1902.

77576. Skin and skull. Adult male. Chicharras, Chiapas, Mexico. February 7, 1896. Collected by E. W. Nelson and E. A. Goldman. Original number 9244.

Well-made skin in good condition; skull Grade A.

†Heteromys goldmani lepturus Merriam.

Proc. Biol. Soc. Washington 15: 42, Mar. 5, 1902.

=Heteromys lepturus Merriam. See Goldman, North Amer. Fauna 34: 25, Sept. 7, 1911.

73382. Skin and skull. Adult male. Mountains near Santo Domingo (a few miles west of Guichicovi), Oaxaca, Mexico. June 20, 1895. Collected by E. W. Nelson and E. A. Goldman. Original number 8120.

Well-made skin in good condition; skull Grade A.

†Heteromys griseus Merriam.

Proc. Biol. Soc. Washington 15: 42, Mar. 5, 1902.

=Heteromys desmarestianus griseus Merriam. See Goldman, North Amer. Fauna 34: 22, Sept. 7, 1911.

76062. Skin and skull. Adult male. Mountains near Tonala, Chiapas, Mexico. Aug. 15, 1895. Collected by E. W. Nelson and E. A. Goldman. Original number 8339.

Well-made skin in good condition; skull Grade A.

†Heteromys (Xylomys) nelsoni Merriam.

Proc. Biol. Soc. Washington 15: 43, Mar. 5, 1902.

=Heteromys nelsoni Merriam. See Goldman, North Amer. Fauna 34: 31, Sept. 7, 1911.

77920. Skin and skull. Adult male. Pinabete, altitude 8,200 feet, Chiapas, Mexico. February 11, 1896. Collected by E. W. Nelson and E. A. Goldman. Original number 9281.

Well-made skin in good condition; skull Grade B.

†Heteromys panamensis Goldman.

Smithsonian Misc. Coll. 56 (36) : 9, Feb. 19, 1912.

=Heteromys desmarestianus panamensis Goldman. See Goldman, Smithsonian Misc. Coll. 69 (5) : 117, Apr. 24, 1920.

171107. Skin and skull. Adult male. Cerro Azul, altitude 2,800 feet, near headwaters of the Chagres River, Panama. March 23, 1911. Collected by E. A. Goldman. Original number 20999.

Well-made skin in good condition except for damaged ears; skull Grade A.

†Heteromys temporalis Goldman.

North Amer. Fauna 34: 26, Sept. 7, 1911.

63719. Skin and skull. Adult female. Motzorongo, Veracruz, Mexico. March 3, 1894. Collected by E. W. Nelson and E. A. Goldman. Original number 5915.

Well-made skin in good condition; skull Grade A.

†Heteromys zonalis Goldman.

Smithsonian Misc. Coll. 56 (36) : 9, Feb. 19, 1912.
=Heteromys desmarestianus zonalis Goldman. See Goldman, Smithsonian Misc. Coll. 69 (5) : 116, Apr. 24, 1920.

170976. Adult female. Rio Indio, near Gatun, Canal Zone, Panama. February 15, 1911. Collected by E. A. Goldman. Original number 20885.

Well-made skin in good condition; skull Grade A.

Genus LIOMYS Merriam

†Heteromys annectens Merriam.

Proc. Biol. Soc. Washington 15: 43, Mar. 5, 1902.
=Liomys annectens (Merriam). See Goldman, North Amer. Fauna 34: 45, Sept. 7, 1911.

71510. Skin and skull. Adult male. Pluma, Oaxaca, Mexico. March 18, 1895. Collected by E. W. Nelson and E. A. Goldman. Original number 7674.

Well-made skin in good condition, except for broken tail; skull Grade A.

†Liomys canus Merriam.

Proc. Biol. Soc. Washington 15: 44, Mar. 5, 1902.
=Liomys irroratus canus Merriam. See Goldman, North Amer. Fauna 34: 60, Sept. 7, 1911.

96259. Skin and skull. Adult male. Near Parral, Chihuahua, Mexico. September 21, 1898. Collected by E. W. Nelson and E. A. Goldman. Original number 13036.

Well-made skin in good condition; skull Grade A.

†Liomys crispus Merriam.

Proc. Biol. Soc. Washington 15: 49, Mar. 5, 1902.

75105. Skin and skull. Adult male. Tonala, Chiapas, Mexico. August 7, 1895. Collected by E. W. Nelson and E. A. Goldman. Original number 8283.

Well-made skin in good condition; skull Grade B.

†Liomys crispus setosus Merriam.

Proc. Biol. Soc. Washington 15: 49, Mar. 5, 1902.

77588. Skin and skull. Adult female. Huehuetan, Chiapas, Mexico. February 22, 1896. Collected by E. W. Nelson and E. A. Goldman. Original number 9364.

Well-made skin in good condition; skull Grade B.

†Liomys guerrerensis Goldman.

North Amer. Fauna 34: 62, Sept. 7, 1911.

127523. Skin and skull. Adult female. Omilteme, Guerrero, Mexico. May 17, 1903. Collected by E. W. Nelson and E. A. Goldman. Original number 16435.

Well-made skin in good condition; skull Grade A.

†Liomys heterothrix Merriam.

Proc. Biol. Soc. Washington 15: 50, Mar. 5, 1902.

90161. Skin and skull. Adult male. San Pedro Sula, Honduras. July 16, 1897. Collected by J. C. Ingersoll. Original number 884–X.

Well-made skin in good condition; skull Grade A.

†Liomys irroratus pretiosus Goldman.

North Amer. Fauna 34; 58, Sept. 7, 1911.

93097. Skin and skull. Adult male. Metlaltoyuca, Puebla, Mexico. January 25, 1898. Collected by E. A. Goldman. Original number 12081.

Well-made skin in good condition, except slightly damaged right front leg; skull Grade B.

†Liomys obscurus Merriam.

Proc. Biol. Soc. Washington 15: 48, Mar. 5, 1902.

=*Liomys pictus obscurus* Merriam. See Goldman, North Amer. Fauna 34: 44, Sept. 7, 1911.

108563. Skin and skull. Adult female. Carrizal, Veracruz, Mexico. May 12, 1901. Collected by E. W. Nelson and E. A. Goldman. Original number 14714.

Well-made skin in good condition; skull Grade A.

†Liomys orbitalis Merriam.

Proc. Biol. Soc. Washington 15: 48, Mar. 5, 1902.

=*Liomys pictus veraecrucis* Merriam. See Goldman, North Amer. Fauna 34: 42, Sept. 7, 1911.

65452. Skin and skull. Adult female. Catemaco, Veracruz, Mexico. April 29, 1894. Collected by E. W. Nelson and E. A. Goldman. Original number 6129.

Well-made skin in good condition; skull Grade A.

251543—42——28

†Liomys parviceps Goldman.

Proc. Biol. Soc. Washington 17: 82, Mar. 21, 1904.

=*Liomys pictus parviceps* Goldman. See Goldman, North Amer. Fauna 34: 38, Sept. 7, 1911.

126477. Skin and skull. Adult female. La Salada, 40 miles south of Uruapan, Michoacan, Mexico. March 19, 1903. Collected by E. W. Nelson and E. A. Goldman. Original number 16194.

Well-made skin in good condition; skull Grade B.

†Liomys phaeura Merriam.

Proc. Biol. Soc. Washington 15: 48, Mar. 5, 1902.

=*Liomys pictus phaeurus* Merriam. See Goldman, North Amer. Fauna 34: 40, Sept. 7, 1911.

71500. Skin and skull. Adult female. Pinotepa, Oaxaca, Mexico. February 21, 1895. Collected by E. W. Nelson and E. A. Goldman. Original number 7553.

Well-made skin in good condition, except that tip of tail is missing; skull Grade A.

†Liomys pictus isthmius Merriam.

Proc. Biol. Soc. Washington 15: 46, Mar. 5, 1902.

73367. Skin and skull. Adult male. Tehuantepec, Oaxaca, Mexico. April 28, 1895. Collected by E. W. Nelson and E. A. Goldman. Original number 7796.

Well-made skin in good condition; skull Grade A.

†Liomys pictus rostratus Merriam.

Proc. Biol. Soc. Washington 15: 46, Mar. 5, 1902.

71488. Skin and skull. Adult male. Near Ometepec, Guerrero, Mexico. February 14, 1895. Collected by E. W. Nelson and E. A. Goldman. Original number 7447.

Well-made skin in good condition; skull Grade B.

†Liomys plantinarensis Merriam.

Proc. Biol. Soc. Washington 15: 46, Mar. 5, 1902.

=*Liomys pictus plantinarensis* Merriam. See Goldman, North Amer. Fauna 34: 37, Sept. 7, 1911.

$\frac{33595}{45630}$. Skin and skull. Adult female. Plantinar, Jalisco, Mexico. April 4, 1892. Collected by E. W. Nelson and E. A. Goldman. Original number 2383.

Well-made skin in good condition; skull Grade A.

†Liomys sonorana Merriam.

Proc. Biol. Soc. Washington 15: 47, Mar. 5, 1902.

=*Liomys pictus sonoranus* Merriam. See Miller, U. S. Nat. Mus. Bull. 128: 267, Apr. 29, 1924.

96252.   Skin and skull.   Adult male.   Alamos, Sonora, Mexico.   December 19, 1898.   Collected by E. A. Goldman.   Original number 13299.

Well-made skin in good condition; skull Grade B.

†Liomys texensis Merriam.

Proc. Biol. Soc. Washington 15: 44, Mar. 5, 1902.
=*Liomys irroratus texensis* Merriam.   See Goldman, North Amer. Fauna 34: 59, Sept. 7, 1911.

58670.   Skin and skull.   Adult female.   Brownsville, Cameron County, Tex.   February 19, 1894.   Collected by J. A. Loring. Original number 1672.

Well-made skin in good condition; skull Grade A.

†Liomys torridus Merriam.

Proc. Biol. Soc. Washington 15: 45, Mar. 5, 1902.
=*Liomys irroratus torridus* Merriam.   See Goldman, North Amer. Fauna 34: 55, Sept. 7, 1911.

69645.   Skin and skull.   Adult female.   Cuicatlan, Oaxaca, Mexico. October 14, 1894.   Collected by E. W. Nelson and E. A. Goldman. Original number 6904.

Well-made skin in good condition; skull Grade A.

†Liomys torridus minor Merriam.

Proc. Biol. Soc. Washington 15: 45, Mar. 5, 1902.
=*Liomys irroratus minor* Merriam.   See Goldman, North Amer. Fauna 34: 56, Sept. 7, 1911.

70301.   Skin and skull.   Adult female.   Huajuapam, Oaxaca, Mexico. November 18, 1894.   Collected by E. W. Nelson and E. A. Goldman.   Original number 7061.

Well-made skin in good condition; skull Grade A.

†Liomys veraecrucis Merriam.

Proc. Biol. Soc. Washington 15: 47, Mar. 5, 1902.
=*Liomys pictus veraecrucis* Merriam.   See Goldman, North Amer. Fauna 34: 42, Sept. 7, 1911.

65457.   Skin and skull.   Adult female.   San Andres Tuxtla, Veracruz, Mexico.   May 7, 1894.   Collected by E. W. Nelson and E. A. Goldman.   Original number 6174.

Well-made skin in good condition; skull Grade A.

Genus MICRODIPODOPS Merriam

†Microdipodops californicus Merriam.

Proc. Biol. Soc. Washington 14: 128, July 19, 1901.

101227.   Skin and skull.   Young adult male.   Sierra Valley, near Vinton, Plumas County, Calif.   August 7, 1900.   Collected by W. K. Fisher.   Original number 1596.

Well-made skin in good condition; skull Grade A.

†**Microdipodops megacephalus** Merriam.

North Amer. Fauna 5: 116, July 30, 1891.

$\frac{24417}{31823}$. Skin and skull. Adult male. Halleck, East Humboldt Valley, Elko County, Nev. October 23, 1890. Collected by Vernon Bailey. Original number 2005.

Well-made skin in good condition; skull Grade A.

†**Microdipodops megacephalus lucidus** Goldman.

Proc. Biol. Soc. Washington 39: 127, Dec. 27, 1926.

210397. Skin and skull. Clayton Valley, 8 miles southeast of Blair, altitude about 4,500 feet, Esmeralda County, Nev. October 19, 1915. Collected by Luther J. Goldman. Original number 2424.

Well-made skin in good condition; skull Grade A.

†**Microdipodops megacephalus oregonus** Merriam.

Proc. Biol. Soc. Washington 14: 127, July 19, 1901.

80128. Skin and skull. Young adult male. Lake Alvord, Alvord Desert, Harney County, Oreg. August 18, 1896. Collected by C. P. Streator. Original number 5430.

Well-made skin in good condition; skull Grade A.

†**Microdipodops pallidus** Merriam.

Proc. Biol. Soc. Washington 14: 127, July 19, 1901.

93520. Skin and skull. Adult female. Ten miles east of Stillwater, Churchill County, Nev. May 11, 1898. Collected by H. C. Oberholser. Original number 101.

Well-made skin in good condition; skull Grade A.

Genus PEROGNATHUS Wied

†**Perognathus amplus** Osgood.

North Amer. Fauna 18: 32, Sept. 20, 1900.

$\frac{34626}{46711}$. Skin and skull. Adult male. Fort Verde, Yavapai County, Ariz. June 26, 1892. Collected by J. A. Loring. Original number 272.

Well-made skin in good condition; skull Grade A.

†**Perognathus amplus jacksoni** Goldman.

Journ. Washington Acad. Sci. 23: 465, Oct. 15, 1933.

212780. Skin and skull. Adult male. Congress Junction, altitude 3,000 feet, Yavapai County, Ariz. June 21, 1916. Collected by H. H. T. Jackson. Original number 381.

Well-made skin in good condition; skull Grade A.

†**Perognathus amplus pergracilis** Goldman.

Journ. Washington Acad. Sci. 22:387, July 19, 1932.

227528. Skin and skull. Young adult male. Hackberry, altitude 3,500 feet, Mohave County, Ariz. September 14, 1917. Collected by E. A. Goldman. Original number 23304.

Well-made skin in good condition; skull Grade A.

†**Perognathus amplus rotundus** Goldman.

Journ. Washington Acad. Sci. 22: 387, July 19, 1932.

250470. Skin and skull. Adult male. Wellton, Yuma County, Ariz. November 9, 1931. Collected by Bernard Bailey. Original number A4353; 27029–X.

Well-made skin in good condition; skull Grade A.

†**Perognathus amplus taylori** Goldman.

Journ. Washingon Acad. Sci. 22:488, Oct. 19, 1932.

250533. Skin and skull. Adult female. Santa Rita Range Reserve, near Northeast Station, 35 miles south of Tucson, altitude about 4,000 feet, Pima County, Ariz. August 3, 1930. Collected by Walter P. Taylor. Original number 1899.

Well-made skin in good condition; skull Grade A.

†**Perognathus anthonyi** Osgood.

North Amer. Fauna 18:56, Sept. 20, 1900.

81058. Skin and skull. Adult female. South Bay, Cerros Island, Lower California, Mexico. July 29, 1896. Collected by A. W. Anthony. Original number 71.

Well-made skin in good condition; skull Grade A.

***Perognathus apache** Merriam.

North Amer. Fauna 1:14, Oct. 25, 1889.

186504. Skin and skull. Adult male. Near Keam's Canyon, Apache County, Ariz. May 22, 1888. Collected by Jere Sullivan. Merriam collection No. $\frac{4253}{4984}$.

Well-made skin in good condition; skull Grade B.

†**Perognathus apache caryi** Goldman.

Proc. Biol. Soc. Washington 31:24, May 16, 1918.

148206. Skin and skull. Adult male. Eight miles west of Rifle, Garfield County, Colo. October 4, 1906. Collected by Merritt Cary. Original number 937.

Well-made skin in good condition; skull Grade A.

†**Perognathus apache cleomophila** Goldman.

Proc. Biol. Soc. Washington 31: 23, May 16, 1918.

226344.   Skin and skull.   Adult male.   Winona, 3 miles northwest, altitude 6,400 feet, Coconino County, Ariz.   July 19, 1917.   Collected by E. A. Goldman.   Original number 23127.

Well-made skin in good condition; skull Grade A.

†**Perognathus apache melanotis** Osgood.

North Amer. Fauna 18: 27, Sept. 20, 1900.

97416.   Skin and skull.   Adult female.   Casas Grandes, Chihuahua, Mexico.   May 21, 1899.   Collected by E. A. Goldman.   Original number 13750.

Well-made skin in good condition; skull Grade A.

†**Perognathus apache relictus** Goldman.

Journ. Mamm. 19: 495, Nov. 14, 1938.

150768.   Skin and skull.   Young adult male.   Medano Springs Ranch, 15 miles northeast of Mosca, San Luis Valley, altitude 7,600 feet, southern Colorado.   November 2, 1907.   Collected by Merritt Cary.   Original number 1222.

Well-made skin in good condition; skull Grade A.

†**Perognathus arenarius ambiguus** Nelson and Goldman.

Proc. Biol Soc. Washington 42: 108, Mar. 25, 1929.

140011.   Skin and skull.   Young adult male.   Yubay, altitude 2,000 feet, 30 miles southeast of Calamahue, Lower California, Mexico.   September 18, 1905.   Collected by E. W. Nelson and E. A. Goldman.   Original number 18141.

Well-made skin in good condition; skull Grade B.

†**Perognathus arenarius sublucidus** Nelson and Goldman.

Proc. Biol. Soc. Washington 42: 109, Mar. 25, 1929.

146896.   Skin and skull.   Adult male.   La Paz, Lower California, Mexico.   February 16, 1906.   Collected by E. W. Nelson and E. A. Goldman.   Original number 19146.

Well-made skin in good condition; skull Grade A.

***Perognathus armatus** Merriam.

North Amer. Fauna 1: 27, Oct. 25, 1889.
=*Perognathus californicus californicus* Merriam.   See Osgood, North Amer. Fauna 18: 58, Sept. 20, 1900.

186505.   Skin and skull.   Adult female.   Mount Diablo, Contra Costa County, Calif.   March 28, 1882.   Collected by W. E. Bryant, Merriam collection No. $\frac{672}{6321}$.

Well-made skin in good condition; tip of tail broken off but tied to specimen; skull Grade C.

†Perognathus artus Osgood.

North Amer. Fauna 18: 55, Sept. 20, 1900.

96298. Skin and skull. Adult female. Batopilas, Chihuahua, Mexico. October 6, 1898. Collected by E. A. Goldman. Original number 13090.

Well-made skin in good condition; skull Grade A.

†Perognathus baileyi Merriam.

Proc. Acad. Nat. Sci. Philadelphia 46: 262, Oct. 23, 1894. (Author's separates dated Sept. 27, 1894.)

$\frac{17838}{24775}$. Skin and skull. Adult female. Magdalena, Sonora, Mexico. November 3, 1889. Collected by Vernon Bailey. Original number 633.

Well-made skin in good condition; skull Grade A.

†Perognathus baileyi domensis Goldman.

Proc. Biol. Soc. Washington 41: 204, Dec. 18, 1928.

248002. Skin and skull. Adult female. Castle Dome, at base of Castle Dome Peak, altitude 1,400 feet, Yuma County, Ariz. April 13, 1927. Collected by George G. Cantwell. Original number 2882.

Well-made skin in good condition; skull Grade A.

†Perognathus baileyi extimus Nelson and Goldman.

Journ. Washington Acad. Sci. 20 (12) : 223, June 19, 1930.

146672. Skin and skull. Adult female. Tres Pachitas, 36 miles south of La Paz, altitude 700 feet, Lower California, Mexico. December 25, 1905. Collected by E. W. Nelson and E. A. Goldman. Original number 18785.

Well-made skin in good condition; skull Grade A.

*Perognathus baileyi insularis Townsend.

Bull. Amer. Mus. Nat. Hist. 31: 122, June 14, 1912.

198410. Skin and skull. Male. Tiburon Island, Gulf of California, Sonora, Mexico. April 13, 1911. Collected by H. E. Anthony. Original number 153.

Well-made skin in good condition; skull Grade A.

*Perognathus bimaculatus Merriam.

North Amer. Fauna 1: 12, Oct. 25, 1889.

=Perognathus flavus bimaculatus Merriam. See Osgood, North Amer. Fauna 18: 24, Sept. 20, 1900.

$\dfrac{8455}{23789}$. Skin and skull. Adult male. Fort Whipple, Yavapai County, Ariz. May 21, 1865. Collected by Elliott Coues. "Expls. in the Rocky Mts.," No. 1499, Elliott Coues.

Fairly well-made skin in good condition. It was probably made up with the skull at first inside; skull grade C.

†Perognathus bombycinus Osgood.

Proc. Biol. Soc. Washington 20: 19, Feb. 23, 1907.
=*Perognathus longimembris bombycinus* Osgood. See Nelson and Goldman, Proc. Biol. Soc. Washington 42: 104, Mar. 25, 1929.

136123. Skin and skull. Adult male. Yuma, Yuma County, Ariz. March 18, 1905. Collected by E. A. Goldman. Original number 16844.

Well-made skin in good condition; skull Grade A.

*Perognathus californicus Merriam.

North Amer. Fauna 1: 26, Oct. 25, 1889.

186506. Skin and skull. Female. Berkeley, Calif. November 8, 1888. Collected by T. S. Palmer and Charles A. Keeler. Merriam collection No. $\dfrac{5132}{5827}$.

Well-made skin in good condition except that tip of tail is missing; skull Grade A.

†Perognathus californicus dispar Osgood.

North Amer. Fauna 18: 58, Sept. 20, 1900.

$\dfrac{32116}{43928}$. Skin and skull. Adult male. Carpenteria, Santa Barbara County, Calif. December 19, 1891. Collected by E. W. Nelson. Original number 1655.

Well-made skin in good condition; skull Grade A.

†Perognathus californicus ochrus Osgood.

Proc. Biol. Soc. Washington 17: 128, June 9, 1904.

130348. Skin and skull. Young adult female. Santiago Springs, 16 miles southwest of McKittrick, Kern County, Calif. July 30, 1903. Collected by L. J. Goldman. Original number 728.

Well-made skin in good condition; skull Grade B.

†Perognathus callistus Osgood.

North Amer. Fauna 18: 28, Sept. 20, 1900.

88245. Skin and skull. Young adult male. Kinney Ranch, Green River Basin, near Bitter Creek, Sweetwater County, Wyo. May 14, 1897. Collected by J. A. Loring. Original number 4122.

Well-made skin in good condition; skull Grade A.

†Perognathus columbianus Merriam.

Proc. Acad. Nat. Sci. Philadelphia 46 : 263, Oct. 23, 1894.   (Author's separates dated Sept. 27, 1894.)

=*Perognathus lordi columbianus* Merriam.   See Osgood, North Amer. Fauna 18 : 40, Sept. 20, 1900.

$\frac{27351}{39450}$. Skin and skull. Young adult male. Pasco, Franklin County, Wash. May 9, 1891. Collected by C. P. Streator. Original number 768.

Well-made skin in good condition; skull Grade A.

*Perognathus (Chaetodipus) eremicus Mearns.

Bull. Amer. Mus. Nat. Hist. 10 : 300, Aug. 31, 1898.

=*Perognathus penicillatus eremicus* Mearns.   See Osgood, North Amer. Fauna 18 : 48, Sept. 20, 1900.

$\frac{21052}{36094}$. Skin and skull. Adult female. Fort Hancock, El Paso County, Tex. June 27, 1893. Collected by E. A. Mearns. Original number 2380.

Well-made skin in good condition, but the tail is broken in both proximal and distal portions. Skull Grade A.

*Perognathus fallax Merriam.

North Amer. Fauna 1 : 19, Oct. 25, 1889.

$\frac{15889}{22684}$. Skin and skull. Adult male. Reche Canyon, 3 miles southeast of Colton, San Bernardino County, Calif. April 21, 1887. Collected by Frank Stephens. Original number 424.

Well-made skin in good condition; skull Grade A.

†Perognathus fallax inopinus Nelson and Goldman.

Proc. Biol. Soc. Washington 42 : 110, Mar. 25, 1929.

81059. Skin and skull. Adult male. Turtle (also known as Bartolome) Bay, Lower California, Mexico. August 1, 1896. Collected by A. W. Anthony. Original number 82.

Well-made skin in good condition; skull Grade A.

*Perognathus fallax pallidus Mearns.

Proc. Biol. Soc. Washington 14 : 135, Aug. 9, 1901.

61007. Skin and skull. Adult female. Mountain Spring, halfway up the east slope of the Coast Range Mountains near the Mexican boundary line, Imperial County, Calif. May 16, 1894. Collected by E. A. Mearns. International Boundary Commission. Original number 3520.

Well-made skin in good condition; skull Grade A.

*Perognathus fasciatus flavescens Merriam.

North Amer. Fauna 1: 11, Oct. 25, 1889.

=*Perognathus flavescens flavescens* Merriam.　See Osgood, North Amer. Fauna 18: 20, Sept. 20, 1900.

186507. Skin and skull. Adult male. Kennedy, Cherry County, Nebr. June 11, 1888. Collected by Vernon Bailey. Original number 23. Merriam collection number $\frac{4303}{5027}$.

Well-made skin in good condition; skull Grade A.

†Perognathus fasciatus litus Cary.

Proc. Biol. Soc. Washington 24: 61, Mar. 22, 1911.

160600. Skin and skull. Adult female. Sun, Sweetwater Valley, Fremont County, Wyo. September 18, 1909. Collected by Merritt Cary. Original number 1778.

Well-made skin in good condition; skull Grade A.

†Perognathus flavescens perniger Osgood.

Proc. Biol. Soc. Washington 17: 127, June 9, 1904.

57725. Skin and skull. Young female. Vermillion, Clay County, S. Dak. August 22, 1889. Collected by G. S. Agersborg.

Skin in fair condition; abdominal incision not sewed up; skull Grade B.

*Perognathus flavus Baird.

Proc. Acad. Nat. Sci. Philadelphia 7: 332, reported for publication Apr. 24, 1855.

$\frac{148}{1130}$. Fragment of skull (skin lost). El Paso, El Paso County, Tex. 1851. Collected by J. H. Clark. United States and Mexican Boundary Survey.

The skull, No. 1130, is represented by the anterior part of the rostrum only. The skin cannot be found.

Type not designated by number. Baird says, "Collected at El Paso by J. H. Clark." Reference to Mammals of North America, p. 425, shows that No. $\frac{148}{1130}$ is the specimen he must have had in mind.

†Perognathus flavus hopiensis Goldman.

Proc. Biol. Soc. Washington 45: 89, June 21, 1932.

248014. Skin and skull. Adult female. Oraibi, altitude 6,000 feet, Hopi Indian Reservation, Navajo County, Ariz. June 5, 1927. Collected by G. G. Cantwell. Original number 3037.

Well-made skin in good condition; skull Grade A.

†Perognathus flavus mexicanus Merriam.

Proc. Acad. Nat. Sci. Philadelphia 46: 265, Oct. 23, 1894. (Author's separates dated Sept. 27, 1894.)

50714. Skin and skull. Young adult male. Tlalpam, Federal District, Mexico. December 4, 1892. Collected by E. W. Nelson. Original number 3978.

Well-made skin in good condition; skull Grade A.

†Perognathus flavus piperi Goldman.

Proc. Biol. Soc. Washington 30: 148, July 27, 1917.

168650. Skin and skull. Adult male. Twenty-three miles southwest of Newcastle, Weston County, Wyo. May 25, 1910. Collected by S. E. Piper. Original number 283.

Well-made skin in good condition; skull Grade A.

†Perognathus flavus sonoriensis Nelson and Goldman.

Journ. Washington Acad. Sci. 24: 267, June 15, 1934.

250885. Skin and skull. Adult female. Costa Rica Ranch, lower Sonora River, Sonora, Mexico. December 13, 1932. Collected by Vernon Bailey and Frederic Winthrop. Original number 11282 (V. Bailey).

Well-made skin in good condition; skull Grade A.

*Perognathus formosus Merriam.

North Amer. Fauna 1: 17, October 25, 1889.

186508. Skin and skull. Adult male. St. George, Washington County, Utah. January 2, 1889. Collected by Vernon Bailey. Original number 469. Merriam collection number $\frac{5213}{5908}$.

Well-made skin in good condition; skull Grade B.

†Perognathus fuliginosus Merriam.

North Amer. Fauna 3: 74, Sept. 11, 1890.
=Perognathus flavus fuliginosus Merriam. See Osgood, North Amer. Fauna 18: 25, Sept. 20, 1900.

$\frac{17708}{24644}$. Skin and skull. Immature male. Cedar belt, northeast of San Francisco Mountain, Coconino County, Ariz. October 4, 1889. Collected by Vernon Bailey. Original number 559.

Well-made skin in good condition; skull Grade C.

†Perognathus goldmani Osgood.

North Amer. Fauna 18: 54, Sept. 20, 1900.

96673. Skin and skull. Adult female. Sinaloa, State of Sinaloa, Mexico. February 15, 1899. Collected by E. A. Goldman. Original number 13428.

Well-made skin in good condition; skull Grade A.

*Perognathus hispidus Baird.

Mammals of North America, p. 421, 1857.

$\frac{577}{1696}$. Skin and skull. Adult female. Charco Escondido, Tamaulipas, Mexico. 1853. Collected by D. N. Couch.

Badly-made skin with bare patches on the right flank and on the back. Tail never skinned out, its tip broken off. Skull Grade C. This skull apparently consists of sections of two different specimens glued together. (See Osgood, North Amer. Fauna 18: 43, Sept. 20, 1900.)

No type designated, but the description is clearly based on No. 577.

†Perognathus hispidus zacatecae Osgood.

North Amer. Fauna 18: 45, Sept. 20, 1900.

91877. Skin and skull. Young adult female. Valparaiso, Zacatecas, Mexico. December 16, 1897. Collected by E. A. Goldman. Original number 11968.

Well-made skin in good condition; skull Grade A.

*Perognathus inornatus Merriam.

North Amer. Fauna 1: 15, Oct. 25, 1889.

$\frac{13394}{23790}$. In alcohol, with skull removed. Young adult male. Fresno, Fresno County, Calif. No date. Collected by Gustav Eisen. Alcoholic cataloged February 6, 1882; skull, July 3, 1889.

Specimen generally well preserved, but color faded; some hair has slipped from the left side. Skull Grade B.

*Perognathus intermedius Merriam.

North Amer. Fauna 1: 18, Oct. 25, 1889.

186509. Skin and skull. Adult male. Mud Spring, Mohave County, Ariz. February 26, 1889. Collected by Vernon Bailey. Original number 616. Merriam collection number $\frac{5309}{6000}$.

Well-made skin in good condition; skull Grade B.

†Perognathus (Chaetodipus) intermedius canescens Merriam.

Proc. Acad. Nat. Sci. Philadelphia 46: 267, Oct. 23, 1894. (Sept. 27, 1894, author's separates.)

=*Perognathus nelsoni canescens* Merriam. See Osgood, North Amer. Fauna 18: 54, Sept. 20, 1900.

51016. Skin and skull. Young adult male. Jaral, Coahuila, Mexico. January 14, 1893. Collected by C. P. Streator. Original number 2557.

Well-made skin in good condition; skull Grade A.

†Perognathus intermedius phasma Goldman.

Proc. Biol. Soc. Washington 31: 22, May 16, 1918.

203003. Skin and skull. Adult female. Tinajas Altas, Gila Mountains, altitude about 1,400 feet, Yuma County, Ariz. November 23, 1913. Collected by E. A. Goldman. Original number 22309.

Well-made skin in good condition; skull Grade A.

*Otognosis longimembris Coues.

Proc. Acad. Nat. Sci. Philadelphia 27: 305, Aug. 31, 1875.

=*Perognathus longimembris* (Coues). See Grinnell, Univ. California Publ. Zool. 40 (2) : 147, 1933.

$\frac{9856}{37356}$. In alcohol; skull removed. Female. Fort Tejon, Cañada de las Uvas, Kern County, Calif. 1857–58. Collected by John Xantus.

Alcoholic specimen in poor condition; it has the appearance of having been completely dried at one time. Skull Grade A.
Designated by number in original description.

†Perognathus longimembris arizonensis Goldman.

Proc. Biol. Soc. Washington 44: 134, Oct. 17, 1931.

250032. Skin and skull. Adult female. Ten miles south of Jacobs Pools, Houserock Valley, north side of Marble Canyon of Colorado River, altitude 4,000 feet, Coconino County, Ariz. June 17, 1931. Collected by E. A. Goldman. Original number 23589.

Well-made skin in good condition; skull Grade A.

*Perognathus longimembris panamintinus Merriam.

Proc. Acad. Nat. Sci. Philadelphia 46: 265, Oct. 23, 1894. (Author's separates dated Sept. 27, 1894.)

$\frac{27767}{39866}$. Skin and skull. Young adult male. Perognathus Flat, altitude 5,200 feet, Emigrant Gap, Panamint Mountains, Inyo County, Calif. April 16, 1891. Collected by Vernon Bailey. Original number 2675.

Well-made skin in good condition; skull Grade B.

†Perognathus merriami gilvus Osgood.

North Amer. Fauna 18: 22, Sept. 20, 1900.

$\frac{35939}{48273}$. Skin and skull. Adult male. Eddy, near Carlsbad, Eddy County, N. Mex. September 18, 1892. Collected by B. H. Dutcher. Original number 329.

Well-made skin with right hind leg missing; otherwise in good condition; skull Grade A.

*Perognathus monticola Baird.

Mammals of North America, p. 422, 1857.

=*Perognathus parvus parvus* Peale. See Osgood, North Amer. Fauna 18: 34, Sept. 20, 1900.

$\frac{451}{1585}$ Skin and skull, formerly mounted. Adult female, probably collected in the neighborhood of The Dalles, Wasco County, Oreg. 1853. Collected by George Suckley. (See Osgood, North Amer. Fauna 18: 36, Sept. 20, 1900.)

The dismounted skin is in poor condition. It is much bleached and the ears are more or less broken; on the posterior parts of body two large areas are without hair. Skull Grade B.

Baird had no other specimen.

†Perognathus (Chaetodipus) nelsoni Merriam.

Proc. Acad. Nat. Sci. Philadelphia 46: 264, Oct. 23 ,1894. (Author's separates dated Sept. 27, 1894.)

=*Perognathus nelsoni nelsoni* Merriam. See Osgood, North Amer. Fauna 18: 53, Sept. 20, 1900.

50214. Skin and skull. Old female. Hacienda La Parada, about 25 miles northwest of the city of San Luis Potosi, State of San Luis Potosi, Mexico. August 19, 1892. Collected by E. W. Nelson. Original number 3207.

Well-made skin in good condition; skull Grade A.

†Perognathus nevadensis Merriam.

Proc. Acad. Nat. Sci. Philadelphia 46: 264, Oct. 23, 1894. (Author's separates dated Sept. 27, 1894.)

=*Perognathus longimembris nevadensis* Merriam. See Grinnell, Univ. California Publ. Zool. 40: 147, Sept. 26, 1933.

54828. Skin and skull. Adult male. Halleck, East Humboldt Valley, Elko County, Nev. July 4, 1893. Collected by Vernon Bailey. Original number 4070.

Well-made skin in good condition; skull Grade A.

*Perognathus obscurus Merriam.

North Amer. Fauna 1: 20, Oct. 25, 1889.

=*Perognathus spinatus occultus* Nelson. See *Perognathus spinatus nelsoni* Townsend.

186510. Skin and skull. Adult female. Camp Apache, Grant County, N. Mex. April 30, 1886. Collected by A. W. Anthony. Merriam collection number $\frac{2340}{2848}$.

Well-made skin in good condition; skull Grade A.

*Perognathus olivaceus Merriam.

North Amer. Fauna 1: 15, Oct. 25, 1889.

=*Perognathus parvus olivaceous* Merriam. See Osgood, North Amer. Fauna 18: 37, Sept. 20, 1900.

186511. Skin and skull. Adult male. Kelton, Box Elder County, Utah. October 24, 1888. Collected by Vernon Bailey. Original number 338. Merriam collection number $\frac{4876}{5623}$.

Well-made skin in good condition; skull Grade B.

*Perognathus olivaceus amoenus Merriam.

North Amer. Fauna 1: 16, Oct. 25, 1889.
=*Perognathus parvus olivaceus* Merriam. See Osgood, North Amer. Fauna 18: 37, Sept. 20, 1900.

186512. Skin and skull. Adult male. Nephi, Juab County, Utah. November 23, 1888. Collected by Vernon Bailey. Original number 404. Merriam collection number $\frac{5103}{5795}$.

Well-made skin in good condition; skull Grade B.

*Perognathus pacificus Mearns.

Bull. Amer. Mus. Nat. Hist. 10: 299, Aug. 31, 1898.
=*Perognathus longimembris pacificus* Mearns. See von Bloeker, Proc. Biol. Soc. Washington 45: 128, Sept. 9, 1932.

61022. Skin and skull. Adult female. Mexican boundary monument, No. 258, shore of Pacific Ocean, San Diego County, Calif. July 12, 1894. Collected by E. A. Mearns. International Boundary Commission. Original number 3787.

Well-made skin in good condition; skull Grade A.

†Perognathus panamintinus arenicola Stephens.

Proc. Biol. Soc. Washington 13: 153, June 13, 1900.
=*Perognathus longimembris arenicola* Stephens. See Osgood, Proc. Biol. Soc. Washington 31: 96, June 29, 1918.

99828. Skin and skull. Adult male. San Felipe Narrows, San Diego County, Calif. April 11, 1892. Collected by Frank Stephens. Original number 2056. (2622-X).

Well-made skin in good condition; skull Grade A.

*Perognathus panamintinus brevinasus Osgood.

North Amer. Fauna 18: 30, Sept. 20, 1900.
=*Perognathus longimembris brevinasus* Osgood. See Miller, U. S. Nat. Mus. Bull. 128: 276, Apr. 29, 1924.

186515. Skin and skull. Adult female. San Bernardino, San Bernardino County, Calif. May 2, 1885. Collected by Frank Stephens. Original number 49. Merriam collection number $\frac{1109}{1661}$.

Well-made skin in good condition; skull Grade A.

*Perognathus paradoxus Merriam.

North Amer. Fauna 1: 24, Oct. 25, 1889.
=*Perognathus hispidus paradoxus* Merriam. See Osgood, North Amer. Fauna 18: 44, Sept. 20, 1900.

18613. Skin and skull. Adult female. Trego County, Kans. October 14, 1884. Collected by A. B. Baker. Merriam collection number $\frac{940}{1544}$.

Well-made skin in good condition; skull Grade A.

*Perognathus paradoxus spilotus Merriam.

North Amer. Fauna 1: 25, Oct. 25, 1889.
=*Perognathus hispidus hispidus* Baird. See Osgood, North Amer. Fauna 18: 42, Sept. 20, 1900.

186514. Skin only. Adult female. Gainesville, Cooke County, Tex. October 8, 1886. Collected by G. H. Ragsdale. Merriam collection number 5293.

Well-made skin in good condition.
Merriam based his description of the skull on No. 23096, a paratype from the type locality. Young adult female. September 24, 1888. Collected by G. H. Ragsdale.
Skull Grade B.

Cricetodipus parvus Peale. See page 574.

†Perognathus parvus clarus Goldman.

Proc. Biol. Soc. Washington 30: 147, July 27, 1917.

178939. Skin and skull. Adult male. Cumberland, Lincoln County, Wyo. May 18, 1912. Collected by Stanley G. Jewett. Original number 976.

Well-made skin in good condition; skull Grade A.

†Perognathus parvus idahoensis Goldman.

Proc. Biol. Soc. Washington 35: 105, Oct. 17, 1922.

236394. Skin and skull. Adult male. Echo Crater, 20 miles southwest of Arco, Blaine County, Idaho. June 14, 1921. Collected by Luther J. Goldman. Original number 2752.

Well-made skin in good condition; skull Grade B.

†Perognathus parvus magruderensis Osgood.

North Amer. Fauna 18: 38, Sept. 20, 1900.

$\frac{28427}{40531}$. Skin and skull. Adult male. Mount Magruder, altitude 8,000 feet, Nev., near boundary between Inyo County, Calif., and Esmeralda County, Nev., June 6, 1891. Collected by Vernon Bailey. Original number 2899.

Well-made skin in good condition; skull Grade A.

†Perognathus parvus plerus Goldman.

Journ. Mamm. 20: 352, Aug. 14, 1939.

263971. Skin and skull. Old adult male. North end of Stansbury Island, Great Salt Lake, altitude 4,250 feet, Utah. June 23, 1938. Collected by William H. Marshall. Original number 117.

Well-made skin in good condition; skull Grade B.

*Perognathus penecillatus [sic] Woodhouse.

Proc. Acad. Nat. Sci. Philadelphia 6: 200, presented at meeting of Dec. 28, 1852.
=*Perognathus penicillatus* Woodhouse. See Woodhouse, *in* Sitgreaves, Report of an Expedition down the Zuni and Colorado Rivers, p. 49, 1853.

$\frac{2676}{37437}$. Skin and skull. Adult male. San Francisco Mountain, Coconino County, Ariz. (Probably a few miles to the northeast. See Osgood, North Amer. Fauna 18: 45, footnote, Sept. 20, 1900.) Collected in October 1851 by S. W. Woodhouse.

Skin formerly mounted, fairly well made up but badly preserved. The hair looks worn and bleached, and there are a couple of bare spots on the specimen. The vertebrae are still in the tail. Skull Grade A.

Type not designated by number. The original description speaks of a single specimen, a male, from San Francisco Mountain; reference to Baird's Mammals of North America, p. 419, shows that No. 2676 is this specimen. It should be observed that the measurements given by Baird do not agree well with those given by Woodhouse.

†Perognathus penicillatus albulus Nelson and Goldman.

Proc. Biol. Soc. Washington 36: 159, May 1, 1923.
=*Perognathus arenarius albulus* Nelson and Goldman. See Huey, Proc. Biol. Soc. Washington 39: 68, July 30, 1926.

146864. Skin and skull. Adult male. Magdalena Island, Lower California, Mexico. December 3, 1905. Collected by E. W. Nelson and E. A. Goldman. Original number 18733.

Well-made skin in good condition; skull Grade A.

†Perognathus penicillatus ammophilus Osgood.

Proc. Biol. Soc. Washington 20: 20, Feb. 23, 1907.
=*Perognathus arenarius ammophilus* Osgood. See Huey, Proc. Biol. Soc. Washington 39: 68, July 30, 1926.

146859. Skin and skull. Adult male. Margarita Island, Lower California, Mexico. November 29, 1905. Collected by E. W. Nelson and E. A. Goldman. Original number 18655.

Well-made skin in good condition; skull Grade A.

†Perognathus penicillatus angustirostris Osgood.

North Amer. Fauna 18: 47, Sept. 20, 1900.

73881. Skin and skull. Adult male. Carrizo Creek, Colorado Desert, Imperial County, Calif. March 31, 1895. Collected by A. W. Anthony. Original number 22.

Well-made skin in good condition; skull Grade A.

*Perognathus penicillatus goldmani Townsend.

Bull. Amer. Mus. Nat. Hist. 31: 122, June 14, 1912.
=*Perognathus penicillatus seri* Nelson. See Nelson, Proc. Biol. Soc. Washington 25: 116, June 29, 1912. (Substitute for *Perognathus penicillatus goldmani* Townsend, not *P. goldmani* Osgood, North Amer. Fauna 18: 54, 1900.)

198411. Skin and skull. Male. Tiburon Island, Gulf of California, Sonora, Mexico. April 13, 1911. Collected by H. E. Anthony. Original number 155.

Well-made skin in good condition; skull Grade A.

†Perognathus penicillatus seorsus Goldman.

Proc. Biol. Soc. Washington 52: 34, Mar. 11, 1939.
=*Perognathus penicillatus sobrinus* Goldman. See Goldman, Journ. Mamm. 20: 257, May 14, 1939.

$\frac{27598}{39697}$. Skin and skull. Adult male. Sand flat along Virgin River, 7 miles north of Bunkerville, Clark County, Nev. May 9, 1891. Collected by Vernon Bailey. Original number 2743.

Well-made skin in good condition; skull Grade A.

Perognathus penicillatus seri Nelson.

See *Perognathus penicillatus goldmani* Townsend.

†Perognathus penicillatus siccus Osgood.

Proc. Biol. Soc. Washington 20: 20, Feb. 23, 1907.
=*Perognathus arenarius siccus* Osgood. See Nelson and Goldman, Proc. Biol. Soc. Washington 42: 108, Mar. 25, 1929.

146890. Skin and skull. Adult male. Ceralbo Island, Lower California, Mexico. February 13, 1906. Collected by E. W. Nelson and E. A. Goldman. Original number 19131.

Well-made skin in good condition; skull Grade A.

Perognathus penicillatus sobrinus Goldman.

See *Perognathus penicillatus seorsus* Goldman.

†Perognathus pernix rostratus Osgood.

North Amer. Fauna 18: 51, Sept. 20, 1900.

95818. Skin and skull. Young adult male. Camoa, Rio Mayo, Sonora, Mexico. October 28, 1898. Collected by E. A. Goldman. Original number 13167.

Well-made skin in good condition; skull Grade A.

*Perognathus spinatus Merriam.

North Amer. Fauna 1: 21, Oct. 25, 1889.

186516. Skin and skull. Adult male. Twenty-five miles south of Needles, Colorado River, San Bernardino County, Calif. March 23, 1889. Collected by Vernon Bailey. Original number 683. Merriam collection No. $\frac{5449}{6137}$.

Well-made skin in good condition; skull Grade B.

†Perognathus spinatus magdalenae Osgood.

Proc. Biol. Soc. Washington 20: 21, Feb. 23, 1907.

146102. Skin and skull. Adult female. Magdalena Island, Lower California, Mexico. November 25, 1905. Collected by E. W. Nelson and E. A. Goldman. Original number 18633.

Well-made skin in good condition; skull Grade B.

*Perognathus spinatus nelsoni Townsend.

Bull. Amer. Mus. Nat. Hist. 31: 122, June 14, 1912.

=Perognathus spinatus occultus Nelson. See Nelson, Proc. Biol. Soc. Washington 25: 116, June 29, 1912. (Substitute for Perognathus penicillatus nelsoni Townsend not P. nelsoni Merriam, Proc. Acad. Nat. Sci. Philadelphia 46: 226, 1894).

198409. Skin and skull. Male. Carmen Island, Gulf of California, Lower California, Mexico. April 3, 1911. Collected by H. E. Anthony. Original number 99.

Well-made skin in good condition; skull Grade A.

Perognathus spinatus occultus Nelson.

See Perognathus spinatus nelsoni Townsend.

†Perognathus (Chaetodipus) stephensi Merriam.

Proc. Acad. Nat. Sci. Philadelphia 46: 267, Oct. 23, 1894. (Author's separates dated Sept. 27, 1894.)

=Perognathus penicillatus stephensi Merriam. See Grinnell, Univ. California Publ. Zool. 40: 153, Sept. 26, 1933.

$\frac{27774}{39873}$. Skin and skull. Adult male. Mesquite Valley, northwest arm of Death Valley, Inyo County, Calif. April 6, 1891. Collected by Frank Stephens. Original number 258.

Well-made skin in good condition; skull Grade A.

Family HYDROCHOERIDAE: Capybaras
Genus HYDROCHOERUS Brisson

*Hydrochoerus hydrochaeris notialis Hollister.

Proc. Biol. Soc. Washington 27: 58, Mar. 20, 1914.

154186. Skin and skeleton. Adult male. Paraguay. Received at National Zoological Park December 7, 1904, from John N. Ruffin, U. S. Consul at Asuncion, Paraguay; died January 6, 1909.

Folded, flat, tanned skin; skull Grade A; skeleton lost.

†**Hydrochoerus isthmius** Goldman.

Smithsonian Misc. Coll. 60 (2) : 11, Sept. 20, 1912.

179703. Skin and skull. Adult male. Marraganti, near the head of tidewater on the Rio Tuyra, eastern Panama. April 4, 1912. Collected by E. A. Goldman. Original number 21591.

Well-made skin in good condition; skull Grade A.

Family HYSTRICIDAE: Old World Porcupines

Genus ATHERURUS F. Cuvier

***Atherurus terutaus** Lyon.

Proc. U. S. Nat. Mus. 32 : 587, June 29, 1907.

=*Atherurus macrourus terutaus* Lyon. See Chasen, Bull. Raffles Mus. 15 : 189, Apr. 1940.

123971. Skin and skull. Adult male. Pulo Terutau (also written Trotau and Trotto), off west coast of the Malay Peninsula. April 10, 1904.   Collected by W. L. Abbott.   Original number 3223.

Well-made skin in good condition; skull Grade A.

***Atherura zygomatica** Miller.

Smithsonian Misc. Coll. 45 : 42, Nov. 6, 1903.

=*Atherurus macrourus zygomaticus* Miller. See Chasen, Bull. Raffles Mus. 15 : 189, Apr. 1940.

112429. Skin and skull. Adult female. Pulo Aor, off coast of Johore, Federated Malay States. June 6, 1901. Collected by W. L. Abbott. Original number 1009.

Well-made skin in good condition; skull Grade A.

Genus THECURUS Lyon

***Thecurus major** Schwarz.

Journ. Mamm. 20 : 246, May 14, 1939.

196777. Skin and skull. Adult male. Near Samarinda, left bank of lower Mahakam River, East Borneo. July 8, 1912. Collected by H. C. Raven. Original number 118.

Well-made skin in good condition, except left forefoot missing; skull Grade A.

***Thecurus sumatrae** Lyon.

Proc. U. S. Nat. Mus. 32 : 583, June 29, 1907.

143432. Skin and skull. Adult male. Aru Bay, east coast of Sumatra. January 17, 1906. Collected by W. L. Abbott. Original number 4637.

Well-made skin in good condition; skull Grade A.

Genus TRICHYS Günther

*Trichys macrotis Miller.

Proc. U. S. Nat. Mus. 26: 469, Feb. 3, 1903.

114488. Skin and skull. Adult female. Tapanuli Bay, northwestern Sumatra. February 20, 1902. Collected by W. L. Abbott. Original number 1555.

Well-made skin in good condition; skull Grade A.

Family IDIURIDAE: African Flying Squirrels
Genus IDIURUS Matschie

*Idiurus macrotis Miller.

Proc. Biol. Soc. Washington 12: 73, Mar. 24, 1898.

83625. Skin and skull. Young adult male. Efulen, Cameroon district, West Africa. June 18, 1895. Collected by G. L. Bates. Original number 4.

Well-made skin in good condition; skull Grade C.

Family MURIDAE: Murine Rats and Mice
Genus ACOMYS Geoffroy

*Acomys hystrella Heller.

Smithsonian Misc. Coll. 56 (17) : 13, Feb. 28, 1911.

164821. Skin and skull. Adult female. Nimule, Uganda, Africa. February 4, 1910. Collected by J. Alden Loring. Original number 8929.

Well-made skin in good condition, skin on terminal half inch of tail lacking; skull Grade A.

*Acomys ignitis montanus Heller.

Smithsonian Misc. Coll. 63 (7) : 12, June 24, 1914.

182901. Skin only. Adult female. North slope of Mount Marsabit, altitude 4,600 feet, British East Africa [=Kenya]. February 26, 1911. Collected by A. Blayne Percival. Original number 309.

Well-made skin in good condition.

Genus AETHOMYS Thomas

*Epimys kaiseri centralis Heller.

Smithsonian Misc. Coll. 63 (7) : 10, June 24, 1914.

=Aethomys kaiseri helleri (Hollister). See Thomas, Ann. Mag. Nat. Hist. (ser. 9) 17: 177, Jan. 1926.

165035. Skin and skull. Adult male. Rhino Camp, Lado, Uganda, Africa. January 11, 1910. Collected by J. Alden Loring. Original number 8633.

Well-made skin in good condition; skull Grade A.

*Epimys kaiseri turneri Heller.

Smithsonian Misc. Coll. 63 (7) : 8, June 24, 1914.

=*Aethomys kaiseri turneri* (Heller). See Thomas, Ann. Mag. Nat. Hist. (ser. 9)
17: 177, Jan. 1926.

183395.   Skin and skull.   Adult female.   Kisumu, British East Africa
[=Kenya].   January 19, 1912.   Collected by H. J. Allen Turner.
Original number (Heller) 5121.

Well-made skin in good condition, left foreleg slightly injured; skull
Grade A.

Genus APODEMUS Kaup

*Mus arianus griseus True.   Cotypes.

Proc. U. S. Nat. Mus. 17: 8, May 8, 1894.   Preoccupied by [*Mus sylvaticus*]
var. *griseus* Palumbo, Ann. Agr. Sci. (ser. 2) 12: 72 (of separate), 1868,
and renamed *Apodemus flavicollis rusiges* Miller, Proc. Biol. Soc. Washington 26: 81, Mar. 22, 1913.

=*Apodemus sylvaticus rusiges* (Miller).   See Wroughton, Journ. Bombay Nat.
Hist. Soc. 26 (4) : 966, Jan. 31, 1920.

No type is mentioned, so that the three following skins and skulls, designated by numbers, on which the description of the species is based, are
taken as cotypes.   They were all collected by W. L. Abbott in Kashmir in
1891.

$\frac{20139}{35502}$.   Adult female.   Central Kashmir, altitude 8,500 feet, in pine
forest.   October 8, 1891.

Skin fairly well made, in good condition; skull Grade C.

$\frac{20144}{35507}$.   Young adult male.   Pir Panjal Range, Kashmir.   August
31, 1891.

Skin fairly well made, in good condition; skull Grade A.

$\frac{20151}{35514}$.   Male, apparently young.   Mountains of central Kashmir,
September 13, 1891.

Skin fairly well made, in fairly good condition; skull cannot be found.

Apodemus flavicollis rusiges Miller.

See *Mus arianus griseus* True.

*Apodemus microtis Miller.

Proc. Biol. Soc. Washington 25: 60, Apr. 13, 1912.

155471.   Skin and skull.   Adult male.   Vicinity of Dzharkent, Russian Turkestan.   November 11, 1909.   Collected by W. Rückbeil.
Original number 12.

Well-made skin in good condition; skull Grade A.

*Apodemus nigritalus Hollister.

Smithsonian Misc. Coll. 60 (24) : 1, Mar. 13, 1913.

175164. Skin and skull. Adult male. Tepucha, 25 miles southeast of Biisk, Altai Mountains, Siberia. August 6, 1912. Collected by N. Hollister. Original number 4438.

Well-made skin in good condition, extreme tip of tail missing; skull Grade A.

*Apodemus praetor Miller.

Proc. Biol. Soc. Washington 27: 89, May 11, 1914.

197792. Skin and skull. Adult male. Sungaree River, 60 miles southwest of Kirin, Kirin Province, Manchuria [=Manchukuo]. July 6, 1913. Collected by Arthur deC. Sowerby. Original number 625.

Well-made skin in good condition; skull Grade A.

Genus APOMYS Mearns

*Apomys bardus Miller.

Proc. U. S. Nat. Mus. 38: 402, Aug. 19, 1910.
=Apomys insignis bardus Miller. See Hollister, Proc. U. S. Nat. Mus. 46: 327, Dec. 31, 1913.

144582. Skin and skull. Adult male. Summit of Mount Bliss, altitude 5,750 feet, Mindanao, Philippine Islands. May 28, 1906. Collected by Edgar A. Mearns. Original number 6166.

Well-made skin in good condition; skull Grade A.

*Apomys hylocoetes Mearns.

Proc. U. S. Nat. Mus. 28: 456, May 13, 1905.

125246. Skin and skull. Adult female. Mount Apo, altitude 6,000 feet, southern Mindanao, Philippine Islands. July 2, 1904. Collected by Edgar A. Mearns. Original number 5696.

Well-made skin in good condition; skull Grade A.

*Apomys insignis Mearns.

Proc. U. S. Nat. Mus. 28: 459, May 13, 1905.

125230. Skin and skull. Adult female. Mount Apo, altitude 6,000 feet, southern Mindanao, Philippine Islands. July 8, 1904. Collected by Edgar A. Mearns. Original number 5711.

Well-made skin in good condition; skull Grade A.

*Apomys major Miller.

Proc. U. S. Nat. Mus. 38: 402, Aug. 19, 1910.

151513. Skin and skull. Adult female. Haights-in-the-Oaks, altitude 7,000 feet, Benguet, Luzon, Philippine Islands. August 2, 1907. Collected by Edgar A. Mearns. Original number 6531.

Well-made skin in good condition; skull Grade A.

*Apomys microdon Hollister.

> Proc. U. S. Nat. Mus. 46: 327, Dec. 31, 1913.

155145.   Skin and skull.   Adult male.   Biga, Catanduanes Island, Philippine Islands.   May 8, 1909.   Collected by D. B. Mackie.   Original number 6.

> Well-made skin but lacks right hindleg; end of tail dried, no wire: skull Grade C.

*Apomys musculus Miller.

> Proc. U. S. Nat. Mus. 38: 403, Aug. 19, 1910.

145770.   Skin and skull.   Adult female.   Camp John Hay, Baguio, altitude 5,000 feet, Benguet, Luzon, Philippine Islands.   May 6, 1907.   Collected by Edgar A. Mearns.   Original number 6409.

> Well-made skin in good condition; skull Grade A.

*Apomys petraeus Mearns.

> Proc. U. S. Nat. Mus. 28: 458, May 13, 1905.

125245.   Skin and skull.   Adult female.   Mount Apo, altitude 7,600 feet, in southern Mindanao, Philippine Islands.   June 30, 1904.   Collected by Edgar A. Mearns.   Original number 5690.

> Well-made skin in good condition; skull Grade A.

Genus ARVICANTHIS Lesson

*Arvicanthis abyssinicus centrosus Hollister.

> Smithsonian Misc. Coll. 66 (10) : 1, Oct. 26, 1916.

165167.   Skin and skull.   Adult male.   Rhino Camp, Lado, Uganda, Africa.   January 21, 1910.   Collected by J. Alden Loring.   Original number 8817.

> Well-made skin in good condition; skull Grade A.

*Arvicanthis abyssinicus virescens Heller.

> Smithsonian Misc. Coll. 63 (7) : 11, June 24, 1914.

183922.   Skin and skull.   Adult male.   Voi, British East Africa [=Kenya].   November 15, 1911.   Collected by Edmund Heller.   Original number 4775.

> Well-made skin in good condition; skull Grade A.

*Arvicanthis jebelae Heller.

> Smithsonian Misc. Coll. 56 (17) : 9, Feb. 28, 1911.
> =Arvicanthis testicularis jebelae Heller.   See Dollman, Ann. Mag. Nat. Hist. (ser. 8) 8 : 338, Sept. 1911.

164826.   Skin and skull.   Male.   Rhino Camp, Lado, Uganda, Africa.   January 16, 1910.   Collected by J. Alden Loring.   Original number 8762.

> Well-made skin in good condition; skull Grade A.

Genus BANDICOTA Gray

*Bandicota siamensis Kloss.

Journ. Nat. Hist. Soc. Siam 3: 282, Dec. 31, 1919.

221559. Skin and skull. Adult male. Tachin, Central Siam. October 23, 1916. Collected by C. Boden Kloss. Original number 2218.

Well-made skin in good condition; skull Grade A.

Genus BATOMYS Thomas

*Batomys dentatus Miller.

Proc. U. S. Nat. Mus. 38: 400, Aug. 19, 1910.

151506. Skin and skull. Adult male. Haights-in-the-Oaks, altitude 7,000 feet, Benguet, Luzon, Philippine Islands. July 31, 1907. Collected by Edgar A. Mearns. Original number 6484.

Well-made skin in good condition; skull Grade A.

Genus BULLIMUS Mearns

*Bullimus bagobus Mearns.

Proc. U. S. Nat. Mus. 28: 450, May 13, 1905.

125248. Skin and skull. Adult female. Todaya, altitude 4,000 feet, Mount Apo, southern Mindanao, Philippine Islands. July 13, 1904. Collected by Edgar A. Mearns. Original number 5729.

Fairly well-made skin in fair condition, slight loss of hair on lower abdomen; skull Grade A.

Genus CHIROPODOMYS Peters

*Chiropodomys niadis Miller.

Smithsonian Misc. Coll. 45: 40, Nov. 6, 1903.

121867. Skin and skull. Adult female. Lafau, Nias Island, off west coast of Sumatra. March 30, 1903. Collected by W. L. Abbott. Original number 2413.

Well-made skin in good condition; skull Grade A.

Genus CRICETOMYS Waterhouse

*Cricetomys gambianus enguvi Heller.

Smithsonian Misc. Coll. 59 (16): 16, July 5, 1912.

181805. Skin and skull. Adult female. Mount Umengo, altitude 5,000 feet, Taita Mountains, British East Africa [=Kenya]. November 13, 1911. Collected by Edmund Heller. Original number 4741.

Well-made skin in good condition; skull Grade A.

*Cricetomys gambianus osgoodi Heller.

Smithsonian Misc. Coll. 59 (16) : 16, July 5, 1912.

181806.   Skin and skull.   Adult male.   Mazeras, British East Africa [=Kenya].   December 20, 1911.   Collected by Edmund Heller.   Original number 4926.

Well-made skin in good condition; skull Grade A.

*Cricetomys gambianus raineyi Heller.

Smithsonian Misc. Coll. 59 (16) : 15, July 5, 1912.

181804.   Skin and skull.   Adult male.   Mount Gargues (Uaragess), altitude 6,000 feet, Mathews Range, British East Africa [=Kenya].   August 31, 1911.   Collected by Edmund Heller. Original number 4187.

Well-made skin in good condition; skull Grade A.

Genus DASYMYS Peters

*Dasymys helukus Heller.

Smithsonian Misc. Coll. 54 (6) : 2, Feb. 28, 1910.

162889.   Skin and skull.   Adult male.   Sirgoit, Guas Ngishu plateau, British East Africa [=Kenya].   November 19, 1909. Collected by Edmund Heller.   Original number 1239.

Well-made skin in good condition; skull Grade A.

*Dasymys helukus nigridius Hollister.

Smithsonian Misc. Coll. 66 (10) : 2, Oct. 26, 1916.

162465.   Skin and skull.   Adult female.   Naivasha Station, British East Africa [=Kenya].   August 20, 1909.   Collected by J. Alden Loring.   Original number 7054.

Well-made skin in good condition; skull Grade A.

*Dasymys orthos Heller.

Smithsonian Misc. Coll. 56 (17) : 13, Feb. 28, 1911.

164824.   Skin and skull.   Adult male.   Butiaba, Albert Nyanza, Uganda, Africa.   January 1, 1910.   Collected by J. Alden Loring.   Original number 8601.

Well-made skin in good condition; skull Grade A.

*Dasymys rufulus Miller.

Proc. Washington Acad. Sci. 2 : 639, Dec. 28, 1900.

83844.   Skin and skull.   Adult male.   Mount Coffee, Liberia, West Africa.   March 30, 1897.   Collected by R. P. Currie. Original number 19.

Well-made skin in good condition; skull Grade A.

*Dasymys savannus Heller.

Smithsonian Misc. Coll. 56 (17) : 14, Feb. 28, 1911.

=*Dasymys helukus savannus* Heller.   See Hollister, U. S. Nat Mus. Bull. 99 (pt. 2) : 122, May 16, 1919.

164471.   Skin and skull.   Adult female.   Fort Hall, British East Africa [=Kenya].   October 28, 1909.   Collected by J. Alden Loring.   Original number 8182.

Well-made skin in good condition; skull Grade A.

Genus DENDROMUS Smith

*Dendromus lineatus Heller.

Smithsonian Misc. Coll. 56 (17) : 4, Feb. 28, 1911.

164816.   Skin and skull.   Adult male.   Rhino Camp, Lado, Uganda, Africa.   February 1, 1910.   Collected by J. Alden Loring.   Original number 8921.

Well-made skin in good condition; skull Grade A.

*Dendromus mesomelas percivali Heller.

Smithsonian Misc. Coll. 59 (16) : 5, July 5, 1912.

=*Dendromus insignis percivali* Heller.   See Hollister, U. S. Nat. Mus. Bull. 99 (pt. 2) : 49, May 16, 1919.

181791.   Skin and skull.   Adult female.   Mount Gargues (Uaragess), altitude 7,000 feet, Mathews Range, British East Africa [=Kenya].   August 26, 1911.   Collected by A. B. Percival. Original number (Heller) 4100.

Well-made skin in good condition; skull Grade A.

*Dendromus whytei capitis Heller.

Smithsonian Misc. Coll. 59 (16) : 6, July 5, 1912.

181792.   Skin and skull.   Adult female.   Mount Lololokui, altitude 6,000 feet, Mathews Range, British East Africa [=Kenya]. September 8, 1911.   Collected by Edmund Heller.   Original number 4263.

Well-made skin in good condition; skull Grade A.

Genus DEPHOMYS Thomas

*Mus defua Miller.

Proc. Washington Acad. Sci. 2: 635, Dec. 28, 1900.

=*Dephomys defua* (Miller).   See Thomas, Ann. Mag. Nat. Hist. (ser. 9) 17: 177, Jan. 1926.

83837.   Skin and skull.   Adult male.   Mount Coffee, altitude 400 or 500 feet, Liberia, West Africa.   May 3, 1897.   Collected by R. P. Currie.   Original number 53.

Well-made skin in good condition; skull Grade A.

Genus ECHIOTHRIX Gray

*Echiothrix brevicula Miller and Hollister.

Proc. Biol. Soc. Washington 34: 67, Mar. 31, 1921.

219744. Skin and skull. Adult male. Pinedapa (about 5 miles inland from the Gulf of Tomini, near Mapane), Middle Celebes. January 29, 1918. Collected by H. C. Raven. Original number 3467.

Well-made skin in good condition, extreme tip of tail missing; skull Grade A.

*Echiothrix centrosa Miller and Hollister.

Proc. Biol. Soc. Washington 34: 67, Mar. 31, 1921.

218706. Skin and skull. Adult male. Winatoe (between Koelawi and Gimpoe), Middle Celebes. January 9, 1917. Collected by H. C. Raven. Original number 3077.

Well-made skin in good condition except for the absence of a small patch of hair on underparts; skull Grade A.

Genus EROPEPLUS Miller and Hollister

*Eropeplus canus Miller and Hollister.

Proc. Biol. Soc. Washington 34: 95, June 30, 1921.

218707. Skin and skull. Female. Goenoeng, altitude 6,000 feet, southwest from Lake Lindoe, Middle Celebes. January 12, 1917. Collected by H. C. Raven. Original number 3079.

Well-made skin in good condition; skull Grade A.

Genus GRAMMOMYS Thomas

*Thamnomys dolichurus littoralis Heller.

Smithsonian Misc. Coll. 59 (16) : 10, July 5, 1912.

=*Grammomys surdaster littoralis* (Heller). See Hollister, U. S. Nat. Mus. Bull. 99 (pt. 2) : 58, May 16, 1919; and St. Leger, Proc. Zool. Soc. London, 1931 (pt. 3) : 986, Sept. 30, 1931.

181799. Skin and skull. Adult male. Mazeras, British East Africa [=Kenya]. December 22, 1911. Collected by Edmund Heller. Original number 4949.

Well-made skin in good condition; skull Grade A.

Genus HYLOMYSCUS Thomas

*Epimys alleni kaimosae Heller.

Smithsonian Misc. Coll. 59 (16) : 7, July 5, 1912.

=*Hylomyscus stella kaimosae* (Heller). See Thomas, Ann. Mag. Nat. Hist. (ser. 9) 17 : 178, Jan. 1926.

181794. Skin and skull. Adult female. Kaimosi, Kakumega Forest, British East Africa [=Kenya]. February 1, 1912. Collected by Edmund Heller. Original number 5527.

Well-made skin in good condition; skull Grade A.

*Epimys endorobae Heller.

Smithsonian Misc. Coll. 56 (9) : 3, July 22, 1910.
=*Hylomyscus denniae* (Thomas). See Thomas, Ann. Mag. Nat. Hist. (ser. 9) 17 : 178, Jan. 1926.

162888. Skin and skull. Adult male. Western edge of Mau Forest, 25 miles north of Edoma Ravine, altitude 8,600 feet, British East Africa [=Kenya]. November 27, 1909. Collected by Edmund Heller. Original number 1261.

Well-made skin in good condition; skull Grade A.

Genus LEGGADA Gray

*Mus bellus enclavae Heller.

Smithsonian Misc. Coll. 56 (17) : 8, Feb. 28, 1911.
=*Leggada bella enclavae* (Heller). See St. Leger, Proc. Zool. Soc. London, 1931 (pt. 3) : 988, Sept. 30, 1931.

164818. Skin and skull. Adult male. Rhino Camp, Lado, Uganda, Africa. January 10, 1910. Collected by J. Alden Loring. Original number 8613.

Well-made skin in good condition; skull Grade A.

*Mus bellus gondokorae Heller.

Smithsonian Misc. Coll. 56 (17) : 8, Feb. 28, 1911.
=*Leggada bella gondokorae* (Heller). See St. Leger, Proc. Zool. Soc. London, 1931 (pt. 3) : 988, Sept. 30, 1931.

164820. Skin and skull. Adult male. Gondokoro, Uganda, Africa. February 25, 1910. Collected by J. Alden Loring. Original number 9089.

Well-made skin in good condition; skull Grade A.

*Mus bellus petilus Hollister.

Smithsonian Misc. Coll. 66 (10) : 3, Oct. 26, 1916.
=*Leggada bella petilus* (Hollister). See St. Leger, Proc. Zool. Soc. London, 1931 (pt. 3) : 988, Sept. 30, 1931.

162397. Skin and skull. Adult male. Southern Guaso Nyiro River, British East Africa [=Kenya]. June 28, 1909. Collected by J. Alden Loring. Original number 6450.

Well-made skin in good condition; skull Grade A.

*Mus gratus soricoides Heller.

Smithsonian Misc. Coll. 63 (7) : 10, June 24, 1914.
=*Leggada grata soricoides* (Heller). See St. Leger, Proc. Zool. Soc. London, 1931 (pt. 3) : 988, Sept. 30, 1931.

183544. Skin and skull. Adult male. Mount Mbololo, Taita Hills, British East Africa [=Kenya]. November 8, 1911. Collected by Edmund Heller. Original number 4675.

Well-made skin in good condition; skull Grade A.

*Mus gratus sungarae Heller.

Smithsonian Misc. Coll. 56 (17) : 7, Feb. 28, 1911.

=Leggada grata grata (Thomas). See G. M. Allen, Bull. Mus. Comp. Zool. 83 : 388, Feb. 1939.

163487. Skin and skull. Old male. Mount Kenia Forest Station, altitude 7,500 feet, British East Africa [=Kenya]. September 20, 1909. Collected by J. Alden Loring. Original number 7425.

Well-made skin in good condition; skull Grade A.

*Mus musculoides emesi Heller.

Smithsonian Misc. Coll. 56 (17) : 5, Feb. 28, 1911.

=Leggada emesi (Heller). See Hollister, U. S. Nat. Mus. Bull. 99 (pt. 2) : 96, May 16, 1919.

164819. Skin and skull. Adult male. Kabula Muliro, Uganda, Africa. December 27, 1909. Collected by J. Alden Loring. Original number 8497.

Well-made skin in good condition, small spot on left side devoid of hair; skull Grade A.

*Leggada naivashae Heller.

Smithsonian Misc. Coll. 54 (4) : 2, Feb. 28, 1910.

=Leggada triton triton Thomas. See Hollister, U. S. Nat. Mus. Bull. 99 (pt. 2) : 95, May 16, 1919; and Thomas, Ann. Mag. Nat. Hist. (ser. 8) 4 : 548, Dec. 1909.

162885. Skin and skull. Adult male. Naivasha Plains at base of Aberdare Mountains, British East Africa [=Kenya]. October 18, 1909. Collected by Edmund Heller. Original number 1186.

Well-made skin in good condition; skull Grade A.

*Mus tenellus acholi Heller.

Smithsonian Misc. Coll. 56 (17) : 6, Feb. 28, 1911.

=Leggada tenella acholi (Heller). See St. Leger, Proc. Zool. Soc. London, 1931 (pt. 3) : 988, Sept. 30, 1931.

164817. Skin and skull. Adult male. Rhino Camp, Lado, Uganda, Africa. January 13, 1910. Collected by J. Alden Loring. Original number 8671.

Well-made skin in good condition; skull Grade A.

*Mus wamae Heller.

Smithsonian Misc. Coll. 56 (17) : 5, Feb. 28, 1911.

=Leggada wamae (Heller).

161777. Skin and skull. Adult female. Kapiti Plains, British East Africa [=Kenya]. May 6, 1909. Collected by J. Alden Loring. Original number 6061.

Well-made skin in good condition but lacks both fore legs; skull Grade A.

Genus LEMNISCOMYS Trouessart

*Lemniscomys dorsalis mearnsi Heller.

Smithsonian Misc. Coll. 63 (7) : 12, June 24, 1914.
=Lemniscomys griselda mearnsi Heller. See Thomas, Ann. Mag. Nat. Hist. (ser. 8) 18: 69, July 1916.

163616. Skin and skull. Adult female. Fort Hall, altitude 6,200 feet, British East Africa [=Kenya]. Sept. 11, 1909. Collected by J. Alden Loring. Original number 7152.

Well-made skin in good condition; skull Grade A.

*Arvicanthis pulchellus micropus Heller.

Smithsonian Misc. Coll. 56 (17) : 9, Feb. 28, 1911.
=Lemniscomys striatus massaicus (Pagenstecher). See Hollister, U. S. Nat. Mus. Bull. 99 (pt. 2) : 139, May 16, 1919.

164825. Skin and skull. Adult female. Rhino Camp, Lado, Uganda, Africa. January 24, 1910. Collected by J. Alden Loring. Original number 8861.

Well-made skin in good condition; skull Grade A.

*Lemniscomys pulchellus spermophilus Heller.

Smithsonian Misc. Coll. 59 (16) : 11, July 5, 1912.
=Lemniscomys striatus massaicus (Pagenstecher). See Hollister, U. S. Nat. Mus. Bull. 99 (pt. 2) : 139, May 16, 1919.

181800. Skin and skull. Adult female. Mount Gargues (Uaragess), altitude 7,000 feet, Mathews Range, British East Africa [=Kenya]. August 26, 1911. Collected by Edmund Heller. Original number 4103.

Well-made skin in good condition; skull Grade A.

Genus LENOMYS Thomas

*Lenomys longicaudus Miller and Hollister.

Proc. Biol. Soc. Washington 34: 95, June 30, 1921.

219712. Skin and skull. Adult female. Gimpoe, Middle Celebes. September 1, 1917. Collected by H. C. Raven. Original number 3203.

Well-made skin in good condition; skull Grade A.

Genus LENOTHRIX Miller

*Lenothrix canus Miller.

Proc. U. S. Nat. Mus. 26: 466, Feb. 3, 1903.
Regarded as a Rattus by Chasen, Bull. Raffles Mus. 15: 182, Apr. 1940.

114386. Skin and skull. Adult male. Pulo Tuanku, west coast of Sumatra. January 27, 1902. Collected by W. L. Abbott. Original number 1477.

Well-made skin in good condition; skull Grade A.

Genus LIMNOMYS Mearns

*Limnomys mearnsi Hollister.

Proc. U. S. Nat. Mus. 46: 324, Dec. 31, 1913.

144622. Skin and skull. Adult female. Summit of Grand Malindang Peak, altitude 9,000 feet, Mindanao, Philippine Islands. June 7, 1906. Collected by Edgar A. Mearns. Original number 6190.

Well-made skin in good condition; skull Grade A.

*Limnomys picinus Hollister.

Proc. U. S. Nat. Mus. 46: 325, Dec. 31, 1913.

144605. Skin and skull. Adult female. Mount Halcon, altitude 4,500 feet, Mindoro, Philippine Islands. November 16, 1906. Collected by Edgar A. Mearns. Original number 6311.

Well-made skin in good condition; skull Grade B.

*Limnomys sibuanus Mearns.

Proc. U. S. Nat. Mus. 28: 452, May 13, 1905.

125228. Skin and skull. Adult female. Mount Apo, altitude 6,600 feet, southern Mindanao, Philippine Islands. June 30, 1904. Collected by Edgar A. Mearns. Original number 5688.

Well-made skin in good condition; skull Grade A.

Genus LOPHUROMYS Peters

*Mus aquilus True.

Proc. U. S. Nat. Mus. 15: 460, Oct. 26, 1892.
=*Lophuromys aquilus aquilus* (True). See Thomas, Proc. Zool. Soc. London, 1896 (pt. 4): 795, Apr. 1897.

$\frac{18997}{34723}$. Skin and skull. Adult male. Mount Kilimanjaro, altitude 8,000 feet, German East Africa [=Tanganyika Territory]. April 11, 1888. Collected by W. L. Abbott.

Fairly well-made skin in good condition; skull Grade C. The specimen was killed by a hawk.

*Lophuromys aquilus margarettae Heller.

Smithsonian Misc. Coll. 59 (16): 7, July 5, 1912.

181793. Skin and skull. Adult male. Mount Gargues (Uaragess), altitude 6,000 feet, Mathews Range, British East Africa [=Kenya]. August 27, 1911. Collected by Edmund Heller. Original number 4126.

Well-made skin in good condition; skull Grade A.

*Lophuromys nudicaudus Heller.

Smithsonian Misc. Coll. 56 (17) : 11, Feb. 28, 1911.

125436. Skin and skull. Adult male. Efulen, Bula country, Cameroons, West Africa. August 4, 1903. Collected by G. L. Bates. Original number 26.

Fairly well-made skin in good condition, small hole on upper side of right hind leg; skull Grade B, numerous minor defects.

*Lophuromys pyrrhus Heller.

Smithsonian Misc. Coll. 56 (17) : 10, Feb. 28, 1911.
=Lophuromys ansorgei pyrrhus Heller. See Hollister, U. S. Nat. Mus. Bull. 99 (pt. 2) : 112, May 16, 1919.

164823. Skin and skull. Adult male. Rhino Camp, Lado, Uganda, Africa. January 24, 1910. Collected by J. Alden Loring. Original number 8853.

Well-made skin in good condition; skull Grade A.

Genus MASTOMYS Thomas

*Epimys coucha durumae Heller.

Smithsonian Misc. Coll. 59 (16) ; 9, July 5, 1912.
=Mastomys coucha durumae (Heller). See St. Leger, Proc. Zool. Soc. London, 1931 (pt. 3) : 990, Sept. 30, 1931.

181796. Skin and skull. Adult male. Mazeras, British East Africa [=Kenya]. December 23, 1911. Collected by Edmund Heller. Original number 5002.

Well-made skin in good condition; skull Grade A.

*Epimys concha (=coucha) ismailiae Heller.

Smithsonian Misc. Coll. 63 (7) : 9, June 24, 1914.
=Mastomys coucha ismailiae (Heller). See St. Leger, Proc. Zool. Soc. London, 1931 (pt. 3) : 990, Sept. 30, 1931.

165108. Skin and skull. Adult male. Gondokoro, Uganda, Africa. February 23, 1910. Collected by J. Alden Loring. Original number 9056.

Well-made skin in good condition; skull Grade A.

*Epimys coucha neumani Heller.

Smithsonian Misc. Coll. 59 (16) : 8, July 5, 1912.
=Mastomys coucha neumani (Heller). See St. Leger, Proc. Zool. Soc. London, 1931 (pt. 3) : 990, Sept. 30, 1931.

181795.   Skin and skull.   Male.   Neuman's Boma, Northern Guaso Nyiro River, British East Africa [=Kenya].   September 26, 1911. Collected by Edmund Heller.   Original number 4372.

Well-made skin in good condition; skull Grade A.

*Rattus coucha tinctus Hollister.

Smithsonian Misc. Coll. 68 (10) : 1, Jan. 16, 1918.
=*Mastomys coucha tinctus* (Hollister).   See St. Leger, Proc. Zool. Soc. London, 1931 (pt. 3) : 990, Sept. 30, 1931.

183294.   Skin and skull.   Adult male.   Kaimosi, Kavirondo, British East Africa [=Kenya].   January 24, 1912.   Collected by Edmund Heller.   Original number 5188.

Well-made skin in good condition; skull Grade A.

*Epimys panya Heller.

Smithsonian Misc. Coll. 56 (9) : 2, pl. 2, July 22, 1910.
=*Mastomys coucha panya* (Heller).   See St. Leger, Proc. Zool. Soc. London, 1931 (pt. 3) : 990, Sept. 30, 1931.

161886.   Skin and skull.   Adult male.   Juja Farm, Athi Plains, British East Africa [=Kenya].   May 23, 1909.   Collected by J. Alden Loring.   Original number 6220.

Well-made skin in good condition; skull Grade A.

Genus MELASMOTHRIX Miller and Hollister

*Melasmothrix naso Miller and Hollister.

Proc. Biol. Soc. Washington 34: 94, June 30, 1921.

219752.   Skin and skull.   Old male.   Rano Rano, Middle Celebes. January 2, 1918.   Collected by H. C. Raven.   Original number 3368.

Well-made skin in good condition; skull Grade A.

Genus MUS Linnaeus

*Mus commissarius Mearns.

Proc. U. S. Nat. Mus. 28: 449, May 13, 1905.

125213.   Skin and skull.   Adult female.   Military commissary building at Davao, southern Mindanao, Philippine Islands.   July 19, 1904.   Collected by Edgar A. Mearns.   Original number 5734.

Fairly well-made skin in fair condition, some naked spots on belly; skull Grade A.

Genus MYLOMYS Thomas

*Pelomys roosevelti Heller.

Smithsonian Misc. Coll. 54 (4) : 1, Feb. 28, 1910.
=*Mylomys roosevelti* (Heller).   See Thomas, Ann. Mag. Nat. Hist. (ser. 8) 20: 363, Nov. 1917.

162881. Skin and skull. Adult male. Nzoia River, Guas Ngishu plateau, British East Africa [=Kenya]. November 16, 1909. Collected by Edmund Heller. Original number 1231.

Well-made skin in good condition; skull Grade A.

Genus MYOMYS Thomas

*Epimys niveiventris ulae Heller.

Smithsonian Misc. Coll. 56 (9) : 3, July 22, 1910.

=*Myomys fumatus fumatus* (Peters). See St. Leger, Proc. Zool. Soc. London, 1931 (pt. 3) : 991, Sept. 30, 1931.

162887. Skin and skull. Adult female. Ulukenia Hills, British East Africa [=Kenya]. November 19, 1909. Collected by J. Alden Loring. Original number 8221.

Well-made skin in good condition; skull Grade A.

*Mus tana True.

Proc. U. S. Nat. Mus. (16) : 602, Oct. 25, 1893.

=*Myomys fumatus tana* (True). See G. M. Allen, Bull. Mus. Comp. Zool. 83 : 406, Feb. 1939.

$\frac{21004}{36055}$ Skin, skull, and body in alcohol. Adult female. Along the Tana River, between the coast and Hameye, British East Africa [=Kenya]. November 1892. Collected by William Astor Chanler and Ludwig von Höhnel.

The specimen was originally in alcohol, but at the time the species was described it was made up into a skin, in good condition; skull Grade A.

Genus OENOMYS Thomas

*Oenomys hypoxanthus vallicola Heller.

Smithsonian Misc. Coll. 63 (7) : 11, June 24, 1914.

=*Oenomys bacchante vallicola* Heller. See Hollister, U. S. Nat. Mus. Bull. 99 (pt. 2) : 66, May 16, 1919.

162614. Skin and skull. Adult female. Lake Naivasha, British East Africa [=Kenya]. July 15, 1909. Collected by J. Alden Loring. Original number 6640.

Well-made skin in good condition; skull Grade B.

Genus OTOMYS Cuvier

*Otomys orestes dollmani Heller.

Smithsonian Misc. Coll. 59 (16) : 5, July 5, 1912.

=*Otomys dollmani* Heller. See Hollister, U. S. Nat. Mus. Bull. 99 (pt. 2) : 147, May 16, 1919.

181790. Skin and skull. Adult male. Mount Gargues (Uaragess), altitude 7,000 feet, Mathews Range, British East Africa [=Kenya]. August 27, 1911. Collected by Edmund Heller. Original number 4125.

Well-made skin in good condition; skull Grade A.

Genus PELOMYS Peters

*Pelomys fallax iridescens Heller.

Smithsonian Misc. Coll. 59 (16) : 12, July 5, 1912.

181801. Skin and skull. Adult male. Mount Mbololo, altitude 5,000 feet, Taita Mountains, British East Africa [=Kenya]. November 5, 1911. Collected by Edmund Heller. Original number 4620.

Well-made skin in good condition; skull Grade A.

Genus POEMYS Thomas

*Dendromys nigrifrons True.

Proc. U. S. Nat. Mus. 15 : 462, Oct. 26, 1892.

=*Poemys nigrifrons* (True). See Thomas, Ann. Mag. Nat. Hist. (ser. 8) 18 : 238, Aug. 1916.

$\frac{19783}{35263}$. Alcoholic, with skull removed. Adult female. Mount Kilimanjaro, altitude 5,000 feet, German East Africa [=Tanganyika Territory]. November 1889. Collected by W. L. Abbott. Original number 10.

Alcoholic in fair condition. A few small bare spots, the under side extensively cut open to remove skull, and then sewed up; skull Grade A.

No type designated by number. A skull is figured and marked "typical specimen." An examination of the five specimens collected by Abbott shows that the figured skull is No. 35263; consequently the specimen to which it belongs may be regarded as the type.

*Dendromus spectabilis Heller.

Smithsonian Misc. Coll. 56 (17) : 3, Feb. 28, 1911.

=*Poemys nigrifrons spectabilis* (Heller). See Thomas, Ann. Mag. Nat. Hist. (ser. 8) 18 : 238, Aug. 1916; and Hollister, U. S. Nat. Mus. Bull. 99 (pt. 2) : 54, May 16, 1919.

164815. Skin and skull. Adult female. Rhino Camp, Lado, Uganda, Africa. January 18, 1910. Collected by J. Alden Loring. Original number 8783.

Well-made skin in good condition; skull Grade A.

Genus PRAOMYS Thomas

*Mus peromyscus Heller.

Smithsonian Misc. Coll. 52 : 472, Nov. 13, 1909.

=*Praomys tullbergi peromyscus* (Heller).

161905. Skin and skull. Adult male. Njoro O Nyiro, Sotik, British East Africa [=Kenya]. June 9, 1909. Collected by Edmund Heller. Original number 1011.

Well-made skin in good condition; skull Grade A.

*Epimys taitae Heller.

Smithsonian Misc. Coll. 59 (16) : 9, July 5, 1912.
=*Praomys taitae* (Heller). See G. M. Allen and Lawrence, Bull. Mus. Comp. Zool. 79: 95, Jan. 1936.

181797. Skin and skull. Adult male. Mount Mbololo, altitude 5,000 feet, Taita Mountains, British East Africa [=Kenya]. November 5, 1911. Collected by Edmund Heller. Original number 4611.

Well-made skin in good condition; skull Grade A.

*Mus tullbergi rostratus Miller.

Proc. Washington Acad. Sci. 2 : 637, Dec. 28, 1900.
=*Praomys tullbergi rostratus* (Miller).

83836. Skin and skull. Adult male. Mount Coffee, altitude 400 to 500 feet, Liberia, West Africa. May 7, 1897. Collected by R. P. Currie. Original number 60.

Well-made skin in good condition; skull Grade A.

Genus RATTUS G. Fischer

*Rattus adspersus Miller and Hollister.

Proc. Biol. Soc. Washington 34: 71, Mar. 31, 1921.

219602. Skin and skull. Adult male. Pinedapa, Middle Celebes. January 22, 1918. Collected by H. C. Raven. Original number 3427.

Well-made skin in good condition; skull Grade A.

*Mus albigularis Mearns.

Proc. U. S. Nat. Mus. 28: 440, May 13, 1905.
=*Rattus albigularis* (Mearns). See Taylor, Philippine Land Mammals, p. 423, June 30, 1934.

125258. Skin and skull. Adult male. Mount Apo, 7,600 feet altitude, southern Mindanao, Philippine Islands. July 3, 1904. Collected by Edgar A. Mearns. Original number 5699.

Well-made skin in good condition; skull Grade A.

*Mus anambae Miller.

Proc. Washington Acad. Sci. 2 : 205, Aug. 20, 1900.
=*Rattus surifer anambae* (Miller). See Chasen and Kloss, Journ. Malay Branch Roy. Asiatic Soc. 6 (3) : 35, Aug. 1928.

101737. Skin and skull. Adult female. Pulo Jimaja, Anambas Islands, South China Sea, between Malay Peninsula and Borneo. September 21, 1899. Collected by W. L. Abbott.

Well-made skin in good condition, feet and tail slightly stained by corrosive sublimate; skull Grade A.

*Mus andrewsi J. A. Allen.

Bull. Amer. Mus. Nat. Hist. 30: 336, Dec. 21, 1911.
=*Rattus andrewsi* (Allen).

175899. Skin and skull. Adult male. Buton Island, Celebes. December 13, 1909. Collected by Roy C. Andrews. Original number 25.

Well-made skin in good condition; skull Grade A.

*Mus asper Miller.

Proc. Biol. Soc. Washington 13: 145, Apr. 21, 1900.
=*Rattus whiteheadi asper* (Miller). See Chasen, Bull. Raffles Mus. 15:181, Apr. 1940.

86767. Skin and skull. Adult female. Khow sai Dow, altitude 1,000 feet, Trong, Peninsular Siam. February 2, 1899. Collected by W. L. Abbott.

Well-made skin in good condition, feet and tail stained by corrosive sublimate; skull Grade A.

*Mus atratus Miller.

Proc. U. S. Nat. Mus. 24:767, May 28, 1902. Name preoccupied by *Mus atratus* Philippi (Anal. Mus. Nac. Chile, Zool. entr., 14: 57, 1900), and renamed *Mus atridorsum* Miller (Proc. Biol. Soc. Washington 16: 50, Mar. 19, 1903).
=*Rattus atridorsum* (Miller).

111868. Skin and skull. Adult female. Barren Island, Andaman Islands, Malay Archipelago. January 7, 1901. Collected by W. L. Abbott. Original number 818.

Well-made skin in good condition; skull Grade A.

Mus atridorsum Miller.

See *Mus atratus* Miller.

*Mus balae Miller.

Smithsonian Misc. Coll. 45: 33, Nov. 6, 1903.
=*Rattus sabanus balae* (Miller). See Chasen, Bull. Raffles Mus. 15:167, Apr. 1940.

121781. Skin and skull. Adult female. Tana Bala, Batu Islands, off west coast of Sumatra. February 12, 1903. Collected by W. L. Abbott. Original number 2274.

Well-made skin in good condition; skull Grade A.

*Rattus balmasus Lyon.

Proc. U. S. Nat. Mus. 52: 447, Dec. 30, 1916.
=*Rattus mülleri balmasus* Lyon. See Chasen, Bull. Raffles Mus. 15:161, Apr. 1940.

121765. Skin and skull. Adult female. Tana Bala, Batu Islands, off west coast of Sumatra. February 13, 1903. Collected by W. L. Abbott. Original number 2286.

Well-made skin in good condition; skull Grade B.

*Epimys barussanus Miller.

Proc. Biol. Soc. Washington 24: 26, Feb. 24, 1911.
=*Rattus cremoriventer barussanus* (Miller). See Chasen, Bull. Raffles Mus. 15, 175, Apr. 1940.

141208. Skin and skull. Adult male. Mojeia River, Nias Island, off west coast of Sumatra. March 10, 1905. Collected by W. L. Abbott. Original number 4016.

Well-made skin in good condition, feet, sides of head, ears, and tail stained by corrosive sublimate; skull Grade A.

*Epimys basilanus Hollister.

Proc. U. S. Nat. Mus. 46: 322, Dec. 31, 1913.
=*Rattus basilanus* (Hollister). See Taylor, Philippine Land Mammals, p. 455, June 30, 1934.

144635. Skin and skull. Adult male. Basilan Island, Philippine Islands. February 1906. Collected by Edgar A. Mearns. Original number 6039.

Well-made skin in good condition; skull Grade A.

*Mus batamanus Lyon.

Proc. U. S. Nat. Mus. 31: 654, Jan. 16, 1907.
=*Rattus whiteheadi batamanus* (Lyon). See Chasen, Bull. Raffles Mus. 10: 19, Oct. 1935.

143232. Skin and skull. Adult male. Senimba Bay, Batam Island, Rhio-Linga Archipelago. March 30, 1906. Collected by C. Boden Kloss. Original number 75.

Well-made skin in good condition; skull Grade A.

*Epimys batus Miller.

Proc. Biol. Soc. Washington 24: 27, Feb. 24, 1911.
=*Rattus whiteheadi batus* (Miller). See Chasen, Bull. Raffles Mus. 15, 181, Apr. 1940.

121792. Skin and skull. Adult female. Pulo Pinie, Batu Islands, off west coast of Sumatra. March 4, 1903. Collected by W. L. Abbott. Original number 2368.

Well-made skin in good condition; skull Grade A.

*Epimys benguetensis Hollister.

Proc. U. S. Nat. Mus. 46: 323, Dec. 31, 1913.
=*Rattus benguetensis* (Hollister). See Taylor, Philippine Land Mammals, p. 443, June 30, 1934.

145790. Skin and skull. Adult female. Camp John Hay, Baguio, altitude 5,000 feet, Benguet Province, Luzon, Philippine Islands. May 1, 1907. Collected by Edgar A. Mearns. Original number 6405.

Well-made skin in good condition, lacks left foreleg; skull Grade A.

*Mus bentincanus Miller.

Smithsonian Misc. Coll. 45: 38, Nov. 6, 1903.
=*Rattus bentincanus* (Miller).

104269. Skin and skull. Adult female. Bentinck Island, Mergui Archipelago. March 11, 1900. Collected by W. L. Abbott. Original number 348.

Well-made skin in good condition, feet, tail, and ears stained by corrosive sublimate; skull Grade A.

*Epimys borneanus Miller.

Smithsonian Misc. Coll. 61 (21) : 15, Dec. 29, 1913.
=*Rattus mülleri borneanus* (Miller). See Chasen and Kloss, Journ. Malay Branch Roy. Asiatic Soc. 6 (pt. 1) : 47, Mar. 1928.

196749. Skin and skull. Adult female. Telok Karang, Tigua, Dutch Southeast Borneo. August 12, 1912. Collected by H. C. Raven. Original number 157.

Well-made skin in good condition; skull Grade A.

*Mus bullatus Lyon.

Proc. U. S. Nat. Mus. 34: 646, Sept. 14, 1908.
=*Rattus annandalei bullatus* (Lyon). See Chasen, Bull. Raffles Mus. 15: 161, Apr. 1940.

143447. Skin and skull. Adult male. Pulo Rupat, off east coast of Sumatra. March 16, 1906. Collected by W. L. Abbott. Original number 4723.

Well-made skin in good condition; skull Grade A.

*Mus burrescens Miller.

Proc. U. S. Nat. Mus. 24: 771, May 28, 1902.
=*Rattus burrescens* (Miller).

111789. Skin and skull. Adult female. Great Nicobar, Nicobar Islands, Malay Archipelago. March 12, 1901. Collected by W. L. Abbott. Original number 926.

Well-made skin in good condition, feet and tail stained by corrosive sublimate; skull Grade A.

*Mus burrulus Miller.

Proc. U. S. Nat. Mus. 24: 770, May 28, 1902.
=*Rattus burrulus* (Miller).

111817. Skin and skull. Adult male. Car Nicobar, Nicobar Islands, Malay Archipelago. January 25, 1901. Collected by W. L. Abbott. Original number 865.

Well-made skin in good condition, feet and tail stained by corrosive sublimate; skull Grade A.

*Mus burrus Miller.

Proc. U. S. Nat. Mus. 24: 768, May 28, 1902.
=*Rattus burrus* (Miller).

111811. Skin and skull. Adult female. Trinkut Island, Nicobar Islands, Malay Archipelago. February 5, 1902. Collected by W. L. Abbott. Original number 881.

Well-made skin in good condition, feet and tail stained by corrosive sublimate; skull Grade A.

*Mus buruensis J. A. Allen.

Bull. Amer. Mus. Nat. Hist. 30: 336, Dec. 21, 1911.
=*Rattus buruensis* (Allen).

175900. Skin and skull. Adult male. Bouru Island, Molucca Islands, Dutch East Indies. December 11, 1909. Collected by Roy C. Andrews. Original number 24.

Well-made skin in good condition; skull Grade B.

*Epimys calcis Hollister.

Proc. Biol. Soc. Washington 24: 89, May 15, 1911.
=*Rattus calcis* (Hollister). See Taylor, Philippine Land Mammals, Bur. Sci. Monogr. 30: 458, June 30, 1934.

145771. Skin and skull. Young adult male. Baguio (Limestone Hills, near Lime Kiln, at 5,000 feet), Benguet Province, Luzon, Philippine Islands. May 8, 1907. Collected by Edgar A. Mearns. Original number 6412.

Fairly well-made skin in good condition except for small spot on belly which lacks hair; skull Grade A.

*Mus carimatae Miller.

Proc. U. S. Nat. Mus. 31: 59, July 23, 1906.
=*Rattus surifer carimatae* (Miller). See Chasen, Bull. Raffles Mus. 15:174, Apr. 1940.

125079. Skin and skull. Adult male. Telok Pai, Karimata Island, off west coast of Borneo. August 20, 1904. Collected by W. L. Abbott. Original number 3612.

Well-made skin in good condition; skull Grade A.

*Mus casensis Miller.

Smithsonian Misc. Coll. 45: 38, Nov. 6, 1903.
=*Rattus surifer casensis* (Miller). See Gyldenstolpe, Journ. Nat. Hist. Soc. Siam 3: 164, Aug. 1, 1919.

104249. Skin and skull. Adult male. Chance Island, Mergui Archipelago. December 28, 1899. Collected by W. L. Abbott. Original number 188.

Fairly well-made skin in good condition, end of tail lost during life; hind feet, tail, and ears stained by corrosive sublimate; skull Grade A.

*Mus catellifer Miller.

Proc. U. S. Nat. Mus. 26: 464, Feb. 3, 1903.
=*Rattus surifer catellifer* (Miller). See Chasen, Bull. Raffles Mus. 15: 173, Apr. 1940.

114590. Skin and skull. Adult female. Pulo Mansalar, off Tapanuli Bay, west coast of Sumatra. March 3, 1902. Collected by W. L. Abbott. Original number 1587.

Well-made skin in good condition, feet, tail, and ears stained by corrosive sublimate; skull Grade A.

*Mus chombolis Lyon.

Proc. U. S. Nat. Mus. 36: 484, June 1, 1909.
=*Rattus mülleri chombolis* (Lyon). See Chasen, Bull. Raffles Mus. 15: 162, Apr. 1940.

144393. Skin and skull. Adult female. Pulo Jombol, Rhio-Linga Archipelago. March 10, 1907. Collected by W. L. Abbott. Original number 5100.

Well-made skin in good condition; skull Grade A.

*Mus clabatus Lyon.

Proc. U. S. Nat. Mus. 31: 596, Dec. 18, 1906.
==*Rattus clabatus* (Lyon).

124888. Skin and skull. Adult female. Klabat Bay, island of Banka, off east coast of Sumatra. June 25, 1904. Collected by W. L. Abbott. Original number 3439.

Well-made skin in good condition; skull Grade B.

*Epimys coloratus Hollister.

Proc. U. S. Nat. Mus. 46: 317, Dec. 31, 1913.
=*Rattus coloratus* (Hollister). See Taylor, Philippine Land Mammals, Bur. Sci. Monogr. 30: 434, June 30, 1934.

144571. Skin and skull. Adult female. Musser's Plantation, 3 miles west of Isobela, Basilan Island, Philippine Islands. February 21, 1906. Collected by Edgar A. Mearns. Original number 6044.

Well-made skin in good condition; skull Grade A.

*Epimys crassus Lyon.

Proc. U. S. Nat. Mus. 40: 103, Apr. 25, 1911.
=*Rattus mülleri crassus* (Lyon). See Chasen, Bull. Raffles Mus. 15: 163, Apr. 1940.

145471. Skin and skull. Adult male. Pulo Lamukotan, off west coast of Borneo. May 8, 1907. Collected by W. L. Abbott. Original number 5190.

Well-made skin in good condition; skull Grade A.

*Mus cremoriventer Miller.

Proc. Biol. Soc. Washington 13: 144, Apr. 21, 1900.
=*Rattus cremoriventer cremoriventer* (Miller). See Gyldenstolpe, Journ. Nat. Hist. Soc. Siam 3: 166, Aug. 1, 1919.

86770. Skin and skull. Adult male. Khow Nok Ram, altitude 3,000 feet, Trong, Peninsular Siam. January 16, 1899. Collected by W. L. Abbott.

Well-made skin in good condition, feet, tail, and head stained by corrosive sublimate; skull Grade A.

*Mus domelicus Miller.

Smithsonian Misc. Coll. 45: 39, Nov. 6, 1903.
=*Rattus domelicus* (Miller).

104257. Skin and skull. Adult female. Domel Island, Mergui Archipelago. February 24, 1900. Collected by W. L. Abbott. Original number 320.

Well-made skin in good condition; skull Grade B.

*Rattus dominator camurus Miller and Hollister.

Proc. Biol. Soc. Washington 34: 96, June 30, 1921.

219566. Skin and skull. Adult male. Pinedapa, Middle Celebes. January 15, 1918. Collected by H. C. Raven. Original number 3384.

Well-made skin in good condition; skull Grade A.

*Mus domitor Miller.

Proc. U. S. Nat. Mus. 26: 461, Feb. 3, 1903.
=*Rattus mülleri domitor* (Miller). See Chasen, Bull. Raffles Mus. 15: 161, Apr. 1940.

114621. Skin and skull. Adult female. Pulo Mansalar, at entrance to Tapanuli Bay, west coast of Sumatra. March 4, 1902. Collected by W. L. Abbott. Original number 1592.

Well-made skin in good condition; skull Grade A.

*Mus enganus Miller.

Proc. U. S. Nat. Mus. 30: 821, June 4, 1906.
=*Rattus enganus* (Miller). See Lyon, Proc. U. S. Nat. Mus. 52: 460, Dec. 30, 1916.

140976. Skin and skull. Adult male. Engano Island, off west coast of Sumatra. December 4, 1904. Collected by W. L. Abbott. Original number 3823.

Well-made skin in good condition; skull Grade A.

*Mus exulans Peale.   Lectotype.

U. S. Exploring Expedition 8 (Mammalia and Ornithology) : 47, 1848.
=*Rattus exulans* (Peale). See Tate, Bull. Amer. Mus. Nat. Hist. 68 (3) : 146,
Feb. 11, 1935.

3730. Mounted skin with cork skull inside. Tahiti, Society Islands.
Collected by U. S. Exploring Expedition (1838–42). Cataloged
December 20, 1859. Peale (1848, pp. 47–48) designates no type
specimen but gives measurements of specimens from Dog Island,
Disappointment Island, Tahiti, Wakes Island, and Hulls Island
(p. 48). Same list of islands on p. 306, but Tahiti placed first.

Specimen old, dirty, much bleached, tail broken off but still present.
It was mounted on a walnut stand with this inscription painted on the
bottom : "3730 *Mus exulans*, Peale (Type) (*Mus penicillatus*, Gould) Tahiti
Rat Society Ids. T. R. Peale." This specimen is, accordingly, now chosen as
the lectotype.

*Rattus facetus Miller and Hollister.

Proc. Biol. Soc. Washington 34 : 96, June 30, 1921.

218677. Skin and skull. Adult female. Goenoeng Lehio, southwest of Lake Lindoe, altitude 6,000 feet, Middle Celebes. January 15, 1917. Collected by H. C. Raven. Original number 3092.

Well-made skin in good condition; skull Grade A.

*Mus ferreocanus Miller.

Proc. Biol. Soc. Washington 13 : 140, Apr. 21, 1900.
=*Rattus bowersii ferreocanus* (Miller). See Chasen, Bull. Raffles Mus. 15 : 183,
Apr. 1940.

86737. Skin and skull. Adult female. Khow Nok Ram, altitude
3,000 feet, Trong, Peninsular Siam. January 15, 1899. Collected
by W. L. Abbott.

Well-made skin in good condition, except for a slight scar on the lower
back; feet and tail stained by corrosive sublimate; skull Grade A.

*Mus firmus Miller.

Proc. Acad. Nat. Sci. Philadelphia 54 : 155, June 11, 1902.
=*Rattus mülleri firmus* (Miller). See Chasen, Bull. Raffles Mus. 10 : 21,
Oct. 1935.

113038. Skin and skull. Adult female. Linga Island, Rhio-Linga
Archipelago. August 25, 1901. Collected by W. L. Abbott.
Original number 1215.

Well-made skin in good condition, feet and ears stained by corrosive
sublimate; skull Grade A.

*Mus flaviventer Miller.

Proc. Washington Acad. Sci. 2 : 204, Aug. 20, 1900.
=*Rattus cremoriventer flaviventer* (Miller). See Chasen, Bull. Raffles Mus. 15 :
175, Apr. 1940.

101739. Skin and skull. Adult male. Pulo Jimaja, Anambas Islands, South China Sea, between Malay Peninsula and Borneo. September 18, 1899. Collected by W. L. Abbott.

Well-made skin in good condition, feet and sides of head slightly stained by corrosive sublimate; skull Grade A.

*Mus flebilis Miller.

Proc. U. S. Nat. Mus. 24 : 762, May 28, 1902.
=Rattus flebilis (Miller).

111841. Skin and skull. Adult female. Henry Lawrence Island, Andaman Islands, Malay Archipelago. January 9, 1901. Collected by W. L. Abbott. Original number 827.

Well-made skin in good condition; feet and tail stained by corrosive sublimate; skull Grade A.

*Mus fremens Miller.

Proc. Acad. Nat. Sci. Philadelphia 54 : 154, June 11, 1902.
=Rattus sabanus fremens (Miller). See Chasen, Bull. Raffles Mus. 15 : 166, Apr. 1940.

113087. Skin and skull. Adult male. Sinkep Island, Rhio-Linga Archipelago. September 4, 1901. Collected by W. L. Abbott. Original number 1273.

Well-made skin in good condition; feet and tail stained by corrosive sublimate; skull Grade A.

*Rattus fremens mansalaris Lyon.

Proc. U. S. Nat. Mus. 52 : 450, Dec. 30, 1916.
=Rattus sabanus mansalaris Lyon. See Chasen, Bull. Raffles Mus. 15 : 167, Apr. 1940.

114583. Skin and skull. Adult male. Pulo Mansalar, off west coast of Sumatra. March 4, 1902. Collected by W. L. Abbott. Original number 1591.

Well-made skin in good condition; feet and tail stained by corrosive sublimate; skull Grade A.

*Rattus fremens tuancus Lyon.

Proc. U. S. Nat. Mus. 52 : 451, Dec. 30, 1916.
=Rattus sabanus tuancus Lyon. See Chasen, Bull. Raffles Mus. 15 : 167, Apr. 1940.

114402. Skin and skull. Adult male. Pulo Tuanku, Banjak Islands, off west coast of Sumatra. January 26, 1902. Collected by W. L. Abbott. Original number 1470.

Well-made skin in good condition; feet and tail stained by corrosive sublimate; skull Grade A.

*Epimys fulmineus Miller.

Smithsonian Misc. Coll. 61 (21) : 9, Dec. 29, 1913.
=Rattus fulmineus (Miller).

112349. Skin and skull. Adult female. Santa Barbe Island, South China Sea, between Sumatra and Borneo. May 27, 1901. Collected by W. L. Abbott. Original number 950.

Well-made skin in good condition; feet and tail stained by corrosive sublimate; skull Grade A.

*Epimys gala Miller.

Proc. U. S. Nat. Mus. 38 : 398, Aug. 19, 1910.

=*Rattus gala* (Miller). See Taylor, Philippine Land Mammals, Bur. Sci. Monogr. 30 : 421, June 30, 1934.

144633. Skin and skull. Adult male. Alag River, Mindoro, Philippine Islands. November 30, 1906. Collected by Edgar A. Mearns. Original number 6334.

Well-made skin in good condition; skull Grade A.

*Mus gilbiventer Miller.

Smithsonian Misc. Coll. 45 : 35, Nov. 6, 1903.

=*Rattus gilbiventer* (Miller).

104153. Skin and skull. Adult male. Sullivan Island, Mergui Archipelago. February 2, 1900. Collected by W. L. Abbott. Original number 295.

Well-made skin in good condition; skull Grade A.

*Epimys gracilis Miller.

Smithsonian Misc. Coll. 61 (21) : 21, Dec. 29, 1913.

=*Rattus gracilis* (Miller).

101520. In alcohol (skull removed). Adult female. Mount Mooleyit, northern Tenasserim. Collected by L. Fea. Received from Genoa Museum.

Skin in fair condition, hair has sloughed from belly and on top of head; skull Grade A.

*Rattus hamatus Miller and Hollister.

Proc. Biol. Soc. Washington 34 : 97, June 30, 1921.

218680. Skin and skull. Adult male. Goenoeng Lehio, Middle Celebes. January 16, 1917. Collected by H. C. Raven. Original number 3095.

Well-made skin in good condition, extreme tip of tail broken off; skull Grade A.

*Rattus hellwaldii cereus Miller and Hollister.

Proc. Biol. Soc. Washington 34 : 74, Mar. 31, 1921.

200232. Skin and skull. Adult male. Toli Toli, northwestern Celebes. November 30, 1914. Collected by H. C. Raven. Original number 1846.

Well-made skin in good condition; skull Grade A.

*Rattus hellwaldii localis Miller and Hollister.

Proc. Biol. Soc. Washington 34: 74, Mar. 31, 1921.

218120. Skin and skull. Adult male. Laboea Sore (north of Parigi), Celebes. December 1, 1916. Collected by H. C. Raven. Original number 2987.

Well-made skin in good condition; skull Grade A.

*Rattus hoffmanni linduensis Miller and Hollister.

Proc. Biol. Soc. Washington 34: 70, Mar. 31, 1921.

218700. Skin and skull. Adult female. Tomado, Lake Lindoe, Middle Celebes. March 28, 1917. Collected by H. C. Raven. Original number 3141.

Well-made skin in good condition except for imperfect ears; skull Grade A.

*Rattus hoffmanni subditivus Miller and Hollister.

Proc. Biol. Soc. Washington 34: 70, Mar. 31, 1921.

219691. Skin and skull. Adult female. Toware, Bada, Middle Celebes. September 18, 1917. Collected by H. C. Raven. Original number 3270.

Well-made skin in good condition; skull Grade A.

*Rattus humiliatus insolatus A. B. Howell.

Proc. Biol. Soc. Washington 40: 44, Mar. 5, 1927.

172569. Skin and skull. Adult female. Twelve miles south of Yenanfu, altitude 4,000 feet, Shensi, China. January 12, 1909. Collected by Arthur deC. Sowerby. Original number 413.

Well-made skin in good condition; skull Grade A.

*Rattus humiliatus sowerbyi A. B. Howell.

Proc. Biol. Soc. Washington 41: 42, Mar. 16, 1928.

199620. Skin and skull. Young adult male. Near Imienpo, altitude 500 feet, north Kirin, Manchuria. October 15, 1914. Collected by Arthur deC. Sowerby. Original number 735.

Well-made skin in good condition; skull Grade A.

*Mus integer Miller.

Proc. Washington Acad. Sci. 3: 119, Mar. 26, 1901.

=Rattus mülleri integer (Miller). See Chasen, Bull. Raffles Mus. 10: 21, Oct. 1935.

104837. Skin and skull. Adult male. Sirhassen Island, Natuna Islands, South China Sea, between Malay Peninsula and Borneo. June 7, 1900. Collected by W. L. Abbott. Original number 455.

Well-made skin in good condition, feet, ears, and several small spots on body stained by corrosive sublimate; skull Grade A.

*Mus julianus Miller.

Smithsonian Misc. Coll. 45 : 34, Nov. 6, 1903.

=*Rattus rattus julianus* (Miller). See Chasen, Bull. Raffles Mus. 15 : 157, Apr. 1940.

112393. Skin and skull. Adult female. St. Julian Island, South China Sea, between Sumatra and Borneo. June 2, 1901. Collected by W. L. Abbott. Original number 987.

Well-made skin in good condition, feet and tail stained by corrosive sublimate; skull Grade A.

*Mus kelleri Mearns.

Proc. U. S. Nat. Mus. 28 : 444, May 13, 1905.

=*Rattus kelleri* (Mearns). See Taylor, Philippine Land Mamm., Bur. Sci. Monogr. 30 : 440, June 30, 1934.

125278. Skin and skull. Adult female. Davao, southern Mindanao, Philippine Islands. July 20, 1904. Collected by Edgar A. Mearns. Original number 5738.

Well-made skin in good condition; skull Grade A.

*Epimys lepidus Miller.

Smithsonian Misc. Coll. 61 (21) : 20, Dec. 29, 1913.

=*Rattus lepidus* (Miller). See Kloss, Journ. Nat. Hist. Soc. Siam 3 : 60, Feb. 25, 1919.

104127. Skin and skull. Adult female. Bok Pyin, southern Tenasserim. February 19, 1900. Collected by W. L. Abbott. Original number 315.

Well-made skin in good condition, feet, tail, ears and top of head stained by corrosive sublimate; skull Grade A.

*Epimys leucophaeatus Hollister.

Proc. U. S. Nat. Mus. 46 : 320, Dec. 31, 1913.

=*Rattus leucophaeatus* (Hollister). See Taylor, Philippine Land Mammals, Bur. Sci. Monogr. 30 : 456, June 30, 1934.

155144. Skin and skull. Adult female. Bagamanoc, Catanduanes Island, Philippine Islands. May 27, 1909. Collected by D. B. Mackie. Original number 5.

Well-made skin in good condition; skull Grade A.

*Mus lingensis Miller.

Proc. Washington, Acad. Sci. 2 : 206, Aug. 20, 1900.

=*Rattus surifer lingensis* (Miller). See Chasen, Bull. Raffles Mus. 15 : 172, Apr. 1940.

101614. Skin and skull. Adult male. Linga Island, Rhio-Linga Archipelago. July 15, 1899. Collected by W. L. Abbott.

Well-made skin in good condition but pelage worn, feet and tail stained by corrosive sublimate; skull Grade B.

*Rattus lingensis antucus Lyon.

Proc. U. S. Nat. Mus. 52: 449, Dec. 30, 1916.
=Rattus surifer antucus Lyon. See Chasen, Bull. Raffles Mus. 15:173, Apr. 1940.

114390. Skin and skull. Adult female. Pulo Tuanku, Banjak Islands, off west coast of Sumatra. January 28, 1902. Collected by W. L. Abbott. Original number 1484.

Well-made skin in good condition, feet and tail stained by corrosive sublimate; skull Grade A.

*Rattus lingensis banacus Lyon.

Proc. U. S. Nat. Mus. 52: 449, Dec. 30, 1916.
=Rattus surifer banacus Lyon. See Chasen, Bull. Raffles Mus. 15: 173, Apr. 1940.

114294. Skin and skull. Adult male. Pulo Bankura, Banjak Islands, off west coast of Sumatra. January 19, 1902. Collected by W. L. Abbott. Original number 1434.

Well-made skin in good condition, tail broken near tip, underparts of body stained bright yellow, feet and tail stained by corrosive sublimate; skull Grade A.

*Rattus lingensis mabalus Lyon.

Proc. U. S. Nat. Mus. 52: 449, Dec. 30, 1916.
=Rattus surifer mabalus Lyon. See Chasen, Bull. Raffles Mus. 15: 174, Apr. 1940.

121825. Skin and skull. Adult female. Tana Masa, Batu Islands, off west coast of Sumatra. February 19, 1903. Collected by W. L. Abbott. Original number 2310.

Well-made skin in good condition; skull Grade A.

*Rattus lingensis pinacus Lyon.

Proc. U. S. Nat. Mus. 52: 450, Dec. 30, 1916.
=Rattus surifer pinacus Lyon. See Chasen, Bull. Raffles Mus. 15: 174, Apr. 1940.

121846. Skin and skull. Adult female. Pulo Pinie, Batu Islands, off west coast of Sumatra. March 2, 1903. Collected by W. L. Abbott. Original number 2349.

Well-made skin in good condition, feet and tail stained by corrosive sublimate; skull Grade A.

*Mus lucas Miller.

Smithsonian Misc. Coll. 45: 30, Nov. 6, 1903.
=Rattus sabanus lucas (Miller). See Chasen, Bull. Raffles Mus. 15: 165, Apr. 1940.

251543—42——31

104190. Skin and skull. Adult female. St. Luke Island, Mergui Archipelago. January 20, 1900. Collected by W. L. Abbott. Original number 253.

Well-made skin in good condition, feet and tail stained by corrosive sublimate; skull Grade A.

*Mus lugens Miller.

Smithsonian Misc. Coll. 45: 33, Nov. 6, 1903.
=*Rattus rattus lugens* (Miller). See Chasen, Bull. Raffles Mus. 15: 158, Apr. 1940.

121533. Skin and skull. Adult female. North Pagi Island, off west coast of Sumatra. November 15, 1902. Collected by W. L. Abbott. Original number 2046.

Well-made skin in good condition, feet and tail stained by corrosive sublimate; skull Grade A.

*Epimys luta Miller.

Smithsonian Misc. Coll. 61 (21) : 18, Dec. 29, 1913.
=*Rattus sabanus luta* (Miller). See Chasen, Bull. Raffles Mus. 15: 164, Apr. 1940.

151917. Skin and skull. Adult female. Pulo Laut, Dutch southeast Borneo. December 24, 1907. Collected by W. L. Abbott. Original number 5682.

Well-made skin in good condition, right ear slightly damaged; skull Grade A.

*Mus luteolus Miller.

Smithsonian Misc. Coll. 45: 36, Nov. 6, 1903.
=*Rattus surifer luteolus* (Miller). See Chasen, Bull. Raffles Mus. 15: 168, Apr. 1940.

104276. Skin and skull. Adult female. St. Matthew Island, Mergui Archipelago. January 15, 1900. Collected by W. L. Abbott. Original number 226.

Well-made skin in good condition, feet and tail stained by corrosive sublimate; skull Grade A.

*Epimys maerens Miller.

Proc. Biol. Soc. Washington 24: 26, Feb. 24, 1911.
=*Rattus rattus maerens* (Miller). See Chasen, Bull. Raffles Mus. 15: 158, Apr. 1940.

141193. Skin and skull. Adult female. Mouth of Mojeia River, Nias Island, off west coast of Sumatra. March 11, 1905. Collected by W. L. Abbott. Original number 4062.

Well-made skin in good condition, feet and tail stained by corrosive sublimate; skull Grade A.

*Mus magnirostris Mearns.

Proc. U. S. Nat. Mus. 28: 441, May 13, 1905.
=*Rattus magnirostris* (Mearns). See Taylor, Philippine Land Mammals, Bur. Sci. Monogr. 30: 430, June 30, 1934.

125212. Skin and skull. Adult female. Zamboanga (old Spanish hospital), western Mindanao, Philippine Islands. January 15, 1904. Collected by Edgar A. Mearns. Original number 5639.

Well-made skin in good condition; skull Grade A.

*Mus mandus Lyon.

Proc. U. S. Nat. Mus. 34: 644, Sept. 14, 1908.
=*Rattus mandus* (Lyon).

144225. Skin and skull. Adult male. Sungei Mandau (tributary to the Siak River), eastern Sumatra. November 23, 1906. Collected by W. L. Abbott. Original number 4898.

Well-made skin in good condition, tail slightly broken with tip missing; skull Grade A.

*Epimys mara Miller.

Smithsonian Misc. Coll. 61 (21): 10, Dec. 29, 1913.
=*Rattus mara* (Miller). See Chasen, Bull. Raffles Mus. 15: 163, Apr. 1940.

196751. Skin and skull. Adult female. Maratua Island, Dutch southeast Borneo. August 28, 1912. Collected by H. C. Raven. Original number 187.

Well-made skin in good condition, tail slightly injured; skull Grade A.

*Mus masae Miller.

Smithsonian Misc. Coll. 45: 32, Nov. 6, 1903.
=*Rattus sabanus masae* (Miller). See Chasen, Bull. Raffles Mus. 15: 167, Apr. 1940.

121822. Skin and skull. Adult female. Tana Masa, Batu Islands, off west coast of Sumatra. February 21, 1903. Collected by W. L. Abbott. Original number 2327.

Well-made skin in good condition; skull Grade A.

*Mus matthaeus Miller.

Smithsonian Misc. Coll. 45: 29, Nov. 6, 1903.
=*Rattus matthaeus* (Miller).

104159. Skin and skull. Adult male. St. Matthew Island, Mergui Archipelago. January 18, 1900. Collected by W. L. Abbott. Original number 243.

Well-made skin in good condition, feet and tail stained by corrosive sublimate; skull Grade A.

*Epimys mayonicus Hollister.

Proc. U. S. Nat. Mus. 46: 319, Dec. 31, 1913.
=*Rattus mayonicus* (Hollister). See Taylor, Philippine Land Mammals, Bur. Sci. Monogr. 30: 457, June 30, 1934.

144600. Skin and skull. Adult male. Mount Mayon, altitude 4,000 feet, Albay Province, Luzon, Philippine Islands. June 5, 1907. Collected by Edgar A. Mearns. Original number 6438.

Fairly well-made skin, lacking hair on top of neck, also a partially bare spot on abdomen; skull Grade A.

*Rattus melanurus Shamel.

Journ. Mamm. 21: 76, Feb. 14, 1940.

197371. Skin and skull. Adult male. Pulo Miang Besar, just out from Sangkulirang Bay, Borneo. September 12, 1913. Collected by H. C. Raven. Original number 1025.

Well-made skin in good condition; skull Grade A.

*Epimys mengurus Miller.

Proc. Biol. Soc. Washington 26: 27, Feb. 24, 1911.
=*Rattus cremoriventer mengurus* (Miller). See Chasen, Bull. Raffles Mus. 15: 175, Apr. 1940.

125021. Skin and skull. Adult male. Bukit Menguru, Billiton Island, off east coast of Sumatra. August 14, 1904. Collected by W. L. Abbott. Original number 3581.

Well-made skin in good condition; skull Grade A.

*Mus mindanensis Mearns.

Proc. U. S. Nat. Mus. 28: 442, May 13, 1905.
=*Rattus mindanensis mindanensis* (Mearns). See Taylor, Philippine Land Mammals, p. 437, June 30, 1934.

125274. Skin and skull. Adult male. Todaya, altitude 4,000 feet, Mount Apo, southern Mindanao, Philippine Islands. July 9, 1904. Collected by Edgar A. Mearns. Original number 5719.

Fairly well-made skin in good condition; skull Grade A.

*Rattus mollicomus Miller and Hollister.

Proc. Biol. Soc. Washington 34: 71, Mar. 31, 1921.

217752. Skin and skull. Adult male. Goenoeng Kalabat, altitude 6,500 feet, northeastern Celebes. April 10, 1916. Collected by H. C. Raven. Original number 2433.

Well-made skin in good condition; skull Grade A.

*Rattus musschenbroekii tetricus Miller and Hollister.

Proc. Biol. Soc. Washington 34: 68, Mar. 31, 1921.

219613. Skin and skull. Adult male. Gimpoe, southwest from Lake Lindoe, Middle Celebes. August 27, 1917. Collected by H. C. Raven. Original number 3184.

Well-made skin in good condition; skull Grade A.

*Epimys nasutus Lyon.

Proc. U. S. Nat. Mus. 40: 104, Apr. 25, 1911.

=*Rattus sabanus nasutus* (Lyon). See Chasen, Bull. Raffles Mus. 15: 164, Apr. 1940.

145519. Skin and skull. Adult male. Pulo Panebangan, off west coast of Borneo. May 21, 1907. Collected by W. L. Abbott. Original number 5270.

Well-made skin in good condition; scar on back; skull Grade A.

*Epimys neglectus ducis Lyon.

Proc. U. S. Nat. Mus. 40: 99, Apr. 25, 1911.

=*Rattus rattus ducis* (Lyon). See Chasen, Bull. Raffles Mus. 15: 158, Apr. 1940.

145511. Skin and skull. Adult male. Pulo Datu, off west coast of Borneo. May 4, 1907. Collected by W. L. Abbott. Original number 5174.

Well-made skin in good condition; skull Grade A.

*Epimys neglectus lamucotanus Lyon.

Proc. U. S. Nat. Mus. 40: 100, Apr. 25, 1911.

=*Rattus rattus lamucotanus* (Lyon). See Chasen, Bull. Raffles Mus. 15: 158, Apr. 1940.

145497. Skin and skull. Adult female. Pulo Lamukotan, off west coast of Borneo. May 10, 1907. Collected by W. L. Abbott. Original number 5224.

Well-made skin in good condition; skull Grade A.

*Rattus nigellus Miller and Hollister.

Proc. Biol. Soc. Washington 34: 72, Mar. 31, 1921.

218140. Skin and skull. Adult male. Bumbaroedjaba, near Toboli, northern Middle Celebes. November 8, 1916. Collected by H. C. Raven. Original number 2936.

Well-made skin in good condition, extreme tip of tail missing; skull Grade A.

*Epimys norvegicus socer Miller.

Proc. Biol. Soc. Washington 27: 90, May 11, 1914.

=*Rattus norvegicus socer* (Miller). See G. M. Allen, Amer. Mus. Nov. 217: 8, June 16, 1926.

144020. Skin and skull. Adult male. Taocheo, Kansu, China, January 30, 1905. Collected by W. W. Simpson. Original number 5.

Well-made skin in good condition; skull Grade A.

*Mus obscurus Miller.

Proc. Washington Acad. Sci. 2: 213, Aug. 20, 1900. Preoccupied by *Mus obscurus* Waterhouse (Proc. Zool. Soc. London 5: 19, 1837), and renamed *Mus pullus* Miller (Proc. Biol. Soc. Washington 14: 178, Sept. 25, 1901).

=*Rattus concolor concolor* (Blyth). See Chasen, Bull. Raffles Mus. 15: 159, Apr. 1940.

101764. Skin and skull. Adult male. Pulo Tioman, off southeast coast of the Malay Peninsula. October 1, 1899. Collected by W. L. Abbott.

Well-made skin in good condition except that tip of tail is shriveled and there is a small bare spot on belly; feet and tail stained by corrosive sublimate; skull Grade A.

*Epimys ornatulus Hollister.

Proc. U. S. Nat. Mus. 46: 322, Dec. 31, 1913.

=*Rattus ornatulus* (Hollister). See Taylor, Philippine Land Mammals, Bur. Sci. Monogr. 30: 457, June 30, 1934.

239245. Skin and skull. Adult female. Cagayancillo, Cagayan Island, Philippine Islands. February 8, 1903. Collected by R. C. McGregor and A. Celestino. Original number 37.

Well-made skin in good condition; skull Grade A.

*Mus pagensis Miller.

Smithsonian Misc. Coll. 45: 39, Nov. 6, 1903.

=*Rattus surifer pagensis* (Miller). See Chasen, Bull. Raffles Mus. 15: 174, Apr. 1940.

121629. Skin and skull. Adult male. South Pagi Island, off west coast of Sumatra. December 23, 1902. Collected by W. L. Abbott. Original number 2153.

Well-made skin in good condition, face slightly stained by corrosive sublimate; skull Grade A.

*Rattus palelae Miller and Hollister.

Proc. Biol. Soc. Washington 34: 69, Mar. 31, 1921.

200063. Skin and skull. Adult female. Pulo Paleleh, north coast of Celebes. August 2, 1914. Collected by H. C. Raven. Original number 1619.

Well-made skin in good condition; skull Grade A.

*Epimys pannellus Miller.

Smithsonian Misc. Coll. 61 (21): 8, Dec. 29, 1913.

=*Rattus rattus pannellus* (Miller). See Gyldenstolpe, Journ. Nat. Hist. Soc. Siam 3: 163, Aug. 1, 1919.

104121. Skin and skull. Adult male. Pulo Rawi, Butang Islands, off west coast of Malay Peninsula. December 19, 1899. Collected by W. L. Abbott. Original number 175.

Well-made skin in good condition, feet and tail stained by corrosive sublimate; skull Grade A.

*Mus pannosus Miller.

Proc. Biol. Soc. Washington 13: 190, Dec. 21, 1900.
=*Rattus rattus pannosus* (Miller). See Gyldenstolpe, Journ. Nat. Hist. Soc. Siam 3: 163, Aug. 1, 1919.

104110. Skin and skull. Adult male. Pulo Adang, Butang Islands, off west coast of Malay Peninsula. December 14, 1899. Collected by W. L. Abbott. Original number 146.

Well-made skin in good condition, feet and tail stained by corrosive sublimate; skull Grade A.

*Mus pantarensis Mearns.

Proc. U. S. Nat. Mus. 28: 448, May 13, 1905.
=*Rattus pantarensis* (Mearns). See Taylor, Philippine Land Mammals, Bur. Sci. Monogr. 30: 453, June 30, 1934.

123294. Skin and skull. Adult female. Pantar, altitude 1,907 feet, Mindanao, Philippine Islands. September 4, 1903. Collected by Edgar A. Mearns. Original number 5622.

Fairly well-made skin in good condition; skull Grade A.

*Mus pellax Miller.

Proc. Biol. Soc. Washington 13: 147, Apr. 21, 1900.
=*Rattus rajah pellax* (Miller). See Chasen, Bull. Raffles Mus. 15: 168, Apr. 1940.

86755. Skin and skull. Adult female. Khow Sai Dow, altitude 1,000 feet, Trong, Peninsular Siam. February 5, 1899. Collected by W. L. Abbott.

Well-made skin in good condition, feet and tail stained by corrosive sublimate; skull Grade A.

*Rattus penitus Miller and Hollister.

Proc. Biol. Soc. Washington 34: 72, Mar. 31, 1921.

218686. Skin and skull. Adult male. Goenoeng Lehio, southwest of Lake Lindoe, altitude 6,000 feet, Middle Celebes. January 21, 1917. Collected by H. C. Raven. Original number 3109.

Well-made skin in good condition; skull Grade A.

*Rattus perasper Shamel.

Journ. Mamm. 21: 76, Feb. 14, 1940.

198255. Skin and skull. Adult male. Gunong Batu, Borneo. December 5, 1913. Collected by H. C. Raven. Original number 1210.

Well-made skin in good condition; skull Grade A.

*Epimys perflavus Lyon.

Proc. U. S. Nat. Mus. 40: 108, Apr. 25, 1911.
=*Rattus surifer perflavus* (Lyon). See Chasen, Bull. Raffles Mus. 15: 174, Apr. 1940.

151918. Skin and skull. Adult male. Pulo Laut, off southeast coast of Borneo. December 25, 1907. Collected by W. L. Abbott. Original number 5684.

Well-made skin in good condition; skull Grade A.

*Rattus pinatus Lyon.

Proc. U. S. Nat. Mus. 52: 448, Dec. 30, 1916.
=*Rattus mülleri pinatus* Lyon. See Chasen, Bull. Raffles Mus. 15: 162, Apr. 1940.

121778. Skin and skull. Adult male. Pulo Pinie, Batu Islands, off west coast of Sumatra. March 4, 1903. Collected by W. L. Abbott. Original number 2367.

Well-made skin in good condition; skull Grade A.

*Epimys pollens Miller.

Smithsonian Misc. Coll. 61 (21) : 17, Dec. 29, 1913.
=*Rattus mülleri pollens* (Miller). See Chasen, Bull. Raffles Mus. 15: 162, Apr. 1940.

124691. Skin and skull. Adult male. Tanjong Rengsam, Banka Island, off east coast of Sumatra. May 22, 1904. Collected by W. L. Abbott. Original number 3250.

Well-made skin in good condition; skull Grade A.

*Epimys potens Miller.

Smithsonian Misc. Coll. 61 (21) : 17, Dec. 29, 1913.
=*Rattus mülleri potens* (Miller). See Chasen, Bull. Raffles Mus. 15:161, Apr. 1940.

114384. Skin and skull. Adult female. Pulo Tuangku, Banjak Islands, off west coast of Sumatra. February 5, 1902. Collected by W. L. Abbott. Original number 1516.

Well-made skin in good condition, feet, base of tail, and ears stained by corrosive sublimate; skull Grade A.

*Mus pulliventer Miller.

Proc. U. S. Nat. Mus. 24: 765, May 28, 1902.
=*Rattus rattus pulliventer* (Miller).

111790. Skin and skull. Adult female. Great Nicobar Island, Nicobar Islands, Malay Archipelago. March 12, 1901. Collected by W. L. Abbott. Original number 927.

Well-made skin in good condition, feet and tail stained by corrosive sublimate; skull Grade A.

Rattus pullus Miller.

See *Mus obscurus* Miller.

*Rattus punicans Miller and Hollister.

Proc. Biol. Soc. Washington 34: 98, June 30, 1921.

219625. Skin and skull. Adult female. Pinedapa, Middle Celebes. February 7, 1918. Collected by H. C. Raven. Original number 3501.

Well-made skin in good condition; skull Grade A.

*Epimys querceti Hollister.

Proc. Biol. Soc. Washington 24: 90, May 15, 1911.
=*Rattus querceti* (Hollister). See Taylor, Philippine Land Mammals, p. 450, June 30, 1934.

145833. Skin and skull. Adult male. Haights-in-the-Oaks, altitude 7,000 feet, Benguet Province, Luzon, Philippine Islands. August 1, 1907. Collected by Edgar A. Mearns. Original number 6491.

Well-made skin in good condition; skull Grade A.

*Rattus rajah koratis Kloss.

Journ. Nat. Hist. Soc. Siam 3: 376, Dec. 31, 1919.

221509. Skin and skull. Adult male. Lat Bua Kao, eastern Siam. October 18, 1916. Collected by C. Boden Kloss. Original number 2187.

Well-made skin in good condition; skull Grade A.

*Rattus rajah kramis Kloss.

Journ. Nat. Hist. Soc. Siam 3: 377, Dec. 31, 1919.

221489. Skin and skull. Adult male. Koh Kram, Inner Gulf of Siam. October 30, 1916. Collected by C. Boden Kloss. Original number 2277.

Well-made skin in good condition; skull Grade A.

*Rattus rallus Miller and Hollister.

Proc. Biol. Soc. Washington 34: 73, Mar. 31, 1921.

219595. Skin and skull. Adult female. Gimpoe, Middle Celebes. September 7, 1917. Collected by H. C. Raven. Original number 3233.

Well-made skin in good condition; skull Grade A.

*Epimys rattus dentatus Miller.

Smithsonian Misc. Coll. 61 (21): 14, Dec. 29, 1913.
=*Rattus rattus dentatus* (Miller). See Chasen, Bull. Raffles Mus. 15: 153, Apr. 1940.

111929. Skin and skull. Adult male. Hastings Island, Mergui Archipelago. December 13, 1900. Collected by W. L. Abbott. Original number 783.

Well-made skin in good condition, feet and tail stained by corrosive sublimate; skull Grade A.

*Rattus rattus exiguus A. B. Howell.

Proc. Biol. Soc. Washington 40 : 43, Mar. 5, 1927.

=*Rattus lorea exiguus* A. B. Howell. See G. M. Allen, Mamm. China and Mongolia 2 : 1005, Sept. 3, 1940.

238185. Skin and skull. Adult female. 70 miles southwest of Yengpingfu, altitude 500 feet, Fukien, China. December 1, 1921. Collected by Arthur deC. Sowerby. Original number 1139.

Well-made skin in good condition; skull Grade A.

*Epimys rattus exsul Miller.

Smithsonian Misc. Coll. 61 (21) : 15, Dec. 29, 1913.

=*Rattus rattus exsul* (Miller).

124046. Skin and skull. Adult male. James Island, Mergui Archipelago. December 31, 1903. Collected by W. L. Abbott. Original number 2958.

Well-made skin in good condition; skull Grade A.

*Epimys rattus fortunatus Miller.

Smithsonian Misc. Coll. 61 (21) : 15, Dec. 29, 1913.

=*Rattus rattus fortunatus* (Miller). See Gyldenstolpe, Journ. Nat. Hist. Soc. Siam 3 : 163, Aug. 1, 1919.

104148. Skin and skull. Adult male. Chance Island, Mergui Archipelago. December 29, 1899. Collected by W. L. Abbott. Original number 191.

Well-made skin in good condition, feet and tail stained by corrosive sublimate; skull Grade A.

*Epimys rattus insulanus Miller.

Smithsonian Misc. Coll. 61 (21) : 14, Dec. 29, 1913.

=*Rattus rattus insulanus* (Miller).

104147. Skin and skull. Adult male. Helfer Island, Mergui Archipelago. March 7, 1900. Collected by W. L. Abbott. Original number 334.

Well-made skin in good condition, feet and tail stained by corrosive sublimate; skull Grade A.

*Rattus rattus koratensis Kloss.

Journ. Nat. Hist. Soc. Siam. 3 : 379, Dec. 31, 1919.

221512. Skin and skull. Adult female. Lat Bua Kao, East Siam. October 19, 1916. Collected by C. Boden Kloss. Original number 2196.

Well-made skin in good condition; skull Grade A.

*Rattus rattus kramensis Kloss.

Journ. Nat. Hist. Soc. Siam 3 : 379, Dec. 31, 1919.

221521. Skin and skull. Adult female. Koh Kram, Inner Gulf of Siam. October 30, 1916. Collected by C. Boden Kloss. Original number 2281.

Well-made skin in good condition; skull Grade A.

*Rattus rattus lanensis Kloss.

Journ. Nat. Hist. Soc. Siam. 3: 378, Dec. 31, 1919.

221523. Skin and skull. Adult female. Koh Lan, Inner Gulf of Siam. October 29, 1916. Collected by C. Boden Kloss. Original number 2261.

Well-made skin in fairly good condition, apparently grease-burned on under parts and small portion of skin broken away; skull Grade A.

*Rattus rattus mesanis Kloss.

Journ. Nat. Hist. Soc. Siam. 3: 379, Dec. 31, 1919.

221535. Skin and skull. Adult male. Koh Mesan Island near Cape Liant, S. E. Siam. November 2, 1916. Collected by C. Boden Kloss. Original number 2320.

Well-made skin in good condition; skull Grade A.

*Epimys rattus pauper Miller.

Smithsonian Misc. Coll. 61 (21) : 13, Dec. 29, 1913.
=Rattus rattus pauper (Miller). See Chasen, Bull. Raffles Mus. 10: 20, Oct. 1935.

104828. Skin and skull. Adult male. Sirhassen Island, South Natuna Islands, South China Sea, between Malay Peninsula and Borneo. June 4, 1900. Collected by W. L. Abbott. Original number 433.

Well-made skin in good condition, feet and tail stained by corrosive sublimate; skull Grade A.

*Epimys rattus shigarus Miller.

Proc. Biol. Soc. Washington 26: 198, Oct. 23, 1913.
=Rattus rattus shigarus (Miller).

176132. Skin and skull. Adult male. Shigar Valley, altitude 9,000 feet, Baltistan, India. October 4, 1912. Collected by W. L. Abbott. Original number 8010.

Well-made skin in good condition, tail injured near base; skull Grade A.

*Epimys rattus turbidus Miller.

Smithsonian Misc. Coll. 61 (21) : 12, Dec. 29, 1913.
=Rattus rattus turbidus (Miller). See Gyldenstolpe, Kungl. Svenska Vet.-Akad. Handl. 60 (6) : 56, Feb. 12, 1920.

196746. Skin and skull. Young adult female. Tanggarung, south bank of Mahakam River, Dutch Southeast Borneo. June 21, 1912. Collected by H. C. Raven. Original number 81.

Well-made skin in good condition; skull Grade A.

*Epimys rattus viclana Miller.

Smithsonian Misc. Coll. 61 (21) : 13, Dec. 29, 1913.
=*Rattus rattus viclana* Miller. See Chasen, Bull. Raffles Mus. 15: 154, Apr. 1940.

123861. Skin and skull. Adult male. Pulo Langkawi, off west coast of Malay Peninsula. November 3, 1903. Collected by W. L. Abbott. Original number 2800.

Well-made skin in good condition; skull Grade A.

*Rattus raveni Miller and Hollister.

Proc. Biol. Soc. Washington 34: 68, Mar. 31, 1921.

199976. Skin and skull. Adult male. Toli Toli, North Celebes. December 16, 1914. Collected by H. C. Raven. Original number 1963.

Well-made skin in good condition; skull Grade A.

*Rattus raveni eurous Miller and Hollister.

Proc. Biol. Soc. Washington 34: 69, Mar. 31, 1921.

199927. Skin and skull. Adult male. Molengkapoti, Kwandang, North Celebes. October 15, 1914. Collected by H. C. Raven. Original number 1724.

Well-made skin in good condition; skull Grade A.

*Epimys roa Miller.

Smithsonian Misc. Coll. 61 (21) : 10, Dec. 29, 1913.
=*Rattus rattus roa* (Miller). See Chasen, Bull. Raffles Mus. 15:157, Apr. 1940.

112444. Skin and skull. Adult female. Pulo Aor, off east coast of Johore, Federated Malay States. June 8, 1901. Collected by W. L. Abbott. Original number 1025.

Well-made skin in good condition, feet and tail stained by corrosive sublimate; skull Grade A.

*Epimys robiginosus Hollister.

Proc. U. S. Nat. Mus. 46: 318, Dec. 31, 1913.
=*Rattus robiginosus* (Hollister). See Taylor, Philippine Land Mammals, Bur. Sci. Monogr. 30: 435, June 30, 1934.

239246. Skin and skull. Adult male. Cagayancillo, Cagayan Island, Philippine Islands. February 7, 1903. Collected by R. C. McGregor and A. Celestino. Original number 33.

Well-made skin in good condition; skull Grade A.

*Epimys saturatus Lyon.

Proc. U. S. Nat. Mus. 40: 109, Apr. 25, 1911.
=*Rattus surifer saturatus* (Lyon). See Chasen, Bull. Raffles Mus. 15: 174, Apr. 1940.

145523. Skin and skull. Adult male. Pulo Panebangan, off west coast of Borneo. May 17, 1907. Collected by W. L. Abbott. Original number 5236.

Well-made skin in good condition; skull Grade A.

*Epimys sebucus Lyon.

Proc. U. S. Nat. Mus. 40: 102, Apr. 25, 1911.
=*Rattus mülleri sebucus* (Lyon). See Chasen, Bull. Raffles Mus. 15: 163, Apr. 1940.

151964. Skin and skull. Adult male. Pulo Sebuku, off southeastern coast of Borneo. January 2, 1908. Collected by W. L. Abbott. Original number 5717.

Well-made skin in good condition, feet stained by corrosive sublimate; skull Grade A.

*Rattus sericatus Miller and Hollister.

Proc. Biol. Soc. Washington 34: 73, Mar. 31, 1921.

219627. Skin and skull. Adult male. Rano Rano, east of Lake Lindoe and north of Lake Poso, altitude 6,000 feet, Middle Celebes. December 19, 1917. Collected by H. C. Raven. Original number 3340.

Well-made skin in good condition; skull Grade A.

*Mus serutus Miller.

Proc. U. S. Nat. Mus. 31: 59, July 23, 1906.
=*Rattus surifer serutus* (Miller). See Chasen, Bull. Raffles Mus. 15: 174, Apr. 1940.

125032. Skin and skull. Adult male. Pulo Serutu, Karimata Islands, off west coast of Borneo. August 17, 1904. Collected by W. L. Abbott. Original number 3590.

Well-made skin in good condition; skull Grade A.

*Mus siantanicus Miller.

Proc. Washington Acad. Sci. 2: 210, Aug. 20, 1900.
=*Rattus rattus siantanicus* (Miller). See Chasen and Kloss, Journ. Malay Branch Roy. Asiatic Soc. 6 (pt. 3) : 36, Aug. 1928.

101705. Skin and skull. Adult male. Pulo Siantan, Anamba Islands, South China Sea, between Malay Peninsula and Borneo. September 11, 1899. Collected by W. L. Abbott.

Fairly well-made skin in good condition; skull Grade B.

*Mus simalurensis Miller.

Proc. U. S. Nat. Mus. 26: 458, Feb. 3, 1903.
=*Rattus rattus simalurensis* (Miller). See Chasen, Bull. Raffles Mus. 15: 158, Apr. 1940.

114216. Skin and skull. Adult female. Simalur Island, off west coast of Sumatra. December 14, 1901. Collected by W. L. Abbott. Original number 1372.

Well-made skin in good condition, feet and tail stained by corrosive sublimate; skull Grade A.

*Rattus simalurensis babi Lyon.

Proc. U. S. Nat. Mus. 52: 447, Dec. 30, 1916.
=*Rattus rattus babi* Lyon. See Chasen, Bull. Raffles Mus. 15: 158, Apr. 1940.

114280. Skull only. Adult male. Pulo Babi, off west coast of Sumatra. January 13, 1902. Collected by W. L. Abbott.

Skull Grade A.

*Rattus simalurensis lasiae Lyon.

Proc. U. S. Nat. Mus. 52: 446, Dec. 30, 1916.
=*Rattus rattus lasiae* Lyon. See Chasen, Bull. Raffles Mus. 15: 158, Apr. 1940.

114254. Skin and skull. Adult female. Pulo Lasia, off west coast of Sumatra. January 6, 1902. Collected by W. L. Abbott. Original number 1400.

Well-made skin in good condition; feet and tail stained by corrosive sublimate; skull Grade A.

*Mus soccatus Miller.

Smithsonian Misc. Coll. 45: 30, Nov. 6, 1903.
=*Rattus sabanus soccatus* (Miller). See Chasen, Bull. Raffles Mus. 15: 167, Apr. 1940.

121549. Skin and skull. Adult male. North Pagi Island, off west coast of Sumatra. December 29, 1902. Collected by W. L. Abbott. Original number 2183.

Well-made skin in good condition, feet and tail stained by corrosive sublimate; skull Grade A.

*Epimys solus Miller.

Smithsonian Misc. Coll. 61 (21): 22, Dec. 29, 1913.
=*Rattus rapit solus* (Miller). See Chasen, Bull. Raffles Mus. 15: 177, Apr. 1940.

123944. Skin and skull. Adult male. Pulo Terutau, off west coast of Malay Peninsula. November 16, 1903. Collected by W. L. Abbott. Original number 2902.

Well-made skin in good condition, edge of ears slightly damaged; skull Grade A (second right upper molar missing).

*Epimys spatulatus Lyon.

Proc. U. S. Nat. Mus. 40: 111, Apr. 25, 1911.
=*Rattus cremoriventer spatulatus* (Lyon). See Chasen, Bull. Raffles Mus. 15: 176, Apr. 1940.

145499. Skin and skull. Adult male. Pulo Lamukotan, off west coast of Borneo. May 10, 1907. Collected by W. L. Abbott. Original number 5214.

Well-made skin in good condition, tail slightly broken near tip; skull Grade A.

*Epimys stentor Miller.

Smithsonian Misc. Coll. 61 (21) : 19, Dec. 29, 1913.
=*Rattus stentor* (Miller).

124044. Skin and skull. Adult female. James Island, Mergui Archipelago. January 2, 1904. Collected by W. L. Abbott. Original number 2983.

Well-made skin in good condition; skull Grade A.

*Mus stoicus Miller.

Proc. U. S. Nat Mus. 24: 759, May 28, 1902.
=*Rattus stoicus* (Miller).

111834. Skin and skull. Adult male. Henry Lawrence Island, Andaman Islands, Malay Archipelago. January 9, 1901. Collected by W. L. Abbott. Original number 820.

Well-made skin in good condition, feet and tail much stained by corrosive sublimate; skull Grade A.

*Mus strepitans Miller.

Proc. Washington Acad. Sci. 2 : 207, Aug. 20, 1900.
=*Rattus sabanus strepitans* (Miller). See Chasen and Kloss, Journ. Malay Branch Roy. Asiatic Soc. 6 (pt. 3) : 35, Aug. 1928.

101697. Skin and skull. Adult female. Pulo Siantan, Anambas Islands, South China Sea, between Malay Peninsula and Borneo. September 10, 1899. Collected by W. L. Abbott.

Well-made skin in good condition; skull Grade A.

*Mus stridens Miller.

Smithsonian Misc. Coll. 45: 28, Nov. 6, 1903.
=*Rattus sabanus stridens* (Miller). See Chasen, Bull. Raffles Mus. 15: 166, Apr. 1940.

104992. Skin and skull. Adult male. Tioman Island, off southeast coast of Malay Peninsula. October 10, 1900. Collected by W. L. Abbott. Original number 702.

Well-made skin in good condition, feet and tail stained by corrosive sublimate; skull Grade A.

*Mus stridulus Miller.

Smithsonian Misc. Coll. 45: 29, Nov. 6, 1903.
=*Rattus stridulus* (Miller).

104196. Skin and skull. Adult female. Bentinck Island, Mergui Archipelago. March 12, 1900. Collected by W. L. Abbott. Original number 350.

Well-made skin in good condition; feet and tail stained by corrosive sublimate; skull Grade A.

*Mus surdus Miller.

Proc. U. S. Nat. Mus. 26: 460, Feb. 3, 1903.
=*Rattus concolor surdus* (Miller). See Lyon, Proc. U. S. Nat. Mus. 52: 457, Dec. 30, 1916.

114184. Skin and skull. Adult male. Simalur Island, off west coast of Sumatra. December 11, 1901. Collected by W. L. Abbott. Original number 1359.

Well-made skin in good condition; skull Grade A.

*Mus surifer Miller.

Proc. Biol. Soc. Washington 13: 148, Apr. 21, 1900.
=*Rattus surifer surifer* (Miller). See Kloss, Treubia 2: 123, Dec. 1921.

86746. Skin and skull. Adult male. Khow Nok Ram, altitude 3,000 feet, Trong, Peninsular Siam. January 14, 1899. Collected by W. L. Abbott.

Well-made skin in good condition except for a break in tail and some damage to left hindleg (probably from jaws of trap), feet and tail stained by corrosive sublimate; skull Grade A.

*Mus surifer butangensis Miller.

Proc. Biol. Soc. Washington 13: 190, Dec. 21, 1900.
=*Rattus surifer butangensis* (Miller). See Gyldenstolpe, Journ. Nat. Hist. Soc. Siam 3: 164, Aug. 1, 1919.

104309. Skin and skull. Adult male. Pulo Adang, Butang Islands, off west coast of Malay Peninsula. December 16, 1899. Collected by W. L. Abbott. Original number 157.

Well-made skin in good condition with exception of slight injury at base of tail; feet stained by corrosive sublimate; skull Grade A.

*Mus surifer flavidulus Miller.

Proc. Biol. Soc. Washington 13: 189, Dec. 21, 1900.
=*Rattus surifer flavidulus* (Miller). See Chasen, Bull. Raffles Mus. 15: 171, Apr. 1940.

104330. Skin and skull. Adult female. Pulo Langkawi, off west coast of Malay Peninsula. December 4, 1899. Collected by W. L. Abbott. Original number 109.

Well-made skin in good condition; skull Grade A.

*Mus taciturnus Miller.

Proc. U. S. Nat. Mus. 24: 762, May 28, 1902.
=*Rattus taciturnus* (Miller).

11828. Skin and skull. Adult male. South Andaman Island Andaman Islands, Malay Archipelago. January 16, 1901. Collected by W. L. Abbott. Original number 854.

Well-made skin in good condition, feet and tail stained by corrosive sublimate; skull Grade A.

*Mus tagulayensis Mearns.

Proc. U. S. Nat. Mus. 28 : 439, May 13, 1905.
=*Rattus tagulayensis* (Mearns). See Taylor, Philippine Land Mammals, Bur. Sci. Monogr. 30 : 422, June 30, 1934.

125264. Skin and skull. Adult male. At sea level, Tagulaya, Gulf of Davao, foot of Mount Apo, southern Mindanao, Philippine Islands. July 15, 1904. Collected by Edgar A. Mearns. Original number 5732.

Well-made skin in good condition; skull Grade A.

*Mus tambelanicus Miller.

Proc. Washington Acad. Sci. 2 : 212, Aug. 20, 1900.
=*Rattus rattus tambelanicus* (Miller). See Chasen, Bull. Raffles Mus. 15 : 157, Apr. 1940.

101665. Skin and skull. Adult male. Big Tambelan Island, South China Sea, between Malay Peninsula and Borneo. August 10, 1899. Collected by W. L. Abbott.

Well-made skin in good condition (tail injured during life and is abnormally short) ; skull Grade A.

*Epimys tingius Miller.

Smithsonian Misc. Coll. 61 (21) : 9, Dec. 29, 1913.
=*Rattus rattus tingius* (Miller). See Chasen, Bull. Raffles Mus. 15 : 156, Apr. 1940.

112723. Skin and skull. Adult male. Pulo Tinggi, off east coast of Johore, Federated Malay States. August 5, 1901. Collected by W. L. Abbott. Original number 1201.

Well-made skin in good condition; skull Grade A.

*Mus tiomanicus Miller.

Proc. Washington Acad. Sci. (2) : 209, Aug. 20, 1900.
=*Rattus rattus tiomanicus* (Miller). See Chasen, Bull. Raffles Mus. 15 : 155, April, 1940.

101763. Skin and skull. Adult male. Pulo Tioman, off southeast coast of Malay Peninsula. October 4, 1899. Collected by W. L. Abbott.

Well-made skin in good condition, feet and tail stained by corrosive sublimate; skull Grade A.

*Mus todayensis Mearns.

Proc. U. S. Nat. Mus. 28: 445, May 13, 1905.
=*Rattus todayensis* (Mearns). See Taylor, Philippine Land Mammals, Bur. Sci. Monogr. 30: 448, June 30, 1934.

125224. Skin and skull. Adult female. Todaya, altitude 4,000 feet, on Mount Apo, southern Mindanao, Philippine Islands. July 11, 1904. Collected by Edgar A. Mearns. Original number 5722.

Well-made skin in good condition; skull Grade A.

*Epimys tua Miller.

Smithsonian Misc. Coll. 61 (21) : 12, Dec. 29, 1913.
=*Rattus rattus tua* (Miller). See Chasen, Bull. Raffles Mus. 15: 158, Apr. 1940.

196752. Skin and skull. Adult female. Maratua Island, Dutch Southeast Borneo. August 28, 1912. Collected by H. C. Raven. Original number 188.

Well-made skin in good condition, tail somewhat shortened and blunt; skull Grade A.

*Epimys tyrannus Miller.

Proc. U. S. Nat. Mus. 38: 397, Aug. 19, 1910.
=*Rattus tyrannus* (Miller). See Taylor, Philippine Land Mammals, Bur. Sci. Monogr. 30: 427, June 30, 1934.

239247. Skin and skull. Adult male. Ticao Island, Philippine Islands. May 15, 1902. Collected by R. C. McGregor and A. Celestino. Original number 8.

Well-made skin in good condition; skull Grade A.

*Epimys ubecus Lyon.

Proc. U. S. Nat. Mus. 40: 109, Apr. 25, 1911.
=*Rattus surifer ubecus* (Lyon). See Chasen, Bull. Raffles Mus. 15: 174, Apr. 1940.

151931. Skin and skull. Adult male. Pulo Sebuku, off southeast coast of Borneo. January 3, 1908. Collected by W. L. Abbott. Original number 5727.

Well-made skin in good condition; skull Grade A.

*Mus umbridorsum Miller.

Smithsonian Misc. Coll. 45: 37, Nov. 6, 1903.
=*Rattus umbridorsum* (Miller).

104227. Skin and skull. Adult male. Loughborough Island, Mergui Archipelago. January 24, 1900. Collected by W. L. Abbott. Original number 269.

Well-made skin in good condition, feet and tail stained by corrosive sublimate; skull Grade A.

*Epimys valens Miller.

Smithsonian Misc. Coll. 61(21) : 18, Dec. 29, 1913.
=*Rattus mülleri valens* (Miller). See Chasen, Bull. Raffles Mus. 15: 164, Apr. 1940.

114285. Skin and skull. Adult female. Pulo Bangkaru, Banjak Islands, off west coast of Sumatra. January 19, 1902. Collected by W. L. Abbott. Original number 1430.

Well-made skin in good condition, feet and tail stained by corrosive sublimate; skull Grade A.

*Mus validus Miller.

Proc. Biol. Soc. Washington 13: 141, Apr. 21, 1900.
=*Rattus mülleri validus* (Miller). See Chasen, Bull. Raffles Mus. 15: 163, Apr. 1940.

86741. Skin and skull. Adult male. Khow Sai Dow, altitude 1,000 feet, Trong, Peninsular Siam. February 18, 1899. Collected by W. L. Abbott.

Well-made skin in good condition, feet stained by corrosive sublimate; skull Grade A.

*Epimys victor Miller.

Smithsonian Misc. Coll. 61 (21) : 16, Dec. 29, 1913.
=*Rattus mülleri validus* (Miller). See Chasen, Bull. Raffles Mus. 15: 163, Apr. 1940.

115422. Skin and skull. Adult female. Near mouth of Rumpin River, Pahang, Federated Malay States. May 25, 1902. Collected by W. L. Abbott. Original number 1706.

Well-made skin in good condition, feet and base of tail stained by corrosive sublimate; skull Grade A.

*Epimys vigoratus Hollister.

Proc. U. S. Nat. Mus. 46: 321, Dec. 31, 1913.
=*Rattus vigoratus* (Hollister). See Taylor, Philippine Land Mammals, Bur. Sci. Monogr. 30: 449, June 30, 1934.

144637. Skin and skull. Adult male. Mount Halcon, spur of main ridge at 4,500 feet, Mindoro, Philippine Islands. November 15, 1906. Collected by Edgar A. Mearns. Original number 6306.

Well-made skin in good condition; skull Grade A.

*Rattus virtus Lyon.

Proc. Biol. Soc. Washington 29: 210, Sept. 22, 1916.

144223. Skin and skull. Adult male. Siak River, near mouth of Gasip River, eastern Sumatra. December 10, 1906. Collected by W. L. Abbott. Original number 4944.

Well-made skin in good condition; skull Grade A.

*Mus vitiensis Peale.   Cotype.

U. S. Exploring Expedition 8 (Mammalia and Ornithology) : 49, 1848.
=*Rattus vitiensis* (Peale).

3731. Skin only. Fiji Islands, Oceania. Collected by U. S. Exploring Expedition (1838–42). Cataloged December 20, 1859.

Skin was originally mounted and on exhibition. In June 1910 it was dismounted and made into a study skin. It is now very much faded and has a bare spot on right flank; otherwise it is in rather good condition.

*Mus vociferans Miller.

Proc. Biol. Soc. Washington 13 : 138, Apr. 21, 1900.
=*Rattus vociferans vociferans* (Miller). See Lyon, Proc. Biol. Soc. Washington 29 : 209, Sept. 22, 1916.

86736. Skin and skull. Adult male. Khow Sai Dow, altitude 1,000 feet, Trong, Peninsular Siam. February 21, 1899. Collected by W. L. Abbott.

Well-made skin in good condition; skull Grade A.

*Epimys vociferans clarae Miller.

Smithsonian Misc. Coll. 61 (21) : 20, Dec. 29, 1913.
=*Rattus vociferans clarae* (Miller).

124115. Skin and skull. Adult male. Clara Island, Mergui Archipelago. January 10, 1904. Collected by W. L. Abbott. Original number 3019.

Well-made skin in good condition, base of tail, hind legs, and ears stained by corrosive sublimate; skull Grade A.

*Epimys vociferans insularum Miller.

Smithsonian Misc. Coll. 61 (21) : 19, Dec. 29, 1913.
=*Rattus vociferans insularum* (Miller).

104167. Skin and skull. Adult female. Domel Island, Mergui Archipelago. February 27, 1900. Collected by W. L. Abbott. Original number 329.

Well-made skin in good condition, base of tail and top of head stained by corrosive sublimate; skull Grade A.

*Mus vociferans lancavensis Miller.

Proc. Biol. Soc. Washington 13 : 188, Dec. 21, 1900.
=*Rattus sabanus lancavensis* (Miller). See Chasen, Bull. Raffles Mus. 15 : 165, Apr. 1940.

104173. Skin and skull. Adult female. Pulo Lankawi, off west coast of Malay Peninsula. December 6, 1899. Collected by W. L. Abbott. Original number 122.

Well-made skin in good condition, feet and tail stained by corrosive sublimate; skull Grade A.

*Rattus vociferans tapanulius Lyon.

Proc. Biol. Soc. Washington 29: 209, Sept. 22, 1916.

114453. Skin and skull. Adult male. Tapanuli Bay, west coast of Sumatra. February 16, 1902. Collected by W. L. Abbott. Original number 1538.

Well-made skin in good condition, feet and tail stained by corrosive sublimate; skull Grade A.

*Mus vulcani Mearns.

Proc. U. S. Nat. Mus. 28: 446, May 13, 1905.
=*Rattus vulcani* (Mearns). See Taylor, Philippine Land Mammals, Bur. Sci. Monogr. 30: 454, June 30, 1934.

125216. Skin and skull. Adult male. Mount Apo, altitude 7,600 feet, southern Mindanao, Philippine Islands. June 26, 1904. Collected by Edgar A. Mearns. Original number 5674.

Well-made skin in good condition; skull Grade B.

*Mus vulcani apicis Mearns.

Proc. U. S. Nat. Mus. 28: 447, May 13, 1905.
=*Rattus vulcani* (Mearns). See Taylor, Philippine Land Mammals, Bur. Sci. Monogr. 30: 454, June 30, 1934.

125229. Skin and skull. Adult female. Summit of Mount Apo, altitude about 9,700 feet, southern Mindanao, Philippine Islands. June 6, 1904. Collected by Edgar A. Mearns. Original number 5709.

Well-made skin in good condition; skull Grade A.

*Mus zamboangae Mearns.

Proc. U. S. Nat. Mus. 28: 443, May 13, 1905.
=*Rattus zamboangae* (Mearns). See Taylor, Philippine Land Mammals, Bur. Sci. Monogr. 30: 442, June 30, 1934.

125279. Skin and skull. Adult male. Zamboanga, western Mindanao, Philippine Islands. January 20, 1904. Collected by Edgar A. Mearns. Original number 5753.

Well-made skin in good condition, a spot without hair on rump and adjoining part of tail; skull Grade A.

Genus SACCOSTOMUS Peters

*Saccostomus isiolae Heller.

Smithsonian Misc. Coll. 59 (16) : 14, July 5, 1912.

181803. Skin and skull. Adult female. Isiola River, Northern Guaso Nyiro, British East Africa [=Kenya]. July 1, 1911. Collected by Edmund Heller. Original number 1908.

Well-made skin in good condition; skull Grade A.

*Saccostomus mearnsi Heller.

Smithsonian Misc. Coll. 54 (4) : 3, Feb. 28, 1910.

162882.   Skin and skull.   Adult male.   Changamwe, British East Africa [=Kenya].   November 28, 1909.   Collected by Edgar A. Mearns.   Original number 7292.

Well-made skin in good condition; skull Grade A.

*Saccostomus umbriventer Miller.

Smithsonian Misc. Coll. 54 (4) : 1, Feb. 28, 1910.

162612.   Skin and skull.   Adult female.   Njori Osolali, Sotik, British East Africa [=Kenya].   June 26, 1909.   Collected by J. Alden Loring.   Original number 6447.

Well-made skin in good condition; skull Grade B.

Genus STEATOMYS Peters

*Steatomys athi Heller.

Smithsonian Misc. Coll. 54 (4) : 3, Feb. 28, 1910.

162883.   Skin and skull.   Adult male.   Lukenia Hills, Athi Plains, British East Africa [=Kenya].   November 22, 1909.   Collected by J. Alden Loring.   Original number 8259.

Well-made skin in good condition; skull Grade A.

Genus TARSOMYS Mearns

*Tarsomys apoensis Mearns.

Proc. U. S. Nat. Mus. 28: 453, May 13, 1905.

125280.   Adult male in alcohol, skull removed.   Mount Apo, altitude 6,750 feet, southern Mindanao, Philippine Islands.   July 5, 1904.   Collected by Edgar A. Mearns.   Original number 5706.

Alcoholic in good condition; skull Grade A.

Genus THALLOMYS Thomas

*Thamnomys loringi Heller.

Smithsonian Misc. Coll. 52 (4) : 471, Nov. 13, 1909.
=*Thallomys loringi* (Heller).   See Thomas, Ann. Mag. Nat. Hist. (ser. 9) 5: 141, Jan. 1920.

161904.   Skin and skull.   Adult female.   Lake Naivasha, British East Africa [=Kenya].   July 17, 1909.   Collected by J. Alden Loring.   Original number 6684.

Well-made skin in good condition; skull Grade A.

Genus TRYPHOMYS Miller

*Tryphomys adustus Miller.

Proc. U. S. Nat. Mus. 38: 399, Aug. 19, 1910.

151511.   Skin and skull.   Old female.   Haights-in-the-Oaks, Benguet, Luzon, Philippine Islands.   July 26, 1907.   Collected by Edgar A. Mearns.   Original number 6457.

Well-made skin in good condition; skull Grade A.

Genus TYPOMYS Thomas

*Arvicanthis planifrons Miller.

Proc. Washington Acad. Sci. 2: 641, Dec. 28, 1900.
=*Typomys planifrons* (Miller).   See St. Leger, Proc. Zool. Soc. London, 1931 (pt. 3) : 997, Sept. 30, 1931.

83814.   Skin and skull.   Adult male.   Mount Coffee, Liberia, West Africa.   April 26, 1897.   Collected by R. P. Currie.   Original number 46.

Well-made skin in good condition except for a small naked area on belly; skull Grade A.   The specimen was first preserved in alcohol, but shortly after coming to the Museum it was made into a skin.

Genus URANOMYS Dollman

*Uranomys ugandae Heller.

Smithsonian Misc. Coll. 56 (17) : 12, Feb. 28, 1911.

164822.   Skin and skull.   Adult male.   Kikonda, Uganda, Africa.   January 2, 1910.   Collected by J. Alden Loring.   Original number 8570.

Well-made skin in good condition; skull Grade A.

Genus ZELOTOMYS Osgood

*Zelotomys hildegardeae vinaceus Heller.

Smithsonian Misc. Coll. 59 (16) : 10, July 5, 1912.

181798.   Skin and skull.   Adult female.   Ndi, Mount Mbololo, altitude 3,000 feet, Taita Mountains, British East Africa [=Kenya].   November 4, 1911.   Collected by Edmund Heller.   Original number 4578.

Well-made skin in good condition; skull Grade A.

Family MUSCARDINIDAE: Dormice

Genus ELIOMYS Wagner

*Eliomys cincticauda Miller.

Proc. Biol. Soc. Washington 14: 39, Apr. 25, 1901.
=*Eliomys pallidus* Barrett-Hamilton.   See Miller, Catalogue of the Mammals of Western Europe, p. 559, 1912.

103030.   Skin and skull.   Adult male.   Sorrento, near Naples, Italy.   May 31, 1900.   Collected by Dane Coolidge.   Original number 1118.

Well-made skin in good condition; skull Grade A.

Family MYOCASTORIDAE: Coypus
Genus MYOCASTOR Kerr

†Myocastor coypus santacruzae Hollister.

Proc. Biol. Soc. Washington 27: 57, Mar. 20, 1914.

96513. Skin and skull. Adult [male]. North bank of Rio Salado, near Los Palmares, Santa Fé (not Santa Cruz as recorded in original description), Argentina. July to September 1896. Collected by W. Frakes. Original number 1977–X.

Well-made skin in good condition; skull Grade A.

Family PEDETIDAE: Cape Jumping Hares
Genus PEDETES Illiger

*Pedetes cafer dentatus Miller.

Proc. Biol. Soc. Washington 40: 113, Sept. 26, 1927.

251879. Skin and skull. Adult male. Near Dodoma, Tanganyika Territory, Africa. July 8, 1926. Collected by Arthur Loveridge.

Well-made skin in good condition; skull Grade A.

*Pedetes surdaster currax Hollister.

Smithsonian Misc. Coll. 68 (10) : 3, Jan. 16, 1918.

181762. Skin and skull. Adult male. Kabalolot Hill, Sotik, British East Africa [=Kenya]. May 7, 1911. Collected by Edmund Heller. Original number 1802.

Well-made skin in good condition; skull Grade A.

*Pedetes surdaster larvalis Hollister.

Smithsonian Misc. Coll. 68 (10) : 2, Jan. 16, 1918.

163304. Skin and skull. Adult female. Ulukenia Hills, Athi Plains, British East Africa [=Kenya]. November 21, 1909. Collected by J. Alden Loring. Original number 8250.

Well-made skin in good condition; skull Grade A.

Family RHIZOMYIDAE: Bamboo Rats
Genus TACHYORYCTES Rüppell

*Tachyoryctes rex Heller.

Smithsonian Misc. Coll. 56 (9) : 4, July 22, 1910.

163088. Skin and skull. Adult male. Western slope of Mount Kenia, altitude 10,000 feet, British East Africa [=Kenya]. October 7, 1909. Collected by J. Alden Loring. Original number 7840.

Well-made skin in good condition; skull Grade A.

Family SCIURIDAE: Squirrels

Genus CALLOSCIURUS Gray

*Sciurus abbottii Miller.

Proc. Washington Acad. Sci. 2: 224, Aug. 20, 1900.
=*Callosciurus vittatus abbottii* (Miller). See Robinson and Kloss, Rec. Indian Mus. 15: 217, Oct. 1918.

101662. Skin and skull. Adult female. Big Tambelan Island, Tambelan Islands, South China Sea, between Malay Peninsula and Borneo. August 10, 1899. Collected by W. L. Abbott.

Well-made skin in good condition; skull Grade A.

*Sciurus adangensis Miller.

Smithsonian Misc. Coll. 45: 17, Nov. 6, 1903.
=*Callosciurus caniceps adangensis* (Miller). See Robinson and Kloss, Rec. Indian Mus. 15: 209, Oct. 1918.

104389. Skin and skull. Adult male. Pulo Adang, Batu Islands, off west coast of Sumatra. December 14, 1899. Collected by W. L. Abbott. Original number 153.

Well-made skin in good condition; skull Grade A.

*Sciurus altinsularis Miller.

Smithsonian Misc. Coll. 45: 21, Nov. 6, 1903.
=*Callosciurus caniceps altinsularis* (Miller). See Robinson and Kloss, Rec. Indian Mus. 15: 208, Oct. 1918.

111975. Skin and skull. Adult female. High Island, Mergui Archipelago. December 31, 1900. Collected by W. L. Abbott. Original number 810.

Well-made skin in good condition; skull Grade A.

*Sciurus anambensis Miller.

Proc. Washington Acad. Sci. 2: 223, Aug. 20, 1900.
=*Callosciurus vittatus anambensis* (Miller). See Robinson and Kloss, Rec. Indian Mus. 15: 208, Oct. 1918.

101686. Skin and skull. Adult female. Pulo Siantan, Anambas Islands, South China Sea, between Malay Peninsula and Borneo. September 12, 1899. Collected by W. L. Abbott.

Well-made skin in good condition; skull Grade A.

*Sciurus aoris Miller.

Smithsonian Misc. Coll. 45: 10, Nov. 6, 1903.
=*Callosciurus vittatus aoris* (Miller). See Robinson and Kloss, Rec. Indian Mus. 15: 217, Oct. 1918.

112418. Skin and skull. Adult female. Pulo Aor, off the coast of Johore, Federated Malay States. June 5, 1901. Collected by W. L. Abbott. Original number 1002.

Well-made skin in good condition; skull Grade A.

*Sciurus arendsis Lyon.

Proc. U. S. Nat. Mus. 40: 87, Apr. 25, 1911.
=*Callosciurus vittatus arendsis* (Lyon). See Robinson and Kloss, Rec. Indian
Mus. 15: 218, Oct. 1918.

154276. Skin and skull. Adult male. Arends Island, Java Sea.
November 24, 1908. Collected by W. L. Abbott. Original number 6251.

Well-made skin in good condition; skull Grade A.

*Sciurus armalis Lyon.

Proc. U. S. Nat. Mus. 40: 82, Apr. 25, 1911.
=*Callosciurus prevostii armalis* (Lyon). See Robinson and Kloss, Rec. Indian
Mus. 15: 212, Oct. 1918.

145420. Skin and skull. Adult male. Pulo Panebangan, off west
coast of Borneo. May 19, 1907. Collected by W. L. Abbott.
Original number 5257.

Well-made skin in good condition; skull Grade A.

*Sciurus atricapillus atrox Miller.

Smithsonian Misc. Coll. 61 (21) : 23, Dec. 29, 1913.
=*Callosciurus prevostii atrox* (Miller). See Robinson and Kloss, Rec. Indian
Mus. 15: 213, Oct. 1918.

196669. Skin and skull. Adult female. Talisaian Mountain,
Dutch Southeast Borneo. February 6, 1913. Collected by H. C.
Raven. Original number 457.

Well-made skin in good condition; skull Grade A.

*Sciurus atristriatus Miller.

Smithsonian Misc. Coll. 61 (21) : 22, Dec. 29, 1913.
=*Callosciurus notatus atristriatus* (Miller). See Gyldenstolpe, Kungl. Svenska
Vet.-Akad. Handl. 60 (6) : 55, Feb. 12, 1920.

196670. Skin and skull. Half-grown female. Lo Bon Bon, Dutch
Southeast Borneo. June 4, 1912. Collected by H. C. Raven.
Original number 13.

Well-made skin in good condition; skull Grade D.

*Sciurus atrodorsalis tachin Kloss.

Journ. Nat. Hist. Soc. Siam. 2: 178, Dec. 1916.
=*Callosciurus atrodorsalis tachin* (Kloss). See Robinson and Kloss, Rec. Indian
Mus. 15: 206, Oct. 1918.

221566. Skin and skull. Adult female. Pak Bu, Tachin, Central
Siam. October 23, 1916. Collected by C. Boden Kloss. Original number 2213.

Well-made skin in good condition except for loss of distal half of tail.
Skull Grade A.

*Sciurus bentincanus Miller.

Smithsonian Misc. Coll. 45: 19, Nov. 6, 1903.
=*Callosciurus caniceps bentincanus* (Miller). See Robinson and Kloss, Rec. Indian Mus. 15: 207, Oct. 1918.

104383. Skin and skull. Adult female. Bentinck Island, Mergui Archipelago. March 11, 1900. Collected by W. L. Abbott. Original number 349.

Well-made skin in good condition; skull Grade A.

*Sciurus bilimitatus Miller.

Smithsonian Misc. Coll. 45: 8, Nov. 6, 1903.
=*Callosciurus nigrovittatus bilimitatus* (Miller). See Robinson and Kloss, Rec. Indian Mus. 15: 222, Oct. 1918.

105072. Skin and skull. Adult female. Tanjong Laboha, Tringanu, Peninsular Siam. September 29, 1900. Collected by C. Boden Kloss. Original number (W. L. Abbott) 671.

Well-made skin in good condition; skull Grade A.

*Sciurus billitonus Lyon.

Proc. U. S. Nat. Mus. 31: 592, Dec. 18, 1906.
=*Callosciurus vittatus billitonus* (Lyon). See Robinson and Kloss, Rec. Indian Mus. 15: 220, Oct. 1918.

124977. Skin and skull. Adult female. Buding Bay, Billiton Island, off east coast of Sumatra. August 5, 1904. Collected by W. L. Abbott. Original number 3539.

Well-made skin in good condition; skull Grade A.

*Sciurus borneoensis palustris Lyon.

Proc. U. S. Nat. Mus. 33: 553, Dec. 24, 1907.
=*Callosciurus prevostii palustris* (Lyon). See Robinson and Kloss, Rec. Indian Mus. 15: 213, Oct. 1918.

142330. Skin and skull. Adult male. North bank of the Kapuas River, below Pulo Limbang, western Borneo. September 22, 1905. Collected by W. L. Abbott. Original number 4467.

Well-made skin in good condition; skull Grade A.

*Sciurus caniceps canigenus A. B. Howell.

Journ. Washington Acad. Sci. 17: 81, Feb. 19, 1927.
=*Callosciurus erythraeus styani* (Thomas). See G. M. Allen, Mamm. China and Mongolia 2: 633, Sept. 3, 1940.

241509. Skin and skull. Adult male. Hai-yen-Hsien, Hangchow Bay, Chekiang, China. December 10, 1925. Collected by Arthur deC. Sowerby. Original number 1515.

Well-made skin in good condition; skull Grade A.

*Sciurus caniceps helvus Shamel.

Journ. Mamm. 11: 72, Feb. 11, 1930.
= *Callosciurus caniceps helvus* (Shamel).

253433. Skin and skull. Adult male. Island of Koh Tau, off east coast of Peninsular Siam. September 17, 1928. Collected by Hugh M. Smith. Original number 2362.

Well-made skin in good condition; skull Grade A.

*Sciurus carimatae Miller.

Proc. U. S. Nat. Mus. 31: 57, July 23, 1906.
=*Callosciurus prevostii carimatae* (Miller). See Robinson and Kloss, Rec. Indian Mus. 15: 212, Oct. 1918.

125076. Skin and skull. Adult male. Telok Pai, Karimata Island, off west coast of Borneo. August 27, 1904. Collected by W. L. Abbott. Original number 3662.

Well-made skin in good condition; skull Grade A.

*Sciurus carimonensis Miller.

Proc. U. S. Nat. Mus. 31: 261, Sept. 11, 1906.
=*Callosciurus prevostii carimonensis* (Miller). See Robinson and Kloss, Rec. Indian Mus. 15: 212, Oct. 1918.

122800. Skin and skull. Adult female. Great Karimon Island, Rhio-Linga Archipelago. May 24, 1903. Collected by W. L. Abbott. Original number 2423.

Well-made skin in good condition; skull Grade A.

*Sciurus casensis Miller.

Smithsonian Misc. Coll. 45: 20, Nov. 6, 1903.
=*Callosciurus caniceps casensis* (Miller). See Robinson and Kloss, Rec. Indian Mus. 15: 208, Oct. 1918.

104370. Skin and skull. Adult female. Chance Island, Mergui Archipelago. December 28, 1899. Collected by W. L. Abbott. Original number 185.

Well-made skin in good condition; skull Grade A.

*Sciurus condurensis Miller.

Proc. U. S. Nat. Mus. 31: 260, Sept. 11, 1906.
=*Callosciurus prevostii condurensis* (Miller). See Robinson and Kloss, Rec. Indian Mus. 15: 211, Oct. 1918.

122876. Skin and skull. Adult female. Pulo Kundur, Rhio-Linga Archipelago. June 13, 1903. Collected by W. L. Abbott. Original number 2486.

Well-made skin in good condition; skull Grade A.

Sciurus conipus Lyon.

See *Sciurus poliopus* Lyon.

*Sciurus datus Lyon.

Proc. U. S. Nat. Mus. 40: 86, Apr. 25, 1911.
=*Callosciurus vittatus datus* (Lyon). See Robinson and Kloss, Rec. Indian Mus. 15: 218, Oct. 1918.

145393. Skin and skull. Adult female. Pulo Datu, off west coast of Borneo. May 2, 1907. Collected by W. L. Abbott. Original number 5153.

Well-made skin in good condition; skull Grade A.

*Sciurus director Lyon.

Proc. U. S. Nat. Mus. 36: 509, June 7, 1909.
=*Callosciurus vittatus director* (Lyon). See Robinson and Kloss, Rec. Indian Mus. 15: 218, Oct. 1918.

145392. Skin and skull. Immature male. Direction Island, off west coast of Borneo. May 1, 1907. Collected by W. L. Abbott. Original number 5152.

Well-made skin in good condition; skull Grade A.

*Sciurus domelicus Miller.

Smithsonian Misc. Coll. 45: 18, Nov. 6, 1903.
=*Callosciurus caniceps domelicus* (Miller). See Robinson and Kloss, Rec. Indian Mus. 15: 207, Oct. 1918.

104381. Skin and skull. Adult female. Domel Island, Mergui Archipelago. February 24, 1900. Collected by W. L. Abbott. Original number 322.

Well-made skin in good condition; skull Grade A.

*Sciurus dulitensis dilutus Miller.

Smithsonian Misc. Coll. 61 (21) : 23, Dec. 29, 1913.
=*Callosciurus vittatus dilutus* (Miller). See Robinson and Kloss, Rec. Indian Mus. 15: 219, Oct. 1918.

196712. Skin and skull. Adult female. Tanjong Batu, Dutch Southeast Borneo. August 24, 1912. Collected by H. C. Raven. Original number 177.

Well-made skin in good condition; skull Grade A.

*Sciurus epomophorus inexpectatus Kloss.

Journ. Nat. Hist. Soc. Siam 2: 178, Dec. 1916.
=*Callosciurus caniceps inexpectatus* (Kloss). See Robinson and Kloss, Rec. Indian Mus. 15: 207, Oct. 1918.

221557. Skin and skull. Adult female. Koh Lak, Pran, Southwest Siam. November 15, 1916. Collected by C. Boden Kloss. Original number 2434.

Well-made skin in good condition; skull Grade A.

*Sciurus erebus Miller.

Proc. U. S. Nat. Mus. 26: 456, Feb. 3, 1903.
=*Callosciurus prevostii piceus* (Peters). See Robinson and Kloss, Rec. Indian Mus. 15: 214, Oct. 1918.

114537. Skin and skull. Adult female. Tapanuli Bay, west coast of Sumatra. March 17, 1902. Collected by W. L. Abbott. Original number 1653.

Well-made skin in good condition; skull Grade A.

*Sciurus erythraeus pranis Kloss.

Journ. Nat. Hist. Soc. Siam 2 : 178, Dec. 1916.

=*Callosciurus atrodorsalis pranis* (Kloss). See Robinson and Kloss, Rec. Indian Mus. 15 : 206, Oct. 1918.

221568. Skin and skull. Adult male. Koh Lak, Pran, Southwest Siam. November 9, 1916. Collected by C. Boden Kloss. Original number 2395.

Well-made skin in good condition; skull Grade A.

*Sciurus finlaysoni trotteri Kloss.

Journ. Nat. Hist. Soc. Siam 2 : 178, Dec. 1916.

=*Callosciurus finlaysoni trotteri* (Kloss). See Robinson and Kloss, Rec. Indian Mus. 15 : 203, Oct. 1918.

236601. Skin and skull. Adult male. Koh Lan, Inner Gulf of Siam. October 29, 1916. Collected by C. Boden Kloss. Original number 2266.

Well-made skin in good condition; skull Grade A.

*Sciurus ictericus Miller.

Smithsonian Misc. Coll. 45 : 12, Nov. 6, 1903.

=*Callosciurus vittatus ictericus* (Miller). See Robinson and Kloss, Rec. Indian Mus. 15 : 218, Oct. 1918.

121727. Skin and skull. Adult female. Tana Bala, Batu Islands, off west coast of Sumatra. February 4, 1903. Collected by W. L. Abbott. Original number 2223.

Well-made skin in good condition; skull Grade A.

*Sciurus klossii Miller.

Proc. Washington Acad. Sci. 2 : 225, Aug. 20, 1900.

=*Callosciurus nigrovittatus klossii* (Miller). See Robinson and Kloss, Rec. Indian Mus. 15 : 223, Oct. 1918.

101678. Skin and skull. Adult male. Kaju Ara, or Saddle Island, Tambelan group, South China Sea, between Malay Peninsula and Borneo. August 15, 1899. Collected by W. L. Abbott.

Well-made skin in good condition; skull Grade A.

*Sciurus lamucotanus Lyon.

Proc. U. S. Nat. Mus. 40 : 85, Apr. 25, 1911.

=*Callosciurus vittatus lamucotanus* (Lyon). See Robinson and Kloss, Rec. Indian Mus. 15 : 218, Oct. 1918.

145405.   Skin and skull.   Adult female.   Pulo Lamukotan, off west coast of Borneo.   May 8, 1907.   Collected by W. L. Abbott. Original number 5201.

Well-made skin in good condition; skull Grade A.

*Sciurus lancavensis Miller.

Smithsonian Misc. Coll. 45: 16, Nov. 6, 1903.
=*Callosciurus caniceps lancavensis* (Miller).   See Robinson and Kloss, Rec. Indian Mus. 15: 209, Oct. 1918.

104390.   Skin and skull.   Adult male.   Pulo Lankawi, off west coast of Malay Peninsula.   December 1, 1899.   Collected by W. L. Abbott.   Original number 101.

Well-made skin in good condition; skull Grade A.

*Sciurus lautensis Miller.

Proc. Washington Acad. Sci. 3: 128, Mar. 26, 1901.
=*Callosciurus vittatus lautensis* (Miller).   See Robinson and Kloss, Rec. Indian Mus. 15: 219, Oct. 1918.

104683.   Skin and skull.   Adult female.   Pulo Laut, Natuna Islands, South China Sea, between Malay Peninsula and Borneo.   August 6, 1900.   Collected by W. L. Abbott.   Original number 612.

Well-made skin in good condition; skull Grade A.

*Sciurus lucas Miller.

Smithsonian Misc. Coll. 45: 20, Nov. 6, 1903.
=*Callosciurus caniceps lucas* (Miller).   See Robinson and Kloss, Rec. Indian Mus. 15: 208, Oct. 1918.

104385.   Skin and skull.   Adult female.   St. Luke Island, Mergui Archipelago.   January 20, 1900.   Collected by W. L. Abbott. Original number 256.

Well-made skin in good condition; skull Grade A.

*Sciurus lutescens Miller.

Proc. Washington Acad. Sci. 3: 124, Mar. 26, 1901.
=*Callosciurus vittatus lutescens* (Miller).   See Robinson and Kloss, Rec. Indian Mus. 15: 218, Oct. 1918.

104668.   Skin and skull.   Adult male.   Sirhassen Island, Natuna Islands, South China Sea, between Malay Peninsula and Borneo. June 3, 1900.   Collected by W. L. Abbott.   Original number 429.

Well-made skin in good condition; skull Grade A.

*Sciurus marinsularis Lyon.

Proc. U. S. Nat. Mus. 40: 89, Apr. 25, 1911.
=*Callosciurus vittatus marinsularis* (Lyon).   See Robinson and Kloss, Rec. Indian Mus. 15: 218, Oct. 1918.

151777. Skin and skull. Adult male. Pulo Laut, off southeastern Borneo. December 17, 1907. Collected by W. L. Abbott. Original number 5619.

Well-made skin in good condition; skull Grade B.

*Sciurus matthaeus Miller.

Smithsonian Misc. Coll. 45: 19, Nov. 6, 1903.
=Callosciurus caniceps matthaeus (Miller). See Robinson and Kloss, Rec. Indian Mus. 15: 207, Oct. 1918.

111920. Skin and skull. Adult female. St. Matthew Island, Mergui Archipelago. December 11, 1900. Collected by W. L. Abbott. Original number 774.

Well-made skin in good condition; skull Grade A.

*Sciurus melanops Miller.

Proc. Acad. Nat. Sci. Philadelphia 54: 151, June 11, 1902.
=Callosciurus prevostii melanops (Miller). See Robinson and Kloss, Rec. Indian Mus. 15: 211, Oct. 1918.

113152. Skin and skull. Adult female. Indragiri River, eastern Sumatra. September 15, 1901. Collected by W. L. Abbott. Original number 1307.

Well-made skin in good condition; skull Grade A.

*Sciurus melanops penialius Lyon.

Proc. U. S. Nat. Mus. 34: 637, Sept. 14, 1908.
=Callosciurus prevostii penialius (Lyon). See Robinson and Kloss, Rec. Indian Mus. 15: 211, Oct. 1918.

144364. Skin and skull. Adult female. Pulo Penjalei, at the mouth of the Kampar River, eastern Sumatra. February 5, 1907. Collected by W. L. Abbott. Original number 5040.

Well-made skin in good condition; skull Grade A.

*Sciurus mendanauus Lyon.

Proc. U. S. Nat. Mus. 31: 589, Dec. 18, 1906.
=Callosciurus prevostii mendanauus (Lyon). See Robinson and Kloss, Rec. Indian Mus. 15: 212, Oct. 1918.

124916. Skin and skull. Adult male. Pulo Mendanau, west coast of Billiton Island, off east coast of Sumatra. July 14, 1904. Collected by W. L. Abbott. Original number 3475.

Well-made skin in good condition; skull Grade A.

*Sciurus mimellus Miller.

Proc. Washington Acad. Sci. 2: 218, Aug. 20, 1900.
=Callosciurus prevostii mimellus (Miller). See Robinson and Kloss, Rec. Indian Mus. 15: 215, Oct. 1918.

101668. Skin and skull. Adult male. Pulo Wai, Tambelan Islands, South China Sea, between Malay Peninsula and Borneo. August 13, 1899. Collected by W. L. Abbott.

Well-made skin in good condition; skull Grade A.

*Sciurus mimiculus Miller.

Proc. Washington Acad. Sci. 2: 219, Aug. 20, 1900.
=*Callosciurus prevostii mimiculus* (Miller). See Robinson and Kloss, Rec. Indian Mus. 15: 215, Oct. 1918.

101616. Skin and skull. Adult male. Santa Barbe Island, South China Sea, between Sumatra and Borneo. August 1, 1899. Collected by W. L. Abbott.

Well-made skin in good condition; skull Grade A.

*Sciurus notatus miniatus Miller.

Proc. Washington Acad. Sci. 2: 79, July 25, 1900.
=*Callosciurus vittatus miniatus* (Miller). See Robinson and Kloss, Rec. Indian Mus. 15: 220, Oct. 1918.

84415. Skin and skull. Adult female. On or near Khow Nom Plu, Trong (or Tarang), Peninsular Siam. February 25, 1897. Collected by W. L. Abbott.

Well-made skin in good condition; skull Grade A.

*Sciurus nyx Lyon.

Proc. U. S. Nat. Mus. 34: 638, Sept. 14, 1908.
=*Callosciurus prevostii nyx* (Lyon). See Robinson and Kloss, Rec. Indian Mus. 15: 215, Oct. 1918.

143392. Skin and skull. Adult female. Pulo Rupat, off east coast of Sumatra. March 10, 1906. Collected by W. L. Abbott. Original number 4691.

Well-made skin in good condition; skull Grade A.

*Sciurus pannovianus Miller.

Smithsonian Misc. Coll. 45: 11, Nov. 6, 1903.
=*Callosciurus vittatus pannovianus* (Miller). See Robinson and Kloss, Rec. Indian Mus. 15: 217, Oct. 1918.

112351. Skin and skull. Adult male. Pulo Pannow, Atas Islands, South China Sea, between Sumatra and Borneo. May 28, 1901. Collected by W. L. Abbott. Original number 952.

Well-made skin in good condition; skull Grade A.

*Sciurus pelapius Lyon.

Proc. U. S. Nat. Mus. 40: 82, Apr. 25, 1911.
=*Callosciurus prevostii pelapius* (Lyon). See Robinson and Kloss, Rec. Indian Mus. 15: 212, Oct. 1918.

145417. Skin and skull. Adult female. Pulo Pelapis (South Island), off west coast of Borneo. May 30, 1907. Collected by W. L. Abbott. Original number 5335.

Well-made skin in good condition; skull Grade A.

*Sciurus pemangilensis Miller.

Smithsonian Misc. Coll. 45: 9, Nov. 6, 1903.
=*Callosciurus vittatus pemangilensis* (Miller). See Robinson and Kloss, Rec. Indian Mus. 15: 217, Oct. 1918.

112460. Skin and skull. Adult female. Pulo Pemangil, off coast of Johore, Federated Malay States. June 12, 1901. Collected by W. L. Abbott. Original number 1062.

Well-made skin in good condition; skull Grade A.

*Sciurus peninsularis Miller.

Smithsonian Misc. Coll. 45: 10, Nov. 6, 1903.
=*Callosciurus vittatus peninsularis* (Miller). See Robinson and Kloss, Rec. Indian Mus. 15: 216, Oct. 1918.

112511. Skin and skull. Adult male. North Bank of Endau River, Pahang, Federated Malay States. June 21, 1901. Collected by W. L. Abbott. Original number 1078.

Well-made skin in good condition; skull Grade A.

*Sciurus poliopus Lyon.

Proc. U. S. Nat. Mus. 40: 88, Apr. 25, 1911.
=*Sciurus conipus* Lyon. See Lyon, Proc. Biol. Soc. Washington 24: 98, May 15, 1911. (Substitute for *Sciurus poliopus* Lyon, not *Sciurus variegatus poliopus* Fitzinger, Sitzber. Akad. Wiss. Wien, math.-nat. Cl., 45 (1): 478, Mar. 1867.)
=*Callosciurus vittatus conipus* (Lyon). See Robinson and Kloss, Rec. Indian Mus. 15: 219, Oct. 1918.

151789. Skin and skull. Adult male. Pamukang Bay, Southern Borneo. April 5, 1908. Collected by W. L. Abbott. Original number 5923.

Well-made skin in good condition; skull Grade A.

*Sciurus pretiosus Miller.

Proc. U. S. Nat. Mus. 26: 454, Feb. 3, 1903.
=*Callosciurus vittatus pretiosus* Miller. See Robinson and Kloss, Rec. Indian Mus. 15: 215, Oct. 1918.

114325. Skin and skull. Adult female. Pulo Bangkaru, Banjak Islands, off west coast of Sumatra. January 20, 1902. Collected by W. L. Abbott. Original number 1442.

Well-made skin in good condition; skull Grade A.

*Sciurus proserpinae Lyon.

Smithsonian Misc. Coll. 48: 275, Feb. 4, 1907.
=*Callosciurus prevostii proserpinae* (Lyon). See Robinson and Kloss, Rec. Indian Mus. 15: 213, Oct. 1918.

142285. Skin and skull. Adult female. Pulo Temaju (also written Temadjoe and Temadju), off the west coast of Borneo. June 9, 1905. Collected by W. L. Abbott. Original number 4180.

Well-made skin in good condition; skull Grade A.

*Sciurus rubeculus Miller.

Smithsonian Misc. Coll. 45 : 22, Nov. 6, 1903.
=*Callosciurus erythraeus rubeculus* (Miller). See Robinson and Kloss, Rec. Indian Mus. 15: 199, Oct. 1918.

86777. Skin and skull. Adult male. Khow Sai Dow, altitude 1,000 feet, Trong (or Tarang), Peninsular Siam. February 21, 1899. Collected by W. L. Abbott.

Well-made skin in good condition; skull Grade A.

*Sciurus rubidiventris Miller.

Proc. Washington Acad. Sci. 3 : 127, Mar. 26, 1901.
=*Callosciurus vittatus rubidiventris* (Miller). See Robinson and Kloss, Rec. Indian Mus. 15 : 219, Oct. 1918.

104671. Skin and skull. Adult female. Bunguran Island, Natuna Islands, South China Sea, between Malay Peninsula and Borneo. June 22, 1900. Collected by W. L. Abbott. Original number 498.

Well-made skin in good condition; skull Grade A.

*Sciurus rutiliventris Miller.

Proc. Washington Acad. Sci. 3 : 126, Mar. 26, 1901.
=*Callosciurus vittatus rutiliventris* (Miller). See Robinson and Kloss, Rec. Indian Mus. 15 : 219, Oct. 1918.

104658. Skin and skull. Adult male. Pulo Midei (Low Island), Natuna Islands, South China Sea, between Malay Peninsula and Borneo. May 24, 1900. Collected by W. L. Abbott. Original number 405.

Well-made skin in good condition; skull Grade A.

*Sciurus sanggaus Lyon.

Proc. U. S. Nat. Mus. 33 : 554, Dec. 24, 1907.
=*Callosciurus prevostii sanggaus* (Lyon). See Robinson and Kloss, Rec. Indian Mus. 15 : 212, Oct. 1918.

142296. Skin and skull. Adult female. Sanggau, south bank of Kapuas River, western Borneo. August 21, 1905. Collected by W. L. Abbott. Original number 4357.

Well-made skin in good condition; skull Grade A.

*Sciurus saturatus Miller.

Proc. U. S. Nat. Mus. 26 : 453, Feb. 3, 1903.
=*Callosciurus vittatus saturatus* (Miller). See Robinson and Kloss, Rec. Indian Mus. 15 : 215, Oct. 1918.

114629. Skin and skull. Adult female. Pulo Mansalar, off Tapanuli Bay, west coast of Sumatra. March 9, 1902. Collected by W. L. Abbott. Original number 1633.

Well-made skin in good condition; skull Grade B.

*Sciurus seraiae Miller.

Proc. Washington Acad. Sci. 3: 125, Mar. 26, 1901.

=*Callosciurus vittatus seraiae* (Miller). See Robinson and Kloss, Rec. Indian Mus. 15: 219, Oct. 1918.

104660. Skin and skull. Adult male. Pulo Seraia, Natuna Islands, South China Sea, between Malay Peninsula and Borneo. May 29, 1900. Collected by W. L. Abbott. Original number 415.

Well-made skin in good condition; skull Grade A.

*Sciurus serutus Miller.

Proc. U. S. Nat. Mus. 31: 58, July 23, 1906.

=*Callosciurus vittatus serutus* (Miller). See Robinson and Kloss, Rec. Indian Mus. 15: 218, Oct. 1918.

125025. Skin and skull. Adult male. Pulo Serutu, Karimata Islands, off west coast of Borneo. August 17, 1904. Collected by W. L. Abbott. Original number 3584.

Well-made skin in good condition; skull Grade A.

*Sciurus siriensis Lyon.

Proc. U. S. Nat. Mus. 40: 87, Apr. 25, 1911.

=*Callosciurus vittatus siriensis* (Lyon). See Robinson and Kloss, Rec. Indian Mus. 15: 218, Oct. 1918.

151768. Skin and skull. Adult male. Pulo Mata Siri, Java Sea. December 7, 1907. Collected by W. L. Abbott. Original number 5580.

Well-made skin in good condition; skull Grade A.

*Sciurus sullivanus Miller.

Smithsonian Misc. Coll. 45: 17, Nov. 6, 1903.

=*Callosciurus caniceps sullivanus* (Miller). See Robinson and Kloss, Rec. Indian Mus. 15: 207, Oct. 1918.

104377. Skin and skull. Adult female. Sullivan Island, Mergui Archipelago. February 1, 1900. Collected by W. L. Abbott. Original number 294.

Well-made skin in good condition; skull Grade A.

*Sciurus tedongus Lyon.

Proc. U. S. Nat. Mus. 31: 591, Dec. 18, 1906.

=*Callosciurus vittatus tedongus* (Lyon). See Robinson and Kloss, Rec. Indian Mus. 15: 220, Oct. 1918.

124717. Skin and skull. Adult male. Tanjong Tedong, island of Banka, off east coast of Sumatra. June 1, 1904. Collected by W. L. Abbott. Original number 3285.

Well-made skin in good condition; skull Grade A.

*Sciurus tenuirostris Miller.

Proc. Washington Acad. Sci. 2: 221, Aug. 20, 1900.

=*Callosciurus vittatus tenuirostris* (Miller). See Robinson and Kloss, Rec. Indian Mus. 15: 217, Oct. 1918.

101753. Skin and skull. Adult female. Pulo Tioman, off southeast coast Malay Peninsula. September 30, 1899. Collected by W. L. Abbott.

Well-made skin in good condition; skull Grade B.

*Sciurus ubericolor Miller.

Proc. U. S. Nat. Mus. 26: 455, Feb. 3, 1903.

=*Callosciurus vittatus ubericolor* (Miller). See Robinson and Kloss, Rec. Indian Mus. 15: 216, Oct. 1918.

114373. Skin and skull. Adult female. Pulo Tuangku, Banjak Islands, off west coast of Sumatra. February 5, 1902. Collected by W. L. Abbott. Original number 1517.

Well-made skin in good condition; skull Grade A.

*Sciurus vittatus rupatius Lyon.

Proc. U. S. Nat. Mus. 34: 640, Sept. 14, 1908.

=*Callosciurus vittatus rupatius* (Lyon). See Robinson and Kloss, Rec. Indian Mus. 15: 216, Oct. 1918.

143406. Skin and skull. Adult female. Pulo Rupat, off east coast of Sumatra. March 17, 1906. Collected by W. L. Abbott. Original number 4733.

Well-made skin in good condition; skull Grade A.

*Sciurus vittatus tapanulius Lyon.

Smithsonian Misc. Coll. 48: 280, Feb. 4, 1907.

=*Callosciurus vittatus tapanulius* (Lyon). See Robinson and Kloss, Rec. Indian Mus. 15: 216, Oct. 1918.

114519. Skin and skull. Adult male. Tapanuli Bay, west coast of Sumatra. February 21, 1902. Collected by W. L. Abbott. Original number 1560.

Well-made skin in good condition; skull Grade A.

*Sciurus vittatus tarussanus Lyon.

Smithsonian Misc. Coll. 48: 279, Feb. 4, 1907.

=*Callosciurus vittatus vittatus* (Raffles). See Robinson and Kloss, Rec. Indian Mus. 15: 215 (footnote), Oct. 1918.

141038. Skin and skull. Adult female. Tarussan Bay, west coast of Sumatra. December 28, 1904. Collected by W. L. Abbott. Original number 3857.

Well-made skin in good condition; skull Grade A.

Genus CITELLUS Oken

†Citellus adocetus Merriam.

Proc. Biol. Soc. Washington 16: 79, May 29, 1903.

126129. Skin and skull. Adult female. La Salada, 40 miles south of Uruapan, Michoacan, Mexico. March 17, 1903. Collected by E. W. Nelson and E. A. Goldman. Original number 16183.

Well-made skin in good condition; skull Grade A.

†Spermophilus annulatus goldmani Merriam.

Proc. Biol. Soc. Washington 15: 69, Mar. 22, 1902.
=*Citellus annulatus goldmani* (Merriam). See Howell, North Amer. Fauna 56: 164, May 18, 1938.

91259. Skin and skull. Adult female. Santiago, Tepic (=Nayarit), Mexico. June 18, 1897. Collected by E. W. Nelson and E. A. Goldman. Original number 11223.

Well-made skin in good condition; skull Grade A.

*Spermophilus armatus Kennicott. Cotypes.

Proc. Acad. Nat. Sci. Philadelphia 15: 158, ordered published June 30, 1863.
=[*Citellus*] *armatus* (Kennicott). See Trouessart, Catalogus Mammalium tam Viventium quam Fossilium, Suppl., p. 339, 1904.

No numbers are mentioned in the original description. Kennicott briefly described four new spermophiles in the collection of the Smithsonian Institution, collected by C. Drexler at Fort Bridger, Utah, now Wyoming. Consequently, all the specimens from Fort Bridger taken by Drexler and in the National collection before 1863 are evidently cotypes of the species.

The extant specimens from Fort Bridger collected by Drexler are listed below. All their labels have *armatus* written on them, possibly by Kennicott's own hand, and they are entered in the catalog as *Spermophilus armatus*. The skins were all collected April to June 1858, and the specimens in alcohol were probably taken at the same time.

$\frac{3463}{4809}$. Female. Skin, cannot be found; anterior half of skull and mandible present. Original number 454. Collected May 26, 1858.

3464. Female. Very poor skin, torn in two; part of skull inside. Original number 728. Collected June 25, 1858.

$\frac{3466}{4808}$. Male. Skin, cannot be found; anterior half of skull and of mandible present. Original number 610.

3467. Male. Skin, cannot be found; no record of a skull. Original number 261. Collected May 2, 1858.

3470. Female. Skin, cannot be found; no record of a skull. Original number 455. Collected May 26, 1858.

$\frac{3472}{4799}$. Skin and skull; neither can be found. Original number 167. Collected April 11, 1858.

3474. Skin, cannot be found; no record of a skull. Original number 215. Collected April 14, 1858.

3475. Male. Skin, cannot be found; no record of a skull. Original number 197. Collected April 14, 1858.

3476. Female. Very poor skin, torn in two; two loose detached legs present; part of skull inside. Original number 229. Collected April 15, 1858.

3478. Male. Skin, cannot be found; no record of a skull. Original number 140. Collected April 2, 1858.

3481. Skin, cannot be found; no record of a skull. Original number 375. Collected May 19, 1858.

5958. Alcoholic, cannot be found.

5959. Alcoholic, in good condition.

5960. Alcoholic, in good condition.

5961. Alcoholic, skull removed and now lost.

$\frac{4221}{4794}$. Skin, cannot be found; anterior half of skull and right half of mandible present. Remarks in catalog say, "Died at S. I., after two years' confinement." It was probably collected at the time the others were taken.

*Spermophilus barrowensis Merriam.

Proc. Washington Acad. Sci. 2: 19, Mar. 14, 1900.
=*Citellus parryii barrowensis* (Merriam). See Howell, North Amer. Fauna 56: 95, May 18, 1938.

$\frac{14061}{37824}$. Skin and skull. Adult male. Point Barrow, Alaska. May 30, 1883. Collected by P. H. Ray. Original number 1428.

Well-made skin in good condition; skull Grade A.

†Spermophilus beecheyi fisheri Merriam.

Proc. Biol. Soc. Washington 8: 133, Dec. 28, 1893.
=*Citellus beecheyi fisheri* (Merriam). See Grinnell, Proc. California Acad. Sci. (ser. 4) 3: 346, Aug. 28, 1913.

$\frac{29318}{41385}$. Skin and skull. Adult male. Kern Valley, 25 miles above Kernville, Kern County, Calif. July 6, 1891. Collected by A. K. Fisher. Original number 741.

Well-made skin in good condition, except for absence of a small patch of hair on right side of abdomen; skull Grade A.

†Citellus beecheyi parvulus Howell.

Journ. Mamm. 12: 160, May 14, 1931.

$\frac{28068}{40167}$. Skin and skull. Young adult female. Shepherd Canyon, Argus Mountains, Inyo County, Calif. April 30, 1891. Collected by A. K. Fisher. Original number 569.

Well-made skin in good condition; skull Grade A.

†Citellus beecheyi sierrae Howell.

North Amer. Fauna 56: 153, May 18, 1938.

88421. Skin and skull. Adult female. Emerald Bay, Lake Tahoe, Eldorado County, California. May 23, 1897. Collected by J. A. Loring. Original number 4166.

Well-made skin in good condition; skull Grade A.

*Spermophilus beldingi Merriam.

Ann. New York Acad. Sci. 4: 317, Dec. 28, 1888.

=[*Citellus*] *beldingi* (Merriam). See Trouessart, Catalogus Mammalium tam Viventium quam Fossilium, Suppl., p. 339, 1904.

186467. Skin and skull. Adult female. Donner, Placer County, Calif. June 22, 1886. Collected by C. A. Allen. Original number 103. Merriam collection No. $\frac{2712}{3342}$.

Well-made skin in good condition; skull Grade A.

*Spermophilus beringensis Merriam.

Proc. Washington Acad. Sci. 2: 20, Mar. 14, 1900.

=*Citellus parryii barrowensis* (Merriam). See Howell, North Amer. Fauna 56: 95, May 18, 1938.

15253. Skin; no skull. Adult male. Cape Lisburne (Coal Veins), Alaska. May 1885. Collected by Henry D. Woolfe.

Fairly well-made skin in good condition.

Spermophilus (Callospermophilus) bernardinus Merriam.

See *Spermophilus chrysodeirus brevicaudus* Merriam.

†Spermophilus canescens Merriam.

North Amer. Fauna 4: 38, Oct. 8, 1890.

=*Citellus spilosoma canescens* (Merriam). See Howell, North Amer. Fauna 56: 125, May 18, 1938.

$\frac{17873}{24810}$. Skin and skull. Immature male. Willcox, Cochise County, Ariz. November 16, 1889. Collected by Vernon Bailey. Original number 676.

Well-made skin in good condition; skull Grade A.

†Citellus canus vigilis Merriam.

Proc. Biol. Soc. Washington 26: 137, May 21, 1913.

=*Citellus townsendii vigilis* Merriam. See Howell, North Amer. Fauna 56: 66, May 18, 1938.

168361. Skin and skull. Adult female. Vale, Malheur County, Oreg. April 29, 1910. Collected by S. G. Jewett. Original number 30.

Well-made skin in good condition; skull Grade A.

†Tamias castanurus Merriam.

North Amer. Fauna 4: 19, Oct. 8, 1890.

=*Citellus lateralis castanurus* (Merriam). See Howell, North Amer. Fauna 56: 201, May 18, 1938.

$\frac{22733}{30197}$. Skin and skull. Adult male. Park City, Wasatch Mountains, altitude 7,000 feet, Summit County, Utah. July 3, 1890. Collected by Vernon Bailey. Original number 1383.

Well-made skin in good condition; skull Grade A.

*Tamias chrysodeirus Merriam.

North Amer. Fauna 4: 19, Oct. 8, 1890.

=*Citellus lateralis chrysodeirus* (Merriam). See Howell, North Amer. Fauna 56: 203, May 18, 1938.

186464. Skin and skull. Adult male. Fort Klamath, Klamath County, Oreg. July 31, 1888. Collected by Samuel Parker. Original number 143. Merriam collection No. $\frac{4966}{5720}$.

Well-made skin in good condition; skull Grade A.

†Spermophilus chrysodeirus brevicaudus Merriam.

Proc. Biol. Soc. Washington 8: 134, Dec. 28, 1893. (Not *Spermophilus brevicauda* Brandt, Bull. Acad. Sci. St. Petersburg 2 (23–24): 369, Mar. 8, 1844.)

=*Spermophilus* (*Callospermophilus*) *bernardinus* Merriam, Science (new ser.) 8: 782, Dec. 2, 1898. (Substitute for *brevicaudus* Merriam.)

=*Citellus lateralis bernardinus* (Merriam). See Howell, North Amer. Fauna 56: 209, May 18, 1938.

56661. Skin and skull. Adult female. San Bernadino Peak, altitude 9,500 feet, San Bernardino County, Calif. October 9, 1893. Collected by J. E. McLellan. Original number 274.

Well-made skin in good condition: skull Grade B.

†Callospermophilus chrysodeirus connectens Howell.

Journ. Mamm. 12: 161, May 14, 1931.

=*Citellus lateralis connectens* (Howell). See Howell, North Amer. Fauna 56: 205, May 18, 1938.

212461. Skin and skull. Adult male. Homestead, Baker County, Oreg. June 1, 1916. Collected by H. H. Sheldon. Original number 535.

Well-made skin in good condition; skull Grade A.

†Callospermophilus chrysodeirus mitratus Howell.

Journ. Mamm. 12: 161, May 14, 1931.

=*Citellus lateralis mitratus* (Howell). See Howell, North Amer. Fauna 56: 210, May 18, 1938.

138125. Skin and skull. Adult male. South Yolla Bolly Mountain, Calif. July 30, 1905. Collected by J. F. Ferry. Original number 13.

Well-made skin in good condition; skull Grade B.

†Callospermophilus chrysodeirus trinitatis Merriam.

Proc. Biol. Soc. Washington 14: 126, July 19, 1901.
=*Citellus lateralis trinitatis* (Merriam). See Howell, North Amer. Fauna 56: 211, May 18, 1938.

95531. Skin and skull. Adult female. Trinity Mountains east of Hoopa Valley, altitude 5,700 feet, Humboldt County, Calif. September 10, 1898. Collected by Vernon Bailey. Original number 6693.

Well-made skin in good condition, except left ear missing; skull Grade A.

*Tamias cinerascens Merriam.

North Amer. Fauna 4: 20, Oct. 8, 1890.
=*Citellus lateralis cinerascens* (Merriam). See Howell, North Amer. Fauna 56: 198, May 18, 1938.

186465. Skin and skull. Adult female. Helena, altitude 4,500 feet, Lewis and Clark County, Mont. August 13, 1888. Collected by C. Hart Merriam. Original number 4. Merriam collection No. $\frac{4525}{5177}$.

Well-made skin, underparts slightly grease-stained; skull Grade A.

†Citellus columbianus ruficaudus Howell.

Proc. Biol. Soc. Washington 41: 212, Dec. 18, 1928.

231942. Skin and skull. Adult female. Wallowa Lake, altitude 4,000 feet, Wallowa County, Oreg. April 13, 1919. Collected by G. G. Cantwell. Original number 1093.

Well-made skin in good condition; skull Grade A.

*Spermophilus couchii Baird.

Proc. Acad. Nat. Sci. Philadelphia 7: 332, reported favorably for publication Apr. 24, 1855.
=*Citellus variegatus couchii* (Baird). See Howell, North Amer. Fauna 56: 139, May 18, 1938.

$\frac{338}{1255}$. Skin and skull. Santa Catarina (not on modern maps; see Baird, Mammals of North America, p. 713), a few miles west of Monterrey, Nuevo Leon, Mexico. April 1853. Collected by D. N. Couch.

The specimen was formerly mounted, but it has recently been made a study skin, in fair condition. Some hair has slipped from the underparts. Instead of being the "glossy black" described by Baird, it has now become a blackish brown, probably because of exposure to light and consequent bleaching. Skull Grade C.

Type not designated by number, but the measurements given in the original description agree exactly with those of No. $\frac{338}{1255}$ as recorded by Baird in Mammals of North America, p. 312.

†Spermophilus cryptospilotus Merriam.

North Amer. Fauna 3: 57, Sept. 11, 1890.

=*Citellus spilosoma cryptospilotus* (Merriam). See Howell, North Amer. Fauna 56: 130, May 18, 1938.

$\frac{17676}{24612}$. Skin and skull. Adult male. Tenebito Wash, Painted Desert, Coconino County, Ariz. August 17, 1889. Collected by C. Hart Merriam. Original number 374.

Well-made skin in good condition; skull Grade A.

*Spermophilus elegans Kennicott.   Cotypes.

Proc. Acad. Nat. Sci. Philadelphia 15: 158, ordered published at meeting of June 30, 1863.

=*Citellus richardsonii elegans* (Kennicott). See Howell, North Amer. Fauna 56: 76, May 18, 1938.

No numbers are mentioned in the original description. Kennicott briefly describes new spermophiles in the collection of the Smithsonian Institution. He speaks of *Spermophilus elegans* as coming from Fort Bridger, Utah (now Wyo.), and collected by C. Drexler. Consequently all the specimens from Fort Bridger collected by C. Drexler and in the collection prior to 1863 become cotypes of the species. In the following list are included all the known existing specimens from Fort Bridger collected by Drexler. The labels all have *elegans* written on them, possibly in Kennicott's hand, and they are entered in the catalog as *Spermophilus elegans*. The skins were collected in April and May of 1858 and the alcoholics were probably taken at the same time.

$\frac{3468}{4796}$. Female. Skin, cannot be found; skull, anterior half present and in fair condition; mandible lost. Original number 168. Collected April 11, 1858.

3469. Female. Very poor skin; no record of a skull. Original number 169. Collected April 11, 1858.

$\frac{3479}{4810}$. Female. Well-made skin in good condition (remade in February 1902); skull has most of mandible and upper tooth row and orbit of right side present. Original number 233. Collected April 17, 1858.

3480. Male. Very poor skin with part of skull inside. Original number 216. Collected April 14, 1858.

4003. Female. Very poor skin; has been mounted; fragmentary skull inside. Original number 3.

$\frac{5950}{4814}$. Skin in alcohol; condition good; skull in good condition.

5951. Alcoholic; abdominal viscera removed; condition fair.

5952. Alcoholic; abdominal viscera removed; condition fair.

5953. Alcoholic; abdominal viscera removed; condition good.

5954. Alcoholic; abdominal viscera removed; young; condition poor.

5955. Body without feet or head, in alcohol; also a poor skin which has been mounted.

5956. Alcoholic; abdominal viscera removed; condition fair.

5957. Body without feet or head, in alcohol; no skin can be found.

†Citellus elegans nevadensis Howell.

Proc. Biol. Soc. Washington 41: 211, Dec. 18, 1928.

=*Citellus richardsonii nevadensis* Howell. See Howell, North Amer. Fauna 56: 77, May 18, 1938.

156788. Skin and skull. Adult female. Paradise, Humboldt County, Nev. March 3, 1908. Collected by Stanley E. Piper. Original number 112.

Well-made skin in good condition; skull Grade B.

†Spermophilus empetra plesius Osgood.

North Amer. Fauna 19: 29, Oct. 6, 1900.

=*Citellus parryii plesius* (Osgood). See Howell, North Amer. Fauna 56: 97, May 18, 1938.

98931. Skin and skull. Adult female. Bennett, head of Lake Bennett, British Columbia, Canada. June 19, 1899. Collected by W. H. Osgood. Original number 465.

Well-made skin in good condition; skull Grade A.

*Citellus grammurus utah Merriam.

Proc. Biol. Soc. Washington 16: 77, May 29, 1903.

=*Citellus variegatus utah* Merriam. See Howell, North Amer. Fauna 56: 146, May 18, 1938.

186468. Skin and skull. Adult female. Near Ogden, from foot of Wasatch Mountains, Weber County, Utah. October 10, 1888. Collected by Vernon Bailey. Original number 291. Merriam collection No. $\frac{4767}{5427}$.

Well-made skin in good condition; skull Grade B.

*Spermophilus harrisii saxicolus Mearns.

Preliminary Diagnoses of New Mammals from the Mexican Border of the United States, p. 2, Mar. 25, 1896. (Reprint: Proc. U. S. Nat. Mus. 18: 444, May 23, 1896.)

=*Citellus harrisii saxicola* (Mearns). See Howell, North Amer. Fauna 56: 169, May 18, 1938.

59869. Skin and skull. Adult female. Tinajas Altas, Gila Mountains, Yuma County, Ariz. February 17, 1894. Collected by Edgar A. Mearns and F. X. Holzner. Original number 2983.

Well-made skin in good condition; skull Grade A.

†**Citellus idahoensis** Merriam.

Proc. Biol. Soc. Washington 26: 135, May 21, 1913.
=*Citellus townsendii idahoensis* Merriam. See Davis, Journ. Mamm. 20: 182, May 14, 1939.

168290. Skin and skull. Adult female. Payette, at junction of Payette and Snake Rivers, Payette County, Idaho. April 23, 1910. Collected by S. G. Jewett. Original number 17.

Well-made skin in good condition; skull Grade A.

†**Tamias interpres** Merriam.

North Amer. Fauna 4: 21, Oct. 8, 1890.
=*Citellus interpres* (Merriam). See Howell, North Amer. Fauna 56: 180, May 18, 1938.

$\frac{18162}{25060}$. Skin and skull. Adult female. El Paso, El Paso County, Tex. December 10, 1889. Collected by Vernon Bailey. Original number 762.

Well-made skin in good condition; skull Grade A.

†**Callospermophilus lateralis arizonensis** Bailey.

Proc. Biol. Soc. Washington 26: 130, May 21, 1913.
=*Citellus lateralis arizonensis* (Bailey). See Howell, North Amer. Fauna 56: 196, May 18, 1938.

$\frac{17527}{24463}$. Skin and skull. Adult male. San Francisco Mountain, Coconino County, Ariz. August 8, 1889. Collected by C. Hart Merriam and Vernon Bailey. Original number 308.

Well-made skin in good condition; skull Grade A.

†**Callospermophilus lateralis caryi** Howell.

Proc. Biol. Soc. Washington 30: 105, May 23, 1917.
=*Citellus lateralis caryi* (Howell). See Howell, North Amer. Fauna 56: 197, May 18, 1938.

176826. Skin and skull. Adult female. Seven miles south of Fremont Peak, Wind River Mountains, altitude 10,400 feet, Fremont County, Wyo. July 19, 1911. Collected by Merritt Cary. Original number 2211.

Well-made skin in good condition; skull Grade A.

†**Callospermophilus lateralis certus** Goldman.

Journ. Mamm. 2: 232, Nov. 29, 1921.
=*Citellus lateralis certus* (Goldman). See Howell, North Amer. Fauna 56: 208, May 18, 1938.

208891. Skin and skull. Adult male. North base of Charleston Peak, Clark County, Nev. June 29, 1915. Collected by L. J. Goldman. Original number 2270.

Well-made skin in good condition; skull Grade B.

*Callospermophilus lateralis tescorum Hollister.

Smithsonian Misc. Coll. 56 (26) : 2, Dec. 5, 1911.
=*Citellus lateralis tescorum* (Hollister). See Howell, North Amer. Fauna 56:
199, May 18, 1938.

174165. Skin and skull. Adult male. Head of Moose Pass Branch of Smoky River, altitude 7,000 feet, Alberta (near Moose Pass, British Columbia, Canada). August 2, 1911. Collected by N. Hollister. Original number 3863.

Well-made skin in good condition; skull Grade A.

*Tamias leucurus Merriam.

North Amer. Fauna 2: 20, Oct. 30, 1889.
=*Citellus leucurus leucurus* (Merriam). See Howell, North Amer. Fauna 56:
170, May 18, 1938.

186466. Skin and skull. Adult male. San Gorgonio Pass, Riverside County, Calif. May 16, 1885. Collected by Frank Stephens. Original number 68. Merriam collection No. $\frac{1108}{1660}$.

Well-made skin in good condition; skull Grade A.

†Tamias leucurus cinnamomeus Merriam.

North Amer. Fauna 3: 51, Sept. 11, 1890.
=*Citellus leucurus cinnamomeus* (Merriam). See Howell, North Amer. Fauna 56: 174, May 18, 1938.

$\frac{17987}{24898}$. Skin and skull. Adult female. Echo Cliffs, Painted Desert, Coconino County, Ariz. September 22, 1889. Collected by C. Hart Merriam and V. Bailey. Original number 510.

Well-made skin in good condition; skull Grade A.

†Ammospermophilus leucurus extimus Nelson and Goldman.

Journ. Washington Acad. Sci. 19: 281, July 19, 1929.
=*Citellus leucurus extimus* (Nelson and Goldman). See Howell, North Amer. Fauna 56: 179, May 18, 1938.

146587. Skin and skull. Adult female. Saccaton, 15 miles north of Cape San Lucas, Lower California, Mexico. December 29, 1905. Collected by E. W. Nelson and E. A. Goldman. Original number 18805.

Well-made skin in good condition; skull Grade A.

†Ammospermophilus leucurus insularis Nelson and Goldman.

Proc. Biol. Soc. Washington 22: 24, Mar. 10, 1909.
=*Citellus insularis* (Nelson and Goldman). See Howell, North Amer. Fauna 56: 181, May 18, 1938.

146783. Skin and skull. Adult female. Espiritu Santo Island, Gulf of California, Lower California, Mexico. February 7, 1906. Collected by E. W. Nelson and E. A. Goldman. Original number 19072.

Well-made skin in good condition; skull Grade A.

†Ammospermophilus leucurus pennipes Howell.

Journ. Mamm. 12: 162, May 14, 1931.
=*Citellus leucurus pennipes* (Howell). See Howell, North Amer. Fauna 56: 175, May 18, 1938.

75683. Skin and skull. Adult female. Grand Junction, Mesa County, Colo. November 11, 1895. Collected by A. H. Howell. Original number 494.

Well-made skin in good condition; skull Grade A.

†Ammospermophilus leucurus tersus Goldman.

Journ. Washington Acad. Sci. 19: 435, Nov. 19, 1929.
=*Citellus leucurus tersus* (Goldman). See Howell, North Amer. Fauna 56: 173, May 18, 1938.

202645. Skin and skull. Young adult male. Lower end of Prospect Valley, altitude 4,500 feet, Grand Canyon, Hualpai Indian Reservation, Ariz. October 3, 1913. Collected by E. A. Goldman. Original number 22269.

Well-made skin in good condition; skull Grade A.

†Citellus leurodon Merriam.

Proc. Biol. Soc. Washington 26: 136, May 21, 1913.
=*Citellus townsendii mollis* (Kennicott). See Howell, North Amer. Fauna 56: 63, May 18, 1938; Davis, Journ. Mamm. 20: 187, May 14, 1939.

169031. Skin and skull. Young adult male. Murphy, in hills west of Snake River, Owyhee County, Idaho. May 30, 1910. Collected by S. G. Jewett. Original number 112.

Well-made skin in good condition; skull Grade A.

†Callospermophilus madrensis Merriam.

Proc. Washington Acad. Sci. 3: 563, Nov. 29, 1901.
=*Citellus madrensis* (Merriam). See Howell, North Amer. Fauna 56: 213, May 18, 1938.

95363. Skin and skull. Adult female. Sierra Madre, near Guadalupe y Calvo, Chihuahua, Mexico. August 27, 1898. Collected by E. W. Nelson and E. A. Goldman. Original number 12923.

Well-made skin in good condition; skull Grade A.

*Spermophilus mexicanus parvidens Mearns.

Preliminary Diagnoses of New Mammals from the Mexican Border of the United States, p. 1, Mar. 25, 1896. (Reprint: Proc. U. S. Nat. Mus. 18: 443, May 23, 1896.)
=*Citellus mexicanus parvidens* (Mearns). See Stone and Rehn, Proc. Acad. Nat. Sci. Philadelphia, 1903: 21, January=May 7, 1903.

63073. Skin and skull. Adult male. Fort Clark, Kinney County, Tex. March 21, 1893. Collected by Edgar A. Mearns. Original number 2312.

Well-made skin in good condition; skull Grade A.

*Spermophilus mohavensis Merriam.

North Amer. Fauna 2: 15, Oct. 30, 1889.

=*Citellus mohavensis* (Merriam). See Trouessart, Catalogus Mammalium tam Viventium quam Fossilium, Suppl., p. 341, 1904.

186469. Skin and skull. Adult male. Mohave River, San Bernardino County, Calif. June 29, 1886. Collected by Frank Stephens. Original number 315. Merriam collection No. $\frac{2594}{3223}$.

Well-made skin in good condition; skull Grade A.

*Spermophilus mollis Kennicott.   Cotypes.

Proc. Acad. Nat. Sci. Philadelphia 15: 157, ordered published at meeting of June 30, 1863.

=*Citellus townsendii mollis* (Kennicott). See Howell, North Amer. Fauna 56: 63, May 18, 1938; Davis, Journ. Mamm. 20: 187, May 14, 1939.

3775. Skin (mounted). Camp Floyd, near Fairfield, Wasatch County, Utah. March 9, 1859. Condition good. May contain fragment of skull.

$\frac{3777}{4798}$. Skin and skull. Camp Floyd, near Fairfield, Wasatch County, Utah. March 18, 1859. Collected by C. S. McCarthy during "explorations with the army in Utah" under Capt. J. H. Simpson. Original number 164.

Skin remade in February 1902, in good condition. Skull Grade C.

†Citellus mollis artemesiae Merriam.

Proc. Biol. Soc. Washington 26: 137, May 21, 1913.

=*Citellus townsendii artemesiae* Merriam. See Howell, North Amer. Fauna 56: 65, May 18, 1938; Davis, Journ. Mamm. 20: 188, May 14, 1939.

$\frac{23489}{30907}$. Skin and skull. Adult male. Birch Creek, Fremont County, Idaho. August 9, 1890. Collected by Vernon Bailey. Original number 1573.

Well-made skin in good condition; skull Grade A.

†Spermophilus mollis canus Merriam.

Proc. Biol. Soc. Washington 12: 70, Mar. 24, 1898.

=*Citellus townsendii canus* (Merriam). See Howell, North Amer. Fauna 56: 67, May 18, 1938.

78681. Skin and skull. Adult female. Antelope, Wasco County, Oreg. June 21, 1896. Collected by Vernon Bailey. Original number 5561.

Well-made skin in good condition; skull Grade A.

†Citellus mollus [sic] pessimus Merriam.

Proc. Biol. Soc. Washington 26: 138, May 21, 1913.

=*Citellus townsendii artemesiae* Merriam. See Howell, North Amer. Fauna 56: 65, May 18, 1938; Davis, Journ. Mamm. 20: 188, May 14, 1939.

$\frac{23925}{31330}$. Skin and skull. Adult male. Lower part of Big Lost River, Fremont County, Idaho. July 23, 1890. Collected by C. P. Streator. Original number 53.

Well-made skin in good condition; skull Grade A.

†Spermophilus mollis stephensi Merriam.

Proc. Biol. Soc. Washington 12: 69, Mar. 24, 1898.
=*Citellus townsendii mollis* (Kennicott). See Howell, North Amer. Fauna 56: 63, May 18, 1938.

$\frac{29492}{41567}$. Skin and skull. Adult male. Queen Station, near head of Owens Valley, Esmeralda County, Nev. July 12, 1891. Collected by Frank Stephens. Original number 718.

Well-made skin in good condition; skull Grade B.

†Citellus mollis washoensis Merriam.

Proc. Biol. Soc. Washington 26: 138, May 21, 1913.
=*Citellus townsendii mollis* (Kennicott). See Howell, North Amer. Fauna 56: 63, May 18, 1938.

$\frac{16946}{23861}$. Skin and skull. Adult. Carson Valley, Douglas County, Nev. May 23, 1889. Collected by Charles A. Keeler. Original number 34.

Well-made skin, slightly grease-burned and tip of tail broken off; skull Grade A.

†Spermophilus mollis yakimensis Merriam.

Proc. Biol. Soc. Washington 12: 70, Mar. 24, 1898.
=*Citellus townsendii townsendii* (Bachman). See Howell, North Amer. Fauna 56: 60, May 18, 1938.

89331. Skin and skull. Adult male. Mabton, Yakima County, Wash. July 16, 1897. Collected by W. K. Fisher. Original number 323.

Well-made skin in good condition; skull Grade A.

*Citellus nebulicola Osgood.

Proc. Biol. Soc. Washington 16: 26, Mar. 19, 1903.
=*Citellus parryii nebulicola* Osgood. See Howell, North Amer. Fauna 56: 100, May 18, 1938.

59145. Skin and skull. Adult female. Nagai Island, Shumagin Islands, Alaska. June 24, 1893. Collected by C. H. Townsend.

Fairly well-made skin in good condition; skull Grade A.

*Spermophilus neglectus Merriam.

North Amer. Fauna 2: 17, Oct. 20, 1889.
=*Citellus tereticaudus neglectus* (Merriam). See Howell, North Amer. Fauna 56: 187, May 18, 1938.

251543—42——34

186470. Skin and skull. Adult male. Dolans Spring, Mohave County, Ariz. February 9, 1889. Collected by Vernon Bailey. Original number 566. Merriam collection No. $\frac{5262}{5952}$.

Well-made skin in good condition; skull Grade B.

†**Spermophilus nelsoni** Merriam.

Proc. Biol. Soc. Washington 8: 129, Dec. 28, 1893.
=*Citellus nelsoni* (Merriam). See Howell, North Amer. Fauna 56: 182, May 18, 1938.

54651. Skin and skull. Adult male. Tipton, San Joaquin Valley, Tulare County, Calif. June 24, 1893. Collected by C. P. Streator. Original number 2968.

Well-made skin in good condition; skull Grade A.

*****Spermophilus obsoletus** Kennicott.   Lectotype.

Proc. Acad. Nat. Sci. Philadelphia 15: 157, ordered published at meeting of June 30, 1863.
=*Citellus spilosoma obsoletus* (Kennicott). See Howell, North Amer. Fauna 56: 130, May 18, 1938.

$\frac{3222}{37998}$. Skin. Female. Fifty miles west of Fort Kearney, Nebr. August 9, 1857. Collected by J. G. Cooper. Original number 44.

Fair skin, remade February 1902. Skull in fair condition; broken about the brain case posteriorly.

†**Spermophilus oregonus** Merriam.

Proc. Biol. Soc. Washington 12: 69, Mar. 24, 1898.
=*Citellus beldingi oregonus* (Merriam). See Howell, North Amer. Fauna 56: 83, May 18, 1938.

89177. Skin and skull. Adult female. Swan Lake Valley, Klamath Basin, Klamath County, Oreg. June 12, 1897. Collected by Vernon Bailey. Original number 6005.

Well-made skin in good condition; skull Grade A.

*****Spermophilus osgoodi** Merriam.

Proc. Washington Acad. Sci. 2: 18, Mar. 14, 1900.
=*Citellus osgoodi* (Merriam). See Osgood, Proc. Biol. Soc. Washington 16: 27, Mar. 19, 1903.

$\frac{12789}{37822}$. Skin and skull. Adult male. Fort Yukon, Alaska. April 29, 1877. Collected by Lucien M. Turner. Original number 1635.

Well-made skin in good condition; skull Grade C.

*****Spermophilus parryii kodiacensis** J. A. Allen.   Lectotype.

Proc. Boston Soc. Nat. Hist. 16: 292, 1874.
=*Citellus kodiacensis* (J. A. Allen). See Howell, North Amer. Fauna 56: 103, May 18, 1938.

$\frac{9242}{38543}$. Skin and skull (originally mounted). Adult male. Kodiak Island, Alaska. June 1868. Collected by F. Bischoff.

Well-made skin in good condition; skull Grade D.

†Spermophilus perotensis Merriam.

Proc. Biol. Soc. Washington 8: 131, Dec. 28, 1893.
=*Citellus perotensis* (Merriam). See Elliot, Field Columbian Mus. Publ. 95 (zool. ser. 4) : 145, 1904.

54274. Skin and skull. Adult female. Perote, Veracruz, Mexico. June 8, 1893. Collected by E. W. Nelson. Original number 4976.

Well-made skin in good condition; skull Grade A.

†Citellus plesius ablusus Osgood.

Proc. Biol. Soc. Washington 16: 25, Mar. 19, 1903.
=*Citellus parryii ablusus* Osgood. See Howell, North Amer. Fauna 56: 98, May 18, 1938.

119815. Skin and skull. Adult male. Nushagak, Alaska. September 16, 1902. Collected by W. H. Osgood and A. G. Maddren. Original number 2043.

Well-made skin in good condition; skull Grade A.

†Spermophilus spilosoma annectens Merriam.

Proc. Biol. Soc. Washington 8: 132, Dec. 28, 1893.
=*Citellus spilosoma annectens* (Merriam). See Trouessart, Catalogus Mammalium tam Viventium quam Fossilium, Suppl., p. 340, 1904.

$\frac{30410}{42396}$. Skin and skull. Young adult male. Padre Island, Cameron County, Tex. August 24, 1891. Collected by W. Lloyd. Original number 694.

Well-made skin in good condition; skull Grade A.

†Spermophilus spilosoma arens Bailey.

Proc. Biol. Soc. Washington 15: 118, June 2, 1902.
=*Citellus spilosoma canescens* (Merriam). See Howell, North Amer. Fauna 56: 125, May 18, 1938.

64977. Skin and skull. Adult male. El Paso, El Paso County, Tex. May 10, 1894. Collected by A. K. Fisher. Original number 1446.

Well-made skin in good condition; skull Grade B.

†Spermophilus spilosoma macrospilotus Merriam.

North Amer. Fauna 4: 38, Oct. 8, 1890.
=*Citellus spilosoma canescens* (Merriam). See Howell, North Amer. Fauna 56: 125, May 18, 1938.

$\frac{16750}{23663}$. Skin and skull. Adult female. Oracle, Pinal County, Ariz. June 11, 1889. Collected by Vernon Bailey. Original number 129.

Well-made skin in good condition; skull Grade A.

†Spermophilus spilosoma major Merriam.

North Amer. Fauna 4: 39, Oct. 8, 1890.
=*Citellus spilosoma major* (Merriam). See Trouessart, Catalogus Mammalium tam Viventium quam Fossilium, Suppl., p. 340, 1904.

$\frac{17116}{24049}$. Skin and skull. Adult female. Albuquerque, Bernalillo County, N. Mex. July 22, 1889. Collected by Vernon Bailey. Original number 225.

Well-made skin in good condition; skull Grade B.

†Spermophilus spilosoma marginatus Bailey.

Proc. Biol. Soc. Washington 15: 118, June 2, 1902.
=*Citellus spilosoma major* (Merriam). See Howell, North Amer. Fauna 56: 126, May 18, 1938.

108927. Skin and skull. Adult male. Alpine, Brewster County, Tex. July 5, 1901. Collected by Vernon Bailey. Original number 7702.

Well-made skin in good condition; skull Grade A.

†Spermophilus spilosoma obsidianus Merriam.

North Amer. Fauna 3: 56, Sept. 11, 1890.
=*Citellus spilosoma pratensis* (Merriam). See Howell, North Amer. Fauna 56: 128, May 18, 1938.

$\frac{17674}{24610}$. Skin and skull. Adult male. Cedar belt northeast of San Francisco Mountain, Coconino County, Ariz. October 1, 1889. Collected by Vernon Bailey. Original number 557.

Well-made skin in fair condition; underparts somewhat grease-stained; skull Grade B.

†Citellus spilosoma pallescens Howell.

Proc. Biol. Soc. Washington 41: 212, Dec. 18, 1928.

79535. Skin and skull. Adult male. La Ventura, Coahuila, Mexico. August 10, 1896. Collected by E. W. Nelson and E. A. Goldman. Original number 10016.

Well-made skin in good condition; skull Grade B.

†Spermophilus spilosoma pratensis Merriam.

North Amer. Fauna 3: 55, Sept. 11, 1890.
=*Citellus spilosoma pratensis* (Merriam). See Trouessart, Catalogus Mammalium tam Viventium quam Fossilium, Suppl., p. 340, 1904.

$\frac{17659}{24595}$. Skin and skull. Adult female. Pine plateau at north base of San Francisco Mountain, Coconino County, Ariz. August 5, 1889. Collected by C. Hart Merriam and Vernon Bailey. Original number 285.

Well-made skin in good condition; skull Grade A.

*Citellus stejnegeri J. A. Allen.

Bull. Amer. Mus. Nat. Hist. 19: 142, Mar. 31, 1903.

63226. Skin and skull. Male (♀), young. Near Petropaulski, southeastern Kamchatka, Siberia. 1895. Collected by L. Stejneger.

Flat skin; all parts present and apparently in good condition; skull Grade A.

*Spermophilus tereticaudus Baird.   Cotypes.

Mammals of North America, p. 315, 1857.
=*Citellus tereticaudus* (Baird). See Elliot, Field Columbian Mus. Publ. 79 (zool. ser. 3) : 211, June 1903.

No type is designated by Baird. The description is apparently equally based upon these three specimens, which are specified by number:

$\frac{1584}{2419}$. Skin and skull. A not fully adult male. Skin in bad condition; most of hair on the posterior half of body, except the legs and tail, is lacking; skull Grade A.

1585. Skin of the head and neck. The body is said to be in alcohol but it cannot be found.

2490. A young female in alcohol. All the hair behind the shoulders, except that on the feet and tail, has sloughed off.

All the specimens were collected at Old Fort Yuma, Imperial County, Calif., on right bank of the Colorado River, opposite present town of Yuma, Ariz., by G. H. Thomas. Skins cataloged June 24, 1856, the alcoholic, April 9, 1857.

†Citellus townsendii brunneus Howell.

Proc. Biol. Soc. Washington 41: 211, Dec. 18, 1928.
=*Citellus brunneus* Howell. See Howell, North Amer. Fauna 56: 72, May 18, 1938.

201963. Skin and skull. Adult female. New Meadows, Adams County, Idaho. July 11, 1913. Collected by L. E. Wyman. Original number 178.

Well-made skin in good condition; skull Grade B.

†Spermophilus tridecemlineatus alleni Merriam.

Proc. Biol. Soc. Washington 12: 71, Mar. 24, 1898.
=*Citellus tridecemlineatus alleni* (Merriam). See Trouessart, Catalogus Mammalium tam Viventium quam Fossilium, Suppl., p. 341, 1904.

56050. Skin and skull. Adult male. West slope of Bighorn Mountains, altitude 8,000 feet, Washakie County, Wyo. September 18, 1893. Collected by V. Bailey. Original number 4383.

Well-made skin in good condition; skull Grade A.

† Citellus tridecemlineatus arenicola Howell.

Proc. Biol. Soc. Washington 41: 213, Dec. 18, 1928.

87686. Skin and skull. Adult male. Pendennis, Lane County, Kans. April 22, 1897. Collected by J. A. Loring. Original number 3988.

Well-made skin in good condition; skull Grade A.

† Citellus tridecemlineatus hollisteri Bailey.

Proc. Biol. Soc. Washington 26: 131, May 21, 1913.

119025. Skin and skull. Adult female. Elk Valley, Mescalero Indian Reservation, Sacramento Mountains, altitude 8,000 feet, Lincoln County, N. Mex. September 11, 1902. Collected by V. Bailey. Original number 7963.

Well-made skin in good condition; skull Grade A.

† Citellus tridecemlineatus monticola Howell.

Proc. Biol. Soc. Washington 41: 214, Dec. 18, 1928.

209255. Skin and skull. Adult male. Marsh Lake (also called Big Lake), White Mountains, altitude 9,000 feet, Apache County, Ariz. June 15, 1915. Collected by E. A. Goldman. Original number 22616.

Well-made skin in good condition; skull Grade A.

*Spermophilus tridecemlineatus pallidus J. A. Allen.   Lectotype.

Monographs of North American Rodentia, p. 872, Aug. 1877.

=Citellus tridecemlineatus pallidus (J. A. Allen).   See Trouessart, Catalogus Mammalium tam Viventium quam Fossilium, Suppl., p. 341, 1904.

16237. Skin only. Mouth of Yellowstone River, Mont. August 18, 1857. Collected by F. V. Hayden.

Skin was formerly poorly made but has recently been remade and is now in fairly good condition.

Allen, Bull. Amer. Mus. Nat. Hist. 7: 328, 1895, writes: "I separated (Proc. Boston Soc. Nat. Hist. 16: 291, 1874) the pale western form here referred to as Spermophilus tridecemlineatus pallidus, without, however, giving any diagnosis. This was supplied three years later in my monographic revision of the American Sciuridae.

"In now separating additional forms of this group, I would restrict pallidus to the arid region of the Plains, from the Upper Missouri southward to eastern Colorado, western Kansas, etc., and designate as its type region the plains of the Lower Yellowstone River."

Howell (North Amer. Fauna 56: 112, 1938) has made No. 16237, taken at the mouth of the Yellowstone, the lectotype.

*Spermophilus tridecemlineatus texensis Merriam.

Proc. Biol. Soc. Washington 12 : 71, Mar. 24, 1898.

=*Citellus tridecemlineatus texensis* (Merriam). See Trouessart, Catalogus Mammalium tam Viventium quam Fossilium, Suppl., p. 342, 1904.

186471. Skin and skull. Adult male. Gainesville, Cooke County, Tex. April 15, 1886. Collected by G. H. Ragsdale. Merriam collection No. $\frac{2117}{2647}$.

Well-made skin in good condition ; skull Grade B.

†Citellus variegatus juglans Bailey.

Proc. Biol Soc. Washington 26 : 131, May 21, 1913.

=*Citellus variegatus grammurus* Say. See Howell, North Amer. Fauna 56 : 142, May 18, 1938.

148289. Skin and skull. Adult male. Glenwood, at 5,000 feet altitude on the Rio San Francisco, at the southwest base of the Mogollon Mountains, Socorro County, N. Mex. November 2, 1906. Collected by Vernon Bailey. Original number 8587.

Well-made skin in good condition ; skull Grade A.

†Citellus washingtoni loringi Howell.

North Amer. Fauna 56 : 71, May 18, 1938.

89805. Skin and skull. Adult male. Douglas, Douglas County, Washington. August 1, 1897. Collected by J. A. Loring. Original number 4547.

Well-made skin in good condition ; skull Grade A.

†Citellus washingtoni washingtoni Howell.

North Amer. Fauna 56 : 69, May 18, 1938.

$\frac{27948}{40068}$. Skin and skull. Adult male. Touchet, Walla Walla County, Washington. May 18, 1891. Collected by Clark P. Streator. Original number 817.

Well-made skin in good condition ; skull Grade A.

Genus CYNOMYS Rafinesque

*Spermophilus gunnisoni Baird.

Proc. Acad. Nat. Sci. Philadelphia 7 : 334, reported favorably for publication April 24, 1855.

=*Cynomys gunnisoni* (Baird). See Baird, Mammals of North America, p. 335, 1857.

$\frac{501}{1636}$. Skin and skull. Young adult. Cochetopa Pass, Saguache County, Colo. September (first week) 1853. Collected by F. Kreutzfeldt, on expedition in charge of Capt. J. W. Gunnison. Original number 22.

Fairly well-made skin, left hindfoot missing ; skull Grade C.

The type is not designated in the original description, but in Baird's Mammals of North America (1857) it is specified by number.

†**Cynomys gunnisoni zuniensis** Hollister.

North Amer. Fauna 40: 32, June 20, 1916.

137555. Skin and skull. Adult male. Wingate, McKinley County, N. Mex. June 26, 1905. Collected by N. Hollister. Original number 2374.

Well-made skin in good condition; skull Grade A.

*****Cynomys leucurus** Merriam.

North Amer. Fauna 3: 59, Sept. 11, 1890; and North Amer. Fauna 4: 33, Oct. 8, 1890.

186472. Skin and skull. Adult female. Fort Bridger, Uinta County, Wyo. September 15, 1888. Collected by Vernon Bailey. Original number 224. Merriam collection No. $\frac{4668}{5319}$.

Well-made skin in good condition; skull Grade A.

†**Cynomys mexicanus** Merriam.

Proc. Biol. Soc. Washington 7: 157, July 27, 1892.

$\frac{26423}{33836}$. Skin and skull. Adult male. La Ventura, Coahuila, Mexico. March 24, 1891. Collected by C. P. Streator. Original number 625.

Well-made skin in good condition; skull Grade A.

Genus DREMOMYS Heude

*****Dremomys rufigenis lentus** A. B. Howell.

Journ. Washington Acad. Sci. 17: 80, Feb. 19, 1927.

=*Dremomys pernyi pernyi* (Milne-Edwards). See G. M. Allen, Mamm. China and Mongolia 2: 647, 648, Sept. 3, 1940.

240384. Skin and skull. Adult male. Wenchuanshein, altitude 6,000 feet, Szechwan, China. August 14, 1924. Collected by D. C. Graham. Original number 14.

Well-made skin in good condition except for slight loss of hair on belly and left side; skull Grade B.

Genus EUTAMIAS Trouessart

†**Tamias alpinus** Merriam.

Proc. Biol. Soc. Washington 8: 137, Dec. 28, 1893.

=*Eutamias alpinus* (Merriam). See Merriam, Proc. Biol. Soc. Washington 11: 191, July 1, 1897.

$\frac{30507}{42491}$. Skin and skull. Young adult female. Big Cottonwood Meadows, altitude 10,000 feet, near Mount Whitney, Tulare County, Calif. August 12, 1891. Collected by B. H. Dutcher. Original number 191.

Well-made skin in good condition; skull Grade A.

*Tamias amoenus J. A. Allen.

Bull. Amer. Mus. Nat. Hist. 3 : 90, June 1890.

=*Eutamias amoenus* (J. A. Allen).   See Merriam, Proc. Biol. Soc. Washington 11 :
191, July 1, 1897.

186460.   Skin and skull.   Adult female.   Fort Klamath, Klamath
County, Oreg.   May 16, 1887.   Collected by J. C. Merrill.
Original number 5.   Merriam collection No. $\frac{3469}{4096}$.

Well-made skin in good condition; skull Grade A.

†Eutamias amoenus ochraceus Howell.

Journ. Mamm. 6 : 54, Feb. 9, 1925.

161049.   Skin and skull.   Adult male.   Stud Horse Canyon, Siskiyou Mountains, altitude 6,500 feet, Siskiyou County, Calif.
September 27, 1909.   Collected by N. Hollister.   Original number 3511.

Well-made skin in good condition; skull Grade A.

†Eutamias amoenus operarius Merriam.

Proc. Biol. Soc. Washington 18 : 164, June 29, 1905.

=*Eutamias minimus operarius* Merriam.   See Howell, Journ. Mamm. 3 : 183,
Aug. 4, 1922.

129808.   Skin and skull.   Young adult female.   Gold Hill, altitude
7,400 feet, Boulder County, Colo.   October 8, 1903.   Collected
by Vernon Bailey.   Original number 8160.

Well-made skin in good condition; skull Grade A.

†Eutamias amoenus vallicola Howell.

Journ. Mamm. 3 : 179, Aug. 4, 1922.

168027.   Skin and skull.   Adult female.   Bass Creek, near Stevens-
ville, altitude 3,725 feet, Ravalli County, Mont.   March 23,
1910.   Collected by Clarence Birdseye.   Original number 1052.

Well-made skin in good condition; skull Grade A.

*Eutamias asiaticus altaicus Hollister.

Proc. Biol. Soc. Washington 25 : 183, Dec. 24, 1912.

=*Eutamias sibiricus altaicus* Hollister.   See G. M. Allen, Mamm. China and
Mongolia 2 : 697, Sept. 3, 1940.

175501.   Skin and skull.   Adult male.   Tapucha, Altai Mountains,
altitude 6,900 feet, Siberia.   August 8, 1912.   Collected by N.
Hollister.   Original number 4474.

Well-made skin in good condition; skull Grade A.

*Tamias asiaticus borealis J. A. Allen.   **Lectotype.**

Monographs of North American Rodentia, p. 793, Aug. 1877.

=*Eutamias minimus borealis* (J. A. Allen).   See Howell, Journ. Mamm. 3 : 183,
Aug. 4, 1922.

6506.   Skin, broken skull inside.   Fort Liard, Mackenzie, Canada. About 1860.   Collected by W. L. Hardisty.   Original number 1086.

Skin in fair condition, portion of tail missing.

No type was selected at the time the species was named. In his second revision of the genus, Allen (Bull. Amer. Mus. Nat. Hist. 3: 107, June 1890) designated as a type (lectotype) U. S. N. M. No. 6506, from Fort Liard, Mackenzie.

*Eutamias asiaticus umbrosus A. B. Howell.

Journ. Washington Acad. Sci. 17: 80, Feb. 19, 1927.
=*Eutamias sibiricus albogularis* J. A. Allen.   See G. M. Allen, Mamm. China and Mongolia 2: 696, Sept. 3, 1940.

240744.   Skin and skeleton.   Adult male.   One hundred and forty miles south of Lanchowfu, Kansu, China.   August 21, 1923. Collected by F. R. Wulsin.   Original number 1118.

Well-made skin in good condition; skull Grade B; skeleton incomplete.

†Eutamias atristriatus Bailey.

Proc. Biol. Soc. Washington 26: 129, May 21, 1913.
=*Eutamias minimus atristriatus* Bailey.   See Howell, Journ. Mamm. 3: 178, Aug. 4, 1922.

119028.   Skin and skull.   Adult female.   Penasco Creek, altitude 7,400 feet, 12 miles east of Cloudcroft, Sacramento Mountains, Lincoln County, N. Mex.   September 6, 1902.   Collected by Vernon Bailey.   Original number 7953.

Well-made skin in good condition; skull Grade A.

†Eutamias bulleri solivagus Howell.

Journ. Mamm. 3: 179, Aug. 4, 1922.

116882.   Skin and skull.   Adult female.   Sierra Guadalupe, Coahuila, Mexico.   May 1, 1902.   Collected by E. W. Nelson and E. A. Goldman.   Original number 15169.

Well-made skin in good condition; skull Grade A.

†Tamias callipeplus Merriam.

Proc. Biol. Soc. Washington 8: 136, Dec. 28, 1893.
=*Eutamias quadrivittatus callipeplus* (Merriam).   See Grinnell, Univ. California Publ. Zool. 40: 130, Sept. 26, 1933.

$\frac{31299}{43164}$.   Skin and skull.   Young adult male.   Summit of Mount Pinos, altitude 9,000 feet, Ventura County, Calif.   October 20, 1891.   Collected by E. W. Nelson.   Original number 1344.

Well-made skin in good condition; skull Grade A.

†Eutamias canicaudus Merriam.

Proc. Biol. Soc. Washington 16: 77, May 29, 1903.
=*Eutamias amoenus canicaudus* Merriam.   See Howell, Journ. Mamm. 3: 184, Aug. 4, 1922.

$\frac{27007}{34428}$. Skin and skull. Adult female. Spokane, Spokane County, Wash. April 11, 1891. Collected by C. P. Streator. Original number 639.

Well-made skin in good condition; skull Grade A.

†Eutamias caniceps Osgood.

North Amer. Fauna 19: 28, Oct. 6, 1900.
=*Eutamias minimus caniceps* Osgood. See Howell, Journ. Mamm. 3: 184, Aug. 4, 1922.

99200. Skin and skull. Adult female. Lake Lebarge, Yukon, Canada. July 13, 1899. Collected by W. H. Osgood. Original number 603.

Well-made skin in good condition; skull Grade A.

†Eutamias caurinus Merriam.

Proc. Acad. Nat. Sci. Philadelphia 50: 352, Oct. 4, 1898.
=*Eutamias amoenus caurinus* Merriam. See Howell, Journ. Mamm. 3: 184, Aug. 4, 1922.

90636. Skin and skull. Adult male. Timberline near head of Soleduck River, Olympic Mountains, Clallam County, Wash. August 27, 1897. Collected by C. Hart Merriam. Original number 6211 (V. Bailey).

Well-made skin in good condition; skull Grade A.

†Tamias cinereicollis J. A. Allen.

Bull. Amer. Mus. Nat. Hist. 3: 94, June 1890.
=*Eutamias cinereicollis* (J. A. Allen). See Miller and Rehn, Proc. Boston Soc. Nat. Hist. 30: 40, Dec. 27, 1901.

$\frac{17597}{24533}$. Skin and skull. Adult female. San Francisco Mountain, Coconino County, Ariz. August 2, 1889. Collected by C. Hart Merriam and Vernon Bailey. Original number 260 (V. Bailey).

Well-made skin in good condition; skull Grade A.

†Eutamias cinereicollis canipes Bailey.

Proc. Biol. Soc. Washington 15: 117, June 2, 1902.

109229. Skin and skull. Adult female. Guadalupe Mountains, El Paso County, Tex. August 24, 1901. Collected by Vernon Bailey. Original number 7827.

Well-made skin in good condition; skull Grade B.

†Eutamias cinereicollis cinereus Bailey.

Proc. Biol. Soc. Washington 26: 130, May 21, 1913.

167029. Skin and skull. Adult male. Copper Canyon, Magdalena Mountains altitude 8,200 feet, Socorro County, N. Mex. September 1, 1909. Collected by E. A. Goldman. Original number 20435.

Well-made skin in good condition; skull Grade A.

†Eutamias consobrinus clarus Bailey.

Proc. Biol. Soc. Washington 31: 31, May 16, 1918.
=*Eutamias minimus consobrinus* J. A. Allen. See Howell, North Amer. Fauna
52: 46, Nov. 30, 1929.

227313. Skin and skull. Swan Lake Valley, Yellowstone National
Park, Wyo. September 13, 1917. Collected by Vernon Bailey.
Original number 9945.

Well-made skin in good condition; skull Grade A.

*Tamias cooperi Baird.   Cotype.

Proc. Acad. Nat. Sci. Philadelphia 7: 334, reported favorably for publication
Apr. 24, 1855.
=*Eutamias townsendii cooperi* (Baird). See Taylor, Proc. California Acad.
Sci. (ser. 4) 9: 110, July 12, 1919.

$\frac{212}{1183}$. Skin and skull. Klickitat Pass, Cascade Mountains, altitude
4,500 feet, Skamania County, Wash. (See Cooper, Amer. Nat.
2: 531, Dec. 1868; Baird's published statements regarding the
locality are inaccurate.) July 1853. Collected by J. G. Cooper.

Skin well preserved. In June 1902 it was remade into a modern study
specimen; skull Grade C.

Another cotype, No. $\frac{211}{1182}$, having the same data as No. $\frac{212}{1183}$, is now **No.**
4754 in the Museum of Comparative Zoology, Cambridge, Mass.

No type is designated in the original description, but on page 301, Mammals
of North America, Baird refers to Nos. 211 and 212 as the ones he had in
view when *Tamias cooperi* was first described.

*Tamias dorsalis Baird.   Cotypes.

Proc. Acad. Nat. Sci. Philadelphia 7: 332, reported favorably for publication
Apr. 24, 1855.
=*Eutamias dorsalis* (Baird). See Merriam, Proc. Biol. Soc. Washington 11: 210,
July 1, 1897.

120. Mounted specimen (skull inside). Fort Webster, copper
mines of the Mimbres River; lat. 32°47′ N., long. 108°04′ W.
Near present town of Santa Rita, Grant County, N. Mex. 1851.
Collected by J. H. Clark.

In fair condition. Some skin is broken about the chin and about right
foreleg; tip of tail missing.

$\frac{119}{3151}$. Data as above. This skin is now No. 4759, Museum of Comparative Zoology, Cambridge, Mass.

These specimens were designated by number by Baird as the basis of
Tamias dorsalis (Mammals of North America, p. 300, 1857).

†Eutamias dorsalis carminis Goldman.

Proc. Biol. Soc. Washington 51: 56, Mar. 18, 1938.

263378. Skin and skull. Young adult male. Carmen Mountains, altitude 7,400 feet, Coahuila, Mexico. September 20, 1937. Collected by R. S. Sturgis. Original number 28066–X (73).

Well-made skin in good condition, except for a small area missing on left side of abdomen; skull Grade A.

*Eutamias dorsalis utahensis Merriam.

Proc. Biol. Soc. Washington 11: 210, July 1, 1897.

186457. Skin and skull. Adult male. Ogden, Weber County, Utah. October 9, 1888. Collected by Vernon Bailey. Original number 289. Merriam collection No. $\frac{4788}{5448}$.

Well-made skin in good condition except for missing tip of tail; skull grade B.

†Eutamias hopiensis Merriam.

Proc. Biol. Soc. Washington 18: 165, June 29, 1905.
=*Eutamias quadrivittatus hopiensis* Merriam. See Howell, Journ. Mamm. 3: 184, Aug. 4, 1922.

67768. Skin and skull. Adult female. Keam Canyon, Painted Desert, Navajo County, Ariz. July 27, 1894. Collected by A. K. Fisher. Original number 1688.

Well-made skin in good condition; skull Grade A.

*Eutamias ludibundus Hollister.

Smithsonian Misc. Coll. 56 (26) : 1, Dec. 5, 1911.
=*Eutamias amoenus ludibundus* Hollister. See Howell, Journ. Mamm. 3: 184, Aug. 4, 1922.

174225. Skin and skull. Adult female. Yellowhead Lake, altitude 3,700 feet, British Columbia, Canada. August 29, 1911. Collected by N. Hollister. Original number 3987.

Well-made skin in good condition; skull Grade A.

*Tamias macrorhabdotes Merriam.

Proc. Biol. Soc. Washington 3: 25, Jan. 27, 1886.
=*Eutamias quadrimaculatus* (Gray). See Merriam, Proc. Biol. Soc. Washington 11: 191, July 1, 1897.

186458. Skin and skull. Adult male. Blue Canyon, Placer County, Calif. October 6, 1885. Collected by C. A. Allen. Original number 1. Merriam collection No. $\frac{1488}{2109}$.

Well-made skin in good condition; skull Grade A.

†Eutamias merriami meridionalis Nelson and Goldman.

Proc. Biol. Soc. Washington 22: 23, Mar. 10, 1909.

139597. Skin and skull. Adult female. Aguaje de San Esteban, about 25 miles northwest of San Ignacio, altitude about 1,200 feet, Lower California, Mexico. October 5, 1905. Collected by E. W. Nelson and E. A. Goldman. Original number 18268.

Well-made skin in good condition; skull Grade B.

†Eutamias minimus arizonensis Howell.

Journ. Mamm. 3 : 178, Aug. 4, 1922.

205869. Skin and skull. Adult male. Prieto Plateau at the south end of Blue Range, altitude 9,000 feet, Greenlee County, Ariz. September 7, 1914. Collected by E. G. Holt. Original number 384.

Well-made skin in good condition; skull Grade A.

†Eutamias minimus caryi Merriam.

Proc. Biol. Soc. Washington 21 : 143, June 9, 1908.

150740. Skin and skull. Young adult male. Medano Ranch, San Luis Valley, Costilla County, Colo. October 24, 1907. Collected by Merritt Cary. Original number 1176.

Well-made skin in good condition; skull Grade A.

†Eutamias minimus confinis Howell.

Journ. Mamm. 6 : 52, Feb. 9, 1925.

168957. Skin and skull. Adult female. Head of Trapper's Creek, altitude 8,500 feet, west slope of Bighorn Mountains, Big Horn County, Wyo. June 7, 1910. Collected by Merritt Cary. Original number 1956.

Well-made skin in good condition; skull Grade A.

*Tamias minimus consobrinus J. A. Allen.

Bull. Amer. Mus. Nat. Hist. 3 ; 112, June 1890.
=Eutamias minimus consobrinus (J. A. Allen). See Miller and Rehn, Proc. Boston Soc. Nat. Hist. 30 : 42, Dec. 27, 1901.

186456. Skin and skull. Adult male. Eighteen miles east of Salt Lake City, Parley's Canyon, Wasatch Mountains, Salt Lake County, Utah. October 31, 1888. Collected by Vernon Bailey. Original number 361. Merriam collection No. $\frac{4883}{5630}$.

Well-made skin in good condition; skull Grade A.

†Eutamias minimus grisescens Howell.

Journ. Mamm. 6 : 52, Feb. 9, 1925.

89701. Skin and skull. Young adult male. Farmer, Douglas County, Wash. July 31, 1897. Collected by J. A. Loring. Original number 4539.

Well-made skin in good condition; skull Grade A.

†**Eutamias minimus jacksoni** Howell.

Journ. Mamm. 6: 53, Feb. 9, 1925.

227423. Skin and skull. Adult male. Crescent Lake, Oneida County, Wis. September 7, 1917. Collected by H. H. T. Jackson. Original number 927.

Well-made skin in good condition; skull Grade A.

†**Tamias minimus melanurus** Merriam.

North Amer. Fauna 4: 22, Oct. 8, 1890.

=*Eutamias minimus pictus* (J. A. Allen). See Miller and Rehn, Proc. Boston Soc. Nat. Hist. 30: 42, Dec. 27, 1901.

$\frac{23048}{30494}$. Skin and skull. Adult male. Snake River, near Blackfoot, Bingham County, Idaho. July 17, 1890. Collected by Vernon Bailey and B. H. Dutcher. Original number 1451.

Well-made skin in good condition; skull Grade C.

*****Tamias minimus pictus** J. A. Allen.

Bull. Amer. Mus. Nat. Hist. 3: 115, June 1890.

=*Eutamias minimus pictus* (J. A. Allen). See Miller and Rehn, Proc. Boston Soc. Nat. Hist. 30: 42, Dec. 27, 1901.

186459. Skin and skull. Adult male. Kelton, Box Elder County, Utah. October 25, 1888. Collected by Vernon Bailey. Original number 342. Merriam collection No. $\frac{4882}{5629}$.

Well-made skin in good condition; skull Grade B.

*****Tamias obscurus** J. A. Allen.

Bull. Amer. Mus. Nat. Hist. 3: 70, June 1890.

=*Eutamias merriami obscurus* (J. A. Allen). See Nelson and Goldman, Proc. Biol. Soc. Washington 22: 23, Mar. 10, 1909.

$\frac{18050}{24954}$. Skin and skull. Adult female. San Pedro Martir Mountains, near Vallecitos, Lower California, Mexico. May 1, 1889. Collected by C. H. Townsend. Original number 7.

Well-made skin in good condition, but no wire in tail; skull Grade A.

†**Eutamias oreocetes** Merriam.

Proc. Biol. Soc. Washington 11: 207, July 1, 1897.

=*Eutamias minimus oreocetes* Merriam. See Howell, Journ. Mamm. 3; 183, Aug. 4, 1922.

72468. Skin and skull. Adult female. Near Summit, Summit Mountain, at timber line on Great Northern R. R., Flathead County, Mont. June 14, 1895. Collected by Vernon Bailey. Original number 5024.

Well-made skin in good condition; skull Grade A.

†**Eutamias pallidus cacodemus Cary.**

Proc. Biol. Soc. Washington 19: 89, June 4, 1906.

=*Eutamias minimus cacodemus* Cary. See Howell, Journ. Mamm. 3: 183, Aug. 4, 1922.

138737 (not 138137, as recorded in original description). Skin and skull. Young adult male. Sheep Mountain, Big Badlands, Fall River County, S. Dak. September 2, 1905. Collected by Merritt Cary. Original number 682.

Well-made skin in good condition; skull Grade A.

†**Eutamias palmeri Merriam.**

Proc. Biol. Soc. Washington 11: 208, July 1, 1897.

$\frac{26075}{33481}$. Skin and skull. Adult male. Charleston Peak, altitude 8,000 feet, Clark County, Nev. February 13, 1891. Collected by T. S. Palmer and E. W. Nelson. Original number 432.

Well-made skin in good condition; skull Grade A.

†**Tamias panamintinus Merriam.**

Proc. Biol. Soc. Washington 8: 134, Dec. 28, 1893.

=*Eutamias panamintinus* (Merriam). See Merriam, Proc. Biol. Soc. Washington 11: 191, July 1, 1897.

$\frac{27603}{39702}$. Skin and skull. Adult male. Johnson Canyon, Panamint Mountains, altitude 6,000 feet, Inyo County, Calif. April 3, 1891. Collected by E. W. Nelson. Original number 723.

Well-made skin in good condition; skull Grade A.

*****Eutamias quadrivittatus animosus Warren.**

Proc. Biol. Soc. Washington 22: 105, June 25, 1909.

=*Eutamias quadrivittatus quadrivittatus* (Say.). See Howell, Journ. Mamm. 3: 184, Aug. 4, 1922.

154163. Skin and skull. Adult female. Irwin Ranch, altitude 5,000 feet, Las Animas County, Colo. April 29, 1909. Collected by E. R. Warren. Original number 3428.

Well-made skin in good condition; skull Grade A.

*****Tamias quadrivittatus gracilis J. A. Allen.**

Bull. Amer. Mus. Nat. Hist. 3: 99, June 1890.

=*Eutamias quadrivittatus quadrivittatus* (Say). See Howell, Journ. Mamm. 3: 184, Aug. 4, 1922.

$\frac{17144}{24077}$. Skin and skull. Adult female. San Pedro, Socorro County, N. Mex. July 4, 1889. Collected by Vernon Bailey. Original number 166.

Well-made skin in good condition; skull Grade A.

†Tamias quadrivittatus luteiventris J. A. Allen.

Bull. Amer. Mus. Nat. Hist. 3: 101, June 1890.

=*Eutamias amoenus luteiventris* (J. A. Allen). See Howell, Journ. Mamm. 3: 179, Aug. 4, 1922.

$\frac{11991}{37996}$. Skin and skull. Adult male. Chief Mountain Lake [=Waterton Lake], Alberta, Canada (3½ miles north of the United States–Canada boundary). August 24, 1874. Collected by Elliott Coues on the U. S. Northern Boundary Survey. Original number 4596.

Remade in February 1902. Now a modern study skin, in good condition; skull Grade B.

*Tamias quadrivittatus pallidus J. A. Allen.   Lectotype.

Proc. Boston Soc. Nat. Hist. 16: 289, 1874.

=*Eutamias minimus pallidus* (J. A. Allen). See Howell, Journ. Mamm. 3: 183, Aug. 4, 1922.

$\frac{11656}{38311}$. Skin and skull. Nearly adult. Camp Thorne, near present town of Glendive, Yellowstone River, Dawson County, Mont. July 18, 1873. Collected by J. A. Allen. Original number 200.

Skin originally had skull inside, but in 1906 the skull was removed and the specimen made into a modern study skin, now in good condition; skull Grade B.

Lectotype chosen out of a series of cotypes by Cary, Proc. Biol. Soc. Washington 19: 88, 1906.

†Eutamias ruficaudus Howell.

Proc. Biol. Soc. Washington 33: 91, Dec. 30, 1920.

72294. Skin and skull. Adult female. Upper St. Marys Lake, Glacier County, Mont. May 30, 1895. Collected by A. H. Howell. Original number 27.

Well-made skin in good condition; skull Grade A.

†Eutamias ruficaudus simulans Howell.

Journ. Mamm. 3: 179, Aug. 4, 1922.

$\frac{28487}{40591}$. Skin and skull. Adult female. Coeur d'Alene, Kootenai County, Idaho. June 1, 1891. Collected by Clark P. Streator. Original number 881.

Well-made skin in good condition; skull Grade A.

*Eutamias senescens Miller.

Proc. Acad. Nat. Sci. Philadelphia 50: 349, Oct. 4, 1898.

=*Eutamias sibiricus senescens* Miller. See G. M. Allen, Mamm. China and Mongolia 2: 693, Sept. 3, 1940.

83395. Skin and skull. Adult female. Low barren hills, 15 miles west of Peking [=Peiping], Chi-li, China. August 21, 1896. Collected by George D. Wilder.

Well-made skin in good condition; skull Grade B.

*Tamias senex J. A. Allen.

Bull. Amer. Mus. Nat. Hist. 3: 83, June 1890.
=*Eutamias townsendii senex* (J. A. Allen). See Howell, Journ. Mamm. 3: 181, Aug. 4, 1922.

186461. Skin and skull. Adult. Summit of Donner Pass, Placer County, Calif. July 1, 1885. Collected by L. Belding. Original number 3. Merriam collection number $\frac{1133}{5882}$.

Well-made skin in good condition; skull Grade A.

*Tamias speciosus Merriam.

In J. A. Allen, Bull. Amer. Mus. Nat. Hist. 3: 86, June 1890.
=*Eutamias quadrivittatus speciosus* (Merriam). See Howell, North Amer. Fauna 52: 89, Nov. 30, 1929.

186462. Adult male. Skin and skull. Head of Whitewater Creek, San Bernardino Mountains, altitude 7,500 feet, San Bernardino County, Calif. June 22, 1885. Collected by Frank Stephens. Original number 108. Merriam collection number $\frac{1148}{1804}$.

Well-made skin in good condition; skull Grade A.

†Eutamias speciosus inyoensis Merriam.

Proc. Biol. Soc. Washington 11: 208, July 1, 1897.
=*Eutamias quadrivittatus inyoensis* Merriam. See Howell, North Amer. Fauna 52: 84, Nov. 30, 1929.

$\frac{29387}{41462}$. Skin and skull. Young adult male. Black Canyon, White Mountains, altitude 8,200 feet, Inyo County, Calif. July 7, 1891. Collected by E. W. Nelson. Original number 1069.

Well-made skin in good condition; skull Grade C.

†Eutamias speciosus sequoiensis Howell.

Journ. Mamm. 3: 180, Aug. 4, 1922.
=*Eutamias quadrivittatus sequoiensis* Howell. See Howell, North Amer. Fauna 52: 88, Nov. 30, 1929.

$\frac{30899}{42799}$. Skin and skull. Adult female. Mineral King, east fork of Kaweah River, altitude 7,300 feet, Tulare County, Calif. September 12, 1891. Collected by V. Bailey. Original number 3259.

Well-made skin in good condition; skull Grade B.

†Eutamias townsendii alleni Howell.

Journ. Mamm. 3: 181, Aug. 4, 1922.
=*Eutamias alleni* Howell. See Howell, North Amer. Fauna 52: 119, Nov. 30, 1929.

135177. Skin and skull. Adult male. Inverness, Marin County, Calif. November 16, 1904. Collected by N. Hollister. Original number 1378.

Well-made skin in good condition; skull Grade A.

†Eutamias townsendii ochrogenys Merriam.

Proc. Biol. Soc. Washington 11: 195, July 1, 1897.

67182. Skin and skull. Adult male. Mendocino, Mendocino County, Calif. July 17, 1894. Collected by J. E. McLellan. Original number 1015.

Well-made skin in good condition; skull Grade B.

†Eutamias townsendii siskiyou Howell.

Journ. Mamm. 3: 180, Aug. 4, 1922.

161033. Skin and skull. Adult female. Near summit of White Mountain, Siskiyou Mountains, altitude 6,000 feet, Siskiyou County, Calif. September 16, 1909. Collected by N. Hollister. Original number 3432.

Well-made skin in good condition; skull Grade A.

*Tamias umbrinus J. A. Allen.

Bull. Amer. Mus. Nat. Hist. 3: 96, June 1890.
=*Eutamias umbrinus* (J. A. Allen). See Miller and Rehn, Proc. Boston Soc. Nat. Hist. 30: 45, Dec. 27, 1901.

186463. Skin and skull. Adult male. Black Fork, Uinta Mountains, altitude about 9,500 feet, Utah. September 19, 1888. Collected by Vernon Bailey. Original number 228. Merriam collection number $\frac{4690}{5341}$.

Well-made skin in good condition; skull Grade C.

Genus GLAUCOMYS Thomas

†Sciuropterus alpinus klamathensis Merriam.

Proc. Biol. Soc. Washington 11: 225, July 15, 1897.
=*Glaucomys sabrinus klamathensis* (Merriam). See Howell, North Amer. Fauna 44: 52, June 13, 1918.

87310. Skin and skull. Adult female. Fort Klamath, altitude 4,200 feet, Klamath County, Oreg. January 11, 1897. Collected by B. L. Cunningham. Original number 355–X.

Well-made skin in good condition; skull Grade A.

†Sciuropterus alpinus zaphaeus Osgood.

Proc. Biol. Soc. Washington 18: 133, Apr. 18, 1905.
=*Glaucomys sabrinus zaphaeus* (Osgood). See Howell, North Amer. Fauna 44: 43, June 13, 1918.

136137. Skin and skull. Adult female. Helm Bay, Cleveland Peninsula, Alaska. January 21, 1905. Collected by C. Catt. Original number 5196–X.

Well-made skin in good condition; skull Grade A.

†Glaucomys bullatus Howell.

Proc. Biol. Soc. Washington 28: 113, May 27, 1915.
=*Glaucomys sabrinus bangsi* Rhoads. See Davis, Recent Mammals of Idaho: 70, 231, Apr. 5, 1939.

$\frac{24271}{31675}$. Skin and skull. Adult female. Sawtooth (Alturas) Lake, east base of Sawtooth Mountains, Blaine County, Idaho. September 28, 1890. Collected by Vernon Bailey and B. H. Dutcher. Original number 1883.

Well-made skin in good condition; skull Grade A.

†Sciuropterus oregonensis stephensi Merriam.

Proc. Biol. Soc. Washington 13: 151, June 13, 1900.
=*Glaucomys sabrinus stephensi* (Merriam). See Howell, North Amer. Fauna 44: 57, June 13, 1918.

99830. Skin and skull. Young adult female. Sherwood, Mendocino County, Calif. May 10, 1894. Collected by Frank Stephens. Original number 2307 (2624–X).

Well-made skin in good condition; skull Grade A.

†Glaucomys sabrinus columbiensis Howell.

Proc. Biol. Soc. Washington 28: 111, May 27, 1915.

94310. Skin and skull. Subadult male. Okanagan, British Columbia, Canada. May 9, 1898. Collected by Allan C. Brooks. Original number 1214 (1762–X).

Well-made skin in good condition; skull Grade A.

*Glaucomys sabrinus fuscus Miller.

Proc. Biol. Soc. Washington 49: 143, Aug. 22, 1936.

260420. Skin and skull. Adult female. Cranberry Glades, altitude 3,300 feet, Pocahontas County, W. Va. June 13, 1936. Collected by Watson Perrygo and Carleton Lingebach. Original number 109.

Well-made skin in good condition; skull Grade A.

*Glaucomys sabrinus griseifrons Howell.

Journ. Mamm. 15: 64, Feb. 15, 1934.

256993. Skin and skull. Adult female. Lake Bay, Prince of Wales Island, Alaska. April 18, 1927. Collected by F. R. Bates. Original number 10.

Well-made skin in good condition; skull Grade A.

†Glaucomys sabrinus latipes Howell.

Proc. Biol. Soc. Washington 28: 112, May 27, 1915.

68753. Skin and skull. Adult female. Glacier, British Columbia, Canada. August 13, 1894. Collected by J. A Loring. Original number 2111.

Well-made skin in good condition except that the left hind foot has been broken off and is now sewed to the skin; skull Grade A.

*Sciuropterus sabrinus macrotis Mearns.

Proc. U. S. Nat. Mus. 21: 353, Nov. 4, 1898.
=*Glaucomys sabrinus macrotis* (Mearns). See Howell, Proc. Biol. Soc. Washington 28: 111, May 27, 1915.

83152. Skin and skull. Adult female. Hunter Mountain, Catskill Mountains, Greene County, N. Y. August 31, 1896. Collected by Edgar A. Mearns. Original number 4036.

Well-made skin in good condition; skull Grade A.

†Sciuropterus volans goldmani Nelson.

Proc. Biol. Soc. Washington 17: 148, Oct. 6, 1904.
=*Glaucomys volans goldmani* (Nelson). See Howell, North Amer. Fauna 44: 28, June 13, 1918.

132833. Skin and skull. Adult male. Twenty miles southeast of Teopisca, Chiapas, Mexico. April 8, 1904. Collected by E. A. Goldman. Original number 16667.

Well-made skin in good condition; skull Grade C.

†Glaucomys volans herreranus Goldman.

Journ. Washington Acad. Sci. 26: 463, Nov. 15, 1936.

261695. Skin and skull. Young adult female. Mountains of Veracruz, Mexico. November 8, 1924. Prepared by Luis G. Rubio. Original number 27589–X.

Well-made specimen, formerly mounted, in good condition; skull Grade C.

†Glaucomys volans madrensis Goldman.

Journ. Washington Acad. Sci. 26: 463, Nov. 15, 1936.

261694. Skin and skull. Adult (sex?). Sierra Madre, Chihuahua, Mexico. Received March 1926 from A. L. Herrera. Original number 27588–X.

Well-made specimen, formerly mounted, in good condition; skull Grade A.

†Glaucomys volans saturatus Howell.

Proc. Biol. Soc. Washington 28: 110, May 27, 1915.

178366. Skin and skull. Adult female. Dothan, Henry County, Ala. March 13, 1912. Collected by A. H. Howell. Original number 1960.

Well-made skin in good condition; skull Grade A.

†Glaucomys volans texensis Howell.

Proc. Biol. Soc. Washington 28: 110, May 27, 1915.

136400. Skin and skull. Adult male. Seven miles northeast of Sour Lake, Hardin County, Tex. March 15, 1905. Collected by James H. Gaut. Original number 3480.

Well-made skin in good condition; skull Grade A.

*Sciuropterus yukonensis Osgood.

North Amer. Fauna 19: 25, Oct. 6, 1900.
=Glaucomys sabrinus yukonensis (Osgood). See Howell, North Amer. Fauna 44: 41, June 13, 1918.

$\frac{19909}{35320}$. Skin and skull. Adult female. Camp Davidson, Yukon River, near Alaska-Canada boundary, Yukon, Canada. December 8, 1890. Collected by R. E. Carson.

Well-made skin in good condition; skull Grade A.

Genus HELIOSCIURUS Trouessart

*Heliosciurus multicolor madogae Heller.

Smithsonian Misc. Coll. 56 (17) : 1, Feb. 28, 1911.

164828. Skin and skull. Adult male. Uma, 50 miles north of Nimule, Uganda, Africa. February 11, 1910. Collected by Kermit Roosevelt. Original number, Loring 8991.

Well-made skin in good condition; skull Grade A.

*Sciurus (Heliosciurus) rufobrachiatus libericus Miller.

Proc. Washington Acad. Sci. 2: 633, Dec. 28, 1900.
=Heliosciurus rufobrachium maculatus (Temminck). See Thomas, Ann. Mag. Nat. Hist. (ser. 9) 11: 524, Apr. 1923.

83834. Skin and skull. Adult male. Mount Coffee, Liberia, West Africa. March 22, 1897. Collected by R. P. Currie. Original number 16.

Well-made skin in good condition; skull Grade A.

*Heliosciurus rufobrachiatus shindi Heller.

Smithsonian Misc. Coll. 63 (7) : 7, June 24, 1914.
=Heliosciurus undulatus shindi Heller. See Hollister, U. S. Nat. Mus. Bull. 99 (pt. 2) : 12, May 16, 1919.

182768. Skin and skull. Adult male. Summit of Mount Umengo, altitude 6,000 feet, Taiti Hills, British East Africa [=Kenya]. November 11, 1911. Collected by Edmund Heller. Original number 4731.

Well-made skin in good condition; skull Grade A.

*Sciurus undulatus True.   Lectotype.

Proc. U. S. Nat. Mus. 15: 465, Oct. 26, 1892.

=*Heliosciurus undulatus undulatus* (True). See Hollister, U. S. Nat. Mus. Bull. 99 (pt. 2) : 11, May 16, 1919.

$\frac{19005}{34731}$. Skin and skull. Adult male (lectotype). Mount Kiliman-jaro, altitude 6,000 feet, German East Africa [=Tanganyika Territory]. June 12, 1888. Collected by W. L. Abbott. Original number 7.

Well-made skin in good condition; skull Grade A.

True had two cotypes, designated by number: Male, No. 19005, and female, No. 19006. It now seems advisable to consider No. $\frac{19005}{34731}$ as the lectotype and No. 19006 (skin only) as a paratype.

Genus HYLOPETES Thomas

*Sciuropterus amoenus Miller.

Proc. U. S. Nat. Mus. 31: 264, Sept. 11, 1906.

=*Hylopetes amoenus* (Miller). See Robinson and Kloss, Rec. Indian Mus. 15: 181, Oct. 1918.

122883. Skin and skull. Adult male. Pulo Kundur, Rhio-Linga Archipelago. June 12, 1903. Collected by W. L. Abbott. Original number 2483.

Well-made skin in good condition; skull Grade A.

Genus IOMYS Thomas

*Iomys lepidus Lyon.

Proc. U. S. Nat. Mus. 40: 78, Apr. 25, 1911.

=*Iomys horsfieldi lepidus* Lyon. See Robinson and Kloss, Rec. Indian Mus. 15: 179, Oct. 1918.

153684. Skin and skull. Adult male. Batu Jurong, southwestern Borneo. June 27, 1908. Collected by W. L. Abbott. Original number 6005.

Well-made skin in good condition; skull Grade A.

Genus LARISCUS Thomas and Wroughton

*Funambulus castaneus Miller.

Proc. Washington Acad. Sci. 2: 217, Aug. 20, 1900.

=*Lariscus insignis castaneus* (Miller). See Chasen and Kloss, Rec. Indian Mus. 15: 233, Oct. 1918.

101696. Skin and skull. Immature male. Pulo Siantan, Anambas Islands, South China Sea, between Malay Peninsula and Borneo. September 10, 1899. Collected by W. L. Abbott.

Fairly well-made skin in good condition; skull Grade A.

*Funambulus obscurus Miller.

Smithsonian Misc. Coll. 45: 23, Nov. 6, 1903.
=*Lariscus niobe obscurus* (Miller). See Chasen and Kloss, Proc. Zool. Soc.
London 1927 (pt. 4) : 826, Jan. 1928.

121640. Skin and skull. Adult female. South Pagi Island off
west coast of Sumatra. November 22, 1902. Collected by W.
L. Abbott. Original number 2086.

Well-made skin in good condition; skull Grade A.

*Funambulus peninsulae Miller.

Smithsonian Misc. Coll. 45: 25, Nov. 6, 1903.
=*Lariscus insignis jalorensis* (Bonhote). See Robinson and Kloss, Journ.
Federated Malay States Mus. 5: 120, Mar. 1915.

86776. Skin and skull. Adult male. Khow Sai Dow, Trong (or
Tarang), Peninsular Siam. February 18, 1899. Collected by
W. L. Abbott.

Well-made skin in good condition; skull Grade A.

*Funambulus rostratus Miller.

Smithsonian Misc. Coll. 45: 24, Nov. 6, 1903.
=*Lariscus insignis rostratus* (Miller). See Chasen and Kloss, Rec. Indian Mus.
15: 234, Oct. 1918.

121801. Skin and skull. Adult female. Tana Bala, Batu Islands,
off west coast of Sumatra. February 12, 1903. Collected by
W. L. Abbott. Original number 2281.

Well-made skin in good condition; tail apparently imperfect in life;
skull Grade A.

Genus MARMOTA Blumenbach

†Marmota caligata cascadensis Howell.

Proc. Biol. Soc. Washington 27: 17, Feb. 2, 1914.

90134. Skin and skull. Adult female. Mount Rainier, altitude
6,000 feet, Pierce County, Wash. August 11, 1897. Collected
by W. K. Fisher. Original number 422.

Well-made skin in good condition; skull Grade A.

†Marmota caligata nivaria Howell.

Proc. Biol. Soc. Washington 27: 17, Feb. 2, 1914.

72235. Skin and skull. Adult female. Mountains near Upper
St. Marys Lake, altitude 6,100 feet, Glacier County, Mont. May
27, 1895. Collected by A. H. Howell. Original number 23.

Well-made skin in good condition; skull Grade A.

†Marmota caligata sheldoni Howell.

Proc. Biol. Soc. Washington 27: 18, Feb. 2, 1914.

137319. Skin and skull. Adult male. Montague Island, Zaikof Bay, Alaska. May 24, 1905. Collected by Charles Sheldon. Original number 12 (5461–X).

Tanned skin in good condition; skull Grade A.

*Arctomys dacota Merriam.

North Amer. Fauna 2: 8, Oct. 30, 1889.

=*Marmota flaviventris dacota* (Merriam). See Howell, Proc. Biol. Soc. Washington 27: 15, Feb. 2, 1914.

186474. Skin and skull. Adult male. Custer, Custer County, Black Hills, S. Dak. July 21, 1888. Collected by Vernon Bailey. Original number 113. Merriam collection number $\frac{4478}{5113}$.

Well-made skin in good condition; skull Grade A.

*Marmota flaviventer luteola Howell.

Proc. Biol. Soc. Washington 27: 15, Feb. 2, 1914.

=*Marmota flaviventris luteola* Howell. See Howell, North Amer. Fauna 37: 50, Apr. 7, 1915.

186520. Skin and skull. Adult male. Woods Post Office, Medicine Bow Mountains, altitude 7,500 feet, Albany County, Wyo. August 13, 1888. Collected by Vernon Bailey. Original number 148. Merriam collection number $\frac{4655}{5306}$.

Well-made skin in good condition; skull Grade A.

†Marmota flaviventer nosophora Howell.

Proc. Biol. Soc. Washington 27: 15, Feb. 2, 1914.

=*Marmota flaviventris nosophora* Howell. See Howell, North Amer. Fauna 37: 46, Apr. 7, 1915.

168494. Skin and skull. Adult female. Willow Creek, altitude 4,000 feet, 7 miles east of Corvallis, Ravalli County, Mont. April 8, 1910. Collected by A. H. Howell. Original number 1723.

Well-made skin in good condition; skull Grade C.

†Marmota flaviventer obscura Howell.

Proc. Biol. Soc. Washington 27: 16, Feb. 2, 1914.

=*Marmota flaviventris obscura* Howell. See Howell, North Amer. Fauna 37: 53, Apr. 7, 1915.

133505. Skin and skull. Adult female. Wheeler Peak, 5 miles south of Twining, altitude 11,300 feet, Taos County, N. Mex. July 24, 1904. Collected by Vernon Bailey. Original number 8181.

Well-made skin in good condition, except claws of hindfeet are missing; skull Grade A.

†**Marmota flaviventer parvula** Howell.

Proc. Biol. Soc. Washington 27: 14, Feb. 2, 1914.
=*Marmota flaviventris parvula* Howell. See Howell, North Amer. Fauna 37: 44, Apr. 7, 1915.

93690. Skin and skull. Adult female. Jefferson, Toquima Range, about 10 miles north of Belmont, Nye County, Nev. June 3, 1898. Collected by Vernon Bailey. Original number 6495.

Well-made skin in good condition; skull Grade A.

†**Marmota flaviventris sierrae** Howell.

North Amer. Fauna 37: 43, Apr. 7, 1915.

$\frac{30984}{42859}$. Skin and skull. Adult female. Head of Kern River, Mount Whitney, altitude 9,300 feet, Tulare County, Calif. September 3, 1891. Collected by Vernon Bailey. Original number 3242.

Well-made skin in good condition; skull Grade A.

†**Marmota flaviventer warreni** Howell.

Proc. Biol. Soc. Washington 27: 16, Feb. 2, 1914.
=*Marmota flaviventris warreni* Howell. See Howell, North Amer. Fauna 37: 52, Apr. 7, 1915.

202937. Skin and skull. Adult female. Crested Butte, Gunnison County, Colo. July 11, 1902. Collected by E. R. Warren. Original number 35 (10639–X).

Well-made skin slightly grease-stained; skull Grade A.

†**Marmota monax petrensis** Howell.

North Amer. Fauna 37: 33, Apr. 7, 1915.

203532. Skin and skull. Adult male. Revelstoke, British Columbia, Canada. May 12, 1890. Collected by W. Spreadborough. Received in exchange from National Museum of Canada. Original number 10712–X.

Well-made specimen in good condition; skull Grade B.

†**Marmota monax preblorum** Howell.

Proc. Biol. Soc. Washington 27: 14, Feb. 2, 1914.

78360. Skin and skull. Adult male. Wilmington, Middlesex County, Mass. April 19, 1896. Collected by A. E. Preble. Original number 127.

Well-made skin in good condition; skull Grade A.

***Marmota monax rufescens** Howell.

Proc. Biol. Soc. Washington 27: 13, Feb. 2, 1914.

186521. Skin and skull. Adult male. Elk River, Sherburne County, Minn. April 9, 1886. Collected by Vernon Bailey. Original number 237. Merriam collection number $\frac{2563}{3173}$.

Well-made skin in good condition; skull Grade A.

†**Arctomys olympus** Merriam.

Proc. Acad. Nat. Sci. Philadelphia 50: 352, Oct. 4, 1898.
=[*Marmota*] *olympus* (Merriam). See Trouessart, Catalogus Mammalium tam Viventium quam Fossilium, Suppl., p. 344, 1904.

90518. Skin and skull. Adult male. Head of Soleduck River, Olympic Mountains, Clallam County, Wash. August 27, 1897. Collected by C. Hart Merriam. Original number 6210 (V. Bailey).

Well-made skin in good condition; skull Grade A.

*****Marmota sibila** Hollister.

Smithsonian Misc. Coll. 56 (35) : 1, Feb. 7, 1912. (Not *Arctomys sibila* Wolf, Linnaeus's Natursystem 2: 481, 1808.)
=*Marmota caligata oxytona* Hollister. See Hollister, Science (new ser.) 39: 251, Feb. 13, 1914.

174503. Skin and skull. Adult female. Head of Moose Pass Branch of Smoky River, altitude 7,200 feet, Alberta (near Moose Pass, British Columbia), Canada. August 3, 1911. Collected by N. Hollister and C. D. Walcott, Jr. Original number (Hollister) 3871.

Well-made skin in good condition; skull Grade A.

Genus MENETES Thomas

*****Lariscus berdmorei amotus** Miller.

Smithsonian Misc. Coll. 61 (21) : 24, Dec. 29, 1913.
=*Menetes berdmorei amotus* (Miller). See Chasen, Bull. Raffles Mus. 15: 145, footnote, Apr. 1940.

124152. Skin and skull. Adult male. Domel Island, Mergui Archipelago, January 30, 1904. Collected by W. L. Abbott. Original number 3081.

Well-made skin in good condition; skull Grade A.

Genus MICROSCIURUS J. A. Allen

†**Microsciurus alfari venustulus** Goldman.

Smithsonian Misc. Coll. 56 (36) : 4, Feb. 19, 1912.

171030. Skin and skull. Adult female. Gatun, Canal Zone, Panama. March 1, 1911. Collected by E. A. Goldman. Original number 20955.

Well-made skin in good condition; skull Grade B.

*****Sciurus (Microsciurus) isthmius** Nelson.

Bull. Amer. Mus. Nat. Hist. 12: 77, Apr. 14, 1899.
=*Microsciurus isthmius* (Nelson). See Goldman, Smithsonian Misc. Coll. 60 (2) : 5, Sept. 20, 1912.

$\frac{3399}{37344}$. Skin and skull. Truando River, northwestern Colombia. Collected by A. Schott. Original number 232. Received from N. Michler. Skin cataloged March 1, 1859; skull, March 25, 1898.

Skin in rather poor condition, tail imperfect; skull Grade C.

†Microsciurus isthmius vivatus Goldman.

Smithsonian Misc. Coll. 60 (2) : 4, Sept. 20, 1912.

179565. Skin and skull. Adult female. Near Cana, altitude 3,500 feet, Pirri Mountains, Panama. June 5, 1912. Collected by E. A. Goldman. Original number 21771.

Well-made skin in good condition; skull Grade A.

Genus NANNOSCIURUS Trouessart

*Nannosciurus bancanus Lyon.

Proc. Biol. Soc. Washington 19: 55, May 1, 1906.
=*Nannosciurus melanotis bancanus* Lyon. See Robinson and Kloss, Rec. Indian Mus. 15: 249, Oct. 1918.

124880. Skin and skull. Adult female. Klabat Bay, island of Banka, east coast of Sumatra. June 24, 1904. Collected by W. L. Abbott. Original number 3430.

Well-made skin in good condition; skull Grade A.

*Nannosciurus borneanus Lyon.

Proc. Biol. Soc. Washington 19: 54, May 1, 1906.
=*Nannosciurus melanotis borneanus* Lyon. See Robinson and Kloss, Rec. Indian Mus. 15: 249, Oct. 1918.

142271. Skin and skull. Adult female. Sanggau, western Borneo. August 23, 1905. Collected by W. L. Abbott. Original number 4368.

Well-made skin in good condition; skull Grade A.

*Nannosciurus pulcher Miller.

Proc. Acad. Nat. Sci. Philadelphia 54: 153, June 11, 1902.
=*Nannosciurus melanotis pulcher* Miller. See Robinson and Kloss, Rec. Indian Mus. 15: 249, Oct. 1918.

113131. Skin and skull. Adult female. Sinkep Island, Rhio-Linga Archipelago. September 4, 1901. Collected by W. L. Abbott. Original number 1274.

Well-made skin in good condition; skull Grade C.

*Nannosciurus sumatranus Lyon.

Proc. Biol. Soc. Washington 19: 53, May 1, 1906.
=*Nannosciurus melanotis sumatranus* Lyon. See Robinson and Kloss, Rec. Indian Mus. 15: 249, Oct. 1918.

141058. Skin and skull. Adult male. Tarussan Bay, west coast of Sumatra. January 16, 1905. Collected by W. L. Abbott. Original number 3946.

Well-made skin in good condition; skull Grade C.

*Nannosciurus surrutilus Hollister.

Proc. U. S. Nat. Mus. 46: 313, Dec. 31, 1913.

144641. Skin and skull. Adult female. Summit of Mount Bliss, altitude 5,750 feet, Mindanao, Philippine Islands. May 28, 1906. Collected by Edgar A. Mearns. Original number 6170.

Well-made skin in good condition; skull Grade A.

Genus PARAXERUS Forsyth-Major

*Paraxerus kahari Heller.

Smithsonian Misc. Coll. 56 (17) : 2, Feb. 28, 1911.

=*Paraxerus ochraceus kahari* Heller. See Hollister, U. S. Nat. Mus. Bull. 99 (pt. 2) : 20, May 16, 1919.

164203. Skin and skull. Adult female. Meru Boma, northeast of Mount Kenia, British East Africa [=Kenya]. September 24, 1909. Collected by Edmund Heller. Original number 1174.

Well-made skin in good condition; skull Grade A.

Genus PETAURISTA Link

*Petaurista batuana Miller.

Smithsonian Misc. Coll. 45: 27, Nov. 6, 1903.

=*Petaurista petaurista batuana* Miller. See Robinson and Kloss, Rec. Indian Mus. 15: 173, Oct. 1918.

121742. Skin and skull. Adult male. Tana Bala, Batu Islands, off west coast of Sumatra. February 5, 1903. Collected by W. L. Abbott. Original number 2233.

Well-made skin in good condition; skull Grade A.

*Petaurista mimicus Miller.

Smithsonian Misc. Coll. 61 (21) : 27, Dec. 29, 1913.

=*Petaurista petaurista mimicus* Miller. See Robinson and Kloss, Rec. Indian Mus. 15: 173, Oct. 1918.

143341. Skin and skull. Adult female. Pulo Rupat, eastern Sumatra. March 10, 1906. Collected by W. L. Abbott. Original number 4695.

Well-made skin in good condition; skull Grade A.

*Petaurista rubicundus A. B. Howell.

Journ. Washington Acad. Sci. 17: 82, Feb. 19, 1927.

=*Petaurista petaurista rubicundus* A. B. Howell. See G. M. Allen, Mamm. China and Mongolia 2: 731, Sept. 3, 1940.

240857. Skin only. Adult female. Mapientung, Szechwan, China. Fall of 1924. Collected by David C. Graham.

A cased skin in good condition.

*Petaurista sulcatus A. B. Howell.

Journ. Washington Acad. Sci. 17: 82, Feb. 19, 1927.

=*Aëretes melanopterus* (Milne-Edwards), Ann. Sci. Nat. Paris (zool. ser. 5) 8: 375, 1867. See G. M. Allen, Mamm. China and Mongolia 2: 746, Sept. 3, 1940.

219206. Skin and skull. Adult female. Hsin-lung-shan, altitude 3,000 feet, 65 miles northeast of Peking [=Peiping], Chi-li, China, August 18, 1917. Collected by Arthur deC. Sowerby. Original number 1017.

Well-made skin in good condition; skull Grade A.

*Petaurista terutaus Lyon.

Proc. Biol. Soc. Washington 20: 17, Feb. 23, 1907.

=*Petaurista petaurista terutaus* Lyon. See Robinson, Journ. Federated Malay States Mus. 7: 224, June 1918.

123934. Skin and skull. Adult male. Pulo Terutau (also written Trotau, Trotto), off west coast of Malay Peninsula. April 9, 1904. Collected by W. L. Abbott. Original number 3219.

Well-made skin in good condition; skull Grade A.

Genus PETINOMYS Thomas

*Sciuropterus crinitus Hollister.

Proc. Biol. Soc. Washington 24: 185, June 23, 1911.

=*Pteromys* (*Petinomys*) *crinitus* (Hollister). See Lawrence, Bull. Mus. Comp. Zool. 86: 67, Nov. 1939.

239217. Skin and skull. Adult male. Basilan Island, Philippine Islands. January 12, 1907. Collected by Richard C. McGregor and A. Celestino. Original number 101.

Well-made skin in good condition; skull Grade A.

*Sciuropterus maerens Miller.

Smithsonian Misc. Coll. 45: 26, Nov. 6, 1903.

=*Petinomys maerens* (Miller). See Robinson and Kloss, Rec. Indian Mus. 15: 183, Oct. 1918.

121531. Skin and skull. Adult female. North Pagi Island, off west coast of Sumatra. January 14, 1902. Collected by W. L. Abbott. Original number 2206.

Well-made skin in good condition; skull Grade A.

Genus PROTOXERUS Forsyth-Major

*Protoxerus stangeri bea Heller.

Smithsonian Misc. Coll. 59 (16): 2, July 5, 1912.

181786. Skin and skull. Adult male. Lukosa River, Kakumega Forest, British East Africa [=Kenya]. February 8, 1912. Collected by Edmund Heller. Original number 5614.

Well-made skin in good condition; skull Grade A.

Genus PTEROMYS G. Cuvier

*Pteromys volans incanus Miller.

Proc. Biol. Soc. Washington 31: 3, Feb. 21, 1918.

200613. Skin and skull. Adult female. Verkhne Kolymsk, East Siberia. April 24, 1915. Collected by Copley Amory, Jr. Original number 374.

Well-made skin in good condition; skull Grade A.

Genus RATUFA Gray

*Ratufa anambae Miller.

Proc. Washington Acad. Sci. 2: 215, Aug. 20, 1900.
=*Ratufa melanopepla anambae* Miller. See Robinson and Kloss, Rec. Indian Mus. 15: 196, Oct. 1918.

101725. Skin and skull. Adult female (not male, as in original description). Pulo Jimaja, Anamba Islands, South China Sea, between Malay Peninsula and Borneo. September 25, 1899. Collected by W. L. Abbott.

Well-made skin in good condition; skull Grade A.

*Ratufa angusticeps Miller.

Proc. Washington Acad. Sci. 3: 130, Mar. 26, 1901.
=*Ratufa melanopepla angusticeps* Miller. See Robinson and Kloss, Rec. Indian Mus. 15: 196, Oct. 1918.

104646. Skin and skull. Adult male. Pulo Lingung, Natuna Islands, South China Sea, between Malay Peninsula and Borneo. June 17, 1900. Collected by W. L. Abbott. Original number 481.

Well-made skin in good conditnon; skull Grade A.

*Ratufa arusinus Lyon.

Proc. U. S. Nat. Mus. 32: 442, May 23, 1907.
=*Ratufa affinis arusinus* Lyon. See Robinson and Kloss, Rec. Indian Mus. 15: 192, Oct. 1918.

143351. Skin and skull. Adult male. Aru Bay, northeastern coast of Sumatra. January 16, 1906. Collected by W. L. Abbott. Original number 4635.

Well-made skin in good condition; skull Grade A.

*Ratufa balae Miller.

Smithsonian Misc. Coll. 45: 6, Nov. 6, 1903.
=*Ratufa affinis balae* Lyon. See Robinson and Kloss, Rec. Indian Mus. 15: 192, Oct. 1918.

121715. Skin and skull. Adult male. Tana Bala, Batu Islands, off west coast of Sumatra. February 5, 1903. Collected by W. L. Abbott. Original number 2224.

Well-made skin in good condition; skull Grade A.

*Ratufa bicolor major Miller.

Proc. Biol. Soc. Washington 24: 28, Feb. 24, 1911.

155666. Skin and skull. Adult female. Tjibodas, Mount Gedé, altitude 4,500 feet, Java. August 15, 1909. Collected by William Palmer. Original number 505.

Well-made skin in good condition; skull Grade A.

*Ratufa bulana Lyon.

Proc. U. S. Nat. Mus. 36: 482, June 1, 1909.
=Ratufa affinis bulana Lyon. See Dammerman, Treubia 8: 317, 1926.

144412. Skin and skull. Adult female. Pulo Bulan, Rhio-Linga Archipelago. March 23, 1907. Collected by W. L. Abbott. Original number 5130.

Well-made skin in good condition; skull Grade A.

*Ratufa carimonensis Miller.

Proc. U. S. Nat. Mus. 31: 257, Sept. 11, 1906.
=Ratufa affinis carimonensis Miller. See Dammerman, Treubia 8: 317, 1926.

122813. Skin and skull. Adult female. Great Karimon Island, Rhio-Linga Archipelago. June 2, 1903. Collected by W. L. Abbott. Original number 2465.

Well-made skin in good condition; skull Grade A.

*Ratufa catemana Lyon.

Proc. U. S. Nat. Mus. 32: 443, May 23, 1907.
=Ratufa affinis catemana Lyon. See Robinson and Kloss, Rec. Indian Mus. 15: 191, Oct. 1918.

123124. Skin and skull. Adult male. Kateman River, southeastern Sumatra. August 27, 1903. Collected by W. L. Abbott. Original number 2759.

Well-made skin in good condition; skull Grade A.

*Ratufa celaenopepla Miller.

Smithsonian Misc. Coll. 61 (21) : 26, Dec. 29, 1913.
=Ratufa melanopepla celaenopepla Miller. See Robinson and Kloss, Rec. Indian Mus. 15: 195, Oct. 1918.

124149. Skin and skull. Adult male. Domel Island, Mergui Archipelago. January 26, 1904. Collected by W. L. Abbott. Original number 3073.

Well-made skin in good condition; skull Grade A.

*Ratufa condurensis Miller.

Proc. U. S. Nat Mus. 31: 258, Sept. 11, 1906.
=*Ratufa affinis condurensis* Miller. See Dammerman, Treubia 8: 317, 1926.

122879. Skin and skull. Adult male. Pulo Kundur (or Kondur), Rhio-Linga Archipelago. June 25, 1903. Collected by W. L. Abbott. Original number 2552.

Well-made skin in good condition; skull Grade A.

*Ratufa confinis Miller.

Proc. U. S. Nat. Mus. 31: 259, Sept. 11, 1906.
=*Ratufa affinis confinis* Miller. See Dammerman, Treubia 8: 317, 1926.

113134. Skin and skull. Adult female. Sinkep Island, Rhio-Linga Archipelago. September 3, 1901. Collected by W. L. Abbott. Original number 1265.

Well-made skin in good condition; skull Grade A.

*Ratufa conspicua Miller.

Smithsonian Misc. Coll. 45: 5, Nov. 6, 1903.
=*Ratufa affinis conspicua* Miller. See Dammerman, Treubia 8: 317, 1926.

115528. Skin and skull. Adult male. Pulo Bintang, Rhio-Linga Archipelago. August 19, 1902. Collected by W. L. Abbott. Original number 1900.

Well-made skin in good condition; skull Grade A.

*Ratufa cothurnata Lyon.

Proc. U. S. Nat. Mus. 40: 93, Apr. 25, 1911.
=*Ratufa affinis cothurnata* Lyon. See Chasen and Kloss, Bull. Raffles Mus. 6: 22, Dec. 1931.

145378. Skin and skull. Adult female. Foot of Mount Palung, near Sukadana, western Borneo. February 9, 1907. Collected by W. L. Abbott. Original number 5537.

Well-made skin in good condition; skull Grade A.

*Ratufa femoralis Miller.

Proc. U. S. Nat. Mus. 26: 447, Feb. 3, 1903.
=*Ratufa affinis femoralis* Miller. See Robinson and Kloss, Rec. Indian Mus. 15: 192, Oct. 1918.

114361. Skin and skull. Adult female. Pulo Tuangku, Banjak Islands, off west coast of Sumatra. January 27, 1902. Collected by W. L. Abbott. Original number 1479.

Well-made skin in good condition; skull Grade A.

*Ratufa griseicollis Lyon.

Proc. U. S. Nat. Mus. 40: 94, Apr. 25, 1911.
=*Ratufa ephippium griseicollis* Lyon. See Robinson and Kloss, Rec. Indian Mus. 15: 190, Oct. 1918.

251543—42——36

145372. Skin and skull. Adult male. Panebangan Island, off west coast of Borneo. May 24, 1907. Collected by W. L. Abbott. Original number 5315.

Well-made skin in good condition; skull Grade A.

*Ratufa insignis Miller.

Smithsonian Misc. Coll. 45 : 4, Nov. 6, 1903.
=*Ratufa affinis insignis* Miller.   See Dammerman, Treubia 8 : 317, 1926.

115531. Skin and skull. Adult male. Pulo Sugi, Rhio-Linga Archipelago. August 26, 1902. Collected by W. L. Abbott. Original number 1960.

Well-made skin in good condition; skull Grade A.

*Ratufa laenata Miller.

Proc. U. S. Nat. Mus. 26 : 449, Feb. 3, 1903.
=*Ratufa bicolor laenata* Miller.   See Robinson and Kloss, Rec. Indian Mus. 15 : 188, Oct. 1918.

114350. Skin and skull. Adult male. Pulo Tuangku, Banjak Islands, off west coast of Sumatra. January 27, 1902. Collected by W. L. Abbott. Original number 1478.

Well-made skin in good condition; skull Grade A.

*Ratufa masae Miller.

Smithsonian Misc. Coll. 45 : 7, Nov. 6, 1903.
=*Ratufa affinis masae* Miller.   See Robinson and Kloss, Rec. Indian Mus. 15 : 192, Oct. 1918.

121818. Skin and skull. Adult male. Tana Masa, Batu Islands, off west coast of Sumatra. February 21, 1903. Collected by W. L. Abbott. Original number 2330.

Well-made skin in good condition; skull Grade A.

*Ratufa melanopepla Miller.

Proc. Washington Acad. Sci. 2 : 71, July 25, 1900.

83230. Skin and skull. Adult male. Telibon Island, Trong (or Tarang), Peninsular Siam. February 27, 1896. Collected by W. L. Abbott.

Well-made skin in good condition; skull Grade A.

*Ratufa melanopepla peninsulae Miller.

Smithsonian Misc. Coll. 61 (21) : 25, Dec. 29, 1913.

$\frac{83478}{49466}$. Skin and skeleton. Adult male. Lay Song Hong, Trong (or Tarang), Peninsular Siam. September 23, 1896. Collected by W. L. Abbott.

Well-made skin in good condition except for feet, which were cut off at ankle in order to make a complete skeleton; skeleton Grade A.

*Ratufa nigrescens Miller.

Proc. U. S. Nat. Mus. 26: 448, Feb. 3, 1903.
=*Ratufa affinis nigrescens* Miller. See Robinson and Kloss, Rec. Indian Mus. 15: 192, Oct. 1918.

114556. Skin and skull. Adult female. Pulo Mansalar, off Tapanuli Bay, west coast of Sumatra. March 11, 1902. Collected by W. L. Abbott. Original number 1641.

Well-made skin in good condition; skull Grade A.

*Ratufa notabilis Miller.

Proc. Acad. Nat. Sci. Philadelphia 54: 150, June 11, 1902.
=*Ratufa affinis notabilis* Miller. See Dammerman, Treubia 8: 317, 1926.

113064. Skin and skull. Adult male. West coast of Linga Island, Rhio-Linga Archipelago. August 24, 1901. Collected by W. L. Abbott. Original number 1210.

Well-made skin in good condition; skull Grade A.

*Ratufa palliata Miller.

Proc. Acad. Nat. Sci. Philadelphia 54: 147, June 11, 1902.
=*Ratufa bicolor palliata* Miller. See Robinson and Kloss, Rec. Indian Mus. 15: 188, Oct. 1918.

113162. Skin and skull. Adult male. Indragiri River, eastern Sumatra. September 23, 1901. Collected by W. L. Abbott. Original number 1327.

Well-made skin in good condition; skull Grade A.

*Ratufa palliata batuana Lyon.

Proc. U. S. Nat. Mus. 52: 445, Dec. 30, 1916.
=*Ratufa bicolor batuana* Lyon. See Robinson and Kloss, Rec. Indian Mus. 15: 188, Oct. 1918.

121707. Skin and skull. Adult male. Tana Bala, Batu Islands, off west coast of Sumatra. February 11, 1903. Collected by W. L. Abbott. Original number 2263.

Well-made skin in good condition; skull Grade A.

*Ratufa phaeopepla Miller.

Smithsonian Misc. Coll. 61 (21): 25, Dec. 29, 1913.
=*Ratufa bicolor phaeopepla* Miller. See Chasen and Kloss, Journ. Siam Nat. Hist. Suppl. 8: 69, Nov. 1930.

124235. Skin and skull. Adult male. Sungei Balik, Tenasserim, Malay Peninsula. February 25, 1940. Collected by W. L. Abbott. Original number 3141.

Well-made skin in good condition; skull Grade A.

*Ratufa piniensis Miller.

Smithsonian Misc. Coll. 45: 8, Nov. 6, 1903.
=*Ratufa affinis piniensis* Miller. See Robinson and Kloss, Rec. Indian Mus. 15: 192, Oct. 1918.

121840. Skin and skull. Adult male. Pulo Pinie, Batu Islands, off west coast of Sumatra. March 1, 1903. Collected by W. L. Abbott. Original number 2343.

Well-made skin in good condition (tail imperfect in life); skull Grade B.

*Ratufa polia Lyon.

Proc. U. S. Nat. Mus. 31: 585, Dec. 18, 1906.
=*Ratufa ephippium polia* Lyon. See Robinson and Kloss, Rec. Indian Mus. 15: 190, Oct. 1918.

125004. Skin and skull. Adult female. Bukit Menguru, Billiton Island, off east coast of Sumatra. August 9, 1904. Collected by W. L. Abbott. Original number 3551.

Well-made skin in good condition; skull Grade A.

*Ratufa polia bancana Lyon.

Proc. U. S. Nat. Mus. 31: 587, Dec. 18, 1906.
=*Ratufa ephippium bancana* Lyon. See Robinson and Kloss, Rec. Indian Mus. 15: 190, Oct. 1918.

124680. Skin and skull. Adult male. Tanjong Rengsam, island of Banka, off east coast of Sumatra. May 27, 1904. Collected by W. L. Abbott. Original number 3277.

Well-made skin in good condition; skull Grade A.

*Ratufa pyrsonota Miller.

Proc. Washington Acad. Sci. 2: 75, July 25, 1900.
=*Ratufa affinis pyrsonota* Miller. See Robinson and Kloss, Rec. Indian Mus. 15: 192, Oct. 1918.

83483. Skin and skull. Adult male. Lay Song Hong, Trong (or Tarang), Peninsular Siam. September 29, 1896. Collected by W. L. Abbott.

Well-made skin in good condition; skull Grade A.

*Ratufa tiomanensis Miller.

Proc. Washington Acad. Sci. 2: 216, Aug. 20, 1900.
=*Ratufa melanopepla tiomanensis* Miller. See Kloss, Journ. Federated Malay States Mus. 2: 149, Sept. 1908.

101751. Skin and skull. Adult male. Pulo Tioman, off southeast coast of Malay Peninsula. October 4, 1899. Collected by W. L. Abbott.

Well-made skin in good condition; skull Grade A.

*Ratufa vittata Lyon.

Proc. U. S. Nat. Mus. 40: 94, Apr. 25, 1911.
=*Ratufa ephippium vittata* Lyon. See Robinson and Kloss, Rec. Indian Mus. 15: 190, Oct. 1918.

151758. Skin and skull. Adult female. Saratok, Pulo Laut, off southeast coast of Borneo. December 19, 1907. Collected by W. L. Abbott. Original number 5632.

Well-made skin in good condition; skull Grade A.

*Ratufa vittatula Lyon.

Proc. U. S. Nat. Mus. 40: 95, Apr. 25, 1911.
=*Ratufa ephippium vittatula* Lyon. See Robinson and Kloss, Rec. Indian Mus. 15: 190, Oct. 1918.

151762. Skin and skull. Adult male. Pulo Sebuku, southeastern Borneo. January 2, 1908. Collected by W. L. Abbott. Original number 5720.

Well-made skin in good condition; skull Grade A.

Genus SCIURUS Linnaeus

Sciurus aberti Woodhouse.

See *Sciurus dorsalis* Woodhouse.

†Sciurus aberti chuscensis Goldman.

Proc. Biol. Soc. Washington 44: 133, Oct. 17, 1931.

158553. Skin and skull. Adult female. Chusca Mountains, altitude 9,000 feet, McKinley County, northwestern New Mexico. October 5, 1908. Collected by Vernon Bailey. Original number 8997.

Well-made skin in good condition; skull Grade A.

*Sciurus aberti concolor True.

Diagnoses of New North American Mammals, p. 1, Apr. 26, 1894. (Reprint: Proc. U. S. Nat. Mus. 17: 241, Nov. 15, 1894.) Preoccupied by *Sciurus concolor* Blyth (Journ. Asiat. Soc. Bengal 24: 474, 1855.) =*Sciurus aberti ferreus* True, Proc. Biol. Soc. Washington 13: 183, Nov. 30, 1900.

$\frac{21423}{36281}$. Skin and skull. Adult female. Loveland, Larimer County, Colo. Collected by William G. Smith. Cataloged October 30, 1893.

Skin in good condition, but not made up in form of a modern study skin; skull Grade A.

Sciurus aberti ferreus True.

See *Sciurus aberti concolor* True.

†Sciurus aberti mimus Merriam.

Proc. Biol. Soc. Washington 17: 130, June 9, 1904.

70908. Skin and skull. Adult female. Hall Peak, Cimarron Mountains, Mora County, N. Mex. January 16, 1895. Collected by C. M. Barber. Original number 61.

Well-made skin in good condition; skull Grade A.

†Sciurus albipes colimensis Nelson.

Proc. Biol. Soc. Washington 12: 152, June 3, 1898.
=*Sciurus poliopus colimensis* Nelson. See Nelson, Proc. Washington Acad.
Sci. 1: 52, May 9, 1899.

$\frac{33197}{45202}$. Skin and skull. Adult male. Hacienda Magdalena, Colima,
Mexico. March 19, 1892. Collected by E. W. Nelson and E. A.
Goldman. Original number 2239.

Well-made skin in fair condition; skull Grade A.

†Sciurus albipes effugius Nelson.

Proc. Biol. Soc. Washington 12: 152, June 3, 1898.
=*Sciurus poliopus effugius* Nelson. See Nelson, Proc. Washington Acad.
Sci. 1: 54, May 9, 1899.

70288. Skin and skull. Adult female. Mountains near Chilpancingo, Guerrero, Mexico. December 24, 1894. Collected by E.
W. Nelson and E. A. Goldman. Original number 7271.

Well-made skin in good condition; skull Grade A.

†Sciurus albipes nemoralis Nelson.

Proc. Biol. Soc. Washington 12: 151, June 3, 1898.
=*Sciurus poliopus nemoralis* Nelson. See Nelson, Proc. Washington Acad.
Sci. 1: 50, May 9, 1899.

$\frac{35358}{47623}$. Skin and skull. Adult male. Patzcuaro, Michoacan, Mexico. July 23, 1892. Collected by E. W. Nelson and E. A. Goldman. Original number 2905.

Well-made skin in good condition; skull Grade A.

†Sciurus albipes quercinus Nelson.

Proc. Biol. Soc. Washington 12: 150, June 3, 1898. (Not *Sciurus quercinus*
Erxleben, Systema Regni Animalis, p. 432, 1777.)
=*Sciurus poliopus hernandezi* Nelson. See Nelson, Proc. Washington Acad.
Sci. 1: 48, May 9, 1899.

68202. Skin and skull. Adult female. Mountains on west side of
valley of Oaxaca, Oaxaca, Mexico. September 15, 1894. Collected by E. W. Nelson and E. A. Goldman. Original number
6768.

Well-made skin in good condition; skull Grade B.

†Sciurus alleni Nelson.

Proc. Biol. Soc. Washington 12: 147, June 3, 1898.

$\frac{25731}{33131}$. Skin and skull. Adult male. Monterrey, Nuevo Leon, Mexico. February 22, 1891. Collected by C. P. Streator. Original
number 563.

Well-made skin in good condition; skull Grade A.

*Sciurus arizonensis Coues.

Amer. Nat. 1: 357, footnote, Sept. 1867.

$\frac{8475}{37607}$. Skin and skull. Female. Fort Whipple, Yavapai County, Ariz. December 20, 1865. Collected by Elliott Coues.

Specimen has evidently been mounted; but it has now been made into a good study skin; skull Grade B.

In the skin catalog, No. 8475 is recorded as having been collected on December 6, 1864. Coues, however, says that the only specimen he obtained was shot December 20, 1865. Ten years later J. A. Allen (Monographs of North American Rodentia, p. 741) gives this same date, probably taking it from Coues, who was working with him, or from an original label that is now lost. Coues did not designate this type by number; but Allen, in his table of measurements of *Sciurus colliaei* (the species to which he then referred *S. arizonensis* as a synonym), entered the specimen No. 8475 as the type of *S. arizonensis*.

In the U. S. National Museum skull catalog under "Remarks" Dr. M. W. Lyon has written "Skull taken from mounted type, not naturally attached to skin, and it is very doubtful if it is the type skull. Oct. 31/98."

†Sciurus aureogaster frumentor Nelson.

Proc. Biol. Soc. Washington 12: 154, June 3, 1898.

54259. Skin and skull. Adult male. Las Vigas, Veracruz, Mexico. June 18, 1893. Collected by E. W. Nelson and E. A. Goldman. Original number 5073.

Well-made skin in good condition; skull Grade B.

†Sciurus boothiae belti Nelson.

Proc. Washington Acad. Sci. 1: 78, May 9, 1899.
=*Sciurus variegatoides belti* Nelson. See Harris, Univ. Michigan Mus. Zool. Misc. Publ. 38: 13, Sept. 4, 1937.

$\frac{36477}{48847}$. Skin and skull. Adult female. Escondido River, 50 miles above Bluefields, Nicaragua. October 12, 1892. Collected by C. W. Richmond. Original number 124.

Well-made skin in good condition; skull Grade A.

*Sciurus boothiae managuensis Nelson.

Proc. Biol. Soc. Washington 13: 150, June 3, 1898.
=*Sciurus variegatoides managuensis* Nelson. See Harris, Univ. Michigan Mus. Zool. Misc. Publ. 38: 17, Sept. 4, 1937.

62476. Skin and skull. Adult male. Along the Managua River, Guatemala. February 12, 1895. Collected by Mrs. C. McElroy.

Well-made skin in good condition; skull Grade A.

†Sciurus boothiae underwoodi Goldman.

Journ. Washington Acad. Sci. 22: 274, May 19, 1932.
=*Sciurus variegatoides underwoodi* Goldman. See Harris, Univ. Michigan Mus. Zool. Misc. Publ. 38: 9, Sept. 4, 1937.

250219. Skin and skull. Adult male. Monte Redondo, altitude 5,100 feet, about 30 miles northwest of Tegucigalpa, Honduras. December 8, 1931. Collected by C. F. Underwood. Original number 644 (26780–X).

Well-made skin in good condition; skull Grade B.

*Sciurus carolinensis hypophaeus Merriam.   Lectotype.

Science 7: 351, Apr. 16, 1886.

193864. Skin and skull. Adult female. Elk River, Sherburne County, Minn. January 20, 1886. Collected by Vernon Bailey. Original number 29.

Well-made skin in good condition; skull Grade A.

*Sciurus carolinensis yucatanensis J. A. Allen.   Cotype.

Monographs of North American Rodentia, p. 705, Aug. 1877.
=*Sciurus yucatanensis* J. A. Allen. See Elliot, Field Columbian Mus. Publ. 11 (zool. ser. 1) : 80, May 1896.

$\frac{8503}{37596}$. Skin and skull. Adult female. Merida, Yucatan, Mexico. March 3, 1865. Collected by A. Schott, "Comision cientifica de Yucatan, Jose Salagar Llarregui." Original number 229.

The specimen has been remade into a modern study skin and is in good condition; skull Grade B.

In the original description (p. 705) J. A. Allen mentions four specimens, all taken at Merida by Schott. In the table of measurements, on page 711, three of them are referred to by number: 8502, 8503, and 8505. These should be regarded as cotypes. Unfortunately, Nos. 8502 and 8505 cannot be found. The fourth specimen, not referred to by number and hence regarded as a paratype, is in good condition and in the collection. It is about half or two-thirds grown, and entered as No. 8504.

*Sciurus castanotus [sic] Baird.

Proc. Acad. Nat. Sci. Philadelphia 7: 332, reported favorably for publication Apr. 24, 1855 (typographical error for *castanonotus*). See Baird, Mammals of North America, p. 266, 1857.
=*Sciurus aberti aberti* Woodhouse. See J. A. Allen, Monographs of North American Rodentia, p. 735, 1877.

$\frac{121}{1107}$. Skin and skull. Adult female. Coppermines, near the present site of Georgetown, Grant County, N. Mex. (On p. 707 of Mammals of North America, Baird says of Coppermines, "A former station of the United States-Mexican Boundary Survey, subsequently called Fort Webster. Not indicated clearly whether on a tributary of the Gila or Mimbres. About lat. 33°, long. 108°." In the original description he writes of this specimen as coming from the Mimbres, 1851, collected by J. H. Clark.

The type specimen has now been made over into a modern study skin, quite complete except for the tail, which is rather fragmentary; skull Grade A.

No numbers are referred to in the original description, but in the Mammals of North America it is seen that there were two specimens, an adult female and a young. Measurements of a skull are given in the first description, which apply to the adult female, No. $\frac{121}{1107}$. Hence it is regarded as the type.

†Sciurus chiricahuae Goldman.

Proc. Biol. Soc. Washington 46: 71, Apr. 27, 1933.

244124. Skin and skull. Adult female. Cave Creek, altitude 5,200 feet, Chiricahua Mountains, Cochise County, Ariz. August 16, 1923. Collected by E. A. Goldman. Original number 23527.

Well-made skin in good condition; skull Grade B.

†Sciurus colliaei nuchalis Nelson.

Proc. Washington Acad. Sci. 1: 59, May 9, 1899.

$\frac{32657}{44580}$. Skin and skull. Adult male. Manzanillo, Colima, Mexico. February 2, 1892. Collected by E. W. Nelson. Original number 1828.

Well-made skin in good condition; skull Grade A.

†Sciurus deppei vivax Nelson.

Proc. Biol. Soc. Washington 14: 131, Aug. 9, 1901.

107932. Skin and skull. Adult female. Apazote, Campeche, Mexico. January 8, 1901. Collected by E. A. Goldman. Original number 14429.

Well-made skin in good condition; skull Grade A.

*Sciurus dorsalis Woodhouse.

Proc. Acad. Nat. Sci. Philadelphia 6: 110, reported favorably for publication June 29, 1852. (Name preoccupied by Sciurus dorsalis Gray, Proc. Zool. Soc. London, 1848, p. 138 =S. adolphei dorsalis.)
=Sciurus aberti Woodhouse. See Woodhouse, Proc. Acad. Nat. Sci. Philadelphia 6: 220, requested to be published Dec. 28, 1852.

2430. Skin, no skull. San Francisco Mountain, Coconino County, Ariz., on the routes of Sitgreaves and Whipple, about lat. 35° N. and long. 111°30′ W. October 1851. Collected by S. W. Woodhouse.

The specimen was formerly mounted, but it has since been taken down and made into a fairly good study skin. The first description reads: "This beautiful squirrel I procured whilst attached to the expedition under the command of Capt. L. Sitgreaves, Topographical Engineer, U. S. Army, exploring the Zuni and the Great and Little Colorado rivers of the West in the month of October 1851, in the San Francisco Mountain, N. Mex." This statement makes it practically certain that the above specimen is the one on which Woodhouse based his description.

Sciurus fossor Peale.   See page 573.

*Sciurus fossor anthonyi Mearns.

Preliminary Diagnoses of New Mammals of the Genera *Sciurus, Castor,
Neotoma,* and *Sigmodon,* from the Mexican border of the United States,
p. 1, Mar. 5, 1897. (Reprint: Proc. U. S. Nat. Mus. 20: 501, Jan. 19,
1898.)
=*Sciurus griseus anthonyi* Mearns. See Elliot, Field Columbian Mus. Publ. 45
(zool. ser. 2) : 57, Mar. 1901.

60928. Skin and skull. Adult female. Campbell's ranch, Laguna
Mountains, San Diego County, Calif. June 10, 1894. Collected
by E. A. Mearns. Original number 3642.

Well-made skin in good condition; skull Grade A.

†Sciurus goldmani Nelson.

Proc. Biol. Soc. Washington 12: 149, June 3, 1898.
=*Sciurus variegatoides goldmani* Nelson. See Dickey, Proc. Biol. Soc. Washington 41: 8, Feb. 1, 1928.

77903. Skin and skull. Adult male. Huehuetan, Chiapas, Mexico.
February 28, 1896. Collected by E. W. Nelson and E. A. Goldman. Original number 9435.

Well-made skin in good condition, except for two small bare patches
on shoulders; skull Grade A.

†Sciurus griseoflavus chiapensis Nelson.

Proc. Washington Acad. Sci. 1: 69, May 9, 1899.

75957. Skin and skull. Adult male. San Cristobal, Chiapas,
Mexico. September 22, 1895. Collected by E. W. Nelson and
E. A. Goldman. Original number 8447.

Well-made skin in good condition; skull Grade B.

*Sciurus infuscatus Cabrera.

Bol. Soc. Esp. Hist. Nat. 5: 227, Apr. 1905.

152266. Skin and skull. Adult male. Navas del Marqués, Province of Avila, Spain. October 26, 1904. Collected by M. M.
de la Escalera.

Well-made skin in good condition; skull Grade A.

†Sciurus kaibabensis Merriam.

Proc. Biol. Soc. Washington 17: 129, June 9, 1904.

130982. Skin and skull. Adult male. Bright Angel Creek, top
of Kaibab Plateau, north side of Grand Canyon, Coconino
County, Ariz. December 1, 1903. Collected by J. T. Stewart.
Original number 4470–X.

Well-made skin in good condition; skull Grade B.

*Sciurus limitis Baird.

Proc. Acad. Nat. Sci. Philadelphia 7: 331, reported favorably for publication Apr. 24, 1855.

=*Sciurus niger limitis* Baird. See Osgood, Proc. Biol. Soc. Washington 20: 45, Apr. 18, 1907.

$\frac{351}{1265}$. Skin and skull. Devils River, Val Verde County, Tex. Collected by J. H. Clark, United States and Mexican Boundary Survey, under Maj. W. H. Emory. Cataloged December 12, 1854.

Well-made skin in good condition except that tail and right ear are slightly damaged; skull Grade A.

The original description says, "Collected by J. H. Clark on Devil's River, Tex.," and by referring to Baird's Mammals of North America, p. 256, it is seen that this specimen is No. $\frac{351}{1265}$, which is consequently considered the type.

†Sciurus negligens Nelson.

Proc. Biol. Soc. Washington 12: 147, June 3, 1898.

93028. Skin and skull. Adult female. Alta Mira, Tamaulipas, Mexico. April 18, 1898. Collected by E. A. Goldman. Original number 12319.

Well-made skin in good condition; skull Grade A.

†Sciurus nelsoni Merriam.

Proc. Biol. Soc. Washington 8: 144, Dec. 29, 1893.

51157. Skin and skull. Adult female. Huitzilac, Morelos, Mexico. January 1, 1893. Collected by E. W. Nelson. Original number 4144.

Well-made skin in good condition; skull Grade A.

†Sciurus nelsoni hirtus Nelson.

Proc. Biol. Soc. Washington 12: 153, June 3, 1898.

55325. Skin and skull. Adult male. Tochimilco, Puebla, Mexico. August 7, 1893. Collected by E. W. Nelson and E. A. Goldman. Original number 5295.

Well-made skin in good condition; skull Grade A.

†Sciurus niger avicennia Howell.

Journ. Mamm. 1: 37, Nov. 28, 1919.

231498. Skin and skull. Adult male. Everglades, Collier County, Fla. March 14, 1919. Collected by A. H. Howell. Original number 2325.

Well-made skin in good condition; skull Grade A.

†Sciurus oculatus tolucae Nelson.

Proc. Biol. Soc. Washington 12: 148, June 3, 1898.

55927. Skin and skull. Adult male. North slope Volcan Toluca, State of Mexico, Mexico. September 8, 1893. Collected by E. W. Nelson and E. A. Goldman. Original number 5419.

Well-made skin in good condition; skull Grade B.

Sciurus poliopus hernandezi Nelson.

See *Sciurus albipes quercinus* Nelson.

†Sciurus poliopus perigrinator Nelson.

Proc. Biol. Soc. Washington 17: 149, Oct. 6, 1904.

70279. Skin and skull. Adult female. Piaxtla, Puebla, Mexico. November 25, 1894. Collected by E. W. Nelson and E. A. Goldman. Original number 7104.

Well-made skin in good condition; skull Grade B.

†Sciurus poliopus senex Nelson.

Proc. Biol. Soc. Washington 17: 148, Oct. 6, 1904.

126208. Skin and skull. Adult female. La Salada, 40 miles south of Uruapan, southern Michoacan, Mexico. March 14, 1903. Collected by E. W. Nelson and E. A. Goldman. Original number 161127.

Well-made skin in good condition; skull Grade A.

†Sciurus richmondi Nelson.

Proc. Biol. Soc. Washington 12: 146, June 3, 1898.

$\frac{36481}{48851}$. Skin and skull. Adult female. Escondido River, 50 miles from Bluefields, Nicaragua. October 4, 1892. Collected by C. W. Richmond. Original number 118.

Well-made skin in good condition; skull Grade A.

†Sciurus socialis cocos Nelson.

Proc. Biol. Soc. Washington 12: 155, June 3, 1898.

70644. Skin and skull. Adult male. Acapulco, Guerrero, Mexico. January 11, 1895. Collected by E. W. Nelson and E. A. Goldman. Original number 7360.

Well-made skin in good condition; skull Grade B.

†Sciurus socialis littoralis Nelson.

Proc. Biol. Soc. Washington 20: 87, Dec. 11, 1907.

71322. Skin and skull. Adult female. Puerto Angel, Oaxaca, Mexico. March 11, 1895. Collected by E. W. Nelson and E. A. Goldman. Original number 7627.

Well-made skin in good condition; skull Grade C.

*Sciurus thomasi Nelson.

Proc. Washington Acad. Sci. 1 : 71, May 9, 1899.
=*Sciurus variegatoides thomasi* Nelson. See Harris, Univ. Michigan Mus. Zool. Misc. Publ. 38 : 24, Sept. 4, 1937.

$\frac{12044}{23367}$. Skin and skull. Talamanca, Costa Rica. 1874. Collected by W. M. Gabb.

The specimen has been remade into a modern study skin and is in good condition; skull Grade A.

†Sciurus truei Nelson.

Proc. Washington Acad. Sci. 1 : 61, May 9, 1899.

96229. Skin and skull. Adult male. Camoa, Rio Mayo, Sonora, Mexico. January 20, 1899. Collected by E. A. Goldman. Original number 13405.

Well-made skin in good condition; skull Grade B.

†Sciurus variabilis choco Goldman.

Smithsonian Misc. Coll. 60 (22) : 4, Feb. 28, 1913.
=*Sciurus gerrardi choco* Goldman. See Goldman, Smithsonian Misc. Coll. 69 (5) : 139, Apr. 24, 1920.

179561. Skin and skull. Adult male. Cana, altitude 3,500 feet, Pirri Mountains, eastern Panama. May 28, 1912. Collected by E. A. Goldman. Original number 21752.

Well-made skin in good condition; skull Grade B.

†Sciurus variegatoides helveolus Goldman.

Smithsonian Misc. Coll. 56 (36) : 3, Feb. 19, 1912.

171540. Skin and skull. Adult male. Corozal, Canal Zone, Panama. June 15, 1911. Collected by E. A. Goldman. Original number 21166.

Well-made skin in good condition; skull Grade B.

*Sciurus vulgaris chiliensis Sowerby.

Ann. Mag. Nat. Hist. (ser. 9) 7 : 253, Mar. 1921.

219185. Skin and skull. Adult female. Wu-ling-shan, Tungling, altitude 3,500 feet, 75 miles northeast of Peking [=Peiping], Chi-li, China. August 25, 1917. Collected by Arthur deC. Sowerby. Original number 1033.

Well-made skin in good condition; skull Grade A.

†Sciurus yucatanensis baliolus Nelson.

Proc. Biol. Soc. Washington 14 : 131, Aug. 9, 1901.

107939. Skin and skull. Adult male. Apazote, Campeche, Mexico. January 8, 1901. Collected by E. A. Goldman. Original number 14428.

Well-made skin in good condition; skull Grade C.

Genus TAMIAS Illiger

*Tamias striatus fisheri Howell.

Journ. Mamm. 6 (1) : 51, Feb. 9, 1925.

193370. Skin and skull. Young adult female. Merritts Corners, 4 miles west of Sing Sing (Ossining), Westchester County, N. Y. August 23, 1884. Collected by A. K. Fisher. Merriam collection No. $\frac{801}{1338}$.

Well-made skin in good condition; skull Grade A.

Genus TAMIASCIURUS J. A. Allen

†Sciurus douglasii cascadensis J. A. Allen.

Bull. Amer. Mus. Nat. Hist. 10: 277, July 22, 1898.
=*Tamiasciurus douglasii cascadensis* (J. A. Allen).

80229. Skin and skull. Adult male. Mount Hood, Oreg. September 9, 1896. Collected by Vernon Bailey. Original number 5874.

Well-made skin in good condition; skull Grade A.

†Sciurus fremonti neomexicanus J. A. Allen.

Bull. Amer. Mus. Nat. Hist. 10: 291, July 22, 1898.
=*Tamiasciurus fremonti neomexicanus* (J. A. Allen).

71690. Skin and skull. Adult male. Rayado Canyon, Colfax County, N. Mex. April 1, 1895. Collected by C. M. Barber. Original number 89.

Well-made skin in good condition; skull Grade A.

*Sciurus hudsonicus abieticola Howell.

Journ. Mamm. 10: 75, Feb. 11, 1929.
=*Tamiasciurus hudsonicus abieticola* (Howell). See Kellogg, Proc. U. S. Nat. Mus. 84: 459, Oct. 7, 1937.

193638. Skin and skull. Adult female. Highlands, Macon County, N. C. March 9, 1886. Collected by C. L. Boynton. Original number 30. Merriam collection No. $\frac{2296}{2806}$.

Well-made skin in good condition; skull Grade A.

†Sciurus hudsonicus baileyi J. A. Allen.

Bull. Amer. Mus. Nat. Hist. 10: 261, July 22, 1898.
=*Tamiasciurus hudsonicus baileyi* (J. A. Allen).

56040. Skin and skull. Adult male. West slope of Bighorn Mountains, altitude 8,400 feet, Washakie County, Wyo. September 19, 1893. Collected by Vernon Bailey. Original number 4390.

Well-made skin in good condition; skull Grade A.

†**Tamiasciurus hudsonicus kenaiensis** Howell.

Proc. Biol. Soc. Washington 49 : 136, Aug. 22, 1936.

107603. Skin and skull. Adult male. Hope, Cook Inlet, Alaska. September 6, 1900. Collected by W. H. Osgood. Original number 1360.

Well-made skin in good condition; skull Grade A.

****Sciurus hudsonicus mearnsi** Townsend.

Proc. Biol. Soc. Washington 11 : 146, June 9, 1897.
=*Tamiasciurus douglasii mearnsi* (Townsend).

$\frac{18266}{25170}$. Skin and skull. San Pedro Martir Mountains, at about 7,000 feet, Lower California, Mexico. May 1889. Collected by C. H. Townsend.

Well-made skin in good condition; skull Grade A.

†**Sciurus hudsonicus petulans** Osgood.

North Amer. Fauna 19 : 27, Oct. 6, 1900.
=*T[amiasciurus] hudsonicus petulans* (Osgood). See Howell, Proc. Biol. Soc. Washington 49 : 136, Aug. 22, 1936.

97457. Skin and skull. Adult female. Glacier, White Pass, altitude 1,870 feet, southern Alaska. June 4, 1899. Collected by W. H. Osgood. Original number 370.

Well-made skin in good condition; skull Grade A.

†**Tamiasciurus hudsonicus preblei** Howell.

Proc. Biol. Soc. Washington 49 : 133, Aug. 22, 1936.

133862. Skin and skull. Adult male (not female as recorded in original description). Fort Simpson, Mackenzie. February 29, 1904. Collected by Edward A. Preble. Original number 5141.

Well-made skin in good condition; skull Grade A.

†**Sciurus hudsonicus ventorum** J. A. Allen.

Bull. Amer. Mus. Nat. Hist. 10 : 263, July 22, 1898.
=*Tamiasciurus hudsonicus ventorum* (J. A. Allen). See Davis, Recent Mamm. Idaho: 229, Apr. 5, 1939.

56030. Skin and skull. Adult male (not female as recorded in original description). South Pass City, Wind River Mountains, Fremont County, Wyo. September 6, 1893. Collected by Vernon Bailey. Original number 4305.

Well-made skin in good condition; skull Grade B.

****Sciurus suckleyi** Baird.

Proc. Acad. Nat. Sci. Philadelphia 7 : 333, reported favorably for publication Apr. 24, 1855.
=*Tamiasciurus douglasii douglasii* (Bachman).

$\frac{272}{37606}$. Skin and skull. Adult male. Steilacoom, Pierce County, Wash. January 13, 1854. Collected by George Suckley, Pacific Railroad Survey. Original number 1.

Specimen made into a modern study skin with skull removed (November 1898). The skin is in fair condition, but the left foreleg is lacking. Only that part of the skull anterior to the brain case and the right half of the mandible are present.

In the original description Baird did not designate a type. He gave three measurements: "Head and body 9 inches, tail vertebrae 4½ inches, to tip of hairs 6 inches." In 1857 (Mammals of North America) he published further details (p. 276). Specimen No. 270, in the table on page 278, being the only one whose measurements agree with those given in the original description, is taken as the type.

Genus TAMIOPS J. A. Allen

*Tamiops macclellandi liantis Kloss.

Journ. Nat. Hist. Soc. Siam 3 : 370, Dec. 31, 1919.

221542. Skin and skull. Adult female. Satahip, near Cape Liant, Shelter Bay, Southeast Siam. November 2, 1916. Collected by C. Boden Kloss. Original number 2337.

Well-made skin in good condition; skull Grade B.

*Sciurus novemlineatus Miller.

Proc. Biol. Soc. Washington 16 : 147, Nov. 12, 1903.

=*Tamiops macclellandi novemlineatus* (Miller). See Robinson and Kloss, Journ. Federated Malay States Mus. 5 : 120, Mar. 1915.

84403. Skin and skull. Adult male. In heavy forest among the hills near Khow Nom Plu, altitude 1,500 feet, Trong (or Tarang), Peninsular Siam. February 19, 1897. Collected by W. L. Abbott.

Well-made skin in good condition; skull Grade A.

*Tamiops vestitus Miller.

Proc. Biol. Soc. Washington 28 : 115, May 27, 1915.

=*Tamiops macclellandi vestitus* Miller. See G. M. Allen, Amer. Mus. Nov. 163; 6, Apr. 2, 1925.

199561. Skin and skull. Adult male. Hsinglungshan, 65 miles northeast of Peking [=Peiping], Chi-li, China, February 15, 1915. Collected by Arthur deC. Sowerby. Original number 754.

Well-made skin in good condition; skull Grade A.

Genus TOMEUTES Thomas

*Sciurus atratus Miller.

Smithsonian Misc. Coll. 45 : 13, Nov. 6, 1903.

=*Tomeutes atratus* (Miller). See Thomas, Ann. Mag. Nat. Hist. (ser. 8) 15 : 386, Apr. 1915.

121524. Skin and skull. Adult female. North Pagi Island, off west coast of Sumatra. November 22, 1902. Collected by W. L. Abbott. Original number 2087.

Well-made skin in good condition; skull Grade A.

*Sciurus balae Miller.

Smithsonian Misc. Coll. 45: 14, Nov. 6, 1903.
=*Tomeutes lowii balae* (Miller). See Robinson and Kloss, Rec. Indian Mus. 15: 230, Oct. 1918.

121799. Skin and skull. Adult male. Tana Bala, Batu Islands, off west coast of Sumatra. February 12, 1903. Collected by W. L. Abbott. Original number 2282.

Well-made skin in good condition, but tail was damaged during life and only 23 mm. remain; skull Grade A.

*Sciurus bancarus Miller.

Proc. U. S. Nat. Mus. 26: 451, Feb. 3, 1903.
=*Tomeutes tenuis bancarus* (Miller). See Robinson and Kloss, Rec. Indian Mus. 15: 229, Oct. 1918 .

114311. Skin and skull. Adult male. Pulo Bangkaru, Banjak Islands, off west coast of Sumatra. January 17, 1902. Collected by W. L. Abbott. Original number 1422.

Well-made skin in good condition; skull Grade A.

*Sciurus evidens Miller and Hollister.

Proc. Biol Soc. Washington 34: 99, June 30, 1921.
=*Tomeutes evidens* (Miller and Hollister).

217814. Skin and skull. Adult female. Pulo Lembeh, off the coast of northeastern Celebes. January 16, 1916. Collected by H. C. Raven. Original number 2525.

Well-made skin in good condition; skull Grade A.

*Sciurus hippurellus Lyon.

Smithsonian Misc. Coll. 50: 27, Apr. 8, 1907.
=*Tomeutes hippurus hippurellus* (Lyon). See Robinson and Kloss, Rec. Indian Mus. 15: 227, Oct. 1918.

142274. Skin and skull. Adult female. Batu Ampar, Landak River, western Borneo. July 11, 1905. Collected by W. L. Abbott. Original number 4260.

Well-made skin in good condition; skull Grade A.

*Sciurus hippurosus Lyon.

Smithsonian Misc. Coll. 50: 26, Apr. 8, 1907.
=*Tomeutes hippurus hippurosus* (Lyon). See Robinson and Kloss, Rec. Indian Mus. 15: 227, Oct. 1918.

251543—42——37

141031. Skin and skull. Adult female. Tarussan Bay, west coast of Sumatra. December 18, 1904. Collected by W. L. Abbott. Original number 3826.

Well-made skin in good condition; skull Grade A.

*Sciurus humilis Miller.

Smithsonian Misc. Coll. 61 (21) : 24, Dec. 29, 1913.
=*Tomeutes lowii humilis* (Miller). See Robinson and Kloss, Rec. Indian Mus. 15: 230, Oct. 1918.

123116. Skin and skull. Immature female. Kateman River, East Sumatra. August 20, 1903. Collected by W. L. Abbott. Original number 2751.

Well-made skin in good condition except for loss of distal half of tail. Skull Grade A.

*Sciurus lingungensis Miller.

Proc. Washington Acad. Sci. 3: 123, Mar. 26, 1901.
=*Tomeutes lowii natunensis* (Thomas).

104693. Skin and skull. Adult male. Pulo Lingung, Natuna Islands, South China Sea, between Malay Peninsula and Borneo. June 19, 1900. Collected by W. L. Abbott. Original number 494.

Well-made skin in good condition; skull Grade A.

*Sciurus mansalaris Miller.

Proc. U. S. Nat. Mus. 26: 451, Feb. 3, 1903.
=*Tomeutes tenuis mansalaris* (Miller). See Robinson and Kloss, Rec. Indian Mus. 15: 229, Oct. 1918.

114633. Skin and skull. Adult male. Pulo Mansalar, off Tapanuli Bay, west coast of Sumatra. March 2, 1902. Collected by W. L. Abbott. Original number 1583.

Well-made skin in good condition; skull Grade A.

*Sciurus mansalaris batus Lyon.

Proc. U. S. Nat. Mus. 52: 443, Dec. 30, 1916.
=*Tomeutes tenuis batus* (Lyon). See Robinson and Kloss, Rec. Indian Mus. 15: 229, Oct. 1918.

121732. Skin and skull. Adult male. Tana Bala, Batu Island, off west coast of Sumatra. February 4, 1903. Collected by W. L. Abbott. Original number 2217.

Well-made skin in good condition; skull Grade B.

*Sciurus murinus necopinus Miller and Hollister.

Proc. Biol. Soc. Washington 34: 98, June 30, 1921.
=*Tomeutes murinus necopinus* (Miller and Hollister).

218712. Skin and skull. Adult male. Goenoeng Lehio (southwest from Lake Lindoe), Middle Celebes. January 20, 1917. Collected by H. C. Raven. Original number 3107.

Well-made skin in good condition; skull Grade A.

*Sciurus parvus Miller.

Proc. Biol. Soc. Washington 14: 33, Apr. 5, 1901.
=*Tomeutes tenuis parvus* (Miller). See Robinson and Kloss, Rec. Indian Mus. 15: 229, Oct. 1918.

84509. Skin and skull. Adult male. Nulu, altitude 1,000 feet, Sarawak, Borneo. October 1894. Collected by Charles Hose.

Well-made skin in good condition; skull Grade A.

*Sciurus piniensis Miller.

Smithsonian Misc. Coll. 45: 14, Nov. 6, 1903.
=*Tomeutes lowii piniensis* (Miller). See Robinson and Kloss, Rec. Indian Mus. 15: 230, Oct. 1918.

121800. Skin and skull. Adult female. Pulo Pinie, Batu Islands, off west coast of Sumatra. March 1, 1903. Collected by W. L. Abbott. Original number 2344.

Well-made skin in good condition; skull Grade A.

*Sciurus procerus Miller.

Proc. Washington Acad. Sci. 3: 122, Mar. 26, 1901.
=*Tomeutes tenuis procerus* (Miller).

104698. Skin and skull. Adult male. Bunguran Island, Natuna Islands, South China Sea, between Malay Peninsula and Borneo. July 18, 1900. Collected by W. L. Abbott. Original number 574.

Well-made skin in good condition; skull Grade A.

*Sciurus pumilus Miller.

Smithsonian Misc. Coll. 45: 15, Nov. 6, 1903.
=*Tomeutes tenuis pumilus* (Miller). See Robinson and Kloss, Rec. Indian Mus. 15: 229, Oct. 1918.

121627. Skin and skull. Adult male. South Pagi Island, off west coast of Sumatra. November 27, 1902. Collected by W. L. Abbott. Original number 2098.

Well-made skin in good condition; skull Grade A.

*Sciurus tenuis surdus Miller.

Proc. Washington Acad. Sci. 2: 80, July 25, 1900.
=*Tomeutes tenuis surdus* (Miller). See Robinson and Kloss, Rec. Indian Mus. 15: 229, Oct. 1918.

84412. Skin and skull. Adult male. Trong (or Tarang), Peninsular Siam. February 3, 1897. Collected by W. L. Abbott.

Well-made skin in good condition; skull Grade B.
Type designated by number. In the original description, under "Measurements," external measurements of the type are said to be given. This is an error, however, as they are measurements of a paratype, No. 83243.

Family SPALACIDAE: Mole Rats

Genus MYOSPALAX Laxmann

*Myotalpa cansus Lyon.

Smithsonian Misc. Coll. 50: 134, July 9, 1907.

=*Myospalax cansus* (Lyon). See Thomas, Proc. Zool. Soc. London, 1908 (pt. 2): 978, Apr. 1909.

144022. Skin and skull. Adult female. Taocheo, Province of Kan-su, China. May 7, 1906. Collected by W. W. Simpson. Original number 7.

Well-made skin in good condition; skull Grade A.

Genus SPALAX Gueldenstaedt

*Spalax berytensis Miller.

Proc. Biol. Soc. Washington 16: 162, Nov. 30, 1903.

$\frac{13009}{36859}$. Skin and skull. Adult female. Beyrout, Syria. April 1878. Collected by W. T. Van Dyck.

Fairly well-made skin in fair condition, a bare patch about chin and throat; skull Grade B.

*Spalax dolbrogeae Miller.

Proc. Biol. Soc. Washington 16: 161, Nov. 30, 1903.

122109. Skin and skull. Adult male. Malcociu near Tulchea, Dobrogea (or Dobruja), Rumania. March 20, 1903. Purchased from Wilhelm Schlüter, of Halle, Germany.

Well-made skin in good condition; skull Grade A.

Family THRYONOMYIDAE: Rush Rats

Genus THRYONOMYS Fitzinger

*Thryonomys gregorianus pusillus Heller.

Smithsonian Misc. Coll. 59 (16): 17, July 5, 1912.

=*Thryonomys pusillus* Heller. See Hollister, U. S. Nat. Mus. Bull. 99 (pt. 2): 163, May 16, 1919.

181807. Skin and skull. Adult female. Ndi, Taita Hills, British East Africa [=Kenya]. November 3, 1911. Collected by Edmund Heller. Original number 4566 (not 4853 as printed in original description).

Well-made skin in good condition, left foreleg shortened, apparently by trap; skull Grade A.

Family ZAPODIDAE: Jumping Mice

Genus NAPAEOZAPUS Preble

†Napaeozapus insignis frutectanus Jackson.

Proc. Biol. Soc. Washington 32: 9, Feb. 14, 1919.

227349. Skin and skull. Adult male. Crescent Lake, Oneida County, Wis. September 6, 1917. Collected by H. H. T. Jackson. Original number 896.

Well-made skin in good condition; skull Grade A.

†Zapus (Napaeozapus) insignis roanensis Preble.

North Amer. Fauna 15: 35, Aug. 8, 1899.
=*Napaeozapus insignis roanensis* (Preble). See Miller, Bull. New York State Mus. 8: 114, Nov. 21, 1900.

66283. Skin and skull. Adult male. Magnetic City, base of Roan Mountain, Mitchell County, N. C. May 22, 1894. Collected by A. G. Wetherby. Original number 5.

Well-made skin in good condition; skull Grade A.

Genus SICISTA Gray

*Sminthus flavus True.

Proc. U. S. Nat. Mus. 17: 341, Nov. 15, 1894.
=*Sicista flavus* (True). See J. A. Allen, Proc. Biol. Soc. Washington 14: 185, Dec. 12, 1901.

$\frac{20140}{35503}$. Skin and skull. Adult male. Central Kashmir, India, at 11,000 feet. July 21, 1891. Collected by W. L. Abbott.

Skin well preserved, but poorly made up; no wires in legs or tail; skull Grade A.

*Sicista napaea Hollister.

Smithsonian Misc. Coll. 60 (14) : 2, Nov. 29, 1912.

175195. Skin and skull. Adult male. Tapucha, Altai Mountains, Siberia. August 6, 1912. Collected by N. Hollister. Original number 4427.

Well-made skin in good condition; skull Grade A.

Genus ZAPUS Coues

†Zapus hudsonius alascensis Merriam.

Proc. Biol. Soc. Washington 11: 223, July 15, 1897.

73584. Skin and skull. Adult male. Yakutat, Alaska. July 5, 1895. Collected by C. P. Streator. Original number 4660.

Well-made skin in good condition; skull Grade A.

†Zapus hudsonius campestris Preble.

North Amer. Fauna 15: 20, Aug. 8, 1899.

65872. Skin and skull. Adult male. Bear Lodge Mountains, Crook County, Wyo. June 12, 1894. Collected by B. H. Dutcher. Original number 600.

Well-made skin in good condition; skull Grade A.

†**Zapus luteus** Miller.

Proc. Biol. Soc. Washington 24: 253, Dec. 23, 1911.

133601. Skin and skull. Adult female. Espanola, altitude 5,000 feet, Rio Arriba County, N. Mex. June 24, 1904. Collected by M. Surber. Original number 162.

Well-made skin in good condition; skull Grade A.

†**Zapus luteus australis** Bailey.

Proc. Biol. Soc. Washington 26: 132, May 21, 1913.

160731. Skin and skull. Young adult female. Socorro, Socorro County, N. Mex. August 23, 1909. Collected by E. A. Goldman. Original number 20402.

Well-made skin in good condition; skull Grade A.

†**Zapus major** Preble.

North Amer. Fauna 15: 24, Aug. 8, 1899.
=*Zapus princeps major* Preble. See Hall, Univ. California Publ. Zool. 37: 10, Apr. 10, 1931.

79983. Skin and skull. Adult female. Warner Mountains, Lake County, Oreg. August 4, 1896. Collected by C. Hart Merriam and Vernon Bailey. Original number 5720.

Well-made skin in good condition; skull Grade A.

†**Zapus nevadensis** Preble.

North Amer. Fauna 15: 25, Aug. 8, 1899.
=*Zapus princeps nevadensis* Preble. See Hall, Univ. California Publ. Zool. 37: 10, Apr. 10, 1931.

94185. Skin and skull. Adult female. Ruby Mountains, Elko County, Nev. June 21, 1898. Collected by Vernon Bailey. Original number 6581.

Well-made skin in good condition; skull Grade A.

†**Zapus pacificus** Merriam.

Proc. Biol. Soc. Washington 11: 104, Apr. 26, 1897.

80445. Skin and skull. Young adult male. Prospect, Rogue River Valley, Jackson County, Oreg. August 29, 1896. Collected by E. A. Preble. Original number 1454.

Well-made skin in good condition; skull Grade A.

†**Zapus princeps minor** Preble.

North Amer. Fauna 15: 23, Aug. 8, 1899.

73673. Skin and skull. Adult female. Wingard, near Carlton House, Saskatchewan, Canada. July 23, 1895. Collected by J. A. Loring. Original number 3123.

Well-made skin in good condition; skull Grade A.

†Zapus princeps oregonus Preble.

North Amer. Fauna 15 : 24, Aug. 8, 1899.

78156. Skin and skull. Adult male. Elgin, Blue Mountains, Union County, Oreg. May 29, 1896. Collected by E. A. Preble. Original number 959.

Well-made skin in good condition; skull Grade A.

†Zapus tenellus Merriam.

Proc. Biol. Soc. Washington 11 : 103, Apr. 26, 1897.

=*Zapus hudsonius tenellus* Merriam. See Hall, Univ. California Publ. Zool. 40 : 377, Nov. 5, 1934.

66932. Skin and skull. Adult female. Kamloops, British Columbia, Canada. August 25, 1894. Collected by C. P. Streator. Original number 4196.

Well-made skin in good condition; skull Grade A.

†Zapus trinotatus montanus Merriam.

Proc. Biol. Soc. Washington 11 : 104, Apr. 26, 1897.

=*Zapus montanus* Merriam. See Preble, North Amer. Fauna 15 : 28, Aug. 8, 1899.

79863. Skin and skull. Adult female. Crater Lake, Mount Mazama, Klamath County, Oreg. August 21, 1896 (not August 19, as in original description). Collected by E. A. Preble. Original number 1388.

Well-made skin in good condition; skull Grade A.

Order XENARTHRA: Edentates

Family BRADYPODIDAE: Three-toed Sloths

Genus BRADYPUS Linnaeus

†Bradypus ignavus Goldman.

Smithsonian Misc. Coll. 60 (22) : 1, Feb. 28, 1913.

179551. Skin and skull. Adult female. Marraganti, about 2 miles above Real de Santa Maria, near head of tidewater on the Rio Tuyra, eastern Panama. April 6, 1912. Collected by E. A. Goldman. Original number 21596.

Well-made skin in good condition; skull Grade A.

Family DASYPODIDAE: Armadillos

Genus CABASSOUS McMurtrie

*Tatoua (Ziphila) centralis Miller.

Proc. Biol. Soc. Washington 13 : 4, Jan. 31, 1899.

=*Cabassous centralis* (Miller). See Palmer, Proc. Biol. Soc. Washington 13 : 72, Sept. 28, 1899.

$\frac{19464}{35382}$. Skin and skull. Adult female. Chamelicon, Honduras. January 8, 1891. Collected by Erich Wittkügel. Original number 8.

Formerly mounted; now a well-made skin in good condition; nine or ten scales missing from carapace. Skull Grade B.

Genus DASYPUS Linnaeus

†Tatu novemcinctum texanum Bailey.

North Amer. Fauna 25: 52, Oct. 24, 1905.
=*Dasypus novemcintus mexicanus* (Peters). See Hollister, Journ. Mamm. 6: 60, Feb. 9, 1925.

$\frac{34352}{46438}$. Skin and skull. Adult male. Brownsville, Cameron County, Tex. June 10, 1892 (not 1902 as given in original description). Collected by F. B. Armstrong. Original number 4.

Well-made skin in good condition; skull Grade A.

Family MEGALONYCHIDAE: Ground Sloths

Genus ACRATOCNUS Miller

*Acratocnus (?) comes Miller.

Smithsonian Misc. Coll. 81 (9) : 26, Mar. 30, 1929.

253178. Right femur (lacking distal extremity) of adult. In large cave near St. Michel, Haiti, Greater Antilles. March 1925. Collected by Gerrit S. Miller, Jr.

Genus PAROCNUS Miller

*Parocnus serus Miller.

Smithsonian Misc. Coll. 81 (9) : 29, Mar. 30, 1929.

253228. Right femur (lacking epiphyses) of immature individual. In large cave near St. Michel, Haiti, Greater Antilles. January 1928. Collected by Arthur J. Poole.

Family MYRMECOPHAGIDAE: Anteaters

Genus CYCLOPES Gray

*Cyclopes mexicanus Hollister.

Proc. Biol. Soc. Washington 27: 210, Oct. 31, 1914.

$\frac{11137}{38534}$. Skin and skull. Adult. Tehuantepec, Oaxaca, Mexico. Collected by John Crawford Spear. Original number 8. Cataloged December 30, 1872.

Well-made skin in good condition; skull Grade A.

Genus MYRMECOPHAGA Linnaeus

*Myrmecophaga centralis Lyon.

Proc. U. S. Nat. Mus. 31: 570, Nov. 14, 1906.

15963. Skull (no skin). Young adult. Pacuare, Costa Rica. June 1876. Collected by José C. Zeledon. Original number 86.
Skull Grade A; no record of a skin.

MISSING TYPE SPECIMENS

TYPE SPECIMENS THAT SHOULD BE IN THE NATIONAL MUSEUM COLLECTION, BUT OF WHICH NO PART CAN NOW BE FOUND

*Lasiurus intermedius H. Allen.

Proc. Acad. Nat. Sci. Philadelphia 14: 246, ordered published Apr. 29, 1862. =*Dasypterus intermedius* (H. Allen). See H. Allen, U. S. Nat. Mus. Bull. 43: 137, Mar. 14, 1894.

6135. In alcohol. Matamoros, Tamaulipas, Mexico. Received from D. N. Couch (Berlandier collection). Cataloged February 7, 1863.

In H. Allen's original description (1862) a table of measurements is given, and, by referring to p. 26 of the same author's Monograph of the Bats of North America (June 1864) it can be seen that those measurements refer to the last specimen in the original table. Unfortunately this individual was not given a number. However, by checking off the six preceding numbers in the "List of specimens" (1864) it is made clear that the single unnumbered specimen in the original table of measurements must have been No. 6136. Since that was the individual measured in the original description, it is here regarded as the type. Of seven paratypes listed in the original description, No. 6135 is the only one that can now be found.

*Macrotus californicus Baird.

Proc. Acad. Nat. Sci. Philadelphia 10: 116, presented for publication May 4, 1858.

2347. In alcohol. Old Fort Yuma, Imperial County, Calif., on right bank of Colorado River, opposite present town of Yuma, Ariz. Collected by G. H. Thomas. Cataloged March 27, 1857.

Specimen cannot be found. H. Allen evidently had it in 1894. See p. 39, A Monograph of the Bats of North America, March 14, 1894.

Type not designated by number in original description. That Baird had only one specimen is implied; and a table of measurements is given agreeing exactly with those published for No. 2347 in Baird's Report U. S. and Mex. Bound. Surv. 2 (pt. 2): 4, 1859.

*Rhogeëssa parvula H. Allen.

Proc. Acad. Nat. Sci. Philadelphia 18: 285, ordered published Aug. 28, 1866.

7841. Adult male. In alcohol. Tres Marias Island, Nayarit, Mexico. Received from A. J. Grayson. Cataloged in first half of 1865.

The specimen cannot be found in the National Museum. James A. G. Rehn informs us that it is in the collection of the Academy of Natural Sciences of Philadelphia and in very bad condition.

*Scotophilus miradorensis H. Allen.

Proc. Acad. Nat. Sci. Philadelphia 18: 287, ordered published Aug. 28, 1866.
=*Eptesicus fuscus miradorensis* (H. Allen). See Miller, U. S. Nat. Mus. Bull. 79: 62, Dec. 31, 1912.

No type mentioned. H. Allen says, "One individual. ♀. Mus. of Smithsonian Institution. Alcohol. Mirador, Veracruz, Mexico. Doctor Sartorius." It is undoubtedly No. 5411, cataloged October 31, 1861, along with other bats that H. Allen was working with at the time. This specimen, No. 5411, has exactly the same data that Allen gives. Also see his second Monograph of Bats of North America, p. 121, 1894, where No. 5411 is entered in the list of specimens of *"Adelonycteris" fuscus.*
It cannot be found.

*Vespertilio agilis H. Allen.

Proc. Acad. Nat. Sci. Philadelphia 18: 282, ordered published Aug. 28, 1866.
=*Myotis californicus mexicanus* (Saussure). See Miller and G. M. Allen, U. S. Nat. Mus. Bull. 144: 159, May 25, 1928.

H. Allen says, "One individual. ♀. No. ? Mus. of Smithsonian Institution. Alcohol. Doctor Sartorius. Mirador, Veracruz, Mexico."
Nothing is known of the specimen.

*Vespertilio exiguus H. Allen.

Proc. Acad Nat. Sci. Philadelphia 18: 281, ordered published Aug. 28, 1866.
=*Myotis nigricans nigricans* (Wied). See Miller and G. M. Allen. U. S. Nat. Mus. Bull. 144: 178, May 25, 1928.

5373. In alcohol. Aspinwall, New Granada, the present Colon, Panama. Received from S. Hayes. Cataloged October 30, 1861.

H. Allen had but one specimen, a female in alcohol, designated by number. It cannot be found.

*V[espertilio] lucifugus LeConte.

McMurtrie, The Animal Kingdom 1: 431, 1831.

4741. Skin. Collected by J. E. LeConte.

"The British Museum has a made-over skin received with the Tomes collection, that was originally No. 4741 of the United States National Museum. It is labeled: *Vespertilio 'lucifugus,'* United States, Maj. LeConte. This is a typical *Myotis lucifugus lucifugus* as now understood, and may well be one of the specimens on which LeConte based his original account of the animal" (Miller and Allen, U. S. Nat. Mus. Bull. 144: 44, 1928).

*Vespertilio mundus H. Allen.

Proc. Acad. Nat. Sci. Philadelphia 18:   280, ordered published Aug. 28, 1866.
=*Myotis albescens* (E. Geoffroy). See Miller and G. M. Allen, U. S. Nat. Mus. Bull. 144: 200, May 25, 1928.

5547. In alcohol. Maracaibo, Venezuela. Young female. Cataloged February 6, 1862.

H. Allen had but one specimen, designated by number. The specimen cannot be found.

*Vespertilio tenuidorsalis H. Allen.

Proc. Acad. Nat. Sci. Philadelphia 18: 283, ordered published Aug. 28, 1866.
=*Myotis californicus californicus* (Audubon and Bachman). See Miller, North Amer. Fauna 13: 69, Oct. 16, 1897.

H. Allen says, "One individual. ♀. No. 5533. Mus. Smithsonian Institution. Alcohol. Cape St. Lucas, Lower California, Mexico. John Xantus." There is some mistake in the number, as the catalog number 5533 calls for a "*V. nitidus*, Puget Sound."

This specimen cannot be found in the National Museum. James A. G. Rehn has informed us that it is now in the collection of the Academy of Natural Sciences of Philadelphia.

*Vespertilio yumanensis H. Allen. Cotypes.

A Monograph of the Bats of North America, p. 58, June 1864.
=*Myotis yumanensis yumanensis* (H. Allen). See Miller, North Amer. Fauna 13: 66, Oct. 16, 1897.

No type designated. Four specimens were measured: 5367, 6019, 6020, and 6021. All must be considered as cotypes; no preference for one over the other was shown; and all came from one locality, Old Fort Yuma, Imperial County, Calif., where they had been collected by G. H. Thomas in 1855. All were in alcohol. None of these specimens can be found. In his "List of Specimens" Allen says that 36 individuals were under No. 5367. The catalog says eight bore that number.

*Sciurus fossor Peale.

U. S. Exploring Expedition 8 (Mamm. and Ornith.) : 55, 1848.
=*Sciurus griseus griseus* Ord. See Rhoads, Amer. Nat. 28: 525, June 1894.

Type locality.—Probably southern Oregon.

The specimen should be in the Museum, with other U. S. Exploring Expedition material, but nothing is known of it. Cassin, U. S. Exploring Expedition 8 (Mamm. and Ornith.), p. 50, 1848, writes: "Specimen in Mus. Acad. Philadelphia, and Nat. Mus. Washington."

*Arvicola montana Peale.

U. S. Exploring Expedition 8 (Mammalia and Ornithology) : 44, 1848.
=*Microtus montanus montanus* (Peale). See Trouessart, Catalogus Mammalium tam Viventium quam Fossilium, p. 563, 1897.

Peale says, "Our specimen was obtained on the 4th of October, near the headwaters of the Sacramento River [=near Mount Shasta, Siskiyou County] in California.

The specimen cannot be found. Its number is not known.

*Arvicola (Pitymys) pinetorum quasiater Coues.

Proc. Acad. Nat. Sci. Philadelphia 26: 191, Dec. 15, 1874.
=*Pitymys quasiater* (Coues). See Miller, U. S. Nat. Mus. Bull. 79: 229, Dec. 31, 1912.

3524. Skin. Jalapa, Veracruz, Mexico. Collected by R. Montes d'Oca. Cataloged March 18, 1859.

The specimen cannot be found. There is no record of a skull. (See Coues, 1874, p. 191.)

Type designated by number.

*Cricetodipus parvus Peale.

U. S. Exploring Expedition 8 (Mamm. and Ornith.) : 53, 1848.

=*Perognathus parvus parvus* (Peale). See Cassin, U. S. Exploring Expedition 8 (Mamm. and Ornith.) : 48, 1858.

Type locality.—Assumed to be The Dalles, Wasco County, Oreg. (See Osgood, North Amer. Fauna 18: 34–36, Sept. 20, 1900.)

Specimen should be in the Museum with the U. S. Exploring Expedition material. Nothing is known of it.

*Mus peruvianus Peale.

U. S. Exploring Expedition 8 (Mamm. and Ornith.) : 51, 1848.

=*Mus musculus musculus* Linnaeus. See Gyldenstolpe, Kungl. Svenska Vet.-Akad. Handl. 11 (3) : 28 (footnote), 1932.

Type locality.—Callao, Peru.

The specimen should be in the Museum, with other U. S. Exploring Expedition material. It is probably No. 4955, an alcoholic, entered in the catalog May 30, 1861, as *Mus musculus* from Callao. This specimen cannot now be found.

*Cervus lewisii Peale.

U. S. Exploring Expedition 8 (Mamm. and Ornith.) : 59, 1848.

=*Odocoileus hemionus columbianus* (Richardson). See Cowan, California Fish and Game 22: 215, July 1936.

There should be two cotypes, one killed on Feather River, upper California, the other killed at the Bay of San Francisco. According to Peale, 1848, p. 40, the Feather River skin was lost in the Sacramento River. The antlers (and ? frontlets) of both of these specimens as well as the skin of the San Francisco Bay animal were originally in the National Institute, and, presumably some years later, they were transferred to the Smithsonian Institution. They cannot be found at present.

Two specimens, one comprising a stuffed skin and a frontlet with small antlers (No. 1487) and the other a stuffed skin without skull (No. 1488), are recorded as having been collected by Titian R. Peale in Oregon, and are marked "typical of the description." After the U. S. Exploring Ship *Peacock* was wrecked on the Columbia River bar on July 18, 1841, Peale became a member of the party under the leadership of Lt. George T. Emmons, which traveled overland during September and October 1841 from Vancouver in the Willamette Valley to San Francisco, Calif. (Charles Wilkes, Narrative of the U. S. Exploring Expedition, 1838–42, 5: 231–266, 1844). It would therefore have been quite possible for Peale to have collected specimens other than the types.

*Cervus macrotis californicus Caton.

Amer. Nat. 10: 464, Aug. 1876.
=*Odocoileus hemionus californicus* (Caton). See Thompson, Forest and Stream 51: 286, Oct. 8, 1898.

Type locality.—Near Gaviota Pass, 40 miles up the coast from Santa Barbara, Calif.

Caton, p. 468, says, "As soon as the deer reached camp I selected a fair specimen, a buck, which I judged to be four years old, and prepared the skin and necessary parts of the skeleton for mounting. This I subsequently sent to the Smithsonian Institution. Professor Baird has expressed much interest about it, and assured me that it would be mounted and added to the collection of American quadrupeds at the Centennial [Exposition, Philadelphia, 1876], when those who take an interest in these studies may examine and compare it with others." Specimen killed March 22, 1876, probably.

An examination of the catalog for 1875–76 shows the specimen to be No. $\frac{12588}{15424}$, cataloged in the spring of 1876. Nothing further is known of it.

*Delphinapterus borealis Peale.

U. S. Exploring Expedition 8 (Mamm. and Ornith.) : 35, 1848.
=*Lissodelphis borealis* (Peale). See Elliot, Field Columbian Mus. Publ. 45 (zool. ser. 2) : 30, Mar. 1901.

Type locality.—Pacific Ocean, lat. 46°6′50″ N., long. 134°5′ W. (10° west of Astoria, Oreg.)

Nothing is known about this specimen. It is not included in Peale's list of specimens, *loc. cit.*, p. 305. Cassin remarked that he had "no specimens for examination." (Cassin, U. S. Exploring Expedition, Mamm. and Ornith., p. 30, 1858.)

*Delphinus albirostratus Peale.

U. S. Exploring Expedition 8 (Mamm. and Ornith.) : 34, 1848. See True, U. S. Nat. Mus. Bull. 36: 62, 1889.

Type locality.—Pacific Ocean, lat. 2°47′5″ S., long. 174°13′ W. (West of Howland and Baker Islands, Oceania).

Nothing is known about this specimen. It is not in Peale's list of specimens, *loc. cit.*, p. 305. Cassin says: "We find no specimen in the collection of the expedition." (U. S. Exploring Expedition, Mamm. and Ornith., p. 32, 1858.)

*Delphinus bairdii Dall.   Cotypes.

Proc. California Acad. Sci. 5: 12, printed in advance Jan. 29, 1873.
For status see Miller, Proc. Biol. Soc. Washington 49: 145, Aug. 22, 1936.

Two females. Point Arguello, Calif. 1872. Collected by C. M. Scammon. "One entire skeleton has been forwarded to Washington."

A search through the Museum collection and catalogs fails to reveal these specimens. They may never have reached the Museum.

The cotypes were not designated by numbers.

*Delphinus lateralis Peale.

U. S. Exploring Expedition 8 (Mamm. and Ornith.) : 35, 1848.
=*Prodelphinus* (?) *lateralis* (Peale). See True, U. S. Nat. Mus. Bull. 36: 65, 1889.

Type locality.—Pacific Ocean, lat. 13°58′ N., long. 161°22′ W. (about 7° southwest of Hawaiian Islands, Oceania).

Nothing is known about this specimen. It is not in Peale's list of specimens, *loc. cit.*, p. 305. Cassin remarks, "We find no specimen in the collection of the expedition." (U. S. Explor. Exped., Mamm. and Ornith., p. 33, 1858.)

*Phocaena australis Peale.

U. S. Exploring Expedition 8 (Mamm. and Ornith.) : 33, 1848.
=?*Lagenorhynchus obscurus* (Gray). See True, U. S. Nat. Mus. Bull. 36: 104, 1889.

Type locality.—South Atlantic Ocean, off coast of Patagonia, Argentina.

Nothing is known about this specimen. It is not included in Peale's list of specimens, *loc. cit.*, p. 205.

*Canis torquatus Baird.

U. S. and Mexican Boundary Survey 2 (2) : 15, 1859.

1379. Skull. Saltillo, Coahuila, Mexico. Collected by J. L. Berlandier. Cataloged January 26, 1855.

The specimen cannot be found in the National Museum.

GEOGRAPHICAL GUIDE TO TYPE LOCALITIES

The countries, islands, States, and territories of the type localities in the foregoing list are here arranged alphabetically under general headings, as follows:

EASTERN HEMISPHERE

	Page		Page
Africa	577	Malay Peninsula	592
Antarctic region	581	Malay States	593
Asia	582	Mergui Archipelago	594
China	582	Oceania	595
East Indies	583	Philippine Islands	595
Europe	590	Siam	597
French Indo-China	591	South China Sea	598
India	591	Soviet Union (Russia)	599
Japan	592	Syria	599
Malay Archipelago	592	Unknown localities	599

WESTERN HEMISPHERE

	Page		Page
Alaska	600	Mexico	607
Arctic region	602	South America	618
Canada	602	United States	620
Central America	604	West Indies	639

Names of species and subspecies in the combinations used by the first describers are arranged alphabetically under the various countries, islands, States, and territories.

EASTERN HEMISPHERE
AFRICA

ANGOLA:
> Hippopotamus constrictus, p. 25.

CAMEROONS:
> Idiurus macrotis, p. 439.
> Lophuromys nudicaudus, p. 451.

ETHIOPIA (formerly Abyssinia):
> Felis leo roosevelti, p. 57.
> Mellivora abyssinica, p. 67.

KENYA (formerly British East Africa):
> Acinonyx jubatus raineyi, p. 52.
> Acinonyx jubatus velox, p. 52.
> Acomys ignitis montanus, p. 439.
> Ammelaphus imberbis australis, p. 15.
> Aonyx capensis helios, p. 61.
> Arvicanthis abyssinicus virescens, p. 442.

577

KENYA—Continued.

Bdeogale crassicauda omnivora, p. 103.
Bubalis cokei kongoni, p. 7.
Bubalis lelwel keniae, p. 7.
Bubalis nakurae, p. 7.
Cephalophus monticola musculoides, p. 8.
Cercopithecus centralis luteus, p. 238.
Cervicapra chanleri, p. 13.
Chaerephon pumilus naivashae, p. 120.
Colobus abyssinicus percivali, p. 239.
Colobus abyssinicus roosevelti, p. 239.
Cricetomys gambianus enguvi, p. 443.
Cricetomys gambianus osgoodi, p. 444.
Cricetomys gambianus raineyi, p. 444.
Crocidura alchemillae, p. 167.
Crocidura alpina, p. 168.
Crocidura hildegardeae altae, p. 169.
Crocidura hildegardeae procera, p. 169.
Crocidura lutreola, p. 171.
Crocidura parvipes nisa, p. 172.
Crocidura raineyi, p. 173.
Crocidura simiolus, p. 174.
Crocidura suahelae, p. 174.
Crocidura turba lakiundae, p. 174.
Crocuta crocuta fisi, p. 61.
Crossarchus fasciatus colonus, p. 104.
Dasymys helukus, p. 444.
Dasymys helukus nigridius, p. 444.
Dasymys savannus, p. 445.
Dendromus mesomelas percivali, p. 445.
Dendromus whytei capitis, p. 445.
Elephantulus phaeus, p. 166.
Elephantulus rufescens mariakenae, p. 166
Eliomys parvus, p. 489.
Epimys alleni kaimosae, p. 446.
Epimys coucha durumae, p. 451.
Epimys coucha neumani, p. 451.
Epimys endorobae, p. 447.
Epimys kaiseri turneri, p. 440.
Epimys niveiventris ulae, p. 453.
Epimys panya, p. 452.
Epimys taitae, p. 455.
Equus quagga cuninghamei, p. 232.
Erinaceus sotikae, p. 165.
Erythrocebus whitei, p. 240.
Felis ocreata nandae, p. 57.
Felis ocreata taitae, p. 57.
Felis pardus fortis, p. 59.
Galago moholi cocos, p. 250.
Galago sotikae, p. 250.
Gazella granti raineyi, p. 9.
Gazella granti roosevelti, p. 9.
Gazella granti serengetae, p. 9.

AFRICA—continued

KENYA—Continued.

Genetta pumila, p. 103.
Georychus kapiti, p. 254.
Gorgon albojubatus mearnsi, p. 8.
Graphiurus murinus isolatus, p. 404.
Graphiurus murinus johnstoni, p. 404.
Heliosciurus rufobrachiatus shindi, p. 536.
Helogale undulata affinis, p. 103.
Heterohyrax brucei albipes, p. 165.
Hippopotamus amphibius kiboko, p. 25.
Ictonyx capensis albescens, p. 64.
Kobus defassa raineyi, p. 9.
Kobus ellipsiprymnus kuru, p. 9.
Lasiopyga albogularis kima, p. 237.
Lasiopyga albogularis maritima, p. 237.
Lasiopyga ascanius kaimosae, p. 238.
Lasiopyga leucampax [sic] mauae, p. 238.
Lasiopyga pygerythra arenaria, p. 238.
Lasiopyga pygerythra callida, p. 238.
Lasiopyga pygerythra contigua, p. 239.
Lasiopyga pygerythra tumbili, p. 239.
Lavia rex, p. 118.
Leggada naivashae, p. 448.
Lemniscomys dorsalis mearnsi, p. 449.
Lemniscomys pulchellus spermophilus, p. 449.
Leo leo hollisteri, p. 56.
Lepus capensis abbotti, p. 210.
Lepus kakumegae, p. 211.
Lepus raineyi, p. 213.
Lophiomys thomasi, p. 269.
Lophuromys aquilus margarettae, p. 450.
Miniopterus natalensis arenarius, p. 149.
Mungos albicaudus dialeucos, p. 104.
Mungos albicaudus ferox, p. 104.
Mungos dentifer, p. 104.
Mungos sanguineus orestes, p. 105.
Mungos sanguineus parvipes, p. 105.
Mus bellus petilus, p. 447.
Mus gratus soricoides, p. 447.
Mus gratus sungarae, p. 448.
Mus peromyscus, p. 454.
Mus tana, p. 453.
Mus wamae, p. 448.
Nandinia binotata arborea, p. 105.
Nesotragus moschatus deserticola, p. 10.
Oenomys hypoxanthus vallicola, p. 453.
Oreotragus oreotragus aureus, p. 10.
Oryx annectens, p. 10.
Otocyon virgatus, p. 46.
Otomys orestes dollmani, p. 453.
Ourebia microdon, p. 10.
Ozanna roosevelti, p. 8.

AFRICA—continued

KENYA—Continued.

Pachyura lixa aequatoria, p. 198.

Papio anubis lestes, p. 246.

Papio anubis vigilis, p. 246.

Paraxerus kahari, p. 543.

Pedetes surdaster currax, p. 490.

Pedetes surdaster larvalis, p. 490.

Pelomys fallax iridescens, p. 454.

Pelomys roosevelti, p. 452.

Petrodromus sultani sangi, p. 166.

Pipistrellus aero, p. 160.

Pipistrellus helios, p. 160.

Proteles cristatus termes, p. 85.

Protoxerus stangeri bea, p. 544.

Rattus coucha tinctus, p. 452.

Redunca redunca tohi, p. 14.

Rhinolophus keniensis, p. 143.

Rhyncotragus kirki myikae, p. 14.

Saccostomus isiolae, p. 487.

Saccostomus mearnsi, p. 488.

Saccostomus umbriventer, p. 488.

Steatomys athi, p. 488.

Strepsiceros strepsiceros bea, p. 15.

Surdisorex polulus, p. 198.

Sylvicapra grimmi altivallis, p. 15.

Sylvicapra grimmia deserti, p. 15.

Tachyoryctes rex, p. 490.

Tatera nigricauda percivali, p. 356.

Tatera pothae, p. 356.

Tatera varia, p. 356.

Thamnomys dolichurus littoralis, p. 446.

Thamnomys loringi, p. 488.

Thos adustus bweha, p. 46.

Thos adustus notatus, p. 47.

Thos aureus bea, p. 41.

Thos mesomelas elgonae, p. 46.

Thos mesomelas mcmillani, p. 46.

Thryonomys gregorianus pusillus, p. 566.

Tragelaphus scriptus olivaceus, p. 16.

Zelotomys hildegardeae vinaceus, p. 489.

LIBERIA:

Arvicanthis planifrons, p. 489.

Dasymys rufulus, p. 444.

Mus defua, p. 445.

Mus tullbergi rostratus, p. 455.

Myosorex muricauda, p. 171.

Pipistrellus minusculus, p. 161.

Sciurus (Heliosciurus) rufobrachiatus libericus, p. 536.

TANGANYIKA TERRITORY (formerly German East Africa):

Cephalophus spadix, p. 8.

Dendrohyrax validus, p. 164.

Dendromys nigrifrons, p. 454.

AFRICA—continued

TANGANYIKA TERRITORY—Continued.
      Mellivora sagulata, p. 67.
      Mungos paludinosus rubescens, p. 102.
      Mus aquilus, p. 450.
      Pedetes cafer dentatus, p. 490.
      Sciurus undulatus (lectotype), p. 537.
UGANDA:
      Acomys hystrella, p. 439.
      Adenota kob alurae, p. 6.
      Arvicanthis abyssinicus centrosus, p. 442.
      Arvicanthis jebelae, p. 442.
      Arvicanthis pulchellus micropus, p. 449.
      Bubalis lelwel roosevelti, p. 7.
      Colobus abyssinicus terrestris, p. 239.
      Crocidura daphnia, p. 168.
      Crocidura littoralis, p. 170.
      Crocidura lutrella, p. 170.
      Crocidura maanjae, p. 171.
      Crocidura mutesae, p. 172.
      Crocidura nilotica, p. 172.
      Crocidura planiceps, p. 173.
      Crocidura sururae, p. 174.
      Dasymys orthos, p. 444.
      Dendromus lineatus, p. 445.
      Dendromus spectabilis, p. 454.
      Epimys concha (=coucha) ismailiae, p. 451.
      Epimys kaiseri centralis, p. 439.
      Eptesicus ugandae, p. 147.
      Felis leo nyanzae, p. 56.
      Felis pardus chui, p. 59.
      Graphiurus personatus, p. 405.
      Heliosciurus multicolor madogae, p. 536.
      Heliosorex roosevelti, p. 173.
      Lophuromys pyrrhus, p. 451.
      Mus bellus enclavae, p. 447.
      Mus bellus gondokorae, p. 447.
      Mus musculoides emesi, p. 448.
      Mus tenellus acholi, p. 448.
      Ourebia montana aequatoria, p. 11.
      Phacochoerus africanus bufo, p. 26.
      Sylvicapra grimmi roosevelti, p. 15.
      Sylvisorex gemmeus, p. 198.
      Uranomys ugandae, p. 489.
AFRICA, off eastern coast:
  SEYCHELLES ISLANDS: ALDABRA ISLAND:
      Nyctinomus pusillus, p. 120.
      Pteropus aldabrensis (cotypes), p. 139.

ANTARCTIC REGION

DECEPTION ISLAND:
      Halichoerus antarcticus, p. 234.

ASIA

Asia, Central:
 Pamir:
  Microtus pamirensis, p. 280.
 Eastern Turkestan:
  Crocidura lignicolor, p. 170.
  Gerbillus arenicolor, p. 265.
  Microtus ravidulus, p. 281.
 Russian Turkestan:
  Apodemus microtis, p. 440.

CHINA

Chekiang:
  Sciurus caniceps canigenus, p. 493.
Chi-li:
  Eutamias senescens, p. 531.
  Petaurista sulcatus, p. 544.
  Sciurus vulgaris chiliensis, p. 559.
  Selenarctos thibetanus wulsini, p. 86.
  Tamiops vestitus, p. 562.
  Taphozous solifer, p. 117.
Fukien:
  Coelops inflata, p. 117.
  Crocidura grisea, p. 169.
  Crocidura grisescens, p. 169.
  Myotis hirsutus, p. 153.
  Myotis sowerbyi, p. 157.
  Pithecus pullus, p. 240.
  Rattus rattus exiguus, p. 476.
Hu-nan: Tung Ting Lake:
  Lipotes vexillifer, p. 113.
Kansu:
  Allactaga mongolica longior, p. 359.
  Capreolus melanotis, p. 16.
  Epimys norvegicus socer, p. 471.
  Eptesicus serotinus pallens, p. 147.
  Euchoreutes naso alashanicus, p. 359.
  Eutamias asiaticus umbrosus, p. 524.
  Mustela tiarata, p. 74.
  Myotalpa cansus, p. 566.
  Ochotona (Pika) alpina argentata, p. 224.
  Ochotona annectens, p. 224.
  Ochotona cansus, p. 224.
  Ochotona erythrotis vulpina, p. 224.
  Pseudois nayaur caesia, p. 13.
Kiangsi:
  Lepus aurigineus, p. 209.
Shansi:
  Lepus swinhoei sowerbyae, p. 214.
  Microtus pullus, p. 281.
Shantung:
  Crocidura shantungensis, p. 174.

CHINA—continued

SHENSI:

> Rattus humiliatus insolatus, p. 465.
> Vormela negans, p. 79.

SZECHWAN:

> Dremomys rufigenis lentus, p. 522.
> Euroscaptor grandis, p. 199.
> Lepus europaeus cinnamomeus, p. 211.
> Lepus grahami, p. 211.
> Petaurista rubicundus, p. 543.

EAST INDIES

BORNEO, mainland:

> Arctogalidia bicolor, p. 101.
> Emballonura pusilla, p. 116.
> Epimys borneanus, p. 458.
> Epimys luta, p. 468.
> Epimys mara, p. 469.
> Epimys rattus turbidus, p. 477.
> Epimys tua, p. 484.
> Galeopterus borneanus, p. 163.
> Hipposideros insolens, p. 118.
> Hylobates cinereus abbotti, p. 251.
> Hylobates mulleri albibarbis, p. 251.
> Iomys lepidus, p. 537.
> Kerivoula bombifrons, p. 147.
> Macaca broca, p. 241.
> Muntiacus rubidus, p. 19.
> Nannosciurus borneanus, p. 542.
> Nycticebus borneanus, p. 251.
> Pithecus mandibularis, p. 244.
> Presbytis arwasca, p. 247.
> Presbytis canicrus, p. 248.
> Pygathrix rubicunda rubida, p. 249.
> Pygathrix ultima, p. 250.
> Rattus melanurus, p. 470.
> Rattus perasper, p. 473.
> Ratufa cothurnata, p. 547.
> Sciurus atricapillus atrox, p. 492.
> Sciurus atristriatus, p. 492.
> Sciurus borneoensis palustris, p. 493.
> Sciurus dulitensis dilutus, p. 495.
> Sciurus hippurellus, p. 563.
> Sciurus parvus, p. 565.
> Sciurus poliopus, p. 494.
> Sciurus sanggaus, p. 501.
> Tana tana besara, p. 203.
> Tarsius borneanus, p. 252.
> Thecurus major, p. 438.
> Tragulus borneanus, p. 31.
> Tragulus virgicollis, p. 38.
> Tupaia longipes salatana, p. 205.

Borneo, off northern coast:
    Mangsi Island:
        Pteropus vociferus, p. 142.
Borneo, off southeastern coast:
    Laut Island:
        Epimys perflavus, p. 473.
        Galeopterus lautensis, p. 163.
        Ratufa vittata, p. 550.
        Sciurus marinsularis, p. 497.
    Sebuku Island:
        Epimys sebucus, p. 479.
        Epimys ubecus, p. 484.
        Ratufa vittatula, p. 551.
        Tragulus sebucus, p. 37.
Borneo, off western coast:
    Datu Island:
        Epimys neglectus ducis, p. 471.
        Sciurus datus, p. 494.
    Direction Island:
        Sciurus director, p. 495.
    Karimata Island:
        Megaderma carimatae, p. 119.
        Mus carimatae, p. 459.
        Mus serutus, p. 479.
        Myotis carimatae, p. 151.
        Pithecus carimatae, p. 242.
        Presbytis carimatae, p. 248.
        Sciurus carimatae, p. 494.
        Sciurus serutus, p. 502.
        Tragulus carimatae, p. 32.
        Tupaia carimatae, p. 203.
        Tupaia gracilis edarata, p. 205.
    Lamukotan Island:
        Epimys crassus, p. 460.
        Epimys neglectus lamucotanus, p. 471.
        Epimys spatulatus, p. 480.
        Sciurus lamucotanus, p. 496.
    Panebangan Island:
        Epimys nasutus, p. 476.
        Epimys saturatus, p. 478.
        Galeopterus abbotti, p. 162.
        Ratufa griseicollis, p. 547.
        Sciurus armalis, p. 492.
    Pelapis Island:
        Sciurus pelapius, p. 499.
    Temaju Island:
        Sciurus proserpinae, p. 500.
Celebes, mainland:
        Cheiromeles parvidens, p. 120.
        Crocidura elongata, p. 168.
        Crocidura lea, p. 170.
        Crocidura levicula, p. 170.

CELEBES, mainland—Continued.
>Crocidura nigripes, p. 172.
>Crocidura nigripes lipara, p. 172.
>Crocidura rhoditus, p. 173.
>Echiothrix brevicula, p. 446.
>Echiothrix centrosa, p. 446.
>Eropeplus canus, p. 446.
>Harpyionycteris celebensis, p. 139.
>Hipposideros gentilis toala, p. 118.
>Lenomys longicaudus, p. 449.
>Megaderma spasma celebensis, p. 119.
>Melasmothrix naso, p. 452.
>Phalanger furvus, p. 232.
>Phoniscus rapax, p. 159.
>Pteropus arquatus, p. 139.
>Rattus adspersus, p. 455.
>Rattus dominator camurus, p. 461.
>Rattus facetus, p. 462.
>Rattus hamatus, p. 464.
>Rattus hellwaldii cereus, p. 464
>Rattus hellwaldii localis, p. 465.
>Rattus hoffmanni linduensis, p. 465.
>Rattus hoffmanni subditivus, p. 465.
>Rattus mollicomus, p. 470.
>Rattus musschenbroekii tetricus, p. 470.
>Rattus nigellus, p. 471.
>Rattus penitus, p. 473.
>Rattus punicans, p. 474.
>Rattus rallus, p. 475.
>Rattus raveni, p. 478.
>Rattus raveni eurous, p. 478.
>Rattus sericatus, p. 479.
>Sciurus murinus necopinus, p. 564.
>Tarsius fuscus dentatus, p. 252.
>Tarsius pumilus, p. 252.

CELEBES, off eastern coast:
>PELING ISLAND:
>>Hipposideros pelingensis, p. 118.

CELEBES, off northern coast:
>PALELEH ISLAND:
>>Rattus palelae, p. 472.

CELEBES, off northeastern coast:
>LEMBEH ISLAND:
>>Cynopithecus lembicus, p. 240.
>>Sciurus evidens, p. 563.

CELEBES, off southeastern coast:
>BUTON ISLAND:
>>Mus andrewsi, p. 456.

JAVA:
>Ratufa bicolor major, p. 546.
>Tragulus focalinus, p. 32.

JAVA SEA:
  ARENDS ISLAND:
    Sciurus arendsis, p. 492.
  BAWEAN ISLAND:
    Pithecus baweanus, p. 241.
    Pteropus baveanus, p. 139.
  MATA SIRI ISLAND:
    Pithecus cupidus, p. 242.
    Sciurus siriensis, p. 502.
MOLUCCA ISLANDS:
  BOURU ISLAND:
    Mus buruensis, p. 459.
RHIO-LINGA ARCHIPELAGO:
  BAKONG ISLAND:
    Tragulus pretiellus, p. 35.
  BATAM ISLAND:
    Arctogalidia mima, p. 102.
    Mus batamanus, p. 457.
    Tragulus perflavus, p. 35.
    Tupaia ferruginea batamana, p. 204.
  BINTANG ISLAND:
    Arctogalidia depressa, p. 101.
    Presbytis rhionis, p. 249.
    Ratufa conspicua, p. 547.
    Tragulus formosus, p. 32.
    Tragulus rubeus, p. 36.
    Tupaia castanea, p. 203.
  BULAN ISLAND:
    Ratufa bulana, p. 546.
  GREAT KARIMON ISLAND:
    Ratufa carimonensis, p. 546.
    Sciurus carimonensis, p. 494.
  JOMBOL ISLAND:
    Galeopterus chombolis, p. 163.
    Mus chombolis, p. 460.
  KUNDUR ISLAND:
    Arctogalidia fusca, p. 101.
    Paradoxurus brunneipes, p. 105.
    Presbytis cana, p. 247.
    Ratufa condurensis, p. 547.
    Sciuropterus amoenus, p. 537.
    Sciurus condurensis, p. 494.
    Tragulus nigrocinctus, p. 35.
  LINGA ISLAND:
    Arctogalidia simplex, p. 102.
    Mus firmus, p. 462.
    Mus lingensis, p. 466.
    Pithecus lingae, p. 243.
    Ratufa notabilis, p. 549.
    Tana lingae, p. 202.
    Tragulus pretiosus, p. 36.
  SEBANG ISLAND:
    Tragulus pretiellus parallelus, p. 36.

RHIO-LINGA ARCHIPELAGO—Continued.
　　SINKEP ISLAND:
　　　　Mus fremens, p. 463.
　　　　Nannosciurus pulcher, p. 542.
　　　　Ratufa confinis, p. 547.
　　　　Tragulus nigricollis, p. 34.
　　　　Tragulus subrufus, p. 37.
　　　　Tupaia phaeura, p. 206.
　　　　Tupaia sincepis, p. 207.
　　SUGI ISLAND.
　　　　Pithecus impudens, p. 242.
　　　　Ratufa insignis, p. 548.
　　　　Tragulus flavicollis, p. 32.
　　　　Tragulus lutescens, p. 34.
　　UNGAR ISLAND.
　　　　Sus rhionis, p. 28.
SUMATRA, mainland:
　　　　Arctogalidia sumatrana, p. 102.
　　　　Crocidura lepidura, p. 170.
　　　　Mus mandus, p. 469.
　　　　Nannosciurus sumatranus, p. 542.
　　　　Niadius minor, p. 138.
　　　　Phoniscus atrox, p. 159.
　　　　Presbytis catemana, p. 248.
　　　　Presbytis percura, p. 249.
　　　　Rattus virtus, p. 485.
　　　　Rattus vociferans tapanulius, p. 487.
　　　　Ratufa arusinus, p. 545.
　　　　Ratufa catemana, p. 546.
　　　　Ratufa palliata, p. 549.
　　　　Sciurus erebus, p. 495.
　　　　Sciurus hippurosus, p. 563.
　　　　Sciurus humilis, p. 564.
　　　　Sciurus melanops, p. 498.
　　　　Sciurus vittatus tapanulius, p. 503.
　　　　Sciurus vittatus tarussanus, p. 503.
　　　　Sus oi, p. 28.
　　　　Taphozous cavaticus, p. 117.
　　　　Thecurus sumatrae, p. 438.
　　　　Tragulus kanchil longipes, p. 33.
　　　　Trichys macrotis, p. 439.
　　　　Tupaia siaca, p. 207.
SUMATRA, off eastern coast:
　　BANKA ISLAND:
　　　　Epimys pollens, p. 474.
　　　　Muntiacus bancanus, p. 18.
　　　　Mus clabatus, p. 460.
　　　　Nannosciurus bancanus, p. 542.
　　　　Nycticebus bancanus, p. 251.
　　　　Paradoxurus hermaphroditus simplex, p. 107.
　　　　Pithecus lapsus, p. 243.
　　　　Ratufa polia bancana, p. 550.

EAST INDIES—continued

SUMATRA, off eastern coast—Continued.
    BANKA ISLAND—Continued.
        Rhinolophus solitarius, p. 144.
        Sciurus tedongus, p. 502.
        Tragulus bancanus, p. 30.
        Tragulus luteicollis, p. 34.
        Tupaia discolor, p. 204.
        Tupaia inflata, p. 205.
    BENGKALIS ISLAND:
        Tragulus fulvicollis, p. 33.
    BILLITON ISLAND:
        Arctogalidia minor, p. 102.
        Epimys mengurus, p. 470.
        Paradoxurus canescens, p. 106.
        Ratufa polia, p. 550.
        Sciurus billitonus, p. 493.
        Tarsius saltator, p. 253.
        Tragulus billitonus, p. 31.
    MENDANAU ISLAND:
        Sciurus mendanauus, p. 498.
    PADANG ISLAND:
        Paradoxurus padangus, p. 107.
    PENJALEI ISLAND:
        Sciurus melanops penialius, p. 498.
    RUPAT ISLAND:
        Mus bullatus, p. 458.
        Petaurista mimicus, p. 543.
        Sciurus nyx, p. 499.
        Sciurus vittatus rupatius, p. 503.
    TEBING TINGGI ISLAND:
        Arctogalidia tingia, p. 102.
        Felis tingia, p. 60.
SUMATRA, off western coast:
    BABI ISLAND:
        Cynopterus babi, p. 137.
        Rattus simalurensis babi, p. 480.
        Sus babi, p. 26.
    BANJAK ISLANDS:
        Epimys potens, p. 474.
        Epimys valens, p. 485.
        Galeopithecus tuancus, p. 164.
        Lenothrix canus, p. 449.
        Pithecus agnatus, p. 241.
        Rattus fremens tuancus, p. 463.
        Rattus lingensis antucus, p. 467.
        Rattus lingensis banacus, p. 467.
        Ratufa femoralis, p. 547.
        Ratufa laenata, p. 548.
        Sciurus bancarus, p. 563.
        Sciurus pretiosus, p. 500.
        Sciurus ubericolor, p. 503.
        Sus babi tuancus, p. 26.

SUMATRA, off western coast—Continued.
  BANJAK ISLANDS—Continued.
      Tana tana tuancus, p. 203.
      Tragulus brevipes, p. 31.
      Tragulus russeus, p. 37.
  BATU ISLANDS:
      Epimys batus, p. 457.
      Funambulus rostratus, p. 538.
      Galeopithecus saturatus, p. 164.
      Mus balae, p. 456.
      Mus masae, p. 469.
      Petaurista batuana, p. 543.
      Presbytis batuanus, p. 247.
      Rattus balmasus, p. 456.
      Rattus lingensis mabalus, p. 467.
      Rattus lingensis pinacus, p. 467.
      Rattus pinatus, p. 474.
      Ratufa balae, p. 545.
      Ratufa masae, p. 548.
      Ratufa palliata batuana, p. 549.
      Ratufa piniensis, p. 549.
      Sciurus adangensis, p. 491.
      Sciurus balae, p. 563.
      Sciurus ictericus, p. 496.
      Sciurus mansalaris batus, p. 564.
      Sciurus piniensis, p. 549.
      Tana cervicalis masae, p. 202.
      Tragulus batuanus, p. 31.
      Tragulus pinius, p. 35.
      Tragulus russulus, p. 37.
      Tragulus russulus masae, p. 37.
      Tupaia cervicalis, p. 202.
      Tupaia tephrura, p. 207.
  ENGANO ISLAND:
      Kerivoula engana, p. 148.
      Mus enganus, p. 461.
      Paradoxurus hermaphroditus enganus, p. 106.
      Pipistrellus curtatus, p. 160.
      Pteropus enganus, p. 140.
      Sus babi enganus, p. 26.
  LASIA ISLAND:
      Megaderma lasiae, p. 119.
      Pithecus fuscus lasiae, p. 242.
      Rattus simalurensis lasiae p. 480.
  MANSALAR ISLAND:
      Mus catellifer, p. 460.
      Mus domitor, p. 461.
      Pithecus mansalaris, p. 244.
      Rattus fremens mansalaris, p. 463.
      Ratufa nigrescens, p. 549.
      Sciurus mansalaris, p. 564.
      Sciurus saturatus, p. 501.

SUMATRA, off western coast—Continued.
 MANSALAR ISLAND—Continued.
  Tragulus amoenus, p. 30.
  Tragulus jugularis, p. 33.
 NIAS ISLAND:
  Arctictis niasensis, p. 100.
  Chiropodomys niadis, p. 443.
  Cynopterus major, p. 137.
  Cynopterus minutus, p. 138.
  Cynopterus princeps, p. 138.
  Epimys barussanus, p. 457.
  Epimys maerens, p. 468.
  Macaca phaeura, p. 245.
  Megaderma niasense, p. 119.
  Myotis niasensis, p. 155.
  Pteropus niadicus, p. 141.
  Rhinolophus circe, p. 143.
  Rhinolophus trifoliatus niasensis, p. 144.
  Sus niadensis, p. 27.
  Tragulus napu niasis, p. 34.
 PAGI ISLANDS:
  Cynopterus pagensis, p. 138.
  Funambulus obscurus, p. 538.
  Hemigale minor, p. 103.
  Macaca pagensis, p. 245.
  Mus lugens, p. 468.
  Mus pagensis, p. 472.
  Mus soccatus, p. 480.
  Myotis abbotti, p. 150.
  Paradoxurus lignicolor, p. 107.
  Sciuropterus maerens, p. 544.
  Sciurus atratus, p. 562.
  Sciurus pumilus, p. 565.
  Simias concolor, p. 250.
  Symphalangus klossii, p. 251.
  Tupaia chrysogaster, p. 204.
 PINIE ISLAND:
  Rattus pinatus, p. 474.
  Tragulus pinius, p. 35.
 SIMALUR ISLAND:
  Macacus fuscus, p. 242.
  Mus simalurensis, p. 479.
  Mus surdus, p. 482.
  Paradoxurus parvus, p. 108.
  Sus mimus, p. 27.
 SIUMAT ISLAND:
  Megaderma siumatis, p. 119.

EUROPE

FRANCE:
  Evotomys vasconiae, p. 264.
  Neomys fodiens minor, p. 181.
  Sorex araneus euronotus, p. 183.

EUROPE—continued

GERMANY:
>Microtus arvalis duplicatus, p. 270.
>Sorex alpinus hercynicus, p. 182.

GREECE:
>Lepus parnassius, p. 213.

ITALY:
>Eliomys cincticauda, p. 489.
>Rupicapra faesula, p. 14.

NORWAY:
>Evotomys norvegicus, p. 263.
>Sorex araneus bergensis, p. 183.

RUMANIA:
>Spalax dolbrogeae, p. 566.

SICILY:
>Crocidura caudata, p. 168.
>Crocidura sicula, p. 174.

SPAIN:
>Sciurus infuscatus, p. 556.

SWEDEN:
>Evotomys hercynicus suecicus, p. 262.

SWITZERLAND:
>Crocidura mimula, p. 171.
>Lepus varronis, p. 215.
>Sorex araneus alticola, p. 182.

FRENCH INDO-CHINA

ANNAM:
>Talpa parvidens, p. 199.

INDIA

BALTISTAN [= KASHMIR]:
>Alticola glacialis, p. 257.
>Crocidura pergrisea, p. 173.
>Epimys rattus shigarus, p. 477.

BURMA, TENASSERIM:
>Epimys gracilis, p. 464.
>Epimys lepidus, p. 466.
>Macaca adusta, p. 240.
>Ratufa phaeopepla, p. 549.

TOUNGOO, BIAPO:
>Kerivoula depressa, p. 148.

KASHMIR:
>Arvicola albicauda, p. 257.
>Arvicola fertilis, p. 267.
>Arvicola montosa, p. 258.
>Crocidura pullata, p. 173.
>Macacus rhesus villosus, p. 245.
>Microtus acrophilus, p. 257.
>Microtus brachelix, p. 266.
>Mus arianus griseus (cotypes), p. 440
>Sminthus flavus, p. 567.
>Sorex planiceps, p. 192.

LADAK:
>Alticola acmaeus, p. 257.
>Microtus cricetulus, p. 257.

JAPAN

Hondo Island:
  Lepus brachyurus angustidens, p. 210.
Korea [=Chosen]:
  Moschus parvipes, p. 25.
Manchuria [=Manchukuo]:
  Apodemus praetor, p. 441.
  Murina huttoni fuscus, p. 150.
  Rattus humiliatus sowerbyi, p.465.
Mongolia:
  Microtus warringtoni, p. 283.
  Procapra altaica, p. 13.
Yenosima:
  Dymecodon pilirostris, p. 198.

MALAY ARCHIPELAGO

Andaman Islands:
  Crocidura anadamanensis, p. 168.
  Mus atratus, p. 456.
  Mus flebilis, p. 463.
  Mus stoicus, p. 481.
  Mus taciturnus, p. 482.
Nicobar Islands:
  Crocidura nicobarica, p. 172.
  Hipposideros nicobarulae, p. 118.
  Macacus umbrosus, p. 246.
  Mus burrescens, p. 458.
  Mus burrulus, p. 458.
  Mus burrus, p. 459.
  Mus pulliventer, p. 474.
  Pipistrellus camortae, p. 160.
  Pteropus faunulus, p. 140.
  Sus nicobaricus, p. 27.
  Tupaia nicobarica surda, p. 205.

MALAY PENINSULA

Peninsular Siam:
  Trong (or Tarang or Trang):
    Arctogalidia major, p. 101.
    Cynopterus angulatus, p. 137.
    Emballonura peninsularis, p. 116.
    Funambulus peninsulae, p. 538.
    Gymnura gymnura minor, p. 165.
    Kerivoula minuta, p. 148.
    Mus asper, p. 456.
    Mus cremoriventer, p. 461.
    Mus ferreocanus, p. 462.
    Mus pellax, p. 473.
    Mus surifer, p. 482.
    Mus validus, p. 485.
    Mus vociferans, p. 486.
    Paradoxurus hermaphroditus ravus, p. 107.
    Paradoxurus robustus, p. 105.
    Pithecus capitalis, p. 241.

MALAY PENINSULA—continued

PENINSULAR SIAM—Continued.

TRONG—Continued.

Pygathrix flavicauda, p. 249.
Ratufa melanopepla, p. 548.
Ratufa melanopepla peninsulae, p. 548.
Ratufa pyrsonota, p. 550.
Sciurus novemlineatus, p. 562.
Sciurus notatus miniatus, p. 499.
Sciurus rubeculus, p. 501.
Sciurus tenuis surdus, p. 565.
Sus jubatus, p. 27.
Tragulus canescens, p. 32.
Tragulus ravus, p. 36.

PENINSULAR SIAM, off eastern coast:

Koh Tau:

Sciurus caniceps helvus, p. 493.
Tupaia lacernata kohtauensis, p. 205.

PENINSULAR SIAM, off western coast:

Butang Island:

Epimys pannellus, p. 492.
Galeopithecus pumilus, p. 164.
Mus pannosus, p. 473.
Mus surifer butangensis, p. 482.
Tragulus ravulus, p. 36.
Tupaia raviana, p. 206.

LANGKAWI ISLAND:

Epimys rattus viclana, p. 478.
Mus surifer flavidulus, p. 482.
Mus vociferans lancavensis, p. 486.
Sciurus lancavensis, p. 497.
Tragulus lancavensis, p. 33.
Tragulus umbrinus, p. 38.

TELIBON ISLAND:

Ratufa melanopepla, p. 548.

TERUTAU ISLAND:

Atherurus terutaus, p. 438.
Epimys solus, p. 480.
Paradoxurus hermaphroditus canus, p. 106.
Petaurista terutaus, p. 544.
Presbytis corvus, p. 248.
Sus jubatulus, p. 26.

MALAY STATES

JOHORE: GUNONG PULAI, near base:

Sus peninsularis, p. 28.

JAMBU LUANG:

Presbytis australis, p. 247.

JOHORE, off eastern coast:

AOR ISLAND:

Atherura zygomatica, p. 438.
Epimys roa, p. 478.

MALAY STATES—continued

JOHORE, off eastern coast—Continued.
    AOR ISLAND—Continued.
        Galeopithecus aoris, p. 162.
        Sciurus aoris, p. 491.
        Tupaia pulonis, p. 206.
    PEMANGIL ISLAND:
        Sciurus pemangilensis, p. 500.
        Tupaia pemangilis, p. 206.
    TINGGI ISLAND:
        Epimys tingius, p. 483.
    TIOMAN ISLAND:
        Mus obscurus, p. 472.
        Mus stridens, p. 481.
        Mus tiomanicus, p. 483.
        Ratufa tiomanensis, p. 550.
        Sciurus tenuirostris, p. 503.
        Tragulus rufulus, p. 37.
        Tupaia sordida, p. 207.
PAHANG: ENDAU RIVER, north bank:
        Sciurus peninsularis, p. 500.
    RUMPIN RIVER:
        Epimys victor, p. 485.
TRENGGANU (OR TRINGANU): TANJONG LABOHA:
        Sciurus bilimitatus, p. 493.

MERGUI ARCHIPELAGO

BENTINCK ISLAND:
        Mus bentincanus, p. 458.
        Mus stridulus, p. 481.
        Sciurus bentincanus, p. 493.
CHANCE ISLAND:
        Epimys rattus fortunatus, p. 476.
        Macaca insulana, p. 242.
        Mus casensis, p. 459.
        Sciurus casensis, p. 494.
CLARA ISLAND:
        Epimys vociferans clarae, p. 486.
        Paradoxurus hermaphroditus pulcher, p. 106.
DOMEL ISLAND:
        Arctogalidia macra, p. 101.
        Epimys vociferans insularum, p. 486.
        Lariscus berdmorei amotus, p. 541.
        Mus domelicus, p, 461.
        Paradoxurus hermaphroditus senex, p. 107.
        Pithecus vitiis, p. 246.
        Ratufa celaenopepla, p. 546.
        Sciurus domelicus, p. 495.
HASTINGS ISLAND:
        Epimys rattus dentatus, p. 475.
HELFER ISLAND:
        Epimys rattus insulanus, p. 476.
HIGH ISLAND:
        Sciurus altinsularis, p. 491.

MERGUI ARCHIPELAGO—continued

JAMES ISLAND:

Epimys rattus exsul, p. 476.

Epimys stentor, p. 481.

Paradoxurus hermaphroditus fuscus, p. 106.

KISSERAING ISLAND:

Paradoxurus hermaphroditus pallens, p. 106.

LOUGHBOROUGH ISLAND

Mus umbridorsum, p. 484.

ST. LUKE ISLAND:

Mus lucas, p. 467.

Sciurus lucas, p. 497.

ST. MATTHEW ISLAND:

Mus luteolus, p. 468.

Mus matthaeus, p. 469.

Paradoxurus hermaphroditus sacer, p. 107.

Pygathrix sanctorum, p. 249.

Sciurus matthaeus, p. 498.

SOUTH TWIN ISLAND:

Pteropus geminorum, p. 140.

SULLIVAN ISLAND, OR PULO LAMPEE:

Mus gilbiventer, p. 464.

Paradoxurus hermaphroditus pugnax, p. 106.

Sciurus sullivanus, p. 502.

Tragulus lampensis, p. 33.

OCEANIA

CAROLINE ISLANDS: UOLA ISLAND:

Emballonura sulcata, p. 116.

FIJI ISLANDS:

Mus vitiensis (cotype), p. 486.

HAWAIIAN ISLANDS:

Atalapha semota, p. 149.

Delphinus lateralis, p. 576.

Phocaena pectoralis, p. 110.

NANTUCKET ISLAND (now BAKER ISLAND):

Delphinus albirostratus, p. 575.

NEW GUINEA, (off north coast), JOBIE ISLAND:

Nyctinomus jobensis (cotypes), p. 119.

SAMOAN ISLANDS:

Pteropus lanigera,* p. 141.

Pteropus samoensis, p. 142.

Vespertilio semicaudatus, p. 116.

SOCIETY ISLANDS:

Mus exulans (lectotype), p. 462.

PHILIPPINE ISLANDS

BALUT ISLAND:

Pteropus balutus, p. 139.

BASILAN ISLAND:

Epimys basilanus, p. 457.

Epimys coloratus, p. 460.

---

* Said (probably incorrectly) to be from the Samoan Islands.

BASILAN ISLAND—Continued.
    Pteropus mearnsi, p. 141.
    Sciuropterus crinitus, p. 544.
BOHOL ISLAND:
    Tarsius fraterculus, p. 252.
CAGAYAN SULU ISLAND, SULU SEA:
    Cynomolgus cagayanus, p. 241.
    Epimys orantulus, p. 472.
    Epimys robiginosus, p. 478.
    Pteropus cagayanus, p. 140.
CATANDUANES ISLAND:
    Apomys microdon, p. 442.
    Epimys leucophaeatus, p. 466.
    Taphonycteris capito, p. 116.
CUYO ISLAND:
    Tupaia cuyonis, p. 204.
GUIMARÁS ISLAND:
    Miniopterus paululus, p. 149.
    Rhinolophus hirsutus, p. 143.
LUZON ISLAND:
    Apomys major, p. 441.
    Apomys musculus, p. 442.
    Batomys dentatus, p. 443.
    Chaerephon luzonus, p. 120.
    Eonycteris robusta, p. 138.
    Epimys benguetensis, p. 457.
    Epimys calcis, p. 459.
    Epimys mayonicus, p. 469.
    Epimys querceti, p. 475.
    Rhinolophus virgo, p. 144.
    Tryphomys adustus, p. 488.
MINDANAO ISLAND:
    Apomys bardus, p. 441.
    Apomys hylocoetes, p. 441.
    Apomys insignis, p. 441.
    Apomys petraeus, p. 442.
    Bullimus bagobus, p. 443.
    Crocidura beatus, p. 168.
    Crocidura grandis, p. 169.
    Cynomolgus mindanensis, p. 244.
    Cynomolgus mindanensis apoensis, p. 244.
    Limnomys mearnsi, p. 450.
    Limnomys sibuanus, p. 450.
    Mus albigularis, p. 455.
    Mus commissarius, p. 452.
    Mus kelleri, p. 466.
    Mus magnirostris, p. 469.
    Mus mindanensis, p. 470.
    Mus pantarensis, p. 473.
    Mus tagulayensis, p. 483.
    Mus todayensis, p. 484.
    Mus vulcani, p. 487.

PHILIPPINE ISLANDS—continued

Mindanao Island—Continued.
    Mus vulcani apicis, p. 487.
    Mus zamboangae, p. 487.
    Nannosciurus surrutilus, p. 543.
    Podogymnura truei, p. 165.
    Pteropus lanensis, p. 140.
    Rhinolophus inops, p. 143.
    Rusa nigellus, p. 25.
    Taphozous pluto, p. 117.
    Tarsomys apoensis, p. 488.
    Urogale cylindrura, p. 207.
Mindoro Island:
    Chilophylla hirsuta, p. 117.
    Crocidura halconus, p. 169.
    Crocidura mindorus, p. 171.
    Epimys gala, p. 464.
    Epimys vigoratus, p. 485.
    Limnomys picinus, p. 450.
    Pithecus mindorus, p. 244.
Palmas Island:
    Pteropus pumilus, p. 141.
Panay Island:
    Pachyura occultidens, p. 198.
Sulu Island, Sulu Archipelago:
    Cynomolgus suluensis, p. 246.
Ticao Island:
    Epimys tyrannus, p. 484.

SIAM

Siam proper (see Malay Peninsula for Peninsular Siam):
    Bandicota siamensis, p. 443.
    Macaca nemestrina indochinensis, p. 244.
    Presbytis argentea (cotypes), p. 247.
    Presbytis cristata koratensis, p. 248.
    Rattus rajah koratis, p. 475.
    Rattus rattus koratensis, p. 476.
    Sciurus atrodorsalis tachin, p. 492.
    Tamiops macclellandi liantis, p. 562.
    Tupaia glis olivacea, p. 204.
    Viverricula malaccensis thai, p. 108.
Siam, inner Gulf of:
  Koh Kram:
    Macaca irus atriceps, p. 243.
    Rattus rajah kramis, p. 475.
    Rattus rattus kramensis, p. 476.
  Koh Lak:
    Sciurus epomophorus inexpectatus, p. 495.
    Sciurus erythraeus pranis, p. 496.
  Koh Lan:
    Rattus rattus lanensis, p. 477.
    Sciurus finlaysoni trotteri, p. 496.
  Koh Mesan.
    Rattus rattus mesanis, p. 477.

SOUTH CHINA SEA

ANAMBAS ISLANDS, between Malay Peninsula and Borneo:
    Emballonura anambensis, p. 115.
    Funambulus castaneus, p. 537.
    Mus anambae, p. 455.
    Mus flaviventer, p. 462.
    Mus siantanicus, p. 479.
    Mus strepitans, p. 481.
    Ratufa anambae, p. 545.
    Rhinolophus minutus, p. 144.
    Rhinolophus nereis, p. 144.
    Sciurus anambensis, p. 491.
    Tupaia anambae, p. 203.
    Tupaia chrysomalla, p. 204.
    Tupaia riabus, p. 206.
NATUNA ISLANDS, between Malay Peninsula and Borneo:
    Arctogalidia inornata, p. 101.
    Epimys rattus pauper, p. 477.
    Galeopithecus gracilis, p. 163.
    Galeopithecus natunae, p. 163.
    Mus integer, p. 465.
    Nycticebus coucang natunae, p. 252.
    Pipistrellus subulidens, p. 161.
    Pithecus lautensis, p. 243.
    Pithecus lingungensis, p. 243.
    Pithecus sirhassenensis, p. 245.
    Presbytis vigilans, p. 250.
    Ratufa angusticeps, p. 545.
    Rhinolophus affinis nesites, p. 143.
    Rhinolophus spadix, p. 144.
    Sciurus lautensis, p. 497.
    Sciurus lingungensis, p. 564.
    Sciurus lutescens, p. 497.
    Sciurus procerus, p. 565.
    Sciurus rubidiventris, p. 501.
    Sciurus rutiliventris, p. 501.
    Sciurus seraiae, p. 502.
    Sus natunensis, p. 27.
    Tragulus bunguranensis, p. 32.
    Tragulus natunae, p. 34.
    Tragulus pallidus, p. 35.
    Tupaia natunae, p. 205.
    Tupaia sirhassenensis, p. 202.
PANNOW ISLAND, ATAS ISLANDS, between Sumatra and Borneo:
    Sciurus pannovianus, p. 499.
ST. BARBE ISLAND, between Sumatra and Borneo:
    Epimys fulmineus, p. 463.
    Hipposideros barbensis, p. 117.
    Sciurus mimiculus, p. 499.
ST. JULIAN ISLAND, between Sumatra and Borneo:
    Mus julianus, p. 466.

SOUTH CHINA SEA—continued

TAMBELAN ISLANDS, between Malay Peninsula and Borneo:
    Mus tambelanicus, p. 483.
    Macacus pumilus, p. 245.
    Pteropus lepidus, p. 141.
    Sciurus abbottii, p. 491.
    Sciurus klossi, p. 496.
    Sciurus mimellus, p. 498.
    Tupaia bunoae, p. 202.

SOVIET UNION (RUSSIA)

SIBERIA:
  ALTAI DISTRICT:
    Allactaga grisescens, p. 359.
    Mustela lineiventer, p. 72.
    Myotis petax, p. 157.
    Ochotona nitida, p. 225.
    Phodopus crepidatus, p. 339.
  ALTAI MOUNTAINS.
    Apodemus nigritalus, p. 440.
    Eutamias asiaticus altaicus, p. 523.
    Lepus quercerus, p. 213.
    Mustela lymani, p. 72.
    Myopus morulus, p. 283.
    Sicista napaea, p. 567.
    Sorex roboratus, p. 193.
  ARIKAM ISLAND, Bering Strait:
    Putorius kaneii, p. 71.
  BERING ISLAND, Bering Sea:
    Berardius bairdii, p. 114.
    Mesoplodon stejnegeri, p. 115
    Phoca stejnegeri, p. 235.
    Vulpes beringensis, p. 40.
    Ziphius grebnitzkii, p. 115.
  KAMCHATKA:
    Citellus stejnegeri, p. 519.
    Lutra stejnegeri, p. 66.
    Phoca ochotensis macrodens, p. 235.
    Rangifer phylarchus, p. 25.
    Sorex macropygmaeus, p. 188.
  PLOVER BAY, Bering Strait:
    Aschizomys lemminus, p. 258.
    Microtus tshuktshorum, p. 282.
  VERKHNE KOLYMSK REGION:
    Pteromys volans incanus, p. 545.

SYRIA

    Spalax berytensis, p. 566.

UNKNOWN LOCALITIES

EXACT LOCALITY UNKNOWN:
    Delphinus longidens, p. 113.
    Delphinus plagiodon, p. 113.
    Sagmatias amblodon, p. 112 (caught at sea).

WESTERN HEMISPHERE

ALASKA

Alaska:

Alces gigas, p. 16.
Arvicola operarius, p. 280.
Canis lupus ligoni, p. 43.
Canis tundrarum, p. 45.
Citellus nebulicola, p. 515.
Citellus plesius ablusus, p. 517.
Dicrostonyx nelsoni, p. 264.
Dicrostonyx unalascensis, p. 264.
Dicrostonyx unalascensis stevensoni, p. 265.
Erethizon epixanthum myops, p. 364.
Evotomys alascensis, p. 260.
Evotomys orca, p. 263.
Evotomys wrangeli, p. 264.
Fiber zibethicus zalophus, p. 301.
Glaucomys sabrinus griseifrons, p. 534.
Lagomys collaris, p. 224.
Lemmus alascensis, p. 268.
Lemmus minusculus, p. 268.
Lemmus yukonensis, p. 269.
Lepus americanus dalli, p. 208.
Lepus othus, p. 213.
Lepus poadromus, p. 213.
Lutra canadensis extera, p. 64.
Lutra canadensis kodiacensis, p. 64.
Lutra canadensis optiva, p. 65.
Lutra canadensis yukonensis, p. 65.
Lutra mira, p. 65.
Lutreola vison ingens, p. 74.
Marmota caligata sheldoni, p. 538.
Microtus abbreviatus, p. 269.
Microtus abbreviatus fisheri, p. 269.
Microtus amakensis, p. 270.
Microtus elymocetes, p. 274.
Microtus innuitus, p. 274.
Microtus kadiacensis, p. 275.
Microtus miurus, p. 277.
Microtus miurus oreas, p. 277.
Microtus muriei, p. 278.
Microtus operarius endoecus, p. 280.
Microtus sitkensis, p. 282.
Microtus unalascensis, p. 283.
Microtus unalascensis popofensis, p. 283.
Microtus yakutatensis, p. 283.
Mustela americana actuosa, p. 66.
Myodes nigripes, p. 268.
Myotis lucifugus alascensis, p. 154.
Odocoileus columbianus sitkensis, p. 20.
Ovis montana dalli (cotypes), p. 12.
Peromyscus hylaeus, p. 322.
Peromyscus sitkensis, p. 331.

ALASKA—Continued.

Phoca richardii pribilofensis, p. 235.
Phocaena dalli, p. 112.
Putorius arcticus, p. 69.
Putorius arcticus kadiacensis, p. 70.
Putorius richardsoni alascensis, p. 73.
Rangifer excelsifrons, p. 24.
Sciuropterus alpinus zaphaeus, p. 533.
Sciurus hudsonicus petulans, p. 561.
Sorex alascensis shumaginensis, p. 182.
Sorex (Microsorex) eximius, p. 179.
Sorex glacialis, p. 186.
Sorex navigator alaskanus, p. 189.
Sorex obscurus alascensis, p. 189.
Sorex obscurus longicauda, p. 190.
Sorex personatus arcticus, p. 192.
Sorex personatus streatori, p. 192.
Sorex pribilofensis, p. 192.
Sorex tundrensis, p. 196.
Spermophilus barrowensis, p. 505.
Spermophilus beringensis, p. 506.
Spermophilus osgoodi, p. 516.
Spermophilus parryii kodiacensis (lectotype), p. 516.
Synaptomys (Mictomys) dalli, p. 354.
Synaptomys (Mictomys) wrangeli, p. 355.
Tamiasciurus hudsonicus kenaiensis, p. 561.
Ursus caurinus, p. 87.
Ursus cressonus, p. 88.
Ursus dalli, p. 89.
Ursus dalli gyas, p. 89.
Ursus eltonclarki, p. 89.
Ursus eltonclarki insularis, p. 89.
Ursus eulophus, p. 89.
Ursus eximius, p. 89.
Ursus holzworthi, p. 90.
Ursus horribilis alascensis (lectotype), p. 90.
Ursus horribilis phaeonyx, p. 91.
Ursus innuitus, p. 92.
Ursus kenaiensis, p. 92.
Ursus kidderi, p. 92.
Ursus kidderi tundrensis, p. 92.
Ursus kwakiutl neglectus, p. 93.
Ursus middendorffi, p. 94.
Ursus mirabilis, p. 94.
Ursus nortoni, p. 95.
Ursus nuchek, p. 95.
Ursus orgiloides, p. 96.
Ursus orgilos, p. 96.
Ursus sheldoni, p. 98.
Ursus shirasi, p. 99.
Ursus sitkensis, p. 99.
Ursus toklat, p. 100.
Ursus townsendi, p. 100.

ALASKA—Continued.
Vulpes alascensis, p. 49.
Vulpes hallensis, p. 40.
Vulpes harrimani, p. 50.
Vulpes kenaiensis, p. 50.
Vulpes lagopus innuitus, p. 40.
Vulpes pribilofensis, p. 41.
Zapus hudsonius alascensis, p. 567.

ARCTIC REGION

ELLESMERE ISLAND:
Lepus arcticus monstrabilis, p. 209.
GREENLAND:
Lepus arcticus porsildi, p. 209.

CANADA

ALBERTA:
Callospermophilus lateralis tescorum, p. 512.
Marmota sibila, p. 541.
Myotis altifrons, p. 150.
Myotis pernox, p. 157.
Ochotona levis, p. 225.
Ochotona princeps lutescens, p. 226.
Rangifer fortidens, p. 24.
Tamias quadrivittatus luteiventris, p. 531.
Thomomys fuscus loringi, p. 389.
Thomomys talpoides andersoni, p. 397.
Ursus dusorgus, p. 89.
Ursus phaeonyx latifrons, p. 97.
Ursus rungiusi rungiusi, p. 98.
Vulpes velox hebes, p. 52.
BRITISH COLUMBIA:
Eutamias ludibundus, p. 527.
Evotomys caurinus, p. 260.
Felis concolor vancouverensis, p. 54.
Glaucomys sabrinus columbiensis, p. 534.
Glaucomys sabrinus latipes, p. 535.
Gulo luscus vancouverensis, p. 64.
Lutra canadensis evexa, p. 64.
Lutra vancouverensis, p. 66.
Marmota monax petrensis, p. 540.
Martes pennanti columbiana, p. 67.
Microtus serpens, p. 282.
Mustela nesophila, p. 67.
Myotis californicus caurinus, p. 151.
Neotoma saxamans, p. 297.
Ochotona princeps brooksi, p. 225.
Peromyscus maniculatus algidus, p. 324.
Peromyscus prevostensis, p. 331.
Procyon lotor vancouverensis, p. 84.
Putorius haidarum, p. 71.
Sorex longicauda elassodon, p. 187.
Sorex longicauda prevostensis, p. 188.

CANADA—continued

BRITISH COLUMBIA—Continued.
Sorex obscurus isolatus, p. 190.
Sorex vancouverensis, p. 197.
Spermophilus empetra plesius, p. 510.
Thomomys talpoides incensus, p. 398.
Thomomys talpoides medius, p. 399.
Ursus atnarko, p. 87.
Ursus (Euarctos) carlottae, p. 86.
Ursus chelidonias, p. 88.
Ursus crassodon, p. 88.
Ursus hoots, p. 90.
Ursus kluane impiger, p. 93.
Ursus kwakiutl, p. 93.
Ursus kwakiutl warburtoni, p. 93.
Ursus ophrus, p. 96.
Ursus pervagor, p. 97.
Ursus pulchellus ereunetes, p. 97.
Ursus selkirki, p. 98.
Ursus shoshone canadensis, p. 99.
Ursus stikeenensis, p. 99.
Ursus tahltanicus, p. 99.
Vespertilio subulatus keenii, p. 158.
Vulpes alascensis abietorum, p. 49.
Zapus tenellus, p. 569.

KEEWATIN:
Dicrostonyx richardsoni, p. 264.
Fiber zibethicus hudsonius, p. 300.
Lepus arcticus canus, p. 208.
Lutreola vison lacustris, p. 74.
Microtus aphorodemus, p. 270.

LABRADOR:
Hesperomys arcticus, p. 312.
Hesperomys bairdii, p. 314.

MACKENZIE:
Evotomys gapperi athabascae, p. 261.
Lepus americanus macfarlani, p. 208.
Lutra canadensis preblei, p. 65.
Microtus macfarlani, p. 276.
Phenacomys mackenzii, p. 338.
Sorex sphagnicola, p. 194.
Synaptomys (Mictomys) bullatus, p. 354.
Tamias asiaticus borealis (lectotype), p. 523.
Tamiasciurus hudsonicus preblei, p. 561.
Ursus macfarlani, p. 94.
Vetularctos inopinatus, p. 92.

MANITOBA:
Sorex (Microsorex) alnorum, p. 179.

NOVA SCOTIA:
Sorex fumeus umbrosus, p. 186.
Vespertilio gryphus var. septentrionalis (lectotype), p. 152.

ONTARIO:
Lutra destructor (lectotype), p. 65.

CANADA—continued

QUEBEC:

    Canis lupus labradorius, p. 43.

    Evotomys ungava, p. 263.

    Lepus labradorius (cotypes), p. 212.

    Microtus pennsylvanicus labradorius, p. 281.

    Mictomys innuitus, p. 355.

    Myotis quebecensis, p. 148.

    Peromyscus maniculatus eremus, p. 325.

    Phenacomys celatus, p. 337.

    Phenacomys latimanus, p. 337.

    Phenacomys ungava, p. 338.

    Vulpes lagopus ungava, p. 40.

SASKATCHEWAN:

    Mustela americana abieticola, p. 66.

    Zapus princeps minor, p. 568.

YUKON:

    Eutamias caniceps, p. 525.

    Fiber spatulatus, p. 300.

    Lepus saliens, p. 214.

    Sciuropterus yukonensis, p. 536.

    Ursus crassus, p. 88.

    Ursus kluane, p. 93.

    Ursus oribasus, p. 96.

    Ursus pallasi, p. 96.

    Ursus pellyensis, p. 96.

    Ursus pulchellus, p. 97.

    Ursus rungiusi sagittalis, p. 98.

CENTRAL AMERICA

COSTA RICA:

    Bassaricyon gabbii, p. 79.

    Carollia castanea, p. 128.

    Cryptotis gracilis, p. 176.

    Dasyprocta punctata underwoodi, p. 359.

    Felis centralis, p. 54.

    Felis costaricensis, p. 55.

    Lepus brasiliensis gabbi (cotypes), p. 218.

    Heteromys desmarestianus planifrons, p. 416.

    Heteromys desmarestianus subaffinis, p. 417.

    Macrogeomys costaricensis, p. 372.

    Macrogeomys dolichocephalus, p. 372.

    Marmosa zeledoni, p. 231.

    Mazama tema cerasina, p. 18.

    Mustela costaricensis, p. 70.

    Myrmecophaga centralis, p. 571.

    Nyctomys sumichrasti costaricensis, p. 299.

    Odocoileus costaricensis, p. 20.

    Oryzomys talamancae, p. 310.

    Philander centralis, p. 232.

    Potos flavus arborensis, p. 80.

    Procyon lotor crassidens, p. 82.

    Proechimys rubellus, p. 363.

    Sciurus thomasi, p. 559.

CENTRAL AMERICA—continued

COSTA RICA—Continued.
    Sturnirops mordax, p. 136.
    Tayassu albirostris spiradens, p. 30.
GUATEMALA:
    Cryptotis goodwini, p. 176.
    Elasmognathus dowii, p. 233.
    Felis concolor mayensis, p. 54.
    Microtus guatemalensis, p. 274.
    Neotoma ferruginea solitaria, p. 287.
    Orthogeomys grandis vulcani, p. 373.
    Orthogeomys latifrons, p. 373.
    Oryzomys angusticeps, p. 305.
    Oryzomys rhabdops, p. 309.
    Oryzomys zygomaticus, p. 311.
    Peromyscus altilaneus, p. 312.
    Peromyscus guatemalensis, p. 322.
    Peromyscus lophurus, p. 323.
    Peromyscus mexicanus saxatillis, p. 329.
    Reithrodontomys dorsalis, p. 342.
    Reithrodontomys microdon, p. 348.
    Reithrodontomys tenuirostris, p. 349.
    Reithrodontomys tenuirostris aureus, p. 349.
    Sciurus boothiae managuensis, p. 553.
    Sorex godmani, p. 186.
    Sorex salvini, p. 193.
    Trachops coffini, p. 136.
    Urocyon guatemalae, p. 48.
HONDURAS:
    Baiomys musculus grisescens, p. 259.
    Canis hondurensis, p. 42.
    Cebus capucinus limitaneus, p. 237.
    Ectophylla alba, p. 129.
    Liomys heterothrix, p. 419.
    Marmosa ruatanica, p. 231.
    Pecari angulatus nigrescens, p. 29.
    Reithrodontomys mexicanus lucifrons, p. 347.
    Reithrodontomys mexicanus minusculus, p. 347.
    Sciurus boothiae underwoodi, p. 553.
    Sitomys (Rhipidomys) decolorus, p. 299.
    Sylvilagus floridanus hondurensis, p. 219.
    Tatoua (Ziphila) centralis, p. 569.
HONDURAS, off coast of, Caribbean Sea, Little Swan Island:
    Capromys brachyurus thoracatus, p. 360.
NICARAGUA:
    Cariacus clavatus, p. 19.
    Dasyprocta punctata richmondi, p. 358.
    Didelphis richmondi, p. 229.
    Micronycteris microtis, p. 133.
    Nasua narica richmondi, p. 80.
    Nyctomys sumichrasti venustulus, p. 299.
    Oryzomys richmondi, p. 309.
    Sciurus boothiae belti, p. 553.
    Sciurus richmondi, p. 558.

CENTRAL AMERICA—continued

NICARAGUA, off coast of, Caribbean Sea, Old Providence Island:
Natalus (Chilonatalus) brevimanus, p. 124.

PANAMA:
Alouatta palliata inconsonans, p. 235.
Aotus zonalis, p. 236.
Ateles dariensis, p. 236.
Bassaricyon gabbi orinomus, p. 79.
Bradypus ignavus, p. 569.
Chiroderma isthmicum, p. 129.
Chironectes panamensis, p. 228.
Cryptotis merus, p. 177.
Dasyprocta punctata dariensis, p. 358.
Elasmognathus bairdii, p. 233.
Euprocyon cancrivorus panamensis, p. 81.
Felis pirrensis, p. 59.
Heteromys australis conscius, p. 416.
Heteromys crassirostris, p. 416.
Heteromys panamensis, p. 417.
Heteromys zonalis, p. 418.
Hoplomys goethalsi, p. 362.
Hydrochoerus isthmius, p. 438.
Icticyon panamensis, p. 46.
Isothrix darlingi, p. 361.
Lonchophylla concava, p. 132.
Lonchophylla robusta, p. 132.
Lutra repanda, p. 66.
Macrogeomys dariensis, p. 372.
Marmosa invicta, p. 230.
Marmosa isthmica, p. 230.
Mazama tema reperticia, p. 18.
Metachirus nudicaudatus dentaneus, p. 232.
Microsciurus alfari venustulus, p. 541.
Microsciurus isthmius vivatus, p. 542.
Mustela frenata panamensis, p. 71.
Neacomys pictus, p. 283.
Nectomys alfari efficax, p. 284.
Oryzomys alfaroi dariensis, p. 305.
Oryzomys bombycinus, p. 305.
Oryzomys frontalis, p. 306.
Oryzomys gatunensis, p. 307.
Oryzomys idoneus, p. 308.
Oryzomys pirrensis, p. 309.
Pecari angulatus bangsi, p. 28.
Peramys melanops, p. 232.
Peromyscus pirrensis, p. 330.
Potos flavus isthmicus, p. 81.
Procyon pumilus, p. 85.
Rheomys raptor, p. 349.
Rhipidomys scandens, p. 350.
Sciurus variabilis choco, p. 559.
Sciurus variegatoides helveolus, p. 559.
Sylvilagus gabbi messorius, p. 220.

CENTRAL AMERICA—continued

PANAMA—Continued.

Uroderma convexum, p. 136.
Vampyressa minuta, p. 136.
Vespertilio exiguus, p. 572.
Zygodontomys cherriei ventriosus, p. 358.

MEXICO

AGUAS CALIENTES:

Dipodomys spectabilis cratodon, p. 415.

CAMPECHE:

Dasyprocta punctata yucatanica, p. 359.
Felis hernandesii goldmani, p. 56.
Heterogeomys hispidus yucatanensis, p. 371.
Jentinkia sumichrasti campechensis, p. 40.
Oryzomys fulvescens mayensis, p. 307.
Ototylomys phyllotis phaeus, p. 311.
Peromyscus texanus castaneus, p. 334.
Peromyscus yucatanicus badius, p. 336.
Potos flavus campechensis, p. 80.
Procyon lotor shufeldti, p. 83.
Sciurus deppei vivax, p. 555.
Sciurus yucatanensis baliolus, p. 559.
Tayassu albirostris ringens, p. 30.

CHIAPAS:

Canis goldmani, p. 42.
Cryptotis griseoventris, p. 176.
Dasyprocta punctata chiapensis, p. 358.
Heterogeomys hispidus chiapensis, p. 371.
Heteromys goldmani, p. 417.
Heteromys griseus, p. 417.
Heteromys (Xylomys) nelsoni, p. 417.
Lepus floridanus chiapensis, p. 219.
Liomys crispus, p. 418.
Liomys crispus setosus, p. 419.
Myotis nigricans extremus, p. 155.
Neotoma ferruginea chamula, p. 287.
Odocoileus nelsoni, p. 21.
Odocoileus thomasi, p. 22.
Orthogeomys grandis annexus, p. 372.
Oryzomys chapmani saturatior, p. 306.
Oryzomys hylocetes, p. 307.
Pecari angulatus nelsoni, p. 29.
Peromyscus allophylus, p. 312.
Peromyscus musculus nigrescens, p. 259.
Peromyscus zarhynchus, p. 336.
Peromyscus zarhynchus cristobalensis, p. 336.
Putorius frenatus goldmani, p. 71.
Reithrodontomys fulvescens chiapensis, p. 343.
Sciuropterus volans goldmani, p. 535.
Sciurus goldmani, p. 556.
Sciurus griseoflavus chiapensis, p. 556.
Scotinomys teguina subnubilis, p. 350.

CHIAPAS—Continued.

Sigmodon hispidus tonalensis, p. 352.
Sorex saussurei cristobalensis, p. 193.
Sorex sclateri, p. 194.
Sorex stizodon, p. 194.
Sorex veraepacis chiapensis, p. 197.
Spilogale angustifrons elata, p. 76.
Tadarida intermedia, p. 124.
Tylomys bullaris, p. 357.
Tylomys tumbalensis, p. 357.

CHIHUAHUA:

Antilocapra americana mexicana, p. 6.
Callospermophilus madrensis, p. 513.
Canis nubilus baileyi, p. 44.
Corynorhinus megalotis mexicanus, p. 146.
Cratogeomys castanops consitus, p. 364.
Dipodomys spectabilis zygomaticus, p. 415.
Felis hippolestes aztecus, p. 56.
Geomys clarkii, p. 366.
Glaucomys volans madrensis, p. 535.
Liomys canus, p. 418.
Microtus mexicanus madrensis, p. 277.
Neotoma mexicana, p. 293.
Neotoma mexicana madrensis, p. 293.
Odocoileus hemionus canus, p. 20.
Onychomys leucogaster albescens, p. 301.
Ovis mexicana, p. 12.
Perognathus apache melanotis, p. 424.
Perognathus artus, p. 425.
Peromyscus melanotis zamelas, p. 328.
Peromyscus polius, p. 331.
Peromyscus sonoriensis blandus, p. 332.
Reithrodon megalotis, p. 345.
Reithrodontomys megalotis obscurus, p. 346.
Spilogale ambigua, p. 75.
Thomomys nelsoni, p. 393.
Thomomys umbrinus caliginosus, p. 400.
Thomomys umbrinus chihuahuae, p. 401.
Thomomys umbrinus madrensis, p. 402.
Ursus nelsoni, p. 95.

COAHUILA:

Canis torquatus, p. 576.
Citellus spilosoma pallescens, p. 518.
Conepatus pediculus, p. 62.
Cratogeomys castanops convexus, p. 365.
Cratogeomys castanops excelsus, p. 365.
Cratogeomys castanops subnubilus, p. 366.
Cratogeomys castanops subsimus, p. 366.
Cynomys mexicanus, p. 522.
Dipodomys nelsoni, p. 411.
Eutamias bulleri solivagus, p. 524.
Eutamias dorsalis carminis, p. 526.
Microtus mexicanus subsimus, p. 277.

MEXICO—continued

COAHUILA—Continued.

Neotoma goldmani, p. 287.
Neotoma mexicana inornata, p. 293.
Neotoma navus, p. 295.
Odocoileus virginianus carminis, p. 22.
Perognathus (Chaetodipus) intermedius canescens, p. 430.
Sigmodon berlandieri, p. 351.
Thomomys sturgisi, p. 397.
Thomomys umbrinus analogus, p. 400.
Ursus americanus eremicus, p. 86.

COLIMA:

Canis vigilis, p. 45.
Conepatus mesoleucus nelsoni, p. 62.
Felis pardalis nelsoni, p. 59.
Geomys fumosus, p. 375.
Nasua narica molaris, p. 80.
Neotoma alleni, p. 266.
Oryzomys melanotis colimensis, p. 308.
Peromyscus allex, p. 258.
Reithrodontomys fulvescens nelsoni, p. 343.
Sciurus albipes colimensis, p. 552.
Sciurus colliaei nuchalis, p. 555.
Sitomys musculus, p. 258.
Tayassu angulatus humeralis, p. 29.
Urocyon cinereoargenteus colimensis, p. 48.
Xenomys nelsoni, p. 357.

DURANGO:

Peromyscus attwateri eremicoides, p. 313.
Peromyscus xenurus, p. 336.
Sorex durangae, p. 185.
Thomomys goldmani, p. 390.
Thomomys simulus parviceps, p. 397.
Thomomys umbrinus durangi, p. 401.

FEDERAL DISTRICT:

Blarina soricina, p. 179.
Oryzomys crinitus, p. 306.
Perognathus flavus mexicanus, p. 428.
Peromyscus gratus, p. 321.
Reithrodontomys levipes toltecus, p. 345.
Spilogale angustifrons, p. 76.

GUANAJUATO:

Cryptotis pergracilis macer, p. 178.
Thomomys umbrinus supernus, p. 403.

GUERRERO:

Blarina mexicana goldmani, p. 177.
Cryptotis guerrerensis, p. 176.
Hodomys alleni guerrerensis, p. 266.
Lepus insonus, p. 221.
Lepus veraecrucis pacificus, p. 223.
Liomys guerrerensis, p. 419.
Liomys pictus rostratus, p. 420.
Neotoma picta, p. 296.
Noctilio leporinus mexicanus, p. 126.

MEXICO—continued

GUERRERO—Continued.
Orthogeomys grandis alleni, p. 372.
Orthogeomys grandis guerrerensis, p. 373.
Oryzomys guerrerensis, p. 307.
Peromyscus comptus, p. 316.
Peromyscus (Megadontomys) thomasi, p. 334.
Potos flavus guerrerensis, p. 80.
Sciurus albipes effugius, p. 552.
Sciurus socialis cocos, p. 558.
Sigmodon guerrerensis, p. 351.
Spilogale pygmaea australis, p. 77.
Sturnira lilium parvidens, p. 135.

HIDALGO:
Blarina obscura, p. 178.
Cratogeomys merriami irolonis, p. 367.
Lepus festinus, p. 211.
Neotoma montezumae, p. 294.
Platygeomys tylorhinus, p. 376.
Thomomys umbrinus albigularis, p. 400.

JALISCO:
Arvicola phaeus, p. 281.
Geomys gymnurus, p. 375.
Geomys nelsoni, p. 375.
Liomys plantinarensis, p. 420.
Micronycteris megalotis mexicanus, p. 133.
Neotoma ferruginea ochracea, p. 287.
Neotoma palatina, p. 296.
Neotoma tenuicauda, p. 298.
Notiosorex gigas, p. 181.
Oryzomys albiventer, p. 304.
Pappogeomys albinasus, p. 374.
Pappogeomys bulleri amecensis, p. 374.
Pappogeomys bulleri lagunensis, p. 374.
Pappogeomys bulleri flammeus, p. 374.
Peromyscus gratus gentilis, p. 321.
Pipistrellus hesperus australis, p. 161.
Platygeomys gymnurus inclarus, p. 375.
Platygeomys zinseri, p. 376.
Reithrodontomys colimae, p. 341.
Reithrodontomys colimae nerterus, p. 342.
Reithrodontomys griseoflavus, p. 343.
Reithrodontomys hirsutus, p. 344.
Reithrodontomys levipes, p. 344.
Reithrodontomys levipes otus, p. 345.
Sigmodon alleni, p. 350.
Sorex emarginatus, p. 185.
Sorex oreopolus, p. 191.
Sorex saussurei, p. 193.
Sylvilagus floridanus restrictus, p. 219.

LOWER CALIFORNIA:
Ammospermophilus leucurus extimus, p. 512.
Ammospermophilus leucurus insularis, p. 512.
Antilocapra americana peninsularis, p. 6.

LOWER CALIFORNIA—Continued.

Antrozous minor, p. 145.

Arctocephalus townsendi, p. 234.

Bassariscus astutus insulicola, p. 39.

Bassariscus astutus palmarius, p. 39.

Bassariscus saxicola, p. 39.

Canis peninsulae, p. 45.

Dipodomys insularis, p. 407.

Dipodomys margaritae, p. 407.

Dipodomys platycephalus, p. 414.

Eutamias merriami meridionalis, p. 527.

Lepus californicus magdalenae, p. 210.

Macrorhinus angustirostris (lectotype), p. 234.

Myotis capitaneus, p. 151.

Myotis micronyx, p. 155.

Natalus mexicanus, p. 125.

Neotoma bryanti, p. 286.

Neotoma insularis, p. 289.

Neotoma intermedia notia, p. 290.

Neotoma intermedia perpallida, p. 290.

Neotoma intermedia pretiosa, p. 290.

Neotoma intermedia ravida, p. 290.

Neotoma intermedia vicina, p. 290.

Neotoma martinensis, p. 293.

Neotoma nudicauda, p. 295.

Odocoileus cerrosensis, p. 19.

Ovis canadensis weemsi, p. 11.

Perodipus simulans peninsularis, p. 414.

Perognathus anthonyi, p. 423.

Perognathus arenarius ambiguus, p. 424.

Perognathus arenarius sublucidus, p. 424.

Perognathus baileyi extimus, p. 425.

Perognathus fallax inopinus, p. 427.

Perognathus penicillatus albulus, p. 435.

Perognathus penicillatus ammophilus, p. 435.

Perognathus penicillatus siccus, p. 436.

Perognathus spinatus magdalenae, p. 437.

Perognathus spinatus nelsoni, p. 437.

Peromyscus eremicus avius, p. 318.

Peromyscus eremicus carmeni, p. 318.

Peromyscus eremicus insulicola, p. 318.

Peromyscus eremicus polypolius, p. 319.

Peromyscus guardia, p. 321.

Peromyscus maniculatus assimilis, p. 324.

Peromyscus maniculatus dorsalis, p. 324.

Peromyscus maniculatus magdalenae, p. 326.

Peromyscus maniculatus margaritae, p. 326.

Peromyscus maniculatus martinensis, p. 326.

Peromyscus stephani, p. 333.

Peromyscus texanus medius, p. 334.

Peromyscus truei lagunae, p. 335.

MEXICO—continued

LOWER CALIFORNIA—Continued.
Phoca richardii geronimensis, p. 235.
Procyon lotor grinnelli, p. 82.
Sciurus hudsonius mearnsi, p. 561.
Sorex californicus juncensis, p. 184.
Sorex lagunae, p. 187.
Spilogale lucasana, p. 77.
Spilogale microdon, p. 77.
Sylvilagus bachmani exiguus, p. 217.
Sylvilagus mansuetus, p. 221.
Tamias obscurus, p. 529.
Thomomys bottae imitabilis, p. 380.
Thomomys bottae incomptus, p. 380.
Thomomys bottae russeolus, p. 382.
Thomomys magdalenae, p. 392.
Vespertilio obscurus, p. 156.
Vespertilio oregonensis (cotype), p. 157.
Vespertilio tenuidorsalis, p. 573.
Vespertilio volans p. 158.
Vulpes macrotis devius, p. 50.
Vulpes macrotis tenuirostris, p. 51.

LOWER CALIFORNIA, Pacific coast, alt. 31° N.:
Globiocephalus scammonii, p. 109.

MEXICO, State of:
Blarina alticola, p. 175.
Cratogeomys oreocetes, p. 368.
Cratogeomys peregrinus, p. 368.
Neotoma fulviventer, p. 288.
Platygeomys planiceps, p. 376.
Reithrodontomys chrysopsis, p. 341.
Reithrodontomys chrysopsis tolucae, p. 345.
Romerolagus nelsoni, p. 215.
Sciurus oculatus tolucae, p. 557.
Thomomys peregrinus, p. 395.
Thomomys umbrinus tolucae, p. 403.
Thomomys umbrinus vulcanius, p. 403.

MICHOACAN:
Artibeus hirsutus, p. 127.
Bassariscus astutus consitus, p. 38.
Citellus adocetus, p. 504.
Lepus floridanus subcinctus, p. 220.
Liomys parviceps, p. 420.
Myotis yumanensis lutosus, p. 158.
Nelsonia goldmani, p. 284.
Neotoma latifrons, p. 291.
Neotomodon alstoni, p. 298.
Oryzomys couesi regillus, p. 306.
Oryzomys fulvescens lenis, p. 307.
Peromyscus banderanus vicinior, p. 314.
Peromyscus hylocetes, p. 322.
Peromyscus melanophrys zamorae, p. 328.
Peromyscus taylori analogus, p. 259.
Peromyscus zelotes, p. 336.

MICHOACAN—Continued.

Platygeomys gymnurus imparilis, p. 375.
Platygeomys tylorhinus angustirostris, p. 376.
Platygeomys varius, p. 376.
Putorius frenatus leucoparia, p. 71.
Sciurus albipes nemoralis, p. 552.
Sciurus poliopus senex, p. 558.
Sigmodon melanotis, p. 353.
Zygogeomys trichopus, p. 403.
Zygogeomys trichopus tarascensis, p. 404.

MORELOS:

Artibeus aztecus, p. 126.
Oryzomys crinitus aztecus, p. 306.
Sciurus nelsoni, p. 557.

NAYARIT:

Chilonycteris mexicana, p. 129.
Cryptotis pergracilis nayaritensis, p. 179.
Molossus nigricans, p. 121.
Oryzomys rufus, p. 310.
Pappogeomys bulleri nayaritensis, p. 374.
Peromyscus spicilegus simulus, p. 332.
Spermophilus annulatus goldmani, p. 504.
Thomomys sheldoni, p. 396.
Thomomys umbrinus extimus, p. 402.
Thomomys umbrinus musculus, p. 402.

NAYARIT, Tres Marias Islands:

Glossophaga mutica, p. 130.
Lepus graysoni, p. 221.
Marmosa insularis, p. 229.
Oryzomys nelsoni, p. 309.
Peromyscus madrensis, p. 324.
Procyon insularis vicinus, p. 81.
Procyon lotor insularis, p. 83.
Rhogeëssa parvula, p. 571.

NUEVO LEON:

Sciurus alleni, p. 552.
Spermophilus couchi, p. 508.
Thomomys perditus, p. 395.

OAXACA:

Ateles tricolor, p. 237.
Blarina fossor, p. 176.
Blarina magna, p. 177.
Blarina mexicana machetes, p. 178.
Blarina mexicana peregrina, p. 178.
Conepatus filipensis, p. 61.
Cryptotis frontalis, p. 176.
Cyclopes mexicanus, p. 570.
Felis glaucula oaxacensis, p. 55.
Hemiderma subrufum, p. 128.
Hesperomys (Vesperimus) affinis, p. 311.
Hesperomys (Vesperimus) melanophrys, p. 327
Heterogeomys hispidus tehuantepecus, p. 371
Heteromys annectens, p. 418.

MEXICO—continued

OAXACA—Continued.
Heteromys goldmani lepturus, p. 417.
Liomys phaeura, p. 420.
Liomys pictus isthmius, p. 420.
Liomys torridus, p. 421.
Liomys torridus minor, p. 421.
Marmosa murina mexicana, p. 230.
Marmosa oaxacae, p. 230.
Microtus fulviventer, p. 274.
Microtus umbrosus, p. 282.
Neotoma isthmica, p. 291.
Neotoma parvidens, p. 296.
Neotoma tropicalis, p. 298.
Nyctomys sumichrasti pallidulus, p. 299.
Odocoileus virginianus oaxacensis, p. 23.
Orthogeomys grandis felipensis, p. 373.
Orthogeomys nelsoni, p. 373.
Oryzomys chapmani caudatus, p. 305.
Peromyscus amplus, p. 312.
Peromyscus auritus, p. 313.
Peromyscus banderanus angelensis, p. 314.
Peromyscus felipensis, p. 319.
Peromyscus lepturus, p. 322.
Peromyscus megalops, p. 327.
Peromyscus megalops melanurus, p. 327.
Peromyscus melanocarpus, p. 327.
Peromyscus mexicanus totontepecus, p. 329.
Peromyscus musculoides, p. 329.
Peromyscus oaxacensis, p. 330.
Peromyscus sonoriensis fulvus, p. 332.
Peromyscus spicilegus evides, p. 332.
Peromyscus tehuantepecus, p. 333.
Reithrodontomys alleni, p. 341.
Reithrodontomys fulvescens mustelinus, p. 343.
Reithrodontomys griseoflavus helvolus, p. 344.
Reithrodontomys microdon albilabris, p. 348.
Reithrodontomys rufescens luteolus, p. 349.
Reithrodontomys saturatus alticolus, p. 349.
Sciurus albipes quercinus, p. 552.
Sciurus socialis littoralis, p. 558.
Sigmodon alticola, p. 350.
Sigmodon planifrons, p. 353.
Sorex obscurus ventralis, p. 190.
Sorex saussurei caudatus, p. 193.
Sorex saussurei oaxacae, p. 193.
Spilogale angustifrons tropicalis, p. 76.
PUEBLA:
Cratogeomys fulvescens, p. 367.
Cratogeomys merriami saccharalis, p. 367.
Cryptotis pergracilis pueblensis, p. 179.
Hodomys vetulus, p. 266.
Lepus orizabae, p. 221.
Liomys irroratus pretiosus, p. 419.

MEXICO—continued

PUEBLA—Continued.

Neotoma orizabae, p. 296.
Neotomodon orizabae, p. 298.
Oryzomys chapmani dilutior, p. 305.
Oryzomys rostratus, p. 310.
Peromyscus mekisturus, p. 327.
Reithrodontomys goldmani, p. 343.
Reithrodontomys orizabae, p. 348.
Reithrodontomys saturatus cinereus, p. 349.
Rhogeëssa gracilis, p. 162.
Sciurus nelsoni hirtus, p. 557.
Sciurus poliopus perigrinator, p. 558.
Sorex orizabae, p. 191.
Tayassu angulatus crassus, p. 28.
Thomomys orizabae, p. 394.
Thomomys umbrinus martinensis, p. 402.

QUERETARO:

Heterogeomys hispidus concavus, p. 371.
Peromyscus attwateri pectoralis, p. 313.
Platygeomys neglectus, p. 376.
Reithrodontomys amoles, p. 341.
Sigmodon alticola amoles, p. 350.

QUINTANA ROO, COZUMEL ISLAND:

Didelphis yucatanensis cozumelae, p. 229.
Mimon cozumelae, p. 133.
Nasua nelsoni, p. 80.
Oryzomys cozumelae, p. 306.
Peromyscus cozumelae, p. 316.
Procyon pygmaeus, p. 85.
Tayassu nanus, p. 30.

SAN LUIS POTOSI:

Cratogeomys castanops peridoneus, p. 365.
Dipodomys merriami atronasus, p. 408.
Lepus asellus, p. 209.
Neotoma leucodon, p. 291.
Neotoma micropus planiceps, p. 294.
Oryzomys mexicanus peragrus, p. 308.
Perognathus (Chaetodipus) nelsoni, p. 432.
Peromyscus eremicus phaeurus, p. 319.
Thomomys umbrinus potosinus, p. 402.

SINALOA:

Kogia floweri, p. 114.
Lepus arizonae goldmani, p. 215.
Perognathus goldmani, p. 429.
Sigmodon hispidus major, p. 352.
Sorex (Notiosorex) evotis, p. 181.
Thomomys sinaloae, p. 397.
Thomomys umbrinus eximius, p. 401.

SONORA:

Canis jamesi, p. 42.
Castor canadensis frondator, p. 254.
Conepatus sonoriensis, p. 63.
Dicotyles angulatus sonoriensis, p. 29.

SONORA—Continued.

Dipodomys deserti sonoriensis, p. 406.
Dipodomys merriami mayensis, p. 408.
Dipodomys mitchelli, p. 411.
Dorcelaphus hemionus eremicus, p. 21.
Felis pardalis sonoriensis, p. 59.
Hesperomys sonoriensis, p. 331.
Lepus alleni tiburonensis, p. 208.
Liomys sonorana, p. 420.
Neotoma albigula seri, p. 285.
Neotoma albigula sheldoni, p. 285.
Neotoma intermedia melanura, p. 289.
Odocoileus hemionus sheldoni, p. 21.
Onychomys torridus yakiensis, p. 304.
Ovis sheldoni, p. 13.
Perognathus baileyi, p. 425.
Perognathus baileyi insularis, p. 425.
Perognathus flavus sonoriensis, p. 429.
Perognathus penicillatus goldmani, p. 436.
Perognathus pernix rostratus, p. 436.
Peromyscus eremicus papagensis, p. 318.
Peromyscus goldmani, p. 320.
Peromyscus merriami, p. 328.
Peromyscus tiburonensis, p. 335.
Procyon hernandezii var. mexicana, p. 81.
Procyon lotor ochraceus, p. 83.
Reithrodon megalotis, p. 345.
Sciurus truei, p. 559.
Sigmodon hispidus eremicus, p. 351.
Taxidea taxus sonoriensis, p. 78.
Teanopus phenax, p. 356.
Thomomys bottae convergens, p. 379.
Thomomys bottae divergens, p. 379.
Thomomys bottae winthropi, p. 382.
Thomomys simulus, p. 397.
Thomomys umbrinus sonoriensis, p. 403.
Ursus kennerleyi, p. 92.

TABASCO:

Didelphis marsupialis tabascensis, p. 228.
Heterogeomys hispidus teapensis, p. 371.
Oryzomys palatinus, p. 309.
Oryzomys rostratus megadon, p. 310.
Oryzomys teapensis, p. 310.
Peromyscus mexicanus teapensis, p. 329.
Pipistrellus cinnamomeus, p. 160.
Putorius tropicalis perdus, p. 74.
Sigmodon hispidus saturatus, p. 352.

TAMAULIPAS:

Blarina berlandieri, (lectotype), p. 175.
Canis microdon, p. 44.
Cratogeomys castanops planifrons, p. 366.
Cratogeomys castanops tamaulipensis, p. 366.
Felis apache, p. 53.

MEXICO—continued

TAMAULIPAS—Continued.

    Felis cacomitli, p. 53.
    Geomys personatus tropicalis, p. 370.
    Lasiurus intermedius, p. 571.
    Lepus merriami altamirae, p. 212.
    Neotoma micropus, p. 294.
    Neotoma micropus littoralis, p. 294.
    Odocoileus virginianus miquihuanensis, p. 23.
    Onychomys torridus surrufus, p. 304.
    Perognathus hispidus, p. 430.
    Scalopus inflatus, p. 200.
    Sciurus negligens, p. 557.

TLAXCALA:

    Peromyscus levipes, p. 323.

VERACRUZ:

    Agouti paca nelsoni, p. 358.
    Alouatta palliata mexicana, p. 236.
    Arvicola (Pitymys) pinetorum quasiater, p. 573.
    Blarina (Soriciscus) mexicana, p. 177.
    Blarina nelsoni, p. 178.
    Centurio mcmurtrii, p. 128.
    Conepatus tropicalis, p. 63.
    Cratogeomys estor, p. 367.
    Cratogeomys fulvescens subluteus, p. 367.
    Cratogeomys perotensis, p. 368.
    Dipodomys perotensis, p. 413.
    Felis onca veraecrucis, p. 58.
    Glaucomys volans herreranus, p. 535.
    Heterogeomys hispidus isthmicus, p. 371.
    Heterogeomys torridus, p. 372.
    Heteromys temporalis, p. 418.
    Lepus floridanus connectens, p. 219.
    Lepus truei, p. 223.
    Liomys obscurus, p. 419.
    Liomys orbitalis, p. 419.
    Liomys veraecrucis, p. 421.
    Metachirus fuscogriseus pallidus, p. 231.
    Mustela frenata perotae, p. 71.
    Myotis longicrus amotus, p. 153.
    Neotoma nelsoni, p. 295.
    Neotomodon perotensis, p. 299.
    Odocoileus virginianus veraecrucis, p. 24.
    Oryzomys goldmani, p. 307.
    Oryzomys jalapae rufinus, p. 308.
    Peromyscus bullatus, p. 315.
    Peromyscus mexicanus orizabae, p. 328.
    Peromyscus (Megadontomys) nelsoni, p. 329.
    Peromyscus simulatus, p. 331.
    Peromyscus texanus mesomelas, p. 334.
    Putorius tropicalis, p. 74.
    Reithrodontomys costaricensis jalapae, p. 342.
    Reithrodontomys difficilis, p. 342.

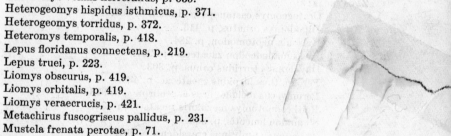

MEXICO—continued

Veracruz—Continued.

Reithrodontomys perotensis, p. 348.
Rhogeëssa tumida, p. 162.
Sciurus aureogaster frumentor, p. 553.
Scotophilus miradorensis, p. 572.
Sorex macrodon, p. 188.
Sorex saussurei veraecrucis, p. 194.
Spermophilus perotensis, p. 517.
Urocyon cinereoargenteus orinomus, p. 48.
Vampyrus spectrum nelsoni, p. 137.
Vespertilio agilis, p. 572.

Yucatan:

Blarina mayensis, p. 177.
Dermanura phaeotis, p. 127.
Didelphis yucatanensis, p. 229.
Felis fossata, p. 55.
Felis glaucula yucatanica, p. 55.
Galictis canaster, p. 63.
Lepus floridanus yucatanicus, p. 220.
Mazama pandora, p. 18.
Nyctinomops yucatanicus, p. 124.
Oryzomys yucatanensis, p. 311.
Ototylomys phyllotis, p. 311.
Sciurus carolinensis yucatanensis (cotype), p. 554.
Sigmodon hispidus microdon, p. 352.
Tayassu angulatus yucatanensis, p. 29.
Urocyon parvidens, p. 49.

Zacatecas:

Cratogeomys castanops goldmani, p. 365.
Dipodomys ornatus, p. 413.
Nelsonia neotomodon, p. 284.
Neotoma leucodon zacatecae, p. 291.
Onychomys torridus canus, p. 303.
Perognathus hispidus zacatecae, p. 430.
Peromyscus melanophrys consobrinus, p. 328.
Reithrodontomys megalotis zacatecae, p. 347.
Sigmodon leucotis, p. 353.
Thomomys umbrinus crassidens, p. 401.
Thomomys umbrinus enixus, p. 401.
Thomomys umbrinus zacatecae, p. 403.

SOUTH AMERICA

Argentina:

Akodon chacoensis, p. 256.
Ctenomys robustus, p. 361.
Ctenomys sericeus, p. 361.
Euneomys petersoni, p. 265.
Felis notialis, p. 57.
Felis puma patagonica, p. 59.
Lagostomus maximus petilidens, p. 256.
Marmosa muscula, p. 230.
Myocastor coypus santacruzae, p. 490.

SOUTH AMERICA—continued

ARGENTINA—Continued.
> Notiomys vestitus alleni, p. 259.
> Oxymycterus microtis, p. 265.
> Reithrodon hatcheri, p. 340.

ARGENTINA, off coast of Patagonia:
> Phocaena australis, p. 576.

BRAZIL:
> Eumops hansae, p. 121.
> Felis concolor greeni, p. 54.
> Felis onca coxi, p. 58.
> Felis onca paulensis, p. 58.
> Lichonycteris degener, p. 132.
> Marmosa purui, p. 231.
> Nyctinomus europs (lectotype), p. 123.
> Proechimys steerei, p. 363.
> Promops pamana, p. 122.
> Vampyrops fumosus, p. 137.

BRAZIL, off coast of:
> Dysopes aurispinosus, p. 122.

CHILE, off coast of:
> Delphinus albimanus, p. 108.

COLOMBIA:
> Sciurus (Microsciurus) isthmius, p. 541.
> Sturnira lilium bogotensis, p. 135.

CURAÇAO, off northern coast of Venezuela:
> Glossophaga elongata, p. 130.
> Leptonycteris curasoae, p. 131.
> Molossus pygmaeus, p. 122.
> Mormoops intermedia, p. 134.
> Myotis nesopolus, p. 155.
> Natalus tumidirostris, p. 126.

ECUADOR:
> Dermanura rava, p. 127.
> Felis aequatorialis, p. 53.

MARGARITA ISLAND, off northern cost of Venezuela:
> Cebus margaritae, p. 237.
> Lepus margaritae, p. 221.
> Rhogeëssa minutilla, p. 162.

PARAGUAY:
> Felis paraguensis, p. 58.
> Glossophaga soricina microtis, p. 131.
> Hemiderma tricolor, p. 128.
> Hydrochoerus hydrochaeris notialis, p. 437.
> Nectomys squamipes pollens, p. 284.

PERU:
> Akodon surdus, p. 256.
> Chraeomys inornatus, p. 260.
> Felis concolor incarum p. 54.
> Hesperomys frida, p. 266.
> Holochilus incarum, p. 266.
> Marmosa caucae albiventris, p. 229.
> Microxus torques, p. 256.
> Mus peruvianus, p. 574.

PERU—Continued.
>Orolestes inca, p. 228.
Oryzomys (Microryzomys) aurillus, p. 356.
Thomasomys daphne, p. 357.
Thomasomys gracilus, p. 357.
Thomasomys notatus, p. 357.

PERU, off coast of:
Orca destructor, p. 112.

TRINIDAD, off northeastern coast of Venezuela:
Mormoops tumidiceps, p. 135.

VENEZUELA:
Glossophaga villosa, p. 131.
Loncheres flavidus, p. 362.
Lophostoma venezuelae, p. 136.
Marmosa demararae meridae, p. 229.
Molossus pretiosus, p. 121.
Mustela meridana, p. 72.
Oryzomys medius, p. 308.
Proechimys guairae, p. 365.
Thyroptera discifera major, p. 145.
Vespertilio mundus, p. 572.

No EXACT LOCALITY:
Amazon River:
Midas elegantulus, p. 236.

UNITED STATES

ALABAMA:
Geomys tuza mobilensis, p. 370.
Glaucomys volans saturatus, p. 535.
Mustela peninsulae olivacea, p. 73.
Procyon lotor varius, p. 84.
Scalopus aquaticus howelli, p. 200.
Spilogale ringens, p. 77.

ARIZONA:
Ammospermophilus leucurus tersus, p. 513.
Arvicola (Mynomes) alticolus, p. 269.
Bassariscus astutus arizonensis, p. 38.
Callospermophilus lateralis arizonensis, p. 511.
Canis mearnsi, p. 44.
Castor canadensis repentinus, p. 255.
Cervus merriami, p. 17.
Citellus tridecemlineatus monticola, p. 520.
Conepatus mesoleucus venaticus, p. 62.
Corynorhinus macrotis pallescens, p. 146.
Dipodomys merriami regillus, p. 409.
Dipodomys microps celsus, p. 410.
Dipodomys microps leucotis, p. 410.
Dipodomys ordii cleomophila, p. 412.
Dipodomys ordii cupidineus, p. 412.
Dipodomys spectabilis, p. 414.
Dipodomys spectabilis perblandus, p. 415.
Dipodops longipes, p. 407.
Erethizon epixanthum couesi, p. 364.

ARIZONA—Continued.

Eutamias hopiensis, p. 527.

Eutamias minimus arizonensis, p. 528.

Felis aztecus browni, p. 53.

Felis concolor kaibabensis, p. 54.

Felis onca arizonensis, p. 58.

Geomys fulvus, p. 386.

Hesperomys leucopus rufinus, p. 323.

Hesperomys megalotis, p. 327.

Hesperomys (Onychomys) torridus, p. 303.

Lepus arizonae major, p. 216.

Lepus sylvaticus arizonae, p. 222.

Lepus sylvaticus holzneri, p. 222.

Lynx baileyi, p. 60.

Mephitis estor, p. 68.

Mephitis milleri, p. 68.

Microtus longicaudus baileyi, p. 275.

Microtus mexicanus hualpaiensis, p. 276.

Microtus montanus arizonensis, p. 278.

Neotoma albigula mearnsi, p. 285.

Neotoma arizonae, p. 285.

Neotoma intermedia devia, p. 289.

Neotoma lepida monstrabilis, p. 291.

Neotoma mexicana bullata, p. 293.

Neotoma pinetorum, p. 297.

Neotoma stephensi, p. 297.

Neotoma stephensi relicta, p. 297.

Nyctinomus mohavensis, p. 124.

Odocoileus virginianus couesi, p. 22.

Ondatra zibethica bernardi, p. 300.

Onychomys fuliginosus, p. 301.

Onychomys leucogaster capitulatus, p. 302.

Onychomys melanophrys pallescens, p. 303.

Onychomys torridus perpallidus, p. 304.

Ovis canadensis gaillardi, p. 11.

Perognathus amplus, p. 422.

Perognathus amplus jacksoni, p. 422.

Perognathus amplus pergracilis, p. 423.

Perognathus amplus rotundus, p. 423.

Perognathus amplus taylori, p. 423.

Perognathus apache, p. 423.

Perognathus apache cleomophila, p. 424.

Perognathus baileyi domensis, p. 425.

Perognathus bimaculatus, p. 425.

Perognathus bombycinus, p. 426.

Perognathus flavus hopiensis, p. 428.

Perognathus fuliginosus, p. 429.

Perognathus intermedius, p. 430.

Perognathus intermedius phasma, p. 430.

Perognathus longimembris arizonensis, p. 431.

Perognathus penecillatus, p. 435.

Peromyscus crinitus disparilis, p. 317.

Peromyscus crinitus peridoneus, p. 317.

UNITED STATES—continued

ARIZONA—Continued.

Peromyscus leucopus ochraceus, p. 323.
Sciurus arizonensis, p. 553.
Sciurus chiricahuae, p. 555.
Sciurus dorsalis, p. 555.
Sciurus kaibabensis, p. 556.
Sigmodon hispidus confinis, p. 351.
Sigmodon hispidus jacksoni, p. 351.
Sigmodon hispidus plenus, p. 352.
Sorex monticolus, p. 188.
Spermophilus canescens, p. 506.
Spermophilus cryptospilotus, p. 509.
Spermophilus harrisii saxicolus, p. 510.
Spermophilus neglectus, p. 515.
Spermophilus spilosoma macrospilotus, p. 517.
Spermophilus spilosoma obsidianus, p. 518.
Spermophilus spilosoma pratensis, p. 518.
Spilogale gracilis, p. 76.
Tamias cinereicollis, p. 525.
Tamias leucurus cinnamomeus, p. 512.
Thomomys alexandrae, p. 377.
Thomomys bottae alienus, p. 379.
Thomomys bottae desitus, p. 379.
Thomomys bottae extenuatus, p. 380.
Thomomys bottae hualpaiensis, p. 380.
Thomomys bottae nicholi, p. 381.
Thomomys bottae parvulus, p. 381.
Thomomys bottae patulus, p. 382.
Thomomys bottae pinalensis, p. 382.
Thomomys bottae virgineus, p. 382.
Thomomys desertorum, p. 384.
Thomomys fossor kaibabensis, p. 385.
Thomomys fulvus catalinae, p. 386.
Thomomys fulvus collinus, p. 386.
Thomomys fulvus flavidus, p. 387.
Thomomys fulvus grahamensis, p. 387.
Thomomys fulvus intermedius, p. 387.
Thomomys fulvus modicus, p. 387.
Thomomys fulvus mutabilis, p. 387.
Thomomys fulvus peramplus, p. 388.
Thomomys fulvus phasma, p. 388.
Thomomys fulvus pusillus, p. 388.
Thomomys fulvus suboles, p. 388.
Thomomys fulvus subsimilis, p. 388.
Thomomys latirostris, p. 391.
Thomomys muralis, p. 393.
Thomomys perpallidus absonus, p. 395.
Thomomys umbrinus chiricahuae, p. 401.
Ursus apache, p. 87.
Ursus arizonae, p. 87.
Vespertilio macropus, p. 154.
Vespertilio melanorhinus, p. 154.
Vulpes macrotis arizonensis, p. 50.

ARIZONA–NEW MEXICO boundary:
  Ursus navaho, p. 95.
ARKANSAS:
  Scalopus aquaticus pulcher, p. 200.
  Vespertilio affinis, p. 150.
CALIFORNIA:
  Antrozous pallidus pacificus, p. 146.
  Aplodontia major (lectotype), p. 253.
  Aplodontia phaea, p. 254.
  Arvicola californica, p. 272.
  Arvicola edax, p. 273.
  Arvicola longirostris, p. 275.
  Arvicola montana, p. 573.
  Arvicola trowbridgii, p. 282.
  Atalapha teliotis, p. 149.
  Callospermophilus chrysodeirus mitratus, p. 507.
  Callospermophilus chrysodeirus trinitatis, p. 508.
  Castor subauratus shastensis, p. 256.
  Cervus lewisii, p. 574.
  Cervus macrotis californicus, p. 575.
  Cervus nannodes, p. 17.
  Chincha platyrhina, p. 69.
  Citellus beecheyi parvulus, p. 505.
  Citellus beecheyi sierrae, p. 506.
  Delphinus bairdii (cotypes), p. 575.
  Delphinus longidens, p. 113.
  Dipodomys californicus, p. 405.
  Dipodomys deserti, p. 406.
  Dipodomys merriami exilis, p. 408.
  Dipodomys merriami kernensis, p. 408.
  Dipodomys merriami nitratoides, p. 408.
  Dipodomys merriami nitratus, p. 409.
  Eutamias amoenus ochraceus, p. 523.
  Eutamias speciosus inyoensis, p. 532.
  Eutamias speciosus sequoiensis, p. 532.
  Eutamias townsendii alleni, p. 532.
  Eutamias townsendii ochrogenys, p. 533.
  Eutamias townsendii siskiyou, p. 533.
  Evotomys californicus, p. 260.
  Grampus stearnsii, p. 109.
  Hesperomys boylii, p. 315.
  Hesperomys eremicus (cotypes), p. 317.
  Hesperomys gambelii (cotypes), p. 319.
  Hesperomys parasiticus, p. 330.
  Lagomys schisticeps, p. 226.
  Latax lutris nereis, p. 63.
  Lepus audubonii, p. 216.
  Lepus campestris sierrae, p. 210.
  Lepus floridanus sanctidiegi, p. 220.
  Lepus trowbridgii (lectotype), p. 223.
  Lepus tularensis, p. 214.
  Lynx rufus californicus, p. 60.

CALIFORNIA—Continued.

Lynx rufus eremicus, p. 60.
Macrotus californicus, p. 571.
Marmota flaviventris sierrae, p. 540.
Mephitis occidentalis (lectotype), p. 68.
Microdipodops californicus, p. 421.
Microtus angusticeps, p. 270.
Microtus californicus constrictus, p. 272.
Microtus californicus vallicola, p. 272.
Microtus dutcheri, p. 273.
Microtus mordax berdardinus, p. 278.
Microtus oregoni adocetus, p. 280.
Microtus scirpensis, p. 281.
Molossus californicus, p. 120.
Myotis californicus pallidus, p. 151.
Myotis occultus, p. 156.
Myotis thysanodes, p. 158.
Neotoma cumulator, p. 286.
Neotoma desertorum, p. 286.
Neotoma desertorum sola, p. 287.
Neotoma fuscipes, p. 288.
Neotoma fuscipes dispar, p. 288.
Neotoma fuscipes streatori, p. 288.
Neotoma macrotis simplex, p. 292.
Neotoma splendens, p. 297.
Neotoma venusta, p. 298.
Neurotrichus gibbsi major, p. 199.
Nyctinomus femorosaccus, p. 123.
Nyctinomus macrotis nevadensis, p 124.
Odocoileus columbianus scaphiotus, p. 19.
Onychomys torridus clarus, p. 304.
Onychomys torridus tularensis, p. 304.
Otognosis longimembris, p. 431.
Perodipus agilis tularensis, p. 405.
Perodipus cabezonae, p. 405.
Perodipus goldmani, p. 406.
Perodipus ingens, p. 407.
Perodipus microps, p. 409.
Perodipus microps levipes, p. 410.
Perodipus morroensis, p. 411.
Perodipus panamintinus, p. 413.
Perodipus perplexus, p. 414.
Perodipus stephensi, p. 415.
Perodipus streatori, p. 415.
Perodipus streatori simulans, p. 415.
Perodipus venustus, p. 416.
Perognathus armatus, p. 424.
Perognathus californicus, p. 426.
Perognathus californicus dispar, p. 426.
Perognathus californicus ochrus, p. 426.
Perognathus fallax, p. 427.
Perognathus fallax pallidus, p. 427.

CALIFORNIA—Continued.

Perognathus inornatus, p. 430.
Perognathus longimembris panamintinus, p. 431.
Perognathus pacificus, p. 433.
Perognathus panamintinus arenicola, p. 433.
Perognathus panamintinus brevinasus, p. 433.
Perognathus penicillatus angustirostris, p. 435.
Perognathus spinatus, p. 436.
Perognathus (Chaetodipus) stephensi, p. 437.
Peromyscus maniculatus elusus, p. 325.
Peromyscus maniculatus exterus, p. 325.
Peromyscus maniculatus santacruzae, p. 326.
Peromyscus maniculatus streatori, p. 326.
Peromyscus oreas rubidus, p. 330.
Peromyscus stephensi, p. 333.
Peromyscus texanus clementis, p. 334.
Phenacomys albipes, p. 337.
Phenacomys intermedius celsus, p. 337.
Phocaena vomerina, p. 111.
Procyon lotor californicus, p. 81.
Procyon pallidus, p. 84.
Reithrodon longicauda (cotypes), p. 345.
Reithrodontomys klamathensis, p. 344.
Scapanus latimanus sericatus, p. 201.
Scapanus truei, p. 202.
Sciuropterus oregonensis stephensi, p. 534.
Sciurus fossor anthonyi, p. 556.
Scotophilus hesperus, p. 160.
Sorex amoenus, p. 182.
Sorex californicus, p. 184.
Sorex montereyensis, p. 188.
Sorex obscurus parvidens, p. 190.
Sorex ornatus, p. 191.
Sorex shastensis, p. 194.
Sorex tenellus, p. 195.
Sorex tenellus lyelli, p. 195.
Sorex tenellus myops, p. 195.
Sorex trowbridgii humboldtensis, p. 196.
Spermophilus beecheyi fisheri, p. 505.
Spermophilus beldingi, p. 506.
Spermophilus chrysodeirus brevicaudus, p. 507.
Spermophilus mohavensis, p. 514.
Spermophilus nelsoni, p. 516.
Spermophilus tereticaudus (cotypes), p. 519.
Spilogale phenax, p. 77.
Sylvilagus audubonii vallicola, p. 217.
Tamias alpinus, p. 522.
Tamias callipeplus, p. 524.
Tamias leucurus, p. 512.
Tamias macrorhabdotes, p. 527.
Tamias panamintinus, p. 530.
Tamias senex, p. 532.

CALIFORNIA—Continued.

Tamias speciosus, p. 532.
Taxidea americana neglecta, p. 78.
Thomomys alpinus, p. 377.
Thomomys alpinus awahnee, p. 377.
Thomomys angularis, p. 377.
Thomomys angularis pascalis, p. 377.
Thomomys aureus perpes, p. 378.
Thomomys bottae minor, p. 381.
Thomomys cabezonae, p. 383.
Thomomys fuscus fisheri, p. 389.
Thomomys laticeps, p. 390.
Thomomys leucodon navus, p. 391.
Thomomys mewa, p. 392.
Thomomys monticola pinetorum, p. 392.
Thomomys neglectus, p. 393.
Thomomys operarius, p. 394.
Thomomys talpoides perpallidus (lectotype), p. 399.
Tursiops gillii, p. 113.
Urocyon californicus townsendi, p. 47.
Urocyon catalinae, p. 47.
Urocyon cinereoargenteus californicus, p. 47.
Urocyon clementae, p. 48.
Urocyon littoralis santacruzae, p. 49.
Ursus californicus tularensis, p. 87.
Ursus colusus, p. 88.
Ursus henshawi, p. 90.
Ursus horribilis californicus (lectotype), p. 91.
Ursus klamathensis, p. 93.
Ursus magister, p. 94.
Ursus mendocinensis, p. 94.
Vespertilio nitidus, p. 155.
Vespertilio oregonensis (cotype), p. 157.
Vespertilio yumanensis (cotype), p. 573.
Vesperugo merriami, p. 161.
Vulpes (Urocyon) littoralis, p. 48.
Vulpes macrotis, p. 50.
Vulpes muticus, p. 51.
Vulpes necator, p. 52.

CALIFORNIA, off coast of:

Lagenorhynchus obliquidens (cotypes), p. 110.

CALIFORNIA-NEVADA boundary:

Ovis nelsoni, p. 12.

COLORADO:

Ammospermophilus leucurus pennipes, p. 513.
Arvicola modesta, p. 277.
Dipodomys montanus, p. 411.
Dipodomys ordii evexus, p. 412.
Dipodomys ordii nexilis, p. 413.
Eptesicus pallidus, p. 147.
Eutamias amoenus operarius, p. 523.
Eutamias minimus caryi, p. 528.

COLORADO—Continued.

Eutamias quadrivittatus animosus, p. 530.
Evotomys galei, p. 261.
Marmota flaviventer warreni, p. 540.
Mustela caurina origenes, p. 67.
Myotis lucifugus phasma, p. 154.
Nemorhoedus palmeri, p. 12.
Neotoma albigula warreni, p. 285.
Neotoma fallax, p. 287.
Neotoma orolestes, p. 296.
Perognathus apache caryi, p. 423.
Perognathus apache relictus, p. 424.
Phenacomys preblei, p. 338.
Pseudostoma castanops, p. 364.
Putorius streatori leptus, p. 74.
Reithrodon montanus, p. 348.
Reithrodontomys megalotis caryi, p. 346.
Sciurus aberti concolor, p. 551.
Sorex tenellus nanus, p. 196.
Spermophilus gunnisoni, p. 521.
Spilogale tenuis, p. 78.
Sylvilagus audubonii warreni, p. 217.
Thomomys bottae howelli, p. 380.
Thomomys bottae internatus, p. 381.
Thomomys bottae optabilis, p. 381.
Thomomys talpoides agrestis, p. 397.
Ursus bairdi, p. 87.
Ursus macrodon, p. 94.
Ursus planiceps, p. 97.
Ursus shoshone, p. 99.

FLORIDA:

Blarina carolinensis peninsulae, p. 167.
Blarina floridana, p. 175.
Canis floridanus, p. 41.
Dasypterus floridanus, p. 146.
Hesperomys macropus, p. 324.
Neofiber alleni, p. 284.
Neofiber alleni nigrescens, p. 285.
Odocoileus virginianus seminolus, p. 23.
Oryzomys natator floridanus, p. 309.
Peromyscus gossypinus restrictus, p. 320.
Peromyscus leucocephalus, p. 322.
Peromyscus polionotus decoloratus, p. 331.
Pitymys parvulus, p. 339.
Procyon lotor auspicatus, p. 81.
Procyon lotor incautus, p. 82.
Procyon lotor inesperatus, p. 83.
Procyon lotor marinus, p. 83.
Sciurus niger avicennia, p. 557.
Sylvilagus floridanus ammophilus, p. 218.
Ursus floridanus, p. 86.

GEORGIA:

Hesperomys cognatus (cotypes), p. 316.
Hesperomys gossypinus (cotypes), p. 320.
Nycticea cynocephala, p. 123.
Odocoileus virginianus nigribarbis, p. 23.
Procyon lotor litoreus, p. 83.

IDAHO:

Arvicola (Mynomes) macropus, p. 276.
Arvicola (Mynomes) mordax, p. 278.
Arvicola (Mynomes) nanus, p. 278.
Citellus idahoensis, p. 511.
Citellus leurodon, p. 513.
Citellus mollis artemisiae, p. 514.
Citellus mollis pessimus, p. 514.
Citellus townsendii brunneus, p. 519.
Eutamias ruficaudus simulans, p. 531.
Evotomys idahoensis, p. 262.
Glaucomys bullatus, p. 534.
Hesperomys crinitus, p. 317.
Lepus idahoensis, p. 208.
Ochotona schisticeps goldmani, p. 226.
Ochotona uinta lemhi, p. 227.
Odocoileus virginianus ochrourus, p. 23.
Onychomys leucogaster brevicaudus, p. 302.
Perognathus parvus idahoensis, p. 434.
Phenacomys orophilus, p. 338.
Reithrodontomys megalotis nigrescens, p. 346.
Sorex dobsoni, p. 184.
Sorex idahoensis, p. 187.
Sorex vagrans similis, p. 197.
Tamias minimus melanurus, p. 529.
Thomomys clusius fuscus, p. 383.
Thomomys idahoensis, p. 390.
Thomomys nevadensis atrogriseus, p. 394.
Thomomys pygmaeus, p. 396.
Thomomys talpoides relicinus, p. 399.
Ursus idahoensis, p. 91.

ILLINOIS:

Neotoma floridana illinoensis, p. 288.

KANSAS:

Arvicola (Synaptomys) gossii (lectotype), p. 354.
Citellus tridecemlineatus arenicola, p. 520.
Fiber zibethicus cinnamominus, p. 300.
Perognathus paradoxus, p. 433.
Scalopus aquaticus machrinoides, p. 200.
Vespertilio ciliolabrum, p. 151.

KENTUCKY:

Clethrionomys gapperi maurus, p. 261.

LOUISIANA:

Canis rufus gregoryi, p. 45.
Felis arundivaga, p. 53.
Geomys breviceps, p. 368.

LOUISIANA—Continued.
> Microtus ludovicianus, p. 276.
> Reithrodontomys mexicanus aurantius, p. 347.
> Sylvilagus aquaticus littoralis, p. 215.

MAINE:
> Lagenorhynchus gubernator (cotypes), p. 109.
> Lutreola macrodon, p. 72.

MARYLAND:
> Myotis winnemana, p. 158.
> Sorex fontinalis, p. 186.

MASSACHUSETTS:
> Arvicola breweri (cotypes), p. 271.
> Lagenorhynchus perspicillatus (cotypes), p. 110.
> Marmota monax preblorum, p. 540.

MICHIGAN:
> Castor canadensis michiganensis, p. 255.
> Hesperomys gracilis, p. 321.

MINNESOTA:
> Marmota monax rufescens, p. 540.
> Mustela vison letifera, p. 75.
> Peromyscus leucopus minnesotae, p. 323.
> Procyon lotor hirtus, p. 82.
> Sciurus carolinensis hypophaeus (lectotype), p. 554.
> Sorex arcticus laricorum, p. 183.
> Vulpes regalis, p. 52.

MISSISSIPPI:
> Blarina exilipes (lectotype), p. 175.
> Microtus pinetorum auricularis, p. 339.

MISSOURI:
> Mustela primulina, p. 73.

MONTANA:
> Canis lupus irremotus, p. 43.
> Eutamias amoenus vallicola, p. 523.
> Eutamias oreocetes, p. 529.
> Eutamias ruficaudus, p. 531.
> Marmota caligata nivaria, p. 538.
> Marmota flaviventer nosophora, p. 539.
> Microtus pennsylvanicus wahema, p. 281.
> Peromyscus leucopus aridulus, p. 322.
> Phenacomys intermedius levis, p. 337.
> Sorex haydeni (lectotype), p. 186.
> Sorex merriami, p. 188.
> Spermophilus tridecemlineatus pallidus (lectotype), p. 520.
> Tamias cinerascens, p. 508.
> Tamias quadrivittatus pallidus (lectotype), p. 531.
> Thomomys fuscus saturatus, p. 389.
> Thomomys pryori, p. 396.
> Thomomys talpoides bullatus, p. 398.
> Thomomys talpoides kelloggi, p. 399.
> Thomomys talpoides trivialis, p. 400.
> Ursus absarokus, p. 86.

UNITED STATES—continued

NEBRASKA:

Canis pallidus, p. 45.
Geomys bursarius lutescens, p. 369.
Mustela campestris, p. 70.
Neotoma baileyi, p. 286.
Perognathus fasciatus flavescens, p. 428.
Peromyscus luteus, p. 324.
Reithrodontomys albescens, p. 341.
Reithrodontomys dychei nebrascensis, p. 342.
Scalopus aquaticus caryi, p. 200.
Spermophilus obsoletus (lectotype), p. 516.
Sylvilagus floridanus similis, p. 220.

NEVADA:

Arvicola curtata, p. 267.
Bassariscus astutus nevadensis, p. 39.
Callospermophilus lateralis certus, p. 511.
Canis lestes, p. 43.
Castor canadensis baileyi, p. 254.
Citellus elegans nevadensis, p. 510.
Citellus mollis washoensis, p. 515.
Dipodomys merriami nevadensis, p. 408.
Eutamias palmeri, p. 530.
Fiber zibethicus mergens, p. 301.
Lutra canadensis nexa, p. 64.
Marmota flaviventer parvula, p. 540.
Microdipodops megacephalus, p. 422.
Microdipodops megacephalus lucidus, p. 422.
Microdipodops pallidus, p. 422.
Microtus nevadensis, p. 279.
Neotoma cinerea lucida, p. 286.
Ochotona uinta nevadensis, p. 227.
Perognathus nevadensis, p. 432.
Perognathus parvus magruderensis, p. 434.
Perognathus penicillatus seorsus, p. 436.
Reithrodontomys megalotis deserti, p. 346.
Sorex nevadensis, p. 189.
Spermophilus mollis stephensi, p. 515.
Thomomys canus, p. 383.
Thomomys nevadensis, p. 394.
Vulpes macrotis nevadensis, p. 51.
Zapus nevadensis, p. 568.

NEW HAMPSHIRE:

Neosorex albibarbis, p. 182.
Synaptomys (Mictomys) sphagnicola, p. 355.
Urocyon cinereoargenteus borealis, p. 47.

NEW JERSEY:

Hesperomys campestris, p. 315.
Kogia goodei, p. 114.

NEW MEXICO:

Canis lupus mogollonensis, p. 43.
Castor canadensis mexicanus, p. 255.
Citellus tridecemlineatus hollisteri, p. 520.

New Mexico—Continued.
 Citellus variegatus juglans, p. 521.
 Cratogeomys castanops hirtus, p. 365.
 Cratogeomys castanops lacrimalis, p. 365.
 Cynomys gunnisoni zuniensis, p. 522.
 Dipodomys spectabilis baileyi, p. 414.
 Dipodomys spectabilis clarencei, p. 414.
 Dorcelaphus crooki, p. 20.
 Eutamias atristriatus, p. 524.
 Eutamias cinereicollis cinereus, p. 525.
 Evotomys limitis, p. 262.
 Fiber zibethicus ripensis, p. 301.
 Hesperomys (Vesperimus) anthonyi, p. 312.
 Hesperomys truei, p. 335.
 Lepus gaillardi, p. 211.
 Lepus sylvaticus rigidus, p. 222.
 Marmota flaviventer obscura, p. 539.
 Myotis baileyi, p. 150.
 Myotis longicrus interior, p. 153.
 Neotoma intermedia angusticeps, p. 289.
 Neotoma mexicana inopinata, p. 293.
 Neotoma micropus leucophaea, p. 294.
 Ochotona nigrescens, p. 225.
 Ochotona saxatilis incana, p. 226.
 Perognathus merriami gilvus, p. 431.
 Perognathus obscurus, p. 432.
 Sciurus aberti chuscensis, p. 551.
 Sciurus aberti mimus, p. 551.
 Sciurus castanotus, p. 554.
 Sciurus fremonti neomexicanus, p. 560.
 Sigmodon minima, p. 353.
 Sigmodon minimus goldmani, p. 353.
 Sorex obscurus neomexicanus, p. 190.
 Spermophilus spilosoma major, p. 518.
 Sylvilagus audubonii cedrophilus, p. 216.
 Sylvilagus audubonii neomexicanus, p. 217.
 Sylvilagus cognatus, p. 218.
 Tamias dorsalis (cotypes), p. 526.
 Tamias quadrivittatus gracilis, p. 530.
 Thomomys apache, p. 378.
 Thomomys aureus pervagus, p. 378.
 Thomomys bottae opulentus, p. 381.
 Thomomys fulvus emotus, p. 386.
 Thomomys mearnsi, p. 392.
 Thomomys pectoralis, p. 395.
 Ursus amblyceps (lectotype), p. 85.
 Ursus horribilis horriaeus (lectotype), p. 91.
 Ursus perturbans, p. 96.
 Vespertilio nitidus henshawii (cotypes), p. 156.
 Vulpes macrotis neomexicanus, p. 51.
 Zapus luteus, p. 568.
 Zapus luteus australis, p. 568.

NEW YORK:

Arvicola scalopsoides, p. 340.

Microtus insularis, p. 274.

Phocaena lineata, p. 110.

Pipistrellus subflavus obscurus, p. 161.

Sciuropterus sabrinus macrotis, p. 535.

Tamias striatus fisheri, p. 560.

NORTH CAROLINA:

Evotomys carolinensis, p. 260.

Mesoplodon mirum, p. 115.

Sciurus hudsonicus abieticola, p. 560.

Zapus (Napaeozapus) insignis roanensis, p. 567.

NORTH DAKOTA:

Arvicola austerus minor, p. 271.

Arvicola (Chilotus) pallidus, p. 267.

Arvicola (Pedomys) cinnamomea, p. 273.

Castor canadensis missouriensis, p. 255.

Evotomys gapperi loringi, p. 261.

Odocoileus virginianus dacotensis, p. 22.

Sorex pachyurus (lectotype), p. 191.

OKLAHOMA:

Canis frustror, p. 41.

Dipodomys oklahomae, p. 412.

Geomys breviceps dutcheri, p. 369.

Microtus pinetorum nemoralis, p. 340.

Onychomys leucogaster breviauritus, p. 302.

OREGON:

Antilocapra americana oregona, p. 6.

Aplodontia pacifica, p. 253.

Atophyrax bendirii, p. 183.

Bison bison oregonus, p. 8.

Callospermophilus chrysodeirus connectens, p. 507.

Cervus lewisii, p. 574.

Chincha occidentalis major, p. 69.

Citellus canus vigilis, p. 506.

Citellus columbianus ruficaudus, p. 508.

Cricetodipus parvus, p. 574.

Dipodomys heermanni gabrielsoni, p. 407.

Evotomys mazama, p. 262.

Evotomys obscurus, p. 263.

Lepus bachmani ubericolor, p. 217.

Lepus klamathensis, p. 212.

Microdipodops megacephalus oregonus, p. 422.

Microtus bairdi, p. 271.

Microtus canicaudus, p. 273.

Neotoma occidentalis fusca, p. 295.

Ochotona fenisex fumosa, p. 225.

Ochotona schisticeps jewetti, p. 226.

Perodipus microps preblei, p. 410.

Perodipus ordii columbianus, p. 412.

Perognathus monticola, p. 432.

Peromyscus truei preblei, p. 336.

Phenacomys longicaudus, p. 337.

OREGON—Continued.

    Procyon lotor excelsus, p. 82.

    Putorius saturatus, p. 73.

    Putorius xanthogenys oregonensis, p. 75.

    Scalops aeneus, p. 200.

    Scapanus alpinus, p. 201.

    Scapanus dilatus, p. 201.

    Sciuropterus alpinus klamathensis, p. 533.

    Sciurus douglasii cascadensis, p. 560.

    Sciurus fossor, p. 573.

    Sorex bairdi, p. 183.

    Sorex (Atophyrax) bendirii palmeri, p. 184.

    Sorex obscurus permiliensis, p. 190.

    Sorex pacificus, p. 191.

    Sorex preblei, p. 192.

    Sorex trigonirostris, p. 196.

    Sorex trowbridgii (lectotype), p. 196.

    Sorex yaquinae, p. 197.

    Spermophilus mollis canus, p. 514.

    Spermophilus oregonus, p. 516.

    Spilogale phenax latifrons, p. 77.

    Tamias amoenus, p. 523.

    Tamias chrysodeirus, p. 507.

    Thomomys douglasii oregonus, p. 384.

    Thomomys hesperus, p. 390.

    Thomomys leucodon, p. 391.

    Thomomys mazama, p. 392.

    Thomomys nasicus, p. 393.

    Thomomys niger, p. 394.

    Thomomys quadratus, p. 396.

    Zapus major, p. 568.

    Zapus pacificus, p. 568.

    Zapus princeps oregonus, p. 569.

    Zapus trinotatus montanus, p. 569.

OREGON, off coast of:

    Delphinapterus borealis, p. 576.

PENNSYLVANIA:

    Arvicola apella, p. 339.

    Mephitis frontata, p. 68.

    Neotoma magister (cotypes), p. 292.

    Sorex fimbripes, p. 185.

SOUTH CAROLINA:

    Hyperodon [sic] semijunctus, p. 115.

    Odocoileus virginianus hiltonensis, p. 23.

    Odocoileus virginianus taurinsulae, p. 24.

    Odocoileus virginianus venatorius, p. 24.

    Procyon lotor solutus, p. 84.

SOUTH DAKOTA:

    Arctomys dacota, p. 539.

    Arvicola (Pedomys) haydenii, p. 274.

    Arvicola (Mynomes) longicaudus, p. 275.

    Eutamias pallidus cacodemus, p. 530.

    Evotomys gapperi brevicaudus, p. 261.

South Dakota—Continued.
 Perognathus flavescens perniger, p. 428.
 Putorius alleni, p. 69.

Tennessee:
 Myotis grisescens, p. 152.

Texas:
 Canis lupus monstrabilis, p. 43.
 Canis nebracensis texensis, p. 44.
 Castor canadensis texensis, p. 255.
 Conepatus leuconotus texensis, p. 62.
 Conepatus mesoleucus mearnsi, p. 62.
 Conepatus mesoleucus telmalestes, p. 62.
 Cratogeomys castanops angusticeps, p. 364.
 Cratogeomys castanops perplanus, p. 366.
 Didelphis marsupialis texensis, p. 228.
 Dipodomys ambiguus, p. 405.
 Dipodomys compactus, p. 406.
 Dipodomys elator, p. 406.
 Dorcelaphus texanus, p. 21.
 Eutamias cinereicollis canipes, p. 525.
 Felis concolor youngi, p. 55.
 Felis limitis, p. 57.
 Geomys arenarius, p. 368.
 Geomys breviceps ammophilus, p. 369.
 Geomys breviceps attwateri, p. 369.
 Geomys breviceps llanensis, p. 369.
 Geomys breviceps sagittalis, p. 369.
 Geomys personatus (cotypes), p. 370.
 Geomys personatus fallax, p. 370.
 Geomys texensis, p. 370.
 Glaucomys volans texensis, p. 536.
 Hesperomys texanus, p. 333.
 Lepus arizonae minor, p. 216.
 Lepus floridanus caniclunis, p. 218.
 Lepus merriami, p. 212.
 Lepus pinetis robustus, p. 222.
 Lepus simplicicanus, p. 222.
 Lepus texianus griseus, p. 214.
 Liomys texensis, p. 421.
 Lutra canadensis texensis, p. 65.
 Microtus mexicanus guadalupensis, p. 276.
 Mormoops megalophylla senicula, p. 134.
 Onychomys longipes, p. 303.
 Onychomys torridus arenicola, p. 303.
 Ovis canadensis texiana, p. 11.
 Perognathus (Chaetodipus) eremicus, p. 427.
 Perognathus flavus, p. 428.
 Perognathus paradoxus spilotus, p. 434.
 Peromyscus boylei laceyi, p. 314.
 Peromyscus boylii penicillatus, p. 315.
 Peromyscus canus, p. 316.
 Peromyscus eremicus arenarius, p. 318.

UNITED STATES—continued

TEXAS—Continued.

Peromyscus pectoralis laceianus, p. 330.

Peromyscus taylori subater, p. 259.

Peromyscus tornillo, p. 335.

Procyon lotor fuscipes, p. 82.

Reithrodontomys griseus, p. 344.

Reithrodontomys merriami, p. 347.

Sciurus limitis, p. 557.

Sigmodon hispidus pallidus, p. 352.

Sigmodon ochrognathus, p. 353.

Sorex (Notiosorex) crawfordi, p. 181.

Spermophilus mexicanus parvidens, p. 513.

Spermophilus spilosoma annectens, p. 517.

Spermophilus spilosoma arens, p. 517.

Spermophilus spilosoma marginatus, p. 518.

Spermophilus tridecemlineatus texensis, p. 521.

Spilogale indianola, p. 76.

Spilogale leucoparia, p. 76.

Tamias interpres, p. 511.

Tatu novemcinctum texanum, p. 570.

Taxidea berlandieri, p. 78.

Thomomys aureus lachuguilla, p. 378.

Thomomys baileyi, p. 378.

Thomomys baileyi spatiosus, p. 379.

Thomomys bottae guadalupensis, p. 380.

Thomomys bottae pervarius, p. 382.

Thomomys fulvus texensis, p. 389.

Thomomys lachuguilla confinalis, p. 390.

Thomomys lachuguilla limitaris, p. 390.

Urocyon cinereoargenteus texensis, p. 48.

Ursus horriaeus texensis, p. 90.

Vespertilio pallidus, p. 145.

UTAH:

Canis estor, p. 41.

Canis lupus youngi, p. 44.

Citellus grammurus utah, p. 510.

Dipodomys microps alfredi, p. 409.

Dipodomys microps bonnevillei, p. 409.

Dipodomys microps russeolus, p. 410.

Dipodomys microps subtenuis, p. 410.

Dipodomys ordii cineraceus, p. 412.

Dipodomys ordii marshalli, p. 413.

Eutamias dorsalis utahensis, p. 527.

Microtus nevadensis rivularis, p. 279.

Neotoma lepida marshalli, p. 291.

Ochotona schisticeps fuscipes, p. 226.

Ochotona uinta, p. 227.

Onychomys leucogaster melanophrys, p. 302.

Onychomys leucogaster utahensis, p. 302.

Onychomys longicaudus, p. 302.

Perodipus montanus utahensis, p. 411.

Perognathus formosus, p. 429.

Perognathus olivaceus, p. 432.

UTAH—Continued.

Perognathus olivaceus amoenus. p. 433.
Perognathus parvus plerus, p. 434.
Peromyscus crinitus pergracilis, p. 317.
Peromyscus maniculatus gunnisoni, p. 325.
Peromyscus maniculatus inclarus, p. 325.
Reithrodontomys megalotis ravus, p. 346.
Sorex leucogenys, p. 187.
Spermophilus mollis (cotypes), p. 514.
Spilogale saxatilis, p. 78.
Tamias castanurus, p. 507.
Tamias minimus consobrinus, p. 528.
Tamias minimus pictus, p. 529.
Tamias umbrinus, p. 533.
Thomomys bottae birdseyei, p. 379.
Thomomys bottae minimus, p. 381.
Thomomys fossor levis, p. 385.
Thomomys fossor moorei, p. 385.
Thomomys fossor parowanensis, p. 385.
Thomomys perpallidus dissimilis, p. 395.
Thomomys perpallidus osgoodi, p. 396.
Thomomys uinta, p. 400.
Ursus utahensis, p. 100.
Vulpes macroura, p. 51.

VERMONT:

Blarina angusticeps, p. 167.
Sorex thompsoni (lectotype), p. 180.

VIRGINIA:

Blarina telmalestes, p. 167.
Fiber macrodon, p. 300.
Microsorex winnemana, p. 180.
Peromyscus nuttalli lewisi, p. 329.
Reithrodontomys humulis virginianus, p. 344.
Sorex fisheri, p. 185.
Sylvilagus floridanus hitchensi, p. 219.
Synaptomys helaletes, p. 355.

WASHINGTON:

Antrozous pallidus cantwelli, p. 145.
Aplodontia major rainieri, p. 253.
Aplodontia olympica, p. 253.
Arctomys olympus, p. 541.
Arvicola occidentalis, p. 279.
Arvicola pauperrima, p. 268.
Balaenoptera davidsoni, p. 108.
Cervus roosevelti, p. 18.
Chincha occidentalis notata, p. 69.
Citellus washingtoni, p. 521.
Citellus washingtoni loringi, p. 521.
Eutamias canicaudus, p. 524.
Eutamias caurinus, p. 525.
Eutamias minimus grisescens, p. 528.
Evotomys nivarius, p. 262.
Evotomys occidentalis, p. 263.

WASHINGTON—Continued.

Felis hippolestes olympus, p. 56.
Hesperomys austerus (lectotype), p. 313.
Lepus texianus wallawalla, p. 214.
Lepus washingtonii, p. 215.
Lynx fasciatus pallescens, p. 60.
Marmota caligata cascadensis, p. 538.
Microsorex hoyi washingtoni, p. 180.
Microtus macrurus, p. 276.
Microtus nanus canescens, p. 279.
Microtus oregoni cantwelli, p. 280.
Mustela caurina, p. 66.
Myotis yumanensis saturatus, p. 159.
Neosorex navigator, p. 189.
Neotoma occidentalis, p. 295.
Ochotona fenisex brunnescens, p. 224.
Perognathus columbianus, p. 427.
Peromyscus maniculatus hollisteri, p. 325.
Phocaena vomerina (cotypes), p. 111.
Procyon psora pacifica, p. 84.
Putorius streatori, p. 73.
Putorius washingtoni, p. 75.
Scapanus orarius, p. 201.
Scapanus orarius schefferi, p. 201.
Sciurus suckleyi, p. 561.
Sorex (Atophyrax) bendirii albiventer, p. 184.
Sorex suckleyi (lectotype), p. 195.
Sorex vagrans (lectotype), p. 197.
Spermophilus mollis yakimensis, p. 515.
Synaptomys (Mictomys) truei, p. 355.
Tamias cooperi (cotype), p. 526.
Thomomys douglasii shawi, p. 384.
Thomomys douglasii tacomensis, p. 384.
Thomomys douglasii yelmensis, p. 385.
Thomomys fuscus columbianus, p. 389.
Thomomys limosus, p. 391.
Thomomys melanops, p. 392.
Thomomys myops, p. 393.
Thomomys talpoides badius, p. 398.
Thomomys talpoides couchi, p. 398.
Thomomys talpoides ericaeus, p. 398.
Urotrichus gibbsii, p. 199.
Ursus chelan, p. 88.
Verspertilio evotis (lectotype), p. 152.
Vespertilio longicrus, p. 153.
Vespertilio nitidus, p. 155.
Vulpes cascadensis, p. 50.

WEST VIRGINIA:

Glaucomys sabrinus fuscus, p. 534.

WISCONSIN:

Arvicola austerus, p. 270.
Eutamias minimus jacksoni, p. 529.

WISCONSIN—Continued.

    Microsorex hoyi intervectus, p. 180.

    Napaeozapus insignis frutectanus, p. 566.

    Sorex hoyi (lectotype), p. 179.

    Sorex palustris hydrobadistes, p. 192.

WYOMING:

    Alces americana shirasi, p. 16.

    Callospermophilus lateralis caryi, p. 511.

    Cervus canadensis nelsoni, p. 17.

    Cynomys leucurus, p. 522.

    Eutamias consobrinus clarus, p. 526.

    Eutamias minimus confinis, p. 528.

    Felis hippolestes, p. 56.

    Lepus baileyi, p. 217.

    Lepus bairdii (cotypes), p. 210.

    Lynx uinta, p. 61.

    Marmota flaviventer luteola, p. 539.

    Microtus montanus caryi, p. 278.

    Ochotona uinta ventorum, p. 227.

    Perodipus ordii luteolus, p. 413.

    Perognathus callistus, p. 426.

    Perognathus fasciatus litus, p. 428.

    Perognathus flavus piperi, p. 429.

    Perognathus parvus clarus, p. 434.

    Phenacomys truei, p. 338.

    Putorius culbertsoni (cotype), p. 70.

    Sciurus hudsonicus baileyi, p. 560.

    Sciurus hudsonicus ventorum, p. 561.

    Spermophilus armatus (cotypes), p. 504.

    Spermophilus elegans (cotypes), p. 509.

    Spermophilus tridecemlineatus alleni, p. 519.

    Thomomys bridgeri, p. 383.

    Thomomys clusius, p. 383.

    Thomomys clusius ocius, p. 384.

    Thomomys talpoides caryi, p. 398.

    Thomomys talpoides nebulosus, p. 399.

    Thomomys talpoides tenellus, p. 400.

    Ursus imperator, p. 91.

    Ursus mirus, p. 95.

    Ursus rogersi, p. 98.

    Ursus rogersi bisonophagus, p. 90.

    Ursus washake, p. 100.

    Zapus hudsonius campestris, p. 567.

ATLANTIC OCEAN (near Portland, Maine):

    Lagenorhynchus perspicillatus (cotypes), p. 110.

EXACT LOCALITY UNKNOWN:

    Atalapha teliotis, p. 149.

    Bassaris raptor, p. 39.

    Synaptomys cooperi, p. 354.

UNITED STATES:

    Nycticea crepuscularis (cotypes), p. 159.

    V[espertilio] lucifugus, p. 572.

"UPPER MISSOURI":
    Ovis canadensis auduboni, p. 11.

WEST INDIES

BAHAMA ISLANDS:
    Chilonatalus tumidifrons, p. 125.
    Erophylla planifrons mariguanensis, p. 130.
    Macrotus waterhousii compressus, p. 132.
    Macrotus waterhousii heberfolium, p. 132.
    Phyllonycteris planifrons, p. 130.
    Vespertilio fuscus bahamensis, p. 146.
EXACT LOCALITY UNKNOWN:
    Monophyllus clinedaphus, p. 133.
GREATER ANTILLES:
  CUBA:
    Boromys offella, p. 360.
    Brachyphylla nana, p. 128.
    Capromys prehensilis gundlachi, p. 361.
    Chilonatalus macer, p. 125.
    Monophyllus cubanus, p. 133.
  DOMINICAN REPUBLIC:
    Brotomys voratus, p. 360.
    Eptesicus hispaniolae, p. 147.
    Natalus major, p. 125.
    Plagiodontia hylaeum, p. 362.
    Tadarida constanzae, p. 123.
  HAITI, REPUBLIC OF:
    Acratocnus (?) comes, p. 570.
    Aphaetreus montanus, p. 360.
    Brachyphylla pumila, p. 128.
    Brotomys (?) contractus, p. 360.
    Hexolobodon phenax, p. 362.
    Ithydontia levir, p. 362.
    Lasiurus minor, p. 148.
    Monophyllus cubanus ferreus, p. 134.
    Nesophontes hypomicrus, p. 166.
    Nesophontes paramicrus, p. 166.
    Nesophontes zamicrus, p. 167.
    Parocnus serus, p. 570.
    Phyllonycteris obtusa, p. 135.
    Plagiodontia spelaeum, p. 363.
    Quemisia gravis, p. 363.
  JAMAICA:
    Lasiurus degelidus, p. 148.
    Macrotus waterhousii jamaicensis, p. 133.
    Nyctinomus orthotis, p. 121.
    Reithronycteris aphylla, p. 135.
  PUERTO RICO:
    Chilonycteris portoricensis, p. 129.
    Eptesicus wetmorei, p. 147.
    Molossus fortis, p. 121.
    Monophyllus portoricensis, p. 134.
    Phyllonycteris bombifrons, p. 130.

WEST INDIES—continued

LESSER ANTILLES:
  BARBADOS:
    Brachyphylla minor, p. 127.
    Monophyllus plethodon, p. 134.
  DOMINICA:
    Myotis dominicensis, p. 152.
    Natalus dominicensis, p. 125.
    Nyctinomus antillularum, p. 122.
  GRENADA:
    Glossophaga rostrata, p. 131.
  GUADELOUPE:
    Ardops annectens, p. 126.
    Artibeus jamaicensis praeceps, p. 127.
    Procyon minor, p. 84.
  ST. KITTS:
    Molossus debilis, p. 121.
  ST. LUCIA:
    Monophyllus luciae, p. 134.
    Stenoderma luciae, p. 126.

COLLECTORS OF THE TYPE SPECIMENS OF MAMMALS IN THE UNITED STATES NATIONAL MUSEUM, INCLUDING THE BIOLOGICAL SURVEYS COLLECTION.

Abbott, James Francis.
Abbott, William Louis, M. D.
Abert, James William, Lt., U. S. A.
Adams, Charles Francis.
Agersborg, Gabriel Smith, M. D.
Akhurst, James.
Alexander, William Henry.
Allen, Charles Andrew.
Allen, Harrison, M. D.
Allen, Joel Asaph.
Amory, Copley, Jr.
Anderson, Eddie Emmanuel.
Anderson, George Smith, Capt., U. S. A.
Anderson, Henry.
Andrews, Roy Chapman.
Anthony, Alfred Webster.
Anthony, Harold Elmer.
Armstrong, Frank Blake.
Aschemeier, Charles Robert.
Ashcraft, Charles E., Jr.
Attwater, Henry Philemon.
Ayres, William Orville, M. D.
Axelson, E. M.

Badger, George Bergen.
Bailey, Alfred Marshall.
Bailey, Bernard Hill.
Bailey, Vernon Orlando.
Baird, Spencer Fullerton.
Baker, Arthur Benoni.
Baldwin, William Plews, Jr.
Ball, Edward F.
Barber, Charles Melvin.
Barnston, George.
Bartsch, Paul.
Bates, Forrest Reuben.
Bates, George Latimer.
Baxter, G. W.
Beccari, Odoardo.
Beckwith, Edward Griffin, Capt., U. S. A.
Beckwith, Paul E.
Belding, Lyman.
Bendire, Charles Emil, Maj., U. S. A.
Benedict, James Everard.

Benson, George Martin.
Berg, Willis Ernest.
Bergen, Paul David, Rev.
Bergh, H. Oscar.
Berlandier, Jean Louis.
Birdseye, Clarence.
Birt, Louis F. H., M. D.
Bischoff, Ferdinand.
Boettcher, Frederick Louis John.
Booy, Theodoor de.
Boyle, C. C., M. D.
Boynton, Charles Lawrence.
Branch, H. Selwyn.
Bretherton, Bernard Joseph.
Brewer, Thomas Mayo, M. D.
Briceño, Solomon [see Solomon Briceño Gabaldon].
Brimley, Clement Samuel.
Brooks, Allan Cyril.
Brown, Herbert.
Brown, John Stafford.
Brown, Joseph Stanley.
Brown, William Lewis.
Brune, Florenz Arnold.
Bryant, Walter [Pierc]E.
Bunch, James Randolph.
Bunnell, Alexander Sterling.
Burbank, Wilbur Swett.
Burlingame, John.
Burnam, Bart.
Busck, August.

Canton, General Francisco.
Canton, M.
Cantwell, George Gordon.
Carson, R. E.
Cary, Merritt.
Case, W. H.
Caton, John Dean.
Catt, Cyrus.
Cavileer, Charles.
Celestino, Andres.
Chanler, William Astor.
Chatelain, H.

Clark, Elton.
Clark, John Henry.
Cluff, Hyrum Albert.
Cole, Henry James.
Comeau, Napolean Alexander.
Coolidge, Dane.
Cook, Orator Fuller.
Cooper, James Graham, M. D.
Cooper, Juan.
Cooper, William.
Cope, Edward Drinker.
Cory, Charles Barney.
Couch, Darius Nash, Lt., U. S. A.
Couch, Leo King.
Coues, Elliott, M. D.
Cox, William Thomas.
Crawford, Samuel Wylie, Asst. Surg.,
    U. S. A.
Cross, Charles Robert, Jr.
Cunningham, B. L.
Currie, Rolla Patteson.

Dall, William Healey.
Darbey, E. W.
Davison, John, Lt., Revenue Cutter
    Service.
Dealy, Joseph MacDonald.
De Long, William Francis.
Derickson, Samuel Hoffman.
Derry, Caulaincourt W.
Devereux, Walter B.
De Weese, Dall.
Dietz, Richard F.
Dippie, George Frederick.
Dixon, T. A.
Dow, John Melmoth, Capt., Merchant
    Marine.
Drexler, Constantin.
Drury, William S.
Dugés, Alfredo.
Dutcher, Basil Hicks, Asst. Surg.,
    U. S. A.

Edson, Charles Farwell.
Edwards, E. H.
Ehrhardt, H.
Eisen, Gustavus Augustus.
Elliott, W. ["W." probably an error for
    I. L.].
Ellsworth, Lincoln.
Emmet, Chris.
Emmet, Hans.
Emmons, George Thornton, Lt., U. S. N.
Emory, William Hemsley, Maj., U. S. A.

Enevoldsen, Fred E. [=Ferdinand
    Eugene].
Erdis, Elwood C.
Escalera, Manuel Martinez de la.
Evermann, Barton Warren.

Fairie, James.
Fannin, John.
Farley, Jim.
Fast, Eli E. [assumed initial].
Fea, Leonardo.
Feilner, John, Capt., U. S. A.
Ferry, John Farwell.
Finley, Charles Otis.
Fisher, Albert Kenrick.
Fisher, Richard Thornton.
Fisher, Walter Kenrick.
Fisk, John W.
Flemming, G.
Foster, William T.
Fox, Carroll.
Frakes, W.
Frantzius, Alexander von.
Funcke, Edward William.
Funk, Jack.

Gabaldon, Solomon Briceño.
Gabb, William More.
Gabrielson, Ira Noel.
Gale, Denis.
Gaumer, George Franklin.
Gaut, James Henry.
Gaylord, Horace Amidon.
Geddis, George (see Smith and Geddis).
Gellineau, Peter.
Gibbs, George.
Gibson, James H.
Gill, Mike.
Gilpin, John Bernard.
Goldman, Edward Alphonso.
Goldman, Luther Chase.
Goldman, Luther Jacob.
Golsan, Lewis Samuel.
Goss, Benjamin Franklin.
Graham, David Crockett.
Graham, James Duncan, Col., U. S. A.
Grasshoff, W.
Grayson, Andrew Jackson, Col.
Green, Edward Clarence.
Green, Morris Miller.
Grinnell, George Bird.
Guesde, L.
Gunnison, John William, Capt., U. S. A.
Guthrie, Leon J.

Hammond, John Fox, Asst. Surg., U. S. A.

Hammond, William Alexander, Asst. Surg., U. S. A.

Hanna, Marcus Albert.

Hansen, Chris.

Hardisty, William L.

Harrington, Mark Raymond.

Hartt, Charles Frederic.

Hasselborg, Allen.

Hastrup, Oluf.

Hatcher, John Bell.

Hayden, Ferdinand Vandiveer, M. D.

Hayes, Sutton., M. D.

Hayes, Thomas.

Heermann, Adolphus Lewis.

Heller, Edmund.

Henry, Ira B.

Henshaw, Henry Wetherbee.

Herndon, William Lewis, Lt., U. S. N.

Herrera, Alfonso Luis.

Hicks, Fred.

Hill, George.

Hittell, Charles Jacob.

Hittell, Franklin Theodore.

Höhnel, Ludwig Ritter von, Capt., Austro-Hungarian Navy.

Hollister, Ned.

Holt, Ernest Golsan.

Holzner, Frank Xavier.

Holzworth, John Michael.

Hose, Charles.

Hose, Ernest.

Howell, Arthur Holmes.

Howland, Henry S.

Hoy, Charles McCaulay.

Hoy, Philo Romayne, M. D.

Hrdlička, Aleš.

Hubrick, J. P., Capt., Merchant Marine.

Humphreys, J. W.

Hurst, John.

Hutton, William R.

Hyland, John.

Ihering, Hermann von.

Ingersoll, Joseph Carleton.

Ives, Joseph Christmas, Lt., U. S. A.

Jackson, Hartley Harrad Thompson.

Jackson, Ray Thomas.

Jennings, Allan Hinson.

Jewett, Ezekial.

Jewett, Stanley Gordon.

Johnson, Albin.

Johnson, John.

Johnson, Walter Rogers.

Johnston, Marius A.

Johnstone, Forrest.

Johnstone, Fred.

Jordan, David Starr.

Jouy, Pierre Louis.

Kaegi, D. N.

Keays, Herbert Henry.

Keeler, Charles Augustus.

Keen, John Henry, Rev.

Kellogg, Arthur Remington.

Kennerly, Caleb Burwell Rowan.

Kennicott, Robert W.

Kent, W. R.

Kidder, James Henry.

Kleineidam, Paul.

Kloss, Cecil Boden.

Knudsen, Valdemar.

Kreutzfeld, F.

Krieger, Herbert William.

Lambert, Charles Alfred.

LeConte, John Eatton, Maj., U. S. A.

LeConte, John Lawrence.

Leigh, Richard (Beaver Dick).

Lemmer, Frank.

Leonard, George.

Lewis, John Barzillai.

Ligon, James Stokley.

Lilly, Benjamin Vernon.

Lingebach, John Carleton.

Llarregui, Jose Salazar.

Lloyd, William.

Loring, John Alden.

Loveridge, Arthur.

Luckey, D. H.

Lyman, Theodore, M. D.

Lyon, Marcus Ward, Jr., M. D.

MacFarlane, Roderick Ross.

Mackay, Walter Grant.

Mackie, David Barclay.

MacTavish, William.

Maddren, Alfred Geddes.

Malleis, Harry.

Manigault, Gabriel Edward.

Mansell, Fred James.

March, William Thomas.

Marcy, Randolph Barnes, Capt., U. S. A

Maria, Nicéforo.
Marsh, Charles Henry.
Marshall, William Hampton.
Martenson, Mart.
Martin, Melvin Emery.
Maynard, Charles Johnson.
McCarthy, Charles S.
McCormick, Lewis Morse.
McDonough, Patrick.
McElroy, Constance Roberts, Mrs.
McGee, William John, M. D.
McGregor, Richard Crittenden.
McGuire, George Montgomery.
McGuire, John Aloysius.
McIlhenny, Edward Avery.
McLellan, James Ellis.
McQuesten, L. N.
Means, John Zachariah.
Mearns, Edgar Alexander, Maj., U. S. A.
Merriam, Clinton Hart, M. D.
Merrill, James Cushing, Maj., U. S. A.
Michler, Nathaniel H., Lt., U. S. A.
Miles, Jack Carroll.
Miller, Gerrit Smith, Jr.
Mills, Joe.
Mitchell, John W.
Möllhausen, Heinrich Balduin.
Moore, Albert Watts.
Moore, Henry Frank.
Morse, Edward Sylvester.
Mullan, John, Lt., U. S. A.
Murdoch, John, Sgt., Signal Corps, War Dept.
Murie, Olaus Johan.
Murray, Alexander Campbell.

Nelson, Edward William.
Neumann, Rudolf.
Newberry, John Strong, M. D.
Niedrach, Robert James.
Norton, George Frederick.

Oberholser, Harry Church.
Oca, Rafael Montes de.
Osgood, Wilfred Hudson.
Owens, James Thomas.

Page, Thomas Jefferson, Capt., U. S. N.
Palache, Charles.
Palmer, Edward, M. D.
Palmer, George W.
Palmer, Theodore Sherman, M. D.
Palmer, William.
Palmer, William Jackson, Gen., U. S. A.

Parker, Samuel.
Pavlof, Willie.
Peale, Titian Ramsay.
Percival, A. Blayne.
Percival, A. V.
Perrygo, Watson Mondell.
Peters, James Lee.
Peterson, Olof August.
Philip, Hoffman, U. S. Consul General.
Piper, Stanley Edward.
Pitcher, John.
Poilane, E.
Poole, Arthur James.
Pope, John, Capt., U. S. A.
Porsild, Morten Pedersen.
Potts, John.
Preble, Alfred Emerson.
Preble, Edward Alexander.
Prentiss, Daniel Webster, Jr., M. D.
Priour, John Marion.

Ragsdale, George Henry.
Rainey, Paul James.
Rairden, Bradstreet Stinson, U. S. Consul.
Ralph, William Le Grange, M. D.
Raven, Henry Cushier.
Ray, Patrick Henry, Lt., U. S. A.
Raynolds, William Franklin, Capt., U. S. A.
Rea, Archibald.
Reed, Howard Sawyer.
Rice, Delmer Sherman.
Richardson, Edward Peirson, M. D.
Richmond, Charles Wallace, M. D.
Riley, Joseph Harvey.
Rindsfoos, William.
Ritter, William Emerson.
Robb, Marcus L.
Robinson, William, Sir.
Robinson, Wirt, Col., U. S. A.
Rogers, Archibald.
Roosevelt, Kermit.
Roosevelt, Theodore.
Rothrock, Joseph Trimble.
Rubio, Luis Gonzalez.
Rückbeil, W. [Vasilii Eugenievich Rükbeil].
Ruffin, John N., U. S. Consul.
Rungius, Carl Clemens Moritz.

Samuels, Emanuel.
Sartorius, Carlos.
Saunders, De Alton.

Saussure, Henri Louis Frédéric de.
Savage, Walter G.
Scammon, Charles Melville, Capt., Revenue Cutter Service.
Scheffer, Theophilus H. [assumed initial].
Schlüter, Wilhelm.
Schmid, Peter.
Schott, Arthur.
Seton, Ernest Thompson.
Sharp, Grover Cleveland.
Sheldon, Charles.
Sheldon, Harry Hargrave.
Shinn, C. H.
Shiras, George Peter, 4th.
Shive, John.
Shufeldt, Percy Welles.
Shufeldt, Robert Wilson, Asst. Surg., U. S. A.
Shumard, George Getz, M. D.
Simpson, James Hervey, Capt., U. S. A.
Simpson, Wallace W.
Sitgreaves, Lorenzo, Capt., U. S. A.
Smith and Geddis [see Thomas Smith and George Geddis].
Smith, Charles H.
Smith, Floyd Tangier.
Smith, Hugh McCormick.
Smith, Thomas.
Smith, William Gilbert.
Smith, William Lord.
Sowerby, Arthur de Carle.
Spaulding, W. H.
Spear, John Crawford, Surg., U. S. N.
Spreadborough, William.
Stansbury, Howard, Capt., U. S. A.
Steere, Joseph Beal.
Stejneger, Leonhard Hess.
Stejneger, Mrs. Leonhard (Marie Reiners).
Stejneger, Thora.
Stephens, Frank.
Stevenson, Donald Harley.
Stewart, Henry Alexander.
Stewart, John Truesdale.
Stimpson, William, M. D.
Streator, Clark Perkins.
Sturgis, Robert Shaw.
Suckley, George, Asst. Surg., U. S. A.
Sullivan, Jeremiah.
Sumichrast, Adrien Louis Francois.
Surber, McClure.
Swanson, C.

Tabb, Richard Howard.
Taylor, Alexander Smith.
Taylor, Walter Penn.
Thayer, Abbott Henderson.
Thomas, George Henry, Maj., U. S. A.
Thompson, James.
Thompson, Russell J.
Thompson, Zadock.
Thurber, Eugene Carlton.
Todd, Caleb Aurelius.
Toney, L. Clark, M. D.
Townsend, Charles Haskins.
Traill, William E.
Trapier, Paul Edmund.
Trook, George H.
Trowbridge, William Petit, Lt., U. S. A.
True, Frederick William.
Turner, Bert Brown.
Turner, H. J. Allen.
Turner, Lucien McShan.

Underwood, Cecil F.
U. S. Exploring Expedition (1838–1842).

Van Dyck, William Thompson.
Van Patten, Charles H., M. D.
Van Vliet, Stewart, Capt., U. S. A.
Varden, John.
Vollum, Edward Perry, Asst. Surg., U. S. A.

Wailes, Benjamin Leonard Covington, Col.
Walcott, Charles Doolittle, Jr.
Wallace, John.
Warmbath, Julian Samuel.
Warren, Edward Royal.
Warren, Gouverneur Kemble, Lt., U. S. A.
Wayne, James.
Weems, Fontaine Carrington.
Weiss, Maximilian.
Weldon, Robert Samuels.
Wetherby, Albert Gallatin.
Wetmore, Frank Alexander.
Whipple, Amiel Weeks, Lt., U. S. A.
Whitaker, Harry L. [assumed initial].
White, John Jay.
White, William Thomas, M. D.
Wilder, George Durand.
Wilkes, Charles, Comdr., U. S. N.
Williams, H. E.

Williamson, Robert Stockton, Lt., U. S. A.
Wilson, Samuel W., M. D.
Winthrop, Frederic, Jr.
Wittfeld, William.
Wittkügel, Erich.
Wood, Ira Turner.
Woodhouse, Samuel Washington, M. D.
Woodruff, Israel Carle, Lt., U. S. A.
Woolfe, Henry D.
Worthen, Charles Kimball.
Wulsin, Frederick Roelker.

Würdemann, Gustavus Wilhelm.
Wyman, Luther Everett.

Xantus, Janos [Louis John Xantus de Vesey].

Young, Robert Thompson.
Yourans, Edmund.

Zeledon, José Castulo.
Zollikofer, Ernst H.

INDEX TO GENERIC, SPECIFIC, AND SUBSPECIFIC NAMES

abbotti, Galeopterus, 162.
    Hylobates, 251.
    Lepus, 210.
    Myotis, 150.
abbottii, Callosciurus, 491.
    Sciurus, 491.
abbreviatus, Microtus, 269.
aberti, Sciurus, 551, 554, 555.
abieticola, Martes, 66.
    Mustela, 66.
    Sciurus, 560.
    Tamiasciurus, 560.
abietorum, Vulpes, 49.
ablusus, Citellus, 517.
absarokus, Ursus, 86.
absonus, Thomomys, 395.
abyssinica, Mellivora, 67.
acholi, Leggada, 448.
    Mus, 448.
Acinonyx, 52.
    raineyi, 52.
    velox, 52.
acmaeus, Alticola, 257.
Acomys, 439.
    hystrella, 439.
    montanus, 439.
Acratocnus, 570.
    comes, 570.
acrophilus, Alticola, 257.
    Microtus, 257.
actuosa, Martes, 66.
    Mustela, 66.
acutus, Lagenorhynchus, 109, 110, 111.
adangensis, Callosciurus, 491.
    Sciurus, 491.
Adelonycteris fuscus, 572.
Adenota, 6.
    alurae, 6.
adocetus, Citellus, 504.
    Microtus, 280.
adspersus, Rattus, 455.
adusta, Macaca, 240.
adustus, Tryphomys, 488.
aeneus, Scalops, 200.
aequatoria, Ourebia, 11.
    Pachyura, 198.
aequatorialis, Alouatta, 235.
    Felis, 53.
    Suncus, 198.
Aëretes melanopterus, 544.
aero, Pipistrellus, 160.
Aethomys, 439.
    helleri, 439.
    turneri, 440.

affinis, Helogale, 103.
    Hesperomys, 311.
    Peromyscus, 311, 329.
    Vespertilio, 150.
agilis, Vespertilio, 572.
agnatus, Pithecus, 241.
Agouti nelsoni, 358.
agrestis, Thomomys, 397.
Akodon, 256.
    chacoensis, 256.
    surdus, 256.
    torques, 256.
alascensis, Evotomys, 260.
    Lemmus, 268.
    Mustela, 73.
    Myotis, 154, 157.
    Putorius, 73.
    Sorex, 186, 189.
    Ursus, 90.
    Vulpes, 49.
    Zapus, 567.
alashanicus, Euchoreutes, 359.
alaskanus, Sorex, 189.
alba, Ectophylla, 129.
    Ondatra, 300.
albescens, Felis, 57.
    Ictonyx, 64.
    Myotis, 155, 572.
    Onychomys, 301.
    Reithrodontomys, 341.
albibarbis, Hylobates, 251.
    Neosorex, 182.
    Sorex, 182.
albicauda, Alticola, 257.
    Arvicola, 257.
albigula, Neotoma, 289.
albigularis, Mus, 455.
    Rattus, 455.
    Thomomys, 400.
albilabris, Reithrodontomys, 348.
albimanus, Delphinus, 108.
albinasus, Pappogeomys, 374.
albipes, Heterohyrax, 165.
    Phenacomys, 337.
albirostratus, Delphinus, 109, 575.
albiventer, Oryzomys, 304.
    Sorex, 184.
albiventris, Marmosa, 229.
albogularis, Eutamias, 524.
albulus, Perognathus, 435.
Alcelaphus, 7.
    keniae, 7.
    kongoni, 7.
    nakurae, 7.
    roosevelti, 7.

Alces, 16.
    gigas, 16.
    shirasi, 16.
alchemillae, Crocidura, 167.
aldabrensis, Pteropus, 139.
alexandrae, Thomomys, 377.
alfredi, Dipodomys, 409.
algidus, Peromyscus, 324.
alienus, Thomomys, 379.
Allactaga, 359.
    grisescens, 359.
    longior, 359.
    saliens, 359.
alleni, Chelemys, 259.
    Citellus, 519.
    Eutamias, 532.
    Hodomys, 266.
    Mustela, 69.
    Neofiber, 284.
    Neotoma, 266.
    Notiomys, 259.
    Orthogeomys, 372.
    Putorius, 69.
    Reithrodontomys, 341.
    Sciurus, 552.
    Sigmodon, 350.
    Spermophilus, 519.
allex, Peromyscus, 258.
allophylus, Peromyscus, 312.
alnorum, Microsorex, 179.
    Sorex, 179.
Alopex, 40.
    beringensis, 40.
    hallensis, 40.
    innuitus, 40.
    pribilofensis, 41.
    ungava, 40.
Alouatta, 235.
    aequatorialis, 235.
    inconsonans, 235.
    mexicana, 236.
alpina, Crocidura, 168.
alpinus, Eutamias, 522.
    Scapanus, 201.
    Tamias, 522.
    Thomomys, 377.
alstoni, Neotomodon, 298.
altae, Crocidura, 169.
altaica, Procapra, 13.
    Prodorcas, 13.
altaicus, Eutamias, 523.
altamirae, Lepus, 212.
Alticola, 257.
    acmaeus, 257.
    acrophilus, 257.
    albicauda, 257.
    glacialis, 257.
    montosa, 258.
    stoliczkanus, 257.
    stracheyi, 257.
alticola, Blarina, 175.
    Cryptotis, 175.
    Microtus, 269.
    Reithrodontomys, 349.
    Sigmodon, 350.
    Sorex, 182.
alticolus, Arvicola, 269.
    Reithrodontomys, 349.

altifrons, Myotis, 150.
altilaneus, Peromyscus, 312.
altinsularis, Callosciurus, 491.
    Sciurus, 491.
altivallis, Sylvicapra, 15.
alurae, Adenota, 6.
amakensis, Microtus, 270.
ambigua, Spilogale, 75.
ambiguus, Dipodomys, 405.
    Perognathus, 424.
amblodon, Sagmatias, 112.
amblyceps, Euarctos, 85.
    Ursus, 85.
amecensis, Pappogeomys, 374.
Ammelaphus australis, 15.
ammophilus, Geomys, 369.
    Perognathus, 435.
    Sylvilagus, 218.
Ammospermophilus, extimus, 512.
    insularis, 512.
    pennipes, 513.
    tersus, 513.
amoenus, Eutamias, 523.
    Hylopetes, 537.
    Perognathus, 433.
    Sciuropterus, 537.
    Sorex, 182, 194.
    Tamias, 523.
    Tragulus, 30.
amoles, Reithrodontomys, 341.
    Sigmodon, 350.
amotus, Lariscus, 541.
    Menetes, 541.
    Myotis, 153.
amplus, Perognathus, 422.
    Peromyscus, 312.
analogus, Baiomys, 259.
    Peromyscus, 259.
    Thomomys, 400.
anambae, Mus, 455.
    Rattus, 455.
    Ratufa, 545.
    Tupaia, 203.
anambensis, Callosciurus, 491.
    Emballonura, 115.
    Sciurus, 491.
andamanensis, Crocidura, 168.
    Macaca, 240, 242, 244.
andersoni, Thomomys, 397.
andrewsi, Mus, 456.
    Rattus, 456.
angelensis, Peromyscus, 314.
angularis, Thomomys, 377.
angulatus, Cynopterus, 137, 138.
angusticeps, Blarina, 167.
    Cratogeomys, 364.
    Microtus, 270.
    Neotoma, 289.
    Oryzomys, 305.
    Ratufa, 545.
angustidens, Lepus, 210.
angustifrons, Spilogale, 76.
angustirostris, Macrorhinus, 234.
    Mirounga, 234.
    Perognathus, 435.
    Platygeomys, 376.
animosus, Eutamias, 530.

annectens, Ardops, 126.
　Citellus, 517.
　Heteromys, 418.
　Liomys, 418.
　Ochotona, 224.
　Oryx, 10.
　Spermophilus, 517.
annexus, Orthogeomys, 372.
antarcticus, Halichoerus, 234.
anthonyi, Hesperomys, 312.
　Perognathus, 423.
　Peromyscus, 312.
　Sciurus, 556.
antillularum, Nyctinomus, 122.
　Tadarida, 122.
Antilocapra, 6.
　mexicana, 6.
　oregona, 6.
　peninsularis, 6.
Antrozous, 145.
　cantwelli, 145.
　minor, 145.
　pacificus, 146.
　pallidus, 145.
antucus, Rattus, 467.
Aonyx, 61.
　helios, 61.
aoris, Callosciurus, 491.
　Galeopithecus, 162.
　Galeopterus, 162.
　Sciurus, 491.
Aotus, 236.
　zonalis, 236.
apache, Felis, 53.
　Perognathus, 423.
　Thomomys, 378.
　Ursus, 87.
apella, Arvicola, 339.
Aphaetreus, 360.
　montanus, 360.
aphorodemus, Microtus, 270.
aphylla, Reithronycteris, 135.
apicis, Mus, 487.
Aplodontia, 253.
　californica, 253.
　major, 253.
　olympica, 253.
　pacifica, 253.
　phaea, 254.
　rainieri, 253.
Apodemus, 440.
　microtis, 440.
　nigritalus, 440.
　praetor, 441.
　rusiges, 440.
apoensis, Cynomolgus, 244.
　Tarsomys, 488.
Apomys, 441.
　bardus, 441.
　hylocoetes, 441.
　insignis, 441.
　major, 441.
　microdon, 442.
　musculus, 442.
　petraeus, 442.
aquilus, Lophuromys, 450.
　Mus, 450.

arborea, Nandinia, 105.
arborensis, Potos, 80.
arctica, Mustela, 69.
Arctictis, 100.
　niasensis, 100.
arcticus, Putorius, 69.
　Sorex, 192, 194.
Arctocephalus, 234.
　townsendi, 234.
Arctogalidia, 101.
　bicolor, 101.
　depressa, 101.
　fusca, 101.
　inornata, 101.
　macra, 101.
　major, 101.
　mima, 102.
　minor, 102.
　simplex, 102.
　sumatrana, 102.
　tingia, 102.
Arctomys, dacota, 539.
　olympus, 541.
　sibila, 541.
Ardops, 126.
　annectens, 126.
　luciae, 126.
arenaria, Cercopithecus, 238.
　Lasiopyga, 238.
arenarius, Geomys, 368.
　Miniopterus, 149.
　Peromyscus, 318.
arendsis, Callosciurus, 492.
　Sciurus, 492.
arenicola, Citellus, 520.
　Onychomys, 303.
　Perognathus, 433.
arenicolar, Gerbillus, 265.
arens, Spermophilus, 517.
argentata, Ochotona, 224.
argentea, Presbytis, 247.
aridulus, Peromyscus, 322.
arizonae, Lepus, 222.
　Neotoma, 285.
　Sylvilagus, 216, 222.
　Ursus, 87.
arizonensis, Bassariscus, 38.
　Callospermophilus, 511.
　Citellus, 511.
　Eutamias, 528.
　Felis, 58.
　Microtus, 278.
　Perognathus, 431.
　Sciurus, 553.
　Vulpes, 50.
armalis, Callosciurus, 492.
　Sciurus, 492.
armatus, Citellus, 504.
　Perognathus, 424.
　Spermophilus, 504.
arquatus, Pteropus, 139.
artemesiae, Citellus, 514.
Artibeus, 126.
　aztecus, 126.
　hirsutus, 127.
　phaeotis, 127.
　praeceps, 127.
　ravus, 127.

articus [sic], Hesperomys, 312.
artus, Perognathus, 425.
arundivaga, Felis, 53.
arusinus, Ratufa, 545.
Arvicanthis, 442.
 centrosus, 442.
 jebelae, 442.
 micropus, 449.
 planifrons, 489.
 virescens, 442.
Arvicola, albicauda, 257.
 alticolus, 269.
 apella, 339.
 austerus, 270.
 breweri, 271.
 californica, 272.
 cinnamomea, 273.
 curtata, 267.
 edax, 273.
 fertilis, 267.
 gossii, 354.
 haydenii, 274.
 longicaudus, 275.
 longirostris, 275.
 macropus, 276.
 minor, 271.
 modesta, 277.
 montana, 278, 573.
 montosa, 258.
 mordax, 278.
 nanus, 278.
 occidentalis, 279.
 operarius, 280.
 pallidus, 267.
 pauperrima, 268.
 phaeus, 281.
 quasiater, 340, 573.
 scalopsoides, 340.
 trowbridgii, 282.
arwasca, Presbytis, 247.
Aschizomys, 258.
 lemminus, 258.
asellus, Lepus, 209.
asper, Mus, 456.
 Rattus, 456.
assimilis, Peromyscus, 324.
Atalapha semota, 149.
 teliotis, 149.
Atelerix, 165.
 hindei, 165.
Ateles, 236.
 dariensis, 236.
 neglectus, 237.
 tricolor, 237.
athabascae, Clethrionomys, 261.
 Evotomys, 261.
Atherura zygomatica, 438.
Atherurus, 438.
 terutaus, 438.
 zygomaticus, 438.
athi, Steatomys, 488.
Atilax, 102.
 rubescens, 102.
atnarko, Ursus, 87.
Atophyrax bendirii, 183.
atratus, Mus, 456.
 Sciurus, 562.

atratus, Tomeutes, 562.
atriceps, Macaca, 243.
atridorsum, Mus, 456.
 Rattus, 456.
atristriatus, Callosciurus, 492.
 Eutamias, 524.
 Sciurus, 492.
atrogriseus, Thomomys, 394.
atronasus, Dipodomys, 408.
atrox, Callosciurus, 492.
 Phoniscus, 159.
 Sciurus, 492.
attenuata, Crocidura, 169.
attwateri, Geomys, 369.
 Peromyscus, 314.
auduboni, Ovis, 11.
audubonii, Lepus, 216.
 Sylvilagus, 216.
aurantius, Reithrodontomys, 347.
aureus, Oreotragus, 10.
 Reithrodontomys, 349.
 Thomomys, 391.
auricularis, Microtus, 339.
 Pitymys, 339.
aurigineus, Lepus, 209.
aurillus, Oryzomys, 356.
 Thallomyscus, 356.
aurispinosa, Tadarida, 122.
aurispinosus, Dysopes, 122.
auritus, Peromyscus, 313, 316.
auspicatus, Procyon, 81.
austerus, Arvicola, 270.
 Hesperomys, 313.
 Peromyscus, 313.
australis, Ammelaphus, 15.
 Phocaena, 109, 576.
 Pipistrellus, 161.
 Presbytis, 247.
 Spilogale, 77.
 Strepsiceros, 15.
 Zapus, 568.
avicennia, Sciurus, 557.
avius, Peromyscus, 318.
awahnee, Thomomys, 377.
azteca, Felis, 56.
aztecus, Artibeus, 126.
 Felis, 56.
 Oryzomys, 306.

babi, Cynopterus, 137.
 Rattus, 480.
 Sus, 26.
bachmani, Sylvilagus, 223.
badius, Peromyscus, 336.
 Thomomys, 398.
bagobus, Bullimus, 443.
bahamensis, Eptesicus, 146.
 Vespertilio, 146.
baileyi, Canis, 44.
 Castor, 254.
 Dipodomys, 414.
 Lepus, 217.
 Lynx, 60.
 Microtus, 275.
 Myotis, 150.
 Neotoma, 286.
 Perognathus, 425.

baileyi, Sciurus, 560.
 Sylvilagus, 217.
 Tamiasciurus, 560.
 Thomomys, 378.
Baiomys, 258.
 analogus, 259.
 grisescens, 259.
 musculus, 258.
 nigrescens, 259.
 paulus, 258.
 subater, 259.
bairdi, Sorex, 183.
 Ursus, 87.
bairdii, Berardius, 114.
 Delphinus, 109, 575.
 Elasmognathus, 233.
 Hesperomys, 314.
 Lepus, 210.
 Microtus, 271.
 Tapirella, 233.
balae, Mus, 456.
 Rattus, 456.
 Ratufa, 545.
 Sciurus, 563.
 Tomeutes, 563.
Balaenoptera, 108.
 davidsoni, 108.
baliolus, Sciurus, 559.
balmasus, Rattus, 456.
balutus, Pteropus, 139.
banacus, Rattus, 467.
bancana, Ratufa, 550.
bancanus, Muntiacus, 18.
 Nannosciurus, 542.
 Nycticebus, 251.
 Tragulus, 30.
bancarus, Sciurus, 563.
 Tomeutes, 563.
Bandicota, 443.
 siamensis, 443.
bangsi, Glaucomys, 534.
 Pecari, 28.
barbensis, Hipposideros, 117.
bardus, Apomys, 441.
barrowensis, Citellus, 505, 506.
 Spermophilus, 505.
barussanus, Epimys, 457.
 Rattus, 457.
basilanus, Epimys, 457.
 Rattus, 457.
Bassaricyon, 79.
 gabbii, 79.
 orinomus, 79.
Bassaris raptor, 39.
Bassariscus, 38.
 arizonensis, 38.
 consitus, 38.
 insulicola, 39.
 nevadensis, 39.
 palmarius, 39.
 raptor, 39.
 saxicola, 39.
batamana, Tupaia, 204.
batamanus, Mus, 457.
 Rattus, 457.
Batomys, 443.
 dentatus, 443.

batuana, Petaurista, 543.
 Ratufa, 549.
batuanus, Presbytes, 247.
 Tragulus, 31.
batus, Epimys, 457.
 Rattus, 457.
 Sciurus, 564.
 Tomeutes, 564.
baveanus, Pteropus, 139.
baweana, Macaca, 241.
baweanus, Pithecus, 241.
Bdeogale, 103.
 omnivora, 103.
bea, Canis, 41.
 Protoxerus, 544.
 Strepsiceros, 15.
 Thos, 41.
beatus, Crocidura, 168.
bedfordi, Capreolus, 16.
beldingi, Citellus, 506.
 Spermophilus, 506.
belti, Sciurus, 553.
bendirii, Atophyrax, 183.
 Sorex, 183.
benguetensis, Epimys, 457.
 Rattus, 457.
bentincanus, Callosciurus, 493.
 Mus, 458.
 Rattus, 458.
 Sciurus, 493.
Berardius, 114.
 bairdii, 114.
bergensis, Sorex, 183.
beringensis, Alopex, 40.
 Spermophilus, 506.
 Vulpes, 40.
berlandieri, Blarina, 175.
 Cryptotis, 175.
 Sigmodon, 351, 352.
 Taxidea, 78.
bernardi, Ondatra, 300.
bernardinus, Citellus, 507.
 Microtus, 278.
 Spermophilus, 506, 507.
berytensis, Spalax, 566.
besara, Tana, 203.
bicolor, Arctogalidia, 101.
bilimitatus, Callosciurus, 493.
 Sciurus, 493.
billitonus, Callosciurus, 493.
 Sciurus, 493.
 Tragulus, 31.
bilobatum, Uroderma, 136.
bimaculatus, Perognathus, 425.
birdseyei, Thomomys, 379.
Bison, 8.
 oregonus, 8.
bisonophagus, Ursus, 98.
blandus, Peromyscus, 332.
Blarina, 167.
 alticola, 175.
 angusticeps, 167.
 berlandieri, 175.
 brevicauda, 167.
 exilipes, 175.
 floridana, 175.
 fossor, 176.

Blarina goldmani, 177.
  machetes, 178.
  magna, 177.
  mayensis, 177.
  mexicana, 177.
  nelsoni, 178.
  obscura, 178.
  peninsulae, 167.
  peregrina, 178.
  soricina, 179.
  telmalestes, 167.
bogotensis, Sturnira, 135.
bombifrons, Erophylla, 130.
  Kerivoula, 147.
  Phyllonycteris, 130.
bombycinus, Oryzomys, 305.
  Perognathus, 426.
bonnevillei, Dipodomys, 409.
borealis, Delphinapterus, 110, 575.
  Eutamias, 523.
  Lasiurus, 148.
  Lissodelphis, 575.
  Synaptomys, 354.
  Tamias, 523.
  Urocyon, 47.
borneanus, Epimys, 458.
  Galeopterus, 163.
  Nannosciurus, 542.
  Nycticebus, 251.
  Rattus, 458.
  Tarsius, 252.
  Tragulus, 31.
Boromys, 360.
  offella, 360.
boylii, Hesperomys, 314.
  Peromyscus, 314.
brachelix, Microtus, 266.
Brachylagus, 208.
  idahoensis, 208.
brachylix, Hyperacrius, 266.
Brachyphylla, 127.
  minor, 127.
  nana, 128.
  pumila, 128.
Bradypus, 569.
  ignavus, 569.
brandti, Microtus, 283.
breviauritus, Onychomys, 302.
brevicauda, Blarina, 167.
  Spermophilus, 507.
brevicaudus, Clethrionomys, 261
  Evotomys, 261.
  Onychomys, 302.
  Spermophilus, 506, 507.
breviceps, Geomys, 368.
  Kogia, 114.
brevicula, Echiothrix, 446.
brevimanus, Chilonatalus, 124.
  Natalus, 124.
brevinasus, Perognathus, 433.
brevipes, Tragulus, 31.
breweri, Arvicola, 271.
  Microtus, 271.
bridgeri, Thomomys, 383.
broca, Macaca, 241.
brooksi, Ochotona, 225.
Brotomys, 360.

Brotomys contractus, 360.
  voratus, 360.
browni, Felis, 53.
brunneipes, Paradoxurus, 105.
brunnescens, Ochotona, 224.
brunneus, Citellus, 519.
bryanti, Neotoma, 286.
Bubalis keniae, 7.
  kongoni, 7.
  nakurae, 7.
  roosevelti, 7.
bufo, Phacochoerus, 26.
bulana, Ratufa, 546.
bullaris, Tylomys, 357.
bullata, Neotoma, 293.
bullatus, Glaucomys, 534.
  Mus, 458.
  Peromyscus, 315.
  Rattus, 458.
  Synaptomys, 354.
  Thomomys, 398.
Bullimus, 443.
  bagobus, 443.
bunguranensis, Tragulus, 32.
bunoae, Tana, 202.
  Tupaia, 202.
burrescens, Mus, 458.
  Rattus, 458.
burrulus, Mus, 458.
  Rattus, 458.
burrus, Mus, 459.
  Rattus, 459.
buruensis, Mus, 459.
  Rattus, 459.
butangensis, Mus, 482.
  Rattus, 482.
bweha, Schaeffia, 36.
  Thos, 46.

Cabassous, 569.
  centralis, 569.
cabezonae, Dipodomys, 405.
  Perodipus, 405.
  Thomomys, 383.
cacodemus, Eutamias, 530.
cacomitli, Felis, 53.
caesia, Pseudois, 13.
cagayana, Macaca, 241.
cagayanus, Cynomolgus, 241.
  Pteropus, 140.
calcis, Epimys, 459.
  Rattus, 459.
californica, Aplodontia, 253.
  Arvicola, 272.
californicus, Cervus, 21, 575.
  Clethrionomys, 260.
  Dipodomys, 405.
  Eumops, 120.
  Evotomys, 260.
  Lynx, 60.
  Macrotus, 132, 571.
  Microdipodops, 421.
  Microtus, 272, 273, 282.
  Molossus, 120.
  Myotis, 155, 156, 157, 158, 573.
  Odocoileus, 575.
  Perognathus, 424, 426.

californicus, Procyon, 81.
    Sorex, 184.
    Urocyon, 47.
    Ursus, 91.
caliginosus, Thomomys, 400.
callida, Lasiopyga, 238.
callidus, Cercopithecus, 238.
callipeplus, Eutamias, 524.
    Tamias, 524.
callistus, Perognathus, 426.
Callosciurus, 491.
    abbottii, 491.
    adangensis, 491.
    altinsularis, 491.
    anambensis, 491.
    aoris, 491.
    arendsis, 492.
    armalis, 492.
    atristriatus, 492.
    atrox, 492.
    bentincanus, 493.
    bilimitatus, 493.
    billitonus, 493.
    carimatae, 494.
    carimonensis, 494.
    casensis, 494.
    condurensis, 494.
    conipus, 500.
    datus, 494.
    dilutus, 495.
    director, 495.
    domelicus, 495.
    helvus, 493.
    ictericus, 496.
    inexpectatus, 495
    klossii, 496.
    lamucotanus, 496.
    lancavensis, 497.
    lautensis, 497.
    lucas, 497.
    lutescens, 497.
    marinsularis, 497.
    matthaeus, 498.
    melanops, 498.
    mendanauus, 498.
    mimellus, 498.
    mimiculus, 499.
    miniatus, 499.
    nyx, 499.
    palustris, 493.
    pannovianus, 499.
    pelapius, 499.
    pemangilensis, 500.
    penialius, 498.
    peninsularis, 500.
    piceus, 495.
    pranis, 496.
    pretiosus, 500.
    proserpinae, 500.
    rubeculus, 501.
    rubidiventris, 501.
    rupatius, 503.
    rutiliventris, 501.
    sanggaus, 501.
    saturatus, 501.
    seraiae, 502.
    serutus, 502.

Callosciurus siriensis, 502.
    styani, 493.
    sullivanus, 502.
    tachin, 492.
    tapanulius, 503.
    tedongus, 502.
    tenuirostris, 503.
    trotteri, 496.
    ubericolor, 503.
    vittatus, 503.
Callospermophilus arizonensis, 511.
    caryi, 511.
    certus, 511.
    connectens, 507.
    madrensis, 513.
    mitratus, 507.
    tescorum, 512.
    trinitatis, 508.
camortae, Pipistrellus, 160.
campechensis, Jentinkia, 40.
    Potos, 80.
campestris, Hesperomys, 315.
    Mustela, 70.
    Zapus, 567.
camurus, Rattus, 461.
cana, Presbytis, 247.
canadensis, Lutra, 65.
    Ovis, 12.
    Ursus, 99.
canaster, Galictis, 63.
    Grison, 63.
canescens, Citellus, 506, 517.
    Microtus, 279.
    Paradoxurus, 106.
    Perognathus, 430.
    Spermophilus, 506.
    Tragulus, 32.
canicaudus, Eutamias, 524.
    Microtus, 273.
caniceps, Eutamias, 525.
caniclunis, Lepus, 218.
canicrus, Presbytis, 248.
canigenus, Sciurus, 493.
canipes, Eutamias, 525.
Canis, 41.
    baileyi, 44.
    bea, 41.
    estor, 41.
    floridanus, 41.
    frustror, 41.
    goldmani, 42.
    gregoryi, 45.
    hondurensis, 42.
    irremotus, 43.
    jamesi, 42.
    labradorius, 43.
    lestes, 43.
    ligoni, 43.
    mearnsi, 44.
    microdon, 44.
    mogollonensis, 43.
    monstrabilis, 43.
    nebracensis, 45.
    pallidus, 45.
    peninsulae, 45.
    rufus, 41.
    texensis, 44.

Canis torquatus, 45, 576.
 tundrarum, 45.
 vigilis, 45.
 youngi, 44.
cansus, Myospalax, 566.
 Myotalpa, 566.
 Ochotona, 224.
cantwelli, Antrozous, 145.
 Microtus, 280.
canus, Citellus, 514.
 Eropeplus, 446.
 Lenothrix, 449.
 Lepus, 208.
 Liomys, 418.
 Odocoileus, 20.
 Onychomys, 303.
 Paradoxurus, 106.
 Peromyscus, 316.
 Rattus, 449.
 Spermophilus, 514.
 Thomomys, 383.
capitalis, Macaca, 241.
 Pithecus, 241.
capitaneus, Myotis, 151.
capitis, Dendromus, 445.
capito, Taphonycteris, 116.
capitulatus, Onychomys, 302.
Capreolus, 16.
 bedfordi, 16.
 melanotis, 16.
Capromys, 360.
 gundlachi, 361.
 thoracatus, 360.
carbo, Trachypithecus, 248.
Cariacus clavatus, 19.
 couesi, 22.
carimatae, Callosciurus, 494.
 Megaderma, 119.
 Mus, 459.
 Myotis, 151.
 Pithecus, 242.
 Presbytis, 248.
 Rattus, 459.
 Sciurus, 494.
 Tragulus, 32.
 Tupaia, 203.
carimonensis, Callosciurus, 494.
 Ratufa, 546.
 Sciurus, 494.
carlottae, Euarctos, 86.
 Ursus, 86.
carmeni, Peromyscus, 318.
carminis, Eutamias, 526.
 Odocoileus, 22.
carolinensis, Clethrionomys, 260.
 Evotomys, 260.
Carollia, 128.
 castanea, 128.
 subrufa, 128.
caryi, Callospermophilus, 511.
 Citellus, 511.
 Eutamias, 528.
 Microtus, 278.
 Perognathus, 423.
 Reithrodontomys, 346.
 Scalopus, 200.
 Thomomys, 398.

cascadensis, Marmota, 538.
 Sciurus, 560.
 Tamiasciurus, 560.
 Vulpes, 50.
casensis, Callosciurus, 494.
 Mus, 459.
 Rattus, 459.
 Sciurus, 494.
castanea, Carollia, 128.
 Tupaia, 203.
castaneus, Funambulus, 537.
 Lariscus, 537.
 Peromyscus, 334.
castanonotus, Sciurus, 554.
castanops, Cratogeomys, 364.
 Pseudostoma, 364.
castanotus [sic], Sciurus, 554.
castanurus, Citellus, 507.
 Tamias, 507.
Castor, 254.
 baileyi, 254.
 frondator, 254.
 mexicanus, 255.
 michiganensis, 255.
 missouriensis, 255.
 repentinus, 255.
 shastensis, 256.
 texensis, 255.
catalinae, Thomomys, 386.
 Urocyon, 47.
catellifer, Mus, 460.
 Rattus, 460.
catemana, Presbytis, 248.
 Ratufa, 546.
caudata, Crocidura, 168.
caudatus, Oryzomys, 305.
 Sorex, 193.
caurina, Martes, 66.
 Mustela, 66.
caurinus, Clethrionomys, 260.
 Eutamias, 525.
 Evotomys, 260.
 Myotis, 151.
 Ursus, 87.
cavaticus, Taphozous, 117.
cavirostris, Ziphius, 115.
Cebus, 237.
 limitaneus, 237.
 margaritae, 237.
cedrophilus, Sylvilagus, 216.
celaenopepla, Ratufa, 546.
celatus, Phenacomys, 337.
celebensis, Harpyionycteris, 139.
 Megaderma, 119.
celsus, Dipodomys, 410.
 Phenacomys, 337.
centralis, Cabassous, 569.
 Epimys, 439.
 Felis, 54.
 Myrmecophaga, 571.
 Philander, 232.
 Tatoua, 569.
centrosa, Echiothrix, 446.
centrosus, Arvicanthis, 442.
Centurio, 128.
 mcmurtrii, 128.
 senex, 128.

Cephalophus, 8.
　　musculoides, 8.
　　spadix, 8.
cerasina, Mazama, 18.
Cercoctenus, 166.
　　sangi, 166.
Cercopithecus, 237.
　　arenaria, 238.
　　callidus, 238.
　　johnstoni, 238, 239.
　　kibonotensis, 237.
　　luteus, 238.
　　neumanni, 238.
　　schmidti, 238.
cereus, Rattus, 464.
cerrosensis, Odocoileus, 19.
certus, Callospermophilus, 511.
　　Citellus, 511.
cervicalis, Tana, 202.
　　Tupaia, 202.
Cervicapra chanleri, 13.
Cervus, 17.
　　californicus, 21, 575.
　　lewisii, 21, 574.
　　merriami, 17.
　　nannodes, 17.
　　nelsoni, 17.
　　occidentalis, 18.
　　roosevelti, 18.
chacoensis, Akodon, 256.
Chaerephon, 119.
　　jobensis, 119.
　　luzonus, 120.
　　naivashae, 120.
　　pusillus, 120.
chamula, Neotoma, 287.
chanleri, Cervicapra, 13.
　　Redunca, 13.
chapmani, Sylvilagus, 218, 222.
Cheiromeles, 120.
　　parvidens, 120.
chelan, Ursus, 88.
Chelemys, 259.
　　alleni, 259.
chelidonias, Ursus, 88.
chiapensis, Dasyprocta, 358.
　　Heterogeomys, 371.
　　Lepus, 219.
　　Reithrodontomys, 343.
　　Sciurus, 556.
　　Sorex, 197.
　　Sylvilagus, 219.
chihuahuae, Thomomys, 401.
chiliensis, Sciurus, 559.
Chilonatalus, 124.
　　brevimanus, 124.
　　macer, 125.
　　tumidifrons, 125.
Chilonycteris, 129.
　　mexicana, 129.
　　portoricensis, 129.
Chilophylla hirsuta, 117.
Chincha, major, 69.
　　notata, 69.
　　platyrhina, 69.
chinchilloides, Euneomys, 265.
chiricahuae, Sciurus, 555.

chiricahuae, Thomomys, 401.
Chiroderma, 129.
　　isthmicum, 129.
Chironectes, 228.
　　panamensis, 228.
Chiropodomys, 443.
　　niadis, 443.
choco, Sciurus, 559.
chombolis, Galeopterus, 163.
　　Mus, 460.
　　Rattus, 460.
Chraeomys, 260.
　　inornatus, 260.
chrysodeirus, Citellus, 507.
　　Tamias, 507.
chrysogaster, Tupaia, 204.
chrysomalla, Tupaia, 204.
chrysomelas, Presbytis, 247.
chrysonotus, Myotis, 155.
　　Thomomys, 387.
chrysopsis, Reithrodontomys, 341.
chui, Felis, 59.
chuscensis, Sciurus, 551.
ciliolabrum, Vespertilio, 151.
cincticauda, Eliomys, 489.
cineraceus, Dipodomys, 412.
cinerascens, Citellus, 508.
　　Tamias, 508.
cinereicollis, Eutamias, 525.
　　Tamias, 525.
cinereus, Eutamias, 525.
　　Reithrodontomys, 349.
　　Sorex, 185, 187.
cinnamomea, Arvicola, 273.
cinnamomeus, Citellus, 512.
　　Lepus, 211.
　　Pipistrellus, 160.
　　Tamias, 512.
cinnamomina, Ondatra, 300.
cinnamominus, Fiber, 300.
circe, Rhinolophus, 143.
Citellus, 504.
　　ablusus, 517.
　　adocetus, 504.
　　alleni, 519.
　　annectens, 517.
　　arenicola, 520.
　　arizonensis, 511.
　　armatus, 504.
　　artemesiae, 514.
　　barrowensis, 505, 506.
　　beldingi, 506.
　　bernardinus, 507.
　　brunneus, 519.
　　canescens, 506, 517.
　　canus, 514.
　　caryi, 511.
　　castanurus, 507.
　　certus, 511.
　　chrysodeirus, 507.
　　cinerascens, 508.
　　cinnamomeus, 512.
　　connectens, 507.
　　couchii, 508.
　　cryptospilotus, 509.
　　elegans, 509.
　　extimus, 512.

Citellus fisheri 505.
goldmani, 504.
grammurus, 521.
hollisteri, 520.
idahoensis, 511.
insularis, 512.
interpres, 511.
juglans, 521.
kodiacensis, 516.
leucurus, 512.
leurodon, 513.
loringi, 521.
madrensis, 513.
major, 518.
mitratus, 507.
mohavensis, 514.
mollis, 513, 514, 515.
monticola, 520.
nebulicola, 515.
neglectus, 515.
nelsoni, 516.
nevadensis, 510.
obsoletus, 516.
oregonus, 516.
osgoodi, 516.
pallescens, 518.
pallidus, 520.
parvidens, 513.
parvulus, 505.
pennipes, 513.
perotensis, 517.
pessimus, 514.
plesius, 510.
pratensis, 518.
ruficaudus, 508.
saxicola, 510.
sierrae, 506.
stejnegeri, 519.
tereticaudus, 519.
tersus, 513.
tescorum, 512.
texensis, 521.
townsendii, 515.
trinitatis, 508.
utah, 510.
vigilis, 506.
washingtoni, 521.
washoensis, 515.
clabatus, Mus, 460.
Rattus, 460.
clarae, Epimys, 486.
Rattus, 486.
clarencei, Dipodomys, 414.
clarkii, Cratogeomys, 366.
Geomys, 366.
clarus, Eutamias, 526.
Onychomys, 304.
Perognathus, 434.
clavatus, Cariacus, 19.
Claviglis, 404.
griseus, 404.
isolatus, 404.
parvus, 404.
personatus, 405.
clementae, Urocyon, 48.
clementis, Peromyscus, 334.
cleomophila, Dipodomys, 412.

cleomophila, Perognathus, 424.
clinedaphus, Monophyllus, 133.
Clethrionomys, 260.
athabascae, 261.
brevicaudus, 261.
californicus, 260.
carolinensis, 260.
caurinus, 260.
dawsoni, 260.
galei, 261.
idahoensis, 262.
limitis, 262.
loringi, 261.
maurus, 261.
mazama, 262.
nivarius, 262.
norvegicus, 263.
obscurus, 263.
occidentalis, 263.
orca, 263.
rufocanus, 258.
suecicus, 262.
ungava, 263.
vasconiae, 264.
wrangeli, 264.
clusius, Thomomys, 383.
cocos, Galago, 250.
Sciurus, 558.
Coelops, 117.
inflata, 117.
robinsoni, 117.
coffini, Trachops, 136.
cognatus, Hesperomys, 316.
Sylvilagus, 218.
colimae, Reithrodontomys, 341.
colimensis, Oryzomys, 308.
Sciurus, 552.
Urocyon, 48.
collaris, Lagomys, 224.
Ochotona, 224.
colliaei, Sciurus, 553.
collinus, Thomomys, 386.
Colobus, 239.
matschiei, 239.
percivali, 239.
roosevelti, 239.
terrestris, 239.
uellensis, 239.
colonus, Crossarchus, 104.
Mungos, 104.
coloratus, Epimys, 460.
Oryzomys, 309.
Rattus, 460.
columbiana, Martes, 67.
columbianus, Dipodomys, 412.
Odocoileus, 19, 574.
Perodipus, 412.
Perognathus, 427.
Thomomys, 389.
columbiensis, Glaucomys, 534.
colusus, Ursus, 88.
comes, Acratocnus, 570.
commissarius, Mus, 452.
compactus, Dipodomys, 406.
compressus, Macrotus, 132.
comptus, Peromyscus, 316.
concava, Lonchophylla, 132.

concavus, Heterogeomys, 371.
concolor, Rattus, 472.
    Sciurus, 551.
    Simias, 250.
condurensis, Callosciurus, 494.
    Ratufa, 547.
    Sciurus, 494.
Conepatus, 61.
    filipensis, 61.
    mearnsi, 62.
    nelsoni, 62.
    pediculus, 62.
    sonoriensis, 63.
    telmalestes, 62.
    texensis, 62.
    tropicalis, 63.
    venaticus, 62.
confinalis, Thomomys, 390.
confinis, Eutamias, 528.
    Ratufa, 547.
    Sigmodon, 351.
conipus, Callosciurus, 500.
    Sciurus, 494, 500.
connectens, Callospermophilus, 507.
    Citellus, 507.
    Lepus, 219.
    Sylvilagus, 219.
Connochaetes, 8.
    mearnsi, 8.
conscius, Heteromys, 416.
consitus, Bassariscus, 38.
    Cratogeomys, 364.
consobrinus, Eutamias, 526, 528.
    Peromyscus, 328.
    Tamias, 528.
conspicua, Ratufa, 547.
constanzae, Tadarida, 123.
constrictus, Hippopotamus, 25.
    Microtus, 272.
contigua, Lasiopyga, 239.
contractus, Brotomys, 360.
convergens, Thomomys, 379.
convexum, Uroderma, 136.
convexus, Cratogeomys, 365.
cooperi, Eutamias, 526.
    Synaptomys, 354.
    Tamias, 526.
corvus, Presbytis, 248.
coryi, Felis, 53.
Corynorhinus, 146.
    mexicanus, 146.
    pallescens, 146.
costaricensis, Felis, 55, 58.
    Macrogeomys, 372.
    Mustela, 70.
    Nyctomys, 299.
    Odocoileus, 20.
cothurnata, Ratufa, 547.
cottoni, Ourebia, 10.
couchi, Thomomys, 398.
couchii, Citellus, 508.
    Spermophilus, 508.
couesi, Cariacus, 22.
    Erethizon, 364.
    Odocoileus, 22.
    Oryzomys, 307, 308, 310.
coxi, Felis, 58.

cozumelae, Didelphis, 229.
    Mimon, 133.
    Oryzomys, 306.
    Peromyscus, 316.
crassidens, Procyon, 82.
    Pseudorca, 112.
    Thomomys, 401.
crassirostris, Heteromys, 416.
crassodon, Ursus, 88.
crassus, Epimys, 460.
    Pecari, 28.
    Rattus, 460.
    Tayassu, 28.
    Ursus, 88.
cratodon, Dipodomys, 415.
Cratogeomys, 364.
    angusticeps, 364.
    castanops, 364.
    clarkii, 366.
    consitus, 364.
    convexus, 365.
    estor, 367.
    excelsus, 365.
    fulvescens, 367.
    goldmani, 365.
    hirtus, 365.
    irolonis, 367.
    lacrimalis, 365.
    oreocetes, 368.
    peregrinus, 368.
    peridoneus, 365.
    perotensis, 368.
    perplanus, 366.
    planifrons, 366.
    saccharalis, 367.
    subluteus, 367.
    subnubilis, 366.
    subsimus, 366.
    tamaulipensis, 366.
crawfordi, Notiosorex, 181.
    Sorex, 181.
cremoriventer, Mus, 461.
    Rattus, 461.
crepidatus, Phodopus, 339.
crepuscularis, Nycticea, 159.
cressonus, Ursus, 88.
Cricetodipus parvus, 434, 574.
Cricetomys, 443.
    enguvi, 443.
    osgoodi, 444.
    raineyi, 444.
cricetulus, Microtus, 257.
crinitus, Hesperomys, 317.
    Oryzomys, 306.
    Peromyscus, 317.
    Petinomys, 544.
    Pteromys, 544.
    Sciuropterus, 544.
crispus, Liomys, 418.
cristatus, Trachypithecus, 250.
cristobalensis, Peromyscus, 336.
    Sorex, 193.
Crocidura, 167.
    alchemillae, 167.
    alpina, 168.
    altae, 169.
    andamanensis, 168.

Crocidura attenauta, 169.
  beatus, 168.
  caudata, 168.
  daphnia, 168.
  elongata, 168.
  fumosa, 167.
  grandis, 169.
  grisea, 169.
  grisescens, 169.
  halconus, 169.
  hildegardeae, 169, 171.
  lakiundae, 174.
  lea, 170.
  lepidura, 170.
  levicula, 170.
  lignicolor, 170.
  lipara, 172.
  littoralis, 170.
  lutrella, 170.
  lutreola, 171.
  maanjae, 171.
  mimula, 171.
  mindorus, 171.
  muricauda, 171.
  mutesea, 172.
  nicobarica, 172.
  nigripes, 172.
  nilotica, 172.
  nisa, 172.
  pergrisea, 173.
  planiceps, 173.
  procera, 169.
  pullata, 173.
  raineyi, 173.
  rhoditis, 173.
  roosevelti, 173.
  shantungensis, 174.
  sicula, 174.
  simiolus, 174.
  suahelae, 174.
  sururae, 174.
  zaodon, 174.
Crocuta, 61.
  fisi, 61.
crooki, Dorcelaphus, 20.
  Odocoileus, 20.
Crossarchus colonus, 104.
cryptospilotus, Citellus, 509.
  Spermophilus, 509.
Cryptotis, 175.
  alticola, 175.
  berlandieri, 175.
  floridana, 175.
  fossor, 176.
  frontalis, 176.
  goldmani, 177.
  goodwini, 176.
  gracilis, 176.
  griseoventris, 176.
  guerrerensis, 176.
  macer, 178.
  machetes, 178.
  magna, 177.
  mayensis, 177.
  merus, 177.
  mexicana, 177.
  nayaritensis, 179.

Cryptotis nelsoni, 178.
  obscura, 178.
  parva, 175.
  peregrina, 178.
  pueblensis, 179.
  soricina, 179.
Ctenomys, 361.
  osgoodi, 361.
  robustus, 361.
  sericeus, 361.
cubanus, Monophyllus, 133.
culbertsoni, Mustela, 70.
  Putorius, 70.
cumulator, Neotoma, 286.
Cuniculus, 358.
  nelsoni, 358.
cuninghamei, Equus, 232.
cupida, Macaca, 242.
cupidineus, Dipodomys, 412.
cupidus, Pithecus, 242.
curasoae, Leptonycteris, 131.
currax, Pedetes, 490.
curtata, Arvicola, 267.
curtatus, Lagurus, 267.
  Lemmiscus, 267.
  Pipistrellus, 160.
cuyonis, Tupaia, 204.
Cyclopes, 570.
  mexicanus, 570.
cylindrura, Urogale, 207.
cynocephala, Nycticea, 123.
  Tadarida, 123.
Cynomolgus, apoensis, 244.
  cagayanus, 241.
  mindanensis, 244.
  suluensis, 246.
Cynomys, 521.
  gunnisoni, 521.
  leucurus, 522.
  mexicanus, 522.
  zuniensis, 522.
Cynopithecus, 240.
  lembicus, 240.
Cynopterus, 137.
  angulatus, 137, 138.
  babi, 137.
  lyoni, 138.
  major, 137.
  minutus, 138.
  pagensis, 138.
  princeps, 138.

dacota, Arctomys, 539.
  Marmota, 539.
dacotensis, Odocoileus, 22.
dalli, Lepus, 208.
  Ovis, 12.
  Phocaena, 112.
  Phocoenoides, 112.
  Synaptomys, 354.
  Ursus, 89.
daphne, Thomasomys, 357.
daphnia, Crocidura, 168.
dariensis, Ateles, 236.
  Dasyprocta, 358.
  Macrogeomys, 372.
  Oryzomys, 305.

darlingi, Diplomys, 361.
  Isothrix, 361.
Dasymys, 444.
  helukus, 444.
  nigridius, 444.
  orthos, 444.
  rufulus, 444.
  savannus, 445.
Dasyprocta, 358.
  chiapensis, 358.
  dariensis, 358.
  richmondi, 358.
  underwoodi, 359.
  yucatanica, 359.
Dasypterus, 146.
  floridanus, 146.
  intermedius, 146, 571.
Dasypus, 570.
  mexicanus, 570.
datus, Callosciurus, 494.
  Sciurus, 494.
davidsoni, Balaenoptera, 108.
dawsoni, Clethrionomys, 260.
debilis, Molossus, 121.
decoloratus, Peromyscus, 331.
decolorus, Nyctomys, 299.
  Sitomys, 299.
defua, Dephomys, 445.
  Mus, 445.
degelidus, Lasiurus, 148.
degener, Lichonycteris, 132.
Delphinapterus borealis, 110, 575.
Delphinus, 108.
  albimanus, 108.
  albirostratus, 109, 575.
  bairdii, 109, 575.
  delphis, 108, 110.
  erebennus, 111.
  lateralis, 113, 576.
  longidens, 113.
  plagiodon, 113.
delphis, Delphinus, 108, 110.
denniae, Hylomyscus, 447.
Dendrohyrax, 164.
  validus, 164.
Dendromus, 445.
  capitis, 445.
  lineatus, 445.
  percivali, 445.
  spectabilis, 454.
Dendromys, nigrifrons, 454.
dentaneus, Metachirus, 232.
dentatus, Batomys, 443.
  Epimys, 475.
  Pedetes, 490.
  Rattus, 475.
  Tarsius, 252.
dentifer, Mungos, 104.
  Myonax, 104.
Dephomys, 445.
  defua, 445.
depressa, Arctogalidia, 101.
  Kerivoula, 148.
Dermanura phaeotis, 127.
  rava, 127.
deserti, Dipodomys, 406.
  Reithrodontomys, 346.

deserti, Sylvicapra, 15.
deserticola, Nesotragus, 10.
desertorum, Neotoma, 286.
  Thomomys, 384.
desitus, Thomomys, 379.
destructor, Lutra, 65.
  Orca, 112.
devia, Neotoma, 289.
  Vulpes, 50.
devius, Vulpes, 50.
dialeucos, Ichneumia, 104.
  Mungos, 104.
diazi, Romerolagus, 215.
Dicotyles sonoriensis, 29.
Dicrostonyx, 264.
  nelsoni, 264.
  richardsoni, 264.
  rubricatus, 264.
  stevensoni, 265.
  unalascensis, 264.
Didelphis, 228.
  cozumelae, 229.
  richmondi, 229.
  tabascensis, 228.
  texensis, 228.
  yucatanensis, 229.
difficilis, Reithrodontomys, 342.
dilatus, Scapanus, 201, 202.
dilutior, Oryzomys, 305.
dilutus, Callosciurus, 495.
  Sciurus, 495.
Diplomys, 361.
  darlingi, 361.
Dipodomys, 405.
  alfredi, 409.
  ambiguus, 405.
  atronasus, 408.
  baileyi, 414.
  bonnevillei, 409.
  cabezonae, 405.
  californicus, 405.
  celsus, 410.
  cineraceus, **412.**
  clarencei, 414.
  cleomophila, 412.
  columbianus, 412.
  compactus, 406.
  cratodon, 415.
  cupidineus, 412.
  deserti, 406.
  elator, 406.
  evexus, 412.
  exilis, 408.
  gabrielsoni, 407.
  goldmani, 406.
  heermanni, 415.
  ingens, 407.
  insularis, 407.
  kernensis, 408.
  leucotis, 410.
  levipes, 410.
  longipes, 407.
  luteolus, 413.
  margaritae, 407.
  marshalli, 413.
  mayensis, 408.
  merriami, 408, 409.

Dipodomys microps, 409.
   mitchelli, 411.
   montanus, 411.
   morroensis, 411.
   nelsoni, 411.
   nevadensis, 408.
   nexilis, 413.
   nitratoides, 408.
   nitratus, 409.
   oklahomae, 412.
   ornatus, 413.
   panamintinus, 413.
   peninsularis, 414.
   perblandus, 415.
   perotensis, 413.
   perplexus, 414.
   platycephalus, 414.
   preblei, 410.
   regillus, 409.
   russeolus, 410.
   simulans, 415.
   sonoriensis, 406.
   spectabilis, 414.
   stephensi, 415.
   subtenuis, 410.
   tularensis, 405.
   utahensis, 411.
   venustus, 416.
   zygomaticus, 415.
Dipodops longipes, 407.
director, Callosciurus, 495.
   Sciurus, 495.
discolor, Tupaia, 204.
dispar, Neotoma, 288.
   Perognathus, 426.
disparilis, Peromyscus, 317.
dissimilis, Thomomys, 395.
divergens, Thomomys, 379.
dobsoni, Sorex, 184.
dolbrogeae, Spalax, 566.
dolichocephalus, Macrogeomys, 372.
dollmani, Otomys, 453.
domelicus, Callosciurus, 495.
   Mus, 461.
   Rattus, 461.
   Sciurus, 495.
domensis, Perognathus, 425.
dominicensis, Myotis, 152.
   Natalus, 125.
domitor, Mus, 461.
   Rattus, 461.
Dorcelaphus crooki, 20.
   eremicus, 21.
   texanus, 21.
dorsalis, Eutamias, 526.
   Peromyscus, 324.
   Reithrodontomys, 342.
   Sciurus, 551, 555.
   Tamias, 526.
douglasii, Tamiasciurus, 561.
dowii, Elasmognathus, 233.
   Tapirella, 233.
Dremomys, 522.
   lentus, 522.
   pernyi, 522.
ducis, Epimys, 471.
   Rattus, 471.

duplicatus, Microtus, 270.
durangae, Sorex, 185.
durangi, Thomomys, 401.
durumae, Epimys, 451.
   Mastomys, 451.
dusorgus, Ursus, 89.
dutcheri, Geomys, 369.
   Microtus, 273.
dychei, Reithrodontomys, 342.
Dymecodon, 198.
   pilirostris, 198.
Dysopes aurispinosus, 122.

Echimys, 362.
   flavidus, 362.
Echinosorex, 165.
   minor, 165.
Echiothrix, 446.
   brevicula, 446.
   centrosa, 446.
Ectophylla, 129.
   alba, 129.
edarata, Tupaia, 205.
edax, Arvicola, 273.
efficax, Nectomys, 284.
effugius, Sciurus, 552.
Egocerus, 8.
   roosevelti, 8.
Elasmognathus bairdii, 233.
   dowii, 233.
elassodon, Sorex, 187.
elata, Spilogale, 76.
elator, Dipodomys, 406.
electra. Lagenorhynchus, 110.
elegans, Citellus, 509.
   Spermophilus, 509.
elegantulus, Midas, 236.
Elephantulus, 166.
   mariakanae, 166.
   phaeus, 166.
elgonae, Lupulella, 46.
   Thos, 46.
Eliomys, 489.
   cincticauda, 489.
   pallidus, 489.
   parvus, 404.
elongata, Crocidura, 168.
   Glossophaga, 130.
eltonclarki, Ursus, 89.
elusus, Peromyscus, 325.
elymocetes, Microtus, 274.
emarginatus, Sorex, 185.
Emballonura, 115.
   anambensis, 115.
   peninsularis, 116.
   pusilla, 116.
   semicaudata, 116.
   sulcata, 116.
emesi, Leggada, 448.
   Mus, 448.
emotus, Thomomys, 386.
enclavae, Leggada, 447.
   Mus, 447.
endoecus, Microtus, 280.
endorobae, Epimys, 447.
engana, Kerivoula, 148.
enganus, Mus, 461.

enganus, Paradoxurus, 106.
  Pteropus, 140.
  Rattus, 461.
  Sus, 26.
enguvi, Cricetomys, 443.
Enhydra, 63.
  nereis, 63.
enixus, Thomomys, 401.
Eonycteris, 138.
  robusta, 138.
Epimys barussanus, 457.
  basilanus, 457.
  batus, 457.
  benguetensis, 457.
  borneanus, 458.
  calcis, 459.
  centralis, 439.
  clarae, 486.
  coloratus, 460.
  crassus, 460.
  dentatus, 475.
  ducis, 471.
  durumae, 451.
  endorobae, 447.
  exsul, 476.
  fortunatus, 476.
  fulmineus, 463.
  gala, 464.
  gracilis, 464.
  insulanus, 476.
  insularum, 486.
  ismailliae, 451.
  kaimosae, 446.
  lamucotanus, 471.
  lepidus, 466.
  leucophaeatus, 466.
  luta, 468.
  maerens, 468.
  mara, 469.
  mayonicus, 469.
  mengurus, 470.
  nasatus, 471.
  neumani, 451.
  ornatulus, 472.
  pannellus, 472.
  panya, 452.
  pauper, 477.
  perflavus, 473.
  pollens, 474.
  potens, 474.
  querceti, 475.
  roa, 478.
  robiginosus, 478.
  saturatus, 478.
  sebucus, 479.
  shigarus, 477.
  socer, 471.
  solus, 480.
  spatulatus, 480.
  stentor, 481.
  taitae, 455.
  tingius, 483.
  tua, 484.
  turbidus, 477.
  turneri, 440.
  tyrannus, 484.
  ubecus, 484.

Epimys ulae, 453.
  valens, 485.
  viclana, 478.
  victor, 485.
  vigoratus, 485.
Eptesicus, 146.
  bahamensis, 146.
  hispaniolae, 147.
  miradorensis, 572.
  pallens, 147.
  pallidus, 147.
  ugandae, 147.
  wetmorei, 147.
Equus, 232.
  cuninghamei, 232.
erebennus, Delphinus, 111.
erebus, Sciurus, 495.
eremicoides, Peromyscus, 313.
eremicus, Dorcelaphus, 21.
  Euarctos, 86.
  Hesperomys, 317.
  Lynx, 60.
  Odocoileus, 21.
  Perognathus, 427.
  Peromyscus, 317, 318, 328.
  Sigmodon, 351.
  Ursus, 86.
eremus, Peromyscus, 325.
Erethizon, 364.
  couesi, 364.
  myops, 364.
ereunetes, Ursus, 97.
ericaeus, Thomomys, 398.
Erinaceus sotikae, 165.
erlangeri, Genetta, 103.
Eropeplus, 446.
  canus, 446.
Erophylla, 130.
  bombifrons, 130.
  mariguanensis, 130.
  planifrons, 130.
Erythrocebus, 240.
  pyrronotus, 240.
  whitei, 240.
estor, Canis, 41.
  Cratogeomys, 367.
  Mephitis, 68.
Euarctos, 85.
  amblyceps, 85.
  carlottae, 86.
  eremicus, 86.
  floridanus, 86.
  thibetanus, 86.
Euchoreutes, 359.
  alashanicus, 359.
eulophus, Ursus, 89.
Eumops, 120.
  californicus, 120.
  glaucinus, 121.
  hansae, 121.
Euneomys, 265.
  chinchilloides, 265.
  petersoni, 265.
Euprocyon panamensis, 81.
euronotus, Sorex, 183.
europs, Nyctinomus, 123.
  Tadarida, 123.

Euroscaptor, 199.
   grandis, 199.
   parvidens, 199.
eurous, Rattus, 478.
Eutamias, 522.
   albogularis, 524.
   alleni, 532.
   alpinus, 522.
   altaicus, 523.
   amoenus, 523.
   animosus, 530.
   arizonensis, 528.
   atristriatus, 524.
   borealis, 523.
   cacodemus, 530.
   callipeplus, 524.
   canicaudus, 524.
   caniceps, 525.
   canipes, 525.
   carminis, 526.
   caryi, 528.
   caurinus, 525.
   cinereicollis, 525.
   cinereus, 525.
   clarus, 526.
   confinis, 528.
   consobrinus, 526, 528.
   cooperi, 526.
   dorsalis, 526.
   grisescens, 528.
   hopiensis, 527.
   inyoensis, 532.
   jacksoni, 529.
   ludibundus, 527.
   luteiventris, 531.
   meridionalis, 527.
   obscurus, 529.
   ochraceus, 523.
   ochrogenys, 533.
   operarius, 523.
   oreocetes, 529.
   pallidus, 531.
   palmeri, 530.
   panamintinus, 530.
   pictus, 529.
   quadrimaculatus, 527.
   quadrivittatus, 530.
   ruficaudus, 531.
   senescens, 531.
   senex, 532.
   sequioensis, 532.
   simulans, 531.
   siskiyou, 533.
   solivagus, 524.
   speciosus, 532.
   umbrinus, 533.
   umbrosus, 524.
   utahensis, 527.
   vallicola, 523.
everetti, Tragulus, 34.
   Urogale, 207.
evexa, Lutra, 64.
evexus, Dipodomys, 412.
evidens, Sciurus, 563.
   Tomeutes, 563.
evides, Peromyscus, 332.
evotis, Myotis, 152.

evotis, Notiosorex, 181.
   Sorex, 181.
   Vespertilio, 152.
Evotomys alascensis, 260
   athabascae, 261.
   brevicaudus, 261.
   californicus, 260.
   carolinensis, 260.
   caurinus, 260.
   galei, 261.
   idahoensis, 262.
   limitis, 262.
   loringi, 261.
   mazama, 262.
   nivarius, 262.
   norvegicus, 263.
   obscurus, 263.
   occidentalis, 263.
   orca, 263.
   suecicus, 262.
   ungava, 263.
   vasconiae, 264.
   wrangeli, 264.
excelsifrons, Rangifer, 24.
excelsus, Cratogeomys, 365.
   Procyon, 82.
exiguus, Peromyscus, 326.
   Rattus, 476.
   Sylvilagus, 217.
   Vespertilio, 572.
exilipes, Blarina, 175.
exilis, Dipodomys, 408.
eximius, Microsorex, 179.
   Sorex, 179.
   Thomomys, 401.
   Ursus, 89.
exsul, Epimys, 476.
   Rattus, 476.
extenuatus, Thomomys, 380.
extera, Lutra, 64.
   exterus, Peromyscus, 325.
extimus, Ammospermophilus, 512.
   Citellus, 512.
   Perognathus, 425.
   Thomomys, 402.
extremus, Myotis, 155.
exulans, Mus, 462.
   Rattus, 462.

facetus, Rattus, 462.
faesula, Rupricapra, 14.
fallax, Geomys, 370.
   Neotoma, 287.
   Perognathus, 427.
faunulus, Pteropus, 140.
felipensis, Orthogeomys, 373.
   Peromyscus, 319.
Felis, 53.
   aequatorialis, 53.
   albescens, 57.
   apache, 53.
   arizonensis, 58.
   arundivaga, 53.
   azteca, 56.
   aztecus, 56.
   browni, 53.
   cacomitli, 53.

Felis centralis, 54.
  chui, 59.
  coryi, 53.
  costaricensis, 55, 58.
  coxi, 58.
  fortis, 59.
  fossata, 55.
  fusca, 59.
  goldmani, 56.
  greeni, 54.
  hippolestes, 56.
  hollisteri, 56.
  incarum, 54.
  kaibabensis, 54.
  limitis, 57.
  mayensis, 54.
  mearnsi, 55, 58.
  nandae, 57.
  nelsoni, 59.
  notialis, 57.
  nyanzae, 56.
  oaxacensis, 55.
  olympus, 56.
  oregonensis, 56.
  paraguensis, 58.
  patagonica, 59.
  paulensis, 58.
  pirrensis, 59.
  roosevelti, 57.
  sonoriensis, 59.
  stanleyana, 54.
  taitae, 57.
  tingia, 60.
  vancouverensis, 54.
  veraecrucis, 58.
  youngi, 54, 55.
  yucatanica, 55.
femoralis, Presbytis, 247, 248, 249.
  Ratufa, 547.
femorosacca, Tadarida, 123.
femorosaccus, Nyctinomus, 123.
ferox, Mungos, 104.
ferreocanus, Mus, 462.
  Rattus, 462.
ferreus, Monophyllus, 134.
  Sciurus, 551.
fertilis, Arvicola, 267.
  Hyperacrius, 267.
festinus, Lepus, 211.
Fiber cinnamominus, 300.
  hudsonius, 300.
  macrodon, 300.
  mergens, 301.
  ripensis, 301.
  spatulatus, 300.
  zalophus, 301.
filchneri, Lepus, 214.
filipensis, Conepatus, 61.
fimbripes, Sorex, 185.
firmus, Mus, 462.
  Rattus, 462.
fisheri, Citellus, 505.
  Microtus, 269.
  Sorex, 185.
  Spermophilus, 505.
  Tamias, 560.
  Thomomys, 389.

fisi, Crocuta, 61.
flammeus, Pappogeomys, 374.
flavescens, Perognathus, 428.
flavicauda, Pygathirx, 249.
  Trachypithecus, 249.
flavicollis, Tragulus, 32.
flavidulus, Mus, 482.
  Rattus, 482.
flavidus, Echimys, 362.
  Loncheres, 362.
  Thomomys, 387.
flaviventer, Mus, 462.
  Rattus, 462.
flavus, Perognathus, 428.
  Sicista, 567.
  Sminthus, 567.
flebilis, Mus, 463.
  Rattus, 463.
floridana, Blarina, 175.
  Cryptotis, 175.
floridanus, Canis, 41.
  Dasypterus, 146.
  Euarctos, 86.
  Oryzomys, 309.
  Peromyscus, 324.
  Ursus, 86.
floweri, Kogia, 114.
focalinus, Tragulus, 32.
fodiens, Neomys, 181.
fontinalis, Sorex, 186.
formosa, Marmosa, 229, 230.
formosus, Perognathus, 429.
  Tragulus, 32.
fortidens, Rangifer, 24.
fortis, Felis, 59.
  Molossus, 121.
fortunatus, Epimys, 476.
  Rattus, 476.
fossata, Felis, 55.
fossor, Blarina, 176.
  Cryptotis, 176.
  Sciurus, 556, 573.
fraterculus, Tarsius, 252.
  Urocyon, 49.
fremens, Mus, 463.
  Rattus, 463.
frida, Hesperomys, 266.
frondator, Castor, 254.
frons, Lavia, 118.
frontalis, Cryptotis, 176.
  Oryzomys, 306.
frontata, Mephitis, 68.
frumentor, Sciurus, 553.
frustror, Canis, 41.
frutectanus, Napaeozapus, 566.
fuliginosus, Onychomys, 301.
  Perognathus, 429.
fulmineus, Epimys, 463.
  Rattus, 463.
fulvescens, Cratogeomys, 367.
fulvicollis, Tragulus, 33.
fulviventer, Microtus, 274.
  Neotoma, 288.
fulvus, Geomys, 286.
  Peromyscus, 332.
  Thomomys, 386.
fumatus, Myomys, 453.

fumosa Crocidura, 167.
  Ochotona, 225.
fumosus, Geomys, 375.
  Platygeomys, 375.
  Vampyrops, 137.
Funambulus castaneus, 537.
  obscurus, 538.
  peninsulae, 538.
  rostratus, 538.
furvus, Phalanger, 232.
fusca, Arctogalidia, 101.
  Felis, 59.
  Macaca, 242.
  Neotoma, 295.
fuscipes, Neotoma, 288.
  Ochotona, 226.
  Procyon, 82.
fuscus, Adelonycteris, 572.
  Glaucomys, 534.
  Macacus, 242.
  Murina, 150.
  Paradoxurus, 106.
  Thomomys, 383.

gabbi, Lepus, 218.
  Sylvilagus, 218.
gabbii, Bassaricyon, 79.
gabrielsoni, Dipodomys, 407.
gaillardi, Lepus, 211.
  Ovis, 11.
gala, Epimys, 464.
  Rattus, 464.
Galago, 250.
  cocos, 250.
  sotikae, 250.
  zanzibaricus, 250.
galei, Clethrionomys, 261.
  Evotomys, 261.
Galeopithecus aoris, 162.
  gracilis, 163.
  natunae, 163.
  pumilus, 164.
  saturatus, 164.
  tuancus, 164.
Galeopterus, 162.
  abbotti, 162.
  aoris, 162.
  borneanus, 163.
  chombolis, 163.
  gracilis, 163.
  lautensis, 163.
  natunae, 163.
  pumilus, 164.
  saturatus, 164.
  tuancus, 164.
Galicitis canaster, 63.
gambelii, Hesperomys, 319.
  Peromyscus, 319, 334.
gatunensis, Oryzomys, 307.
Gazella, 9.
  raineyi, 9.
  roosevelti, 9.
  serengetae, 9.
geminorum, Pteropus, 140.
gemmeus, Sylvisorex, 198.
Genetta, 103.
  erlangeri, 103.

Genetta pumila, 103.
gentilis, Peromyscus, 321.
Geomys, 368.
  ammophilus, 369.
  arenarius, 368.
  attwateri, 369.
  breviceps, 368.
  clarkii, 366.
  dutcheri, 369.
  fallax, 370.
  fulvus, 386.
  fumosus, 375.
  gymnurus, 375.
  llanensis, 369.
  lutescens, 369.
  mobilensis, 370.
  nelsoni, 375.
  personatus, 370.
  sagittalis, 369.
  texensis, 370.
  tropicalis, 370.
Georychus kapiti, 254.
Geoxus, 265.
  michaelseni, 265.
Gerbillus, 265.
  arenicolor, 265.
germani, Trachypithecus, 248.
geronimensis, Phoca, 235.
gibbsii, Neürotrichus, 199.
  Urotrichus, 199.
gigas, Alces, 16.
  Notiosorex, 181.
gilbiventer, Mus, 464.
  Rattus, 464.
gillii, Tursiops, 113.
gilva, Neotoma, 287.
gilvus, Perognathus, 431.
glacialis, Alticola, 257.
  Sorex, 186.
glaucinus, Eumops, 121.
Glaucomys, 533.
  bangsi, 534.
  bullatus, 534.
  columbiensis, 534.
  fuscus, 534.
  goldmani, 535.
  griseifrons, 534.
  herreranus, 535.
  klamathensis, 533.
  latipes, 535.
  macrotis, 535.
  madrensis, 535.
  saturatus, 535.
  stephensi, 534.
  texensis, 536.
  yukonensis, 536.
  zaphaeus, 533.
Globicephala, 109.
  scammonii, 109.
Globicephalus, 109.
  scammonii, 109.
Glossophaga, 130.
  elongata, 130.
  microtis, 131.
  mutica, 130.
  rostrata, 131.
  soricina, 131.

Glossophaga villosa, 131.
godmani, Sorex, 186.
goethalsi, Hoplomys, 362.
goldmani, Blarina, 177.
　　Canis, 42.
　　Citellus, 504.
　　Cratogeomys, 365.
　　Cryptotis, 177.
　　Dipodomys, 406.
　　Felis, 56.
　　Glaucomys, 535.
　　Heteromys, 417.
　　Lepus, 215.
　　Mustela, 71.
　　Nelsonia, 284.
　　Neotoma, 289.
　　Ochotona, 226.
　　Oryzomys, 307.
　　Perodipus, 406.
　　Perognathus, 429, 436.
　　Peromyscus, 320.
　　Putorius, 71.
　　Reithrodontomys, 343.
　　Sciuropterus, 535.
　　Sciurus, 556.
　　Sigmodon, 353.
　　Spermophilus, 504.
　　Sylvilagus, 215.
　　Thomomys, 390.
gondokorae, Leggada, 447.
　　Mus, 447.
goodei, Kogia, 114.
goodwini, Cryptotis, 176.
Gorgon mearnsi, 8.
gossii, Arvicola, 354.
　　Synaptomys, 354.
gossypinus, Hesperomys, 320.
　　Peromyscus, 316, 320.
gracilis, Cryptotis, 176.
　　Epimys, 464.
　　Galeopithecus, 163.
　　Galeopterus, 163.
　　Hesperomys, 321.
　　Peromyscus, 321.
　　Rattus, 464.
　　Rhogeëssa, 162.
　　Spilogale, 76.
　　Tamias, 530.
　　Thomasomys, 357.
grahamensis, Thomomys, 387.
grahami, Lepus, 211.
Grammomys, 446.
　　littoralis, 446.
grammurus, Citellus, 521.
Grampidephis, 109.
　　griseus, 109.
Grampus, stearnsii, 109.
grandis, Crocidura, 169.
　　Euroscaptor, 199.
Graphiurus, isolatus, 404.
　　johnstoni, 404.
　　personatus, 405.
grata, Leggada, 448.
gratus, Peromyscus, 321, 336.
gravis, Quemisia, 363.
graysoni, Lepus, 221.
　　Sylvilagus, 221.

grebnitzkii, Ziphius, 115.
greeni, Felis, 54.
gregoryi, Canis, 45.
grinnelli, Procyon, 82.
grisea, Crocidura, 169.
griseicollis, Ratufa, 547.
griseifrons, Glaucomys, 534.
griseoflavus, Reithrodontomys, 343.
griseoventris, Cryptotis, 176.
grisescens, Allactaga, 359.
　　Baiomys, 259.
　　Crocidura, 169.
　　Eutamias, 528.
　　Myotis, 152.
griseus, Claviglis, 404.
　　Grampidelphis, 109.
　　Heteromys, 417.
　　Lepus, 214.
　　Mus, 440.
　　Reithrodontomys, 344.
　　Sciurus, 573.
Grison, 63.
　　canaster, 63.
guadalupensis, Microtus, 276.
　　Thomomys, 380.
guairae, Proechimys, 363.
guardia, Peromyscus, 321.
guatemalae, Urocyon, 48.
guatemalensis, Microtus, 274.
　　Peromyscus, 322.
gubernator, Lagenorhynchus, 109, 111.
guerrerensis, Cryptotis, 176.
　　Hodomys 266.
　　Liomys, 419.
　　Orthogeomys, 373.
　　Oryzomys, 307.
　　Potos, 80.
　　Sigmodon, 351.
Gulo, 64.
　　vancouverensis, 64.
gundlachi, Capromys, 361.
gunnisoni, Cynomys, 521.
　　Peromyscus, 325.
　　Spermophilus, 521.
gyas, Ursus, 89.
Gymnura minor, 165.
gymnurus, Geomys, 375.
　　Platygeomys, 375.

haidarum, Mustela, 71.
　　Putorius, 71.
halconus, Crocidura, 169.
Halichoerus antarcticus, 234.
hallensis, Alopex, 40.
　　Vulpes, 40.
hamatus, Rattus, 464.
hansae, Eumops, 121.
Harpyionycteris, 139.
　　celebensis, 139.
harrimani, Vulpes, 50.
hatcheri, Reithrodon, 340.
haydeni, Sorex, 186.
haydenii, Arvicola, 274.
　　Microtus, 274.
heberfolium, Macrotus, 132.
hebes, Vulpes, 52.
heermanni, Dipodomys, 415.

helaletes, Synaptomys, 355.
Heliophobius, 254.
    kapiti, 254.
helios, Aonyx, 61.
    Pipistrellus, 160.
Heliosciurus, 536.
    libericus, 536.
    maculatus, 536.
    madogae, 536.
    shindi, 536.
    undulatus, 537.
Heliosorex roosevelti, 173.
helleri, Aethomys, 439.
Helogale affinis, 103.
helukus, Dasymys, 444.
helveolus, Sciurus, 559.
helvolus, Reithrodontomys, 344.
helvus, CalloSciurus, 493.
    Sciurus, 493.
Hemiderma perspicillata, 128.
    subrufum, 128.
    tricolor, 128.
Hemigale minor, 103.
Hemigalus, 103.
    minor, 103.
henshawi, Ursus, 90.
henshawii, Vespertilio, 156.
hercynicus, Sorex, 182.
hernandezi, Sciurus, 552, 558.
herreranus, Glaucomys, 535.
Hesperomys, 266.
    affinis, 311.
    anthonyi, 312.
    articus [sic], 312.
    austerus, 313.
    bairdii, 314.
    boylii, 314.
    campestris, 315.
    cognatus, 316.
    crinitus, 317.
    eremicus, 317.
    frida, 266.
    gambelii, 319.
    gossypinus, 320.
    gracilis, 321.
    leucopus, 321.
    macropus, 324.
    megalotis, 327.
    melanophrys, 327.
    parasiticus, 330.
    rufinus, 323.
    sonoriensis, 331.
    texanus, 333.
    torridus, 303.
    truei, 335.
hesperus, Pipistrellus, 160,
    Scotophilus, 160.
    Thomomys, 390.
Heterogeomys, 371.
    chiapensis, 371.
    concavus, 371.
    isthmicus, 371.
    teapensis, 371.
    tehuantepecus, 371.
    torridus, 372.
    yucatanensis, 371.
Heterohyrax, 165.

Heterohyrax albipes, 165.
Heteromys, 416.
    annectens, 418.
    conscius, 416.
    crassirostris, 416.
    goldmani, 417.
    griseus, 417.
    lepturus, 417.
    nelsoni, 417.
    panamensis, 417.
    planifrons, 416.
    subaffinis, 417.
    temporalis, 418.
    zonalis, 418.
heterothrix, Liomys, 419.
Hexolobodon, 362.
    phenax, 362.
hildegardeae, Crocidura, 169, 171.
hiltonensis, Odocoileus, 23.
hindei, Atelerix, 165.
hippolestes, Felis, 56.
Hippopotamus, 25.
    constrictus, 25.
    kiboko, 25.
Hipposideros, 117.
    barbensis, 117.
    insolens, 118.
    nicobarulae, 118.
    pelingensis, 118.
    toala, 118.
hipposideros, Rhinolophus, 144.
hippurellus, Sciurus, 563.
    Tomeutes, 563.
hippurosus, Sciurus, 563.
    Tomeutes, 563.
hirsuta, Chilophylla, 117.
hirsutus, Artibeus, 127.
    Myotis, 153.
    Reithrodontomys, 344.
    Rhinolophus, 143.
hirtus, Cratogeomys, 365.
    Procyon, 82.
    Sciurus, 557.
hispaniolae, Eptesicus, 147.
hispidus, Perognathus, 430, 434.
hitchensi, Sylvilagus, 219.
Hodomys, 266.
    alleni, 266.
    guerrerensis, 266.
    vetulus, 266.
hollisteri, Citellus, 520.
    Felis, 56.
    Leo, 56.
    Peromyscus, 325.
    Sorex, 192.
Holochilus, 266.
    incarum, 266.
holzneri, Lepus, 222.
    Sylvilagus, 222.
holzworthi, Ursus, 90.
hondurensis, Canis, 42.
    Sylvilagus, 219.
hoots, Ursus, 90.
hopiensis, Eutamias, 527.
    Perognathus, 428.
Hoplomys, 362.
    goethalsi, 362.

horriaeus, Ursus, 91.
hosei, Presbytis, 248.
  Tragulus, 38.
howelli, Scalopus, 200.
  Thomomys, 380.
hoyi, Microsorex, 179.
  Sorex, 179.
hualpaiensis, Microtus, 276.
  Thomomys, 380.
hudsonius, Fiber, 300.
humboldtensis, Sorex, 196.
humeralis, Nycticeius, 159.
  Pecari, 29.
  Tayassu, 29.
humilis, Sciurus, 564.
  Tomeutes, 564.
hydrobadistes, Sorex, 192.
Hydrochoerus, 437.
  isthmius, 438.
  notialis, 437.
hylaeum, Plagiodontia, 362.
hylaeus, Peromyscus, 322.
Hylobates, 251.
  abbotti, 251.
  albibarbis, 251.
  klossii, 251.
hylocetes, Oryzomys, 307.
  Peromyscus, 322.
hylocoetes, Apomys, 441.
hylodromus, Ursus, 98.
Hylomyscus, 446.
  denniae, 447.
  kaimosae, 446.
Hylopetes, 537.
  amoenus, 537.
Hyperacrius, 266.
  brachylix, 266.
  fertilis, 267.
Hyperaodon [sic] semijunctus, 115.
Hyperodon [sic] semijunctus, 115.
hypomicrus, Nesophontes, 166.
hypophaeus, Sciurus, 554.
hystrella, Acomys, 439.

ibeana, Ichneumia, 104.
Ichneumia, 104.
  dialeucos, 104.
  ibeana, 104.
ictericus, Callosciurus, 496.
  Sciurus, 496.
Icticyon, 46.
  panamensis, 46.
Ictonyx, 64.
  albescens, 64.
idahoensis, Brachylagus, 208.
  Citellus, 511.
  Clethrionomys, 262.
  Evotomys, 262.
  Lepus, 208.
  Perognathus, 434.
  Sorex, 187.
  Sylvilagus, 208.
  Thomomys, 390.
  Ursus, 91.
Idiurus, 439.
  macrotis, 439.
idoneus, Oryzomys, 308.

ignavus, Bradypus, 569.
illinoensis, Neotoma, 288.
imitabilis, Thomomys, 380.
imparilis, Platygeomys, 375.
imperator, Ursus, 91.
impiger, Ursus, 93.
impudens, Pithecus, 242.
inca, Lestoros, 228.
  Orolestes, 228.
incana, Ochotona, 226.
incanus, Pteromys, 545.
incarum, Felis, 54.
  Holochilus, 266.
incautus, Procyon, 82.
incensus, Thomomys, 398.
inclarus, Peromyscus, 325.
  Platygeomys, 375.
incomptus, Thomomys, 380.
inconsonans, Alouatta, 235.
indianola, Spilogale, 76.
indochinensis, Macaca, 244.
inesperatus, Procyon, 83.
inexpectatus, Callosciurus, 495.
  Sciurus, 495.
inflata, Coelops, 117.
  Tupaia, 205.
inflatus, Scalopus, 200.
infuscatus, Sciurus, 556.
ingens, Dipodomys, 407.
  Lutreola, 74.
  Mustela, 74.
  Perodipus, 407.
innuitus, Alopex, 40.
  Microtus, 274.
  Mictomys, 355.
  Synaptomys, 355.
  Ursus, 92.
  Vulpes, 40.
inopinata, Neotoma, 293.
inopinatus, Ursus, 92.
  Vetularctos, 92.
inopinus, Perognathus, 427.
inops, Rhinolophus, 143.
inornata, Arctogalidia, 101.
  Neotoma, 293.
inornatus, Chraeomys, 260.
  Perognathus, 430.
insignis, Apomys, 441.
  Ratufa, 548.
insolatus, Rattus, 465.
insolens, Hipposideros, 118.
insonus, Lepus, 221.
  Sylvilagus, 221.
insulana, Macaca, 242.
insulanus, Epimys, 476.
  Rattus, 476.
insularis, Ammospermophilus, 512.
  Citellus, 512.
  Dipodomys, 407.
  Marmosa, 229.
  Microtus, 274, 279.
  Neotoma, 289.
  Perognathus, 425.
  Procyon, 83.
  Pteropus, 141.
  Ursus, 89.
insulatum, Epimys, 486.

insulatum, Rattus, 486.
insulicola, Bassariscus, 39.
  Peromyscus, 318.
integer, Mus, 465.
  Rattus, 465.
interior, Myotis, 153.
intermedia, Mormoops, 134.
  Tadarida, 124.
intermedius, Dasypterus, 146, 571.
  Lasiurus, 146, 571.
  Perognathus, 430.
  Phenacomys, 338.
  Thomomys, 387.
internatus, Thomomys, 381.
interpres, Citellus, 511.
  Tamias, 511.
intervectus, Microsorex, 180.
invicta, Marmosa, 230.
inyoensis, Eutamias, 532.
Iomys, 537.
  lepidus, 537.
iridescens, Pelomys, 454.
irolonis, Cratogeomys, 367.
irremotus, Canis, 43.
irus, Macaca, 241, 242, 243, 244.
isiolae, Saccostomus, 487.
ismailliae ,Epimys, 451.
  Mastomys, 451.
isolatus, Claviglis, 404.
  Graphiurus, 404.
  Sorex, 190.
Isolobodon, 362.
  levir, 362.
Isothrix darlingi, 361.
isthmica, Marmosa, 230.
  Neotoma, 291.
isthmicum, Chiroderma, 129.
isthmicus, Heterogeomys, 371.
  Potos, 81.
isthmius, Hydrochoerus, 438.
  Liomys, 420.
  Microsciurus, 541.
  Sciurus, 541.
Ithydontia levir, 362.

jacksoni, Eutamias, 529.
  Perognathus, 422.
  Sigmodon, 351.
jalapae, Reithrodontomys, 342.
jalorensis, Lariscus, 538.
jamaicensis, Macrotus, 133.
jamesi, Canis, 42.
jebelae, Arvicanthis, 442.
Jentinkia, 40.
  campechensis, 40.
jewetti, Ochotona, 226.
jobensis, Chaerephon, 119.
  Nyctinomus, 119.
johnstoni, Cercopithecus, 238, 239.
  Graphiurus, 404.
jubatulas, Sus, 26.
jubatus, Sus, 27.
juglans, Citellus, 521.
jugularis, Tragulus, 33.
julianus, Mus, 466.
  Rattus, 466.
juncensis, Sorex, 184.

kadiacensis, Microtus, 275.
  Mustela, 70.
  Putorius, 70.
kahari, Paraxerus, 543.
kaibabensis, Felis, 54.
  Sciurus, 556.
  Thomomys, 385.
kaimosae, Epimys, 446.
  Hylomyscus, 446.
  Lasiopyga, 238.
kakumegae, Lepus, 211.
kaneii, Mustela, 71.
  Putorius, 71.
kapiti, Georychus, 254.
  Heliophobius, 254.
keenii, Myotis, 158.
  Vespertilio, 158.
kelleri, Mus, 466.
  Rattus, 466.
kelloggi, Thomomys, 399.
kenaiensis, Tamiasciurus, 561.
  Ursus, 92.
  Vulpes, 50.
keniae, Alcelaphus, 7.
  Bubalis, 7.
keniensis, Rhinolophus, 143.
kennerleyi, Ursus, 92.
Kerivoula, 147.
  bombifrons, 147.
  depressa, 148.
  engana, 148.
  minuta, 148.
kernensis, Dipodomys, 408.
kiboko, Hippopotamus, 25.
kibonotensis, Cercopithecus, 237.
kidderi, Ursus, 92.
kima, Lasiopyga, 237.
klamathensis, Glaucomys, 533.
  Lepus, 212.
  Reithrodontomys, 344.
  Sciuropterus, 533.
  Ursus, 93.
klossii, Callosciurus, 496.
  Hylobates, 251.
  Sciurus, 496.
  Symphalangus, 251.
kluane, Ursus, 93.
Kobus, 9.
  kuru, 9.
  raineyi, 9.
kodiacensis, Citellus, 516.
  Lutra, 64.
  Spermophilus, 516.
Kogia, 114.
  breviceps, 114.
  floweri, 114.
  goodei, 114.
kohtauensis, Tupaia, 205.
kongoni, Alcelaphus, 7.
  Bubalis, 7.
koratensis, Presbytis, 248.
  Rattus, 476.
koratis, Rattus, 475.
kramensis, Rattus, 476.
kramis, Rattus, 475.
kuru, Kobus, 9.
kwakiutl, Ursus, 93.

labradorius, Canis, 43.
   Lepus, 208, 212.
   Microtus, 281.
laceianus, Peromyscus, 330.
laceyi, Peromyscus, 315.
lachuguilla, Thomomys, 378.
lacrimalis, Cratogeomys, 365.
lacustris, Lutreola, 74.
   Mustela, 74.
laenata, Ratufa, 548.
Lagenorhynchus, 109.
   acutus, 109, 110, 111.
   electra, 110.
   gubernator, 109, 111.
   obliquidens, 110.
   obscurus, 576.
   perspicillatus, 110, 111.
Lagomys collaris, 224.
   schisticeps, 226.
Lagostomus, 256.
   petilidens, 256.
lagunae, Peromyscus, 335.
   Sorex, 187.
lagunensis, Pappogeomys, 374.
Lagurus curtatus, 267.
lakiundae, Crocidura, 174.
lampensis, Tragulus, 33.
lamucotanus, Callosciurus, 496.
   Epimys, 471.
   Rattus, 471.
   Sciurus, 496.
lancavensis, Callosciurus, 497.
   Mus, 486.
   Rattus, 486.
   Sciurus, 497.
   Tragulus, 33.
lanensis, Pteropus, 140.
   Rattus, 477.
laniger, Myotis, 157.
lanigera, Pteropus, 141.
lapsus, Pithecus, 243.
laricorum, Sorex, 183, 191.
Lariscus, 537.
   amotus, 541.
   castaneus, 537.
   jalorensis, 538.
   obscurus, 538.
   rostratus, 538.
larvalis, Pedetes, 490.
lasiae, Macaca, 242.
   Megaderma, 119.
   Pithecus, 242.
   Rattus, 480.
Lasiopyga arenaria, 238.
   callida, 238.
   contigua, 239.
   kaimosae, 238.
   kima, 237.
   maritima, 237.
   mauae, 238.
   tumbili, 239.
Lasiurus, 148.
   borealis, 148.
   degelidus, 148.
   intermedius, 146, 571.
   minor, 148.
   semota, 149.

Lasiurus teliotis, 149.
Latax, nereis, 63.
lateralis, Delphinus, 113, 576.
   Prodelphinus, 576.
laticeps, Thomomys, 390.
latifrons, Neotoma, 291.
   Orthogeomys, 373.
   Spilogale, 77.
   Ursus, 97.
latimanus, Phenacomys, 337.
latipes, Glaucomys, 535.
latirostris, Thomomys, 391.
lautensis, Callosciurus, 497.
   Galeopterus, 163.
   Pithecus, 243.
   Sciurus, 497.
Lavia, 118.
   frons, 118.
   rex, 118.
lea, Crocidura, 170.
Leggada, 447.
   acholi, 448.
   emesi, 448.
   enclavae, 447.
   gondokorae, 447.
   grata, 448.
   naivashae, 448.
   petilus, 447.
   soricoides, 447.
   triton, 448.
   wamae, 448.
leibii, Myotis, 158.
lembicus, Cynopithecus, 240.
lemhi, Ochotona, 227.
lemminus, Aschizomys, 258.
Lemmiscus, 267.
   curtatus, 267.
   pallidus, 267.
   pauperrimus, 268.
Lemmus, 268.
   alascensis, 268.
   minusculus, 268.
   nigripes, 268.
   yukonensis, 269.
Lemniscomys, 449.
   massaicus, 449.
   mearnsi, 449.
   spermophilus, 449.
lenis, Oryzomys, 307.
Lenomys, 449.
   longicaudus, 449.
Lenothrix, 449.
   canus, 449.
lentus, Dremomys, 522.
Leo hollisteri, 56.
lepida, Neotoma, 286.
lepidura, Crocidura, 170.
lepidus, Epimys, 466.
   Iomys, 537.
   Pteropus, 141.
   Rattus, 466.
Leptonycteris, 131.
   curasoae, 131.
lepturus, Heteromys, 417.
   Peromyscus, 322.
leptus, Mustela, 74.
   Putorius, 74.

Lepus, 208.
  abbotti, 210.
  altamirae, 212.
  angustidens, 210.
  arizonae, 222.
  asellus, 209.
  audubonii, 216.
  aurigineus, 209.
  baileyi, 217.
  bairdii, 210.
  caniclunis, 218.
  canus, 208.
  chiapensis, 219.
  cinnamomeus, 211.
  connectens, 219.
  dalli, 208.
  festinus, 211.
  filchneri, 214.
  gabbi, 218.
  gaillardi, 211.
  goldmani, 215.
  grahami, 211.
  graysoni, 221.
  griseus, 214.
  holzneri, 222.
  idahoensis, 208.
  insonus, 221.
  kakumegae, 211.
  klamathensis, 212.
  labradorius, 208, 212.
  macfarlani, 208, 214.
  magdalenae, 210.
  major, 216.
  margaritae, 221.
  merriami, 212.
  minor, 216.
  monstrabilis, 209.
  orizabae, 221.
  othus, 213.
  pacificus, 223.
  parnassius, 213.
  poadromus, 213.
  porsildi, 209.
  quercerus, 213.
  raineyi, 213.
  richardsonii, 214.
  rigidus, 222.
  robustus, 222.
  saliens, 214.
  sanctidiegi, 220.
  sierrae, 210.
  simplicicanus, 222.
  sowerbyae, 214.
  subcinctus, 220.
  texianus, 214.
  tiburonensis, 208.
  trowbridgii, 223.
  truei, 223.
  tularensis, 214.
  ubericolor, 217.
  varronis, 215.
  wallawalla, 214.
  washingtonii, 215.
  yucatanicus, 220.
lestes, Canis, 43.
  Papio, 246.
Lestoros, 228.

Lestoros inca, 228.
letifera, Mustela, 75.
leucocephalus, Peromyscus, 322.
leucodon, Neotoma, 291.
  Thomomys, 391.
leucogenys, Sorex, 187.
leucoparia, Mustela, 71.
  Putorius, 71.
  Spilogale, 76.
leucophaea, Neotoma, 294.
leucophaeatus, Epimys, 466.
  Rattus, 466.
leucopus, Hesperomys, 321.
leucotis, Dipodomys, 410.
  Sigmodon, 353.
leucurus, Citellus, 512.
  Cynomys, 522.
  Tamias, 512.
leurodon, Citellus, 513.
levicula, Crocidura, 170.
levipes, Dipodomys, 410.
  Perodipus, 410.
  Peromyscus, 323.
  Reithrodontomys, 344.
levir, Isolobodon, 362.
  Ithydontia, 362.
levis, Ochotona, 225.
  Phenacomys, 337.
  Thomomys, 385.
lewisi, Peromyscus, 329.
lewisii, Cervus, 21, 574.
liantis, Tamiops, 562.
libericus, Sciurus, 536.
Lichonycteris, 132.
  degener, 132.
lignicolor, Crocidura, 170.
  Paradoxurus, 107.
ligoni, Canis, 43.
limitaneus, Cebus, 237.
limitaris, Thomomys, 390.
limitis, Clethrionomys, 262
  Evotomys, 262.
  Felis, 57.
  Sciurus, 557.
Limnomys, 450.
  mearnsi, 450.
  picinus, 450.
  sibuanus, 450.
limosus, Thomomys, 391.
linduensis, Rattus, 465.
lineata, Phocaena, 110, 111.
lineatus, Dendromus, 445.
lineiventer, Mustela, 72.
lingae, Pithecus, 243.
  Tana, 202.
lingensis, Mus, 466.
  Rattus, 466.
lingungensis, Pithecus, 243.
  Sciurus, 564.
Liomys, 418.
  annectens, 418.
  canus, 418.
  crispus, 418.
  guerrerensis, 419.
  heterothrix, 419.
  isthmius, 420.
  minor, 421.

Liomys obscurus, 419.
　orbitalis, 419.
　parviceps, 420.
　phaeura, 420.
　phaeurus, 420.
　plantinarensis, 420.
　pretiosus, 419.
　rostratus, 420.
　setosus, 419.
　sonorana, 420.
　sonoranus, 420.
　texensis, 421.
　torridus, 421.
　veraecrucis, 419, 421.
lipara, Crocidura, 172.
Lipotes, 113.
　vexillifer, 113.
Lissodelphis, 110.
　borealis, 575.
litoreus, Procyon, 83.
littoralis, Crocidura, 170.
　Grammomys, 446.
　Neotoma, 294.
　Sciurus, 558.
　Sylvilagus, 215.
　Thamnomys, 446.
　Urocyon, 48.
　Vulpes, 48.
litus, Perognathus, 428.
llanensis, Geomys, 369.
localis, Rattus, 465.
Loncheres, flavidus, 362.
Lonchophylla, 132.
　concava, 132.
　robusta, 132.
longicauda, Reithrodon, 345.
　Sorex, 190.
longicaudus, Arvicola, 275.
　Lenomys, 449.
　Microtus, 275.
　Onychomys, 302.
　Phenacomys, 337.
　Reithtodontomys, 344, 345.
longicrus, Myotis, 150, 153.
　Vespertilio, 153.
longidens, Delphinus, 113.
longimembris, Otognosis, 431.
　Perognathus, 431.
longior, Allactaga, 359.
longipes, Dipodomys, 407.
　Dipodops, 407.
　Onychomys, 303.
　Tragulus, 33.
longirostris, Arvicola, 275.
Lophiomys, 269.
　thomasi, 269.
Lophostoma venezuelae, 136.
Lophuromys, 450.
　aquilus, 450.
　margarettae, 450.
　nudicaudus, 451.
　pyrrhus, 451.
lophurus, Peromyscus, 323.
loringi, Citellus, 521.
　Clethrionomys, 261.
　Evotomys, 261.
　Thallomys, 488.

loringi, Thamnomys, 488.
　Thomomys, 389.
lucas, Callosciurus, 497.
　Mus, 467.
　Rattus, 467.
　Sciurus, 497.
lucasana, Spilogale, 77.
luciae, Ardops, 126.
　Monophyllus, 134.
　Stenoderma, 126.
lucida, Neotoma, 286.
lucidus, Microdipodops, 422.
lucifrons, Reithrodontomys, 347.
lucifugus, Myotis, 150, 572.
　Vespertilio, 154, 572.
ludibundus, Eutamias, 527.
ludovicianus, Microtus, 276.
lugens, Mus, 468.
　Rattus, 468.
Lupulella, 46.
　elgonae, 46.
luta, Epimys, 468.
　Rattus, 468.
luteicollis, Tragulus, 34.
luteiventris, Eutamias, 531.
　Tamias, 531.
luteola, Marmota, 539.
luteolus, Dipodomys, 413.
　Mus, 468.
　Perodipus, 413.
　Rattus, 468.
　Reithrodontomys, 349.
lutescens, Callosciurus, 497.
　Geomys, 369.
　Ochotona, 226.
　Sciurus, 497.
　Tragulus, 34.
luteus, Cercopithecus, 238.
　Peromyscus, 324.
　Zapus, 568.
lutosus, Myotis, 158.
Lutra, 64.
　canadensis, 65.
　destructor, 65.
　evexa, 64.
　extera, 64.
　kodiacensis, 64.
　mira, 65.
　nexa, 64.
　optiva, 65.
　preblei, 65.
　repanda, 66.
　stejnegeri, 66.
　texensis, 65.
　vancouverensis, 66.
　yukonensis, 65.
lutrella, Crocidura, 170.
Lutreola ingens, 74.
　lacustris, 74.
　macrodon, 72.
lutreola, Crocidura, 171.
luzonus, Chaerephon, 120.
lyelli, Sorex, 195.
lymani, Mustela, 72.
Lynx, 60.
　baileyi, 60.
　californicus, 60.

Lynx eremicus, 60.
  pallescens, 60.
  uinta, 61.
lyoni, Cynopterus, 138.
Lyssodes, 240.
  melli, 240.

maanjae, Crocidura, 171.
mabulus, Rattus, 467.
Macaca, 240.
  adusta, 240.
  andamensis, 240, 242, 244.
  atriceps, 243.
  baweana, 241.
  broca, 241.
  cagayana, 241.
  capitalis, 241.
  cupida, 242.
  fusca, 242.
  indochinensis, 244.
  insulana, 242.
  irus, 241, 242, 243, 244.
  lasiae, 242.
  mindanensis, 244.
  mindorus, 244.
  nemestrina, 241.
  pagensis, 245.
  phaeura, 245.
  pumila, 243, 245.
  suluensis, 246.
  umbrosa, 246.
  villosa, 245.
  vitiis, 246.
Macacus fuscus, 242.
  pagensis, 245.
  phaeura, 245.
  pumilus, 245.
  umbrosus, 246.
  villosus, 245.
macer, Chilonatalus, 125.
  Cryptotis, 178.
macfarlani, Lepus, 208, 214.
  Microtus, 276.
  Ursus, 94.
machetes, Blarina, 178.
  Cryptotis, 178.
machrinoides, Scalopus, 200.
mackenzii, Phenacomys, 338.
macklotii, Pteropus, 142.
macra, Arctogalidia, 101.
macrodens, Phoca, 235.
macrodon, Fiber, 300.
  Lutreola, 72.
  Mustela, 72.
  Ondatra, 300.
  Sorex, 188.
  Ursus, 94.
Macrogeomys, 372.
  costaricensis, 372.
  dariensis, 372.
  dolichocephalus, 372.
macropus, Arvicola, 276.
  Hesperomys, 324.
  Microtus, 276.
  Vespertilio, 154.
macropygmaeus, Sorex, 188.
macrorhabdotes, Tamias, 527.

Macrorhinus angustirostris, 234.
macrospilotus, Spermophilus, 517.
macrotis, Glaucomys, 535.
  Idiurus, 439.
  Sciuropterus, 535.
  Tadarida, 124.
  Trichys, 439.
  Vulpes, 50.
Macrotus, 132.
  californicus, 132, 571.
  compressus, 132.
  heberfolium, 132.
  jamaicensis, 133.
macroura, Vulpes, 51.
macrurus, Microtus, 276.
maculatus, Heliosciurus, 536.
madogae, Heliosciurus, 536.
madrensis, Callospermophilus, 513.
  Citellus, 513.
  Glaucomys, 535.
  Microtus, 277.
  Neotoma, 293.
  Peromyscus, 324.
  Thomomys, 402.
maerens, Epimys, 468.
  Petinomys, 544.
  Rattus, 468.
  Sciuropterus, 544.
magdalenae, Lepus, 210.
  Perognathus, 437.
  Peromyscus, 325.
  Thomomys, 392.
magister, Neotoma, 292.
  Ursus, 94.
magna, Blarina, 177.
  Cryptotis, 177.
magnirostris, Mus, 469.
  Rattus, 469.
magruderensis, Perognathus, 434.
major, Aplodontia, 253.
  Apomys, 441.
  Arctogalidia, 101.
  Chincha, 69.
  Citellus, 518.
  Cynopterus, 137.
  Lepus, 216.
  Mephitis, 69.
  Natalus, 125.
  Neürotrichus, 199.
  Ratufa, 546.
  Sigmodon, 352.
  Spermophilus, 518.
  Thecurus, 438.
  Thyroptera, 145.
  Zapus, 568.
managuensis, Sciurus, 553.
mandarinus, Microtus, 281.
mandibularis, Pithecus, 244.
mandus, Mus, 469.
  Rattus, 469.
maniculatus, Peromyscus, 312, 314.
mansalaris, Pithecus, 244.
  Rattus, 463.
  Sciurus, 564.
  Tomeutes, 564.
mansuetus, Sylvilagus, 221.
mara, Epimys, 469.

mara, Rattus, 469.
margarettae, Lophuromys, 450.
margaritae, Cebus, 237.
    Dipodomys, 407.
    Lepus, 221.
    Peromyscus, 326.
    Sylvilagus, 221.
marginatus, Spermophilus, 518.
mariakanae, Elephantulus, 166.
mariguanensis, Erophylla, 130.
marinsularis, Callosciurus, 497.
    Sciurus, 497.
marinus, Procyon, 83.
maritima, Lasiopyga, 237.
Marmosa, 229.
    albiventris, 229.
    formosa, 229, 230.
    insularis, 229.
    invicta, 230.
    isthmica, 230.
    meridae, 229.
    mexicana, 230.
    muscula, 229, 230.
    oaxacae, 230.
    purui, 231.
    ruatanica, 231.
    zeledoni, 231.
Marmota, 538.
    cascadensis, 538.
    dacota, 539.
    luteola, 539.
    nivaria, 538.
    nosophora, 539.
    obscura, 539.
    olympus, 541.
    oxytona, 541.
    parvula, 540.
    petrensis, 540.
    preblorum, 540.
    rufescens, 540.
    sheldoni, 538.
    sibila, 541.
    sierrae, 540.
    warreni, 540.
marshalli, Dipodomys, 413.
    Neotoma, 291.
Martes, 66.
    abieticola, 66.
    actuosa, 66.
    caurina, 66.
    columbiana, 67.
    nesophila, 67.
    origines, 67.
martinensis, Neotoma, 293.
    Peromyscus, 326.
    Thomomys, 402.
masae, Mus, 469.
    Rattus, 469.
    Ratufa, 548.
    Tana, 202.
    Tragulus, 37.
massaicus, Lemniscomys, 449.
Mastomys, 451.
    duramae, 451.
    ismailiae, 451.
    neumani, 451.
    panya, 452.

Mastomys tinctus, 452.
matschiei, Colobus, 239.
matthaeus, Callosciurus, 498.
    Mus, 469.
    Rattus, 469.
    Sciurus, 498.
mauae, Lasiopyga, 238.
maurus, Clethrionomys, 261.
mayensis, Blarina, 177.
    Cryptotis, 177.
    Dipodomys, 408.
    Felis, 54.
    Oryzomys, 307.
mayonicus, Epimys, 469.
    Rattus, 469.
Mazama, 18.
    cerasina, 18.
    pandora, 18.
    reperticia, 18.
mazama, Clethrionomys, 262.
    Evotomys, 262.
    Thomomys, 392.
mcmillani, Thos, 46.
mcmurtrii, Centurio, 128.
mearnsi, Canis, 44.
    Conepatus, 62.
    Connochaetes, 8.
    Felis, 55, 58.
    Gorgon, 8.
    Lemniscomys, 449.
    Limnomys, 450.
    Neotoma, 285.
    Pteropus, 141.
    Saccostomus, 488.
    Sciurus, 561.
    Tamiasciurus, 561.
    Thomomys, 392.
medius, Oryzomys, 308.
    Peromyscus, 334.
    Thomomys, 399.
megacephalus, Microdipodops, 422.
Megaderma, 119.
    carimatae, 119.
    celebensis, 119.
    lasiae, 119.
    niasense, 119.
    siumatis, 119.
megadon, Oryzomys, 310.
megalops, Peromyscus, 327.
megalotis, Hesperomys, 327.
    Reithrodon, 345.
    Reithrodontomys, 345, 346.
mekisturus, Peromyscus, 327.
melalophus, Presbytis, 247, 249.
melanocarpus, Peromyscus, 327.
melanopepla, Ratufa, 548.
melanophrys, Hesperomys, 327.
    Onychomys, 302, 303.
    Peromyscus, 327.
melanops, Callosciurus, 498.
    Monodelphis, 232.
    Peramys, 232.
    Sciurus, 498.
    Thomomys, 392.
melanopterus, Aëretes, 544.
melanorhinus, Myotis, 154, 156.
    Vespertilio, 154.

melanotis, Capreolus, 16.
  Perognathus, 424.
  Peromyscus, 328.
  Sigmodon, 353.
melanura, Neotoma, 289.
melanurus, Peromyscus, 327.
  Rattus, 470.
  Tamias, 529.
Melasmothrix, 452.
  naso, 452.
melli, Lyssodes, 240.
Mellivora, 67.
  abyssinica, 67.
  sagulata, 67.
mendanauus, Callosciurus, 498.
  Sciurus, 498.
mendocinensis, Ursus, 94.
Menetes, 541.
  amotus, 541.
mengurus, Epimys, 470.
  Rattus, 470.
Mephitis, 68.
  estor, 68.
  frontata, 68.
  major, 69.
  milleri, 68.
  nigra, 68.
  notata, 69.
  occidentalis, 68.
  platyrhina, 69.
mergens, Fiber, 301.
  Ondatra, 301.
meridae, Marmosa, 229.
meridana, Mustela, 72.
meridionalis, Eutamias, 527.
merriami, Cervus, 17.
  Dipodomys, 408, 409.
  Lepus, 212.
  Peromyscus, 328.
  Pipistrellus, 161.
  Reithrodontomys, 347.
  Sorex, 188.
  Vesperugo, 161.
merus, Cryptotis, 177.
mesanis, Rattus, 477.
mesomelas, Peromyscus, 334.
Mesoplodon, 115.
  mirum, 115.
  stejnegeri, 115.
messorius, Sylvilagus, 220.
Metachirops, 231.
  pallidus, 231.
Metachirus dentaneus, 232.
  pallidus, 231.
mewa, Thomomys, 392.
mexicana, Alouatta, 236.
  Antilocapra, 6.
  Blarina, 177.
  Chilonycteris, 129.
  Cryptotis, 177.
  Marmosa, 230.
  Micronycteris, 133.
  Neotoma, 293.
  Ovis, 12.
  Procyon, 81.
  Tadarida, 124.
mexicanus, Castor, 255.

mexicanus, Corynorhinus, 146.
  Cyclopes, 570.
  Cynomys, 522.
  Dasypus, 570.
  Micronycteris, 133.
  Myotis, 572.
  Natalus, 125.
  Noctilio, 126.
  Oryzomys, 310.
  Perognathus, 428.
  Peromyscus, 333.
  Procyon, 81.
  Reithrodontomys, 342.
michaelseni, Geoxus, 265.
michiganensis, Castor, 255.
Microdipodops, 421.
  californicus, 421.
  lucidus, 422.
  megacephalus, 422.
  oregonus, 422.
  pallidus, 422.
microdon, Apomys, 442.
  Canis, 44.
  Ourebia, 10.
  Reithrodontomys, 346.
  Sigmodon, 352.
  Spilogale, 77.
Micronycteris, 133.
  mexicana, 133.
  mexicanus, 133.
  microtis, 133.
micronyx, Myotis, 155.
microps, Dipodomys, 409.
  Perodipus, 409.
micropus, Arvicanthis, 449.
  Neotoma, 294.
Microsciurus, 541.
  isthmius, 541.
  venustulus, 541.
  vivatus, 542.
Microsorex, 179.
  alnorum, 179.
  eximius, 179.
  hoyi, 179.
  intervectus, 180.
  thompsoni, 180.
  washingtoni, 180.
  winnemana, 180.
microtis, Apodemus, 440.
  Glossophaga, 131.
  Micronycteris, 133.
Microtus, 269.
  abbreviatus, 269.
  acrophilus, 257.
  adocetus, 280.
  alticola, 269.
  amakensis, 270.
  angusticeps, 270.
  aphorodemus, 270.
  arizonensis, 278.
  auricularis, 339.
  baileyi, 275.
  bairdii, 271.
  bernardinus, 278.
  brachelix, 266.
  brandti, 283.
  breweri, 271.

Microtus californicus, 272, 273, 282.
  canescens, 279.
  canicaudus, 273.
  cantwelli, 280.
  caryi, 278.
  constrictus, 272.
  cricetulus, 257.
  duplicatus, 270.
  dutcheri, 273.
  elymocetes, 274.
  endoecus, 280.
  fisheri, 269.
  fulviventer, 274.
  guadalupensis, 276.
  guatemalensis, 274.
  haydenii, 274.
  hualpaiensis, 276.
  innuitus, 274.
  insularis, 274, 279.
  kadiacensis, 275.
  labradorius, 281.
  longicaudus, 275.
  ludovicianus, 276.
  macfarlani, 276.
  macropus, 276.
  macrurus, 276.
  madrensis, 277.
  mandarinus, 281.
  minor, 271.
  miurus, 277.
  modestus, 277.
  montanus, 275, 573.
  mordax, 278.
  muriei, 278.
  nanus, 278.
  nemoralis, 340.
  nesophilus, 274, 279.
  nevadensis, 279.
  ochrogaster, 270, 273.
  operarius, 280.
  oreas, 277.
  pamirensis, 280.
  phaeus, 281.
  popofensis, 283.
  pullus, 281.
  ravidulus, 281.
  rivularis, 279.
  scirpensis, 281.
  serpens, 282.
  sitkensis, 282.
  subsimus, 277.
  townsendii, 279.
  tshuktshorum, 282.
  umbrosus, 282.
  unalascensis, 283.
  vallicola, 272.
  wahema, 281.
  warringtoni, 283.
  yakutatensis, 283.
microtus, Oxymycterus, 265.
Microxus torques, 256.
Mictomys innuitus, 355.
Midas elegantulus, 236.
middendorffi, Ursus, 94.
milleri, Mephitis, 68.
mima, Arctogalidia, 102.
mimellus, Callosciurus, 498.

mimellus, Sciurus, 498.
mimiculus, Callosciurus, 499.
  Sciurus, 499.
mimicus, Petaurista, 543.
Mimon, 133.
  cozumelae, 133.
mimula, Crocidura, 171.
mimus, Sciurus, 551.
  Sus, 27.
mindanensis, Cynomolgus, 244.
  Macaca, 244.
  Mus, 470.
  Rattus, 470.
mindorus, Crocidura, 171.
  Macaca, 244.
  Pithecus, 244.
miniatus, Callosciurus, 499.
  Sciurus, 499.
minima, Sigmodon, 353.
minimus, Thomomys, 381.
Miniopterus, 149.
  arenarius, 149.
  paululus, 149.
minnesotae, Peromyscus, 323.
minor, Antrozous, 145.
  Arctogalidia, 102.
  Arvicola, 271.
  Brachyphylla, 127.
  Echinosorex, 165.
  Gymnura, 165.
  Hemigale, 103.
  Hemigalus, 103.
  Lasiurus, 148.
  Lepus, 216.
  Liomys, 421.
  Microtus, 271.
  Neomys, 181.
  Niadius, 138.
  Procyon, 84.
  Sylvilagus, 216.
  Thomomys, 381.
  Zapus, 568.
minusculus, Lemmus, 268.
  Pipistrellus, 161.
  Reithrodontomys, 347.
minuta, Kerivoula, 148.
  Vampyressa, 136.
minutilla, Rhogeëssa, 162.
minutillus, Rhinolophus, 143, 144.
minutus, Cynopterus, 138.
  Rhinolophus, 143, 144.
miquihuanensis, Odocoileus, 23.
mira, Lutra, 65.
mirabilis, Ursus, 94.
miradorensis, Eptesicus, 572.
  Scotophilus, 572.
Mirounga, 234.
  angustirostris, 234.
mirum, Mesoplodon, 115.
mirus, Ursus, 95.
missouriensis, Castor, 255.
mitchelli, Dipodomys, 411.
mitratus, Callospermophilus, 507.
  Citellus, 507.
miurus, Microtus, 277.
mobilensis, Geomys, 370.
modesta, Arvicola, 277.

modestus, Microtus, 277.
modicus, Thomomys, 387.
mogollonensis, Canis, 43.
mohavensis, Citellus, 514.
    Nyctinomus, 124.
    Spermophilus, 514.
molaris, Nasua, 80.
mollicomus, Rattus, 470.
mollis, Citellus, 513, 514, 515.
    Spermophilus, 514.
Molossus, 121.
    californicus, 120.
    debilis, 121.
    fortis, 121.
    nigricans, 121.
    pretiosus, 121.
    pygmaeus, 122.
monochroura, Neotoma, 297.
Monodelphis, 232.
    melanops, 232.
Monophyllus, 133.
    clinedaphus, 133.
    cubanus, 133.
    ferreus, 134.
    luciae, 134.
    plethodon, 134.
    portoricensis, 134.
monstrabilis, Canis, 43.
    Lepus, 209.
    Neotoma, 291.
montana, Arvicola, 278, 573.
montanus, Acomys, 439.
    Aphaetreus, 360.
    Dipodomys, 411.
    Microtus, 275, 573.
    Reithrodon, 348.
    Reithrodontomys, 348.
    Zapus, 569.
montereyensis, Sorex, 188.
montezumae, Neotoma, 294.
monticola, Citellus, 520.
    Perognathus, 432.
    Sorex, 184, 188.
monticolus, Sorex, 188.
montosa, Alticola, 258.
    Arvicola, 258.
moorei, Thomomys, 385.
mordax, Arvicola, 278.
    Microtus, 278.
    Sturnirops, 136.
Mormoops, 134.
    intermedia, 134.
    senicula, 134.
    tumidiceps, 135.
morroensis, Dipodomys, 411.
    Perodipus, 411.
morulus, Myopus, 283.
Moschus, 25.
    parvipes, 25.
mundus, Vespertilio, 155, 572.
Mungos, 104.
    colonus, 104.
    dentifer, 104.
    dialeucos, 104.
    ferox, 104.
    orestes, 105.
    parvipes, 105.

Mungos rubescens, 102.
Muntiacus, 18.
    bancanus, 18.
    rubidus, 19.
muralis, Thomomys, 393.
muricauda, Crocidura, 171.
    Myosorex, 171.
muriei, Microtus, 278.
Murina, 150.
    fuscus, 150.
Mus, 452.
    acholi, 448.
    albigularis, 455.
    anambae, 455.
    andrewsi, 456.
    apicis, 487.
    aquilus, 450.
    asper, 456.
    atratus, 456.
    atridorsum, 456.
    balae, 456.
    batamanus, 457.
    bentincanus, 458.
    bullatus, 458.
    burrescens, 458.
    burrulus, 458.
    burrus, 459.
    buruensis, 459.
    butangensis, 482.
    carimatae, 459.
    casensis, 459.
    catellifer, 460.
    chombolis, 460.
    clabatus, 460.
    commissarius, 452.
    cremoriventer, 461.
    defua, 445.
    domelicus, 461.
    domitor, 461.
    emesi, 448.
    enclavae, 447.
    enganus, 461.
    exulans, 462.
    ferreocanus, 462.
    firmus, 462.
    flavidulus, 482.
    flaviventer, 462.
    flebilis, 463.
    fremens, 463.
    gilbiventer, 464.
    gondokorae, 447.
    griseus, 440.
    integer, 465.
    julianus, 466.
    kelleri, 466.
    lancavensis, 486.
    lingensis, 466.
    lucas, 467.
    lugens, 468.
    luteolus, 468.
    magnirostris, 469.
    mandus, 469.
    masae, 469.
    matthaeus, 469.
    mindanensis, 470.
    musculus, 574.
    obscurus, 472, 474.

Mus pagensis, 472.
  pannosus, 473.
  panterensis, 473.
  pellax, 473.
  peromyscus, 454.
  peruvianus, 574.
  petilus, 447.
  pulliventer, 474.
  pullus, 472.
  rostratus, 455.
  serutus, 479.
  siantanicus, 479.
  simalurensis, 479.
  soccatus, 480.
  soricoides, 447.
  stoicus, 481.
  strepitans, 481.
  stridens, 481.
  stridulus, 481.
  sungarae, 448.
  surdus, 482.
  surifer, 482.
  taciturnus, 482.
  tagulayensis, 483.
  tambelanicus, 483.
  tana, 453.
  tiomanicus, 483.
  todayensis, 484.
  umbridorsum, 484.
  validus, 485.
  vitiensis, 486.
  vociferans, 486.
  vulcani, 487.
  wamae, 448.
  zamboangae, 487.
muscula, Marmosa, 229, 230.
musculoides, Cephalophus, 8.
  Peromyscus, 329.
musculus, Apomys, 442.
  Baiomys, 258.
  Mus, 574.
  Sitomys, 258.
  Thomomys, 402.
Mustela, 69.
  abieticola, 66.
  actuosa, 66.
  alascensis, 73.
  alleni, 69.
  arctica, 69.
  campestris, 70.
  caurina, 66.
  costaricensis, 70.
  culbertsoni, 70.
  goldmani, 71.
  haidarum, 71.
  ingens, 74.
  kadiacensis, 70.
  kaneii, 71.
  lacustris, 74.
  leptus, 74.
  letifera, 75.
  leucoparia, 71.
  lineiventer, 72.
  lymani, 72.
  macrodon, 72.
  meridana, 72.
  nesophila, 67.

Mustela olivacea, 73.
  oregonensis, 75.
  origines, 67.
  panamensis, 71.
  perda, 74.
  perotae, 71.
  primulina, 73.
  saturata, 73.
  streatori, 73.
  tiarata, 74.
  tropicalis, 74.
  washingtoni, 75.
mustelinus, Reithrodontomys, 343.
mutabilis, Sorex, 193.
  Thomomys, 387.
mutesae, Crocidura, 172.
mutica, Glossophaga, 130.
  Vulpes, 51.
muticus, Vulpes, 51.
Mylomys, 452.
  roosevelti, 452.
Myocastor, 490.
  santacruzae, 490.
Myodes nigripes, 268.
Myomys, 453.
  fumatus, 453.
  tana, 453.
Myonax, 104.
  dentifer, 104.
  orestes, 105.
  parvipes, 105.
myops, Erethizon, 364.
  Sorex, 195.
  Thomomys, 393.
Myopus, 283.
  morulus, 283.
Myosorex muricauda, 171.
Myospalax, 566.
  cansus, 566.
Myotalpa cansus, 566.
Myotis, 150.
  abbotti, 150.
  alascensis, 154, 157.
  albescens, 155, 572.
  altifrons, 150.
  amotus, 153.
  baileyi, 150.
  californicus, 155, 156, 157, 158, 573.
  capitaneus, 151.
  carimatae, 151.
  caurinus, 151.
  chrysonotus, 155.
  dominicensis, 152.
  evotis, 152.
  extremus, 155.
  grisescens, 152.
  hirsutus, 153.
  interior, 153.
  keenii, 158.
  laniger, 157.
  leibii, 158.
  longicrus, 150, 153.
  lucifugus, 150, 572.
  lutosus, 158.
  melanorhinus, 154, 156.
  mexicanus, 572.
  micronyx, 155.

Myotis nesopolus, 155.
  niasensis, 155.
  nigricans, 572.
  occultus, 150, 156.
  pallidus, 151.
  pernox, 157.
  petax, 157.
  phasma, 154.
  quebecensis, 148.
  saturatus, 159.
  septentrionalis, 152.
  sowerbyi, 157.
  subulatus, 151.
  thysanodes, 158.
  volans, 151, 158.
  winnemana, 158.
  yumanensis, 154, 156, 158, 573.
Myrmecophaga, 571.
  centralis, 571.
Mystax, 236.
  rufiventer, 236.

naivashae, Chaerephon, 120.
  Leggada, 448.
nakurae, Alcelaphus, 7.
  Bubalis, 7.
nana, Brachyphylla, 128.
nandae, Felis, 57.
Nandinia, 105.
  arborea, 105.
nannodes, Cervus, 17.
Nannosciurus, 542.
  bancanus, 542.
  borneanus, 542.
  pulcher, 542.
  sumatranus, 542.
  surrutilus, 543.
nanus, Arvicola, 278.
  Microtus, 278.
  Pecari, 30.
  Sorex, 196.
  Tayassu, 30.
napaea, Sicista, 567.
Napaeozapus, 566.
  frutectanus, 566.
  roanensis, 567.
napu, Tragulus, 32.
nasicus, Thomomys, 393.
naso, Melasmothrix, 452.
Nasua, 80.
  molaris, 80.
  nelsoni, 80.
  richmondi, 80.
nasutus, Epimys, 471.
  Rattus, 471.
Natalus, 125.
  brevimanus, 124.
  dominicensis, 125.
  major, 125.
  mexicanus, 125.
  tumidirostris, 126.
natunae, Galeopithecus, 163.
  Galeopterus, 163.
  Nycticebus, 252.
  Tragulus, 34.
  Tupaia, 205.
natunensis, Sus, 27.

natunensis, Tomeutes, 564.
navaho, Ursus, 95.
navigator, Neosorex, 189.
  Sorex, 189.
navus, Neotoma, 295.
  Thomomys, 391.
nayaritensis, Cryptotis, 179.
  Pappogeomys, 374.
Neacomys, 283.
  pictus, 283.
nebracensis, Canis, 45.
nebrascensis, Peromyscus, 324.
  Reithrodontomys, 342.
nebulicola, Citellus, 515.
nebulosus, Thomomys, 399.
necator, Vulpes, 52.
necopinus, Sciurus, 564.
  Tomeutes, 564.
Nectomys, 284.
  efficax, 284.
  pollens, 284.
negans, Vormela, 79.
neglecta, Taxidea, 78.
neglectus, Ateles, 237.
  Citellus, 515.
  Platygeomys, 376.
  Spermophilus, 515.
  Thomomys, 393.
  Ursus, 93.
negligens, Sciurus, 557.
nelsoni, Agouti, 358.
  Blarina, 178.
  Cervus, 17.
  Citellus, 516.
  Conepatus, 62.
  Cryptotis, 178.
  Cuniculus, 358.
  Dicrostonyx, 264.
  Dipodomys, 411.
  Felis, 59.
  Geomys, 375.
  Heteromys, 417.
  Nasua, 80.
  Neotoma, 295.
  Odocoileus, 21.
  Orthogeomys, 373.
  Oryzomys, 309.
  Ovis, 12.
  Pappogeomys, 375.
  Pecari, 29.
  Perognathus, 432, 437.
  Peromyscus, 329.
  Reithrodontomys, 343.
  Romerolagus, 215.
  Sciurus, 557.
  Spermophilus, 516.
  Thomomys, 393.
  Ursus, 95.
  Vampyrum, 137.
  Vampyrus, 137.
  Xenomys, 357.
Nelsonia, 284.
  goldmani, 284.
  neotomodon, 284.
nemestrina, Macaca, 241.
nemoralis, Microtus, 240.
  Pitymys, 340.

nemoralis, Sciurus, 552.
Nemorhoedus palmeri, 12.
Neofiber, 284.
  alleni, 284.
  nigrescens, 285.
neomexicana, Vulpes, 51.
neomexicanus, Sciurus, 560.
  Sorex, 190.
  Sylvilagus, 217.
  Tamiasciurus, 560.
  Vulpes, 51.
Neomys, 181.
  fodiens, 181.
  minor, 181.
Neosorex albibarbis, 182.
  navigator, 189.
Neotoma, 285.
  albigula, 289.
  alleni, 266.
  angusticeps, 289.
  arizonae, 285.
  baileyi, 286.
  bryanti, 286.
  bullata, 293.
  chamula, 287.
  cumulator, 286.
  desertorum, 286.
  devia, 289.
  dispar, 288.
  fallax, 287.
  fulviventer, 288.
  fusca, 295.
  fuscipes, 288.
  goldmani, 289.
  illinoensis, 288.
  inopinata, 293.
  inornata, 293.
  insularis, 289.
  isthmica, 291.
  latifrons, 291.
  lepida, 286.
  leucodon, 291.
  leucophaea, 294.
  littoralis, 294.
  lucida, 286.
  madrensis, 293.
  magister, 292.
  marshalli, 291.
  martinensis, 293.
  mearnsi, 285.
  melanura, 289.
  mexicana, 293.
  micropus, 294.
  monochroura, 297.
  monstrabilis, 291.
  montezumae, 294.
  navus, 295.
  nelsoni, 295.
  notia, 290.
  nudicauda, 295.
  occidentalis, 295.
  ochracea, 287.
  orizabae, 296.
  orolestes, 296.
  palatina, 296.
  parvidens, 296.
  perpallida, 290.

Neotoma picta, 296.
  pinetorum, 297
  planiceps, 294.
  pretiosa, 290.
  ravida, 290.
  relicta, 297.
  saxamans, 297.
  seri, 285.
  sheldoni, 285.
  simplex, 288, 292.
  sola, 287.
  solitaria, 287.
  splendens, 297.
  stephensi, 297.
  streatori, 288.
  tenuicauda, 298.
  torquata, 288, 296.
  tropicalis, 298.
  venusta, 286, 298.
  vicina, 290.
  warreni, 285.
  zacatecae, 291.
Neotomodon, 298.
  alstoni, 298.
  orizabae, 298.
  perotensis, 299.
neotomodon, Nelsonia, 284.
nereis, Enhydra, 63.
  Latax, 63.
  Rhinolophus, 144.
nerterus, Reithrodontomys, 342.
nesites, Rhinolophus, 143.
nesophila, Martes, 67.
  Mustela, 67.
nesophilus, Microtus, 274, 279.
Nesophontes, 166.
  hypomicrus, 166.
  paramicrus, 166.
  zamicrus, 167.
nesopolus, Myotis, 155.
Nesotragus, 10.
  deserticola, 10.
neumani, Epimys, 451.
  Mastomys, 451.
neumanni, Cercopithecus, 238.
Neürotrichus, 199.
  gibbsii, 199.
  major, 199.
nevadensis, Bassariscus, 39.
  Citellus, 510.
  Dipodomys, 408.
  Microtus, 279.
  Nyctinomus, 124.
  Ochotona, 227.
  Perognathus, 432.
  Sorex, 189.
  Thomomys, 394.
  Vulpes, 51.
  Zapus, 568.
nexa, Lutra, 64.
nexilis, Dipodomys, 413.
niadensis, Sus, 27.
niadicus, Pteropus, 141.
niadis, Chiropodomys, 443.
Niadius minor, 138.
niasense, Megaderma, 119.
niasensis, Arctictis, 100.

niasensis, Myotis, 155.
    Rhinolophus, 144.
niasis, Tragulus, 34.
nicholi, Thomomys, 381.
nicobarica, Crocidura, 172.
nicobaricus, Sus, 27.
nicobarulae, Hipposideros, 118.
nigellus, Rattus, 471.
    Rusa, 25.
niger, Thomomys, 394.
nigra, Mephitis, 68.
nigrescens, Baiomys, 259.
    Neofiber, 285.
    Ochotona, 225.
    Pecari, 29.
    Peromyscus, 259
    Ratufa, 549.
    Reithrodontomys, 346.
nigribarbis, Odocoileus, 23.
nigricans, Molossus, 121.
    Myotis, 572.
nigricollis, Tragulus, 34.
nigridius, Dasymys, 444.
nigrifrons, Dendromys, 454.
    Poemys, 454.
nigripes, Crocidura, 172.
    Lemmus, 268.
    Myodes, 268.
nigritalus, Apodemus, 440.
nigrocinctus, Tragulus, 35.
nilotica, Crocidura, 172.
nisa, Crocidura, 172.
nitida, Ochotona, 225.
nitidus, Vespertilio, 155.
nitratoides, Dipodomys, 408.
nitratus, Dipodomys, 409.
nivaria, Marmota, 538.
nivarius, Clethrionomys, 262.
    Evotomys, 262.
Noctilio, 126.
    mexicanus, 126.
nortoni, Ursus, 95.
norvegicus, Clethrionomys, 263.
    Evotomys, 263.
nosophora, Marmota, 539.
notabilis, Ratufa, 549.
notata, Chincha, 69.
    Mephitis, 69.
notatus, Schaeffia, 47.
    Thomasomys, 357.
    Thos, 47.
notia, Neotoma, 290.
notialis, Felis, 57.
    Hydrochoerus, 437.
Notiomys alleni, 259.
Notiosorex, 181.
    crawfordi, 181.
    evotis, 181.
    gigas, 181.
noveboracensis, Peromyscus, 315, 323.
novemlineatus, Sciurus, 562.
    Tamiops, 562.
nuchalis, Sciurus, 555.
nuchek, Ursus, 95.
nudicauda, Neotoma, 295.
nudicaudus, Lophuromys, 451.
nyanzae, Felis, 56.

Nycticea crepuscularis, 159.
    cynocephala, 123.
Nycticebus, 251.
    bancanus, 251.
    borneanus, 251.
    natunae, 252.
Nycticeius, 159.
    humeralis, 159.
Nyctinomops yucatanicus, 124.
Nyctinomus antillularum, 122.
    europs, 123.
    femorosaccus, 123.
    jobensis, 119.
    mohavensis, 124.
    nevadensis, 124.
    orthotis, 121.
    pusillus, 120.
Nyctomys, 299.
    costaricensis, 299.
    decolorus, 299.
    pallidulus, 299.
    venustulus, 299.
nyikae, Rhynchotragus, 14.
nyx, Callosciurus, 499.
    Sciurus, 499.

oaxacae, Marmosa, 230.
    Sorex, 193.
oaxacensis, Felis, 55.
    Odocoileus, 23.
    Peromyscus, 330.
obliquidens, Lagenorhynchus, 110.
obscura, Blarina, 178.
    Cryptotis, 178.
    Marmota, 539.
obscurus, Clethrionomys, 263.
    Eutamias, 529.
    Evotomys, 263.
    Funambulus, 538.
    Lagenorhynchus, 576.
    Lariscus, 538.
    Liomys, 419.
    Mus, 472, 474.
    Perognathus, 432.
    Pipistrellus, 161.
    Reithrodontomys, 346.
    Sorex, 189, 197.
    Tamias, 529.
    Vespertilio, 156.
obsidianus, Spermophilus, 518.
obsoletus, Citellus, 516.
    Spermophilus, 516.
obtusa, Phyllonycteris, 135.
occidentalis, Arvicola, 279.
    Crevus, 18.
    Clethrionomys, 263.
    Evotomys, 263.
    Mephitis, 68.
    Neotoma, 295.
occultidens, Pachyura, 198.
    Suncus, 198.
occultus, Myotis, 150, 156.
    Perognathus, 432, 437.
Ochotona, 224.
    annectens, 224.
    argentata, 224.
    brooksi, 225.

Ochotona, brunnescens, 224.
  cansus, 224.
  collaris, 224.
  fumosa, 225.
  fuscipes, 226.
  goldmani, 226.
  incana, 226.
  jewetti, 226.
  lemhi, 227.
  levis, 225.
  lutescens, 226.
  nevadensis, 227.
  nigrescens, 225.
  nitida, 225.
  schisticeps, 226.
  uinta, 227.
  ventorum, 227.
  vulpina, 224.
ochracea, Neotoma, 287.
ochraceus, Eutamias, 523.
  Peromyscus, 323.
  Procyon, 83.
ochrogaster, Microtus, 270, 273.
ochrogenys, Eutamias, 533.
ochrognathus, Sigmodon, 353.
ochrourus, Odocoileus, 23.
ochrus, Perognathus, 426.
ocius, Thomomys, 384.
Odocoileus, 19.
  californicus, 575.
  canus, 20.
  carminis, 22.
  cerrosensis, 19.
  columbianus, 19, 574.
  costaricensis, 20.
  couesi, 22.
  crooki, 20.
  dacotensis, 22.
  eremicus, 21.
  hiltonensis, 23.
  miquihuanensis, 23.
  nelsoni, 21.
  nigribarbis, 23.
  oaxacensis, 23.
  ochrourus, 23.
  scaphiotus, 19.
  seminolus, 23.
  sheldoni, 21.
  sitkensis, 20.
  taurinsulae, 24.
  texanus, 21.
  thomasi, 22.
  truei, 19.
  venatorius, 24.
  veraecrucis, 24.
Oenomys, 453.
  vallicola, 453.
offella, Boromys, 360.
oi, Sus, 28.
oklahomae, Dipodomys, 412.
olivacea, Mustela, 73.
  Tupaia, 204.
olivaceus, Perognathus, 432, 433.
  Tragelaphus, 16.
olympica, Aplodontia, 253.
olympus, Arctomys, 541.
  Felis, 56.

olympus, Marmota, 541.
omnivora, Bdeogale, 103.
Ondatra, 300.
  alba, 300.
  bernardi, 300.
  cinnamomina, 300.
  macrodon, 300.
  mergens, 301.
  ripensis, 301.
  spatulata, 300.
  zalopha, 301.
Onychomys, 301.
  albescens, 301.
  arenicola, 303.
  breviauritus, 302.
  brevicaudus, 302.
  canus, 303.
  capitulatus, 302.
  clarus, 304.
  fuliginosus, 301.
  longicaudus, 302.
  longipes, 303.
  melanophrys, 302, 303.
  pallescens, 303.
  perpallidus, 304.
  surrufus, 304.
  torridus, 303.
  tularensis, 304.
  utahensis, 302.
  yakiensis, 304.
operarius, Arvicola, 280.
  Eutamias, 523.
  Microtus, 280.
  Thomomys, 394.
ophrus, Ursus, 96.
optabilis, Thomomys, 381.
optiva, Lutra, 65.
opulentus, Thomomys, 381.
orarius, Scapanus, 201.
orbitalis, Liomys, 419.
Orca destructor, 112.
orca, Clethrionomys, 263.
  Evotomys, 263.
oreas, Microtus, 277.
oregona, Antilocapra, 6.
oregonensis, Felis, 56.
  Mustela, 75.
  Putorius, 75.
  Vespertilio, 157.
oregonus, Bison, 8.
  Citellus, 516.
  Microdipodops, 422.
  Spermophilus, 516.
  Thomomys, 384.
  Zapus, 569.
oreocetes, Cratogeomys, 368.
  Eutamias, 529.
oreopolus, Sorex, 191.
Oreotragus, 10.
  aureus, 10.
orestes, Mungos, 105.
  Myonax, 105.
orgiloides, Ursus, 96.
orgilos, Ursus, 96.
oribasus, Ursus, 96.
origines, Martes, 67.
  Mustela, 67.

orinomus, Bassaricyon, 79.
Urocyon, 48.
orizabae, Lepus, 221.
Neotoma, 296.
Neotomodon, 298.
Peromyscus, 328.
Reithrodontomys, 348.
Sorex, 191.
Sylvilagus, 221.
Thomomys, 394.
ornatulus, Epimys, 472.
Rattus, 472.
ornatus, Dipodomys, 413.
Sorex, 191.
Orolestes inca, 228.
orolestes, Neotoma, 296.
orophilus, Phenacomys, 338.
Orthogeomys, 372.
alleni, 372.
annexus, 372.
felipensis, 373.
guerrerensis, 373.
latifrons, 373.
nelsoni, 373.
vulcani, 373.
orthos, Dasymys, 444.
orthotis, Nyctinomus, 121.
Oryx, 10.
annectens, 10.
Oryzomys, 304.
albiventer, 304.
angusticeps, 305.
aurillus, 356.
aztecus, 306.
bombycinus, 305.
caudatus, 305.
colimensis, 308.
coloratus, 309.
couesi, 307, 308, 310.
cozumelae, 306.
crinitus, 306.
dariensis, 305.
dilutior, 305.
floridanus, 309.
frontalis, 306.
gatunensis, 307.
goldmani, 307.
guerrerensis, 307.
hylocetes, 307.
idoneus, 308.
lenis, 307.
mayensis, 307.
medius, 308.
megadon, 310.
mexicanus, 310.
nelsoni, 309.
palatinus, 309.
peragrus, 308.
pirrensis, 309.
regillus, 306.
rhabdops, 309.
richmondi, 309.
rostratus, 310.
rufinus, 308.
rufus, 310.
saturatior, 306.
talamancae, 310.

Oryzomys teapensis, 310.
yucatanensis, 311.
zygomaticus, 311.
osgoodi, Citellus, 516.
Cricetomys, 444.
Ctenomys, 361.
Spermophilus, 516.
Thomomys, 396.
othus, Lepus, 213.
Otocyon, 46.
virgatus, 46.
Otognosis, longimembris, 431.
Otomys, 453.
dollmani, 453.
Ototylomys, 311.
phaeus, 311.
phyllotis, 311.
otus, Reithrodontomys, 344.
Ourebia, 10.
aequatoria, 11.
cottoni, 10.
microdon, 10.
Ovis, 11.
auduboni, 11.
canadensis, 12.
dalli, 12.
gaillardi, 11.
mexicana, 12.
nelsoni, 12.
sheldoni, 13.
texiana, 11.
weemsi, 11.
Oxymycterus, microtus, 265.
oxytona, Marmota, 541.
Ozanna, roosevelti, 8.

Pachyura, aequatoria, 198.
occultidens, 198.
pachyurus, Sorex, 191.
pacifica, Aplodontia, 253.
Procyon, 84.
pacificus, Antrozous, 146.
Lepus, 223.
Perognathus, 433.
Procyon, 84.
Sorex, 191.
Sylvilagus, 223.
Zapus, 568.
padangus, Paradoxurus, 107.
pagensis, Cynopterus, 138.
Macaca, 245.
Macacus, 245.
Mus, 472.
Rattus, 472.
Paguma, 105.
robusta, 105.
palatina, Neotoma, 296.
palatinus, Oryzomys, 309.
palelae, Rattus, 472.
pallasi, Ursus, 96.
pallens, Eptesicus, 147.
Paradoxurus, 106.
pallescens, Citellus, 518.
Corynorhinus, 146.
Lynx, 60.
Onychomys, 303.
palliata, Ratufa, 549.

pallidulus, Nyctomys, 299.
pallidus, Antrozous, 145.
  Arvicola, 267.
  Canis, 45.
  Citellus, 520.
  Eliomys, 489.
  Eptesicus, 147.
  Eutamias, 531.
  Lemmiscus, 267.
  Metachirops, 231.
  Metachirus, 231.
  Microdipodops, 422.
  Myotis, 151.
  Perognathus, 427.
  Procyon, 84.
  Sigmodon, 352.
  Spermophilus, 520.
  Tamias, 531.
  Tragulus, 35.
  Vespertilio, 145.
palmarius, Bassariscus, 39.
palmeri, Eutamias, 530.
  Nemorhoedus, 12.
  Sorex, 184.
palustris, Callosciurus, 493.
  Sciurus, 493.
pamana, Promops, 122.
pamirensis, Microtus, 280.
panamensis, Chironectes, 228.
  Euprocyon, 81.
  Heteromys, 417.
  Icticyon, 46.
  Mustela, 71.
  Procyon, 81.
panamintinus, Dipodomys, 413.
  Eutamias, 530.
  Perodipus, 413.
  Perognathus, 431.
  Tamias, 530.
pandora, Mazama, 18.
pannellus, Epimys, 472.
  Rattus, 472.
pannosus, Mus, 473.
  Rattus, 473.
pannovianus, Callosciurus, 499.
  Sciurus, 499.
pantarensis, Mus, 473.
  Rattus, 473.
panya, Epimys, 452.
  Mastomys, 452.
papagensis, Peromyscus, 318.
Papio, 246.
  lestes, 246.
  vigilis, 246.
Pappogeomys, 374.
  albinasus, 374.
  amecensis, 374.
  flammeus, 374.
  lagunensis, 374.
  nayaritensis, 374.
  nelsoni, 375.
Paradoxurus, 105.
  brunneipes, 105.
  canescens, 106.
  canus, 106.
  enganus, 106.
  fuscus, 106.

Paradoxurus lignicolor, 107.
  padangus, 107.
  pallens, 106.
  parvus, 108.
  pugnax, 106.
  pulcher, 106.
  ravus, 107.
  robustus, 105.
  sacer, 107.
  senex, 107.
  simplex, 107.
paradoxus, Perognathus, 433.
paraguensis, Felis, 58.
parallelus, Tragulus, 36.
paramicrus, Nesophontes, 166.
parasiticus, Hesperomys, 330.
  Peromyscus, 330.
Paraxerus, 543.
  kahari, 543.
parnassius, Lepus, 213.
Parocnus, 570.
  serus, 570.
parowanensis, Thomomys, 385.
parva, Cryptotis, 175.
parviceps, Liomys, 420.
  Thomomys, 397.
parvidens, Cheiromeles, 120.
  Citellus, 513.
  Euroscaptor, 199.
  Neotoma, 296.
  Sorex, 190.
  Spermophilus, 513.
  Sturnira, 135.
  Talpa, 199.
  Urocyon, 49.
parvipes, Moschus, 25.
  Mungos, 105.
  Myonax, 105.
parvula, Marmota, 540.
  Rhogeëssa, 162, 571.
parvulus, Citellus, 505.
  Pitymys, 339.
  Thomomys, 381.
parvus, Claviglis, 404.
  Cricetodipus, 434, 574.
  Eliomys, 404.
  Paradoxurus, 108.
  Perognathus, 432, 574.
  Sciurus, 565.
  Tomeutes, 565.
pascalis, Thomomys, 377.
patagonica, Felis, 59.
patulus, Thomomys, 382.
paulensis, Felis, 58.
paululus, Miniopterus, 149.
paulus, Baiomys, 258.
pauper, Epimys, 477.
  Rattus, 477.
pauperrima, Arvicola, 268.
pauperrimus, Lemmiscus, 268.
pealii, Phoca, 234.
Pecari, 28.
  bangsi, 28.
  crassis, 28.
  humeralis, 29.
  nanus, 30.
  nelsoni, 29.

Pecari nigrescens, 29.
    sonoriensis, 29.
    yucatanensis, 29.
pectoralis, Peromyscus, 313.
    Phocaena, 110.
    Thomomys, 395.
Pedetes, 490.
    currax, 490.
    dentatus, 490.
    larvalis, 490.
pediculus, Conepatus, 62.
pelapius, Callosciurus, 499.
    Sciurus, 499.
pelingensis, Hipposideros, 118.
pellax, Mus, 473.
    Rattus, 473.
pellyensis, Ursus, 96.
Pelomys, 454.
    iridescens, 454.
    roosevelti, 452.
pemangilensis, Callosciurus, 500.
    Sciurus, 500.
pemangilis, Tupaia, 206.
penecillatus [sic], Perognathus, 435.
penialius, Callosciurus, 498.
    Sciurus, 498.
penicillatus, Perognathus, 435.
    Peromyscus, 315.
peninsulae, Blarina, 167.
    Canis, 45.
    Funambulus, 538.
    Ratufa, 548.
peninsularis, Antilocapra, 6.
    Callosciurus, 500.
    Dipodomys, 414.
    Emballonura, 116.
    Perodipus, 414.
    Sciurus, 500.
    Sus, 28.
penitus, Rattus, 473.
pennipes, Ammospermophilus, 513.
    Citellus, 513.
peragrus, Oryzomys, 308.
peramplus, Thomomys, 388.
Peramys melanops, 232.
perasper, Rattus, 473.
perblandus, Dipodomys, 415.
percivali, Colobus, 239.
    Dendromus, 445.
    Tatera, 356.
percura, Presbytis, 249.
perda, Mustela, 74.
perditus, Thomomys, 395.
perdus, Putorius, 74.
peregrina, Blarina, 178.
    Cryptotis, 178.
peregrinus, Cratogeomys, 368.
    Thomomys, 395.
perflavus, Epimys, 473.
    Rattus, 473.
    Tragulus, 35.
pergracilis, Perognathus, 423.
    Peromyscus, 317.
pergrisea, Crocidura, 173.
peridoneus, Cratogeomys, 365.
    Peromyscus, 317.
perigrinator, Sciurus, 558.

permiliensis, Sorex, 190.
perniger, Perognathus, 428.
pernox, Myotis, 157.
pernyi, Dremomys, 522.
Perodipus, cabezonae, 405.
    columbianus, 412.
    goldmani, 406.
    ingens, 407.
    levipes, 410.
    luteolus, 413.
    microps, 409.
    morroensis, 411.
    panamintinus, 413.
    peninsularis, 414.
    perplexus, 414.
    preblei, 410.
    simulans, 415.
    stephensi, 415.
    streatori, 415.
    tularensis, 405.
    utahensis, 411.
    venustus, 416.
Perognathus, 422.
    albulus, 435.
    ambiguus, 424.
    ammophilus, 435.
    amoenus, 433.
    amplus, 422.
    angustirostris, 435.
    anthonyi, 423.
    apache, 423.
    arenicola, 433.
    arizonensis, 431.
    armatus, 424.
    artus, 425.
    baileyi, 425.
    bimaculatus, 425.
    bombycinus, 426.
    brevinasus, 433.
    californicus, 424, 426.
    callistus, 426.
    canescens, 430.
    caryi, 423.
    clarus, 434.
    cleomophila, 424.
    columbianus, 427.
    dispar, 426.
    domensis, 425.
    eremicus, 427.
    extimus, 425.
    fallax, 427.
    flavescens, 428.
    flavus, 428.
    formosus, 429.
    fuliginosus, 429.
    gilvus, 431.
    goldmani, 429, 436.
    hispidus, 430, 434.
    hopiensis, 428.
    idahoensis, 434.
    inopinus, 427.
    inornatus, 430.
    insularis, 425.
    intermedius, 430.
    jacksoni, 422.
    litus, 428.
    longimembris, 431.

Perognathus magdalenae, 437.
  magruderensis, 434.
  melanotis, 424.
  mexicanus, 428.
  monticola, 432.
  nelsoni, 432, 437.
  nevadensis, 432.
  obscurus, 432.
  occultus, 432, 437.
  ochrus, 426.
  olivaceus, 432, 433.
  pacificus, 433.
  pallidus, 427.
  panamintinus, 431.
  paradoxus, 433.
  parvus, 432, 574.
  penecillatus [sic], 435.
  penicillatus, 435.
  pergracilis, 423.
  perniger, 428.
  phasma, 430.
  piperi, 429.
  plerus, 434.
  relictus, 424.
  rostratus, 436.
  rotundus, 423.
  seorsus, 436.
  seri, 436.
  siccus, 436.
  sobrinus, 436.
  sonoriensis, 429.
  spilotus, 434.
  spinatus, 436.
  stephensi, 437.
  sublucidus, 424.
  taylori, 423.
  zacatecae, 430.
Peromyscus, 311.
  affinis, 311, 329.
  algidus, 324.
  allex, 258.
  allophylus, 312.
  altilaneus, 312.
  amplus, 312.
  analogus, 259.
  angelensis, 314.
  anthonyi, 312.
  arenarius, 318.
  aridulus, 322.
  assimilis, 324.
  attwateri, 315.
  auritus, 313, 316.
  austerus, 313.
  avius, 318.
  badius, 336.
  blandus, 332.
  boylii, 315.
  bullatus, 315.
  canus, 316.
  carmeni, 318.
  castaneus, 334.
  clementis, 334.
  comptus, 316.
  consobrinus, 328.
  cozumelae, 316.
  crinitus, 317.
  cristobalensis, 336.

Peromyscus decoloratus, 331.
  disparilis, 317.
  dorsalis, 324.
  elusus, 325.
  eremicoides, 313.
  eremicus, 317, 318, 328.
  eremus, 325.
  evides, 332.
  exiguus, 326.
  exterus, 325.
  felipensis, 319.
  floridanus, 324.
  fulvus, 332.
  gambelii, 319, 334.
  gentilis, 321.
  goldmani, 320.
  gossypinus, 316, 320.
  gracilis, 321.
  gratus, 321, 336.
  guardia, 321.
  guatemalensis, 322.
  gunnisoni, 325.
  hollisteri, 325.
  hylaeus, 322.
  hylocetes, 322.
  inclarus, 325.
  insulicola, 318.
  laceianus, 330.
  laceyi, 314.
  lagunae, 335.
  lepturus, 322.
  leucocephalus, 322.
  levipes, 323.
  lewisi, 329.
  lophurus, 323.
  luteus, 324.
  madrensis, 324.
  magdalenae, 326.
  maniculatus, 312, 314.
  margaritae, 326.
  martinensis, 326.
  medius, 334.
  megalops, 327.
  mekisturus, 327.
  melanocarpus, 327.
  melanophrys, 327.
  melanotis, 328.
  melanurus, 327.
  merriami, 328.
  mesomelas, 334.
  mexicanus, 333.
  minnesotae, 323.
  musculoides, 329.
  nebrascensis, 324.
  nelsoni, 329.
  nigrescens, 259.
  noveboracensis, 315, 323.
  oaxacensis, 330.
  ochraceus, 323.
  orizabae, 328.
  papagensis, 318.
  parasiticus, 330.
  pectoralis, 313.
  penicillatus, 315.
  pergracilis, 317.
  peridoneus, 317.
  phaeurus, 319.

Peromyscus, pirrensis, 330.
  polius, 331.
  polypolius, 319.
  preblei, 336.
  prevostensis, 331.
  restrictus, 320.
  rowleyi, 315.
  rubidus, 330.
  rufinus, 323.
  santacruzae, 326.
  saxatilis, 329.
  simulatus, 331.
  simulus, 332.
  sitkensis, 331.
  sonoriensis, 331.
  stephani, 333.
  stephensi, 333.
  streatori, 326.
  subater, 259.
  teapensis, 329.
  tehuantepecus, 333.
  texanus, 316, 333.
  thomasi, 334.
  tiburonensis, 335.
  tornillo, 335.
  totontepecus, 328, 329.
  truei, 327, 335.
  vicinior, 314.
  xenurus, 336.
  zamelas, 328.
  zamorae, 328.
  zarhynchus, 336.
  zelotes, 336.
peromyscus, Mus, 454.
  Praomys, 454.
perotae, Mustela, 71.
perotensis, Citellus, 517.
  Cratogeomys, 368.
  Dipodomys, 413.
  Neotomodon, 299.
  Reithrodontomys, 348.
  Spermophilus, 517.
perpallida, Neotoma, 290.
perpallidus, Onychomys, 304.
  Thomomys, 399.
perpes, Thomomys, 378.
perplanus, Cratogeomys, 366.
perplexus, Dipodomys, 414.
  Perodipus, 414.
personatus, Claviglis, 405.
  Geomys, 370.
  Graphiurus, 405.
perspicillata, Hemiderma, 128.
perspicillatus, Lagenorhynchus, 110, 111.
perturbans, Ursus, 96.
peruvianus, Mus, 574.
pervagor, Ursus, 97.
pervagus, Thomomys, 378.
pervarius, Thomomys, 382.
pessimus, Citellus, 514.
Petaurista, 543.
  batuana, 543.
  mimicus, 543.
  rubicundus, 543.
  sulcatus, 544.
  terutaus, 544.
petax, Myotis, 157.

petersoni, Euneomys, 265.
  petilidens, Lagostomus, 256.
petilus, Leggada, 447.
  Mus, 447.
Petinomys, 544.
  crinitus, 544.
  maerens, 544.
petraeus, Apomys, 442.
petrensis, Marmota, 540.
Petrodromus sangi, 166.
petulans, Sciurus, 561.
  Tamiasciurus, 561.
Phacochoerus, 26.
  bufo, 26.
phaea, Aplodontia, 254.
phaeonyx, Ursus, 91.
phaeopepla, Ratufa, 549.
phaeotis, Artibeus, 127.
  Dermanura, 127.
phaeura, Liomys, 420.
  Macaca, 245.
  Macacus, 245.
  Tupaia, 206.
phaeurus, Liomys, 420.
  Peromyscus, 319.
phaeus, Arvicola, 281.
  Elephantulus, 166.
  Microtus, 281.
  Ototylomys, 311.
Phalanger, 232.
  furvus, 232.
phasma, Myotis, 154.
  Perognathus, 430.
  Thomomys, 388.
phayrei, Trachypithecus, 247.
Phenacomys, 337.
  albipes, 337.
  celatus, 337.
  celsus, 337.
  intermedius, 338.
  latimanus, 337.
  levis, 337.
  longicaudus, 337.
  mackenzii, 338.
  orophilus, 338.
  preblei, 338.
  truei, 338.
  ungava, 337, 338.
phenax, Hexolobodon, 362.
  Spilogale, 77.
  Teanopus, 356.
Philander, 232.
  centralis, 232.
Phoca, 234.
  geronimensis, 235.
  macrodens, 235.
  pealii, 234.
  pribilofensis, 235.
  richardii, 234.
  stejnegeri, 235.
Phocaena, 110.
  australis, 109, 576.
  dalli, 112.
  lineata, 110, 111.
  pectoralis, 110.
  phocoena, 111.
  vomerina, 111.

phocoena, Phocaena, 111.
Phocoenoides, 112.
    dalli, 112.
Phodopus, 339.
    crepidatus, 339.
Phodotes, 126.
    tumidirostris, 126.
Phoniscus, 159.
    atrox, 159.
    rapax, 159.
phylarchus, Rangifer, 25.
Phyllonycteris, 135.
    bombifrons 130.
    obtusa 135.
    planifrons 130.
phyllotis, Ototylomys, 311.
piceus, Callosciurus, 495.
picinus, Limnomys, 450.
picta, Neotoma, 296.
pictus, Eutamias, 529.
    Neacomys, 283.
    Tamias, 529.
pilirostris, Dymecodon, 198.
pinacus, Rattus, 467.
pinalensis, Thomomys, 382.
pinatus, Rattus, 474.
pinetorum, Neotoma, 297.
    Thomomys, 392.
piniensis, Ratufa, 549.
    Sciurus, 565.
    Tomeutes, 565.
pinius, Tragulus, 35.
piperi, Perognathus, 429.
Pipistrellus, 160.
    aero, 160.
    australis, 161.
    camortae, 160.
    cinnamomeus, 160.
    curtatus, 160.
    helios, 160.
    hesperus, 160.
    merriami, 161.
    minusculus, 161.
    obscurus, 161.
    stampflii, 161.
    subulidens, 161.
pirrensis, Felis, 59.
    Oryzomys, 309.
    Peromyscus, 330.
Pithecus agnatus, 241.
    baweanus, 241.
    capitalis, 241.
    carimatae, 242.
    cupidus, 242.
    impudens, 242.
    lapsus, 243.
    lasiae, 242.
    lautensis, 243.
    lingae, 243.
    lingungensis, 243.
    mandibularis, 244.
    mansalaris, 244.
    mindorus, 244.
    pullus, 240.
    sirhassenensis, 245.
    vitiis, 246.
Pitymys, 339.

Pitymys auricularis, 339.
    nemoralis, 340.
    parvulus, 339.
    quasiater, 340, 573.
    scalopsoides, 339, 340.
plagiodon, Delphinus, 113.
    Stenella, 113.
Plagiodontia, 362.
    hylaeum, 362.
    spelaeum, 363.
planiceps, Crocidura, 173.
    Neotoma, 294.
    Platygeomys, 376.
    Sorex, 192.
    Ursus, 97.
planifrons, Arvicanthis, 489.
    Cratogeomys, 366.
    Erophylla, 130.
    Heteromys, 416.
    Phyllonycteris, 130.
    Sigmodon, 353.
    Typomys, 489.
plantinarensis, Liomys, 420.
platycephalus, Dipodomys, 414.
Platygeomys, 375.
    angustirostris, 376.
    fumosus, 375.
    gymnurus, 375.
    imparilis, 375.
    inclarus, 375.
    neglectus, 376.
    planiceps, 376.
    tylorhinus, 376.
    varius, 376.
    zinseri, 376.
platyrhina, Chincha, 69.
    Mephitis, 69.
plenus, Sigmodon, 352.
plerus, Perognathus, 434.
plesius, Citellus, 510.
    Spermophilus, 510.
plethodon, Monophyllus, 134.
pluto, Taphonycteris, 117.
    Taphozous, 117.
poadromus, Lepus, 213.
Podogymnura, 165.
    truei, 165.
Poemys, 454.
    nigrifrons, 454.
    spectabilis, 454.
polia, Ratufa, 550.
poliopus, Sciurus, 494, 500.
polius, Peromyscus, 331.
pollens, Epimys, 474.
    Nectomys, 284.
    Rattus, 474.
polulus, Surdisorex, 198.
polypolius, Peromyscus, 319.
popofensis, Microtus, 283.
porsildi, Lepus, 209.
portoricensis, Chilonycteris, 129.
    Monophyllus, 134.
potens, Epimys, 474.
    Rattus, 474.
pothae, Tatera, 356.
Potos, 80.
    arborensis, 80.

Potos campechensis, 80.
  guerrerensis, 80.
  isthmicus, 81.
potosinus, Thomomys, 402.
praeceps, Artibeus, 127.
praetor, Apodemus, 441.
pranis, Callosciurus, 496.
  Sciurus, 496.
Praomys, 454.
  peromyscus, 454.
  rostratus, 455.
  taitae, 455.
pratensis, Citellus, 518.
  Spermophilus, 518.
preblei, Dipodomys, 410.
  Lutra, 65.
  Perodipus, 410.
  Peromyscus, 336.
  Phenacomys, 338.
  Sorex, 192.
  Tamiasciurus, 561.
preblorum, Marmota, 540.
Presbytes batuanus, 247.
  rhionis, 249.
Presbytis, 247.
  argentea, 247.
  arwasca, 247.
  australis, 247.
  cana, 247.
  canicrus, 248.
  carimatae, 248.
  catemana, 248.
  chrysomelas, 247.
  corvus, 248.
  femoralis, 247, 248, 249.
  hosei, 248.
  koratensis, 248.
  melalophus, 247, 249.
  percura, 249.
  rubicunda, 248, 249.
  vigilans, 250.
pretiellus, Tragulus, 35.
pretiosa, Neotoma, 290.
pretiosus, Callosciurus, 500.
  Liomys, 419.
  Molossus, 121.
  Sciurus, 500.
  Tragulus, 36.
prevostensis, Peromyscus, 331.
  Sorex, 188.
pribilofensis, Alopex, 41.
  Phoca, 235.
  Sorex, 192.
  Vulpes, 41.
primulina, Mustela, 73.
princeps, Cynopterus, 138.
Procapra, altaica, 13.
procera, Crocidura, 169.
procerus, Sciurus, 565.
  Tomeutes, 565.
Procyon, 81.
  auspicatus, 81.
  californicus, 81.
  crassidens, 82.
  excelsus, 82.
  fuscipes, 82.
  grinnelli, 82.

Procyon hirtus, 82.
  incautus, 82.
  inesperatus, 83.
  insularis, 83.
  litoreus, 83.
  marinus, 83.
  mexicana, 81.
  mexicanus, 81.
  minor, 84.
  ochraceus, 83.
  pacifica, 84.
  pacificus, 84.
  pallidus, 84.
  panamensis, 81.
  pumilus, 85.
  pygmaeus, 85.
  shufeldti, 83.
  solutus, 84.
  vancouverensis, 84.
  varius, 84.
  vicinus, 81.
Prodelphinus lateralis, 576.
Prodorcas, 13.
  altaica, 13.
Proechimys, 363.
  guairae, 363.
  rubellus, 363.
  steerei, 363.
Promops, 122.
  pamana, 122.
proserpinae, Callosciurus, 500.
  Sciurus, 500.
Proteles, 85.
  termes, 85.
Protoxerus, 544.
  bea, 544.
pryori, Thomomys, 396.
Pseudois, 13.
  caesia, 13.
  szechuanensis, 13.
Pseudorca, 112.
  crassidens, 112.
Pseudostoma castanops, 364.
Pteromys, 545.
  crinitus, 544.
  incanus, 545.
Pteropus, 139.
  aldabrensis, 139.
  arquatus, 139.
  balutus, 139.
  baveanus, 139.
  cagayanus, 140.
  enganus, 140.
  faunulus, 140.
  geminorum, 140.
  insularis, 141.
  lanensis, 140.
  lanigera, 141.
  lepidus, 141.
  macklotii, 142.
  mearnsi, 141.
  niadicus, 141.
  pumilus, 141.
  samoensis, 142.
  vociferus, 142.
pueblensis, Cryptotis, 179.
pugnax, Paradoxurus, 106.

pulchellus, Ursus, 97.
pulcher, Nannosciurus, 542.
  Paradoxurus, 106.
  Scalopus, 200.
pullata, Crocidura, 173.
pulliventer, Mus, 474.
  Rattus, 474.
pullus, Microtus, 281.
  Mus, 472.
  Pithecus, 240.
  Rattus, 474.
pulonis, Tupaia, 206.
pumila, Brachyphylla, 128.
  Genetta, 103.
  Macaca, 243, 245.
pumilus, Galeopithecus, 164.
  Galeopterus, 164.
  Macacus, 245.
  Procyon, 85.
  Pteropus, 141.
  Sciurus, 565.
  Tarsius, 252.
  Tomeutes, 565.
punicans, Rattus, 474.
purui, Marmosa, 231.
pusilla, Emballonura, 116.
pusillus, Chaerephon, 120.
  Nyctinomus, 120.
  Thomomys, 388.
  Thryonomys, 566.
Putorius alascensis, 73.
  alleni, 69.
  arcticus, 69.
  culbertsoni, 70.
  goldmani, 71.
  haidarum, 71.
  kadiacensis, 70.
  kaneii, 71.
  leptus, 74.
  leucoparia, 71.
  oregonensis, 75.
  perdus, 74.
  saturatus, 73.
  streatori, 73.
  tropicalis, 74.
  washingtoni, 75.
putorius, Spilogale, 77.
Pygathrix flavicauda, 249.
  rubida, 249.
  sanctorum, 249.
  ultima, 250.
pygmaeus, Molossus, 122.
  Procyon, 85.
  Thomomys, 396.
pyrrhus, Lophuromys, 451.
pyrronotus, Erythrocebus, 240.
pyrsonota, Ratufa, 550.

quadratus, Thomomys, 396.
quadrimaculatus, Eutamias, 527.
quadrivittatus, Eutamias, 530.
quasiater, Arvicola, 340, 573.
  Pitymys, 340, 573.
quebecensis, Myotis, 148.
Quemisia, 363.
  gravis, 363.
quercerus, Lepus, 213.

querceti, Epimys, 475.
  Rattus, 475.
quercinus, Sciurus, 552, 558.

raineyi, Acinonyx, 52.
  Cricetomys, 444.
  Crocidura, 173.
  Gazella, 9.
  Kobus, 9.
  Lepus, 213.
rainieri, Aplodontia, 253.
rallus, Rattus, 475.
Rangifer, 24.
  excelsifrons, 24.
  fortidens, 24.
  phylarchus, 25.
  stonei, 24.
rapax, Phoniscus, 159.
raptor, Bassaris, 39.
  Bassariscus, 39.
  Rheomys, 349.
Rattus, 455.
  adspersus, 455.
  albigularis, 455.
  anambae, 455.
  andrewsi, 456.
  antucus, 467.
  asper, 456.
  atridorsum, 456.
  babi, 480.
  balae, 456.
  balmasus, 456.
  banacus, 467.
  barussanus, 457.
  basilanus, 457.
  batamanus, 457.
  batus, 457.
  benguetensis, 457.
  benticanus, 458.
  borneanus, 458.
  bullatus, 458.
  burrescens, 458.
  burrulus, 458.
  burrus, 459.
  buruensis, 459.
  butangensis, 482.
  calcis, 459.
  camurus, 461.
  canus, 449.
  carimatae, 459.
  casensis, 459.
  catellifer, 460.
  cereus, 464.
  chombolis, 460.
  clabatus, 460.
  clarae, 486.
  coloratus, 460.
  concolor, 472.
  crassus, 460.
  cremoriventer, 461.
  dentatus, 475.
  domelicus, 461.
  domitor, 461.
  ducis, 471.
  enganus, 461.
  eurous, 478.
  exiguus, 476.

Rattus exsul, 476.
 exulans, 462.
 facetus, 462.
 ferreocanus, 462.
 firmus, 462.
 flavidulus, 482.
 flaviventer, 462.
 flebilis, 463.
 fortunatus, 476.
 fremens, 463.
 fulmineus, 463.
 gala, 464.
 gilbiventer, 464.
 gracilis, 464.
 hamatus, 464.
 insolatus, 465.
 insulanus, 476.
 insularum, 486.
 integer, 465.
 julianus, 466.
 kelleri, 466.
 koratensis, 476.
 koratis, 475.
 kramensis, 476.
 kramis, 475.
 lamucotanus, 471.
 lancavensis, 486.
 lanensis, 477.
 lasiae, 480.
 lepidus, 466.
 leucophaeatus, 466.
 linduensis, 465.
 lingensis, 466.
 localis, 465.
 lucas, 467.
 lugens, 468.
 luta, 468.
 luteolus, 468.
 mabalus, 467.
 maerens, 468.
 magnirostris, 469.
 mandus, 469.
 mansalaris, 463.
 mara, 469.
 masae, 469.
 matthaeus, 469.
 mayonicus, 469.
 melanurus, 4,0.
 mengurus, 470.
 mesanis, 477.
 mindanensis, 470.
 mollicomus, 470.
 nasutus, 471.
 nigellus, 471.
 ornatulus, 472.
 pagensis, 472.
 palelae, 472.
 pannellus, 472.
 pannosus, 473.
 pantarensis, 473.
 pauper, 477.
 pellax, 473.
 penitus, 473.
 perasper, 473.
 perflavus, 473.
 pinacus, 467.
 pinatus, 474.

Rattus pollens, 474.
 potens, 474.
 pulliventer, 474.
 pullus, 474.
 punicans, 474.
 querceti, 475.
 rallus, 475.
 raveni, 478.
 roa, 478.
 robiginosus, 478.
 saturatus, 478.
 sebucus, 479.
 sericatus, 479.
 serutus, 479.
 shigarus, 477.
 siantanicus, 479.
 simalurensis, 479.
 soccatus, 480.
 socer, 471.
 solus, 480.
 sowerbyi, 465.
 spatulatus, 480.
 stentor, 481.
 stoicus, 481.
 strepitans, 481.
 stridens, 481.
 stridulus, 481.
 subditivus, 465.
 surdus, 482.
 surifer, 482.
 taciturnus, 482.
 tagulayensis, 483.
 tambelanicus, 483.
 tapanulius, 487.
 tetricus, 470.
 tinctus, 452.
 tingius, 483.
 tiomanicus, 483.
 todayensis, 484.
 tua, 484.
 tuancus, 463.
 turbidus, 477.
 tyrannus, 484.
 ubecus, 484.
 umbridorsum, 484.
 valens, 485.
 validus, 485.
 viclana, 478.
 vigoratus, 485.
 virtus, 485.
 vitiensis, 486.
 vociferans, 486.
 vulcani, 487.
 zamboangae, 487.
Ratufa, 545.
 anambae, 545.
 angusticeps, 545.
 arusinus, 545.
 balae, 545.
 bancana, 550.
 batuana, 549.
 bulana, 546.
 carimonensis, 546.
 catemana, 546.
 celaenopepla, 546.
 condurensis, 547.
 confinis, 547.

Ratufa conspicua, 547.
  cothurnata, 547.
  femoralis, 547.
  griseicollis, 547.
  insignis, 548.
  laenata, 548.
  major, 546.
  masae, 548.
  melanopepla, 548.
  nigrescens, 549.
  notabilis, 549.
  palliata, 549.
  peninsulae, 548.
  phaeopepla, 549.
  piniensis, 549.
  polia, 550.
  pyrsonota, 550.
  tiomanensis, 550.
  vittata, 550.
  vittatula, 551.
rava, Dermanura, 127.
raveni, Rattus, 478.
raviana, Tupaia, 206.
ravida, Neotoma, 290.
ravidulus, Microtus, 281.
ravulus, Tragulus, 36.
ravus, Artibeus, 127.
  Paradoxurus, 107.
  Reithrodontomys, 346.
  Tragulus, 36.
Redunca, 13.
  chanleri, 13.
  tohi, 14.
regalis, Vulpes, 52.
regillus, Dipodomys, 409.
  Oryzomys, 306.
Reithrodon, 340.
  hatcheri, 340.
  longicauda, 345.
  megalotis, 345.
  montanus, 348.
Reithrodontomys, 341.
  albescens, 341.
  albilabris, 348.
  alleni, 341.
  alticola, 349.
  alticolus, 349.
  amoles, 341.
  aurantius, 347.
  aureus, 349.
  caryi, 346.
  chiapensis, 343.
  chrysopsis, 341.
  cinereus, 349.
  colimae, 341.
  deserti, 346.
  difficilis, 342.
  dorsalis, 342.
  dychei, 342.
  goldmani, 343.
  griseoflavus, 343.
  griseus, 344.
  helvolus, 344.
  hirsutus, 344.
  jalapae, 342.
  klamathensis, 344.
  levipes, 344.

Reithrodontomys longicaudus, 344, 345.
  lucifrons, 347.
  luteolus, 349.
  megalotis, 345, 346.
  merriami, 347.
  mexicanus, 342.
  microdon, 348.
  minusculus, 347.
  montanus, 348.
  mustelinus, 343.
  nebrascensis, 342.
  nelsoni, 343.
  nerterus, 342.
  nigriscens, 346.
  obscurus, 346.
  orizabae, 348.
  otus, 345.
  perotensis, 348.
  ravus, 346.
  tenuirostris, 349.
  tenuis, 343.
  toltecus, 345.
  tolucae, 341.
  virginianus, 344.
  zacatecae, 346, 347.
Reithronycteris, 135.
  aphylla, 135.
relicinus, Thomomys, 399.
relicta, Neotoma, 297.
relictus, Perognathus, 424.
repanda, Lutra, 66.
repentinus, Castor, 255.
reperticia, Mazama, 18.
restrictus, Peromyscus, 320.
  Sylvilagus, 219.
rex, Lavia, 118.
  Tachyoryctes, 490.
rhabdops, Oryzomys, 309.
Rheomys, 349.
  raptor, 349.
Rhinolophus, 143.
  circe, 143.
  hipposideros, 144.
  hirsutus, 143.
  inops, 143.
  keniensis, 143.
  minutillus, 143.
  minutus, 143, 144.
  nereis, 144.
  nesites, 143.
  niasensis, 144.
  solitarius, 144.
  spadix, 144.
  virgo, 144.
rhionis, Presbytes, 249.
  Sus, 28.
Rhipidomys, 350.
  scandens, 350.
rhoditis, Crocidura, 173.
Rhogeëssa, 162.
  gracilis, 162.
  minutilla, 162.
  parvula, 162, 571.
  tumida, 162.
Rhynchotragus, 14.
  nyikae, 14.
riabus, Tupaia, 206.

richardii, Phoca, 234.
richardsoni, Dicrostonyx, 264.
richardsonii, Lepus, 214.
richmondi, Dasyprocta, 358.
    Didelphis, 229.
    Nasua, 80.
    Oryzomys, 309.
    Sciurus, 558.
rigidus, Lepus, 222.
ringens, Spilogale, 77.
    Tayassu, 30.
ripensis, Fiber, 301.
    Ondatra, 301.
rivularis, Microtus, 279.
roa, Epimys, 478.
    Rattus, 478.
roanensis, Napaeozapus, 567.
    Zapus, 567.
robiginosus, Epimys, 478.
    Rattus, 478.
robinsoni, Coelops, 117.
roboratus, Sorex, 193.
robusta, Eonycteris, 138.
    Lonchophylla, 132.
    Paguma, 105.
robustus, Ctenomys, 361.
    Lepus, 222.
    Paradoxurus, 105.
    Sylvilagus, 222.
rogersi, Ursus, 98.
Romerolagus, 215.
    diazi, 215.
    nelsoni, 215.
roosevelti, Alcelaphus, 7.
    Bubalis, 7.
    Cervus, 18.
    Colobus, 239.
    Crocidura, 173.
    Egocerus, 8.
    Felis, 57.
    Gazella, 9.
    Heliosorex, 173.
    Mylomys, 452.
    Ozanna, 8.
    Pelomys, 452.
    Sylvicapra, 15.
rostrata, Glossophaga, 131.
rostratus, Funambulus, 538.
    Lariscus, 538.
    Liomys, 420.
    Mus, 455.
    Oryzomys, 310.
    Perognathus, 436.
    Praomys, 455.
rotundus, Perognathus, 423.
rowleyi, Peromyscus, 315.
ruatanica, Marmosa, 231.
rubeculus, Callosciurus, 501.
    Sciurus, 501.
rubellus, Proechimys, 363.
rubescens, Atilax, 102.
    Mungos, 102.
rubeus, Tragulus, 36.
rubicunda, Presbytis, 248, 249.
rubicundus, Petaurista, 543.
rubida, Pygathrix, 249.
rubidiventris, Callosciurus, 501.

rubidiventris, Sciurus, 501.
rubidus, Muntiacus, 19.
    Peromyscus, 330.
rubricatus, Dicrostonyx, 264.
rufescens, Marmota, 540.
ruficaudus, Citellus, 508.
    Eutamias, 531.
rufinus, Hesperomys, 323.
    Oryzomys, 308.
    Peromyscus, 323.
rufiventer, Mystax, 236.
rufocanus, Clethrionomys, 258.
rufulus, Dasymys, 444.
    Tragulus, 37.
rufus, Canis, 41.
    Oryzomys, 310.
rungiusi, Ursus, 98.
rupatius, Callosciurus, 503.
    Sciurus, 503.
Rupicapra, 14.
    faesula, 14.
    rupicapra, 14.
rupicapra, Rupicapra, 14.
Rusa, 25.
    nigellus, 25.
rusiges, Apodemus, 440.
russeolus, Dipodomys, 410.
    Thomomys, 382.
russeus, Tragulus, 37.
russulus, Tragulus, 37.
rutiliventris, Callosciurus, 501.
    Sciurus, 501.

saccharalis, Cratogeomys, 367.
Saccostomus, 487.
    isiolae, 487.
    mearnsi, 488.
    umbriventer, 488.
sacer, Paradoxurus, 107.
sagittalis, Geomys, 369.
    Ursus, 98.
Sagmatias, 112.
    amblodon, 112.
sagulata, Mellivora, 67.
salatana, Tupaia, 205.
saliens, Allactaga, 359.
    Lepus, 214.
saltator, Tarsius, 253.
salvini, Sorex, 193.
samoensis, Pteropus, 142.
sanctidiegi, Lepus, 220.
    Sylvilagus, 220.
sanctorum, Pygathrix, 249.
sanggaus, Callosciurus, 501.
    Sciurus, 501.
sangi, Cercoctenus, 166.
    Petrodromus, 166.
santacruzae, Myocastor, 490.
    Peromyscus, 326.
    Urocyon, 49.
saturata, Mustela, 73.
saturatior, Oryzomys, 306.
saturatus, Callosciurus, 501.
    Epimys, 478.
    Galeopithecus, 164.
    Galeopterus, 164.
    Glaucomys, 535.

saturatus, Myotis, 159.
    Putorius, 73.
    Rattus, 478.
    Sciurus, 501.
    Sigmodon, 352.
    Thomomys, 389.
saussurei, Sorex, 193.
savannus, Dasymys, 445.
saxamans, Neotoma, 297.
saxatilis, Peromyscus, 329.
    Spilogale, 78.
saxicola, Bassariscus, 39.
    Citellus, 510.
saxicolus, Spermophilus, 510.
Scalops aeneus, 200.
scalopsoides, Arvicola, 340.
    Pitymys, 339, 340.
Scalopus, 200.
    caryi, 200.
    howelli, 200.
    inflatus, 200.
    machrinoides, 200.
    pulcher, 200.
scammonii, Globicephala, 109.
    Globicephalus, 109.
scandens, Rhipidomys, 350.
Scapanus, 200.
    alpinus, 201.
    dilatus, 201, 202.
    orarius, 201.
    schefferi, 201.
    sericatus, 201.
    townsendii, 200.
    truei, 202.
scaphiotus, Odocoileus, 19.
Schaeffia, 46.
    bweha, 46.
    notatus, 47.
schefferi, Scapanus, 201.
schisticeps, Lagomys, 226.
    Ochotona, 226.
schmidti, Cercopithecus, 238.
scirpensis, Microtus, 281.
Sciuropterus amoenus, 537.
    crinitus, 544.
    goldmani, 535.
    klamathensis, 533.
    macrotis, 535.
    maerens, 544.
    stephensi, 534.
    yukonensis, 536.
    zaphaeus, 533.
Sciurus, 551.
    abbottii, 491.
    aberti, 551, 554, 555.
    abieticola, 560.
    adangensis, 491.
    alleni, 552.
    altinsularis, 491.
    anambensis, 491.
    anthonyi, 556.
    aoris, 491.
    arendsis, 492.
    arizonensis, 553.
    armalis, 492.
    atratus, 562.
    atristriatus, 492.

Sciurus atrox, 492.
    avicennia, 557.
    baileyi, 560.
    balae, 563.
    baliolus, 559.
    bancarus, 563.
    batus, 564.
    belti, 553.
    bentincanus, 493.
    bilimitatus, 493.
    billitonus, 493.
    canigenus, 493.
    carimatae, 494.
    carimonensis, 494.
    cascadensis, 560.
    casensis, 494.
    castanonotus, 554.
    castanotus [sic], 554.
    chiapensis, 556.
    chiliensis, 559.
    chiricahuae, 555.
    choco, 559.
    chuscensis, 551.
    cocos, 558.
    colimensis, 552.
    colliaei, 553.
    concolor, 551.
    condurensis, 494.
    conipus, 494, 500.
    datus, 494.
    dilutus, 495.
    director, 495.
    domelicus, 495.
    dorsalis, 551, 555.
    effugius, 552.
    erebus, 495.
    evidens, 563.
    ferreus, 551.
    fossor, 556, 573.
    frumentor, 553.
    goldmani, 556.
    griseus, 573.
    helveolus, 559.
    helvus, 493.
    hernandezi, 552, 558.
    hippurellus, 563.
    hippurosus, 563.
    hirtus, 557.
    humilis, 564.
    hypophaeus, 554.
    ictericus, 496.
    inexpectatus, 495.
    infuscatus, 556.
    isthmius, 541.
    kaibabensis, 556.
    klossii, 496.
    lamucotanus, 496.
    lancavensis, 497.
    lautensis, 497.
    libericus, 536.
    limitis, 557.
    lingungensis, 564.
    littoralis, 558.
    lucas, 497.
    lutescens, 497.
    managuensis, 553.
    mansalaris, 564.

Sciurus marinsularis, 497.
  matthaeus, 498.
  mearnsi, 561.
  melanops, 498.
  mendanauus, 498.
  mimellus, 498.
  mimiculus, 499.
  miniatus, 499.
  mimus, 551.
  necopinus, 564.
  negligens, 557.
  nelsoni, 557.
  nemoralis, 552.
  neomexicanus, 560.
  novemlineatus, 562.
  nuchalis, 555.
  nyx, 499.
  palustris, 493.
  pannovianus, 499.
  parvus, 565.
  pelapius, 499.
  pemangilensis, 500.
  penialius, 498.
  peninsularis, 500.
  perigrinator, 558.
  petulans, 561.
  piniensis, 565.
  poliopus, 494, 500.
  pranis, 496.
  pretiosus, 500.
  procerus, 565.
  proserpinae, 500.
  pumilus, 565.
  quercinus, 552, 558.
  richmondi, 558.
  rubeculus, 501.
  rubidiventris, 501.
  rupatius, 503.
  rutiliventris, 501.
  sanggaus, 501.
  saturatus, 501.
  senex, 558.
  seraiae, 502.
  serutus, 502.
  siriensis, 502.
  suckleyi, 561.
  sullivanus, 502.
  surdus, 565.
  tachin, 592.
  tapanulius, 503.
  tarussanus, 503.
  tedongus, 502.
  tenuirostris, 503.
  thomasi, 559.
  tolucae, 557.
  trotteri, 496.
  truei, 559.
  ubericolor, 503.
  underwoodi, 553.
  undulatus, 537.
  ventorum, 561.
  vivax, 555.
  yucatenensis, 554.
sclateri, Sorex, 194.
Scotinomys, 350.
  subnubilis, 350.
Scotophilus hesperus, 160.

Scotophilus miradorensis, 572.
scottii, Urocyon, 48.
sebucus, Epimys, 479.
  Rattus, 479.
  Tragulus, 37.
Selenarctos, 86.
  ussuricus, 86.
  wulsini, 86.
selkirki, Ursus, 98.
semicaudata, Emballonura, 116.
semicaudatus, Vespertilio, 116.
semijunctus, Hyperaodon [sic], 115.
  Hyperodon [sic], 115.
seminolus, Odocoileus, 23.
semota, Atalapha, 149.
  Lasiurus, 149.
senescens, Eutamias, 531.
senex, Centurio, 128.
  Eutamias, 532.
  Paradoxurus, 107.
  Sciurus, 558.
  Tamias, 532.
senicula, Mormoops, 134.
seorsus, Perognathus, 436.
septentrionalis, Myotis, 152.
  Vespertilio, 152.
sequoiensis, Eutamias, 532.
seraiae, Callosciurus, 502.
  Sciurus, 502.
serengetae, Gazella, 9.
seri, Neotoma, 258.
  Perognathus, 436.
sericatus, Rattus, 479.
  Scapanus, 201.
sericeus, Ctenomys, 361.
serpens, Microtus, 282.
serus, Parocnus, 570.
serutus, Callosciurus, 502.
  Mus, 479.
  Rattus, 479.
  Sciurus, 502.
setosus, Liomys, 419.
shantungensis, Crocidura, 174.
shastensis, Castor, 256.
  Sorex, 194.
shawi, Thomomys, 384.
sheldoni, Marmota, 538.
  Neotoma, 285.
  Odocoileus, 21.
  Ovis, 13.
  Thomomys, 396.
  Ursus, 98.
shigarus, Epimys, 477.
  Rattus, 477.
shindi, Heliosciurus, 536.
shirasi, Alces, 16.
  Ursus, 99.
shoshone, Ursus, 99.
shufeldti, Procyon, 83.
shumaginensis, Sorex, 182.
siaca, Tupaia, 207.
siamensis, Bandicota, 443.
siantanicus, Mus, 479.
  Rattus, 479.
sibila, Arctomys, 541.
  Marmota, 541.
sibuanus, Limnomys, 450.

siccus, Perognathus, 436.
Sicista, 567.
    flavus, 567.
    napaea, 567.
sicula, Crocidura, 174.
sierrae, Citellus, 506.
    Lepus, 210.
    Marmota, 540.
Sigmodon, 350.
    alleni, 350.
    alticola, 350.
    amoles, 350.
    berlandieri, 351, 352.
    confinis, 351.
    eremicus, 351.
    goldmani, 353.
    guerrerensis, 351.
    jacksoni, 351.
    leucotis, 353.
    major, 352.
    melanotis, 353.
    microdon, 352.
    minima, 353.
    ochrognathus, 353.
    pallidus, 352.
    planifrons, 353.
    plenus, 352.
    saturatus, 352.
    tonalensis, 352.
simalurensis, Mus, 479.
    Rattus, 479.
Simias, 250.
    concolor, 250.
similis, Sorex, 189, 194, 197.
    Sylvilagus, 220.
simiolus, Crocidura, 174.
simplex, Arctogalidia, 102.
    Neotoma, 288, 292.
    Paradoxurus, 107.
simplicicanus, Lepus, 222.
simulans, Dipodomys, 415.
    Eutamias, 531.
    Perodipus, 415.
simulatus, Peromyscus, 331.
simulus, Thomomys, 397.
    Peromyscus, 332.
sinaloae, Thomomys, 397.
sincepis, Tupaia, 207.
sirhassenensis, Pithecus, 245.
    Tana, 202.
    Tupaia, 202.
siriensis, Callosciurus, 502.
    Sciurus, 502.
siskiyou, Eutamias, 533.
sitkensis, Microtus, 282.
    Odocoileus, 20.
    Peromyscus, 331.
    Ursus, 99.
Sitomys, decolorus, 299.
    musculus, 258.
siumatis, Megaderma, 119.
Sminthus flavus, 567.
sobrinus, Peroganthus, 436.
soccatus, Mus, 480.
    Rattus, 480.
socer, Epimys, 471.
    Rattus, 471.

sola, Neotoma, 287.
solifer, Taphozous, 117.
solitaria, Neotoma, 287.
solitarius, Rhinolophus, 144.
solivagus, Eutamias, 524.
solus, Epimys, 480.
    Rattus, 480.
solutus, Procyon, 84.
sonorana, Liomys, 420.
sonoranus, Liomys, 420.
sonoriensis, Conepatus, 63.
    Dicotyles, 29.
    Dipodomys, 406.
    Felis, 59.
    Hesperomys, 331.
    Pecari, 29.
    Perognathus, 429.
    Peromyscus, 331.
    Taxidea, 78.
    Thomomys, 403.
sordida, Tupaia, 207.
Sorex, 182.
    alascensis, 186, 189.
    alaskanus, 189.
    albibarbis, 182.
    albiventer, 184.
    alnorum, 179.
    alticola, 182.
    amoenus, 182, 194.
    arcticus, 192, 194.
    bairdi, 183.
    bendirii, 183.
    bergensis, 183.
    californicus, 184.
    caudatus, 193.
    chiapensis, 197.
    cinereus, 185, 187.
    crawfordi, 181.
    cristobalensis, 193.
    dobsoni, 184.
    durangae, 185.
    elassodon, 187.
    emarginatus, 185.
    euronotus, 183.
    evotis, 181.
    eximius, 179.
    fimbripes, 185.
    fisheri, 185.
    fontinalis, 186.
    glacialis, 186.
    godmani, 186.
    haydeni, 186.
    hercynicus, 182.
    hollisteri, 192.
    hoyi, 179.
    humboldtensis, 196.
    hydrobadistes, 192.
    idahoensis, 187.
    isolatus, 190.
    juncensis, 184.
    lagunae, 187.
    laricorum, 183, 191.
    leucogenys, 187.
    longicauda, 190.
    lyelli, 195.
    macrodon, 188.
    macropygmaeus, 188.

Sorex merriami, 188.
  montereyensis, 188.
  monticola, 184, 188.
  monticolus, 188.
  mutabilis, 193.
  myops, 195.
  nanus, 196.
  navigator, 189.
  neomexicanus, 190.
  nevadensis, 189.
  oaxacae, 193.
  obscurus, 189, 197.
  oreopolus, 191.
  orizabae, 191.
  ornatus, 191.
  pachyurus, 191.
  pacificus, 191.
  palmeri, 184.
  parvidens, 190.
  permiliensis, 190.
  planiceps, 192.
  preblei, 192.
  prevostensis, 188.
  pribilofensis, 192.
  roboratus, 193.
  salvini, 193.
  saussurei, 193.
  sclateri, 194.
  shastensis, 194.
  shumaginensis, 182.
  similis, 189, 194, 197.
  sphagnicola, 194.
  stizodon, 194.
  streatori, 192.
  suckleyi, 195.
  tenellus, 195.
  tetragonurus, 182.
  thompsoni, 180.
  trigonirostris, 196.
  trowbridgii, 196.
  tundrensis, 196.
  umbrosus, 186.
  vagrans, 195, 197.
  vancouverensis, 197.
  ventralis, 190.
  veraecrucis, 194.
  yaquinae, 197.
soricina, Blarina, 179.
  Cryptotis, 179.
  Glossophaga, 131.
soricoides, Leggada, 447.
  Mus, 447.
sotikae, Erinaceus, 165.
  Galago, 250.
sowerbyae, Lepus, 214.
sowerbyi, Myotis, 157.
  Rattus, 465.
spadix, Cephalophus, 8.
  Rhinolophus, 144.
Spalax, 566.
  berytensis, 566.
  dolbrogeae, 566.
spatiosus, Thomomys, 379.
spatulata, Ondatra, 300.
spatulatus, Epimys, 480.
  Fiber, 300.
  Rattus, 480.

speciosus, Eutamias, 532.
  Tamias, 532.
spectabilis, Dendromus, 454.
  Dipodomys, 414.
  Poemys, 454.
spelaeum, Plagiodontia, 363.
Spermophilus alleni, 519.
  annectens, 517.
  arens, 517.
  armatus, 504.
  barrowensis, 505.
  beldingi, 506.
  beringensis, 506.
  bernardinus, 506, 507.
  brevicauda, 507.
  brevicaudus, 506, 507.
  canescens, 506.
  canus, 514.
  couchii, 508.
  cryptospilotus, 509.
  elegans, 509.
  fisheri, 505.
  goldmani, 504.
  gunnisoni, 521.
  kodiacensis, 516.
  macrospilotus, 517.
  major, 518.
  marginatus, 518.
  mohavensis, 514.
  mollis, 514.
  neglectus, 515.
  nelsoni, 516.
  obsidianus, 518.
  obsoletus, 516.
  oregonus, 516.
  osgoodi, 516.
  pallidus, 520.
  parvidens, 513.
  perotensis, 517.
  plesius, 510.
  pratensis, 518.
  saxicolus, 510.
  stephensi, 515.
  tereticaudus, 519.
  texensis, 521.
  yakimensis, 515.
spermophilus, Lemniscomys, 449.
sphagnicola, Sorex, 194.
  Synaptomys, 355.
Spilogale, 75.
  ambigua, 75.
  angustifrons, 76.
  australis, 77.
  elata, 76.
  gracilis, 76.
  indianola, 76.
  latifrons, 77.
  leucoparia, 76.
  lucasana, 77.
  microdon, 77.
  phenax, 77.
  putorius, 77.
  ringens, 77.
  saxatilis, 78.
  tenuis, 78.
  tropicalis, 76.
spilotus, Perognathus, 434.

spinatus, Perognathus, 436.
spiradens, Tayassu, 30.
splendens, Neotoma, 297.
stampflii, Pipistrellus, 161.
stanleyana, Felis, 54, 55.
stanleyanus, Tragulus, 35.
stearnsii, Grampus, 109.
Steatomys, 488.
    athi, 488.
steerei, Proechimys, 363.
stejnegeri, Citellus, 519.
    Lutra, 66.
    Mesoplodon, 115.
    Phoca, 235.
Stenella, 113.
    plagiodon, 113.
Stenoderma, luciae, 126.
stentor, Epimys, 481.
    Rattus, 481.
stephani, Peromyscus, 333.
stephensi, Dipodomys, 415.
    Glaucomys, 534.
    Neotoma, 297.
    Perodipus, 415.
    Perognathus, 437.
    Peromyscus, 333.
    Sciuropterus, 534.
    Spermophilus, 515.
stevensoni, Dicrostonyx, 265.
stikeenensis, Ursus, 99.
stizodon, Sorex, 194.
stoicus, Mus, 481.
    Rattus, 481.
stoliczkanus, Alticola, 257.
stonei, Rangifer, 24.
stracheyi, Alticola, 257.
streatori, Mustela, 73.
    Neotoma, 288.
    Perodipus, 415.
    Peromyscus, 326.
    Putorius, 73.
    Sorex, 192.
strepitans, Mus, 481.
    Rattus, 481.
Strepsiceros, 15.
    australis, 15.
    bea, 15.
stridens, Mus, 481.
    Rattus, 481.
stridulus, Mus, 481.
    Rattus, 481.
sturgisi, Thomomys, 397.
Sturnira, 135.
    bogotensis, 135.
    parvidens, 135.
Sturnirops, 136.
    mordax, 136.
styani, Callosciurus, 493.
suahelae, Crocidura, 174.
subaffinis, Heteromys, 417.
subater, Baiomys, 259.
    Peromyscus, 259.
subcinctus, Lepus, 220.
    Sylvilagus, 220.
subditivus, Rattus, 465.
sublucidus, Perognathus, 424.
subluteus, Cratogeomys, 367.

subnubilis, Scotinomys, 350.
subnubilus, Cratogeomys, 366.
suboles, Thomomys, 388.
subrufa, Carollia, 128.
subrufum, Hemiderma, 128.
subrufus, Tragulus, 37.
subsimilis, Thomomys, 388.
subsimus, Cratogeomys, 366.
    Microtus, 277.
subtenuis, Dipodomys, 410.
subulatus, Myotis, 151.
subulidens, Pipistrellus, 161.
suckleyi, Sciurus, 561.
    Sorex, 195.
suecicus, Clethrionomys, 262.
    Evotomys, 262.
sulcata, Emballonura, 116.
sulcatus, Petaurista, 544.
sullivanus, Callosciurus, 502.
    Sciurus, 502.
suluensis, Cynomolgus, 246.
    Macaca, 246.
sumatrae, Thecurus, 438.
sumatrana, Arctogalidia, 102.
sumatranus, Nannosciurus, 542.
Suncus, 198.
    aequatorius, 198.
    occultidens, 198.
sungarae, Mus, 448.
supernus, Thomomys, 403.
surda, Tupaia, 205.
Surdisorex, 198.
    polulus, 198.
surdus, Akodon, 256.
    Mus, 482.
    Rattus, 482.
    Sciurus, 565.
    Tomeutes, 565.
surifer, Mus, 482.
    Rattus, 482.
surrufus, Onychomys, 304.
surrutilus, Nannosciurus, 543.
sururae, Crocidura, 174.
Sus, 26.
    babi, 26.
    enganus, 26.
    jubatulus, 26.
    jubatus, 27.
    mimus, 27.
    natunensis, 27.
    niadensis, 27.
    nicobaricus, 27.
    oi, 28.
    peninsularis,28.
    rhionis, 28.
    tuancus, 26.
Sylvicapra, 15.
    altivallis, 15.
    deserti, 15.
    roosevelti, 15.
Sylvilagus, 215.
    ammophilus, 218.
    arizonae, 216, 222.
    audubonii, 216.
    bachmani, 223.
    baileyi, 217.
    cedrophilus, 216.

Sylvilagus chapmani, 218, 222.
    chiapensis, 219.
    cognatus, 218.
    connectens, 219.
    exiguus, 217.
    gabbi, 218.
    goldmani, 215.
    graysoni, 221.
    hitchensi, 219.
    holzneri, 222.
    hondurensis, 219.
    idahoensis, 208.
    insonus, 221.
    littoralis, 215.
    mansuetus, 221.
    margaritae, 221.
    messorius, 220.
    minor, 216.
    neomexicanus, 217.
    orizabae, 221.
    pacificus, 223.
    restrictus, 219.
    robustus, 222.
    sanctidiegi, 220.
    similis, 220.
    subcinctus, 220.
    truei, 223.
    ubericolor, 217.
    vallicola, 217.
    warreni, 217.
    yucatanicus, 220.
Sylvisorex, 198.
    gemmeus, 198.
Symphalangus klossii, 251.
Synaptomys, 354.
    borealis, 354.
    bullatus, 354.
    cooperi, 354.
    dalli, 354.
    gossii, 354.
    helaletes, 355.
    innuitus, 355.
    sphagnicola, 355.
    truei, 355.
    wrangeli, 355.
szechuanensis, Pseudois, 13.

tabascensis, Didelphis, 228.
tachin, Callosciurus, 492.
    Sciurus, 492.
Tachyoryctes, 490.
    rex, 490.
taciturnus, Mus, 482.
    Rattus, 482.
tacomensis, Thomomys, 384.
Tadarida, 122.
    antillularum, 122.
    aurispinosa, 122.
    constanzae, 123.
    cynocephala, 123.
    europs, 123.
    femorosacca, 123.
    intermedia, 124.
    macrotis, 124.
    mexicana, 124.
    yucatanica, 124.
tagulayensis, Mus, 483.

tagulayensis, Rattus, 483.
tahltanicus, Ursus, 99.
taitae, Epimys, 455.
    Felis, 57.
    Praomys, 455.
talamancae, Oryzomys, 310.
Talpa parvidens, 199.
tamaulipensis, Cratogeomys, 366.
tambelanicus, Mus, 483.
    Rattus, 483.
Tamias, 560.
    alpinus, 522.
    amoenus, 523.
    borealis, 523.
    callipeplus, 524.
    castanurus, 507.
    chrysodeirus, 507.
    cinerascens, 508.
    cinereicollis, 525.
    cinnamomeus, 512.
    consobrinus, 528.
    cooperi, 526.
    dorsalis, 526.
    fisheri, 560.
    gracilis, 530.
    interpres, 511.
    leucurus, 512.
    luteiventris, 531.
    macrorhabdotes, 527.
    melanurus, 529.
    obscurus, 529.
    pallidus, 531.
    panamintinus, 530.
    pictus, 529.
    senex, 532.
    speciosus, 532.
    umbrinus, 533.
Tamiasciurus, 560.
    abieticola, 560.
    baileyi, 560.
    cascadensis, 560.
    douglasii, 561.
    kenaiensis, 561.
    mearnsi, 561.
    neomexicanus, 560.
    petulans, 561.
    preblei, 561.
    ventorum, 561.
Tamiops, 562.
    liantis, 562.
    novemlineatus, 562.
    vestitus, 562.
Tana, 202.
    besara, 203.
    bunoae, 202.
    cervicalis, 202.
    lingae, 202.
    masae, 202.
    sirhassenensis, 202.
    tuancus, 203.
tana, Mus, 453.
    Myomys, 453.
tapanulius, Callosciurus, 503.
    Rattus, 487.
    Sciurus, 503.
Taphonycteris, 116.
    capito, 116.

Taphonycteris pluto, 117.
Taphozous, 117.
  cavaticus, 117.
  pluto, 117.
  solifer, 117.
Tapirella, 233.
  bairdii, 233.
  dowii, 233.
tarascensis, Zygogeomys, 404.
Tarsius, 252.
  borneanus, 252.
  dentatus, 252.
  fraterculus, 252.
  pumilus, 252.
  saltator, 253.
Tarsomys, 488.
  apoensis, 488.
tarussanus, Sciurus, 503.
Tatera, 356.
  percivali, 356.
  pothae, 356.
  varia, 356.
Tatoua centralis, 569.
Tatu texanum, 570.
taurinsulae, Odocoileus, 24.
Taxidea, 78.
  berlandieri, 78.
  neglecta, 78.
  sonoriensis, 78.
Tayassu, 30.
  crassus, 28.
  humeralis, 29.
  nanus, 30.
  ringens, 30.
  spiradens, 30.
  yucatanensis, 29.
taylori, Perognathus, 423.
Teanopus, 356.
  phenax, 356.
teapensis, Heterogeomys, 371.
  Oryzomys, 310.
  Peromyscus, 329.
tedongus, Callosciurus, 502.
  Sciurus, 502.
tehuantepecus, Heterogeomys, 371.
  Peromyscus, 333.
teliotis, Atalapha, 149.
  Lasiurus, 149.
telmalestes, Blarina, 167.
  Conepatus, 62.
temporalis, Heteromys, 418.
tenellus, Sorex, 195.
  Thomomys, 400.
  Zapus, 569.
tenuicauda, Neotoma, 298.
tenuidorsalis, Vespertilio, 158, 573.
tenuirostris, Callosciurus, 503.
  Reithrodontomys, 349.
  Sciurus, 503.
  Vulpes, 51.
tenuis, Reithrodontomys, 343.
  Spilogale, 78.
tephrura, Tupaia, 207.
tereticaudus, Citellus, 519.
  Spermophilus, 519.
termes, Proteles, 85.
terrestris, Colobus, 239.

tersus, Ammospermophilus, 513.
  Citellus, 513.
terutaus, Atherurus, 438.
  Petaurista, 544.
tescorum, Callospermophilus, 512.
  Citellus, 512.
tetragonurus, Sorex, 182.
tetricus, Rattus, 470.
texanum, Tatu, 570.
texanus, Dorcelaphus, 21.
  Hesperomys, 333.
  Odocoileus, 21.
  Peromyscus, 316, 333.
texensis, Canis, 44.
  Castor, 255.
  Citellus, 521.
  Conepatus, 62.
  Didelphis, 228.
  Geomys, 370.
  Glaucomys, 536.
  Liomys, 421.
  Lutra, 65.
  Spermophilus, 521.
  Thomomys, 389.
  Urocyon, 48.
  Ursus, 90.
texiana, Ovis, 11.
texianus, Lepus, 214.
thai, Viverricula, 108.
Thallomys, 488.
  loringi, 488.
Thallomyscus, 356.
  aurillus, 356.
Thamnomys littoralis, 446.
  loringi, 488.
Thecurus, 438.
  major, 438.
  sumatrae, 438.
thibetanus, Euarctos, 86.
thomasi, Lophiomys, 269.
  Odocoileus, 22.
  Peromyscus, 334.
  Sciurus, 559.
Thomasomys, 357.
  daphne, 357.
  gracilis, 357.
  notatus, 357.
Thomomys, 377.
  absonus, 395.
  agrestis, 397.
  albigularis, 400.
  alexandrae, 377.
  alienus, 379.
  alpinus, 377.
  analogus, 400.
  andersoni, 397.
  angularis, 377.
  apache, 378.
  atrogriseus, 394.
  aureus, 391.
  awahnee, 377.
  badius, 398.
  baileyi, 378.
  birdseyei, 379.
  bridgeri, 383.
  bullatus, 398.
  cabezonae, 383.

Thomomys caliginosus, 400.
    canus, 383.
    caryi, 398.
    catalinae, 386.
    chihuahuae, 401.
    chiricahuae, 401.
    chrysonotus, 387.
    clusius, 383.
    collinus, 386.
    columbianus, 389.
    confinalis, 390.
    convergens, 379.
    couchi, 398.
    crassidens, 401.
    desertorum, 384.
    desitus, 379.
    dissimilis, 395.
    divergens, 379.
    durangi, 401.
    emotus, 386.
    enixus, 401.
    ericaeus, 398.
    eximius, 401.
    extenuatus, 380.
    extimus, 402.
    fisheri, 389.
    flavidus, 387.
    fulvus, 386.
    fuscus, 383.
    goldmani, 390.
    grahamensis, 387.
    guadalupensis, 380.
    hesperus, 390.
    howelli, 380.
    hualpaiensis, 380.
    idahoensis, 390.
    imitabilis, 380.
    incensus, 398.
    incomptus, 380.
    intermedius, 387.
    internatus, 381.
    kaibabensis, 385.
    kelloggi, 399.
    lachuguilla, 378.
    laticeps, 390.
    latirostris, 391.
    leucodon, 391.
    levis, 385.
    limitaris, 390.
    limosus, 391.
    loringi, 389.
    madrensis, 402.
    magdalenae, 392.
    martinensis, 402.
    mazama, 392.
    mearnsi, 392.
    medius, 399.
    melanops, 392.
    mewa, 392.
    minimus, 381.
    minor, 381.
    modicus, 387.
    moorei, 385.
    muralis, 393.
    musculus, 402.
    mutabilis, 387.
    myops, 393.

Thomomys nasicus, 393.
    navus, 391.
    nebulosus, 399.
    neglectus, 393.
    nelsoni, 393.
    nevadensis, 394.
    nicholi, 381.
    niger, 394.
    ocius, 384.
    operarius, 394.
    optabilis, 381.
    opulentus, 381.
    oregonus, 384.
    orizabae, 394.
    osgoodi, 396.
    parowanensis, 385.
    parviceps, 397.
    parvulus, 381.
    pascalis, 377.
    patulus, 382.
    pectoralis, 395.
    peramplus, 388.
    perditus, 395.
    peregrinus, 395.
    perpallidus, 399.
    perpes, 378.
    pervagus, 378.
    pervarius, 382.
    phasma, 388.
    pinalensis, 382.
    pinetorum, 392.
    potosinus, 402.
    pryori, 396.
    pusillus, 388.
    pygmaeus, 396.
    quadratus, 396.
    relicinus, 399.
    russeolus, 382.
    saturatus, 389.
    shawi, 384.
    sheldoni, 396.
    simulus, 397.
    sinaloae, 397.
    sonoriensis, 403.
    spatiosus, 379.
    sturgisi, 397.
    suboles, 388.
    subsimilis, 388.
    supernus, 403.
    tacomensis, 384.
    tenellus, 400.
    texensis, 389.
    tolucae, 403.
    townsendii, 394.
    trivialis, 400.
    uinta, 400.
    virgineus, 382.
    vulcanius, 403.
    winthropi, 382.
    yelmensis, 385.
    zacatecae, 403.
thompsoni, Microsorex, 180.
    Sorex, 180.
thoracatus, Capromys, 360.
Thos bea, 41.
    bweha, 46.
    elgonae, 46.

Thos mcmillani, 46.
  notatus, 47.
Thryonomys, 566.
  pusillus, 566.
Thryoptera, 145.
  major, 145.
thysanodes, Myotis, 158.
tiarata, Mustela, 74.
tiburonensis, Lepus, 208.
  Peromyscus, 335.
tinctus, Mastomys, 452.
  Rattus, 452.
tingia, Arctogalidia, 102.
  Felis, 60.
tingius, Epimys, 483.
  Rattus, 483.
tiomanensis, Ratufa, 550.
tiomanicus, Mus, 483.
  Rattus, 483.
toala, Hipposideros, 118.
todayensis, Mus, 484.
  Rattus, 484.
tohi, Redunca, 14.
toklat, Ursus, 100.
toltecus, Reithrodontomys, 345.
tolucae, Reithrodontomys, 341.
  Sciurus, 557.
  Thomomys, 403.
Tomeutes, 562.
  atratus, 562.
  balae, 563.
  bancarus, 563.
  batus, 564.
  evidens, 563.
  hippurellus, 563.
  hippurosus, 563.
  humilis, 564.
  mansalaris, 564.
  natunensis, 564.
  necopinus, 564.
  parvus, 565.
  piniensis, 565.
  procerus, 565.
  pumilus, 565.
  surdus, 565.
tonalensis, Sigmodon, 352.
Tonatia, 136.
  venezuelae, 136.
tornillo, Peromyscus, 335.
torquata, Neotoma, 288, 296.
torquatus, Canis, 45, 576.
torques, Akodon, 256.
  Microxus, 256.
torridus, Hesperomys, 303.
  Heterogeomys, 372.
  Liomys, 421.
  Onychomys, 303.
totontepecus, Peromyscus, 328, 329.
townsendi, Arctocephalus, 234.
  Urocyon, 47.
  Ursus, 100.
townsendii, Citellus, 515.
  Microtus, 279.
  Scapanus, 200.
  Thomomys, 394.
Trachops, 136.
  coffini, 136.

Trachypithecus carbo, 248.
  cristatus, 250.
  flavicauda, 249.
  germani, 248.
  phayrei, 247.
Tragelaphus, 16.
  olivaceus, 16.
Tragulus, 30.
  amoenus, 30.
  bancanus, 30.
  batuanus, 31.
  billitonus, 31.
  borneanus, 31.
  brevipes, 31.
  bunguranensis, 32.
  canescens, 32.
  carimatae, 32.
  everetti, 34.
  flavicollis, 32.
  focalinus, 32.
  formosus, 32.
  fulvicollis, 33.
  hosei, 38.
  jugularis, 33.
  lampensis, 33.
  lancavensis, 33.
  longipes, 33.
  luteicollis, 34.
  lutescens, 34.
  masae, 37.
  napu, 32.
  natunae, 34.
  niasis, 34.
  nigricollis, 34.
  nigrocinctus, 35.
  pallidus, 35.
  parallelus, 36.
  perflavus, 35.
  pinius, 35.
  pretiellus, 35.
  pretiosus, 36.
  ravulus, 36.
  ravus, 36.
  rubeus, 36.
  rufulus, 37.
  russeus, 37.
  russulus, 37.
  sebucus, 37.
  stanleyanus, 35.
  subrufus, 37.
  umbrinus, 38.
  virgicollis, 38.
trichopus, Zygogeomys, 403.
Trichys, 439.
  macrotis, 439.
tricolor, Ateles, 237.
  Hemiderma, 128.
trigonirostris, Sorex, 196.
trinitatis, Callospermophilus, 508.
  Citellus, 508.
triton, Leggada, 448.
trivialis, Thomomys, 400.
tropicalis, Conepatus, 63.
  Geomys, 370.
  Mustela, 74.
  Neotoma, 298.
  Putorius, 74.

tropicalis, Spilogale, 76.
trotteri, Callosciurus, 496.
  Sciurus, 496.
trowbridgii, Arvicola, 282.
  Lepus, 223.
  Sorex, 196.
truei, Hesperomys, 335.
  Lepus, 223.
  Odocoileus, 19.
  Peromyscus, 327, 335.
  Phenacomys, 338.
  Podogymnura, 165.
  Scapanus, 202.
  Sciurus, 559.
  Sylvilagus, 223.
  Synaptomys, 355.
Tryphomys, 488.
  adustus, 488.
tshuktshorum, Microtus, 282.
tua, Epimys, 484.
  Rattus, 484.
tuancus, Galeopithecus, 164.
  Galeopterus, 164.
  Rattus, 463.
  Sus, 26.
  Tana, 203.
tularensis, Dipodomys, 405.
  Lepus, 214.
  Onychomys, 304.
  Perodipus, 405.
  Ursus, 87.
tumbalensis, Tylomys, 357.
tumbili, Lasiopyga, 239.
tumida, Rhogeëssa, 162.
tumidiceps, Mormoops, 135.
tumidifrons, Chilonatalus, 125.
tumidirostris, Natalus, 126.
  Phodotes, 126.
tundrarum, Canis, 45.
tundrensis, Sorex, 196.
  Ursus, 92.
Tupaia, 203.
  anambae, 203.
  batamana, 204.
  bunoae, 202.
  carimatae, 203.
  castanea, 203.
  cervicalis, 202.
  chrysogaster, 204.
  chrysomalla, 204.
  cuyonis, 204.
  discolor, 204.
  edarata, 205.
  inflata, 205.
  kohtauensis, 205.
  natunae, 205.
  olivacea, 204.
  pemangilis, 206.
  phaeura, 206.
  pulonis, 206.
  raviana, 206.
  riabus, 206.
  salatana, 205.
  siaca, 207.
  sincepis, 207.
  sirhassenensis, 202.
  sordida, 207.

Tupaia surda, 205.
  tephrura, 207.
turbidus, Epimys, 477.
  Rattus, 477.
turneri, Aethomys, 440.
  Epimys, 440.
Tursiops, 113.
  gillii, 113.
Tylomys, 357.
  bullaris, 357.
  tumbalensis, 357.
tylorhinus, Platygeomys, 376.
Typomys, 489.
  planifrons, 489.
tyrannus, Epimys, 484.
  Rattus, 484.

ubecus, Epimys, 484.
  Rattus, 484.
ubericolor, Callosciurus, 503.
  Lepus, 217.
  Sciurus, 503.
  Sylvilagus, 217.
uellensis, Colobus, 239.
ugandae, Eptesicus, 147.
  Uranomys, 489.
uinta, Lynx, 61.
  Ochotona, 227.
  Thomomys, 400.
ulae, Epimys, 453.
ultima, Pygathrix, 250.
umbridorsum, Mus, 484.
  Rattus, 484.
umbrinus, Eutamias, 533.
  Tamias, 533.
  Tragulus, 38.
umbriventer, Saccostomus, 488.
umbrosa, Macaca, 246.
umbrosus, Eutamias, 524.
  Macacus, 246.
  Microtus, 282.
  Sorex, 186.
unalascensis, Dicrostonyx, 264.
  Microtus, 283.
underwoodi, Dasyprocta, 359.
  Sciurus, 553.
undulatus, Heliosciurus, 537.
  Sciurus, 537.
ungava, Alopex, 40.
  Clethrionomys, 263.
  Evotomys, 263.
  Phenacomys, 337, 338.
  Vulpes, 40.
Uranomys, 489.
  ugandae, 489.
Urocyon, 47.
  borealis, 47.
  californicus, 47.
  catalinae, 47.
  clementae, 48.
  colimensis, 48.
  fraterculus, 49.
  guatamalae, 48.
  littoralis, 48.
  orinomus, 48.
  parvidens, 49.
  santacruzae, 49.

Urocyon scottii, 48.
 texensis, 48.
 townsendi, 47.
Uroderma, 136.
 bilobatum, 136.
 convexum, 136.
Urogale, 207.
 cylindrura, 207.
 everetti, 207.
Urotrichus, gibbsii, 199.
Ursus, 86.
 absarokus, 86.
 alascensis, 90.
 amblyceps, 85.
 apache, 87.
 arizonae, 87.
 atnarko, 87.
 bairdi, 87.
 bisonophagus, 98.
 californicus, 91.
 canadensis, 99.
 carlottae, 86.
 caurinus, 87.
 chelan, 88.
 chelidonias, 88.
 colusus, 88.
 crassodon, 88.
 crassus, 88.
 cressonus, 88.
 dalli, 89.
 dusorgus, 89.
 eltonclarki, 89.
 eremicus, 86.
 ereunetes, 97.
 eulophus, 89.
 eximius, 89.
 floridanus, 86.
 gyas, 89.
 henshawi, 90.
 holzworthi, 90.
 hoots, 90.
 horriaeus, 91.
 hylodromus, 98.
 idahoensis, 91.
 imperator, 91.
 impiger, 93.
 innuitus, 92.
 inopinatus, 92.
 insularis, 89.
 kenaiensis, 92.
 kennerleyi, 92.
 kidderi, 92.
 klamathensis, 93.
 kluane, 93.
 kwakiutl, 93.
 latifrons, 97.
 macfarlani, 94.
 macrodon, 94.
 magister, 94.
 mendocinensis, 94.
 middendorffi, 94.
 mirabilis, 94.
 mirus, 95.
 navaho, 95.
 neglectus, 93.
 nelsoni, 95.
 nortoni, 95.

Ursus nuchek, 95.
 ophrus, 96.
 orgiloides, 96.
 orgilos, 96.
 oribasus, 96.
 pallasi, 96.
 pellyensis, 96.
 perturbans, 96.
 pervagor, 97.
 phaeonyx, 91.
 planiceps, 97.
 pulchellus, 97.
 rogersi, 98.
 rungiusi, 98.
 sagittalis, 98.
 selkirki, 98.
 sheldoni, 98.
 shirasi, 99.
 shoshone, 99.
 sitkensis, 99.
 stikeenensis, 99.
 tahltanicus, 99.
 texensis, 90.
 toklat, 100.
 townsendi, 100.
 tularensis, 87.
 tundrensis, 92.
 utahensis, 100.
 warburtoni, 93.
 washake, 100.
ussuricus, Selenarctos, 86.
utah, Citellus, 510.
utahensis, Dipodomys, 411.
 Eutamias, 527.
 Onychomys, 302.
 Perodipus, 411.
 Ursus, 100.

vagrans, Sorex, 195, 197.
valens, Epimys, 485.
 Rattus, 485.
validus, Dendrohyrax, 164.
 Mus, 485.
 Rattus, 485.
vallicola, Eutamias, 523.
 Microtus, 272.
 Oenomys, 453.
 Sylvilagus, 217.
Vampyressa, 136.
 minuta, 136.
Vampyrops, 137.
 fumosus, 137.
Vampyrum, 137.
 nelsoni, 137.
Vampyrus nelsoni, 137.
vancouverensis, Felis, 54.
 Gulo, 64.
 Lutra, 66.
 Procyon, 84.
 Sorex, 197.
varia, Tatera, 356.
varius, Platygeomys, 376.
 Procyon, 84.
varronis, Lepus, 215.
vasconiae, Clethrionomys, 264.
 Evotomys, 264.
velox, Acinonyx, 52.

venatorius, Odocoileus, 24.
venaticus, Conepatus, 62.
venezuelae, Lophostoma, 136.
   Tonatia, 136.
ventorum, Ochotona, 227.
   Sciurus, 561.
   Tamiasciurus, 561.
ventralis, Sorex, 190.
ventriosus, Zygodontomys, 358.
venusta, Neotoma, 286, 298.
venustulus, Nyctomys, 299.
   Microsciurus, 541.
venustus, Dipodomys, 416.
   Perodipus, 416.
veraecrucis, Felis, 58.
   Liomys, 419, 421.
   Odocoileus, 24.
   Sorex, 194.
Vespertilio affinis, 150.
   agilis, 572.
   bahamensis, 146.
   ciliolabrum, 151.
   evotis, 152.
   exiguus, 572.
   henshawii, 156.
   keenii, 158.
   longicrus, 153.
   lucifugus, 154, 572.
   macropus, 154.
   melanorhinus, 154.
   mundus, 155, 572.
   nitidus, 155.
   obscurus, 156.
   oregonensis, 157.
   pallidus, 145.
   semicaudatus, 116.
   septentrionalis, 152.
   tenuidorsalis, 158, 573.
   volans, 158.
   yumanensis, 158, 573.
Vesperugo merriami, 161.
vestitus, Tamiops, 562.
Vetularctos, 92.
   inopinatus, 92.
vetulus, Hodomys, 266.
vexillifer, Lipotes, 113.
vicina, Neotoma, 290.
vicinior, Peromyscus, 314.
vicinus, Procyon, 81.
viclana, Epimys, 478.
   Rattus, 478.
victor, Epimys, 485.
vigilans, Presbytis, 250.
vigilis, Canis, 45.
   Citellus, 506.
   Papio, 246.
vigoratus, Epimys, 485.
   Rattus, 485.
villosa, Glossophaga, 131.
   Macaca, 245.
villosus, Macacus, 245.
vinaceus, Zelotomys, 489.
virescens, Arvicanthis, 442.
virgatus, Otocyon, 46.
virgicollis, Tragulus, 38.
virgineus, Thomomys, 382.
virginianus, Reithrodontomys, 344.

virgo, Rhinolophus, 144.
virtus, Rattus, 485.
vitiensis, Mus, 486.
   Rattus, 486.
vitiis, Macaca, 246.
   Pithecus, 246.
vittata, Ratufa, 550.
vittatula, Ratufa, 551.
vittatus, Callosciurus, 503.
vivatus, Microsciurus, 542.
vivax, Sciurus, 555.
Viverricula, 108.
   thai, 108.
vociferans, Mus, 486.
   Rattus, 486.
vociferus, Pteropus, 142.
volans, Myotis, 151, 158.
   Vespertilio, 158.
vomerina, Phocaena, 111.
voratus, Brotomys, 360.
Vormela, 79.
   negans, 79.
vulcani, Mus, 487.
   Orthogeomys, 373.
   Rattus, 487.
vulcanius, Thomomys, 403.
Vulpes, 49.
   abietorum, 49.
   alascensis, 49.
   arizonensis, 50.
   beringensis, 40.
   cascadensis, 50.
   devia, 50.
   devius, 50.
   hallensis, 40.
   harrimani, 50.
   hebes, 52.
   innuitus, 40.
   kenaiensis, 50.
   littoralis, 48.
   macrotis, 50.
   macroura, 51.
   mutica, 51.
   muticus, 51.
   necator, 52.
   neomexicana, 51.
   neomexicanus, 51.
   nevadensis, 51.
   pribilofensis, 41.
   regalis, 52.
   tenuirostris, 51.
   ungava, 40.
vulpina, Ochotona, 224.

wahema, Microtus, 281.
wallawalla, Lepus, 214.
wamae, Leggada, 448.
   Mus, 448.
warburtoni, Ursus, 93.
warreni, Marmota, 540.
   Neotoma, 285.
   Sylvilagus, 217.
warringtoni, Microtus, 283.
washake, Ursus, 100.
washingtoni, Citellus, 521.
   Microsorex, 180.
   Mustela, 75.

washingtoni, Putorius, 75.
washingtonii, Lepus, 215.
washoensis, Citellus, 515.
weemsi, Ovis, 11.
wetmorei, Eptesicus, 147.
whitei, Erythrocebus, 240.
winnemana, Microsorex, 180.
    Myotis, 158.
winthropi, Thomomys, 382.
wrangeli, Clethrionomys, 264.
    Evotomys, 264.
    Synaptomys, 355.
wulsini, Selenarctos, 86.

Xenomys, 357.
    nelsoni, 357.
xenurus, Peromyscus, 336.

yakiensis, Onychomys, 304.
yakimensis, Spermophilus, 515.
yakutatensis, Microtus, 283.
yaquinae, Sorex, 197.
yelmensis, Thomomys, 385.
youngi, Canis, 44.
    Felis, 54, 55.
yucatanensis, Didelphis, 229.
    Heterogeomys, 371.
    Oryzomys, 311.
    Pecari, 29.
    Sciurus, 554.
    Tayassu, 29.
yucatanica, Dasyprocta, 359.
    Felis, 55.
    Tadarida, 124.
yucatanicus, Lepus, 220.
    Nyctinomops, 124.
    Sylvilagus, 220.
yukonensis, Glaucomys, 536.
    Lemmus, 269.
    Lutra, 65.
    Sciuropterus, 536.
yumanensis, Myotis, 154, 156, 158, 573.
    Vespertilio, 158, 573.

zacatecae, Neotoma, 291.
    Perognathus, 430.
    Reithrodontomys, 346, 347.

zacatecae, Thomomys, 403.
zalopha, Ondatra, 301.
zalophus, Fiber, 301.
zamboangae, Mus, 487.
    Rattus, 487.
zamelas, Peromyscus, 328.
zamicrus, Nesophontes, 167.
zamorae, Peromyscus, 328.
zanzibaricus, Galago, 250.
zaodon, Crocidura, 174.
zaphaeus, Glaucomys, 533.
    Sciuropterus, 533.
Zapus, 567.
    alascensis, 567.
    australis, 568.
    campestris, 567.
    luteus, 568.
    major, 568.
    minor, 568.
    montanus, 569.
    nevadensis, 568.
    oregonus, 569.
    pacificus, 568.
    roanensis, 567.
    tenellus, 569.
zarhynchus, Peromyscus, 336.
zeledoni, Marmosa, 231.
zelotes, Peromyscus, 336.
Zelotomys, 489.
    vinaceus, 489.
zinseri, Platygeomys, 376.
Ziphius, 115.
    cavirostris, 115.
    grebnitzkii, 115.
zonalis, Aotus, 236.
    Heteromys, 418.
zuniensis, Cynomys, 522.
Zygodontomys, 358.
    ventriosus, 358.
Zygogeomys, 403.
    tarascensis, 404.
    trichopus, 403.
zygomatica, Atherura, 438.
zygomaticus, Atherurus, 438.
    Dipodomys, 415.
    Oryzomys, 311.

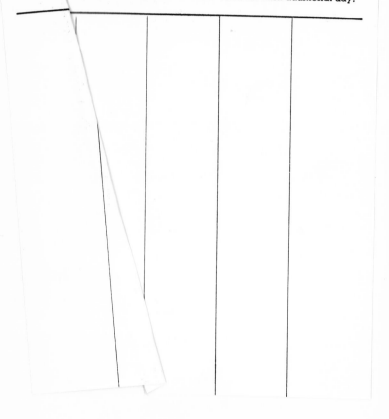